P9-AFA-458

Cells and Tissues in Culture

METHODS, BIOLOGY AND PHYSIOLOGY

VOLUME 3

Cells and Tissues in Culture

METHODS, BIOLOGY AND PHYSIOLOGY

Edited by
E. N. WILLMER
Physiological Laboratory
University of Cambridge, England

VOLUME 3

1966
ACADEMIC PRESS
LONDON • NEW YORK

ACADEMIC PRESS INC. (LONDON) LTD
Berkeley Square House
Berkeley Square
London, W.1.

U.S. Edition published by
ACADEMIC PRESS INC.
111 Fifth Avenue
New York, New York 10003

Library of Congress Catalog Card Number: 64–14227

PRINTED IN GREAT BRITAIN BY
WILLMER BROTHERS LIMITED, BIRKENHEAD

Contributors

FREDERIK B. BANG, *Department of Pathobiology, Johns Hopkins University, School of Hygiene and Public Health, Baltimore, Maryland, U.S.A.* (p. 151)

ARMIN C. BRAUN, *The Rockefeller University, New York, New York, U.S.A.* (p. 691)

G. G. HENSHAW, *Department of Botany, University College of Swansea, Wales* (p. 459)

SYLVIA FITTON JACKSON, *Strangeways Research Laboratory, Cambridge, England* (p. 1)

W. JACOBSON, *Sir Halley Stewart Research Fellow, Strangeways Research Laboratory, Cambridge, England* (p. 351)

BRYN M. JONES, *Department of Zoology, University College of Wales, Aberystwyth, Wales* (p. 397)

JACQUES LIPETZ, *The Rockefeller University, New York, New York, U.S.A.* (p. 691)

JOSEPH L. MELNICK, *Department of Virology and Epidemiology, Baylor University College of Medicine, Houston, Texas, U.S.A.* (p. 263)

G. J. V. NOSSAL, *The Walter and Eliza Hall Institute and Department of Medical Biology, University of Melbourne, Melbourne, Australia* (p. 317)

FRED RAPP, *Department of Virology and Epidemiology, Baylor University College of Medicine, Houston, Texas, U.S.A.* (p. 263)

V. M. ROSENOER, *Medical Unit and Department of Pharmacology, Royal Free Hospital, London, England* (p. 351)

H. E. STREET, *Department of Botany, University College of Swansea, Wales* (pp. 459, 533, 631)

O. A. TROWELL, *Medical Research Council Radiobiological Unit, Harwell, Berkshire, England* (p. 63)

Foreword to Volume 3

In this third volume there are considered some of the applications of the methods of Tissue Culture to a wide variety of fields of investigation. Such methods have been of exceptional importance in the study of viruses and indeed of great practical and medical value in several branches of virology, immunology and preventive medicine. They are also the methods of choice for the study of the cytological effects of radiation.

Tissue Culture methods have so far been applied only in a more limited way to the tissues of the invertebrates, but the importance of these studies can now be clearly recognized. Curiously enough, their application to the study of plant tissues lagged behind the corresponding research on animal tissues, but the last four chapters in this volume make it quite clear that great progress has now been made in this field too, and biologists in general will find that the comparison of the observations on plant tissues with those on animal tissues makes a fascinating study.

The compilation of these volumes has been achieved by the ready co-operation of the authors, the publishers and the printers. As might well have been expected, there have been difficulties, delays, defections and deaths; nevertheless, it is hoped that the final result, though perhaps not so "up to the minute" as one might have wished, will give the reader a valuable and general picture of the scientific progress achieved by Tissue-Culture methods during their first sixty or so years of existence, and that it will prove to be a stimulus to future research for many years to come.

The editor wishes again to express his thanks not only to the authors, but also to those who have helped him in the preparation of the indexes, without which much of the valuable information contained in these volumes might for ever lie buried and inaccessible. The subject index for this third volume was prepared with the assistance of Miss J. Lapwood and Mr. P. Shoenberg. His thanks also go to all those who have given permission for the use of photographs and illustrations for the illumination of the text.

Finally, those who make use of these volumes and gain benefit therefrom may wish to add their quota to the tribute which the editor extends to his wife for her endless patience during the prolonged editorial labours.

PHYSIOLOGICAL LABORATORY
CAMBRIDGE
July 1966

E. N. WILLMER

Foreword to Volume 1

Since 1907, Tissue Culture has been used and misused in a wide variety of ways and in a number of branches of biology. A few years ago, the idea was mooted that it was time to make an assessment of the achievements of Tissue Culture. This assessment should not only consider the technique in itself, but more particularly should evaluate the effects that Tissue Culture has had in the solution of problems in cellular and histological biology. What, indeed, are the contributions which Tissue Culture has made to biology, and what are they likely to be in the future? Has Tissue Culture altered our approach to cellular behaviour or opened up any new fields?

This book is an attempt to show what has been achieved so far and to discuss where, when and how the technique may be most profitably employed.

In 1960, a number of investigators in the various fields of Tissue Culture were approached and asked if they would evaluate the uses and applications of the technique in their particular areas of study. They were asked to assess what contributions the method had made, was making, or was likely to make to our understanding of normal or pathological cells and tissues, and to point out those features which, though they may be peculiar to life *in vitro*, are nevertheless of value to our understanding of cells and tissues in general.

The problem of selecting suitable authors for the task was, of course, both difficult and invidious. For the final choice, the editor accepts full responsibility, well-knowing that, despite his efforts, there will be many who would have chosen quite differently. Some investigators, whose contributions would have been most valuable, were unfortunately, for one reason or another, unable to accept the challenge; a few accepted the challenge and then found it impossible to carry on with the task; finally, in two cases, alas, illness and untimely death intervened.

The first volume covers many of the more general fields of Tissue Culture, including such topics as the evaluation of the methods as such, the study of metabolic processes and growth, the action of hormones and vitamins and the use of the method in genetics. The second volume is devoted to studies of certain particular tissues or systems which have either been extensively investigated in themselves or which, for one reason or another, accentuate some achievement or contribution which the method has made to biology. In the third volume, some of the uses of Tissue Culture in the study of invertebrate and plant tissues will be reviewed, together with some of the applications to pathology and virus research.

The editor wishes to express his most sincere thanks to the contributors, not only for their contributions but also for their forbearance and patience during the long period of gestation. He also wishes to thank all those authors and proprietors of journals who have kindly allowed their illustrations to be used to enrich the text. Dr. R. L. Tapp has provided invaluable assistance in the compilation of the index and his efforts will greatly increase the value of these volumes as a work of reference for years to come. Finally, the Academic Press and their printers are deserving of high praise for their splendid efficiency and patience.

PHYSIOLOGICAL LABORATORY
CAMBRIDGE

E. N. WILLMER

October 1964

Foreword to Volume 2

In this volume, which is devoted to those aspects of Tissue Culture which are applicable to particular classes of cells and tissues, the aim has been to give the reader some idea of the manner in which culture methods are being used in the special problems of cell and tissue physiology. The reader will find that, just as the problems connected with each tissue are different, so the methods which have been applied to their solution are many and various. The chapters, each by a different author, vary very much in their approach. This variety is partly determined by the nature of the topic and partly by the inclination of the author, but it emphasizes the wide scope and importance of Tissue Culture in biology.

PHYSIOLOGICAL LABORATORY
CAMBRIDGE

E. N. WILLMER

October 1964

Contents

Contents of Volume 1

Contents of Volume 2

CHAPTER 1

The Molecular Organization of Cells and Tissues in Culture

SYLVIA FITTON JACKSON*

Strangeways Research Laboratory, Cambridge, England

1. Introduction

Tissue-culture cells have not been used yet to any great extent for the study of molecular organization, but their potential value should not be overlooked. The advantage of direct observations, the selection of precise sequential stages in, for example, development processes, the possible tendency towards spatial simplification of complex interrelationships, and the ease and speed with which thorough fixation can be obtained suggests that analysis by electron-microscopy of the fine-structure of various types of cells in tissue culture might contribute to the understanding of many problems. A certain reserve should be maintained, however, over equating results obtained in *in vitro* systems with

*Member of the External Scientific Staff of the Medical Research Council.

those that occur *in vivo*. Conversely, the Tissue Culture method offers the possibility of studying closed systems in which extrinsic factors can be under the full control of the investigator. The present-day development of micro-techniques for the estimation of most biological substances, and the ability to follow metabolic processes in great detail provide additional tools that can be used on the same cells as are being studied, for instance, by electron-microscopy.

In the present chapter, a brief outline is given of methods available for the study of the fine-structure of cells in tissue culture; certain facets of cellular organization at the molecular level are then described. Finally, the contribution that the use of tissue cultures have made towards our present understanding of fibrogenesis is discussed; the study of fibre-formation in cultures has proved tractable since collagen has characteristic features that may be used to great advantage. The results so far obtained in this field support the idea that the elucidation of many other problems of modern biology will be greatly aided by studies of the molecular organization of cells in culture.

II. Methods

A. PREPARATIVE PROCEDURES FOR THE STUDY OF MOLECULAR ORGANIZATION

Techniques for the preparation of biological material for the study of molecular organization by electron-microscopy are based essentially on classical histological procedures, but certain necessary modifications have had to be introduced to meet the requirements of the high resolution of the electron-microscope. Three basic considerations are necessary; first, the specimen must be of a sufficient thinness to allow penetration by the electron beam; secondly, the specimen must be preserved in such a way as to prevent gross coagulation and displacement of the molecular architecture for many procedures ideal for use with specimens to be viewed by light microscopy introduce severe disruption of fine-structure; thirdly, the specimen must be able to withstand complete desiccation.

Histological techniques have been developed to meet these requirements, and, in addition, to facilitate the localization of certain substances by specific reactions. Basically, osmium tetroxide, in a suitable physiological salt solution buffered to a pH similar to that of the specimen has been used most generally as a fixative; recent findings have shown that a buffered glutaraldehyde solution, used either first or alone, frequently increases the detail of the macromolecular organization visible in the specimen. Methacrylates and epoxy-resins have been developed as embedding media, and methods have been devised to enable sections of the necessary thinness to be cut from all types of tissue. The use of heavy metals for the staining of sections in order to increase contrast, or as a negative stain of dispersed material, has facilitated studies at the molecular level. Many methods are available and much depends on the requirements of a particular tissue; the techniques have been given with great clarity and in excellent detail in "Techniques for Electron Microscopy" 2nd ed. edited by D. H. Kay (1965).

B. HANDLING OF CULTURES FOR ELECTRON-MICROSCOPY

Cultures for examination by the electron-microscope fall into four categories, the handling of which differs in certain respects. A brief outline of some methods is given below.

1. *Whole Mounts of Monolayer Cultures*

Whole mounts of cell cultures were examined first in the electron-microscope by Porter, Claude and Fullam (1945). The technique was based on obtaining a thin well-spread layer of cells which was grown on a plastic film, such as could be prepared, for example, from 0·3% Formvar in ethylene dichloride and supported on a coverslip. Such coated coverslips were sterilized by u.v. irradiation. After fixation of the culture, the cells together with the underlying film were stripped off, placed on specimen grids, and examined in the electron-microscope either without further treatment, or after being first shadowed with a metal such as gold-palladium. Alternatively, steel specimen grids were used and inserted beneath the Formvar film while the cultures were still growing, thus eliminating much of the handling (Fitton Jackson, 1953).

2. *Sections of Monolayer Cultures*

More recently, cultures have been grown on coverslips prepared with either plastic films covered with a film of sublimed carbon, or on films prepared from a solution of collagen and covered with a carbon film (Heyner, 1963). After fixation, subsequent dehydration and impregnation with the requisite resin, gelatine capsules filled with the embedding medium are inverted over the required cells (e.g. Micou, Collins and Crocker, 1962). Special areas can be chosen previously by examining the culture by phase-contrast microscopy and marking the area with a diamond (e.g. Bloom, 1960). After polymerization, the marked area of the block can be sectioned, and stained as required after mounting on a specimen grid.

3. *Organ Cultures*

Thin sections of organ cultures can be prepared by the use of techniques for the appropriate tissue (e.g. Glauert and Phillips, 1965); the lengths of time for fixation, dehydration and impregnation by the embedding medium should be varied according to the size of the specimen, the density of the molecular components of the tissue, and the water content. In general, specimens should not exceed 4 mm in thickness.

4. *Cell Suspensions and Cell Fractions*

Cells grown in suspension can be collected by gentle centrifugation and then processed like a small piece of tissue; occasionally it is a help if such preparations are embedded first in agar (e.g. Glauert, 1965). When homogenized cells are fractionated under various centrifugal forces, the resultant pellets may be treated similarly. Alternatively when homogenates are subjected to fractionation by, for example, sucrose density gradients, the various fractions can be studied by means of negative-contrast methods (e.g. Horne, 1965). In this method, small drops of each fraction are mixed with an equal volume of a solution of an heavy metal, for example phosphotungstic acid, which "impregnates" the specimen so that the molecular organization is seen against the dense background of the metal (e.g. Parsons, 1963).

III. Cellular Organization at the Molecular Level

A. The Cell Surface

Tissue cultures are particularly amenable to studies of the nature of the cell surface and its response to alterations in physiological conditions. Cinemicrophotographic observations of various types of living cells maintained in culture have emphasized not only the heterogeneity but the dynamic nature of the surface; they show, for example, that the advancing edge of migrating cells may form into thin sheets of undulating cytoplasm (Fig. 1), while numerous cytoplasmic projections of varying length, and sometimes of extreme thinness, may extend out into the surrounding culture medium (Fig. 2). Certain cells, such as macrophages, undergo rapid changes in shape, and a further striking characteristic of most cells is the marked extensibility of the surface,

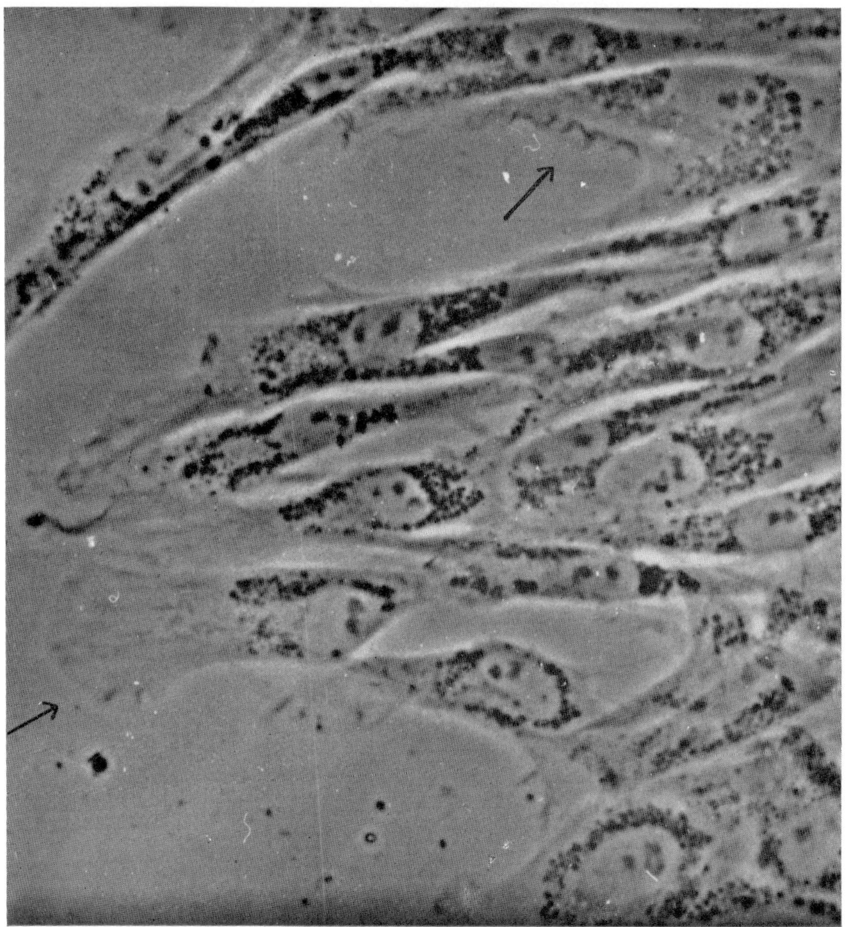

FIG. 1. Phase-contrast photomicrograph of cells migrating from an explant of metatarsal tendon of a 10-day chick embryo in serum exudate. Note the ruffled edges of the cells and the extreme thinness of the outer parts of the cytoplasm of some cells. × 550.

which appears to be capable of a considerable degree of distortion when a cell is subjected, for instance, to severe compression. In addition, the cell surface may be seen to react in a variety of ways during the passage of substances of different molecular weight into and out of the cell. A fundamental problem in the field of biology is an understanding of the various functions of the cell surface and how these may be expressed in terms of molecular architecture; certain aspects of this problem, in which tissue-culture investigations have contributed, will be discussed briefly.

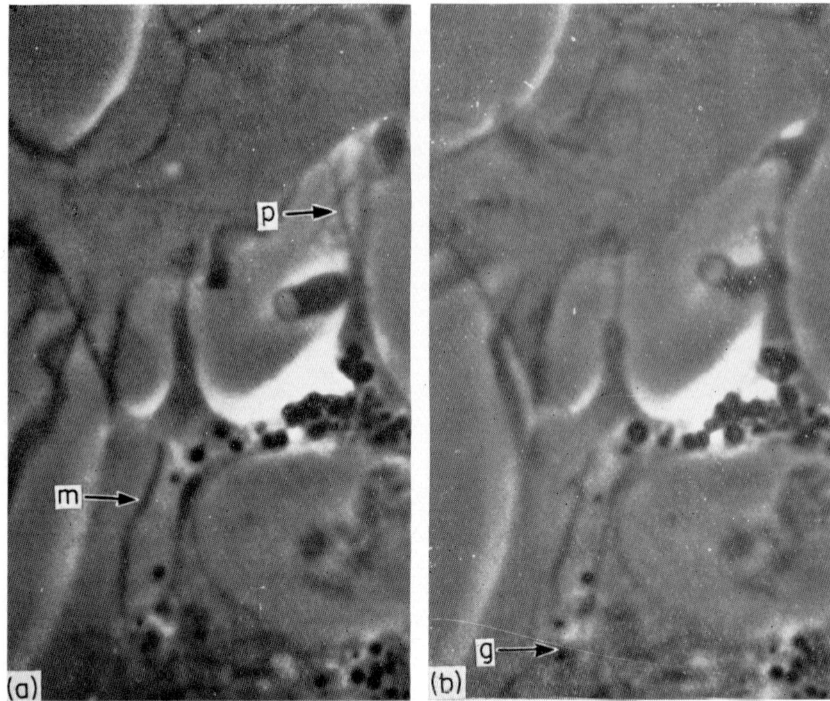

FIG. 2. Adjacent phase-contrast photomicrographs taken from a ciné-film of osteoblasts growing from an explant of frontal bone of 11-day chick embryo. Note the long cytoplasmic processes (p), mitochondria (m) and a Golgi zone (g) near the nucleus. There is a 3 sec interval between frames. × 2,500.

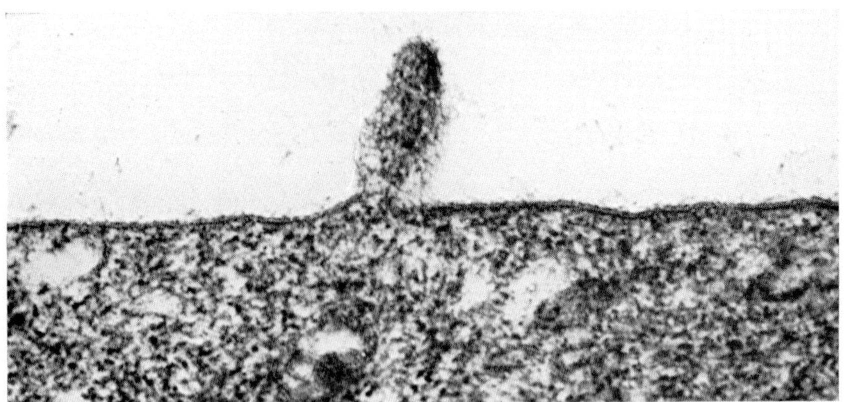

FIG. 3. Electron-micrograph of a thin section of epidermal cells growing in organ culture. The triple layers of the cell surface can be seen clearly. × 72,000.

1. *Structure of the Cell Surface*

Electron-microscopy of sectioned tissues has demonstrated that a characteristic morphological feature of the surface of most metazoan cells is a triple-layered structure (Fig. 3) consisting of two dense lines, each about 25 Å wide, separated by a less dense region of about 25 Å, the whole being termed the (75 Å) unit membrane by Robertson (1959). Detailed studies have not been made of the dimensions of this membrane in cells in culture, but at present there is no evidence to suggest that they differ from those in the corresponding cell *in vivo*. The width of the membrane may well vary in different cell types and depend upon the physiological activity of the cell; for instance, Sjöstrand and Zetterqvist (1957) noted a transitory increase in width shortly after the intake of food in the intestinal epithelium of the mouse. Further studies by Sjöstrand and Elfvin (1962) and Sjöstrand (1963b) have shown that in cells from the kidney and pancreas, the triple-layered structure of the cell surface measures between 90 and 100 Å after fixation by either osmium tetroxide or potassium permanganate; the structure appeared to be asymmetrical with a thicker opaque layer at the cytoplasmic surface, and a thinner opaque layer at the external surface of the cell; occasionally, however, the opaque layers were of equal width after potassium permanganate treatment. In a detailed comparative study of the dimensions and structural patterns of various unit membranes, present in the same cells, Sjöstrand (1963a, b) noted that the total width of the triple-layered structure of the cell surface was greater than that of certain other cytoplasmic organelles, and furthermore that a globular sub-structure, evident in the membranes of the organelles, was not observed in the membrane of the cell surface.

In general it has been assumed that the triple-layered structure, seen in sections of cells by electron-microscopy, might well represent a bimolecular leaflet of mixed lipids with a monolayer of protein or other material on either interface as first proposed by Danielli and Harvey (1934) for the possible structure of the cell surface membrane; in their model the lipid molecules were orientated so that their hydrocarbon tails were opposed to one another with the respective polar heads either towards the exterior or interior of the cell. The identity of such lipid or protein components with any part of the triple-layered structure seen by electron-microscopy has not yet been established. Nor is the precise molecular structure of the cell surface membrane known; much of the evidence is indirect, and based, in the main, on work on membranes of erythrocytes or studies of physico-chemical systems. Although it seems indisputable that water insoluble lipoproteins form part of the cell surface, various other molecular configurations to that suggested by Danielli and Harvey have been proposed. Winkler and Bungenberg de Jong (1941) suggested that the surface might consist of a single compact monolayer of lipid with a second diffuse layer adhering discontinuously, and in addition that cholesterol might play an important part by stabilizing the phospholipid molecules. Finean (1957) was in agreement with this latter suggestion and also considered that water formed an integral part of the structure proposed by Danielli and Harvey by being spatially related to the hydrophilic groups of the lipid and protein components. Although the amount of water in the cell surface is not known, it has been found to vary between 30% (Schmitt, Bear and Palmer, 1941) and 65% (Shanes and Berman, 1955) in myelin; in this respect it is interesting that the birefringent properties of the cell surface change on drying. Danielli (1958) has extended his earlier hypothesis with Harvey to suggest that the protein moiety may well interdigitate between the oriented lipid molecules since such a structure would facilitate expansion of the membrane; Haydon (1962), however, has questioned the validity of this proposal, in view of the low surface tension of mammalian cells (2 dynes/cm) and since he failed to demonstrate that added protein reduced the surface tension of a phospholipid film (36 dynes/cm).

The fact that Sjöstrand (1963a, b) has observed a globular structure in certain membranes of cellular organelles, though not in the triple-layered structure of the cell surface, suggests a different molecular configuration from that of a bimolecular leaflet. It is interesting therefore that Lucy and Glauert (1964), in studies of artificial mixtures of lipids by electron-microscopy, have observed lamellar, tubular, hexagonal and helical complexes which appeared to contain specific arrangements of small globular sub-units. These findings led to the suggestion that biological membranes may, under certain circumstances, be present in the form of globular micelles of phospholipid, about 40–50 Å in diameter, with aqueous pores, approximately 4 Å in radius, extending throughout the lipid layer. In a theoretical discussion of globular lipid micelles and cell membranes, Lucy (1964) has suggested that within the plane of the membrane the globular micelles would probably be arranged in an hexagonal lattice but would be in continuous random motion about their mean positions. The stability of the structure would depend on hydrogen bonding and electrostatic interactions between adjacent micelles. Furthermore, transitions to and from a micellar-type membrane might be particularly important in relation to the movement of molecules at the surface and to membrane permeability. Functional enzymes might also form an integral part of the structure of the membrane in such regions. Thus, the structure of the cell surface may well be heterogeneous in the sense that the configuration of the composite molecules may vary; hence an orientated bimolecular leaflet and globular micelles may not necessarily be mutually exclusive.

For purposes of further discussion, the surface of the cell will be taken not only to be represented by a unit membrane but will include also those regions immediately adjacent to it both within and without the cell. Much evidence now supports the idea that each cell lies within its own microenvironment, in the sense that the substances associated with the outer layer of the membrane of the cell surface may differ from time to time and from place to place. Although most of the evidence is indirect, various experimental results suggest that in all metazoan cells part of such a microenvironment is mucoid in nature and of varying thickness. When cells are treated with proteolytic enzymes, and, in particular, with trypsin, cellular attachment is weakened and a mucinous material is liberated. L. Weiss (1958) noted that there was a 20% loss in the dry mass of ascites cells after such treatment, but there was no appreciable loss in cellular diameter; he suggested therefore that the change in weight represented a "slime coat" lost from the cell surface. Examination of epidermal cells after short-term trypsinization by the author has shown, however, that the osmiophilic membrane of the cell surface was not disrupted, and that there was no change in the electron density of the regions immediately adjacent as compared with controls; the basement membrane, visible as an electron dense line, about 400 Å wide, was removed, however, by such treatment. The treatment with trypsin also affects the capacity of cells to adhere to various surfaces, which again suggests an alteration in the properties of the cell surface. Further studies by Weiss (1962) demonstrated that neuraminidase produced a significant reduction of the shear-strength of the surface of foetal rat fibroblasts in culture, the results indicating that sialic acid was a structural component of the surface of the cells. Earlier, Cook Heard and Seaman (1960) had shown that trypsin released a sialomucoprotein from the surface of erythrocytes, and both Ponder (1952–3) and Seaman and Heard (1960) recorded a 20% reduction in the net negative charge of the erythrocytes after treatment with trypsin. These results strongly implied that a mucoid substance was associated with the surface of certain cells, and that the net negative charge of the cell may be due, in part, to this material. Subsequent work by Cook, Heard and Seaman (1962) confirmed that the carboxyl group of sialic acid(s), probably located at the surface of Ehrlich ascites tumour cells, was responsible for their negative electrophoretic charge. Gasic and Berwick (1963) have shown also by electron-microscopy that sialic acid was largely associated with the surface regions of mouse ascites cells.

In an elegant study Rosenberg (1960) found that a microexudate, that he defined as a substance of submicroscopical dimensions roughly 20–40 Å in width was given off by fibroblasts in culture. He showed that, upon contact with certain surfaces, i.e. clean glass, silicone and transferred stearate films, these cells deposited a complex molecular "carpet" that had strong affinities for the respective surfaces. Rosenberg's results indicated that this microexudate consisted, not only of the cell's own secretory product, but of molecules transferred from the surfaces of the cells. Furthermore the surfaces of the cells in culture appeared to possess a molecular configuration and charge distribution such that molecular adsorption could take place; for instance trypsin became adsorbed to the surface of the cells and remained enzymatically active. Since the "bridge" of microexudate between cell and, for example, glass surface was resistant to both trypsin and Versene, Rosenberg suggested that the microexudate might act as an ionic bridge, or that the bonding forces involved London-van-der-Waals forces (cf. Curtis, 1960). The microexudate was not given off when cells rested upon transferred or adsorbed films of protein; it would be interesting to know, therefore, whether the microexudate was still present in the sense that it was adhering to the cell surface. This leads one to the question of whether the microexudate is synonymous with the mucinous substance of the cell surface discussed previously. The simplest hypothesis would be that the microexudate forms an integral part of the cell surface, and that, when it is shed from the cell, it undergoes renewal at the cell surface. Future studies of this culture system by, for instance, electron-microscopy and other physical and chemical techniques should yield much new information.

Studies by P. Weiss (1933, 1945), indicated that a colloidal substance, visible by light microscopy, was produced by cultured cells. He found that this substance determined the orientation and the arrangement of the cells growing outward from an explant, suggesting that cells, in conjunction with their growth medium, modified their environment in such a way that their movement was affected. The question arises whether this colloidal substance is related to the mucinous material of the cell surface or should it be taken to represent part of the ground substance; the work of Castor (1962) and others has suggested that, in culture, many cells produce hyaluronate, which is a characteristic constituent of some ground substances.

In a study of the response of cells to pH changes in the medium, Taylor (1962) noted that cells changed their polarity and their direction of movement in response to a microstream of fluid applied in such a way that only a part of the cell surface would be effected by the change in pH*. Taylor suggested that the change in pH was sufficient to induce a gelation or contraction in the cytoplasm adjacent to the affected area, and thus brought about an asymmetrical change in the general cell outline; he also found that free cells displayed greater surface activity when they lay in the path of the microstream. The work of Taylor supports the view that local pH changes in the microenvironment of part of the surface of a cell, may be a significant factor in controlling cellular behaviour. Both Danielli (1937) and McLaren and Babcock (1959) have emphasized that the pH of a particular region of the cell surface may differ by as much as 2 pH units from that of the bulk phase.

The suggestion by Willmer (1961) that steroids may become localized within the membrane of the cell surface, leaving large polar groups projecting outwards, leads to the idea that a concentration of steroids could also alter the surface properties to a considerable extent.

2. *Morphological Specialization of the Cell Surface*

One function of the cell surface is to act as a bounding layer within which cellular organization is maintained. Some revealing features demonstrated by cinemicrophotography of tissue-culture cells are the quick changes in their shape, the rapid formation of cytoplasmic blebs, elongated protrusions, and narrow cytoplasmic processes of extreme length, some of which appear to be attached at their tips (Fig. 4), while others wave about freely in the medium. Porter *et al.* (1945) were the first to examine the morphology of the cell in tissue culture by viewing whole mounts of thinly spread cells in the electron-microscope (Fig. 5); they described narrow cellular processes that appeared to be composed of thin cytoplasmic sheets with occasional dense swellings, presumably representing small cytoplasmic organelles. Some of these processes measured about 2000 Å in diameter while others were well below the resolution of the light microscope. Further observations on such processes in various different types of cells were recorded by De Robertis and Setelo (1952), Fitton Jackson (1953) and Gey (1956). More recently P. Weiss (1961) has commented on the rigidity of some cytoplasmic extensions of cells in culture; he suggested they contained a rigid core and designated them "microspikes". Subsequent studies by Taylor and Robbins (1963) have shown that in living cells such microspikes were most frequently present at an active border of a cell, were about 15 μ long and waved about continuously. The microspikes were

*Changes were induced by the alteration of the concentration of H^+, HCO_3^- and CO_2 in the medium; the response failed to occur when either HCO_3 or CO_2 were varied without changing the pH. Elevation of pH accelerated cell movement while lowering the pH retarded and eventually stopped cellular activity.

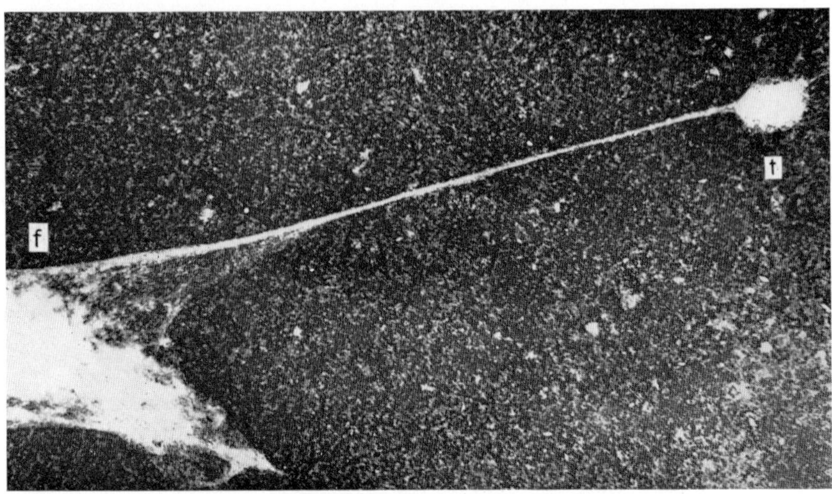

FIG. 4. Electron-micrograph of a whole mount of part of a dermal fibroblast (f) showing a flattened tip (t) attached to the substratum; note the extreme thinness of the process proximal to the tip. × 7,000.

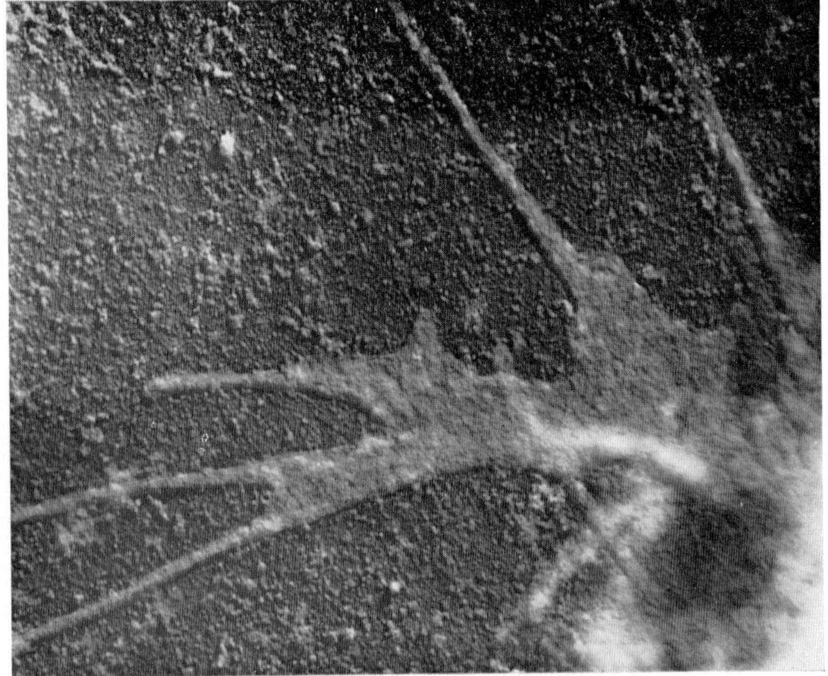

FIG. 5. Electron-micrograph of a whole mount of part of a fibroblast from chick tendon growing in culture, showing long narrow processes. × 8,000.

stiff and, either of uniform diameter, or thicker at their base, where they appeared to be hinged to the main body of the cell; occasionally they were forked at their tip. In general, the life of such microspikes was short, and regression occurred either by a general collapse or by a folding back onto the cell. Studies of such whole cells by electron-microscopy demonstrated the presence of extremely dense processes of about 1000 Å in diameter which consisted of a single axial core about 500–800 Å in diameter surrounded by a thin sleeve of cytoplasm; in some of these processes, however, more than one core of varying length was present and the total diameter was upwards of 2000 Å, depending on the number of cores. Unless the unit processes have undergone considerable shrinkage during preparation, or appear larger in living cultures because of their rapid movement, it would seem that only the processes with multiple cores would be observed by light microscopy, and would correspond to the microspikes. The authors suggested that, although there was as yet little direct evidence, the microspikes were in fact real cell organelles in the sense that they were ideally adapted for tactile exploration of, and selective attachment to, solid structures such as may be required in cell to cell contacts. Taylor and Robbins (1963) further described other cytoplasmic extensions which appeared to flutter passively in living cultures but which, when anchored to the substratum were straight; they were longer than 15 μ and about 0·5 μ or less in width. Most of these processes appeared to be formed by strands of cytoplasm spun out from the retreating border of a cell, and were named "retraction fibrils" by the authors. Electron-microscopy showed thin processes without a dense core; they were greatly elongated, with less regular contours than the microspikes, and various swellings along their length appeared to contain granular cytoplasm. When cytoplasmic processes anchored the cell to the substratum the tips of the cell processes became extremely flattened. Such processes often showed an active streaming of cytoplasmic matter; Fitton Jackson and Randall (1956) noted that when living cultures of osteoblasts were studied by interferometer microscopy, the mass of a process increased and diminished in alternating sequence, suggesting that there were variations in the concentration of material in the process.

These various studies of cytoplasmic processes tend to emphasize the remarkable plasticity of the cell; it is of interest, therefore, that tissue cultures have been used to measure the relative extensibility of the cell surface; Rosenberg (1963) found that, on application of a controlled pressure, bulges or protrusions (termed "herniations" by Rosenberg) developed at the cell surface but quickly receded on decompression; 5–30 min later the surface contour of the cell had returned to normal. The initiation and enlargement of any one protrusion did not prevent the development of others in the same cell, and although they appeared rapidly, there was no undue disturbance of the adjacent ectoplasm. Successive application and release of the deforming force led to protrusions arising in different places at the cell surface, thus demonstrating that the surface was heterogeneous with respect to its ability to form protrusions. Measurements made on cultures prepared directly from the liver and heart of embryonic chickens, and on a tissue culture strain of human conjunctival cells were different, the last showing the lowest value for extensibility. An abrupt increase in surface extensibility of chicken heart cells occurred between 7 and 10 days of embryonic development, but the value for embryonic liver cells did not alter. Although considerable fluctuations in extensibility occurred during the first 4 days in culture, heart cells kept for about 3 weeks showed the same degree of extensibility as on explanation. It is interesting that the dispersion of monolayer cultures of human conjunctival cells in several different ways failed to show a change in surface extensibility. The mechanism of such surface extensibility is not yet understood, but these results demonstrate that under the same conditions the extensibility of the cell surface varies in different types of cells, and implies therefore that the molecular configuration of the surface layers may differ. In any discussion on the structure of the cell surface, it is necessary to formulate a molecular architecture that is capable of permitting such tremendous extensions of cytoplasmic processes and protrusions without loss of the coherence of the surface.

Tissue cultures have been used in many detailed studies of cell contact (see Vol. 1); contact guidance (P. Weiss, 1929) and contact inhibition (Abercrombie and Heaysman, 1954) must have a profound importance in all morphogenetic mechanisms. Studies of the fine-structure of adjacent cells in culture are not many, but adjacent cell surfaces ordinarily maintain a separation of 100–200 Å, depicted as an electron-lucent region (Fig. 6), and found, for example, in organ cultures of epidermis by Fitton Jackson and Fell (1963). The gap between cells can be narrowed to about 15 Å, however, by treatment with hypertonic solutions (L. Weiss, 1962), a finding that supports the idea that such intercellular regions may consist of mucoid material with an high water content.

Devis and James (1962) have observed a complex relationship between adult guinea-pig fibroblasts, obtained from granulation tissue of 10-day-old wounds, explanted and cultured in plasma clots. After fixation by osmium tetroxide, adjacent cells were separated by a distance of about 160 Å; in this zone a central dense line about 20 Å wide was present between the respective unit membranes, but after fixation with permanganate the line increased to double this width. A

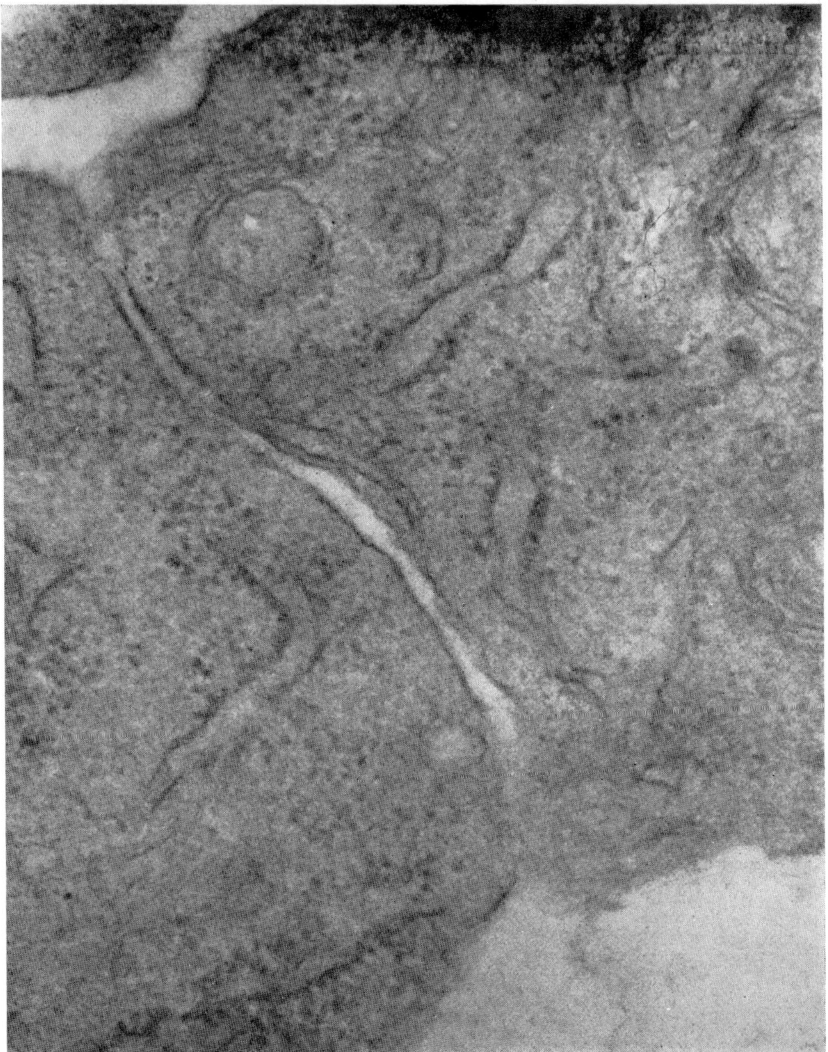

FIG. 6. Electron-micrograph of a section of a corneal culture showing the close association of adjacent cells. × 105,000.

similar appearance has also been reported by Robertson (1959) in Schwann cell membranes. Devis and James suggested that this structural feature between fibroblasts might be of importance for intercellular adhesion.

In a study of the fine-structure of vertebrate epidermis, Porter (1954) observed occasional dense thickenings of opposing cell surfaces and correlated this feature with the presence of desmosomes. Subsequent studies of a number of tissues have demonstrated the marked degree of symmetry and alignment within the desmosome; these structures consist essentially of intermittent areas of the adjacent cytoplasm of different cells, where dense plaques have formed directly beneath the surface of each cell and from which fibrillar tufts extend into the cytoplasm (Fig. 7); the intercellular gap is denser and often slightly wider than elsewhere and usually an electron-dense stratum marks the midline between the cells. The dimensions of the desmosomal complex vary in different cell types and also with the use of different fixatives and staining procedures.

The importance of desmosomes in certain morphogenetic movements of cells and their capacity to form firm and localized sites of cell adhesion is well recognized. Overton (1962) has studied the sequential development of desmosomes in chick blastoderms by means of electron-microscopy. Desmosomes were not present at the primitive streak stage but became more and more frequent at subsequent stages (5–11). In view of the importance attached to the capacity of cells to reorganize normal tissue patterns in culture after their dissociation, Overton studied also the reassociation of blastodermal cells. Separation was achieved by trypsinization of stages 9–11 and the dispersed cells were reassociated in Maximow depression slides; Overton succeeded in picking out a developmental sequence for desmosomes based on her observations of the normal development in the blastoderm; she thought that it was possible that remnants of desmosomes were reorganized, as well as new ones formed. A sequence of samples were fixed $1\frac{1}{2}$, 4 and 13 h after dispersion, and corresponded to three stages of the symmetrical development of the desmosome. First, localized electron-dense regions were associated with adjacent cell surfaces; secondly, desmosomal plaques appeared and widening of the intercellular spaces occurred; thirdly, numerous fibres sprouted from the plaques into the cytoplasm and the intercellular stratum developed. Densitometer tracings of the newly formed desmosome indicated that the intercellular region was 300–350 Å wide and that the plaque to cell membrane measured 125 Å. Overton observed also that desmosomal components were present in one cell in the absence of any in the opposite cell 13 h after dispersion, indicating that under these circumstances a half desmosome does not necessarily induce a counterpart in the opposite cell. This finding suggests that desmosomes may form only at specific sites of the cell surface.

3. *Cytosis and Secretion*

The passage of various substances into and out of the cell must involve a number of mechanisms; such movement must depend on the

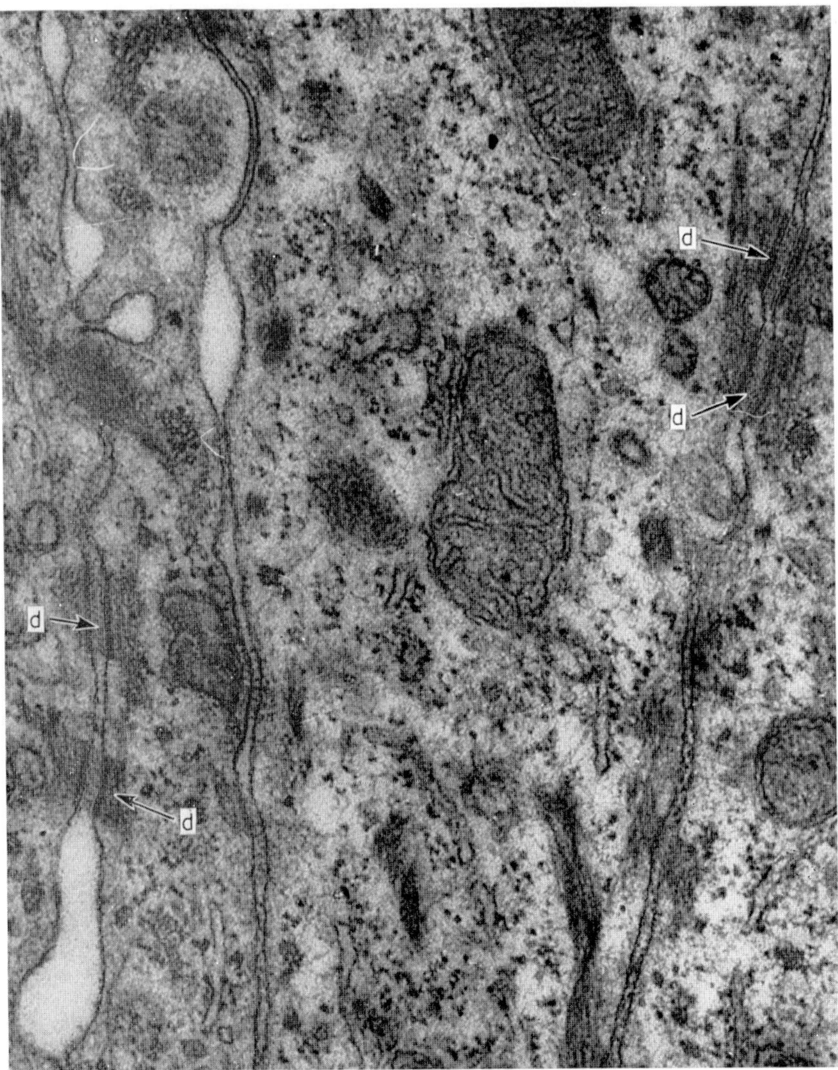

FIG. 7. Electron-micrograph of part of a section of chick skin grown in organ culture showing the detailed structure of the desmosomes (d) of the epidermal cells. × 72,000.

requirements of the cell, on environmental factors, on the size and shape of the molecules, and on the distribution of positive and negative charges on the molecule and on the cell surface.

The mode of passage may well differ from one cell type to another. The simple diffusion of ions, for instance, may be dependent upon the nature of the cell surface, as discussed above; in addition ions may be pumped against an active gradient in which an enzyme or enzymes may play an essential part. The localization of alkaline phosphatase within, or just beneath, the surface layer of epithelial cells of rat kidney tubules by means of a lead-phosphate staining method and electron-microscopy (Mölbert, Duspive and von Deimling, 1960) supports this concept.

An important feature of cellular activity, however, was first noted by Lewis (1931) in living cultures of fibroblasts; he commented on the apparent inbibition of the surrounding fluid medium by means of an enfolding of part of the cell surface, which then became pinched off to form intracellular vacuoles, a process of pinocytosis. Since then, many cinemicrophotographic films of different cells have depicted this activity with great clarity. Observations have also shown that the intake of solid material of various sizes could occur by cytoplasmic engulfment, or phagocytosis. Novikoff (e.g. 1963) has suggested that pinocytosis and phagocytosis involve similar cellular mechanisms and has proposed that the general term "cytosis" should be used. It seems possible that secretory processes may involve the discharge of substances from the cell by a reversal of mechanisms used in cytotic activity.

Tissue cultures, in which cytosis is so evident in the living cells, have not yet been used to any great extent to study the mechanisms that may be involved at the molecular level. The potentiality of such material, however, has been indicated by a study of surface antigens and pinocytosis by Easton, Goldberg and Green (1962). In this work, fibroblasts were incubated for a short period with rabbit immune ferritin-linked γ-globulin. Electron-microscopy demonstrated labyrinthine folding of the cell surfaces and characteristic arrays of ferritin molecules were associated with them, indicating that conjugated antibody was fixed to the surface antigen. Subsequently most of the ferritin was observed in small vesicles bounded by a 70 Å membrane, but it was not identified in mitochondria or in ergastoplasm. These results implied that the ferritin antibody was not able to pass directly through the cell membrane but rather had become included within pinocytotic vesicles by an infolding of the cell surface. Clearly, further work along these lines, in which observations on living cells are correlated with various methods applicable to molecular studies, will be of great value.

B. THE CYTOPLASM

1. *Basic Structural Features*

Studies of the fine-structure of cells in culture are, at present, comparatively few in number, but those that have been made indicate that the major structural features of the cytoplasm (Figs. 7 and 8) conform with observations on similar cells *in vivo*.

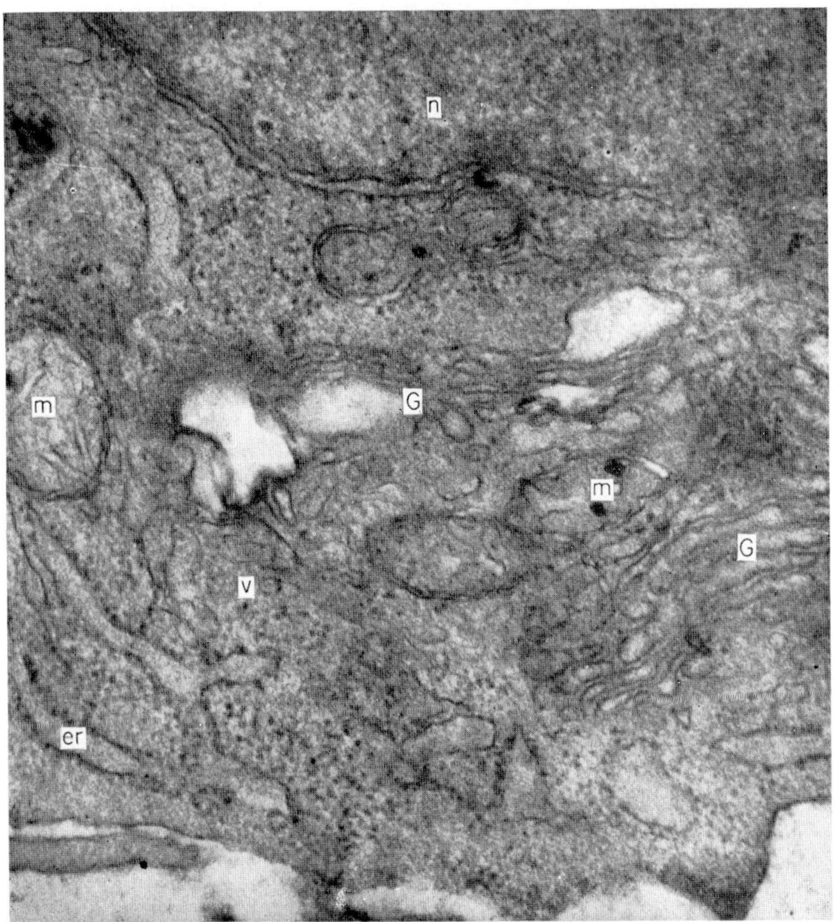

FIG. 8. Electron-micrograph of part of the fibroblast growing in monolayer culture from dispersed dermal cells of the embryo chick. The cytoplasmic organization is extremely complex; mitochondria (m), Golgi zone (G), numerous vesicles (v), endoplasmic reticulum (er) and part of the nucleus (n) are visible. × 72,000.

The cytoplasmic sap in which the organelles are bathed appears as a comparatively electron-lucent substance by electron-microscopy, although new features of this region are beginning to become apparent when glutaraldehyde is used as an initial fixative. The cytoplasmic sap corresponds essentially to the supernatant fraction, obtained when cells are broken up and submitted to differential centrifugation, and many metabolic processes are carried out in this region of the cell (e.g. Zamecnik, Stephenson and Hecht, 1958; Lehninger, 1959). The presence of metabolically-active molecules suggests that the sap must be organized in a definitive spatial manner so as to facilitate the functioning of the various activities. Studies of sub-fractions of the supernatant, obtained by centrifugation under various centrifugal forces in the region of $200{,}000 \times g$, by means of negative stains and high resolution electron-microscopy may well reveal details of the structure of various molecular components, the biochemical histories of which are known. Tissue cultures should prove to be a valuable tool in this respect.

The behaviour of mitochondria has been studied in considerable detail in living cells in tissue culture; many ciné films have shown that the mitochondria move about constantly in the cytoplasm, have a remarkable plasticity of shape and undergo rhythmic swelling and contraction (e.g. Canti, 1928), but such movements may be exaggerated on account of the flattening of the cell on the substratum. Sections of cultured fibroblasts, and indeed of most cells in culture, examined by electron-microscopy demonstrate that the mitochondrion is bounded by a triple-layered (unit) membrane with a total thickness of the order of 60 Å; the opaque inner and outer layers are each about 20 Å wide, and the intermediate region is approximately 20 Å wide also (Fig. 9).

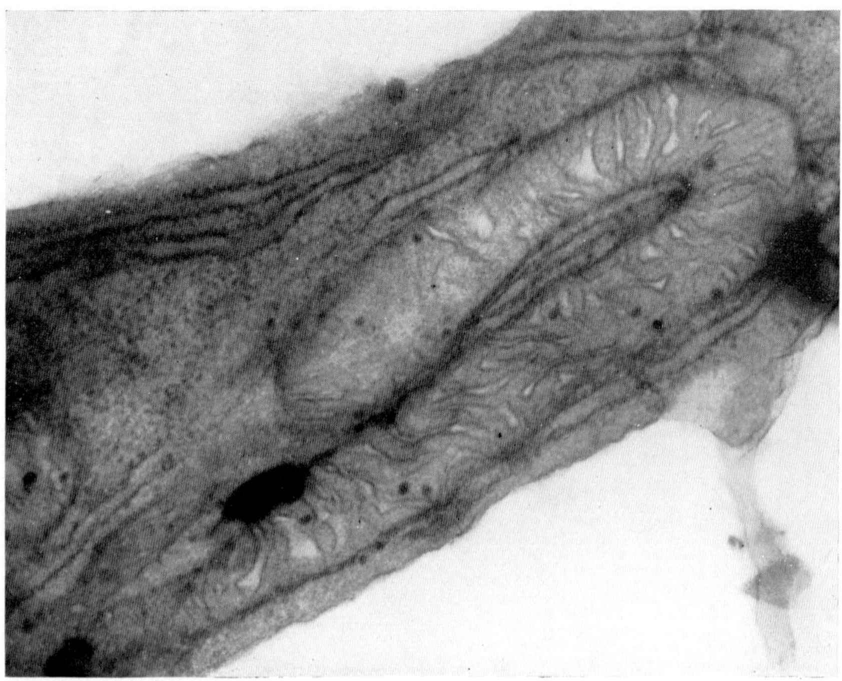

FIG. 9. A thin section of a mitochondrion lying within a cytoplasmic process of a corneal fibroblast growing in culture. Note the way in which the mitochondrion is bent back on itself. $\times$ 105,000.

Internal membranes project into the interior of the mitochondrion and may be surrounded by an electron-lucent homogeneous matrix; these membranes appear to arise as folds of the inner limiting membrane. Membranes composed of globular units as observed by Sjöstrand (1963a) in mitochondria of kidney cells have not yet been described in mitochondria of cells in culture.

Mitochondrial structure in relation to function has been discussed in a detailed treatise by Lehninger (1965). Various small particles, associated with mitochondrial membranes, first described by Fernandez-Moran (1963) and Parsons (1963), and implicated with electron transport, oxidative reactions and with the catalyzing of certain synthetic reactions, have not yet been demonstrated as a feature of mitochondria in cultured cells. The facility with which controlled alterations can be made in the metabolic state of the cell in culture, however, and the speed with which such cells can be fixed may well prove that cells in tissue culture are excellent experimental material for future studies of the molecular structure of mitochondria in relation to function.

It is important to emphasize the dynamic nature of the cell; the superb and detailed molecular organization of cells seen by means of electron-microscopy may perhaps leave one with an impression of the complete static precision of the various cellular constituents in relation to each other. The remarkable ability of rapid movement inherent within the individual organelles, however, is clearly depicted in all ciné-films taken of many different cell-types.

Porter and Thompson (1947) examined, by means of electron-microscopy, whole mounts made from thinly spread tumour cells growing in cultures from explants of rat endothelioma. They noted that the cytoplasm contained rounded or oval elements 100–300 mμ in diameter; these vesicular bodies were usually connected to each other in strands or strings to form an irregular reticulated system (Fig. 10), differential fixation and extraction procedures helped to clarify the organization of these components from the rest of the cytoplasm. Porter and Kallman (1952) compared the fine structure of chick macrophages, obtained from buffy-coat cells, *in situ* and in thin sections; the irregular reticulated system usually appeared to be excluded from the thinnest margins of the cells and was confined essentially to the endoplasm; the endoplasmic localization and the reticulated nature of the system led Porter (1953) to apply the term "endoplasmic reticulum" to this morphological entity. Thus the concept, initially derived from cultured cells of a finely-divided and continuous vesicular or vacuolated system has survived to the present time.

In view of the rapid movement of many cytoplasmic organelles in

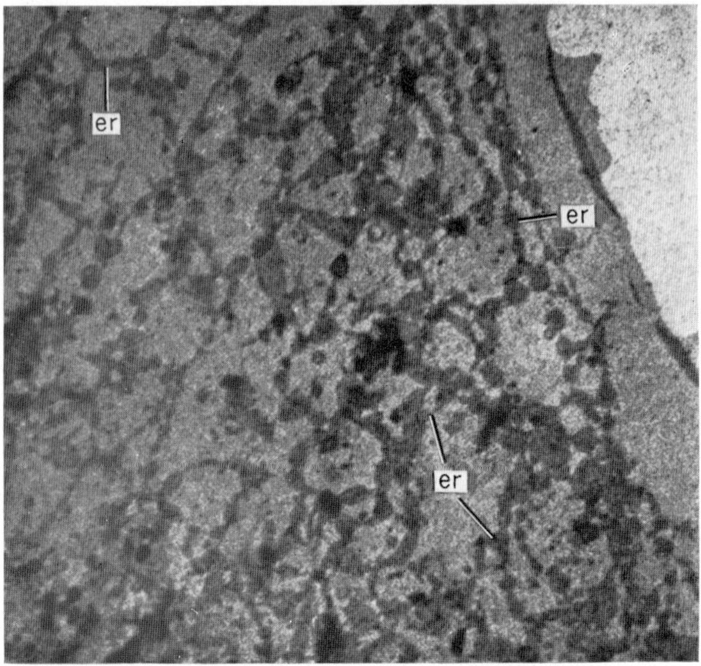

FIG. 10. Electron-micrograph of a marginal area of a thinly spread tumour cell grown in culture from an explant of rat endothelioma. Part of the cell surface is on the right of the micrograph. Note the round and oval elements connected to form strands (er). × 12,000. Micrograph by courtesy of Dr. K. R. Porter.

cells in culture, some controversy exists as to whether the endoplasmic reticulum is necessarily so well-formed in living cells *in vivo* as would be suggested by the appropriate thin sections. Profiles of endoplasmic reticulum, however, do not seem to be so abundant in sections of some cultured cells (Fig. 11) as in their corresponding cells *in vivo*; the difference may well be a reflection of their synthetic state and of their change in environment. That the endoplasmic reticulum does exist as a continous reticulated system in cells in culture is supported by the observations of Fawcett and Ito (1958) and Rose and Pomerat (1960) who have recorded, by means of phase-contrast cinemicrophotography, appropriate reticulated masses, of considerable density, forming a network in the cytoplasm.

Although the description of the Golgi zone seen in living cells in culture varies widely, the ovoid complex is usually located in a juxtanuclear position and consists of a mass of granules or droplets of varying density. The Golgi zone may be seen clearly for example in osteoblasts grown from explants of frontal bone of the embryo chicken and under

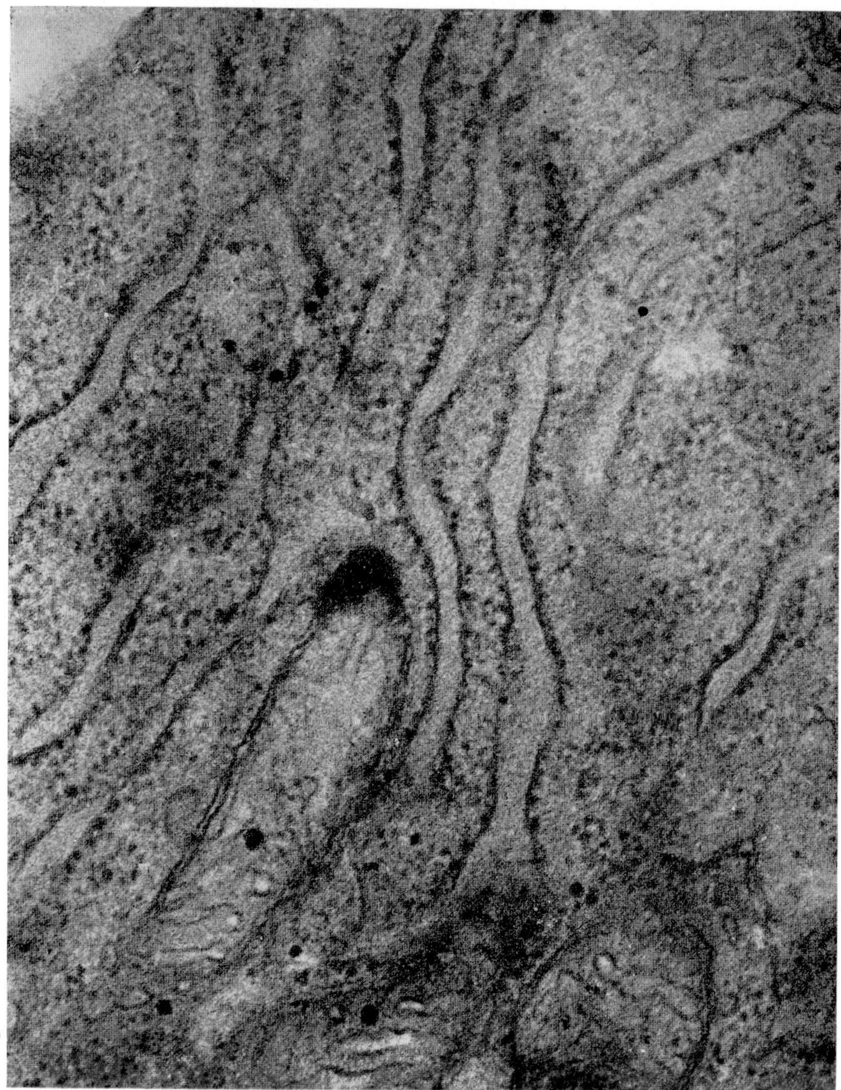

FIG. 11. Electron-micrograph of part of the cytoplasm of a fibroblast growing from a suspension of dermal cells of embryo chick. The variations in the organization of the endoplasmic reticulum are clearly visible although the amount present is not great. × 105,000.

ultraviolet illumination has a low absorption in the range characteristic of nucleic acids (i.e. $\lambda = 265$ mμ). Rose (1961) has studied the behaviour of this region in osteoblasts grown from embryo chicken long bones cultivated under sheets of cellophane; by phase-contrast microscopy the Golgi complex appeared essentially grey with many associated white droplets and occasional strands of material interwoven within the general mass. Observations by cinemicrophotography demonstrated rapid changes in shape and size, while cytochemical tests gave a strongly positive reaction for alkaline phosphatase, and a negative reaction for the periodic acid–Schiff test. The vital dyes, methylene blue and neutral red were taken up strongly by the complex, but it failed to stain for lipid material with Sudan IV. Rose's observations suggested that the droplets were formed in the Golgi zone and were not derived by pinocytotic activity. The fine-structure of the Golgi zone in cultured cells has not been described in any detail; in osteoblast and dermal fibroblasts (Fig. 12), however, it appears to consist essentially of a mass of rounded vesicles, of varying size and density and a complex of elongated sacs, frequently stacked closely together, the membranes of which are smooth.

In addition to the major cytoplasmic organelles described briefly above, numerous particles and vesicles of varying size and density are seen in electron-micrographs of thin sections of cultured cells. The particles measure from 150 to 400 Å across, and some may probably represent free ribosomes. The vesicles range in size from about 500 to 3000 Å in diameter and are characterized by a smooth bounding membrane; whether some of the vesicles are synonymous with pinocytotic vacuoles is at present open to question. In addition, dense ovoid bodies of considerable size are occasionally present in the cytoplasm and may represent lysosomes, but descriptions of their fine-structure in cultured cells have not yet been published.

2. *Alterations in Molecular Organization*

As mentioned previously, cells in culture provide ideal experimental material for studies on the effects of changes in the environment on the molecular organization of cells. For example, the sequence of changes, produced by the addition of vitamin A alcohol, in structural features of rat dermal fibroblasts in culture has been studied by Daniel, Glauert, Dingle and Lucy (1965). Monolayer cultures were grown on films of collagen for 7 days in a medium consisting of 80% Eagle's medium, 10% bovine serum and 10% embryo fowl extract; 33 μg/ml of vitamin A was added and incubation was continued for the next 12 h. Examination of appropriate thin sections by electron-microscopy indicated that there was some variation in the rate at which the cells became affected. Small invaginations of the cell surface occurred first, followed by swelling of the mitochondria, the cristae of which became disorganized after 9 h treatment, a finding which may be correlated with a reduction of respiration. The cisternae of the endoplasmic reticulum became distended for some hours, and then collapsed and diminished in amount;

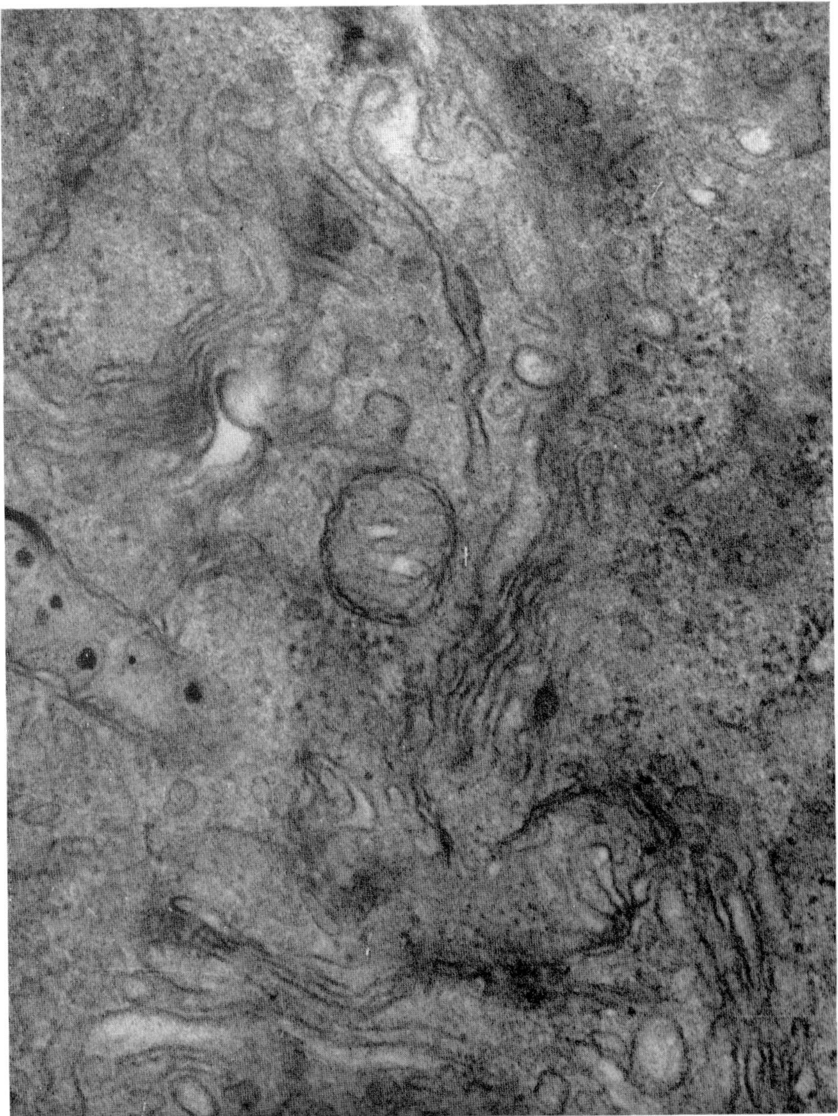

FIG. 12. Electron-micrograph of the Golgi zone of an osteoblast growing in culture. × 72,000.

ribosomes were released from the membranes into the surrounding cytoplasm, leading to a marked rise in the number of free ribosomes; in addition the amount of smooth membranous material increased. The Golgi zone of the treated cells became extensive and its vesicles were swollen and empty, even after 1 h of treatment. Large, dense granules possibly representing lysosomes were present in the cytoplasm throughout the culture period in both control and treated cells; lysosomal granules could be distinguished by light microscopy by the use of the Gomori technique for acid phosphatase. The authors concluded that the vitamin altered the structure of the various membranes of the cell; comparative observations of the structure of the membranes of different cytoplasmic organelles, and of the cell surface at high resolution may well provide much new information and aid in the elucidation of the molecular organization of these structures.

C. INTERPHASE NUCLEI AND THE NUCLEAR MEMBRANE

The condensation of chromatin often in association with the nuclear membrane may be observed as areas of increased density when sections of most cells in culture, and also cells *in vivo*, are studied by electron-microscopy. Interphase nuclei are notable, however, for their inherent lack of readily characterized structure (Fig. 13); the apparent lack of visible order does not, however, necessarily imply absence of molecular order, but rather that it has either not been resolved or not been preserved by the preparative methods now in use.

The matrix of nuclei consists essentially of irregularly dispersed material, which may be somewhat filamentous, and in addition, particles of about 200–300 Å may be randomly dispersed throughout the area. Although the nucleoli form distinctive dense regions within the nuclei, their border is not bounded by a membrane, and their structure appears to consist essentially of closely-packed dense particles of about 200 Å diameter; occasionally dense thread-like processes appear to be randomly twisted within this region.

A survey of published electron-micrographs of cells in culture and many specimens belonging to the author indicate that the nuclear membrane has not undergone any radical alteration due to the change in the environment of the cell. This membrane, seen in cross-section appears to consist of two dense lines forming the inner and outer membranes; each are about 70 Å wide and are separated from each other by a perinuclear space of varying width (Fig. 13). In many tissue cultures, the nuclear membrane is deeply invaginated, while in some instances the outer membrane appears to merge outwards into the cytoplasm; the author, however, has not observed any direct connection between this membrane and any of those in the cytoplasm. The presence of pores in the membrane has long been postulated, and in some cultured cells may be seen as discontinuities in the structure, the outer membrane usually being joined to the inner membrane on either side of the orifice which measures 300–500 Å across. Sjöstrand (1959) has emphasized that a membrane may extend across the orifice, while Bernhard (1959)

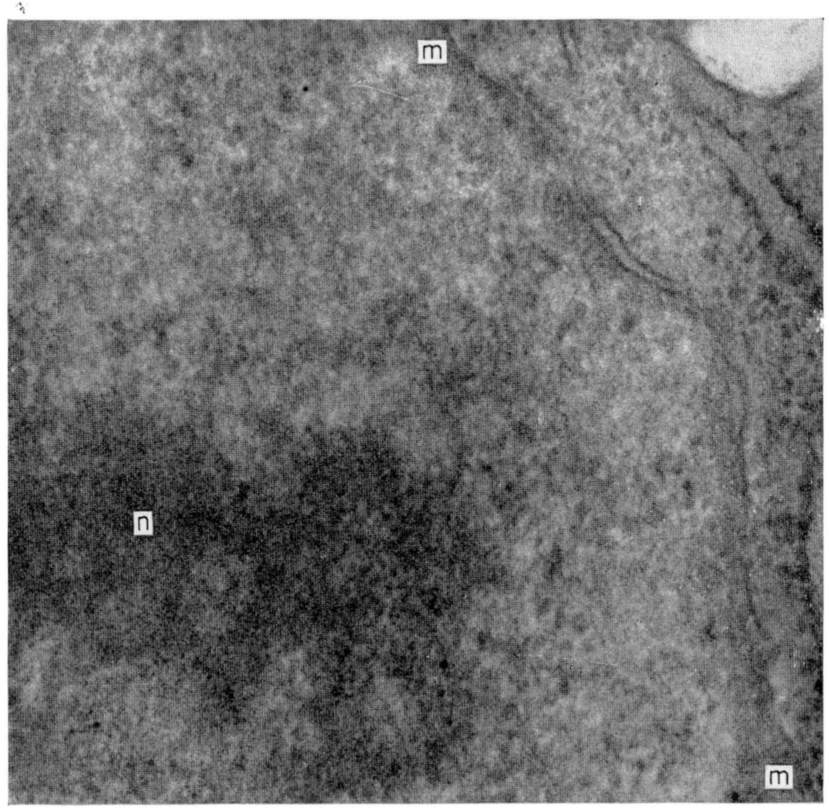

FIG. 13. Electron-micrograph of part of an interphase nucleus of a corneal fibroblast growing in culture. Part of the nuclear membrane (m) can be seen on the right, and the dense mass represents part of a nucleolus (n). × 105,000.

has suggested that a diaphragm is present; either structural arrangement could help in the regulation of material passing through the pore.

D. THE FINE-STRUCTURE OF TISSUE CULTURE CELLS DURING MITOSIS

Many studies have been made of living tissue culture cells in mitosis, with particular reference to the movement of chromosomes and the spindle (see Vol. 1), but there is a paucity of information about cellular fine-structure at different stages of the mitotic cycle. A major problem, at present, is lack of adequate preparative procedures for the preservation of chromosomes; although the general spatial organization of the chromosomal material is retained, the methods for electron-microscopy that have proved more than adequate to maintain the organization of the cytoplasm are practically useless to demonstrate any macromolecular order within the chromosomes.

Bloom and Leider (1962) attempted to investigate the effect of irradiation, with 10^{-1}ergs/μ^2 of heterochromatic ultraviolet light, on chromosomes of the cells of cardiac mesothelium of *Triturus viridescens* and *Amblystoma tigrinum* grown in tissue culture. Although there was a marked change in the refractive index, indicating a loss of substance, of the chromosomes, and a reduction in the amount of Feulgen-positive material, little information was gained by electron-microscopy. There was a marked lowering of the electron density in the irradiated area of the chromosomes, but details of structural organization were not apparent. In further studies, phase contrast and electron-microscopy have been used by Robbins and Gonatas (1964) to describe certain features of HeLa cells during the mitotic cycle, and by Barnicott and Huxley (1965) to investigate the mitotic chromosome.

In their study of cells from newt heart cultures (*Triturus triturus carnifex*) and monolayers of human fibroblasts, Barnicott and Huxley noted that in prophase the nuclear membrane was well-defined at first, but subsequently, on disruption, the two layers became separated from each other, prior to fragmentation. The chromosomes were irregular in outline, very dense, and they stood out from the surrounding material; sometimes they appeared to consist of two chromatids. One to two dense tubular structures representing the centrioles lay in the adjacent cytoplasm (Fig. 14). Robbins and Gonatas (1964) have noted that in HeLa cells centriolar replication is one of the earliest events in the mitotic cycle, two centrioles being observed at each pole of the cell. Spindle fibres were present in the cytoplasm in association with the centrioles and appeared to be similar in structure to the microtubules seen in the cytoplasm of various cells by Behnke (1964) after glutaraldehyde fixation. The spindle fibres were not observed in the nucleus during prophase in newt cells, but in HeLa cells several spindle tubules appeared to pass towards and into chromosomal material. Robbins and Gonatas have suggested that the marked undulation of the nuclear membrane that precedes its dissolution may be intimately related to the spindle-forming activity of the centriole.

Owing to the radial orientation of the chromosomes that occurs during metaphase in the newt cells one, or possibly two centrioles lay at the centre of the clear region round which the chromosomes were disposed. The chromosomes appeared uniformly dense and consisted of two chromatids lying parallel to each other; the centromere regions were flattened against the periphery of the spindle and were attached

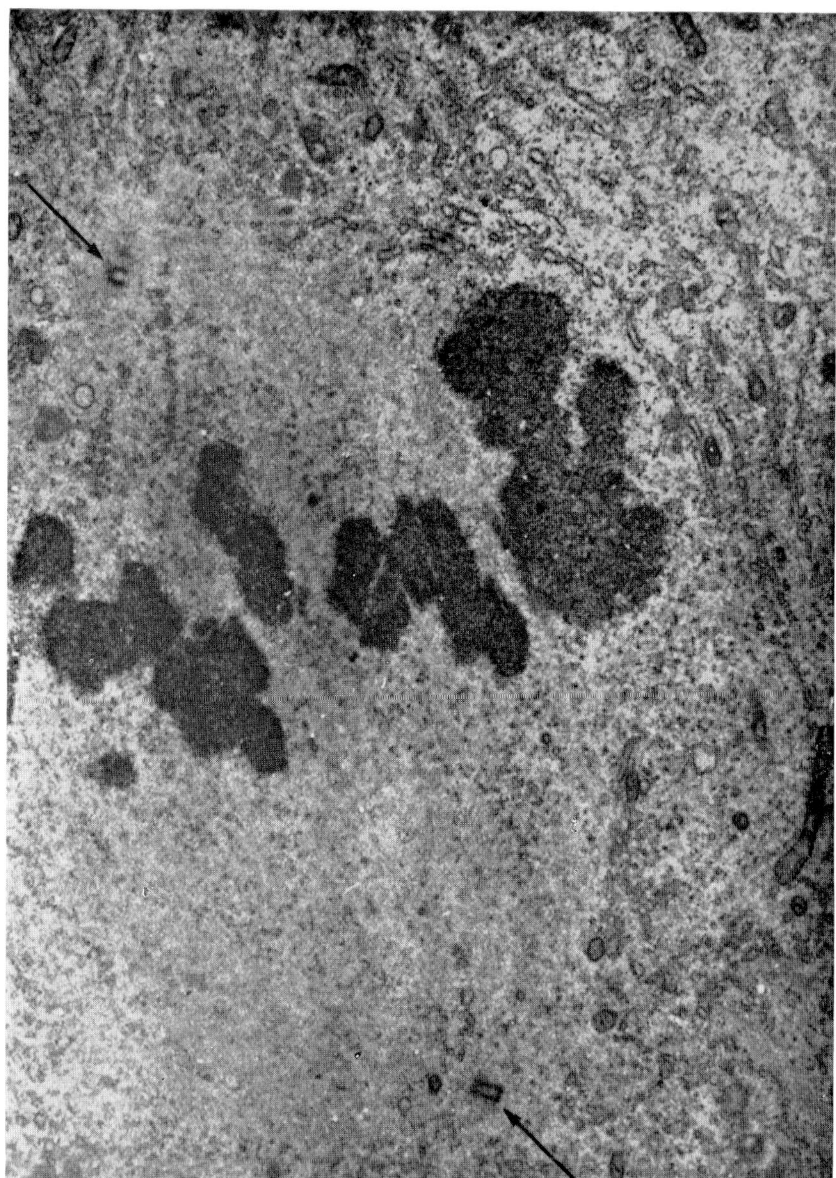

FIG. 14. Electron-micrograph of a cultured human fibroblast in metaphase. The cell has been sectioned through the longitudinal axis of the spindle, and shows centrioles (arrows) at each end of the spindle. Some of the chromosomes are seen within the spindle, while mitochondria and strands of reticulum are visible in the surrounding cytoplasm. × 12,000. Micrograph by courtesy of Dr. N. A. Barnicott and Dr. H. E. Huxley and *Quart J. micr. Sci.*

at various points. The spindle consisted of numerous fibres about 150 Å in diameter, with a denser surface layer giving a tubular appearance; the fibres were slightly wavy but no periodic structure was visible. The chromosomes were attached to centriolar regions by conspicuous bundles of about twenty fibres which converged into the centromere (Fig. 15), the fibres interlacing around the centrioles. In HeLa cells, Robbins and Gonatas have indicated that some spindle tubules pass through condensed chromosomes in a continuous manner.

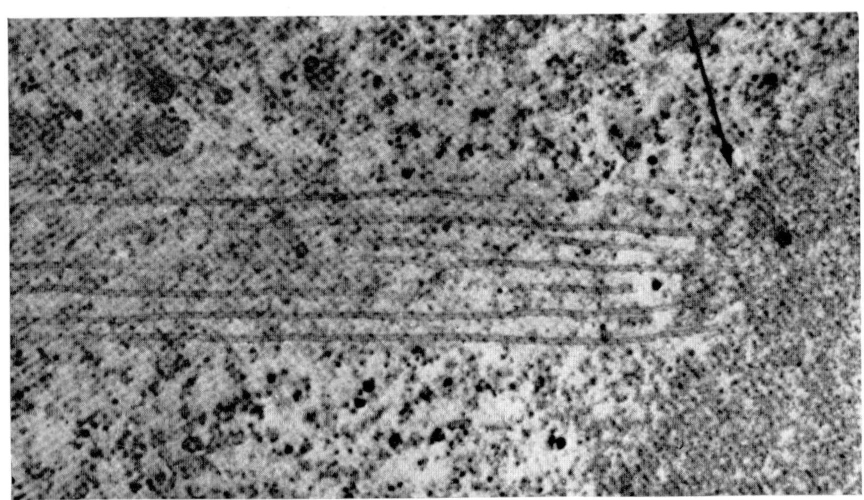

FIG. 15. Electron-micrograph of a newt cell undergoing mitosis in culture; spindle-fibre bundles may be seen converging on to a centromere (arrow). × 25,000. Micrograph by courtesy of Dr. N. A. Barnicott and Dr. H. E. Huxley and *Quart. J. micr. Sci.*

During anaphase, Barnicott and Huxley (1965) have observed that in newt cells the chromosomes first become more compact, and that, although the fibre bundles connecting the centromeres and centrioles must shorten by about one-third to one-half of their length at metaphase, their diameter was not increased. There was no evidence to suggest that the anaphase chromosomes were composed of two chromatids. The subsequent separation of the daughter cells was accompanied by an elongation of the spindle in the intervening regions. Small vacuoles which lay around the chromosomal material appeared to fuse to reconstitute the nuclear membrane. In HeLa cells, the nuclear membrane appeared to be derived from polar aggregates of endoplasmic reticulum, formation being initiated at the respective poles of the cells, within 2 min of the onset of karyokinesis. Two to four minutes later equatorial constriction occurred, with the concomitant formation of the mid-body, in a region where many bundles of spindle tubules lay. During telophase, spindle tubules were in continuity throughout the dense mid-body of the intercellular bridge.

In discussion, Barnicott and Huxley stressed that there was no evidence in the chromosomes of an helical internal structure or structural regularity at any level of organization down to 10–20 Å, and that the centromere regions did not become attached to a continuous spindle-fibre bundle, but each chromatid established a connection by means of its own kinetochore with the appropriate pole.

Robbins and Gonatas (1964) reported also that in HeLa cells, the Golgi complex disappeared during the mitotic cycle; in early prophase the Golgi zone became vesicular and then dispersed by metaphase. Rudimentary vesicles appeared subsequently in late anaphase and a fully-recognizable Golgi complex was once more evident by telophase. Conversely many dense membrane-bound bodies about 0·8 μ across became scattered in the cytoplasm, close to the periphery, during metaphase; during anaphase such bodies gave a positive result for acid phosphatase, but by telophase their number had diminished markedly.

IV. Fibrogenesis in Tissue Culture

A. Introduction

Fibrogenesis involves a number of sequential developmental steps; mechanisms concerned in two of these have received particular attention in tissue-culture investigations and they will form the basis of discussion in this section. One step concerns the determination of the size of the macromolecular particle of the fibrous protein, collagen, that is produced by the cell. The other concerns the localization of the site or sites where such particles become aggregated into a definitive fibril, and, as a part of this problem, the mechanisms that are involved in the enlargement of individual collagen fibrils until their characteristic size for the particular tissue is attained. Furthermore, it must be borne in mind that distinctive constituents of the ground substance may play essential and varied roles. Detailed investigations of macromolecular formation, the conditions under which this occurs and the requirements necessary for the subsequent growth of collagen fibrils should yield a better understanding of a process which is basic to the whole physiology of connective tissue.

Since tissue cultures are used so frequently in studies of fibrogenic mechanisms, the technique being often adapted to meet new methods of analysis, it is important to ask to what degree are the cells in such cultures capable of producing and organizing the same type of extracellular material as that from which the cells were derived. The nature of any one connective tissue depends, at least in part, on the maintenance of a specific balance between the various constituents peculiar to that tissue; hence the production of the appropriate complex matrix must imply that the various types of connective tissue cells are each capable of synthesizing all the different products required (e.g. Fitton Jackson, 1960). Certain facets of these problems, as they apply to cultured connective tissue, will be discussed later in this section.

Much of the tissue-culture work concerning fibrogenesis, until about 1950, was based on histological observations of various connective tissues, grown in the main by the hanging-drop method of culture. The question of the relationship of the fibrous protein, collagen, to the cells has been a controversial issue since the time of Schleiden (1838) and Schwann (1839). In early tissue-culture studies M. R. Lewis (1917) made an elegant investigation of chicken cells cultured for long periods and, as a result of this work, suggested that collagen fibres arose from the surface of the cell. Long cytoplasmic extensions are, however, a characteristic feature of most connective-tissue cells grown in culture; hence, it may have been difficult for her to distinguish clearly between these processes and true fibrous arrays of collagen at the resolution of the light microscope and with the methods then available.

On the other hand, a popular concept was that collagen fibres developed extracellularly, and involved the conversion of fibrin into collagen; this view was supported by the observations of Baitsell (e.g. 1915) of amphibian and chick tissue cultures in which individual fibres in the intercellular regions appeared to be gradually transformed into a fibrous matrix; since the individual fibres were present at a very early stage of culture (the medium was blood plasma), it was assumed that they were fibrin and that they were subsequently incorporated into collagenous material. On the other hand, much evidence indicated that collagen was not derived from fibrin.

Many other tissue-culture studies supported the idea of the extracellular formation of collagen fibrils, but not in association with fibrin. In most of these investigations a distinction was made between reticular fibres, stained by silver methods, and collagen fibres stained by the Mallory technique. Maximow (1929) noted that fibres always appeared in the neighbourhood of cells grown from rabbit thymus by the double coverslip method; he suggested that the fibres developed by the precipitation of soluble substances in the medium. At first the fibres were argyrophil, but after 25–35 days growth they began to take the Mallory stain for collagen. From these results Maximow concluded that reticular fibres represented an early stage in the formation of collagen. McKinney

(1929) produced rather similar results in cultures of rabbit lymph nodes, but the Mallory stain for collagen became positive within 6 days of culture; he claimed that this alteration in staining reaction represented a chemical and physical difference in the fibres analogous to that which occurs with ageing. The experiments of Doljanski and Roulet (1933) laid additional emphasis on the extracellular development of collagen fibres; these authors placed small pieces of tissue in a clot of plasma and embryo extract on one side of a porous glass filter and after a few days demonstrated that fibres had developed in the plasma on the opposite side of the filter, away from the tissue, and that these fibres stained positively for collagen and negatively for elastin and fibrin. The filter was presumed to be too fine for cellular processes to penetrate; it was suggested therefore that a cellular secretion had diffused through the filter and interacted with the subjacent medium to form it into fibres.

These and many other tissue-culture studies were clearly handicapped by the lack of resolution of the light microscope, and also by the available methods of determining the metabolic processes of the cell. The increased optical resolution obtainable with the advent of the electron-microscope provided a much better technique for studies of fibrogenic mechanisms at the molecular level, and can now be used in conjunction with more refined methods of microanalysis. While these investigations are contributing much information about processes involved in the formation of the extracellular materials *in vitro*, the validity of the results can be strengthened also by information gained from studies of similar tissues developing *in vivo*.

B. CULTURE SYSTEMS USED IN FIBROGENIC STUDIES

Four basic methods of culture have been used to study fibrogenic mechanisms, the different methods each providing certain advantages for the particular aspects under investigation. While many of these studies have been orientated towards elucidating the formative processes involved in collagen fibre-formation, extensive studies of the production of mucopolysaccharides, important constituents of the ground substance, have also been made (see Vol. 1, Chap. 2). Few combined morphological and biochemical studies have been made, however, in which the development of collagen and the components of the ground substance have been followed simultaneously.

1. *Hanging-drop Cultures*

Explants of such tissues as skin, cornea, tendon and bone have been grown by the hanging-drop method in fluid medium, and have been subsequently examined in the electron-microscope either as whole mounts or in section, the cultures being prepared for electron-microscopy by methods described briefly in Section II. These investigations attempted to establish the site of the initial formation of definitive collagen fibrils and the results will be discussed later (p. 49).

2. *Organ Cultures*

The organ-culture technique has been used extensively to study the effect of different environmental conditions on the development of, for example, long-bone rudiments, and chemical assays of the tissues, and of the medium in which they have been grown, have been made. Much of this work has been discussed by Biggers in Vol. 2, Chap. 4. More recently, however, such cultures have been prepared for electron-microscopy by the normal techniques used for tissue preparation, and variations in the fine structure of the cells and of the matrix have been observed.

Preliminary studies on the effect of excess vitamin A on explanted limb-bone rudiments from late foetal mice have demonstrated certain changes in the fine structure of treated rudiments as compared with the controls (Fell, 1964). In the treated explants the chondrocytes undergo a loss of cytoplasm, the Golgi zone is reduced and glycogen disappears while the cartilage matrix becomes fibrillar and the intercellular partitions reduced in width. In the bony shaft of the explant, there is a loss of pre-osseous zones of matrix, the mitochondria of the osteoblasts are swollen, the cisternae of their endoplasmic reticulum are reduced in volume but the Golgi zone appears unaffected.

Clearly, detailed studies at the fine-structure level of long-bone rudiments cultured in different environmental conditions should yield much valuable new information, especially if such changes can be correlated with biochemical information. As an example the recent work of O'Dell (1965a) in which collagenase has been used to deplete, specifically, the collagen from growing rudiments, and his demonstration that the intercellular materials regenerate on removal of the enzyme, indicate the potency of such experimental approaches to the study of the embryology of the intercellular materials at the macromolecular level.

Organ cultures of embryonic chick tibiae have been used to study collagen fibrogenesis in cartilage and also certain aspects of osteogenesis (Winell, Bassett, Wiener and Spiro, 1966). In this work, the proximal and distal cartilaginous condyles were removed from 11-day-old tibiae, the central portion of each rudiment was then grown in organ culture on a plasma clot in an atmosphere of 35% oxygen, 5% carbon dioxide and 60% nitrogen. After 7 days, thin layers of cells had developed over the cut surfaces of the cartilage; after 14 days in culture, the bony shaft had thickened by the addition of new osteoid, which also grew over the ends of the anlagen to cover the cartilage core (Shaw and Bassett, 1964).

Thin sections of these rudiments viewed in the electron-microscope showed many intact chondrocytes on either side of the central hypertrophied zone of cartilage; such cells contained many cytoplasmic organelles including ergastoplasm and large amounts of smooth-surfaced endoplasmic reticulum and the Golgi complex, but little glycogen. The healthy cells were closely surrounded by cartilage matrix, but many other cells were in various stages of degeneration, the lacunae containing only cellular debris or even being empty. Cells deep within the osteoid cap that had developed over the exposed cartilage contained relatively few mitochondria, vesicles and cisternae of the endoplasmic reticulum, but those nearer to the exterior surface contained numerous mitochondria, vesicles, vacuoles and well-developed systems of ergastoplasm.

After 14 days in culture, sections showed that the cartilage matrix adjacent to the central zone was composed of randomly orientated filaments, of 100–200 Å in diameter, without periodic structure, and separated from each other by an homogeneous amorphous material. In the zones of cartilage underlying the newly formed caps of osteoid, two types of characteristic collagen fibrils, with a well-defined periodicity of 640 Å, were observed, those of 500–700 Å in diameter lying within the extracellular regions and fibrils of 2000–4000 Å in diameter found within the lacunar spaces of degenerate cartilage cells (Fig. 16). Some of the fibrils close to the central zone were tapered and appeared to be extensions of the non-banded filaments. In the regions where the larger fibrils were observed, metachromasia was reduced. The source of the collagen macromolecules used in the formation of the large collagen fibrils is not known, but, as pointed out by the authors, the cells of the overlying caps of osteoid may well be associated with their production. The collagen fibrils in these regions, however, were only about 700 Å in diameter, with a characteristic periodicity.

It is of interest that, although well-defined collagen fibrils were not present in the cartilaginous zones when culturing started, characteristic fibrils subsequently appeared. When articular cartilage begins to differentiate in the 17-day-old embryo as an extension of the perichondrium, typical collagen fibrils of 1000 Å or more in diameter begin to appear, and, by 5 days post-embryo, it forms a thick zone at either end of the long-bone (Fitton Jackson, 1960). Hence the development of thin layers of cells over the cut surfaces of the explanted rudiments during culture is somewhat analogous to that which occurs *in vivo*, but the explanation as to why some of the fibrils lying within the lacunal

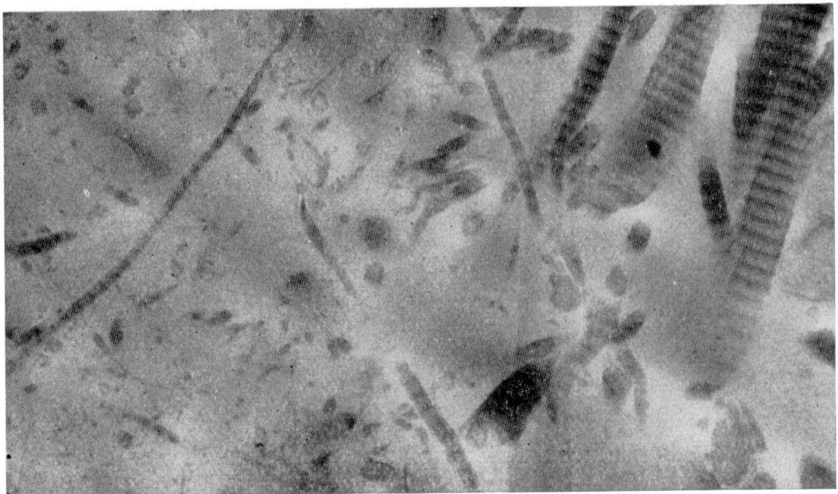

Fig. 16. Electron-micrograph of section through cartilage underlying the osteoid cap. Note collagen fibrils of 500–700 Å in diameter on the matrix and those of about 3500 Å in diameter lying within a lacunal area. × 30,000. Micrograph by courtesy of Dr. C. A. L. Bassett.

spaces are of an unusually large diameter is not yet clear. The unbanded filaments observed within certain zones of the cartilage matrix in culture may be similar to those first reported by Martin (1953) in the cartilage matrix of long-bone rudiments of chick embryos, and may possibly represent filaments of protein-polysaccharide as described by Fitton Jackson (1964).

Winell *et al.* (1966) also reported that, although the bulk of the newly formed osteoid was not mineralized, needle-shaped crystals were observed in the deeper, and hence more mature, portions of the osteoid cap and also in the superficial layers of the diaphysis; such crystals were 1000–2000 Å in length and 25–50 Å in width and were assumed to be hydroxyapatite in nature. Small particles 50–100 Å in diameter were also randomly associated with collagen fibrils in these regions and may well represent a developmental stage in the formation of the crystals (e.g. Fitton Jackson, 1957). The fact that osteoid formed in organ culture can mineralize to the degree described by these authors is of considerable interest since doubts have frequently been expressed as to its potentialities in this respect; that such mineralization occurred in the deeper zones of the osteoid cap and in the superficial zones of the diaphysis, both of which had formed earlier than the other regions of new osteoid, indicates that a number of factors, as yet not understood, must be involved in such mineralization.

3. *Primary Cell Cultures*

Cells derived directly from the embryo have been used in a number of studies in which attempts have been made to relate certain synthetic steps with morphological observations. To investigate the initial stages of formation of collagen, suspensions of osteoblasts, obtained by trypsinization of frontal bones of fowl embryos (10–11 days old), were grown on glass plates in a fluid fibrin-free natural medium. These primary cultures consisted predominantly of one type of collagen-forming cell; the cultures differentiated into typical young osteogenic tissue in the course of 5–6 days (Fitton Jackson and Randall, 1956). Since cell suspensions were used at the beginning of the culture period all the extracellular material present in the cultures must have been formed by the cells; chemical analysis by Fitton Jackson and Smith (1957) showed that there was a tenfold increase in the dry weight of the cultures, about 20% of which was collagen (based on hydroxyproline analysis). Although appreciable amounts of protein-bound hydroxyproline were formed during the first 24 h period (12–15% collagen), electron-microscopy failed to demonstrate the presence of any typical collagen fibrils during this time. Subsequently, characteristic collagen fibrils appeared in the cultures (Fig. 17) but there was no significant rise in the mean hydroxyproline content. This finding led to the conclusion that collagen fibrils were formed by the synthesis and secretion by the cell of an hydroxyproline-containing precursor, of a protein or large peptide nature, which itself had no banded structure, as resolved by electron-microscopy, but which subsequently became directly transformed, without marked change in hydroxyproline content, into banded fibrils. Further studies of the same culture system by Smith and Fitton Jackson (1957) confirmed the observation of Stetten (1949) that the hydroxyproline of collagen was derived directly from proline, the rate of the formation of the protein-bound ^{14}C-hydroxyproline from ^{14}C-proline was maximal in cultures grown for 15 h and fell exponentially with the increase in age of the cultures.

Fitton Jackson and Randall (1956) noted also that a hyaluronic acid-like substance was produced initially by the primary osteogenic cultures; subsequently, chondroitin sulphate-like material appeared (although it was low in sulphate) which closely paralleled the formation of characteristic collagen fibrils seen by electron-microscopy. Whether a correlation exists between these two events is still open to question.

Primary cultures have also been used by Fessler and Bailey (1965) to investigate the initial stages in the synthesis of collagen. The cells were obtained by trypsinization of 11-day-old chick embryos and the

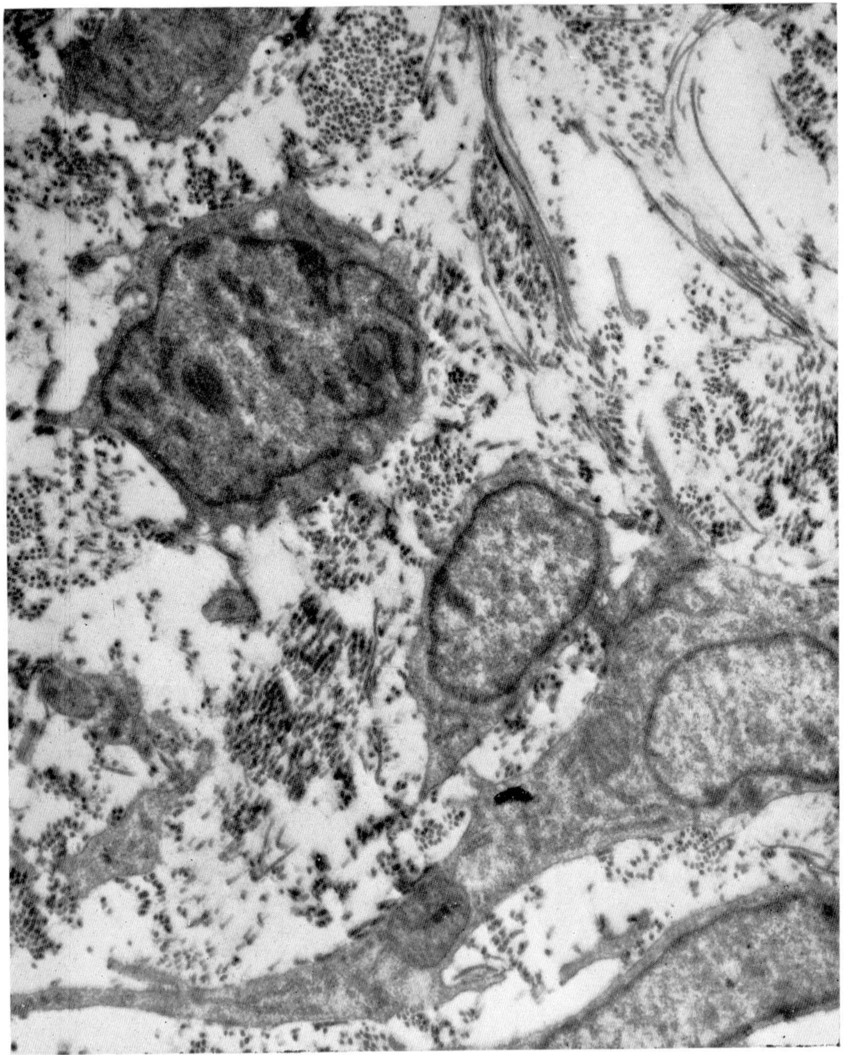

FIG. 17. Electron-micrograph of part of an osteoblastic culture grown for 48 h. Many collagen fibrils are visible between the cells. × 5,500.

resultant cultures were found to incorporate ^{14}C-proline and synthesize ^{14}C-hydroxyproline into non-dialysable compounds.

Further investigations of primary cultures of cells derived from frontal bone and from epiphyseal cartilage of 10 – 11-day-old chick embryos have been made to see whether the mode of formation of collagen fibrils in an osteogenic system differed from that in a chondrogenic system (Fitton Jackson, 1965). The spatial organization of the cells in these primary cultures showed some differences; whereas the chondroblasts tended to aggregate together into groups and thence develop into whorls, the osteogenic cells tended to grow in sheets, layer upon layer, the cells of each succeeding layer being aligned at right angles to each other. Characteristic collagen fibrils were not visible in the cartilage cultures before about 48 h, whereas, as mentioned previously, typical fibrils appeared in the osteogenic cultures after 24–30 h growth. The chemical analyses after 48 h of culture indicated that the amount of collagen (as judged by hydroxyproline analysis) produced by the osteoblasts was about double that by the chondroblasts (i.e. 17·2% and 9·1% respectively), but a reverse balance was found with respect to hexosamine-containing products. It is not yet known among which constituents the hexosamine may be distributed but, based on the amount of hexosamine contained in various connective tissues an approximate estimate would indicate the presence of 3·6% and 12·8% of hexosamine-containing constituents in the primary cultures of bone and cartilage respectively.

This preliminary comparative study of two markedly dissimilar types of skeletal tissue indicates that, when such cells are grown under the same environmental conditions, they have the capacity to display the type of growth normal to their origin, and this implies that at the time of explanation the cells have been programmed to such an extent that they synthesize certain balanced amounts of their characteristic macromolecular components in a defined sequence of events.

4. *Established Cell Lines*

Cultures of established cell lines have been used to study the synthesis of collagen and the concomitant morphological development of collagen fibrils has been followed by means of electron-microscopy. In this work Goldberg, Green and Todaro (1963) and Goldberg and Green (1964) have used established lines of mouse fibroblasts in which cells, having been cultured for a number of weeks, underwent a period of rapid division followed by a stationary phase, the latter correlating with the appearance of extracellular collagen fibrils and the accumulation of hydroxyproline. One established line of cells (3T6) was derived from primary cultures of dissociated cells of whole mouse embryos (Todaro and Green, 1963), which were serially subcultured three times a week at an initial density of 6×10^5 cells per Petri dish of 50 mm diameter. At first the growth of cells was slow, the intermitotic time extending to about 100 h; the growth rate then increased, and after about fifteen transfers, the intermitotic period was less than 13 h. At this stage, hydroxyproline was not detected in the cultures. After about 100 mitotic divisions the density of the cells was permitted to increase, and by not subculturing, division was arrested; in such cultures, a log phase of growth occurred for the first 3 days and a state of non-proliferation was attained by the sixth day, with a density of 10^7 cells per Petri dish. Analysis for hydroxyproline indicated that its synthesis began on the fourth to fifth day and continued at a constant rate for about 3 weeks, but the cell number did not change. In cell line 3T6, 5–16 μg collagen per 10^7 cells per day was produced, this figure resting on the assumption that the hydroxyproline synthesized represented collagen with a 13% content of hydroxyproline (Green and Hamerman, 1964). Characteristic collagen fibrils were observed in thin sections of appropriate cultures and will be discussed in more detail below.

That such cells, maintained under saturation density, were clearly viable was demonstrated by the facts that about 80% formed macroscopical colonies when plated out on X-irradiated feeder cells, and that they retained the capacity for division when culture conditions of low density were restored. Goldberg and Green (1964) suggested that every cell of the 3T6 line had the capacity to produce collagen as a fairly stable property and pointed out that other lines also possessed this activity to a lesser degree. Subsequent studies by Green and Goldberg (1964a) with ^{14}C-proline indicated that in fact a very small amount of collagen was synthesized in the earlier stages, about 0·25% of the total protein produced during the log phase of culture being collagen, rising to about 3·5% in the stationary phase; since the cellular proteins turned over rapidly however, collagen accumulated to form about 15% of the total protein. A further point of interest was the finding that the lactic acid concentration increased markedly during the exponential growth phase, the pH dropping to 6·6. Green and Goldberg suggested that the increase in hydrogen-ion concentration might inhibit the synthesis of cellular protein, and hence mitosis, but that the increase of lactate ion might specifically stimulate collagen synthesis.

Green and Hamerman (1964) noted also that the 3T6 line of cells was capable of synthesizing an hexuronic acid containing polysaccharide; since both streptococcal and testicular hyaluronidase degraded the polysaccharide, they assumed it consisted essentially of hyaluronate. The rate of synthesis was of the order of 100–200 μg per 10^7 per day, that is to say about fifteen times the amount of collagen synthesized in the same cultures.

Green and his colleagues have suggested that the 3T6 line consists of a single cell type which is capable of carrying out two specialized functions simultaneously in that they produce two of the major constituents found in intercellular material. Whether the cultures really represent a single cell type is, perhaps, open to question. Neither is it clear whether every cell is actively concerned in the two specialized functions, particularly since the amount of collagen formed per cell is very small. Furthermore, the proportions of products produced are grossly dissimilar to those which are required to form and maintain any of the major connective and skeletal tissues of the mammalian body. It would be interesting to know, therefore, if such cells would be capable of initiating other types of differentiation if they were grown under different conditions, since environmental factors are of great importance in influencing the type of development in culture.

5. *Environmental Requirements for Growth and Differentiation*

Many studies concerned with the development of intercellular material in both primary cell and organ cultures have been made in which natural media were used; for certain investigations at the molecular level however, cultures should be grown in a defined environment. Owing to the pioneer work of Earle, Parker and Waymouth (see Vol. 1, Chap. 3) cell lines can be maintained indefinitely in synthetic media, but in such systems the inherent capacity of the cell for specific differentiation is usually quickly lost. Recent evidence from studies of established cell lines derived from mouse embryos indicates, however, that some specific differentiations, e.g. collagen formation, may be related, at least in part, to the density at which the cells are grown (e.g. Goldberg, Green and Todaro, 1963). Much work in the past few years has also been orientated towards the formulation of a chemically defined medium suitable for use with organ cultures of skeletal tissues (see Vol. 2, Chap. 4).

Inevitably, the choice of constituents for any synthetic medium must be somewhat arbitary since there are too many parameters for the effects of each constituent to be tested individually; the necessity for certain amino acids in various media, however, has been well established (see Vol. 1, Chaps. 8 and 9). Biggers, Gwatkin and Heyner (1961) demonstrated that young long-bone rudiments from embryonic chicks could be maintained for a reasonable period in a medium devised by them (known as BGJ), that differentiation followed a similar pattern to that *in ovo*, but that the intercellular material was clearly abnormal (e.g. Biggers, Lawson, Lucy and Webb, 1961; Biggers, 1963). The rudiments also underwent progressive hydration during culture (Biggers, 1963; Schryver, 1965; Dingle, Fell and Lucy, 1966) though this could be reduced by the addition of hydrocortisone to the medium (Reynolds, 1966a). Furthermore the size and dry weight of rudiments grown in the BGJ medium were much less than those of comparable rudiments *in vivo*, presumably due, at least in part, to a reduction or cessation of synthesis of intercellular materials (O'Dell, 1965b).

It has long been accepted that lack of ascorbic acid reduces or inhibits the production of collagen, although the way in which the vitamin acts is still an open question (see Gould, 1963). It is significant, therefore, that Jeffrey and Martin (1964) found that, with the addition of 5 mg % of ascorbic acid to a defined medium, collagen continued to be synthesized in organ cultures of 8–9-day tibiae of chick embryos, but that the synthesis virtually ceased after 4 days if tibiae were grown in defined medium without the vitamin; synthesis of collagen could be restored immediately in such rudiments on their transfer to the ascorbic acid-containing medium. Treatment of the rudiments with various inhibitory compounds indicated that the action of ascorbic acid on collagen synthesis was independent of any general effect upon protein or nucleic acid synthesis or on electron transport.

Subsequent investigations by Reynolds (1966b) have shown that the addition of ascorbic acid, at dose levels of at least 50 μg/ml in a slightly modified version of BGJ medium (Reynolds, 1966a), to cultures of tibiae of 7-day chick embryos completely prevented the terminal water-logging referred to previously, greatly stimulated the synthesis of collagen, but had little effect on either the DNA content or synthesis of hexo-samine-containing material. Reynolds found that, after 6 days in culture, the ratio of collagen (calculated from the content of hydroxyproline) to hexosamine was 2, a figure comparable to that found in rudiments of 9-day-old embryos (Reynolds, 1966a), whereas the ratio of collagen to hexosamine in cultures of tibiae grown in the absence of the vitamin was only 0·9. That ascorbic acid is an essential constituent of any synthetic medium which is being used in studies of the development of inter-cellular material is further emphasized by the fact that Green and Goldberg (1964b) and Schimizu, McCann and Keech (1965) have shown that the addition of ascorbic acid enhances the synthesis of collagen in cultures of established cell lines (see also Vol. 1, Chap. 17).

The gas phase in which cultures are grown affects the development of intercellular material. For instance Bassett (1962) observed that the new outgrowth from pieces of midshaft of the tibiae of 20-day-old chick embryos calcified heavily when grown in an atmosphere of 35% O_2, 60% N and 5% CO_2; the region of ossification was limited, how-ever, to the surface of the culture and electron-microscopy showed that the fine-structure of such areas was typical of young bone. On the other hand, low levels of oxygen (5%) promoted the development of cartilage in similar cultures. It is of interest that excess levels of oxygen, of the order of 85–95%, have been shown to stimulate the resorption of bone in culture, and have been correlated with the appearance of osteoclasts (Goldhaber, 1958). Furthermore, Sledge (1965) has shown that long-bone rudiments of 7-day chick embryos grown in synthetic medium in an atmosphere of 85% O_2, 10% N and 5% CO_2 brought about the resorption of cartilage matrix through the release of lysosomal enzymes, the oxygen having a direct effect on the stabilization of the chondroblast lysosomes (Sledge and Dingle, 1965).

In summary, certain extrinsic factors may introduce marked changes in the growth and the differentiation of the cultures and much more knowledge about these effects is required. Certain basic conditions have been laid down however, and, although they may not be optimal, it is evident that a number of worthwhile culture systems are now available for use in studies of fibre formation.

C. FINE-STRUCTURE OF FIBROGENIC CELLS

Certain features of the fine-structure of cells in culture have been described earlier in this chapter. The purpose now is to discuss briefly certain points in the cytoplasmic morphology of those cells in culture which are held to be directly concerned in the production of intercellular material.

Stearns (1940) reported the presence of cytoplasmic granules in fibroblasts of healing wounds in the ears of rabbits and suggested they were directly concerned in the formation of collagen fibres. Fitton Jackson (1955) and Fitton Jackson and Randall (1956) noted similar sized granules (0·7–2·0 μ) in living fibroblasts growing in cultures of tendon and cornea and in osteoblasts of frontal bone and long-bone rudiments; a detailed analysis strongly supported the view that they contained both an acid mucopolysaccharide and protein, and, since both alkaline phosphatase and cytochrome oxidase were associated with the granular region of the cell, it was suggested that the granules were centres of metabolic activity and were concerned with the production of intercellular material. Electron-microscopy of sections of the cultures showed that the content of the granules was somewhat fibrous (Fig. 18). Robbins, Watson, Pappas and Porter (1955) found similar granules in cultures of skin, and related them to collagen production; the basis for this suggestion rested on the facts that the staining properties of the granules were similar to those of collagen and that the granules diminished in number when the cultures were grown in the presence of anti-collagen serum. Subsequently Sheldon (1959) and Cameron (1961) equated the granules with the dilated cisternae of the endoplasmic reticulum, but, in the view of the present author, the nature of the granules in living osteoblasts observed by phase contrast (N.A. 1.32) is not consistent with this suggestion; first, they may be seen to be individual oval organelles that can move about in a random fashion, and,

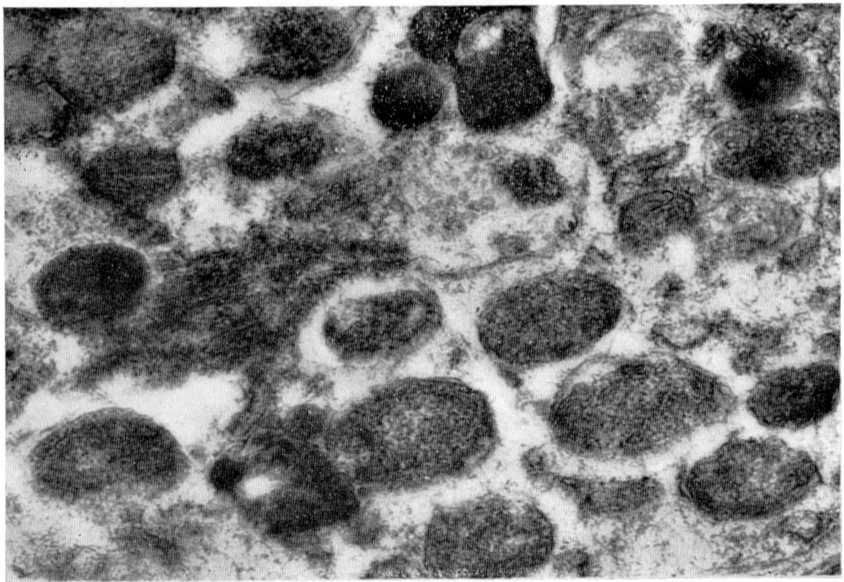

FIG. 18. Electron-micrograph of part of an osteoblast showing the filamentous nature of some cytoplasmic granules. × 35,000.

second, the fine-structure of the granules is clearly different from that of dilated cisternae (Fig. 18).

Goldberg and Green (1964) studied the fine structure of the established mouse fibroblasts referred to above by use of thin sections and the electron-microscope, and correlated certain morphological features with synthetic events. In the log-phase of growth, the cytoplasm showed poorly developed profiles of endoplasmic reticulum; a large complement of free ribosomes, a small Golgi zone and small spherical mitochondria with simple cristae and a matrix of low density. During the phase of diminished growth rate in the cultures the amount of endoplasmic reticulum increased, the mitochondria elongated and the matrix became denser. In the stationary phase of growth, sections cut at right angles to the plane of the culture showed that the cells overlapped each other, and that from twenty to thirty cell layers had formed. At this stage the mitochondria had become considerably elongated, sometimes branched, and contained well-defined cristae. The total amount of endoplasmic reticulum or ergastoplasm had increased and the cisternae had enlarged; the number of free ribosomes was reduced, while in tangential sections ergastoplasmic ribosomes formed curved chains of from ten to twenty particles. No rough-surfaced membranes were seen close to the surface of the cells. The

Golgi zone had become structurally more complex, and consisted of vesicles and flattened membranous figures composed of 70 Å wide smooth membranes. Some of the Golgi structures appeared to be associated with smooth-surfaced endoplasmic reticulum. Some smooth vesicular profiles and vesicles with dense limiting membranes appeared to lie near the cell surface, and it was suggested that the latter might be concerned with pinocytotic activity. Study of cells in the late stationary phase of culture showed an increase in a number of dense membrane-limited bodies which might be equated with lysosomes.

Goldberg and Green suggested that the increase in the complexity of the fine-structure of the cytoplasm in the stationary phase compared with that in the log-phase was connected with specific synthesis of intercellular materials, and that the two types of morphology represented the two extremes in cyto-differentiation.

It is interesting that the present author has observed that the cells of primary cultures derived directly from embryonic tissues are lacking in complex cytoplasmic organization. Profiles of endoplasmic reticulum or ergastoplasm are scarce; the Golgi zone, although prominent, is small; mitochondria are elongated; the number of free ribosomes is high and, in addition, there are many small vesicles of varying density scattered throughout the cytoplasm. As mentioned previously, the amount of collagen being synthesized by such cultures is considerable and certainly much more per cell than that in established cell lines.

D. THE FUNCTION OF CYTOPLASMIC ORGANELLES IN RELATION TO FIBROGENESIS

A number of investigations have supported the idea that there is a progression of synthetic steps that move through different cytoplasmic organelles (Caro, 1961). Considerable controversy rages around the vexed question of whether the Golgi zone of fibrogenic cells is indeed concerned in any way with the synthesis of collagen and/or with storing and/or preparing it for secretion from the cell (cf. Porter, 1964). From their observations of established mouse fibroblasts, Goldberg and Green (1964) have suggested that collagen is synthesized in association with the rough-surfaced endoplasmic reticulum and is transported as a soluble protein to the cell surface via smooth vesicles which represented a stage in the secretory cycle; they believe that the vesicles may have migrated from the Golgi zone or may have formed from endoplasmic reticulum denuded of ribosomes. In their view there was little evidence to support the idea that the Golgi zone in the mouse fibroblasts was concerned with storage of specialized cellular products.

Combined autoradiography and electron-microscopy enables the relationship between individual silver grains, due to labelled substances that have become bound into specific constituents, and their site in the cell to be assessed more precisely than previously. Certain observations made on connective tissues used in this way are relevant to the present discussion; proline and its conversion to hydroxyproline is used frequently as a marker for the synthesis of collagen. Ross and Benditt (1962) noted that many grains were localized in the dilated cisternae of the endoplasmic reticulum and also in the Golgi zone of fibroblasts after injection of tritiated proline into guinea-pigs at various stages during the healing of wounds; subsequently grains were localized predominently outside the cells where many collagen fibrils were present. Revel and Hay (1963) reported that they had observed a progressive movement of ^{3}H-proline passing via the endoplasmic reticulum to vesicles of the Golgi zone of chondroblasts in the anlages of regenerating limbs of *Amblystoma* larvae; subsequently the labelled material appeared to leave the cells by fusion of the vesicular membranes with the cell surface, and became localized within the extracellular domain several microns from the cells. Detailed counts by Ross and Benditt (1965) have now indicated that in wounds, the grains, representing ^{3}H-proline, passed directly from the ergastoplasm to the extracellular environment. The chemical distribution of ^{3}H-proline in different constituents of the wounds is not known, but the amount of collagen present normally exceeds that of other proteins of the ground substance by quite a large margin. On the other hand, non-collagenous protein forms a considerable proportion of cartilage matrix and about 7% of this protein is proline; hence, in the observations of Revel and Hay (1963), tritiated proline may have traced, at least in part, the production of non-collagenous protein in addition to the formation of collagen. Thus, in cartilage the dominant movement of labelled material from the endoplasmic reticulum to the Golgi vesicles may well represent sequential stages in the synthesis of non-collagenous protein rather than that of collagen.

This view is supported, first, by the fact that the label subsequently appeared some microns from the chondroblasts, rather than near to the cell surface, and second, by the observations of Campo and Dziewiatkowski (1962) and Godman and Lane (1964). These authors have studied the uptake of ^{35}S-sulphate in cartilage; Godman and Lane noted that it accumulated within the microvesicles of the Golgi zone within 3 min of the application of the isotope. They suggested that the sulphate was being used in the assembly of macromolecular components of the ground substance; that the non-collagenous protein is probably synthesized before the polysaccharide moiety of the chondroitin sulphate-protein complex is indicated by the work of Telser, Robinson and Dorfman (1965). At present, therefore, the balance of evidence favours the view that the Golgi zone is not directly concerned in either a definitive step in the synthesis of collagen, or in the transport of collagenous protein through the cell.

The investigation of the function of the different organelles in cellular fractions has also contributed some information relevant to the process of fibrogenesis. That considerable amounts of protein-bound hydroxyproline were located within osteoblasts grown in culture was shown by the present author (Fitton Jackson, 1958, 1960). In these experiments, primary cultures were used before collagen fibrils were distinguished outside the cells by means of electron-microscopy. Chemical analysis of cellular fractions obtained from such cultures by homogenization followed by differential centrifugation showed that about 50% of the bound hydroxyproline synthesized by the cells within the first 12 h of culture was located in fractions which were undoubtedly cytoplasmic, the rest being found mainly in the heavier fractions containing nuclei, mitochondria etc. with a small amount in the microsomal fraction. The amount of intracellular hydroxyproline was reduced with age. It is interesting therefore that Prockop, Peterkofsky and Udenfriend (1962) found also that the bulk of protein-bound hydroxyproline was present in a non-dialysable form in a $15{,}000 \times g$ fraction obtained directly from 9-day-old chick embryos. The highest specific activity, however, was located in a microsomal fraction, and further work with a cell-free system showed that the substrate for hydroxylation was a microsomal-bound polypeptide of considerable size (Peterkofsky and Udenfriend, 1963). This finding was in agreement with that of Lowther, Green and Chapman (1961) in studies of fractions derived from carageenan granuloma in guinea-pigs; they noted that the highest rate of conversion of ^{14}C-proline to ^{14}C-hydroxyproline occurred in peptide-bound hydroxyproline in a microsomal preparation. Such synthetic activity was associated with particle-studded fragments of endoplasmic reticulum as seen by electron-microscopy, and Eastoe (1961) established that the amino-acid pattern of the fraction was collagenous in nature.

The hydroxylation of proline to hydroxyproline (and lysine to hydroxylysine) has been used as a marker in many studies of the synthesis of collagen. It is an open question, however, at what stage the hydroxylation occurs during the synthesis of the collagen molecules. On the one hand, much evidence supports the contention, first proposed by Stetten (1949), that oxidation occurs when the proline or lysine is already in peptide linkage. On the other hand, some evidence supports the idea that oxidation occurs at an early stage in the synthetic cycle namely in association with sRNA (Gould, Manner, Levi and Schantz, 1963).

The question arises as to whether the assembly of the collagen molecule is associated with relatively small ribosomal aggregates which would be required for sub-units of low molecular weight, with medium-sized aggregates, which might represent the formation of one of the three polypeptide chains, or with very large aggregates which would indicate the simultaneous synthesis of all three chains of the collagen monomer. In studies of sucrose gradients of homogenates of 9-day chick embryos, Kretsinger, Manner, Gould and Rich (1964) found that rapidly sedimenting material contained a large proportion of collagen-forming sites suggesting that very large polysomes were concerned in the synthesis of collagen. Their experiments showed that these polysomes were larger than those involved in the synthesis of other proteins and that they were more resistant to attack by ribonuclease. Malt and Speakman (1965) have suggested, however, that such large ribosomal aggregates are not exclusively concerned in collagen production as similar patterns occur in material from both scorbutic and non-scorbutic guinea-pigs. Since an ill-defined membrane, resistant to attack by deoxycholate (which normally lyses the membranes of the ergastoplasm) is visible behind ribosomal clusters observed by electron-microscopy, Malt and Speakman have suggested that other substances may influence the aggregation of ribosomes to form polysomal masses.

Studies of the distribution of material from homogenates of primary cultures of osteoblasts and chondroblasts in sucrose density-gradients have demonstrated, in addition to some larger aggregates, small aggregates of from six to eleven ribosomes, as seen by electron-microscopy (Fig. 19), and as distinguished by increased ultraviolet absorption and radioactivity of ^{14}C-hydroxyproline (Fitton Jackson, 1965). The

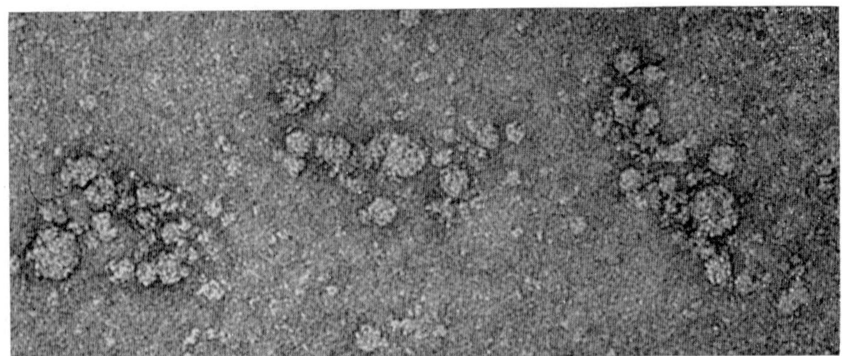

FIG. 19. Electron-micrograph of ribosomal clusters, obtained from a sucrose density gradient of a homogenate from cartilage cells obtained from a culture derived from cell suspensions of chick epiphysis. The specimen has been negatively stained with phosphotungstic acid. × 380,000.

suggestion has been made that such aggregates may represent a primary stage in the assembly of the collagen molecule. It is important to note that it was only possible to precipitate out recognizable collagen fibrils from material obtained from the heaviest pellet, a finding that supports the idea that the collagen monomer must be in a certain state before it can be induced to aggregate into fibrils.

Examination of homogenates from primary cultures of 11-day-old chick embryos by Fessler and Bailey (1965) indicated that the cells synthesized material that was chromatographically similar to the hydroxamation products of gelatin, which have been shown to correspond in part to the postulated sub-units of collagen (Hodge, Petruska and Bailey, 1965), but the validity of the idea of sub-units has been queried by Bornstein and Piez (1965).

It is evident from the above brief discussion that the size of the ribosomal aggregates that may be involved in the synthesis of the collagen molecule and the size of the collagen particle that is produced by the cell is still open to question.

E. THE INITIAL FORMATION OF DEFINITIVE COLLAGEN FIBRILS AND THEIR GROWTH

Porter and Vanamee (1949) and Porter (1951) made a detailed study of fibrogenesis of intact tissue cultures of embryonic skin. The initial study showed that the cultures produced a luxuriant crop of cells within 3 days, quickly followed by the development of extensive fibrous arrays; electron-microscopy demonstrated numerous fibrils, of about 400 Å in diameter, and compound fibrils composed of parallel arrays of the individual fibrils. A characteristic periodicity of 640 Å, apparent in certain regions of the compound fibrils identified them as collagen. Porter and Vanamee commented that since it was difficult to see the interrelationship between the fibrils and the cells there was no evidence to indicate whether they were derived from within the cells or spun off their surfaces. Porter (1951) stressed that the fibrous arrays were arranged in planes above and below one another, and were not interwoven; hence the formation of the fibrils had not proceeded freely in all directions, but rather that the fibrous mat must have been organized by the cells. A detailed study of the cell surfaces (Fig. 20) thrown into relief by the use of the shadowing technique, suggested that there was a very intimate relation between small unit fibrils and the surface of the cells; these observations led Porter to conclude that either a gelated layer just beneath the cell membrane became organized into fibrils, or that this gelated material passed through the cell surface as an exudate and became "polymerized" into definitive fibrils on the

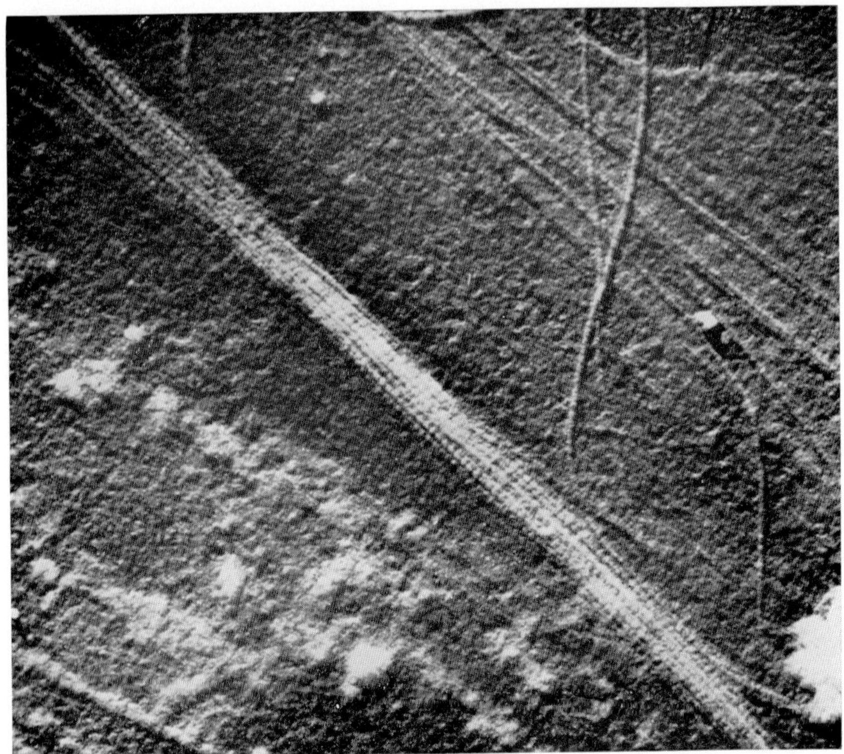

Fig. 20. Electron-micrograph of a small part of the surface of a cultured fibroblast from skin of 12-day-old chick embryo. Note the bundle of unit fibrils of collagen, some of which are continuous with the cell surface; part of the cell margin can be seen in the upper right-hand corner. The specimen has been shadowed. × 25,000. Micrograph by courtesy of Dr. K. R. Porter.

cell surface. The first fibrils showed a periodic structure of about 210 Å, when the cultures were grown in balanced salt plus bouillon medium, or in a clot of fowl plasma and embryo extract; fibrils with a periodicity of 640 Å were only obtained after several days in the latter medium. The most active stage of synthesis, based on the rapid appearance of fibrils, occurred between 72 and 96 h growth; at 48 h the most notable feature was a thickening of the cell surface and an indication of fibrous condensations. Porter also commented on the appearance of an amorphous material, possibly akin to a mucinous substance, in association with the cell surface.

The present writer also made a detailed study of fibrogenesis, using both the tissue-culture technique and observations on the corresponding normal tissues in the embryo (Fitton Jackson, 1953). Osteoblasts grown from frontal bone and fibroblasts from tendon and cornea were examined whole in the electron-microscope. The results obtained from observations on these three tissues were essentially the same as those on embryonic skin discussed above; the initial network of fibrils present in the extracellular regions, however, showed a regular periodicity of 70–80 Å, with a diameter of the fibrils of about 200 Å. At a later stage of growth, the fibrils increased in diameter and showed a periodic structure of 210 Å, with greater apparent density of one out of every three bands; some of the fibrils became aggregated into small bundles with the banding of the fibrils in register with each other.

These studies of whole tissue cultures established that collagen fibrils, and fibril bundles, were present in the culture and they distinguished clearly the difference in morphology between fibrous arrays and long cytoplasmic processes. Porter's observations strongly suggested that the surfaces of the cells were intimately concerned in the initial formation of collagen fibrils. Furthermore, it was clearly established that once the collagen fibrils were in an extracellular domain, further enlargement proceeded outside the cell.

In a further detailed analysis of whole mounts of chick dermal tissue grown in culture and viewed by electron-microscopy, Porter and Pappas (1959) stressed that the appearance and amount of newly formed collagen fibrils bore a direct density relationship to the cell surface, and that fibrils were not present in the free medium at the periphery of the culture. Moreover, Porter and Pappas were unable to reproduce the results of Doljanski and Roulet (1933) referred to earlier, suggesting that a cellular secretion was either not produced by the cells, or, if produced, failed to penetrate the interposed filter, and thus was unable to interact with the underlying culture medium to form fibres. Porter and Pappas pointed out that the differences in results might be explained by the fact that the fibrils formed at the surface of the cells and used up the available material synthesized by the cell as fast as it was produced. On the other hand, it is possible that the skin cultures may have synthesized hyaluronic acid, which could conceivably clog the pores of the filter and thus prevent penetration by other material.

Porter and Pappas (1959) stressed that longitudinal thickenings occurred in the cytoplasm of many cells after about 48 h in culture, and that collagen fibrils appeared to condense on the cell surface in these regions; they correlated this observation with areas of increased density seen at the cell surface in thin sections of 14–16-day-old embryonic skin. Such regions were often intimately associated with extracellular bundles of unit fibrils. In addition, Porter and Pappas noted areas of increased density at the cell surface, without closely associated bundles of unit fibrils, and other areas, in which bundles of fibrils were close to the cell but that the density of the surface was normal. Porter and Pappas concluded from their observations of whole cells in skin cultures and sectioned skin from the embryo that unit fibrils of 200–300 Å diameter formed from material at the cell surface and were then shed into the extracellular regions by a mechanism similar to "ecdysis"; they put forward the hypothesis that collagen fibrils were perhaps induced to "polymerize" by enzymes resident in templates at the cell surface, or in the unit fibril. They stated that intracellular fibrils were not observed and that studies of whole cultures by electron-microscopy might enhance the appearance of fibril formation at the cell surface, whereas under certain conditions fibrils might be capable of forming at some distance from the cell.

In an electron-microscope study of the morphogenesis of osteogenic cultures derived from cell suspensions of frontal bone of young chick embryos, and grown in sheets, in a fibrin-free medium, the present writer has observed that in sections cut at right angles to the plane of the culture, where two layers of cells have formed, collagen fibrils were situated not only close to the cell surface but appeared at considerable distance from the cells. Many of the fibrils were seen in cross-section, which aided in the definition of the spatial relationship of cells to fibrils. Another interesting feature in these cultures was the fact that although some collagen fibrils lay immediately adjacent to the cell surface, here delineated as an electron-dense line, most of the fibrils were separated from the cells by a halo, composed of a structureless substance similar in electron-density to the material surrounding individual collagen fibrils in the extracellular phase. Such a morphological feature might be an artifact caused by slight retraction of the cytoplasm during preparative procedures, or may indicate that the osteoblasts secreted a material that was capable of being transformed into fibrils at some distance from the cell.

In an electron-microscope study of chondrogenesis in the epiphysis of foetal rats, Godman and Porter (1960) and Godman (1962) suggested that unit or primary fibrils were first laid down by the cell and that collagen monomers were added to these cores to form collagen fibrils. More recently, Porter (1964) has remarked that "In mature fibrils, a core of low density is uniformly present, suggesting that the central element is indeed of a different nature from collagen". This is certainly an interesting suggestion and implies that some initiating element may be concerned in collagen fibril formation. Rudall (1965) has recently suggested that measurements of the growth rate of collagen fibrils and the corresponding amount of matrix in developing tendon of the chick embryo (Fitton Jackson, 1956) point to the existence of a central core, 20–30 Å diam., of three tropocollagen molecules acting as the "nucleus" of the fibril and that these are deposited by one process, while additional molecules are added by another method depending on the amount of matrix present. Wood's observations (1962) support also the idea that two stages may be involved in fibril formation, a nucleation stage followed by a growth period. The fact that Wood's experiments were based on purified solutions of collagen is against the idea of a collagen fibril with a central core of a substance other than collagen.

Morphological features associated with the formation of recognizable collagen fibrils have been followed by means of electron-microscopy also in thin sections of the cultures of established mouse fibroblasts (Goldberg and Green, 1964). Extracellular fibrils were not seen in the first 3 days of rapid proliferation of the cells (log phase) but during the next 3 days in culture some fine fibrils of 50–160 Å in diameter, with no detectable periodicity, appeared outside the cells. Subsequently during the stationary phase of culture, the extracellular appearance of characteristic collagen fibrils was correlated with the accumulation of hydroxyproline. These fibrils were 280–420 Å in diameter, with a periodicity of 550 Å, consisting of an asymmetric intra-period pattern. The proportion of these fibrils in the culture rose with time. During both the log and stationary phases of culture, the cell surfaces appeared as well-defined membranes about 70 Å wide in section when cut at right angles to the plane of growth; in sections cut in the horizontal plane the surface appeared as a hazy region, with which, in the stationary phase, characteristic collagen fibrils were associated. In these sections of about 500 Å thickness the long cytoplasmic processes, a feature of these cells in culture, would be seen as a relatively wide zone of indefinite structure. Goldberg and Green held that the diffuse appearance of the cell surface, variously associated with collagen fibrils, did not imply that the surface was involved in the formation of collagen fibrils, and that such loss of cell surface during fibrogenesis would lead to loss of cell viability. They suggested that their morphological evidence supported the idea that collagen monomers were secreted from the cell by a merocrine process, which then formed extracellularly into long fibrils of 85 Å in diameter, which rapidly grew by deposition of the monomers till they were about 400 Å in diameter and a characteristic periodicity was present; the increase in hydroxyproline content of the cultures represented an increase in fibril number and length rather than an increase in fibril size. The fibrils were orientated parallel to the horizontal plane of the culture and tended to form in layers at right angles to each other.

In addition, Goldberg and Green (1964) noted during both the log and stationary phases of culture that fibrils of about 50 Å diameter were randomly distributed in the cytoplasm and also lay in parallel array just beneath the surface of the cells. The occurrence of these fibrils was almost similar in both phases of culture. Since hydroxyproline was not identified chemically in these cultures during the log phase it was suggested that such intracellular fibrils did not represent collagen but that they might be correlated with cell motility and cytoplasmic streaming. In a later paper, however, Green and Goldberg (1964a) found that ^{14}C-proline was hydroxylated in small amounts during the log phase. Thus whether such intracellular fibrils represent a stage in the formation of collagen fibrils must be left open to question.

A rather converse view of certain aspects of fibrogenesis has been proposed by Yardley, Heaton, Gaines and Shulman (1960) and Yardley (1962). Thin sections of cultures of heart tissue from embryo chicks were examined by electron-microscopy, and it was noted that marginal condensations of the surface of fibroblasts were associated with intracytoplasmic filaments, some of which appeared to be in direct continuity with characteristic collagen fibrils in the extracellular phase. The observations suggested that a breakdown occurred in the cell surface during the extrusion of collagen and the implication was made that the filaments were collagenous; it appeared as if the disruption of the cell surface occurred at the marginal condensations permitting the extrusion of large regions of associated cytoplasm. Yardley and colleagues compared their observations with those on the extrusion of cellular material from apocrine cells. The question arises whether the apparent disintegration of the cell surface and extrusion of cytoplasmic material and associated filaments is a general feature of fibrogenesis. Yardley (1962) found that sections cut perpendicular to the plane of the cultures demonstrated marginal condensations both inside and outside the unit membrane, and at other sites on the surface of the cell the membrane disappeared or merged with the marginal condensations; many of the micrographs, however, were of sections cut parallel to the surface of the culture, and hence it was inevitable that the cell surface-membrane appeared indistinct or disrupted and it was impossible to gauge the precise spatial relationship between the fibrous elements and the unit membrane. Kuwabara (1959) also studied tissue cultures by electron-microscopy and noted an amorphous material in association with the cell surface, and the indistinctness of the unit-membrane in many areas. Yardley (1962) came to the conclusion that when the secretion from which collagen was derived was exposed to "extracellular space", characteristic collagen fibrils were formed; he proposed that such exposure could occur by transfer through an intact cell membrane, by rupture of the cell membrane or by fragmentation of cytoplasmic masses from the main body of the cell. In the view of the writer the bulk of the evidence on the mode of formation of collagen fibrils *in vivo* and *in vitro* is against the hypothesis that the cell surface-membrane undergoes severe disruption during fibrogenesis.

F. CONCLUSIONS

Various steps that are known to be involved in the synthesis of the collagen molecule are surrounded by much controversy, and many steps have not been studied at all. Likewise, the function of the different cytoplasmic organelles is still open to question. Some of the variations in results may be due to different interpretations of similar data, but they may well be due also to the use of different cells and experimental conditions. Fundamentally, the formation of collagen protein most likely follows a basic pathway in all metazoan cells, but this may be modified in certain ways if the metabolic regulation at the molecular level becomes out of phase due, for instance, to the experimental handling of the cells.

As yet there is no knowledge of the size of the collagen unit that is extruded from the metazoan cell but there is some evidence to support the idea that primary collagen fibrils are formed at the cell surface or in the cortex just beneath it; it is unlikely, however, that the cell surface membrane undergoes severe disruption during fibrogenesis. Once such primary fibrils are laid down, growth occurs by the addition of further collagen units which must be secreted from the cell. There is little doubt now that much of the collagen produced by the metazoan cell is secreted and that there may be more than one method, possibly depending on the type of cell. That the secretion or secretions are capable also of being transformed into fibrils at some distance from the cell is indisputable. Such transformation is in accord with the hypothesis put forward by Fitton Jackson (1956) that collagen fibril-formation can occur when cellular secretions come into contact with interstitial fluid, although whether the fluid provides additional organic and/or enzymatic substances essential for fibrogenesis, or whether it supplies a medium of appropriate ionic strength and pH for the necessary transformation of cytoplasmic precursors is not yet clear. Whether any regulation of fibre-formation may be exerted by constituents of the ground substance is also open to question. In this connection it is of considerable interest to draw a parallel with observations of the cross-linking process that occurs during the biosynthesis of elastin (Partridge, Elsden, Thomas, Dorfman, Telser and Pei-Lee Ho, 1964). It is possible that the structural features of the collagen protein extruded from the cell are such that, when they attain a specific juxtaposition one with the other, they possess an inherent capacity to form the necessary cross-links within the extracellular phase, and hence form characteristic fibrous arrays.

References

Abercrombie, M. and Heaysman, J. E. M. (1954). Observations on the social behaviour of cells in tissue culture. *Exp. Cell Res.* **6**, 293.

Baitsell, G. A. (1915). The origin and structure of a fibrous tissue which appears in living cultures of adult frog tissues. *J. exp. Med.* **21**, 455.

Barnicott, N. A. and Huxley, H. E. (1965). Electron microscope observations on mitotic chromosomes. *Quart. J. micr. Sci.* **106**, 197.

Bassett, C. A. L. (1962). Current concept of bone formation. *J. Bone Jt. Surg.* **44A**, 1217.

Behnke, O. (1964). A preliminary report on 'microtubules' in undifferentiated and differentiated vertebrate cells. *J. Ultrastruct. Res.* **11**, 139.

Bernhard, W. (1959). Ultrastructural aspects of nucleo-cytoplasmic relationship. *Exp. Cell Res. Suppl.* **6**, 17.

Biggers, J. D. (1963). Studies on the development of embryonic cartilaginous long-bone rudiments *in vitro*. *Nat. Cancer Inst. Monogr.* **11**, 1.

Biggers, J. D., Gwatkin, R. B. L. and Heyner, S. (1961). Growth of embryonic avian and mammalian tibiae on a relatively simple chemically defined medium. *Exp. Cell Res.* **25**, 41.

Biggers, J. D., Lawson, K. A., Lucy, J. A. and Webb, M. (1961). The chemical composition of long-bone rudiments from the embryonic chick. *Biochim. biophys. Acta* **54**, 236.

Bloom, W. (1960). Preparation of a selected cell for electron microscopy. *J. biophys. biochem. Cytol.* **7**, 191.

Bloom, W. and Leider, R. J. (1962). Optical and electron microscopic changes in ultraviolet irradiated chromosome segments. *J. Cell Biol.* **13**, 269.

Bornstein, P. and Piez, K. A. (1965). Collagen. Structural studies based on the cleavage of methionyl bonds. *Science* **148**, 1353.

Cameron, D. A. (1961). The fine structure of osteoblasts in the metaphysis of the tibia of the young rat. *J. biophys. biochem. Cytol.* **9**, 883.

Campo, R. D. and Dziewiatkowski, D. P. (1962). Intracellular synthesis of protein-polysaccharide by slices of bovine costal cartilage. *J. biol. Chem.* **237**, 2729.

Canti, R. G. (1928). Cinemicrograph demonstration of living tissue cells growing *in vitro*. *In* "Verhandlungen de Abteilung für experimentelle Zellforschung auf der X internationale Zoologenkongress, Budapest," p. 86.

Caro, L. G. (1961). Electron microscopic radioautography of thin sections. The Golgi zone as a site of protein concentration in pancreatic acinar cells. *J. biophys. biochem. Cytol.* **10**, 37.

Castor, C. W. (1962). Do the functional capacities of connective tissue cells change with age or disease? *In* "The Biology of Connective Tissue Cells", pp. 223–226. Arthritis and Rheumatism Foundation, U.S., New York.

Cook, G. M. W., Heard, D. H. and Seaman, G. V. F. (1960). A sialomucopeptide liberated by trypsin from the human erythrocyte. *Nature, Lond.* **188**, 1011.

Cook, G. M. W., Heard, D. H. and Seaman, G. V. F. (1962). The electrokinetic characterization of the Ehrlich ascites carcinoma cell. *Exp. Cell Res.* **28**, 27.

Curtis, A. S. G. (1960). Cell contacts: some physical considerations. *Amer. Nat.* **94**, 37.

Daniel, M. R., Glauert, A. M., Dingle, J. T. and Lucy, J. A. (1965). The action of vitamin A (retinol) on the fine structure of rat dermal fibroblasts in culture. Strangeways Annual Report, pp. 13–14.

Danielli, J. F. (1937). The relations between surface pH, ion concentrations and interfacial tension. *Proc. roy. Soc.* B, **122**, 155.

Danielli, J. F. (1958). *In* "Surface Phenomena in Chemistry and Biology" (J. F. Danielli, K. G. A. Pankhurst and R. C. Riddiford, eds.), p. 246. Pergamon Press, Oxford.

Danielli, J. F. and Harvey, F. N. (1934). The tension at the surface of mackerel egg oil, with remarks on the nature of the cell surface. *J. cell. comp. Physiol.* **5**, 483.

De Robertis, E. and Setelo, J. R. (1952). Electron microscope study of cultured nervous tissue. *Exp. Cell Res.* **3** (Suppl. 2), 433.

Devis, R. and James, D. W. (1962). Electron microscopic appearance of close relationships between adult guinea-pig fibroblasts in tissue culture. *Nature, Lond.* **194**, 695.

Dingle, J. T., Fell, H. B. and Lucy, J. A. (1966). Synthesis of connective tissue components. The effect of retinol and hydrocortisone on cultured limb-bone rudiments. *Biochem. J.* **98**, 173.

Doljanski, L. and Roulet, F. (1933). Studien über die Entstehung der Bindegewebsfibrille. *Virchows Arch.* **293**, 260.

Eastoe, J. E. (1961). The composition of collagen from subcellular fractions of guinea-pig granuloma tissue. *Biochem. J.* **79**, 648.

Easton, J. M., Goldberg, B. and Green, H. (1962). Demonstration of surface antigens and pinocytosis in mammalian cells with ferritin-antibody conjugates. *J. Cell Biol.* **12**, 437.

Fawcett, D. W. and Ito, S. (1958). Observations on the cytoplasmic membranes of testicular cells examined by phase contrast and electron microscopy. *J. biophys. biochem. Cytol.* **4**, 130.

Fell, H. B. (1964). Some factors in the regulation of cell physiology in skeletal tissue. *In* "Bone Biodynamics" (H. M. Frost, ed.), p. 189. Little Brown, Boston.

Fernandez-Moran, H. (1963). Molecular basis of specificity in membranes. *In* "Macromolecular Specificity and Biological Memory" (F. O. Schmitt, ed.), pp. 39–48. M.I.T. Press, Cambridge, Mass.

Fessler, J. H. and Bailey, A. J. (1965). A search for subunit precursors of tropocollagen. *In* "Structure and Function of Connective and Skeletal Tissue", pp. 287–288. Butterworth, London.

Finean, J. B. (1957). The role of water in the structure of peripheral nerve myelin. *J. biophys. biochem. Cytol.* **3**, 95.

Fitton Jackson, S. (1953). Fibrogenesis *in vivo* and *in vitro*. *In* "Nature and Structure of Collagen" (J. T. Randall, ed.), pp. 140–152. Butterworth, London.

Fitton Jackson, S. (1955). Cytoplasmic granules in fibrogenic cells. *Nature, Lond.* **175**, 39.

Fitton Jackson, S. (1956). The morphogenesis of avian tendon. *Proc. roy. Soc.* B, **144**, 556.

Fitton Jackson, S. (1957). The fine structure of developing bone in the embryonic fowl. *Proc. roy. Soc.* B, **146**, 270.

Fitton Jackson, S. (1958). The synthesis of hydroxyproline within osteoblasts. *In* "Microsomal Particles and Protein Synthesis" (R. D. Roberts, ed.), p. 121. Pergamon Press, Oxford.

Fitton Jackson, S. (1960). Fibrogenesis and the formation of matrix. *In* "Bone as a Tissue" (K. Rodahl, J. T. Nicholson and E. M. Brown, eds.), pp. 165–186. McGraw-Hill, New York.

Fitton Jackson, S. (1964). Connective tissue cells. *In* "The Cell" (J. Brachet and A. E. Mirsky, eds.), Vol. 6, pp. 387–520. Academic Press, New York.

Fitton Jackson, S. (1965). Antecedent phases in matrix formation. *In* "Structure and Function of Connective and Skeletal Tissue", pp. 277–281. Butterworth, London.

Fitton Jackson, S. and Fell, H. B. (1963). Epidermal fine structure in embryonic chicken skin during atypical differentiation induced by vitamin A in culture. *Devl. Biol.* **7**, 394.

Fitton Jackson, S. and Randall, J. T. (1956). Fibrogenesis and the formation of matrix in developing bone. *In* "Bone Structure and Metabolism" (G. E. W. Wolstenholme and C. M. O'Connor, eds.). Ciba Foundation Symposium, Churchill, London.

Fitton Jackson, S. and Smith, R. H. (1957). Studies on the biosynthesis of collagen. I. The growth of fowl osteoblasts and the formation of collagen in tissue culture. *J. biophys. biochem. Cytol.* **3**, 897.

Gasic, G. and Berwick, L. (1963). Hale stain for sialic acid-containing mucins. *J. Cell Biol.* **19**, 223.

Gey, G. O. (1956). Some aspects of the constitution and behaviour of normal and malignant cells maintained in continuous culture. *Harvey Lect.* **50**, 154.

Glauert, A. M. (1965). The fixation and embedding of biological specimens. *In* "Techniques for Electron Microscopy" (D. H. Kay, ed.), pp. 166–212. Blackwell, Oxford.

Glauert, A. M. and Phillips, R. (1965). The preparation of thin sections. *In* "Techniques for Electron Microscopy" (D. H. Kay, ed.), pp. 213–253. Blackwell, Oxford.

Godman, G. C. (1962). Do the functional capacities of connective tissue cells change with age or disease? *In* "The Biology of Connective Tissue Cells", p. 227. Arthritis and Rheumatism Foundation, U.S., New York.

Godman, G. C. and Lane, N. (1964). On the site of sulphation in the chondrocyte. *J. Cell Biol.* **21**, 353.

Godman, G. C. and Porter, K. R. (1960). Chondrogenesis studied with the electron microscope. *J. biophys. biochem. Cytol.* **8**, 719.

Goldberg, B. and Green, H. (1964). An analysis of collagen secretion by established mouse fibroblast lines. *J. Cell Biol.* **22**, 227.

Goldberg, B., Green, H. and Todaro, G. J. (1963). Collagen formation *in vitro* by established mammalian cell lines. *Exp. Cell Res.* **31**, 444.

Goldhaber, P. (1958). The effect of hyperoxia on bone resorption in tissue culture. *Arch. Path.* **66**, 635.

Gould, B. S. (1963). Collagen formation and fibrogenesis with special reference to the role of ascorbic acid. *Int. Rev. Cytol.* **15**, 301.

Gould, B. S., Manner, G., Levi, A. and Schantz, A. (1963). Collagen biosynthesis. Formation of an S-RNA hydroxylysine complex. *Fed. Proc.* **22**, 411.

Green, H. and Goldberg, B. (1964a). Collagen and cell protein synthesis by an established mammalian fibroblast line. *Nature, Lond.* **204**, 347.

Green, H. and Goldberg, B. (1964b). Collagen synthesis by human fibroblast strains. *Proc. Soc. exp. Biol., N.Y.* **117**, 258.

Green, H. and Hamerman, D. (1964). Production of hyaluronate and collagen by fibroblast clones in culture. *Nature, Lond.* **201**, 710.

Haydon, D. A. (1962). Quoted by L. Weiss (1962).

Heyner, S. (1963). *In situ* embedding of cultured cells or tissues grown on glass in epoxy resins for electron microscopy. *Stain. Technol.* **38**, 335.

Hodge, A. J., Petruska, J. A. and Bailey, A. J. (1965). The subunit structure of the tropocollagen macromolecule and its relation to various ordered aggregation states. *In* "Structure and Function of Connective and Skeletal Tissue", pp. 31–41. Butterworth, London.

Horne, R. W. (1965). Negative staining methods. *In* "Techniques for Electron Microscopy" (D. H. Kay, ed.), p. 328. Blackwell, Oxford.

Jeffrey, J. J. and Martin, C. R. (1964). Ascorbic acid dependent synthesis of collagen by embryonic chick tibia grown in tissue culture. VIth int. Congr. Biochem., New York. *Collagen Currents* **5**, 114 (Abst.).

Kay, D. H. (Ed.) (1965). "Techniques for Electron Microscopy". Blackwell, Oxford.

Kretsinger, R., Manner, G., Gould, B. S. and Rich, A. (1964). Synthesis of collagen on polyribosomes. *Nature, Lond.* **202**, 438.

Kuwabara, H. (1959). Collagen formation on tissue culture of fibroblasts from chick embryo hearts. *Jap. J. exp. Med.* **29**, 627.

Lehninger, A. L. (1959). Respiratory energy transformation. *In* "Biophysical Science" (J. L. Oncley, ed.), pp. 136–146. Wiley, New York.

Lehninger, A. L. (1965). "The Mitochondrion". W. A. Benjamin, Inc., New York.

Lewis, M. R. (1917). Development of connective tissue fibers in tissue cultures of chick embryos. *Contr. Embryol. Carneg. Inst. Wash.* **8**, 45.

Lewis, W. H. (1931). Pinocytosis. *Bull. Johns Hopk. Hosp.* **49**, 17.

Lowther, D. A., Green, N. M. and Chapman, J. A. (1961). Morphological and chemical studies of collagen formation. II. Metabolic activity of collagen associated with sub-cellular fractions of guinea-pig granulomata. *J. biophys. biochem. Cytol.* **10**, 373.

Lucy, J. A. (1964). Globular lipid micelles and cell membranes. *J. theoret. Biol.* **7**, 360.

Lucy, J. A. and Glauert, A. M. (1964). Structure and assembly of macromolecular lipid complexes composed of globular micelles. *J. mol. Biol.* **8**, 727.

McKinney, R. L. (1929). Studies of fibers in tissue culture. III. The development of reticulum into collagenous fibers in cultures of adult rabbit lymph nodes. *Arch. exp. Zellforsch.* **9**, 14.

McLaren, A. D. and Babcock, K. L. (1959). Some characteristics of enzyme reactions at surfaces. *In* "Subcellular Particles" (T. Hayashi, ed.), pp. 23–35. Ronald Press, New York.

Malt, R. A. and Speakman, P. T. (1965). Cellular synthesis of collagen, ribosomal aggregates in hyperthyroidism, hypothyroidism and ascorbic acid depletion. *Surgery* **58**, 248.

Martin, A. V. W. (1953). Fine structure of cartilage matrix. *In* "Nature and Structure of Collagen" (J. T. Randall, ed.), p. 129. Butterworth, London.

Maximow, A. (1929). Nach des Verfassers Tode geschrieben und veröffentlicht. *Z. mikr.-anat. Forsch.* **17**, 625.

Micou, J., Collins, C. C. and Crocker, T. T. (1962). Nuclear-cytoplasmic relationships in human cells in tissue culture. *J. Cell Biol.* **12**, 195.

Mölbert, E. R. G., Duspive, F. and von Deimling, O. M. (1960). The demonstration of alkaline phosphatase in the electron microscope. *J. biophys. biochem. Cytol.* **7**, 387.

Novikoff, A. (1963). Lysosomes and related particles. *In* "The Cell" (J. Brachet and A. E. Mirsky, eds.), Vol. 2, pp. 423–488. Academic Press, New York.

O'Dell, D. S. (1965a). The use of collagenase in investigating the synthetic balance of the intercellular materials. *Exp. Cell Res.* **40**, 432.

O'Dell, D. S. (1965b). The formation and regulation of intercellular materials in the chicken embryo. Ph.D.Dissertation, Cambridge University.

Overton, J. (1962). Desmosome development in normal and reassociating cells in the early chick blastoderm. *Devl. Biol.* **4**, 532.

Parsons, D. F. R. (1963). Mitochondrial structure: two types of subunits on negatively stained mitochondrial membranes. *Science* **140**, 985.

Partridge, S. M., Elsden, D. F., Thomas, J., Dorfman, A., Telser, A. and Pei-Lee Ho (1964). Biosynthesis of the desmosine and isodesmosine cross-bridges in elastin. *Biochem. J.* **93**, 30c.

Peterkofsky, B. and Udenfriend, S. (1963). Localisation of the site of proline hydroxylation during the cell-free biosynthesis of collagen. *Biochem. biophys. Res. Commun.* **12**, 257.

Ponder, E. (1952–3). Volume changes, ion exchanges, and fragilities of human red cells in solutions of the chlorides of the alkaline earths. *J. gen. Physiol.* **36**, 767.

Porter, K. R. (1951). Repair processes in connective tissues. *In* "Connective Tissues" (C. Ragan, ed.), p. 136. Josiah Macy Jr. Foundation, New York.

Porter, K. R. (1953). Observations on a submicroscopic basophilic component of cytoplasm. *J. exp. Med.* **97**, 727.

Porter, K. R. (1954). Observations on the submicroscopic structure of animal epidermis. *Anat. Rec.* **118**, 433.

Porter, K. R. (1964). Cell fine structure and biosynthesis of intercellular macromolecules. *In* "Connective Tissue. Intercellular Macromolecules", pp. 167–196. Little Brown, Boston.

Porter, K. R. and Kallman, F. L. (1952). Significance of cell particles as seen by electron microscopy. *Ann. N.Y. Acad. Sci.* **54**, 882.

Porter, K. R. and Pappas, G. D. (1959). Collagen formation by fibroblasts of the chick embryo dermis. *J. biophys. biochem. Cytol.* **5**, 153.

Porter, K. R. and Thompson, H. P. (1947). Some morphological features of cultured rat sarcoma cells as revealed by the electron microscope. *Cancer Res.* **7**, 431.

Porter, K. R. and Vanamee, P. (1949). Observations on the formation of connective tissue fibers. *Proc. Soc. exp. Biol., N.Y.* **71**, 513.

Porter, K. R., Claude, A. and Fullam, E. F. (1945). A study of tissue culture cells by electron microscopy. Methods and preliminary observations. *J. exp. Med.* **81**, 233.

Prockop, D. J., Peterkofsky, B. and Udenfriend, S. (1962). Studies on the intracellular localization of collagen synthesis in the intact chick embryo. *J. biol. Chem.* **237**, 1581.

Revel, J. P. and Hay, E. L. (1963). An autoradiographic and electron microscopic study of collagen synthesis in differentiating cartilage. *Z. Zellforsch.* **61**, 110.

Reynolds, J. J. (1966a). The effect of hydrocortisone on the growth of chick bone rudiments in chemically defined medium. *Exp. Cell Res.* **41**, 174.

Reynolds, J. J. (1966b). The effect of ascorbic acid on the growth of chick bone rudiments in chemically defined medium. *Exp. Cell Res.* **42**, 178.

Robertson, J. D. (1959). The ultrastructure of cell membranes and their derivatives. *Biochem. Soc. Symp.* No. 16, 3.

Robbins, E. and Gonatas, N. K. (1964). The ultrastructure of a mammalian cell during the mitotic cycle. *J. Cell Biol.* **21**, 439.

Robbins, W. C., Watson, R. F., Pappas, G. D. and Porter, K. R. (1955). Some effects of anti-collagen serum on collagen formation in tissue culture. A preliminary report. *J. biophys. biochem. Cytol.* **1**, 381.

Rose, G. G. (1961). The Golgi complex in living osteoblasts. *J. biophys. biochem. Cytol.* **9**, 463.

Rose, G. G. and Pomerat, C. M. (1960). Phase contrast observations of the endoplasmic reticulum in living tissue cultures. *J. biophys. biochem. Cytol.* **8**, 423.

Rosenberg, M. D. (1960). Microexudates from cells grown in tissue culture. *Biophys. J.* **1**, 137.

Rosenberg, M. D. (1963). The relative extensibility of cell surfaces. *J. Cell Biol.* **17**, 298.

Ross, R. and Benditt, E. P. (1962). Wound healing and collagen formation. III. A quantitative radioautographic study of the utilization of proline-H^3 in wounds from normal and scorbutic guinea-pigs. *J. Cell Biol.* **15**, 99.

Ross, R. and Benditt, E. P. (1965). Wound healing and collagen formation. V. Quantitative electron microscope radioautoradiographic observations of proline-H^3 utilization by fibroblasts. *J. Cell Biol.* **27**, 83.

Rudall, K. M. (1965). Tissue maintenance and catabolism. *In* "Structure and Function of Connective and Skeletal Tissue", pp. 464–465. Butterworth, London.

Schimizu, Y., McCann, D. S. and Keech, M. K. (1965). The effect of ascorbic acid on human dermal fibroblasts in monolayer tissue culture. *J. Lab. clin. Med.* **65**, 286.

Schleiden, M. J. (1838). Beiträge zur Phytogenesis. *Arch. Anat. Physiol. u. wiss. Med. (Berlin)* **2**, 137.

Schmitt, F. O., Bear, R. S. and Palmer, K. J. (1941). X-ray diffraction studies on the structure of the nerve myelin sheath. *J. cell. comp. Physiol.* **18**, 31.

Schryver, H. F. (1965). The influence of hydrocortisone on the water uptake of embryonic tibiotarsi in organ culture. *Exp. Cell Res.* **37**, 327.

Schwann, Th. (1839). "Mikroskopische Untersuchungen über die Übereinstimmung unter Struktur und dem Wachstum der Tiere und Pflanzen." Vol. 3. Sander, Berlin.

Seaman, G. V. F. and Heard, D. H. (1960). The surface of the washed human erythrocyte as a polyanion. *J. gen. Physiol.* **44**, 251.

Shanes, A. M. and Berman, M. D. (1955). Penetration of the desheathed toad sciatic nerve by ions and molecules. 1. Steady state and equilibrium distributions. *J. cell. comp. Physiol.* **45**, 177.

Shaw, J. L. and Bassett, C. A. L. (1964). An improved method for evaluating osteogenesis *in vitro*. *Anat. Rec.* **149**, 57.

Sheldon, H. (1959). Electron microscope observations on rickets. *Bull. Johns Hopk. Hosp.* **105**, 52.

Sjöstrand, F. S. (1959). Fine structure of cytoplasm: the organisation of membranous layers. *In* "Biological Science" (J. C. Oncley, ed.), pp. 301–318. Wiley, New York.

Sjöstrand, F. S. (1963a). A new ultrastructural element of the membranes in mitochondria and of some cytoplasmic membranes. *J. Ultrastruct. Res.* **9**, 340.

Sjöstrand, F. S. (1963b). A comparison of plasma membrane, cytomembranes and mitochondrial membrane elements with respect to ultrastructural features. *J. Ultrastruct. Res.* **9**, 561.

Sjöstrand, F. S. and Elfvin, L. G. (1962). The layered, asymmetric structure of the plasma membrane in the exocrine pancreas cells of the cat. *J. Ultrastruct. Res.* **7**, 504.

Sjöstrand, F. S. and Zetterqvist, H. (1957). Functional changes of the free cell surface membrane of the intestinal absorbing cell. *In* "Electron Microscopy", pp. 150–151. Almqvist and Wiksell, Stockholm.

Sledge, C. B. (1965). The effect of hyperoxia on cartilage in organ culture. *In* "Structure and Function of Connective and Skeletal Tissue", pp. 436–442. Butterworth, London.

Sledge, C. B. and Dingle, J. T. (1965). Oxygen-induced resorption of cartilage in organ culture. *Nature, Lond.* **205**, 140.

Smith, R. H. and Fitton Jackson, S. (1957). Studies on the biosynthesis of collagen. II. The conversion of C^{14} proline to C^{14} hydroxyproline by fowl osteoblasts in tissue culture. *J. biophys. biochem. Cytol.* **3**, 913.

Stearns, M. L. (1940). Studies on the development of connective tissue in transparent chambers in the rabbits ear. I and II. *Amer. J. Anat.* **66**, 133; **67**, 55.

Stetten, M. R. (1949). Some aspects of the metabolism of hydroxyproline, studied with the aid of isotopic nitrogen. *J. biol. Chem.* **181**, 31.

Taylor, A. C. (1962). Response of cells to pH changes in the medium. *J. Cell Biol.* **15**, 201.

Taylor, A. C. and Robbins, E. (1963). Observations on microextensions from the surface of isolated vertebrate cells. *Dev. Biol.* **7**, 660.

Telser, A., Robinson, H. C. and Dorfman, A. (1965). The biosynthesis of chondroitin sulphate protein complex. *Proc. nat. acad. Sci. Wash.* **54**, 912.

Todaro, G. J. and Green, H. (1963). Quantitative studies of the growth of mouse embryo cells in culture and their development into established lines. *J. Cell Biol.* **17**, 299.

Weiss, L. (1958). The effects of trypsin on the size, viability and dry mass of sarcoma 37 cells. *Exp. Cell Res.* **14**, 80.

Weiss, L. (1962). The mammalian tissue cell surface. *Biochem. Soc. Symp.* No. 22, p. 32.

Weiss, P. (1929). Erzwingung elementarer Strukturverschledenheiten am *in vitro* wachsenden Gewebe. *Roux Arch. EntwMech. Organ.* **116**, 438.

Weiss, P. (1933). Functional adaptation and the role of ground substances in development. *Amer. Nat.* **67**, 322.

Weiss, P. (1945). Experiments on cell and axon orientation *in vitro*: the role of colloidal exudates in tissue organization. *J. exp. Zool.* **100**, 353.

Weiss, P. (1961). From cell to molecule. *In* "The Molecular Control of Cellular Activity" (J. M. Allen, ed.), pp. 1–72. McGraw-Hill, New York.

Willmer, E. N. (1961). Steroids and cell surfaces. *Biol. Rev.* **36**, 368.

Winell, M., Bassett, C. A. L., Wiener, J. and Spiro, D. (1966). Ultrastructural aspects of osteogenesis and fibrogenesis in tissue culture. (In preparation).

Winkler, K. C. and Bungenberg de Jong, H. G. (1941). Structure of the erythrocyte-membrane. *Arch. neerl. Physiol.* **25**, 431.

Wood, G. C. (1962). The heterogeneity of collagen solutions and its effect on fibril formation. *Biochem. J.* **84**, 429.

Yardley, J. H. (1962). What is the role of connective tissue cells in the formation of the extracellular components of the tissue? *In* "The Biology of Connective Tissue Cells", p. 179. Arthritis and Rheumatism Foundation, U.S., New York.

Yardley, J. H., Heaton, M. W., Gaines, L. M., Jr. and Shulman, L. E. (1960). Collagen formation by fibroblasts. Preliminary electron microscopic observations using thin sections of tissue culture. *Bull. Johns Hopk. Hosp.* **106**, 381.

Zamecnik, P. C., Stephenson, M. L. and Hecht, L. I. (1958). Intermediate reactions in amino acid incorporation. *Proc. nat. Acad. Sci. Wash.* **44**, 73.

CHAPTER 2

Tissue Culture in Radiobiology

O. A. TROWELL

Medical Research Council Radiobiological Unit, Harwell, Berkshire, England

I. Historical Introduction

Within a few years of its inception the method of tissue culture was used to observe the direct effects of X and γ rays on living cells (Price Jones and Mottram, 1914; Wood and Prime, 1914). This early interest arose from the practical necessity of finding some rational basis for the radiation treatment of human tumours. Over the years radiotherapists have learnt a great deal from such tissue culture studies, but much remains to be discovered and each new advance in culture technique has been quickly exploited to this end. In addition to the demands of radiotherapists there is now a great incentive to find ways of protecting human cells from the hazards of the atomic age. There is therefore, and there has been for many years, a powerful and practical urge to fundamental studies on the action of radiation on both normal and malignant cells, and, thanks to tissue culture, it has been possible to investigate the effects of radiation on cells living in a controlled environment and free from the disturbing influence of other parts of the body. Because the import of this work is readily apparent to the lay mind a great deal of money and time has been expended on it; some would say a disproportionate amount. Fortunately, however, much has been discovered, especially during the past ten years, and fresh light has been thrown not only on the effects of radiation but on the normal processes of cell multiplication and cell metabolism. In this field, as in many others, the distinction between pure and applied research is no longer meaningful.

The history of radiobiology divides rather strikingly into a "pre-war" period, up to about 1940, and a "post-war" period dating from about 1945. In the pre-war epoch, hanging-drop tissue cultures of fibroblasts were the principle test object and the only radiation sources available were X rays and radium. The visible effects of radiation on the living cell were qualitatively described and the time sequence of events was established. But since the roentgen for X rays was not defined until 1928 and the international roentgen for X and γ rays was not agreed upon until 1937, quantitative results during this period were usually relative rather than absolute. Most of the classical contributions came from the Strangeways Laboratory in Cambridge, England, and were associated with the names of Strangeways, Canti, Spear and Lasnitzki.

In the post-war epoch the major advances have come from the use of cell cultures. These were eminently suitable for accurate analysis of the effects of radiation upon growth. Radiation dosimetry, too, was now very accurate, so that absolute quantitative data became available. The most important contributions in this period have come from laboratories in the United States and Canada.

When a whole animal is exposed to radiation, the harmful effects observed in any one organ may not be entirely due to the *direct* effects of radiation on the cells, for there may be additional *indirect* effects resulting from damage to the local blood vessels (haemorrhage or thrombosis) or from circulating toxic substances released from damaged tissues elsewhere. In the pre-war period it was generally believed that these indirect effects were of considerable magnitude, and one of the chief objects of tissue culture work was to measure the direct effect and so assess its contribution to the *in vivo* situation. But in the post-war period it became increasingly clear that these indirect effects are quantitatively small and after doses up to 2000r, which are those of greatest biological interest, it is doubtful if they exist at all. There are now certain instances in which quantitative results obtained from Tissue Culture have completely accounted for the results observed in the whole animal. The modern view therefore is that most of the biological and clinical effects of radiation can be wholly explained at the cellular level as involving cell death in certain sensitive tissues, inhibition of cell division and mutagenic effects arising from chromosome damage. All these have now been studied in Tissue Culture under closely controlled conditions and in a quantitative way.

The most spectacular contributions of Tissue Culture to radiobiology are the recent ones, made since about1956. They were made possible by the availability of some radically new techniques which may briefly be listed as follows: (1) quantitative methods for the continuous propagation of pure cell strains in monolayer or suspension; (2) the Puck method for assessing the reproductive capacity of isolated cells by their ability to form macroscopic colonies, and (3) autoradiography with ^{3}H thymidine for labelling individual cells and measuring deoxyribonucleic acid (DNA) synthesis within them. By the use of these methods a great deal of fundamental information has been acquired about the effects of radiation on cell population dynamics and on various intracellular synthetic mechanisms and about inherent cell radiosensitivity. The observations were made on cell populations in which cytological, genetic and biochemical variations were reduced to a minimum. But it must be emphasized that, so far, this information is available only for certain established strains of either embryonic or malignant cells, and these strains may behave somewhat differently from the cells of origin and from the cells of the normal adult body.

In Tissue-Culture work so far, attention has been limited to the "acute" effects of radiation. These are the effects observed within a few hours or days of a single short exposure. The "chronic" effects, such as ageing and carcinogenesis, which occur many months later, are not yet accessible to *in vitro* investigation. With regard to chronic irradiation, that is continuous or intermittent exposure to very low intensity radiation for some weeks, only a very few Tissue-Culture reports have appeared and it is to be hoped that the method will be more assiduously applied in this rather important field.

Earlier reviews on the use of Tissue Culture in radiobiology have been made by Spear (1935), Stroud and Brues (1954) and Gärtner (1957).

Before embarking on a systematic description of radiation effects it is perhaps worth making two general points. The first is that every cell in the body can be killed outright if the dose is high enough, but such results are of no particular interest. In warm-blooded animals, biological as well as therapeutic interest is confined to doses extending up to about 5000r and this may be called the biological dose range. Within this range certain cell types and certain physiological processes are very much more sensitive than others and this is the starting point for almost all radiobiological inquiries, for here is a clue which should help in our search for the underlying mechanism of radiation damage. The second point to be made is that none of the effects of ionizing radiation so far discovered is specific, exactly similar effects can be produced by other types of radiation, such as ultraviolet, and by certain (radiomimetic) chemical poisons.

Perhaps the most important, certainly the most studied, effect of radiation is inhibition of growth. Accordingly, the first and in fact the greater part of this chapter will deal with the effects of radiation on cell growth *in vitro*.

II. The Effects of Radiation on Cell Proliferation

The commonly observed effects of radiation on proliferating cells in general have all been well known for more than forty years. They have been consistently found in all biological material, both animal and plant, *in vivo* and *in vitro*, and before proceeding to Tissue-Culture studies it may be helpful to summarize them as follows.

(1) *Mitotic inhibition.* Shortly after a small dose of radiation the percentage of cells in mitosis drops to a low level, but returns to normal again within a few hours. After higher doses, inhibition is more prolonged but the eventual recovery is usually complete. Cells which have already embarked upon mitosis at the time of irradiation usually complete the process in a normal fashion. Radiation affects only the cells which were about to enter mitosis and temporarily prevents them from doing so.

(2) *Mitotic retardation.* The duration of mitosis, the time taken for mitosis to be completed (normally 30–40 min), is considerably prolonged, and this is generally due to some hold-up at metaphase. It is important not to confuse this with mitotic inhibition, though it must be admitted that the terminology is somewhat confusing. The term "inhibition" is now universally used to mean a slower rate of entry of cells into mitosis, so a different term must be used to designate the slowing of mitosis itself, and for this I have chosen "retardation".

(3) *Giant-cell formation.* After irradiation some cells may slowly grow to an abnormal size, both nucleus and cytoplasm being involved. Such cells are often multinucleate. In this process continued growth of the cell as a whole takes place in the face of repeated failure of cell or cytoplasmic division.

(4) *Chromosome abnormalities.* These are of two distinct kinds, which are thought to represent two different actions of radiation.

(a) *Stickiness.* In the later stages of mitosis the daughter chromosomes tend to stick together instead of moving to the two poles. This may produce "clumping" of the chromosomes at metaphase and "lagging" in the movement of chromosomes at anaphase. The stickiness is a temporary phenomenon and it is seen in cells which were already in mitosis at the time of exposure, as well as in those which divide later. It is thought to represent a "physiological" effect rather than overt structural damage, probably some change in the surface properties of chromosomes.

(b) *Breakage.* The chromosome is broken across transversely at one point along its length, and usually several chromosomes are broken in the same cell. Most, but not all, of the broken ends reunite but many of them join on to the wrong chromosomes. This leads to "deletion", "translocation" or "inversion" of the material in one or more of the chromosomes. It is unnecessary to describe these rearrangements in detail; the upshot is that the chromosome material gets muddled up and at the next division it becomes unequally divided between the two daughter cells. Furthermore, any fragments which have failed to reunite are left outside the daughter nuclei altogether. For these reasons one or both of the daughter nuclei may be deficient in chromosome parts and the deficiency may be so great that the cell is non-viable. For the most part, the chromosomes are damaged during the resting (intermitotic) phase, but the broken chromosomes do not become visible until the metaphase and anaphase of the next mitosis. It has of course been suggested that the chromosome break is caused by the passage of a single ionizing particle through the chromosome, but this seems unlikely now that we know that similar breaks can be produced by radiomimetic chemicals.

(5) *Mitotic or delayed death.* It has been found in most proliferating tissues exposed to relatively small doses of radiation that no cells die until mitosis is resumed after its temporary inhibition, and the cells then die either during division or shortly afterwards. This is readily understandable in terms of chromosome breakage. The chromosomes of all the resting cells are damaged, more or less, and owing to faulty reunion or deletion of fragments many of the cells are left with a highly abnormal set of chromosomes. When such cells next divide they may die *during* division owing to the mechanical difficulties posed by the bizarrely shaped chromosomes, or, if they succeed in dividing, the daughter cells may be genetically so deficient that they cannot survive, in which case they die *shortly after* division. This is the most important mechanism of cell death in proliferating tissues, at any rate after relatively low doses of radiation.

(6) *Non-mitotic or immediate death.* After somewhat higher doses of radiation, some of the cells in proliferating tissues die at once or within a few hours. This death is unrelated to mitosis and its mechanism is obscure, but it seems to be essentially the same as that found in certain radiosensitive types of non-proliferating cells, such as small lymphocytes.

III. Effects of Radiation on the Growth of Tissue and Cell Cultures

The first major contribution of Tissue Culture to this subject was that of Strangeways and Oakley (1923). These workers exposed hanging-drop cultures of chick fibroblasts to small doses of X rays and in a classical paper they described in some detail almost all the phenomena listed in the preceding section, as seen in living cells. Both authors were good pathologists and their report was a model of accurate description which has well stood the test of time. Many of the facts were already known from serially-sampled *in vivo* material, but this was the first detailed account of the mitotic abnormalities produced by radiation and it was the first time they had been followed through by continuous observation of living vertebrate cells. It is interesting to recall these authors' statement that *all* the changes described had previously been seen by them in unirradiated cultures in unfavourable media, and they doubted if any were specific for radiation. Here again their observation has been fully vindicated, though in the intervening years many seemed to lose sight of it.

The observations of Strangeways and Oakley were purely qualitative, but over the next twenty years quantitative studies were made on similar cultures in the same laboratory, chiefly by Canti, Spear and Lasnitzki, whose work will frequently be mentioned in the ensuing pages. Canti (1928) introduced time-lapse cinematography specifically for recording the effects of radiation on individual living cells and this line of investigation has been pursued by Simon-Reuss and Spear (1947), Stroud (1956), Pomerat, Kent and Logie (1957b) and Pomerat (1958).

In the preceding section the effects of radiation on proliferating cells were listed (1) to (6). This does not imply that radiation has six independent actions, indeed several of the effects are known to be interrelated. It is nevertheless a convenient classification of observed phenomena and we shall now deal with each effect in turn and consider the part which Tissue-Culture methods have played in elucidating it. The extent to which these six effects are interdependent will, it is hoped, become apparent as the discussion proceeds. It has been necessary also to interpolate an account of recent work on the effects of radiation on DNA synthesis and the cell cycle because this has important bearings on mitotic inhibition, mitotic retardation and giant-cell formation.

A. MITOTIC INHIBITION

This was first shown in tissue cultures by Price Jones and Mottram (1914) for γ rays and by Kimura (1919) for X rays. These early workers used hanging-drop cultures of rodent tumour cells and they noted that whereas mitosis was suppressed, the "outgrowth" due to cell migration was quite unaffected. It is fortunate that the effects of radiation on these two components of "growth" in tissue culture were thus differentiated from the start and the confusion which arose in many other fields of inquiry into the growth of tissue cultures was almost entirely avoided.

The classical work of Strangeways and Oakley (1923) on hanging-drop cultures of chick fibroblasts using X rays, established that cells were temporarily restrained from entering mitosis. Strangeways and

Hopwood (1926) extended this work with some quantitative observations which enabled them to conclude that the cells were most sensitive to inhibition during a relatively short period just before prophase. In the same laboratory it was shown that γ rays from radium had exactly the same effect (Canti and Donaldson, 1926; Canti and Spear, 1927, 1929; Spear, 1931b). The effects of X and γ rays on mitosis in fibroblast cultures reported from the Strangeways laboratory were completely confirmed by Juul and Kemp (1933) in Copenhagen.

Canti and Spear (1929) made the further point that when the mitotic index recovers after inhibition it temporarily "overshoots", that is it rises above normal before settling down. Furthermore, whatever the dose, the size of the overshoot seemed to be almost exactly complementary to that of the initial trough. This suggested that radiation affected only those cells which were just about to enter mitosis and that when released from inhibition these quickly caught up with the other cells, so that in the end no cells were permanently delayed and the overall mitotic index remained unchanged. This explanation was generally accepted, but Canti and Spear were careful to point out that the overshooting mitotic index could also be explained on the alternative assumption that the duration of the mitotic process itself was lengthened during the recovery period, and they mentioned that "some evidence obtained by direct examination suggests that the latter alternative may be the cause". Recent work, to be described in the next section, has shown that the duration of mitosis is in fact considerably prolonged during the period of recovery from mitotic inhibition and it now seems that Canti and Spear's "latter alternative" is probably the correct explanation.

If the cells are sensitive to inhibition for only a very brief period just before prophase, then one might expect that a given dose of radiation spaced out over a period of several hours would produce more inhibition than the same dose given in a few minutes, because more cells would be caught in the sensitive stage. But in point of fact the reverse was found to be true; decreasing the dose rate decreased the effect (Canti and Spear, 1927; Cox, 1931a; Spear and Grimmett, 1933) and there was a critical dose rate below which no inhibition occurred whatever the dose (Canti and Spear, 1927). This simply means that any catching of cells in the sensitive phase was overshadowed by a more important opposing factor, which their experiments clearly revealed. This is that the inhibitory effect of radiation on mitosis is not cumulative, in other words recovery processes are at work. The fact that total recovery occurs so quickly after irradiation leads of course to the same conclusion. On the other hand, it has been reported recently that decreasing the dose rate did increase the amount of mitotic inhibition in cultures of chick fibroblasts, and this was true for X rays and fast electrons (Gärtner and Peters, 1953) and also β rays (Gärtner and Zoeppritz, 1958). At present this result seems puzzling.

Mitotic inhibition is produced by quite small doses of radiation. In fibroblast cultures 50r produces a peak depression of about 50% and 300r produces almost 100% (Lasnitzki and Lea, 1940), while 2000r abolishes mitosis completely for 24 h (Lasnitzki, 1947). The same doses produce about the same degree of inhibition in the dividing erythroblasts and myelocytes in cultures of bone marrow (Osgood and Bracher, 1939; Osgood, 1942; Rachmilewitz, Rosin, Goldhaber and Doljanski, 1947; Astaldi, Mauri and di Guglielmo, 1950; Boll, Koppe, Schaaf and Trautmann, 1956). As far as is known the sensitivity of all dividing cells is about the same, both *in vivo* and *in vitro*. Breitling and Peters (1957) detected a depression of mitosis in HeLa cell cultures continuously exposed to only 0·1r/day of γ rays, as compared with controls; and Peters (1962) claimed that a dose of only 0·02r given over 48 h produced a detectable effect on cultures of HeLa and human amnion cells.

Lasnitzki (1943a) made the point that the higher the dose the more prolonged the inhibition. This relationship has now been fully worked out in various cell strains maintained in continuous culture. The average period of mitotic delay or preprophase arrest was measured after graded doses of radiation. In mouse L cells, Whitfield and Rixon (1959) found that mitotic delay was linearly proportional to dose over the range 200–4000r, but Whitmore, Stanners, Till and Gulyas (1961) thought that delay was proportional to logarithm of dose over the range 2000–5000r. In HeLa cells, Tolmach (1961) found a direct proportionality which amounted to a delay of 1 min/r. It must be made clear that after high doses of radiation, say 5000r, although mitoses eventually reappear and mitotic inhibition is therefore recovered from, practically all the dividing cells die either during mitosis or shortly afterwards, so that growth soon comes to a stop. After high doses of radiation therefore, growth is permanently arrested, but not because of mitotic inhibition as here defined.

All these facts about mitotic inhibition were discovered by the use of Tissue Culture. Many of them have since been confirmed by the much more tedious process of serially sampling tissues in the whole animal. The advantages of Tissue Culture were that the cell population could be continuously observed and quantitative results were easily obtained. It must also be remembered that, at the time, indirect effects of radiation loomed large and it seemed very necessary to exclude them. But we now know that the mitotic inhibition produced by a given dose of radiation is about the same *in vivo* as *in vitro* (Lasnitzki, 1945).

The question of how radiation prevents cells from entering mitosis is an intriguing one and the answer remains elusive. For many years it was thought that inhibition of DNA synthesis was a likely explanation but, as will be shown in Section III, E, this has now been ruled out. It is therefore worth considering a more recent theory which postulates an increase in cell permeability. It has been found that when tissue cultures are exposed to hypertonic saline or to certain polyamines such as spermine or agmatine (decarboxylated arginine), the cells round up and their nuclear chromatin becomes condensed, so much so that they all appear to be in early prophase. And this change is completely reversible. This suggested that chromosome coiling, which is the basic phenomenon of prophase, normally results from the action of certain intracellular cations on the anionic chromatin. From the radiation point of view it was then postulated that radiation increases cell permeability with the result that the normal cations leak out and are no longer available to bring about the normal prophase changes. If this hypothesis is correct, the mitotic inhibition which normally follows irradiation could perhaps be prevented by raising the concentration of cations in the culture medium before exposure. And this has been found to be the case. Gaulden (1956) had already shown that hypertonic saline prevented radiation-induced mitotic delay in cultures of grasshopper neuroblasts, and Whitfield, Rixon and Youdale (1962) found that 0·05 M agmatine completely prevented the mitotic inhibition produced by 1000r of X rays in suspension cultures of L-strain fibroblasts. The agmatine had to be removed immediately after irradiation otherwise it itself retarded the later stages of mitosis. Whitfield and Rixon (1962) then found that calcium was a particularly effective cation for this purpose and showed that 0·01 M calcium salt completely prevented the mitotic delay induced by 1400r. It is known from other work that radiation does increase cell permeability and that calcium is a particularly effective agent for reducing the permeability of radiation-damaged cells. So this may be a second way in which calcium reduces the loss of chromosome-condensing cations from the irradiated cell. It is obvious that this problem could only be tackled by Tissue-Culture methods and further important discoveries in this field can confidently be expected.

B. MITOTIC RETARDATION

As mitotic inhibition wears off, mitosis reappears and it is then found that the time which each cell takes to carry out its division is longer than normal, and this mitotic retardation is a feature which persists for many hours. The phenomenon was first noted by Strangeways and Oakley (1923) in fibroblast cultures and defined more precisely by Lasnitzki (1940). In similar fibroblast cultures Simon-Reuss and Spear (1947) followed individual mitotic cells by time-lapse cinematography and found that after 88r about half of the mitoses were delayed for an hour or more in metaphase. They were unable to say whether prophase was similarly prolonged or not.

Modern observations have been made on cell strains in continuous culture. With L fibroblasts Whitmore *et al.* (1961) found that 200r increased the average duration of mitosis by an hour or more, and with U-12 fibroblasts Harrington (1961) found that 15 h after 500r the average duration of mitosis was 172 min as compared with the normal 64 min. Pomerat *et al.* (1957b) studied various human cell strains with time-lapse cinematography and found many instances of very prolonged metaphase delay after 2000r.

Stroud and Brues (1954) and Stroud (1956) found a marked retardation of mitosis in cultures of chick-embryo muscle cells continuously irradiated by means of ^3H_2O present in the culture medium. Their most important finding was that a dose rate of 47 rep/h, which was too low to cause any mitotic inhibition (preprophase arrest) was nevertheless sufficient to increase the average duration of mitosis from 40 to 61 min. So, under these conditions, mitotic retardation is a more sensitive indicator of radiation damage than is mitotic inhibition. An important technical consequence was that at these low dose rates the mitotic index (% of cells in mitosis) was actually greater than normal. If the mitotic index alone had been scored the results might have been interpreted as a stimulation of mitosis, and it is interesting to recall that there were several such claims for a stimulating action of radiation in the early literature. Stroud and Brues point out that colchicine was originally claimed to be a mitotic stimulant on just such a basis as this.

In insects the effects of radiation on mitosis seem to be somewhat different. Carlson and his co-workers have cultured portions of grasshopper embryo and studied the effect of X rays on the proliferating neuroblasts in great detail. This work has been summarized by Carlson (1961) and the chief points are as follows. The main effect of radiation was to arrest the cells in late prophase. Carlson called this mitotic inhibition, and it is of course reasonable to do so, but in the terminology adopted in this article (p. 67) we should call it mitotic retardation. A dose of 3r produced detectable retardation and the passage of a single α particle through a cell was sufficient to halt it in prophase. Recovery from this retardation could be accelerated by adding grasshopper egg yolk to the medium, and it could be slowed by high oxygen concentration. It was also noted that cells irradiated in prophase often reverted to interphase before proceeding normally.

The question of mitotic inhibition and mitotic retardation in relation to the cell cycle as a whole will be discussed in the next sections.

C. DNA SYNTHESIS AND THE CELL CYCLE IN NORMAL CELLS

In this section we shall put aside the question of radiation and briefly summarize the important information which is now available about the time sequence of DNA synthesis in normal proliferating cells (for more detailed discussions of this the reader is referred to Vol. 1, Chaps. 7, 10 and 12). With modern methods of cell culture it is possible to study the growth of a homogeneous population of cells (a cell strain) under standardized conditions, and, by analysis of serial samples, to follow the increase in cell number, total protein, DNA, RNA, etc. with great precision. Furthermore, if thymidine labelled with ^{3}H or ^{14}C is added to the culture medium, the process of DNA synthesis can be followed, for this compound is incorporated into newly forming DNA and nothing else. Cells synthesizing DNA incorporate labelled thymidine into the nucleus and this can be recognized by autoradiography. Usually the labelled thymidine is added to the medium at a particular stage of the experiment, left there for a certain time (half an hour or less) and then removed. In this way all the cells are uniformly exposed to thymidine over a precisely defined period, and the information obtained is of two kinds. First, the percentage of cells labelled tells us what percentage of the cells were synthesizing DNA during the period, and, second, the "heaviness" of the label, which can be determined by grain counting, tells us the rate of DNA synthesis in individual cells. Information of this kind cannot be obtained with anything approaching this precision in experiments on the whole animal, though it can be obtained in certain other biological material such as plant root tips.

The key fact discovered was that the process of DNA synthesis, wherein the DNA content of the nucleus is doubled in preparation for the next division, does not occur as previously supposed just before division, nor does it occur throughout the intermitotic period, it occurs during a sharply restricted period roughly midway between one division and the next. Each new daughter cell passes first through a resting period called G_1, then through the period of DNA synthesis (S), then through a second resting period called G_2, and finally through the period of mitosis (M). The complete cell cycle is shown in Fig. 1, and it is believed that in cultures of pure cell strains the cycles of the individual cells are pretty uniform. The terminology G_1, S, G_2, M, was introduced by Howard and Pelc (1953) and has proved very useful. The letter G simply meant "gap" so as to be quite non-committal.

It has been possible to deduce the approximate duration of each phase of the cell cycle by exposing the cells to ^{3}H-thymidine for a brief period and then seeing how long the labelled cells took to pass into and

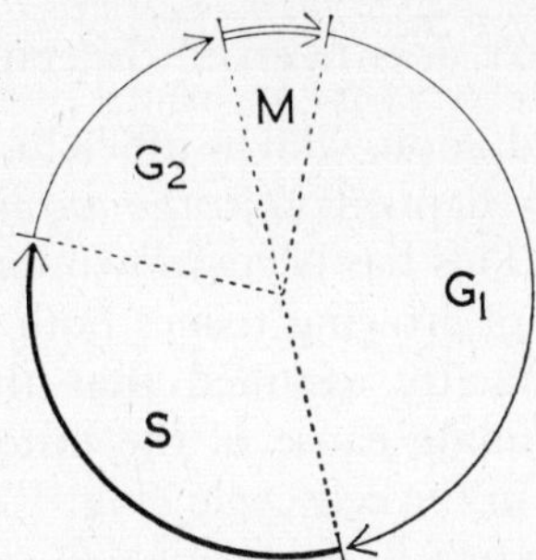

FIG. 1. The cell cycle in proliferating cells.

out of mitosis. The results obtained for several mammalian cell lines are shown in Table I, from which it may be seen that the variation between different cell types is not very great.

We can now proceed to examine the effect of radiation on the cell cycle and correlate this with the mitotic inhibition and mitotic retardation already described.

TABLE I

The duration in hours of the phases of the cell cycle, in various mammalian cells cultured *in vitro*

	G_1	S	G_2	M	
L fibroblasts	9–11	6–7	2–4	1	Stanners and Till, 1960
L fibroblasts	9	7	3	1	Whitmore *et al.*, 1961
U–12 fibroblasts	16	9	4	1	Harrington, 1960
Chinese hamster fibroblasts	2·7	5·8	2·1	0·4	Hsu *et al.*, 1962
Chinese hamster fibroblasts	5–6	6	2–3		Taylor, 1960
HeLa cells in 10% horse serum	14	8·5	3–10		Painter and Drew, 1959
HeLa cells in 15% calf serum	14	5–6	2–8		Painter and Drew, 1959
Chinese hamster embryo cells	12–14[a]	8	2–4		Chu, 1962
Human bone-marrow cells	25–30	12–15	3–4		Lajtha *et al.*, 1954

[a] G_1 plus M.

D. THE EFFECT OF RADIATION ON THE CELL CYCLE

Moderate doses of radiation, which suffice to inhibit mitosis, produce a partial and temporary depression in the *overall* rate of DNA synthesis in proliferating tissues. This has been known for a long time and it has been found in all sorts of growing tissues both *in vivo* and *in vitro,* and until recently it was tacitly assumed that this depression of DNA synthesis was the proximate cause of the mitotic inhibition. But discovery of the G_2 phase in the cell cycle (Fig. 1) disposed of this theory. Howard (1956) was the first to point out that since the onset of mitotic inhibition is immediate, the cells which are prevented from entering mitosis, at any rate during the first few hours, must have been in G_2 at the time of irradiation and these cells have already completed their DNA synthesis. Radiation therefore blocks the movement of cells from G_2 to M and this will interfere with the passage of cells round the cycle in the following way. All the cells which were in M, G_1 and S at the time of irradiation will proceed normally and for the time being the overall rate of DNA synthesis in the culture will be maintained. But about 10 h later all these cells will have passed through S, and, since no new cells are moving round to enter S, the overall rate of synthesis falls off. This has been verified experimentally. It has been shown in many proliferating cell systems that after irradiation the overall rate of DNA synthesis is maintained until every cell has accumulated the double (4c) complement; this takes 12 h or so depending on the system, and after this long "latent period" the rate of synthesis falls almost to zero (if mitotic inhibition was complete) and remains there until mitosis is resumed.

This was shown first *in vivo,* using ascites tumour cells, by Kelly, Hirsch, Beach and Petrakis (1957), and Caspersson, Klein and Ringertz (1958). The results were confirmed and shown more convincingly in experiments on fibroblasts grown in suspension culture. Whitmore, Till, Gwatkin, Siminovitch and Graham (1958) followed the increase in total DNA per culture flask after a dose of 5000r, and Whitfield and Rixon (1959) did the same for a dose of 1000r. Whitmore *et al.* (1961) measured DNA synthesis with ^{3}H-thymidine at intervals after a dose of 2000r, and Harrington (1961) did the same for a dose of 500r.

The above workers all concluded that the depression of overall DNA synthesis observed in growing tissues after irradiation was chiefly due to the G_2 arrest which ultimately reduced the number of cells moving round the cycle and entering S. In other words mitotic inhibition is the cause of reduced DNA synthesis, not the result of it. This idea was confirmed by some other observations which they made. Whitmore *et al.* (1961) and Whitfield and Rixon (1959) found that the synthesis of ribonucleic acid (RNA) and of protein was depressed parallel to that of DNA. This seems to show quite clearly that radiation does not inhibit DNA synthesis specifically; it is simply a question of fewer cells undergoing general protoplasmic growth. Whitfield and Rixon also found that simple dilution of the cell suspension led to a temporary arrest of mitosis which was followed by exactly the same pattern of depressed DNA synthesis.

Although the weight of evidence against any specific effect of radiation on DNA synthesis is substantial, the matter is not yet finally settled. Dickson and Paul (1961) irradiated monolayer cultures of mouse fibroblasts (strain-L) and found a temporary but *immediate* depression of overall DNA synthesis, amounting to 50% after 2300r. There was no depression of RNA synthesis and the depression of DNA synthesis occurred only if the cultures were well-oxygenated. It was clearly shown that the magnitude of the radiation-induced depression of DNA synthesis was directly proportional to oxygen tension. The results of other workers will therefore have to be re-examined in this light and much further work seems necessary.

It is interesting at this point to recall some early work on radiation-induced mitotic inhibition in hanging-drop cultures of fibroblasts. Strangeways and Hopwood (1926) had already proved that the cells were arrested just before prophase and this work was continued by Love (1931) who deduced from mathematical calculations (not understood by the present writer) that the cells were most sensitive during the 3 h period preceding mitosis, which corresponds very well to the G_2 period for fibroblasts shown in Table I.

While it is universally agreed that the major effect of radiation is an arrest of cells in G_2, it seems that, in addition, there is some lesser slowing of the movement of cells through the other parts of the cycle. In L fibroblasts, Whitmore *et al.* (1961) at first concluded that radiation caused no change in the rate of movement of cells through G_1 and S, but in later work from the same laboratory Till (1961) reported that 2000r slowed the rate of passage through M, G_1 and S by about 20%, so that the duration of each of these phases was lengthened. In HeLa cells, Painter and Robertson (1959) found a similar lengthening of S phase. In bone marrow and lymphoid cells the lengthening of G_1 and S is much more marked (Lajtha, Oliver, Kumatori and Ellis, 1958) and this will be discussed more fully in the next section. Lajtha *et al.* found that 200r was sufficient to double the duration of G_1 in bone marrow cells, whereas over 500r was required to lengthen S at all, and from this they speculated that some unidentified process preceding DNA synthesis is particularly sensitive to radiation.

The general conclusion to be drawn is that radiation slows all stages

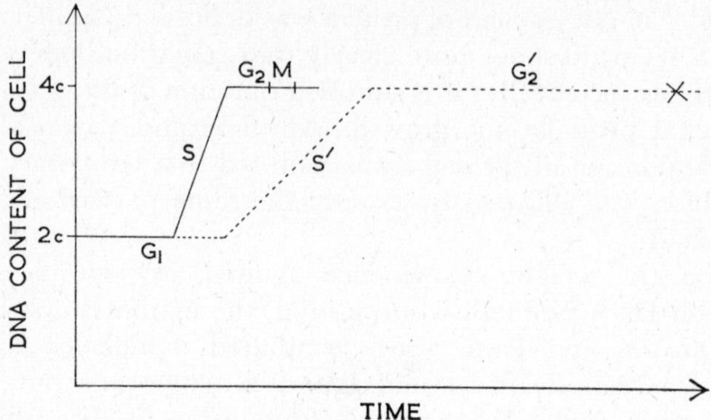

FIG. 2. The effects of radiation on the cell cycle. ———, Normal; ...., irradiated.

of the cell cycle, but the slowing is most marked, amounting to complete arrest, in G_2. This is represented schematically in Fig. 2.

The G_2 arrest corresponds to the mitotic inhibition dealt with in Section III, A. The lengthening of M corresponds to the mitotic retardation dealt with in Section III, B. The lengthening of S means that the rate of DNA synthesis in individual cells *during S phase* is reduced and this matter will be dealt with in the next section.

This work on the cell cycle must be acclaimed as a brilliant contribution of modern cell-culture methods combined with autoradiography to the study of normal growth and the effects of radiation upon it. The technical details and the scientific reasoning involved were too complex for description here but they merit careful reading as elegant examples of what modern culture methods can achieve when strategically planned, and in this connection the papers of Whitmore and Till from Toronto can be especially recommended.

But all new techniques raise their own problems and it is necessary to conclude this section with a few cautionary notes. When ^{3}H-thymidine is used to label cells the risk arises that the β radiation from incorporated ^{3}H may damage the cells. Drew and Painter (1959) found that 0·1 μc/ml of ^{3}H-thymidine continuously applied was ultimately lethal to HeLa cells in culture, and Sanders, Peterson and Langham (1961) found that 4 μc/ml inhibited growth. Subsequently Painter and Hughes (1961) showed that 0·05 μc/ml of ^{3}H-thymidine applied for half an hour did not alter the viability, generation time or mitotic activity of the cells, and this seems to be about the only control so far available. In general this dose has not been exceeded; Harrington (1960), for example, applied 0·05 μc/ml for 6 h in her experiments, which was probably safe, but Whitmore *et al.* (1961) applied 0·25 μc/ml for 80 h which seems more doubtful.

Goodheart (1961) devised a formula for calculating the radiation dose distribution within a cell containing intranuclear ^{3}H, and from this Sanders *et al.* (1961) calculated that 4 μc/ml ^{3}H-thymidine in the medium resulted in a radiation dose of 19r per day to the nuclei of labelled cells and 1·2r per day to the medium; and this inhibited growth. As a control they tried the effect of adding ^3H_2O instead of ^{3}H-thymidine and were very surprised to find that a concentration which delivered a calculated dose of 26r per day to both cells and medium had no harmful effect at all. This result seems very important for it suggests that ^{3}H-thymidine has some specific action over and above a generalized β irradiation of the cell. Sanders *et al.* suggested that perhaps the N–glycoside bond of the thymidylate incorporated into DNA polymer is specifically ruptured, thereby making a hole in the template used for subsequent replication.

The next question is, can it be assumed that ^{3}H-thymidine uptake is a reliable measure of DNA synthesis under all circumstances? There seems to be overwhelming evidence that in the normal whole animal this is a valid assumption, but in tissue cultures and in radiation damaged tissues it is less certain. Stroud, Brues and Svoboda (1961) experimented with two different strains of kidney cells, one from a pig, the other from a monkey, maintained in continuous culture. They found that, although both strains were proliferating at about the same rate and the pig cells could be labelled with ^{3}H-thymidine in the usual way, the monkey cells could hardly be labelled at all. The only explanation of this seems to be that the monkey cells were synthesizing their own thymidine. After exposure to 500r, labelling of the pig cells was depressed in the usual way, but labelling of the monkey cells, negligible before, now became quite marked. This was interpreted to mean that the synthesis of thymidine in monkey kidney cells is very sensitive to radiation. Reports such as this emphasize that results obtained by thymidine labelling should be treated with caution until it is shown that they are a valid index of DNA synthesis in the particular cultures under study. Lajtha, Oliver, Berry and Noyes (1958) have pointed out another error which may arise in the case of radiation studies. After high doses of radiation unlabelled thymidine liberated from autolysing dead cells will dilute the radioactivity of the total thymidine pool.

So far the various phases of the cell cycle *in vitro* have been established in cells of embryonic or malignant origin which have been kept in continuous culture for many years and which may, by mutation, have deviated considerably from their progenitors. It is interesting to note that Seed (1962) found that in three freshly isolated cell types, derived from monkey kidney, human skin and mouse embryo, nuclear protein synthesis occurred only during S phase, whereas in the old established strains HeLa and L it went on throughout the cell cycle. Further studies on freshly isolated cells from adult animals seem very desirable.

In the case of certain mammalian cells information is now available about their cell cycle *in vivo*. The durations of G_1, S, G_2 and M found for epidermal, intestinal epithelial, bone and liver cells *in vivo* have been tabulated by Post, Huang and Hoffman (1963) and the figures are roughly of the same order as those listed in Table I.

E. THE EFFECT OF RADIATION ON DNA SYNTHESIS

We must now return to the vexed question of the effect of radiation on DNA synthesis and try to disentangle the apparently contradictory results which have confused this subject for many years.

With reference first to the overall rate of DNA synthesis by the *whole culture,* which is measured by estimating total DNA, this simply depends on the total number of cells passing through S phase, and, as explained in the previous section, this number does not begin to decline until about 10 h after irradiation. It follows that measurements made during the first few hours after irradiation should show no effect, but those made later should. Apart from Dickson and Paul (1961), whose results were mentioned in the preceding section, the great majority of workers have found that this is in fact true.

We must now consider a totally different measurement, the rate of DNA synthesis in *individual cells during S phase*. This rate, which is determined from grain counts in autoradiographs, is represented by the slopes S and S′ in Fig. 2. The effect of radiation is to prolong the duration of S and slow the rate of DNA synthesis in each cell. But the final double complement (4c) of DNA is always reached, so this factor does not appreciably affect the overall synthesis by the whole culture. Now this slower rate of synthesis in S phase will be detected only if the period of observation is short—not longer than S; if the period of observation is long, both the irradiated and the control cells will have had time to reach the 4c value and no effect will be observed. A further point is that S is prolonged only if the cells are irradiated during S phase; when they are irradiated in G_1 the subsequent S phase is not affected (Terasima and Tolmach, 1963).

In any particular experiment, therefore, an inhibitory effect of radiation on DNA synthesis may or may not be observed, depending on what is measured, when it is measured and over how long a period of time. Some of the apparently contradictory reports in the literature can thus be reconciled even without taking into account a further factor, giant-cell formation, which will be dealt with in the next section.

In recent years the inhibitory effect of radiation on the rate of DNA synthesis by individual cells in S phase has been studied in some detail in cell suspension cultures, chiefly by Lajtha and his colleagues. Lajtha *et al.* (1958) used human bone marrow cells; Cooper and Alpen (1959) used rat thoracic duct lymphocytes; Berry, Hell, Lajtha and Ebert (1961) used mouse ascites tumour cells; and Huntley and Lajtha (1962) used mouse spleen lymphocytes. The effects of graded doses of radiation were accurately measured and a dose-effect curve constructed. In all these four systems it was found that the dose-effect curve was biphasic, indicating the existence of two independent radiosensitive components, S_1 and S_2 as shown in Fig. 3. The use of S_1 and S_2 in this connection (S for slope) must not be confused with the use of S to mean the synthetic phase in the cell cycle.

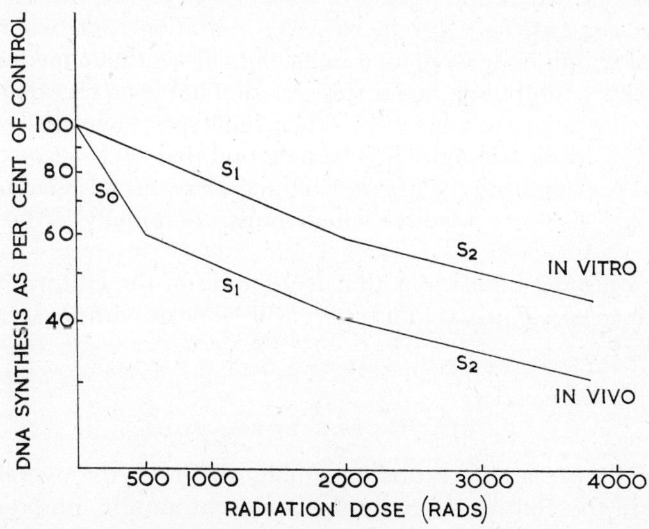

FIG. 3. Inhibition of DNA synthesis in proliferating lymphocytes. The X ray dose-effect curves *in vivo* and *in vitro*. (Modified from Lajtha, 1963.)

Similar experiments in the whole animal on thymus lymphocytes (Ord and Stocken, 1958b) and mouse spleen lymphocytes (Huntley and Lajtha, 1962) revealed the existence of a third and even more radiosensitive component, S_0, which apparently exists *in vivo* but not *in vitro*. The dose-effect curve for lymphocytes *in vivo* is therefore triphasic as indicated in Fig. 3. It must be made clear that the lymphocytes involved here are the medium sized and large ones only; the small lymphocytes do not normally divide and they do not synthesize DNA. Huntley and Lajtha suggested that S_0 represents inhibition of the intranuclear generation of ATP, S_1 inhibition of nucleoside phosphorylation, and S_2 represents damage to the DNA template. Be this as it may, the important point is that by the time lymphocytes have been explanted *in vitro* they have entirely lost the sensitive S_0 component and their DNA synthesis is already 35% inhibited. Presumably, mechanical trauma or some unphysiological factor in the *in vitro* environment destroys their power of intranuclear ATP synthesis and with it a very radiosensitive fraction of their original capacity for DNA synthesis. *In vitro*, therefore, they appear to be much less radiosensitive than *in vivo* (Alpen, Cooper and Barkley, 1960). The experiments of Ord and Stocken (1956, 1958a) showed the same sort of thing, but since they measured DNA synthesis in a different way, they are not quantitatively comparable. Ord and Stocken found that when lymphocyte suspensions were cultured in Ringer phosphate, even 2000r had no effect on DNA synthesis; but when the medium was improved by increasing the potassium content, 600r produced 14% inhibition; and when organ cultures of lymph node were used in a complete synthetic medium 600r produced 30% inhibition. So far this situation has been revealed only in medium and large lymphocytes; other cell types have not yet been investigated. More and more it is being found that cells *in vitro* differ in important respects from their *in vivo* counterparts, and this is a limitation of the Tissue-Culture method which must continually be taken into account.

There are some indications that irradiation of the culture medium may inhibit DNA synthesis, and these will be dealt with in Sections V, D, and XII.

F. GIANT-CELL FORMATION

As already explained, radiation usually depresses the overall DNA synthesis in the culture. Initially this is due to mitotic inhibition, but the rate remains permanently less than in the controls because the irradiated cultures contain fewer cells. But it must now be stated that in the case of certain long-established cell strains this depression of DNA synthesis may not occur. In HeLa cells, Levine and Kritchevsky (1958) found that DNA synthesis continued at the normal rate for several days after 1500r; and Sheek, Des Armier, Sagik and Magee (1960) found that the synthesis of both DNA and protein continued normally for 10 days after 1400r. In L fibroblasts, Dickson, Paul and Davidson (1958) found that synthesis of DNA, RNA, protein and lipid continued at the normal rate after 800r, and Whitfield and Rixon (1959) found that DNA synthesis continued normally after 1000r. All these workers noted that most of the cells in their irradiated cultures enlarged and became "giant cells", and this explains why synthesis went on. It seems that under certain circumstances, DNA synthesis does not stop when the 4c value is reached; it and the synthesis of other protoplasmic constituents go on unimpaired despite the absence of mitosis, with the result that both nucleus and cytoplasm increase greatly in size.

In hanging-drop cultures of chick fibroblasts a *few* giant cells can usually be found after irradiation (Prime, 1917; Strangeways and Oakley, 1923; Paterson, 1942). Strangeways and Oakley noted that the cytoplasm, nucleus and nucleolus were all enlarged and ascribed this to continued growth of the cell in the absence of division.

Giant-cell formation has been studied quantitatively in appropriate cell strains in continuous culture. Whitmore *et al.* (1958) used L fibroblasts and found that after 5000r, which permanently stopped mitosis, the average DNA, RNA and protein contents per cell increased logarithmically and in parallel fashion for 6 days, at a rate which was one-third to one-half that found in normal cultures. After 4 days the average cell contents of DNA, RNA and protein had increased about threefold, that is, more than enough to make two daughter cells. It was shown that the incremental DNA was newly synthesized and not scavenged from dead cells. Fogh, Biedler and Denues (1961) used a strain of human amnion cells and found that the average cell volume had increased about threefold 2 days after 3000r, while after 1000 and 300r the increases were correspondingly less. Tolmach and Marcus (1960) used HeLa cells and found that after 1300r the mean cell volume increased exponentially for 6 days at a rate corresponding to about half the growth rate of normal cultures. Ultimately the population consisted of giant cells twenty-to-forty times the normal size, but they all died within a few more days. Painter and Hughes (1961) performed an ingenious experiment with HeLa cells. They first exposed the cultures briefly to ^{3}H-thymidine so as to label all the cells in S phase. Different cultures were then irradiated at selected times after the labelling so that the labelled cells were all in G_1 or all in S, or all in G_2, at the time of irradiation. They found that the labelled cells all grew into giant cells irrespective of the stage in the cell cycle at which they had been irradiated. Terasima and Tolmach (1963) reached the same conclusion from experiments on "synchronized" populations of HeLa cells (the preparation of synchronized populations is explained on p. 91).

After 5000r cell enlargement is less than after 1250r (Tolmach, 1961), presumably because radiation now begins to inhibit protoplasmic synthesis. Giant-cell formation has also been described in various human tumour cell lines by Puck and Marcus (1956), Painter (1960) and Schleich, Gey and Gey (1961), in a mouse lymphoma cell line by Alexander (1961) and in cultures of bone marrow by Rachmilewitz *et al.* (1947).

Since the DNA content of these giant cells exceeds the 4c value, the question arises where is it located. Till and Whitmore (1959) observed that although giant cells do not divide in the ordinary way a certain number of abortive nuclear divisions nevertheless occurs. Metaphases occur and, in spite of severe structural damage, the chromosomes manage to divide, but they fail to separate. The nuclei thus become polyploid and this accounts for their high DNA content. It seems therefore that the cells can go through several cycles (S phases) without actually dividing. Till and Whitmore thought that radiation impaired spindle formation and this was the fundamental defect which prevented these cells from dividing. At any rate the mechanism must be something quite different from the temporary G_2 arrest which is responsible for ordinary mitotic inhibition.

In some cases the nuclei do in fact divide but the cytoplasm fails to do so. Fogh *et al.* (1961) found that many of the giant cells in their amnion cell cultures were multinucleate. Pomerat, Kent and Logie (1957a) have illustrated a great variety of giant cells showing multilobulation of the nucleus or multinucleation, with up to sixty micronuclei present in one cell, produced by irradiation of various human cell strains. The same authors (1957b) used time-lapse cinematography of cells in a Rose chamber to observe the origin of these bizarre giant cells by abnormal and abortive mitoses during the first 5 days after exposure to 2000 or 4000r of γ rays. They found that the nuclei of multinucleate cells often divide again synchronously to produce a cell with twice as many nuclei. This indicates that radiation may have some rather specific effect on cytoplasmic division.

Giant-cell formation does not occur to any great extent *in vivo,* though it has been recorded in irradiated human cervical carcinomas (Huwer, 1933; Glucksmann, 1941) and in some animal tumours (Luther, 1940, 1943). Pomerat *et al.* (1957a) irradiated nine different established human cell strains with 2000–4000r and observed extensive giant cell formation in all, but no giant cells could be found in primary explants from six different human sources, after similar irradiation. Harper, Pomerat and Kent (1958) found that irradiation of the Chang cell line, originally derived from human conjunctiva, regularly produced many giant cells, whereas irradiation of primary explants of human conjunctiva, cornea, sclera, choroid or retina produced none at all. Pomerat, Fernandes, Nakanishi and Kent (1958) then showed that giant cells could not be produced in primary explants of human amnion, but they appeared in some numbers when 20-day-old second-passage cultures were irradiated. All this goes to show that extensive giant-cell formation is a peculiar feature restricted to established cell lines. Now it is known that most established cell lines are polyploid (Bender, 1957) and the nine human lines used by Pomerat *et al.* (1957a) were known to be so. It seems therefore that, in respect of general protoplasmic growth, polyploid cells are much less sensitive to radiation than diploid ones. One may speculate that they are also less sensitive to other adverse influences, such as those presenting *in vitro,* and this may be why such cells are "selected" during establishment of a permanent cell strain.

Finally it may be noted that a few giant cells can sometimes be found in unirradiated cultures. Puck and Marcus (1956) found 0·19% in HeLa cultures, and Nakanishi and Nakahara (1956) watched the formation of multinucleated giant cells in normal cultures of ascites tumour cells.

G. CHROMOSOME ABNORMALITIES

These are visible at metaphase or anaphase in both fixed and living cells. From the observational point of view there is no particular case for studying them in tissue culture rather than in fixed preparations from the whole animal, except that in flattened and extended cells they may be easier to see and count. Chromosome fragmentation can be more accurately observed in the fixed cell than in the living, but chromosome stickiness can be more fully appreciated when the living cell is watched throughout division. Another point which observation of the living cells in tissue culture has revealed is that when the chromosomes are greatly altered in size and shape (from fragmentation and abnormal rejoining) mitotic division may be difficult and prolonged for purely mechanical reasons. It is often surprising that such a cell is able to complete division at all.

The various chromosome abnormalities produced by radiation were first clearly described by Strangeways and Oakley (1923) in fibroblast cultures. Since then they have been redescribed *ad nauseam* in almost every variety of growing tissue, both *in vivo* and *in vitro,* but no new points have emerged. One of the best recent descriptions is that of Fogh *et al.* (1961) in cultures of human amnion cells.

In what follows we shall be concerned only with chromosome fragmentation and its consequences; chromosome stickiness is difficult to measure and very little work has been done on it. Chromosome structural abnormalities (such as anaphase bridges) can easily be seen and scored and they provide a very sensitive index of radiation damage. For example, Simon-Reuss and Spear (1947) found in chick fibroblast cultures that about 40% of the mitotic figures were abnormal shortly after exposure to 55r. The quantitative effects of different doses, dose rates, etc. have been worked out in cultures of various mammalian cell types by Puck (1958), Chu and Giles (1958), Wakonig and Ford (1960), Bender (1960), and Hsu, Dewey and Humphrey (1962). It has usually been found that when the same dose is given at a slower rate or as a series of interrupted fractions the amount of chromosome damage is somewhat reduced, which implies that a certain amount of recovery occurs.

The question arises whether the chromosomes are more sensitive to radiation damage during one or other phase of the cell cycle, and this can be answered by the following type of experiment. Cultures are briefly exposed to ^{3}H-thymidine so as to label all the cells in S phase, a procedure known as "pulse" or "flash" labelling. The cultures are then immediately irradiated and examined at time intervals afterwards. The amount of chromosome damage in the metaphases is separately assessed for the labelled and unlabelled cells. It can then be assumed, from existing data on the cell cycle, that all labelled metaphases were in S at the time of irradiation, unlabelled metaphases seen 1–5 h post-irradiation were in G_2 at the time of irradiation, and unlabelled metaphases seen at 10–13 h were mostly in G_1 at the time of irradiation. The results obtained so far have varied with the cell strain. In L fibroblasts and mouse ascites tumour cells, Dewey and Humphrey (1962) found that the chromosomes were more sensitive in S phase than in G_1 or G_2. But in Chinese hamster fibroblasts Hsu *et al.* (1962) found them three-to-four times more sensitive in G_2 than in S. In plant cells the chromosomes are relatively insensitive to damage during mitosis itself (M phase), and the same is probably true of vertebrate cells in tissue culture (Strangeways and Oakley, 1923), but the point has never been clearly established and it must be remembered that Carlson (1961) thought that the chromosomes of insect cells in culture were most sensitive during mid prophase and mid telophase.

The fact that these chromosome abnormalities are in no way specific for radiation is often forgotten. Paterson and Thompson (1949) showed that exactly the same chromosome stickiness, chromosome fragmentation and mitotic inhibition could be produced in fibroblast cultures by urethane, and it is now known that many other "mitotic poisons" and even high oxygen concentration can do the same. Furthermore exactly the same chromosome abnormalities occur to some extent in supposedly normal and unirradiated tissues. Thus Lasnitzki (1943b) found that 1% of the mitoses in ordinary chick fibroblast cultures showed abnormal chromosomes and Bender (1957) found a similar figure in cultures of human kidney epithelium cells. Fogh *et al.* (1961) found 20–30% of abnormal mitoses in cultures of human amnion cells, and Dubinin, Kerkis and Lebedeva (1961) found 1·5% in human fibroblast cultures. One also recalls that Strangeways and Oakley (1923) found many chromosome abnormalities in chick fibroblast cultures when an "unfavourable" culture medium was used. By the same standards Glucksmann (1947) found that 11% of the mitoses in regenerating human epidermis and 20–32% of those in various untreated human epitheliomata were abnormal. All this makes the quantitative assessment of radiation damage much more difficult.

The conclusion seems inescapable that the effect of radiation is simply to enhance the occurrence of some natural defects. Or are they defects, in the ultimate sense? Perhaps this is part of some physiological process of growth control which we do not yet understand.

Although not strictly a "chromosome" defect, this is a convenient point to mention the one or two reports that radiation damages the mitotic spindle. Koller (1947) noted "incomplete or abnormal spindle formation" in histological sections of human tumours that had been treated by radiation. Brues, Stroud and Svihla (1951), Stroud and Brues (1954) and Stroud (1956) added ^3H_2O to the culture medium of chick embryo muscle cells, so that the cells were exposed to continuous irradiation at a rate of 40–200r/h for long periods of time. This led to various disturbances and failures at metaphase and anaphase which they ascribed to impairment of spindle formation, though (rather surprisingly) chromosome structural damage was rarely seen. They realized from the microbeam work of Zirkle and Bloom, which is described in Section V, that this was probably not a direct destructive effect of radiation on the spindle itself but some earlier effect which interfered with spindle formation. Apart from Till and Whitmore (1959) who thought that 5000r impaired spindle formation in giant HeLa cells, other workers have not reported this particular feature. Levis and Marin (1963) have described the occurrence of multipolar mitoses in a strain of guinea-pig cells. The percentage of multipolar mitoses increased with dose over the range 200–600r and increased with time up to 4½ days. It seems that this may be related to the production of multinucleated giant cells.

On the whole, the study of chromosome and spindle irregularities by tissue-culture methods has not borne much fruit; it has certainly thrown no light on how they are produced. But tissue culture has recently made a remarkable contribution to the general study of human chromosomes as will now be described.

Until quite recently any detailed study of the chromosomes of individual human beings was virtually impossible. In biopsy specimens of growing tissues such as skin or bone marrow, not many mitoses are present any way and with ordinary methods of histological preparation the chromosomes in the mitotic figures are too closely crowded for analysis. Now however, and rather belatedly, it has been realized that these difficulties can be overcome by short-term tissue culture (see Vol. 1, Chap. 12). The procedure is to culture a small biopsy fragment in a suitable growth promoting medium so as to provide an actively dividing monolayer on glass. Colchicine is then added to "collect" a large number of mitoses in metaphase, after which the cells are swollen by treatment with hypotonic saline and squashed under a coverslip. In the "squashed" metaphases the chromosomes are usually well separated and can be individually identified from their size and shape. By this means the chromosomal changes associated with certain diseases have for the first time been recognized and this has opened up a new chapter in clinical medicine. Short-term human cell cultures such as these have also been used for radiation studies. Dubinin *et al.* (1961) used fibroblast cultures, in which 1·5% of the mitoses were abnormal to start with, and found that 10r of X rays just about doubled the incidence. The percentage of abnormal mitoses was directly proportional to dose and worked out at 0·19% per r. In similar experiments Kerkis, Lebedeva and Osetrova (1962) found that 7r was sufficient to double the spontaneous chromosome mutation rate in human fibroblasts. They also showed that whereas in human fibroblasts the percentage of mitoses showing abnormal chromosomes after irradiation was 0·141% per r, in the case of rabbit fibroblasts the figure was 0·053% and in hamster fibroblasts it was 0·036%. Since the whole-animal LD_{50} dose is for man 400r, for the rabbit 800r and for the hamster 900r, it appeared that the sensitivity of chromosomes in tissue culture correlates well with the sensitivity of the organism as a whole. Bender (1957) used kidney epithelium cells and scored the mitotic abnormalities present 2–3 days after 25 and 50r. In control cultures one chromosome break was found per 100 mitoses and the radiation dose required to double this incidence was calculated to be only 3·3r, which is only one-third of the "maximal permissible dose" laid down for human exposure. This suggests that human cells may be more sensitive to radiation than hitherto supposed. More studies of this kind are urgently needed, for there is very little concrete information about the radiosensitivity of human cells; the figures for permissible human exposure have been calculated from data obtained on laboratory animals.

It is now possible to culture "lymphocytes" from human blood, using phytohaemagglutinin to stimulate mitosis (as described in Vol. 2, Chap. 2, Section XI, D), and this method has been widely used for the study of human chromosomes. Ohnuki, Awa and Pomerat (1961) exposed such cultures to 400r of X rays and found that two days later 56% of the mitoses showed abnormal chromosomes. In similar experiments Bender and Gooch (1962b) made a detailed quantitative study of the different types of chromosome abnormalities resulting from exposure of the cultures to 50, 100 or 200r of X rays.

Once abnormal chromosomes have been produced they are likely to persist and the method of culturing blood "lymphocytes" has been used to detect the presence of abnormal chromosomes in the cells of human beings who had been exposed to radiation some time previously.

Bender and Gooch (1962c) cultured blood from eight men who had, $2\frac{1}{2}$ years previously, received doses ranging from 23 to 365 rads of mixed γ rays and neutrons as the result of a laboratory accident, and they found that 2–20% of the cells contained grossly abnormal chromosomes. Buckton, Jacobs, Court Brown and Doll (1962) cultured blood from patients who had been exposed to therapeutic X radiation (for ankylosing spondylitis) as long as 20 years previously, and found that a considerable number of cells contained abnormal chromosomes.

H. MITOTIC DEATH

Strangeways and Oakley (1923) found that when mitosis is resumed after its inhibition, many of the cells die either during division or shortly afterwards, and they described two different ways in which the cells might break down. In the first, the chromatin clumped, leading to what is now called pyknosis, while in the second the whole cell simply "exploded", usually during prophase or telophase. Subsequent observers have seen predominantly the pyknotic type of death, though Pomerat *et al.* (1957b) recorded a good deal of "explosive" death in their cinematographic studies of irradiated HeLa cells.

This mitotic death does not occur unless and until mitosis is resumed, and many of the cells do not die until after several divisions, so the effect is spread out over several days. Hence it is also called "delayed" death.

Lasnitzki (1940, 1943a) irradiated fibroblasts with 100 and 1000r of X rays and counted the dying cells in the cultures and subcultures over the next 10 days. After either dose the onset of cell death paralleled the return of mitotic activity and death continued for 2 days after 100r and 5 days after 1000r. She thought that most of the cells died in prophase.

Cox (1931b) irradiated fibroblast cultures which were initially growing at different rates and showed that the amount of cell death produced was proportional to the mitotic activity at the time of irradiation. Alexander (1961) has recently found the same thing with lymphoma cells in suspension culture. Laser (1930) and Fischer (1931) had also shown that the inhibition of outgrowth in hanging-drop cultures (which is mostly due to mitotic death) was directly proportional to the mitotic activity of the culture at the time of irradiation. Rachmilewitz *et al.* (1947) cultured pre-irradiated fragments of bone marrow and studied the cell death which occurred during the first 24 h. They found that late erythroblasts and normoblasts were the most sensitive cells, followed by promyelocytes and myelocytes, while the haemocytoblasts were relatively insensitive. They claimed that the sensitivity of the different cell types was strictly proportional to their normal mitotic activity, but few would agree that normoblasts are the most mitotically active cells in the marrow. A more likely explanation of their findings is that normoblasts are particularly susceptible to non-mitotic death, as will be described in Section VII, B.

Experiments in which the dose rate was varied, or the dose fractionated, have yielded variable results which are not easy to summarize. Spear (1930, 1931a, b) measured the "delayed lethal" effect of γ rays on hanging-drop fibroblast cultures by subculturing them every 2 days and seeing how many days elapsed before outgrowth completely ceased. This does not look a very accurate method and it is by no means certain that the effect measured was entirely due to mitotic death. Be that as it may, he found that the effect of a standard dose could be diminished by decreasing the dose rate but not by splitting the dose into six fractions given at daily intervals and at the original dose rate. He went on to show (Spear, 1932) that twenty-four exposures of 2·5 min, given at 80 min intervals (total exposure time = 1 h) produced the same effect as 4·5 h continuous exposure. In similar experiments Paterson (1944) found that two doses spaced 21 days apart had more effect than when they were spaced only 3 days apart. In recent and probably more reliable experiments Gärtner and Zoeppritz (1958) exposed chick fibroblast cultures to β rays and found that variations in dose rate had no effect on the amount of delayed cell death recorded.

It has been reported that HeLa cell cultures continuously exposed to 0·1r/day of γ rays contain significantly more dead cells than control cultures (Breitling and Peters, 1957) and, later, the same was reported in cultures of HeLa cells, L fibroblasts and human amnion cells after exposure to a total dose of only 0·02r spread over a period of 2 days (Peters, 1962). Until confirmed, these results must be treated with some reserve. But the matter should be settled as the answer may affect our thinking on human tolerance levels.

The question whether susceptibility to delayed death depends on the position of the cell in the cell cycle at the time of irradiation has been investigated by experiments with ^{3}H-thymidine similar to those described in the previous section. Cultures of HeLa cells were flash-labelled and irradiated at various time intervals thereafter. In cultures irradiated immediately it is assumed that the labelled cells were in S phase at the time of irradiation; in cultures irradiated 5 h after labelling the labelled cells must have been in G_2 phase at the time of irradiation, while in cultures irradiated 11–17 h after labelling most of them would have been in G_1. Painter and Hughes (1961) found that in all three cases the labelled cells survived for exactly the same length of time as the unlabelled ones and they concluded that the survival of a cell does not depend on its position in the cell cycle at the time of irradiation, and it is therefore unrelated to any inhibition of DNA synthesis.

This problem has also been studied by using "synchronized" cell populations. When the cells of monolayer cultures undergo mitosis they round up and are easily detachable from the glass. If the mitotic cells are detached from the glass (by gentle agitation) at a particular moment in time they will constitute a population synchronized in respect of the cell cycle and they can then be used for further studies. Such a population can be irradiated at different stages in the cell cycle and the ensuing cell death measured. Terasima and Tolmach (1963) used HeLa cells and found that the cells were most sensitive when irradiated in M phase or in the late G_1-early S phase; and least sensitive in G_2 and early G_1. Sinclair and Morton (1963) used Chinese hamster lung cells and found them least sensitive in S phase. At present it is not possible to reconcile these rather different findings.

Most writers have taken it for granted that mitotic death is a direct consequence of the chromosomal damage sustained at the time of irradiation, but there is in fact no proof of this. From the admittedly rather fragmentary evidence available on the sensitivity of the cell at different stages of the cell cycle, sensitivity to mitotic death does not correlate very well with sensitivity to chromosome damage. Some further evidence bearing on this point is given in Section IV, C.

Given chromosome damage, it is of course easy to visualize that the cell may be "unable to survive the ordeal of mitosis" (Tansley, Spear and Glücksmann, 1937) or that, even if it does, one or other of the daughter cells may be so deficient in genetic material as to be non-viable (Koller, 1947), but there may be more to it than this. The exact causes of cell death are very difficult to ascertain and it may eventually turn out that the mechanisms of mitotic and non-mitotic cell death after irradiation are not so different as is presently thought.

I. NON-MITOTIC DEATH

When cultures of the commonly used fibroblasts or epithelial cells are exposed to high doses of radiation, doses much greater than those which suffice to produce mitotic inhibition and mitotic death, some of the cells are killed outright and immediately. This does not depend in any way upon the mitotic state of the cells, so it is called "non-mitotic" or "immediate" death to distinguish it from the mitotic or delayed variety. Nor is this effect confined to growing cells, it is found equally in fully differentiated adult tissues. The effect is listed here because it is observed in growing cultures, but since it does not involve the process of growth itself, description of it is deferred to Section VII.

IV. Effect of Radiation on the Growth of Isolated Cells

A. Measurement of the Growth Capacity of Individual Irradiated Cells

Puck, Marcus and Cieciura (1956) introduced a method for the clonal growth of mammalian cells *in vitro* which has opened up a new chapter in radiobiology. They first showed that if a small number (about 100) of isolated HeLa cells, obtained by tryptic digestion, are placed in a suitable fluid growth-medium in a Petri dish, each cell adheres to the glass and in the course of a few days multiplies to form a macroscopic colony. If the cells are irradiated shortly after planting, it is found that some of them form only abortive microscopic colonies or none at all, and by counting the number of proper macroscopic colonies which are produced after different doses of radiation this effect can be accurately and statistically analysed.

It was shown that each macroscopic colony, once formed, is capable of unlimited further growth on subcultivation, whereas the abortive colonies are not. What is measured therefore is the effect of radiation on the capacity of a cell for unlimited growth, or what Gray (1959) has called its "reproductive integrity". This is not some newly discovered effect of radiation; loss of reproductive integrity is almost certainly due to a combination of mitotic death and prolonged mitotic inhibition. The novelty of Puck's method is that it enables us for the first time to discover the ultimate fate of a statistically significant number of individual cells and to construct true dose-survival curves for a number of mammalian cell types, as has been done for other organisms such as bacteria. The exact shape and position of this dose-survival curve is a matter of very great interest to radiobiologists for certain practical and theoretical deductions can be made from it. The work of Puck and his associates is therefore one of the most important contributions which Tissue-Culture methods have made to radiobiology.

Defining survival as "the ability of a cell to proliferate and form a macroscopic colony within 15 days", Puck *et al.* (1956) found that the dose-effect curve was exponential; the logarithm of the surviving fraction was linearly proportional to dose, except for a small "shoulder" at the origin which points to the existence of a dose threshold (Fig. 4). In shape this curve was exactly similar to those which had already been found in the case of irradiated suspensions of bacteria or virus particles. As a measure of mean radiosensitivity it is customary to read off the 37% survival dose, that is the dose which reduces the surviving fraction

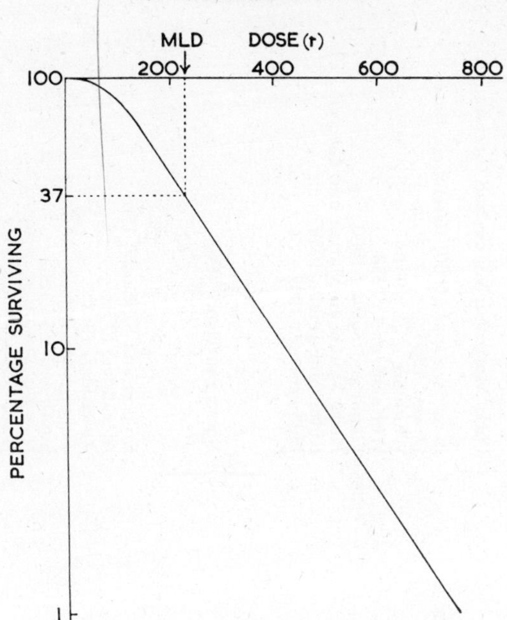

Fig. 4. Shape of the dose-survival curve for the colony-forming ability of mammalian cell strains in culture. MLD, mean lethal dose.

to 0·37 or e^{-1} (e being the base of natural logarithms), as indicated in Fig. 4. This value is also referred to as the mean lethal dose (MLD), or the D_0. The reasons for choosing 37% are theoretical and need not detain us here; for all ordinary purposes the 50% killing dose or LD_{50} might just as well have been chosen. Some authors have used the term LD_{37} to mean the MLD, but this is incorrect; the MLD $= LD_{63}$.

The MLD values so far reported are listed in Table II, from which it may be seen that the differences between different cell types are not so great as might have been expected. Indeed, Puck and his associates, who felt that this was the first time the inherent radiosensitivity of mammalian cells had been properly measured, went on to claim that the inherent sensitivity of all mammalian cell types is substantially the same. This rather sweeping conclusion was widely accepted in many quarters (e.g. Gray, 1959) and the figures were used to calculate and predict various results in the whole animal. But since then, MLD figures well outside the narrow range found by Puck *et al.* have been reported (Table II) and doubts have arisen whether this measure of sensitivity is so fundamental and inviolate after all, and also whether it can legitimately be extrapolated to cells *in vivo*. Some of these doubts must now be examined.

TABLE II

The mean lethal dose (MLD) of X radiation for various types of cell, determined from their reproductive capacity

Cell type	MLD[a]	Reference
HeLa	138 rads[b]	Puck and Marcus, 1956
HeLa	150r	Bases, 1959a
Epithelial strain from human lung	240 rads[b]	
Epithelial strains from human conjunctiva, liver and appendix	~138 rads[b]	Puck, Morkovin, Marcus and Cieciura, 1957
Epithelial strain from human kidney	110–180 rads[c]	Barendsen *et al.*, 1960; Barendsen, 1962
Epithelial strain from human liver	119 rads	Dewey, 1960
L-strain mouse fibroblasts	240 rads	Whitmore *et al.*, 1961
AMK strain from monkey kidney[d]	150–200r	Whitmore *et al.*, 1958
Chinese hamster fibroblasts	117 rads	Elkind and Sutton, 1960
Six different strains of human fibroblasts	108 rads[b]	Puck, Morkovin, Marcus and Cieciura, 1957
Chick fibroblasts	~600r[e]	Rubin and Temin, 1959
Chick embryo wing-bud cells	268 rads	Philpott *et al.*, 1962
Human kidney, cultured 22 days, mainly epithelial cells	480 rads	
Human kidney, cultured 8 days, mainly fibroblasts	99 rads	
Human kidney, cultured 44 days, mainly fibroblasts	47 rads	
Human lung, cultured 22 days, fibroblasts	108 rads	Norris and Hood, 1962
Human lung, cultured 72 days, fibroblasts	41 rads	
Human skin, strain 1, cultured 4 weeks, fibroblasts	104 rads	
Human skin, strain 2, cultured 4 weeks, fibroblasts	51 rads	
Strain from human bone marrow	180r	Erikson and Szybalski, 1961
Strain of mouse lymphoma cells	200r	Alexander, 1961
A mutant strain of the above	75r	Alexander, 1962
In vivo assay: Mouse bone-marrow cells	115r	Till and McCulloch, 1961
In vivo assay: Mouse bone-marrow cells	84r	Smith and Vos, 1962
In vivo assay: CBA mouse leukaemia cells	165r	Hewitt and Wilson, 1959
In vivo assay: P 388 mouse leukaemia cells	160 rads	Berry and Andrews, 1961

[a] In most cases the cells were irradiated as a monolayer on glass, under which conditions 1 rad = 0·7r (Morkovin and Feldman, 1959).

[b] The figures originally given by Puck *et al.* were later found to be too low, owing to an error in dosimetry. The corrected figures given by Morkovin and Feldman (1959) are quoted here.

[c] Survival curve not exponential.

[d] Later thought to be L-strain mouse fibroblasts (Whitmore *et al.*, 1961).

[e] Read from the published curve, full data not available.

B. CRITICISM OF PUCK'S METHOD

The first point is that whereas HeLa cells (Puck and Marcus, 1956) and certain other human epithelial cells (Marcus, Cieciura and Puck, 1956) exhibit 100% plating efficiency in normal cultures, that is every cell forms a colony, in the case of many other cells this is not so. In human fibroblast cultures Puck, Cieciura and Fisher (1957) found a plating efficiency of only 50–60%, and with freshly isolated cells, as opposed to well established strains, the figure is even lower (Zaroff, Sato and Mills, 1961; Norris and Hood, 1962). When plating efficiency is low, the MLD can still be estimated, but with much less accuracy; and a further error is that the MLD refers not to the whole population but only to those cells which are normally capable of colony formation under *in vitro* conditions. The fact that plating efficiency is much higher in established strains shows that continuous strains probably arise by selection of cells of high reproductive capacity. The results of Norris and Hood (Table II) show that mean cell radiosensitivity increases during the establishment of a strain which points to selection of the more sensitive, perhaps the less differentiated cells. There is of course much other evidence that established cell strains differ considerably from the normal cells of origin and it would be surprising if they did not differ in radiosensitivity as well.

A more serious criticism of the Puck method concerns the end point —"a macroscopic colony within 15 days". This seems a somewhat arbitrary standard. Puck and Marcus (1956) admitted that "it is impossible to avoid a certain degree of arbitrariness in the criterion which will indicate loss of reproductive function". Till and Whitmore (1959) pointed out that inhibition of growth is not an all or nothing phenomenon and the ability of a cell to form a macroscopic colony within a given time is an arbitrary criterion of its viability. Many of the "failed" cells do form microscopic colonies, and the growth rate of some macroscopic colonies is subnormal. Till and Whitmore (1959) showed with HeLa cells that the average number of cells per colony on the fifth day after irradiation was inversely and exponentially proportional to dose up to 1500r, which showed that there is no clear-cut distinction between macroscopic and abortive colonies. Sinclair (1962) found with hamster lung cells that the macroscopic colonies formed after irradiation grew at very different rates, and these differences were maintained on subculture. It also seems probable that the growth-promoting capacity of the culture medium would influence the number of colonies formed, but no one seems to have investigated this point.

The most important question is whether, in actual practice, slight changes in the criteria or the culture technique do in fact alter the survival curve. Unfortunately, however, this question has never been fully answered. It is true that Elkind and Sutton (1960) tried counting all the colonies instead of just the macroscopic ones and found that this made surprisingly little difference to the survival curve. This result goes some way toward restoring confidence in the Puck method, but more information of this type would be very welcome.

Despite the above criticisms there are still some reasons for believing that the Puck method does measure something fundamental. In the first place, the MLD values obtained by different workers in different laboratories have usually shown remarkably close agreement. More important is the fact that it has been possible in a few cases to measure the colony-forming power of irradiated cells by certain methods of *in vivo* assay, and in all cases the MLD has turned out to be much the same as that found by tissue-culture assay. In these experiments the cells were irradiated *in vitro* and a few of them were then injected intravenously into a homologous animal. Till and McCulloch (1961) irradiated mouse bone-marrow cells, injected them into normal mice, and subsequently counted the number of "naked eye" colonies (nodules) which grew in the spleen. They had previously established that each viable cell entering the spleen gave rise to a visible colony. Hewitt and Wilson (1959) irradiated mouse leukaemia cells, injected serial dilutions into a series of normal mice, and found out how many of these animals developed leukaemia. They knew that an average of two viable cells sufficed to produce leukaemia and from this they could deduce the percentage of viable cells in the irradiated material. Smith and Vos (1962) injected irradiated bone-marrow cells into mice which had just received a supralethal dose of whole-body radiation, and found out how many of the mice were protected from death. They knew the average number of cells required to protect these animals and from this deduced the percentage of viable cells in the injected material. The MLD values found by these *in vivo* methods are shown in Table II (last four entries) and it can be seen that they do not differ very much from the values found in similar cells by the Puck method. Finally there is an interesting piece of evidence from radiotherapy. The dose required to "sterilize" a tumour composed of (say) 10^9 cells may reasonably be defined as that which reduces survival to "less than one" cell in 10^9. Now this dose could be read off from a dose-survival curve. Morkovin and Feldman (1960) pointed out that extrapolation of the usual Puck survival curves indicates a sterilizing dose of round about 3000r for a 10 g tumour and that this agrees quite well with actual radiotherapeutic experience.

C. RECOVERY FROM SUBLETHAL RADIATION DAMAGE

Although it is generally assumed that the dose-survival curve for X rays, as determined by the Puck method, is always exponential, it must be pointed out that Bender and Gooch (1962a) found that their data were equally consistent with other mathematical relationships. Furthermore in at least one case, that of human kidney cells, the curve is definitely not exponential (Barendsen, Beusker, Vergroesen and Budke, 1960; Barendsen, 1962; Vos, Budke and Vergroesen, 1962; Vos and Kaalen, 1962).

If the dose-survival curve is exponential this is held to prove that the radiation injury involved is cumulative and irreparable. Puck (1960) was firmly convinced that "breakage of one or more of the chromosomes by direct hits is the primary damage which leads to loss of reproductive integrity", and the idea is that chromosome damage leads ultimately to mitotic cell death (as described in Section III, H) and abortion of the colony. But further work has not altogether supported this belief. Elkind and Sutton (1960) were interested in the initial "shoulder" on the Puck survival curve (Fig. 4). This indicates that a certain amount of radiation damage (about 50r worth) has to be accumulated before the reproductive integrity of the cells is affected at all. Elkind and Sutton wanted to find out whether this initial sublethal damage was recovered from or not. They argued that *all* the cells in an irradiated culture would sustain this initial damage, even the ones which did not succumb, so that if a second dose of radiation was given shortly after the first, the second dose-survival curve should show no shoulder or dose-threshold, provided of course that the initial damage had not meanwhile been repaired. When they performed the experiment they found that the second survival curve did show some dose threshold. If the time interval between the irradiations was 9 h or more the second dose threshold was similar to the first, but if the interval was shorter the second threshold was correspondingly reduced. They concluded that the sublethal damage sustained during the first irradiation was partially repaired within 1 h and completely in 9 h, that is well before the first post-irradiation division. They further showed that this recovery system was not attenuated by repeated exposures at 24 h intervals, and they came to "doubt whether chromosome damage is the only or primary cause of cell death". The detailed argument and elegant results of Elkind and Sutton cannot be fully expounded here. Their paper was quickly acclaimed a classic and Fig. 5 gives some idea of the extraordinary precision which modern cell-culture methods can bring to bear in the solution of this sort of problem.

It can be predicted from the above findings that if a specified dose is

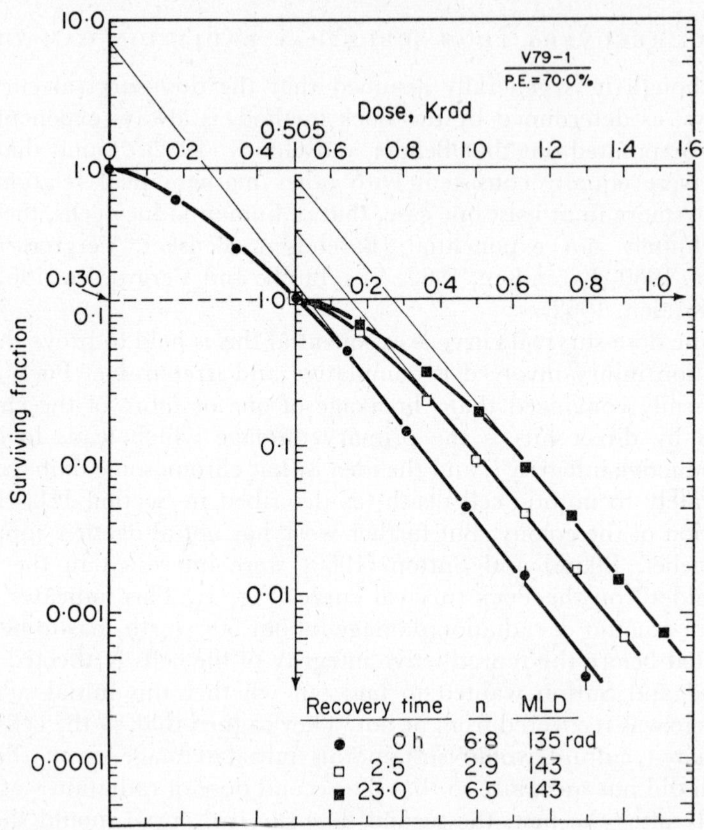

Fig. 5. Fractionated survival curves with V79–1 cells after 2·5 and 23 h of incubation at 37°C after a first dose of 505 rads. Non-fractionated curve after 2 h at 37°C for attachment. (Elkind and Sutton, 1960, Fig. 11.)

given at a lower dose rate or as a series of separated fractions the effect on reproductive integrity should be less. The point does not appear to have been adequately checked by direct experiment, though it has been reported that mitotic death in fibroblast cultures can be reduced by reducing the dose rate (Spear, 1930) but not by dose fractionation (Spear, 1931a). It is important that this point should be cleared up because fractionation is often employed in radiotherapy. Elkind and Sutton used X rays and their findings were completely confirmed by Barendsen (1962) who went on to show however that no such recovery process can be detected when α rays are used. This difference is of some importance for radiobiological theory but it cannot be expounded here.

Another important paper which is too complex for description here is that of Bender and Wolff (1961). They compared the kinetics of X ray induced chromosome aberrations with the kinetics of cell survival and reached the conclusion that the relation of chromosome aberrations to cell killing is obscure and that in any case the aberrations could not account for all the killing. They felt that all current explanations of mitotic death were unsatisfactory and that targets other than the chromosomes would have to be considered. And this thought may appropriately conclude our examination of this branch of the subject.

D. OTHER EFFECTS OF RADIATION ON ISOLATED CELLS

The original Puck method has been extended and developed on some different lines which are of considerable interest. Tolmach (1961), after plating out the HeLa cells, identified a number of individual cells and followed each one under the microscope throughout the post-irradiation period. The growth of each microcolony was followed in detail, every mitosis and cell death being recorded. Mitotic inhibition occurred and the average delay of the first post-irradiation division was 1 min per r. Cell death started on the second day and 70% were dead by the fifth day. The final percentage lost by the fifth day was independent of dose within the range 1000–10,000r but after the higher doses the cells died earlier. After the fifth day, survival followed an exponential pattern and was thought to represent the natural life span of cells which were unable to divide. Further studies such as this should throw more light on what Puck's original method really measures.

Another line of study has been the induction of mutation. Puck, Morkovin, Marcus and Cieciura (1957) found a high proportion of mutant strains among the colonies which grew from cells exposed to 500–900r. These differed from the parent strain either in morphology or growth requirements, and sometimes also in chromosome pattern (Puck, 1958); and these differences were maintained in subculture. Sinclair (1962), with hamster lung cells, found that the colonies developing after 1500r had different growth rates which were maintained on subculture. So this is evidently a further way in which radiation may influence growth. Mutation towards increased radioresistance might also occur and such mutants could be selected by exposing the cultures to repeated further doses of radiation. In experiments of this type Rhynas and Newcombe (1960) did produce a more resistant strain of L fibroblasts by four doses of 1000r given at 5-month intervals, but in HeLa cells Bases (1959a) failed to select out any strains differing in either radioresistance or growth rate after eight exposures to 500r. In similar experiments on human amnion cells, Kohn and Fogh (1959) also failed to induce any permanent changes in radioresistance or growth rate. It is also known that after a single dose of radiation (500–

1000r) the growth rate of cultures of chick fibroblasts (Lasnitzki, 1943a) and L fibroblasts (Reid and Gifford, 1952) returns almost exactly to normal after about 2 weeks, which again provides no evidence of mutation.

This is the first time that Tissue-Culture methods have been applied to the important problem of radiation-induced mutation and a very interesting field seems to have opened up, especially as the susceptibility of different cell strains seems to vary so much.

V. Irradiation of Selected Parts of the Cell

A. TECHNIQUE

Methods have been devised by which irradiation can be restricted to just one part of a living cell, such as the nucleus, nucleolus, the metaphase chromosomes or the mitotic spindle. For this work well expanded cells growing as a monolayer on a coverslip are essential and it is usually desirable that some of them should be in mitosis. The methods of tissue and cell culture are therefore an indispensable adjunct to the technique.

There are two different ways of providing the restricted irradiation field. The first exploits the very short range of α rays which is $<35\mu$ after suitable filtration. A tiny source of α rays, usually a minute piece of polonium, is mounted on the tip of a micro-needle and by means of an ordinary micromanipulator this can be moved to any desired position in relation to a selected cell. The dose delivered to different parts of the cell depends on their distance from the source, which can be measured. It is possible to compare irradiation of cytoplasm with irradiation of the whole cell, but any sharper localization is hardly possible. This method was introduced by Buchsbaum and Zirkle (1949) and it has been developed by Munro (1958).

The second method is to use a collimated microbeam of radiation which is produced from an ordinary macrobeam by use of a suitable micro-aperture. The following microbeams of defined aperture have been used: soft X rays, $2{\cdot}5\mu$ (Seed, 1960); α rays, 1–5μ (Davis and Smith, 1957; Smith, 1959), 2–3μ (Clegg, 1964a); protons, $2{\cdot}5\mu$ (Zirkle and Bloom, 1953); ultraviolet, 7μ (Bloom, Zirkle and Uretz, 1955), 3μ (Gaulden and Perry, 1958; Dendy, 1962). With these microbeams radiation can be confined to quite small volumes and such structures as the nucleolus or a single chromosome can be irradiated.

B. IRRADIATION OF CHROMOSOMES

Irradiation of the whole chromosome mass at metaphase with a microbeam of protons (Zirkle and Bloom, 1953) or ultraviolet (Bloom *et al.*, 1955), or with α rays (Munro, 1959) produced chromosome stickiness and consequent anaphase bridges. Bloom *et al.* found that when irradiation was confined to one end of the metaphase plate the subsequent anaphase bridges were similarly localized. On a few occasions they were able to irradiate just one of the metaphase chromosomes and this was followed by non-disjunction of the two daughter chromosomes at anaphase. They also succeeded in irradiating the centromere of a single chromosome during metakinesis, with the result that the chromosome lost all capacity for directed movement; it was left to drift in the cytoplasm where it eventually formed a micronucleus. Smith (1959) irradiated the metaphase chromosomes with a microbeam of α rays, and found that very small doses produced some increase of the normal cytoplasmic "bubbling" which occurs during mitosis, while larger doses caused failure of cytoplasmic division at the succeeding telophase so that a binucleated cell was produced; and very large doses caused clumping of the metaphase chromosomes followed by cell death. Bloom and co-workers used newt heart cells, while both Munro and Smith used chick fibroblasts. They all showed that irradiation of the cytoplasm alone, even with much higher doses, had no effect on the chromosomes.

Munro (1959, 1961) irradiated one of the two separating groups of chromosomes at anaphase and found that it failed to reconstruct a nucleus at telophase, whereas the unirradiated one formed a normal nucleus. Cells were irradiated at various stages of anaphase and telophase and it was found that nuclear reconstruction could be prevented by irradiating at any time up to 2–3 min before the reappearance of the nuclear membrane.

C. IRRADIATION OF THE MITOTIC SPINDLE

Bloom *et al.* (1955) irradiated the mitotic spindle in metaphase cells and found that while moderate doses of ultraviolet radiation destroyed the spindle completely, relatively enormous doses of protons had no effect. After destruction of the spindle the chromosomes lost their orientation completely and at the subsequent "false anaphase" two irregular groups of chromosomes (instead of chromatids) separated.

D. IRRADIATION OF THE NUCLEOLUS

In interphase cells the nucleolus is an obvious target for microbeam irradiation. Gaulden and Perry (1958) irradiated the nucleolus of grasshopper neuroblasts with a 3μ beam of u.v. and found that this inhibited mitosis. Irradiation at the very beginning of prophase was equally effective, which seemed to exclude any mechanism dependent on DNA synthesis. This observation might throw some light on the mechanism of the mitotic inhibition discussed in Section III, A, but it has not yet been confirmed in any vertebrate cells.

Seed (1960) measured the total nucleic acid content of the nucleus in individual fibroblasts by u.v. absorption photometry, and found that this quantity was reduced 3–7 h after irradiation of the nucleolus with a $2{\cdot}5\mu$ beam of soft X rays. A similar dose to the nuclear sap had no effect. In later work from the same laboratory however, Smith (1962) using a 5μ beam of α rays and measuring the DNA synthesis in individual fibroblasts by ^{3}H-thymidine autoradiography, found that DNA synthesis could be inhibited by irradiating either the nucleolus or the nuclear sap. It was therefore concluded that the nucleolus plays no special role in DNA synthesis. He went on to show that DNA synthesis could also be inhibited by irradiating the cytoplasm and even by irradiating the culture medium close to the cell. This latter observation is of great interest and may be the most important finding that microbeam studies have so far contributed.

Perry, Hell and Errera (1961) irradiated the nucleolus of HeLa cells with a u.v. microbeam and found that this inhibited the uptake of ^{3}H-cytidine into the cytoplasmic RNA. They concluded that about two-thirds of the normal synthesis of cytoplasmic RNA depended on the nucleolus and probably took place within it. A good deal of earlier work had implicated the nucleolus in cytoplasmic RNA synthesis, so this result was not unexpected.

E. IRRADIATION OF THE CYTOPLASM

Clegg (1964a) used an ingenious technique to irradiate parts of individual fibroblasts growing on a very thin plastic coverslip. A polonium source together with a $2–3\mu$ collimating aperture was mounted entirely within the central part of the upper condenser lens of a phase contrast microscope. The source lay within the phase rings so it did not obstruct the optical path. A few minutes after irradiation of a selected cell the whole culture was fixed and sectioned in Araldite for electron-microscopy. The sections were cut parallel to the expanded plane of the cells, and by special means it was possible to locate the irradiated cell under the electron-microscope. The most important finding was that a small dose (10 α particles in 15 sec) delivered to a small area (3μ diam.) of the cytoplasm produced, within a few minutes, changes which were uniformly distributed throughout the whole cytoplasm (Clegg, 1964b). These changes comprised disintegration of the mitochondrial cristae, breaking up of the endoplasmic reticulum into small globules, and a darker staining of the various cell membranes. No changes were seen in the nucleus. This work constitutes an important technical advance in radiobiology and the results of irradiating other parts of the cell and other types of cell will be awaited with great interest.

F. CONCLUSIONS

So far these observations have not thrown much light on the two major problems of radiobiology which are the mechanism of chromosome breakage and the mechanism of cell death. No one has yet produced any satisfactory evidence that chromosomes can be broken more easily by irradiating any specific part of the cell. It is true that Bloom *et al.* (1955) claimed that they had produced chromosome breaks by local irradiation of prophase chromosomes, but their photographs are far from convincing. There is therefore no support for any "direct hit" theory of chromosome damage and this is in line with the conclusions reached in Section III, G.

As regards cell death, it is still not known whether this can be produced more readily by irradiating the nucleus or the cytoplasm. It should be possible to irradiate selected parts of individual cells which have been plated out by the Puck technique and to see what effect this has on colony formation. Munro (1961) has developed some methods for this, using HeLa cells, but no results are yet to hand. Munro (1961) has also pointed out that instead of comparing irradiation of the nucleus with irradiation of an equal volume of cytoplasm, as is usually done, it might be fairer to compare irradiation of the whole nucleus with that of the whole cytoplasm. This could best be done by shielding the nucleus and this will call for the development of "microshield" techniques.

The effect on the cells of irradiating the culture medium might logically be dealt with next, but there are reasons for deferring this to Section XII.

VI. Some Fallacious Methods of Growth Measurement

Having described the effect of radiation on several of the fundamental processes responsible for growth, we may now pause to consider the overall effect of radiation on the growth of tissue and cell cultures. It is clear that the various cellular activities involved in normal growth are very unequal in their sensitivity to radiation. Respiration and glycolysis are usually not affected at all in the biological dose range, protein synthesis is not specifically affected either, and any observed depression of DNA synthesis appears to be the result of growth inhibition rather than its primary cause. Only two sensitive points have so far been identified. The first is the G_2 stage in the cell cycle and the second is the chromosomes themselves, whose breakage is thought to be responsible for some, at any rate, of the subsequently observed cell death. It seems increasingly doubtful, however, whether the observed effect of radiation on growth can be wholly accounted for in these terms and some additional sensitive spot must sooner or later be discovered.

In tissue-culture work many different methods have at various times been used for measuring "growth". It is now known that some of these do not measure true growth at all and others may register it inaccurately. In the past some of these fallacious methods have been employed in radiation studies, with the result that incorrect conclusions have been reached concerning the effect of radiation upon growth. It seems important therefore to re-examine the question of growth measurement in the light of modern knowledge.

The earliest method was simply to measure the increase in area of a hanging-drop culture, usually of fibroblasts. It is now known of course that this "outgrowth" is due as much, if not more, to the migration of cells from the original explant as it is to cell multiplication; so the method does not measure true growth with any reliability. Fortunately for radiobiology this fact was fully appreciated by Price Jones and Mottram, in 1914, but it did not fully penetrate into general tissue-culture circles until about twenty years later, by which time the term "growth" in tissue culture had come to mean little more than cell migration.

Another much abused measurement is the "mitotic index", which is the percentage of cells in mitosis at any given moment of time. It is disturbing to think of the countless authors who have assumed that a change in the mitotic index is proof of a corresponding change in the rate of cell multiplication. Here again the fallacy was exposed by radiobiologists. As long ago as 1929, Canti and Spear noted that one effect of radiation was to prolong the duration of each mitosis and they appreciated that this, taken alone, would automatically raise the mitotic index. Later students of the effect of radiation on the mitotic index of tissue cultures (Stroud and Brues, 1954; Harrington, 1961; Tolmach, 1961) made the same point, but they did not pursue the matter any further. The first clear thought on the subject was that of Evans, Neary and Tonkinson (1957). They considered the cell cycle, as depicted in Fig. 1, and pointed out that an increased rate of cell multiplication which affected all stages of the cycle equally (i.e. each cell simply moved faster round the cycle) would not affect the mitotic index at all. And also, that a rise in the mitotic index could be due either to a prolongation of M relative to the other phases or to a speeding up of one or more of the other phases relative to M. It seemed clear therefore that an increase in the mitotic index could be associated with either a speeding up or a slowing down in the rate of passage of cells through the cycle, that is with either an increased or decreased rate of cell multiplication. All this is doubtless true in the case of pure cell strains maintained in continuous culture, for here all the cells are cycling and at approximately the same rate. But in the old-fashioned hanging-drop cultures there is reason to think that only a proportion of the cells are cycling (Jacoby, Trowell and Willmer, 1937) and here a rise in the mitotic index could represent the recruitment of more cells. But in any case it seems that the mitotic index, taken alone, must be regarded as an unreliable measure of growth.

In the case of pure cell strains, the increase in total cell number or total DNA would seem at first sight to be a valid index of growth. But it is not, for it represents only the balance between cell multiplication and cell death, and after irradiation the latter looms quite large. Ideally both cell multiplication and cell loss should be separately recorded and so far this has been done only by Tolmach (1961) in the microcolonies of HeLa cells developing on Puck plates.

From the point of view of interpreting effects in the whole animal and in radiotherapy, the Puck assay of reproductive integrity is perhaps the most useful growth measurement because it assesses the ultimate outcome. But even this may have its limitations. Kohn and Fogh (1959) have pointed out that in the Puck test the irradiated cells are widely separated so that the developing clones do not compete with one another. In normal tissues, on the other hand, survival may also be influenced by the pressures of natural selection, and subnormal clones may not survive in competition with unaffected cells. There is also some evidence that cells are more sensitive when irradiated in isolation, after trypsin separation, than when they are irradiated *en masse*. In the case of HeLa cells, Reid and Gifford (1952) irradiated monolayer cultures with 500r and concluded from a careful study of the population changes that 25% of the original cells survived and repopulated the culture. Whereas Puck and Marcus (1956) with their method found that only 1% survived 500r.

Finally it must be stressed that the tissue culture evidence so far available relates almost entirely to the growth of embryonic or dedifferentiated or malignant cells. It would be more interesting to study normal lymphoid, bone-marrow, epidermal, intestinal epithelial or germ cells, but sustained growth of these *in vitro* is not yet feasible.

From time to time claims have been made that very small doses of radiation stimulate cellular activity. Several early claims that radiation stimulates growth were based on the mitotic index and can be dismissed for the reasons given above. More recently Boll (1957) showed that small doses of ^{32}P increased the mitotic index in bone-marrow cultures, but Fieschi and Sacchetti (1960) showed that this was simply due to a more rapid loss of non-mitotic cells. Prime (1917) and Kimura (1919) stated that small doses of radiation stimulated the migration of cells, while Chambers and Cameron (1941) made the rather astounding claim that 50,000r increased the migration of epithelial cells from fragments of chick mesonephros. Any question of a stimulating action of radiation could reasonably be dismissed were it not for the work of Hoffman and Wollman (1949). They put up fresh hanging-drop plasma-clot cultures of chick heart, irradiated them at once and then measured the time which elapsed before the first cells migrated out. In control cultures this was 28 h but in cultures exposed to 30r it was only 17 h. The effect was graded over the dose range 0–1000r with an optimum at 30r. This seems to be a genuine effect so the question of radiostimulation must still remain open.

Another dubious point is whether exposure of a culture to one dose of radiation makes it either more or less sensitive to a second dose given some time later. In other words is there any evidence for an immunizing or a sensitizing action? Laser (1930) found the cultures more sensitive at the second exposure but Fischer (1931) found them less sensitive, though it is doubtful if either result would withstand statistical scrutiny. Although the matter has never been finally settled, it might be anticipated that a culture would be less sensitive at a second exposure because the first exposure had already removed the most radiosensitive cells. With a longer time interval between exposures, the effect might depend on the production of mutant strains of either greater or lesser radiosensitivity (as described in Section IV, D), and hence be quite variable.

VII. Non-mitotic Cell Death

A. PROLIFERATING CELLS

Non-mitotic death in proliferating cells has been defined in Section III, I. When hanging-drop fibroblast cultures are exposed to very high doses of radiation the emigration of cells is immediately and permanently arrested. This escaped the attention of Strangeways and Oakley, (1923) because they did not use big enough doses. The effect was noted after high doses of γ radiation by Laser and Halberstaedter (1929), Canti (1929), Doljanski, Trillat, Lecomte du Noüy and Rogozinski (1931), Spear (1931a), and Halberstaedter and Doljansky (1937).

It was later observed after X radiation by Cox (1931a) and Vollmar (1939). Doljanski and Goldhaber (1942) found that a slight effect could first be detected at 2500r but 260,000r was required for complete cessation of cell migration.

In the light of later knowledge it can be assumed that the above effect was almost entirely due to immediate and direct killing of the cells. Lasnitzki (1943b) was the first to investigate cell death directly. She counted the percentage of degenerate (dead) cells present in the outgrowth zone of fibroblast cultures 3 h after irradiation, and found 0% after 1000r, 53% after 2500r and 75% after 10,000r. The sharp dose threshold is rather remarkable. In similar experiments, Cox (1931a) used a single dose of 12,000r and showed that increasing the dose rate increased the effect.

All the above relates to chick fibroblasts. Meanwhile Goldfeder (1940) had reported on the sensitivity of some other tissues. She exposed small fragments of moist fresh tissue to X radiation and then set them up as hanging-drop cultures and observed the minimum dose which would completely inhibit "outgrowth". The criterion was that not a single cell should migrate out during the observation period of 72 h. Her results, together with those of some other workers who used a similar criterion, are given in Table III. These figures must be taken for what they are worth, which is not a great deal. Obviously what has been measured is the LD_{100} and this is not a very satisfactory end point to choose. Dose-

TABLE III

Non-mitotic (immediate) cell death
(The dose of radiation required to kill all the cells in a hanging-drop culture.)

Cell or tissue	Dose rate (r/min)	LD_{100}(r)	Reference
Chick fibroblasts	81·5	117,000	Spear, 1930
Chick fibroblasts	22,260	120,000	Doljanski *et al.*, 1931
Chick fibroblasts	85,000	260,000	Doljanski and Goldhaber, 1942
Rat fibroblasts	90,000	200,000	Halberstaedter *et al.*, 1942
Rat sarcoma cells	90,000	200,000	
Heart, chicken embryo	936	140,000–150,000	Goldfeder, 1940
Heart, chicken embryo	10,000	250,000–260,000	
Kidney, newborn rat	234	75,000–80,000	
Kidney, newborn rat	936	90,000–95,000	
Kidney, newborn rat	10,000	130,000–140,000	
Spleen, newborn rat	936	50,000–60,000	
Mouse sarcoma	936	50,000–60,000	
Mouse sarcoma	10,000	85,000–90,000	
Nerve cells, spinal ganglion, chick embryo	2,400	32,000	Goldring, 1956

survival curves are always S shaped and neither the upper limit (LD_{100}) nor the lower limit (LD_0) can ever be defined with accuracy. This is why the LD_{50} should be chosen for measurement whenever possible.

The results of Goldfeder (Table III) seemed to show that increasing the dose rate diminished the effect, thus contradicting the observations of Cox (1931a) referred to above. She realized that her results ran contrary to general radiobiological experience and suggested that perhaps total exposure time was the important factor, and that the longer exposure entailed by a lower dose rate "caught" more cells in some specially sensitive phase of the life cycle. It is doubtful however if any of the differences shown in Table III between different doses or even between different tissues would withstand statistical investigation on the basis of the data provided. The results simply show that the lowest dose which will kill *all* the cells immediately is of the order of 100,000r; and the different tissues did not differ much in this respect. It is important to note that these LD_{100} doses did not produce any *immediate* change in the rates of respiration or glycolysis of the cultures (Goldfeder and Fershing, 1938; Goldfeder, 1939).

In the experiments of Goldfeder listed in Table III, small fragments of fresh tissue were irradiated *before* being put up in culture. This was done because she had earlier found that if established cultures (a few days old) were irradiated, the LD_{100} was lower by a factor of about 5 (Goldfeder, 1938). But if these irradiated cultures were transplanted into fresh medium immediately after irradiation the LD_{100} was the same as with the fresh fragments. This was all taken to show that the radiation effect was in part due to inactivation of growth-promoting substances in the plasma–embryo extract medium. But growth-promoting substances are not necessary for cell migration and it seems more likely that radiation generated some toxic product in the medium. There is every reason to suppose that these high doses of radiation would decompose the culture medium quite markedly, but experimental evidence on the toxicity of irradiated culture medium is still uncertain (see Section XII).

As remarked above it would be much more informative to measure the LD_{50} in these cultures, but this has never been done. It is possible however to deduce from the results of Lasnitzki (1943b) that the LD_{50} for chick fibroblasts *in vitro* is about 2500r.

B. NON-PROLIFERATING CELLS

In this chapter so far we have confined our attention to cells which have the ability to proliferate, and these, naturally enough, are relatively undifferentiated. But the greater part of the adult body is made up of fully differentiated cells which are mostly incapable of proliferation, and it is upon these cells that the bodily functions largely depend. The effects of radiation on these mature cells, most of them subserving some specific function, would therefore seem to be a matter of some importance. But surprisingly little is known. This is partly because these cells are, with a few notable exceptions, relatively insensitive to radiation and so they have attracted less interest.

The only proven effect of radiation on mature cells is the lethal one. The cells die shortly after exposure and there is no reason to suppose that the phenomenon differs in any way from the non-mitotic death encountered in proliferating tissues. It is true of course that the overall function of an organ may be depressed after a sufficiently high dose of radiation, but this is simply due to loss of cells. No impairment of function in surviving cells has so far been demonstrated, though the possibility cannot be ruled out.

In order to study the lethal effect of radiation on mature cells *in vitro* it is necessary to employ some sort of organ-culture technique. The requirement is that small organs or pieces of tissue shall survive *in vitro* for several days without any necrosis or dedifferentiation. In the case of some organs this can be achieved (Trowell, 1959). The effect of radiation may be measured by counting the percentage of dead (degenerate) cells at time intervals afterwards. This, however, is open to the same fallacy as the mitotic index, in that the length of time for which the dead cells persist will affect the count. Lajtha (1961) went so far as to say that the apparent differences in radiosensitivity of different organs are entirely due to differences in the rate at which the cells die and in the time for which the dead cells persist (before removal by autolysis or phagocytosis). But this is a great exaggeration. The difficulty can be overcome by waiting until the radiation effect is all over and then counting the absolute number of surviving cells. The number of surviving cells in the irradiated cultures can be expressed as a percentage of the number in parallel unirradiated cultures and in this way a true survival curve can be obtained. The technical problems involved have been discussed by Trowell (1961a). So far, the only cells which have been quantitatively investigated in this way are the small lymphocytes in rat lymph nodes (Trowell, 1961a) and the visual cells in guinea-pig retina (Lucas, 1962a).

The radiosensitivity of small lymphocytes has been dealt with in Vol. 2, Chap. 2, Section XIII. This section should be read at this point and taken as an integral part of the present chapter. The important point established was that the LD_{50} for small lymphocytes *in vitro* was 190r, while that for visual cells was 2600r. This may be compared with the figure of 2500r for fibroblasts mentioned in the preceding section. Another difference was that in the case of lymphocytes the threshold dose was virtually zero, whereas in the case of visual cells it appeared to be at least 1500r. As regards the other fully differentiated cells, such as muscle and nerve cells, and the parenchymal cells of all the glandular organs, no precise figures are available but observation indicates that in most cases the LD_{50} is very high, running to many thousand roentgens. It must be mentioned however that the germ cells, of some species at any rate, are extraordinarily sensitive to radiation during the early non-proliferative phase of their development. In the mouse the LD_{50} for spermatogonia (*in vivo*) is 20–24r (Oakberg, 1957) and for primary oocytes 8·4r (Oakberg, 1962).

The position is therefore that whereas the different types of proliferating cells, whether fibroblastic, epithelial or haemopoietic, exhibit a rather uniform sensitivity to radiation as regards both mitotic (Table II) and non-mitotic (Table III) death, in the case of non-proliferating cells a very wide range of sensitivity is found. The statement that non-proliferating cells are much less sensitive to radiation than proliferating ones is true only as a broad generalization, notable exceptions exist in the small lymphocyte and the normoblast, as has been discussed more fully in Vol. 2, Chap. 2. The fact that the LD_{50} for small lymphocytes is just about the same as the MLD for various proliferating cells (Table II) is probably a pure coincidence.

Cell death can also be measured *in vivo*, but usually with less accuracy. The *in vitro* measurement affords the following additional advantages. First, the cell population remains unchanged. In the whole animal, as modern studies with marked cells have so clearly shown, there may be considerable movement of cells from one organ to another, especially in the haemopoietic system. Second, any indirect effects arising from vascular occlusion or circulating radiotoxins are excluded. Third, the cell environment is controlled and the effects of environmental changes can be investigated. It is of some interest to compare *in vitro* with *in vivo* results and this is done in Section XIII.

The only other cell about which any information exists is the macrophage and here it is conflicting. Chambers and Cameron (1941) found that 25,000r killed all the macrophages in cultures of chick-embryo kidney within 24 h. Goldring (1956) reported that the migration of macrophages from explants of chick spinal ganglia was inhibited by 500r and virtually abolished by 2000r. Gilman and Trowell (1965) studied the macrophages in organ cultures of rat thymus and lymph node and found that neither their morphological appearance nor their ability to segregate vital dyes were affected by X ray doses up to 40,000r. The term "macrophage" is a loose one and it may include cell types which are really very different in their origin, function and radiosensitivity.

There are a few reports on the effect of radiation on amoeboid, muscular and ciliary movement *in vitro*, but most of them rather meagre. Levy and Ketchel (1962) showed that 200,000r had no effect on the amoeboid movement of human neutrophil leucocytes, provided that the medium was immediately renewed so as to dispose of toxic products. Goldhaber and Back (1941) found that the dose required to stop the spontaneous contractions of muscle cells in cultures of chick embryo heart or intestine, within 10 min of irradiation, was 500,000–700,000r, which probably corresponds to the killing dose. The same observers found that at least 10^6r was required to abolish ciliary activity in oral epithelium from the toad. Umeda (1927) used cultures of ox tracheal epithelium and found that very high doses produced a transitory slowing of the ciliary beat which fully recovered within one hour. This seems a very interesting observation which would be worth further investigation. Heine (1936) used rabbit tracheal epithelium and noted a slight inhibition after 11,200r. He concluded with the rather curious piece of reasoning that "since cilia are ancient structures, biologically, it follows that in the order of events they should be the last to be destroyed".

VIII. Degenerative Changes in the Cytoplasm

In the great majority of cases cell death, whether mitotic or non-mitotic, is not preceded by any notable morphological changes. The cell simply dies and this is *followed* by autolytic changes in the nucleus which take the form of pyknosis, karyorrhexis or karyolysis. These nuclear changes are often referred to as pyknotic, etc. "degeneration", but this is a confusing use of the term for the changes simply represent post-mortem autolysis, and of course they are quite unspecific.

Nevertheless, in some instances, particularly in tissue cultures, certain changes have been seen in the cytoplasm while the cell is still alive and moving, and these, being *ante mortem* may properly be called degenerative. Such changes have been sought for assiduously in the hope that they might throw some light on the mechanism of cell death.

The change most frequently reported is an increasing granularity followed by multiple vacuolation of the cytoplasm. Bisceglie and Bucciardi (1928) described vacuolation of the cytoplasm in chick fibroblasts exposed to γ rays. They also discovered that application of 1% KCl for 48 h had exactly the same effect and that the effects of KCl and radiation were additive. Interest in the subject was revived by Stroud and Brues (1954), who saw a good deal of vacuolation in their cultures of chick muscle cells continuously irradiated with ^3H_2O at 200–400r/min. The first change was increasing granularity of the cytoplasm which went on to multiple vacuolation. Under higher dose rates, larger vacuoles often developed quite suddenly leading to explosive destruction of the cell within a minute. Other workers (Strangeways and Oakley, 1923; Canti, 1929; Pomerat *et al.*, 1957b; Schleich *et al.*, 1961) have also noted explosive death of cells though not all of them related it to vacuolation. Pomerat *et al.* (1957a) illustrated degenerative vacuolation in a number of human cell lines after exposure to 2000–4000r, and Pomerat (1958) found that it was especially evident in one particular strain of human epidermal cells. In this latter about 20% of the cells developed large multiple vacuoles within 5 days. In ciné records it was observed that individual vacuoles might suddenly expel their content and then slowly reform, after the manner of contractile vacuoles. Cytoplasmic vacuolation was seen regularly by Goldfeder (1961) in cultures of mouse mammary tumour cells and by Fogh *et al.* (1961) in human amnion cells after 600r. Schleich *et al.* (1961), in cultures of a human fibrosarcoma, found that increased granularity and vacuolation of the cytoplasm were first detectable 24 h after irradiation and became more marked in the succeeding days. Some change was apparent after 300r, but after 900r vacuolation became extreme and the cells resembled multilocular cysts.

Under the electron-microscope, Fogh *et al.* (1961) found that some of the human amnion cells fixed 4 days after 100r showed disintegration of the cytoplasmic matrix. Clear empty areas were found in the cytoplasm, usually around the nucleus. The mitochondria and Golgi apparatus, however, were well preserved. The nucleus was often lobulated and the nucleolus sometimes showed evidence of disintegration.

It seems unlikely that any of these degenerative changes are specific for radiation. Similar changes are often seen in cells poisoned with cyanide or SH poisons, and the vacuolation may in all cases be due to failure of the intracellular water pump. It is also possible that these changes are not due to a direct effect of radiation upon the cytoplasm at all. Most observers have found that the cytoplasmic changes are not noticeable until several days after irradiation and they may therefore be the expression of chromosome deficiences in newly formed cells.

These observations throw no light at all on the central problem of how and why radiation kills cells. Any hypothesis is therefore open to consideration. The fact that purified DNA in solution can readily be depolymerized by exposure to radiation has led to the suggestion that depolymerization and destruction of the nuclear DNA might account for chromosome breakage and also perhaps for cell death. But in chromosomes DNA seems to be much more resistant than it is in dilute solution in a test tube. Montgomery and Warren (1953) irradiated rat carcinoma cells *in vitro* and found that even after 60,000r there was no change in the cellular content of DNA and RNA, as determined by u.v. absorption. Nor was there any change in the content of lipid, SH groups, or various enzymes, as determined histochemically.

The search for a "biochemical lesion" involving the specific inactivation of some enzyme system has been equally unsuccessful. In some cases indeed the earliest biochemical change appears to be an *increase* in the activity of certain intracellular enzymes and this led Bacq and Alexander (1961) to put forward an "enzyme-release" hypothesis of radiation damage. The biochemical organization of the cell depends to a great extent on the localization of specific enzymes within specific structures such as the nucleus, mitochondria, lysosomes and endoplasmic reticulum. The intracellular membranes which divide the cell into these compartments, and which often separate enzymes from potential substrates, are remarkably uniform in thickness and appear to be protein-phospholipid-protein in structure. It is postulated that radiation (and presumably radiomimetic chemicals) damages these membranes with the result that enzymes leak from their normal compartment and proceed to attack and destroy various structures within the cell. This is an attractive hypothesis which could explain a good many facts, but at present there is no direct evidence in support of it.

Searching for a specific morphological or biochemical lesion as the primary event in radiation damage has much in common with the search for the "cause" of cancer—the longer the quest continues and the wider the field of inquiry the more remote does any single unifying explanation seem to become.

IX. Radiation and Cell Differentiation

A. THE EFFECT OF RADIATION ON DIFFERENTIATION

There is a certain amount of evidence from animal experiments and from human radiotherapy that, in certain situations, radiation may actually promote the process of cell differentiation (Lasnitzki, 1961a), and the cure of malignancy by radiotherapy might in part depend on this effect. But there is no tissue culture evidence to support the idea.

Lasnitzki (1961b) reported a case in which radiation appeared to inhibit differentiation. In organ cultures of immature mouse vagina the epithelium underwent squamous differentiation and keratinization during the first 3 days, in either synthetic or natural culture medium. In natural medium 300r apparently prevented this squamous differentiation, though in synthetic medium it did not. It is apparent from her description however, that what happened in the normal cultures was not keratinization of the existing epithelium but the development of an entirely new (keratinizing) epithelium from the basal cell layer, the original epithelium being cast off. There was therefore no evidence that radiation inhibited the process of differentiation itself; it prevented the formation of a potentially squamous epithelium, which is not quite the same thing.

No one else seems to have investigated the effect of radiation on differentiation *in vitro*, and this seems to be a field wide open to exploration by the methods of organ culture.

B. THE EFFECT OF DIFFERENTIATION ON RADIOSENSITIVITY

In the genesis of mature differentiated cells two successive stages can generally be recognized. The first is the mitotic proliferation of relatively undifferentiated cells. In the second, mitosis ceases and the differentiation of each cell proceeds to completion. From what has been said in Section VII, B, it will be evident that as soon as cell proliferation ceases the cells are *ipso facto* much less sensitive to the lethal action of radiation. The interesting question is what happens from then on. Do the cells become more and more resistant as differentiation proceeds, or do they stay the same, or are there fluctuations in sensitivity?

There is some information on this point from whole-animal experiments. It has been established that, in the developing brain, the radiosensitivity of neurones decreases progressively as differentiation proceeds, and it has been tacitly assumed that this is the pattern for all developing tissues. Lucas (1961) however has shown that the radiosensitivity of developing visual cells, though it falls at first, rises again about twofold during the last stages of differentiation. So there is evidently scope for variation and other types of cell will have to be investigated.

To date, there are only two tissue culture results which bear on this question. Goldring (1956) cultured spinal ganglia which had been taken from chick embryos at various stages of development. She found that the fully differentiated neurones present in the ganglia of 12-day embryos were less radiosensitive than the partially differentiated ones present in ganglia of 6-day embryos. Chambers and Cameron (1941) cultured chick mesonephric tubules and found that the intact tubules were *more* radiosensitive than the dedifferentiated epithelial cells which grew out from them. They showed therefore that dedifferentiation decreases sensitivity, so presumably differentiation increased it—which is contrary to general expectation.

It would be very well worth while to investigate the changes in radiosensitivity which accompany cell differentiation in a systematic way. In some cases at any rate the modern methods of organ culture provide a suitable tool. It is important in the first place to establish that the changes found in the whole animal do represent real changes in cell sensitivity and are not just secondary effects. Then there is a point of great biochemical interest. It is known that the whole pattern of cell metabolism undergoes profound changes as differentiation proceeds. The change over from glycolysis to respiration represents one aspect of this, and the elaboration of specific enzymes is another. If these shifts in metabolic state could be correlated with changes in radiosensitivity some light might be thrown on the relative sensitivity of certain biochemical processes. Some other ways in which organ culture might be employed in this field of radiobiology have been discussed by Borghese (1961b).

X. The Radiosensitivity of Malignant Cells

Many workers have tried hard to prove that malignant cells are more sensitive than normal ones, in an effort to provide a more rational basis for the practice of radiotherapy. Clearly this is an important question and one which can best be answered by experiments in tissue culture. It would seem essential to compare the malignant cells with their non-malignant counterparts, but in the early work this was not feasible because the culture of normal adult tissues had proved too difficult. The following workers were content to compare chick embryo fibroblasts with the cells of rat sarcoma or mouse carcinoma: Wood and Prime (1914); Canti (1928, 1929); Vollmar and Rajewsky (1937); Vollmar (1939); Goldfeder (1940); Doljanski, Goldhaber and Halberstaedter (1944); Goldhaber, Doljanski and Halberstaedter (1944). Although some measured the delayed effect of low doses and others the immediate effect of high doses, these authors were unanimous in their conclusion that malignant cells are more sensitive than normal ones. But of course this is quite unacceptable because mammalian cells were compared with chick cells.

Some workers have made more valid comparisons. Rat fibroblasts were compared with rat sarcoma cells by Laser and Halberstaedter (1929) who found the sarcoma cells "not certainly more" sensitive, by Laser (1930) who found the sarcoma cells slightly more sensitive, and by Halberstaedter, Goldhaber and Doljanski (1942) who found no difference. Santesson (1929) compared chick fibroblasts with Rous (fowl) sarcoma cells and found that the sarcoma cells were slightly less sensitive. Whitman (1933) also found that rat sarcoma cells were less sensitive than the normal macrophages which were also present in the cultures. Evidently the differences, if any, are quite small and of doubtful significance.

The results collected in Table II do not indicate any difference between normal and malignant cell strains. It must be concluded, on present evidence, that malignant cells and normal cells are equally sensitive.

Radiotherapists have found that different types of human tumour differ somewhat in radiosensitivity. It would be interesting to see if these differences could be substantiated *in vitro,* but little work has been done on these lines except in the case of the leukaemias (Schrek, Leithold, Friedman and Best, 1962). Some experiments of Goldfeder on animal tumours are of interest in this connection. Two different mammary carcinomas were used, one derived from C3H strain mice, the other from dba strain mice. In culture it was found that the dba tumour was about twice as sensitive to radiation as the C3H tumour (Goldfeder, 1949). But if, after irradiation, the cultures were grafted into homologous mice to test survival it was found that the C3H tumour was the more sensitive (Goldfeder, 1947). From these experiences she concluded that tissue culture could be very valuable in revealing the intrinsic radiosensitivity of a tumour because in the whole animal this might be obscured by other factors.

Goldfeder (1961) also studied two other mouse mammary tumours, one an adenocarcinoma which grew in epithelial sheets, the other an anaplastic spindle cell carcinoma. The spindle-cell tumour was much the more sensitive to radiation *in vitro,* as judged by growth inhibition, abnormal mitoses, giant-cell formation and cytoplasmic vacuolation. She then compared the mitochondria in these two tumours and found that those of the spindle-cell tumour were fewer in number and poorer in cristae, and they also had a lower capacity for oxidative phosphorylation. This suggested that the spindle-cell tumour was more radiosensitive because it had a poorer mitochondrial equipment. A similar explanation for the high radiosensitivity of lymphocytes had been put forward by Trowell (1958).

XI. Chemical Factors Influencing Radiosensitivity

A. Introduction

The question now to be considered is, does the radiosensitivity of a cell depend in any way upon its environment, and, more specifically, is the sensitivity of cells in tissue culture influenced by the chemical composition of the culture medium?

It can be said at once that the concentration of dissolved oxygen in the medium is of considerable importance, but, apart from this, none of the other physiological variables seem to have any influence. Changes of pH or osmotic strength, changes in the concentrations of inorganic ions, glucose or protein, and even changes of temperature, seem to have little or no effect on radiosensitivity. This means that apart from the question of oxygen, which will be discussed later, the fact that different workers have used different media, ranging from simple salt solution to a plasma clot, is of no great importance. So far in this article, when the results of different workers have been compared, this factor has, with some confidence, been discounted.

Passing now from physiology to pharmacology, it has been found that the radiosensitivity of cells *in vitro* can be considerably altered by adding certain specific chemical substances to the culture medium. Most of these substances have to be added beforehand so that they are present during irradiation, but a few are effective when added immediately afterwards. Some of these "drugs" are "radioprotective" while others are "radiosensitizing". The radioprotective substances are, of course, fruits of the intensive research which followed the creation by man of various atomic hazards to man. The radiosensitizing substances are chiefly of interest to radiotherapists.

Although in most cases the effect of the drug was first discovered in the whole animal, tissue culture experiments have proved indispensable for quantitative evaluation at the cellular level. This is the only way in which a known concentration can be applied to known cells for a known period of time, and the subsequent effect on radiosensitivity be accurately measured. Already this has proved to be one of the most valuable uses of tissue culture in radiobiology and there is no doubt that it will be exploited even more fully in the future, especially by organ culture (Trowell, 1961a).

B. RADIOSENSITIZING SUBSTANCES

1. *Oxygen*

The most important radiosensitizer known is a natural one, oxygen. If cultures are irradiated under completely anaerobic conditions, for example in nitrogen, they are less sensitive than in air or oxygen. Sensitivity increases with oxygen concentration up to a certain maximum. The overall or maximum effect of oxygen in any particular case can conveniently be designated by a figure which is variously called the "maximal oxygen sensitivity factor", the "oxygen enhancement ratio", or simply the "oxygen factor". This is the radiation dose required to produce some standard effect in nitrogen divided by the dose required to produce the same effect in an optimal concentration of oxygen.

The values which have been found in various tissue-culture systems are listed in Table IV. Apart from the rather low figures for visual cells and amnion cells, which may have been due to technical difficulties in achieving zero oxygen concentration, all the others are remarkably consistent and lie between 2 and 3. The figures which have been obtained in whole-animal experiments and in plant material also fall in this range, all of which suggests that something fundamental is being measured.

TABLE IV

The oxygen factor for various mammalian cells cultured and irradiated *in vitro*

Cell type	Culture method	Assay of radiation effect	Oxygen factor	Reference
Strain from human liver	Puck	Colony formation	2·2	Dewey, 1960
Strain from human kidney	Puck	Colony formation	2·6	Voss and Kaalen, 1962
Human bone marrow	Suspension	Inhibition of DNA synthesis in S phase	3	Berry *et al.*, 1961
Mouse ascites tumour	Suspension	Inhibition of DNA synthesis in S phase	3	Berry *et al.*, 1961
Human amnion cells	Rose chamber	Absolute cell survival	~1·3	Rounds *et al.*, 1959
Rat thymus lymphocytes	Suspension	Absolute cell survival	2·5	Patt, 1955
Rat lymph node lymphocytes	Organ	Absolute cell survival	2·7	Trowell, 1961a
Visual cells, guinea-pig retina	Organ	Absolute cell survival	1·3	Lucas, 1962a

The oxygen effect was not demonstrated in mammalian cells until 1953. Prior to this most of the radiobiological work had been done with hanging-drop cultures and it is now realized that in such cultures the cells are relatively if not absolutely anoxic. So in retrospect it seems likely that in all this earlier work the cells were less radiosensitive than they would have been under more normal conditions. Whether differences in oxygenation could have accounted for some of the differences observed by different workers it is not now possible to judge.

More recently it has been discovered, in bacteria, that nitric oxide has the same effect as oxygen, and Dewey (1960) has confirmed this in the case of cultured HeLa cells. He showed that 10% NO in N_2 had quantitatively the same radiosensitizing effect as 100% O_2. Various theories have been put forward to explain the oxygen effect, but since tissue culture is not implicated, they need not detain us here.

2. *Drugs*

Mitchell and Simon-Reuss (1952) studied the effect of tetra-sodium 2-methyl-1,4-naphthohydroquinone diphosphate, which is marketed under the trade name of "Synkavit" and used, clinically, as a substitute for vitamin K. They used hanging-drop cultures of chick fibroblasts growing in plasma plus embryo extract and found that addition of Synkavit in 2–4 μM concentration sensitized the cells to X rays, as judged by mitotic inhibition and chromosome fragmentation. Synkavit itself produced some mitotic inhibition; what they showed was that the combined effect of Synkavit plus X rays was more than simply additive. Schleich *et al.* (1961) however could find no sensitizing action of Synkavit on the human tumour strains HeLa and AFi grown on glass in serum saline. They covered the same dose range of Synkavit and X rays, and in respect of mitotic inhibition, cell death and ultimate survival time they found that Synkavit had, if anything, a slight protective action. It is not yet known whether this discrepancy in findings is due to the different cells used or to the different culture media. It is known that Synkavit is to some extent inactivated by SH compounds in the medium so different media might well vary in this respect. Since Synkavit is sometimes used as an adjunct to clinical radiotherapy it seems important that its effect upon human cells should be properly established.

Alexander (1961) showed that 20 μM iodoacetate sensitized mouse lymphoma cells cultured in suspension. Iodoacetate, like Synkavit, combines with SH groups and it seems that the radiosensitizing action of both could be explained on the hypothesis that they inactivate certain intracellular SH compounds (such as glutathione) which normally act as "physiological" radioprotectors (the protective effect of SH compounds is described in the succeeding section).

We must now mention several unrelated compounds, whose mode of action is obscure. Peters and Gärtner (1956) found that N-(3′-dimethylamino)-propyl-3-chlorphenothiazin, marketed under the trade name of "Megaphen", sensitized chick fibroblasts to X rays (as judged by mitotic inhibition and cell death). Bases (1959b) showed that the antibiotic Actinomycin D sensitized HeLa cells to radiation (as judged by the Puck survival test), and that it was effective in the extraordinarily low concentration of 0·1 μg/100 ml. Even more interesting is the fact that Actinomycin was also effective when applied immediately *after* irradiation, which suggests that it acts by inhibiting some repair process. This repair process probably involves RNA synthesis, for it has been shown that Actinomycin D is a highly specific inhibitor of RNA synthesis in cultured L fibroblasts (Reich, Franklin, Shatkin and Tatum, 1961). Bagshaw (1961) showed that post-irradiation treatment of HeLa cells with 1·56 μM 5-fluorouracil increased their sensitivity by a factor of 1·4, again presumably by inhibiting repair.

Erikson and Szybalski (1961) found that cells could be "presensitized" by growing them for some time in medium containing a halogenated thymidine analogue (5-chlorodeoxyuridine, or the corresponding 5-bromo or 5-iodo compounds), after which they were irradiated in normal medium. Radiosensitivity was assayed by the Puck cell-survival method and the X ray MLD was 180r for the controls, 110r for cells treated with the chloro-compound, 100r for the bromo-compound, and 75r for the iodo-compound. The thymidine analogue is incorporated into the nuclear DNA and this makes the cells more sensitive to X rays and ultraviolet, but not to thermal neutrons. To some extent this supports the old theory (p. 112) that cell death is due to direct destruction of the nuclear DNA, the assumption being that the "halogenated" DNA is less stable, as it might well be. Bases (1959b) found that HeLa cells could be presensitized by growing them in a medium in which 85% of the H_2O had been replaced with D_2O, and again this suggests that instability was built into some cellular structure.

C. RADIOPROTECTIVE SUBSTANCES

1. *Thiol Compounds*

The search for protective substances has proceeded on rather more rational lines. Several compounds have been developed on the basis of a reasonable theory as to their mode of action. This is particularly true in the case of the first-discovered and still the most important group of protective substances, the thiol or SH compounds.

It is thought nowadays that the primary action of radiation is to ionize some of the cell water with production of certain free radicals. These radicals are chemically very reactive and they act upon the protoplasm thereby producing the biological damage. Now it is known that these free radicals also react with SH groups, though this is not why they produce radiation damage because the cytological effects of SH poisons are different from those of radiation. It does mean however that if SH compounds of one sort or another could be introduced into the cell they might inactivate these toxic radicals and so protect the cell.

The natural thiols cysteine and glutathione were the first to be tried and they proved moderately effective. Other thiols were then developed in the hope of finding greater activity and the most important of these are: cysteamine, cystamine, thiourea, diethyldithiocarbamate, and aminoethylisothiouronium bromide-hydrobromide (AET). All these compounds give some protection to the whole animal when injected just before irradiation. But when tested in tissue culture the results were more variable, as may be seen in Table V. On the whole it seems that cysteine and cysteamine are as effective to cells in tissue culture as they are to the corresponding cells in the whole animal; the one or two negative results may well have been due to oxidation of the compound before it got into the cells, for both are very unstable in solution. The S—S compounds cystine and cystamine, both of which are effective *in vivo* have been found by most observers to be ineffective *in vitro*. The reason may be that the whole animal reduces these compounds to the SH form whereas tissue cultures cannot do so. The most consistent protection in tissue cultures has been obtained with AET, probably because this substance is relatively stable in solution. The degree of protection obtainable with AET is however no greater than with cysteine under favourable conditions. The maximum protection obtainable with any of these thiol compounds corresponds to a "dose reduction factor" (measured in the same way as the oxygen factor) of about 3.

The SH compounds all have an affinity for oxygen, becoming oxidized to the S—S form. This means that they will reduce the concentration of dissolved oxygen in both the medium and the cells. It has therefore been suggested that they act as radioprotectors only in this indirect way, and the fact that the maximum dose reduction factor obtainable (3) corresponds so closely to the maximum oxygen factor certainly supports this idea. The question could best be settled by seeing if thiol compounds have any protective effect in the absence of oxygen, but no satisfactory experiments using mammalian cells have yet been reported. It seems essential in future that, in all experiments claiming to show a change in radiosensitivity, the effect should be demonstrated in cultures irradiated under nitrogen, so as to exclude any indirect effect due to oxygen (Trowell, 1961a).

2. *Amines*

The biological amines histamine, adrenalin, noradrenalin and 5-hydroxytryptamine, will all protect the whole animal to some extent. But none of them has any effect on cultures of fibroblasts, epithelial cells or lymphocytes (van Bekkum and de Groot, 1956; Schleich, 1961; Booz and Betz, 1961; Grant and Vos, 1962; Vos *et al.*, 1962). The protective effect seen in the whole animal is probably due to diminished oxygen supply resulting from vasoconstriction. This was a case in which the negative results obtained in tissue culture were of great value in elucidating the mechanism.

3. *RNA*

Rounds (1961) showed that yeast RNA would protect certain strains of normal human cells. In order to measure radiosensitivity, the cells

TABLE V

Radioprotective substances tested in tissue culture

Substance	Concentration[a]	Cells	Assay of radiation effect	Protection	Reference
Cysteine	0·21 mM	Chick fibroblasts	Mitotic inhibition; outgrowth	–	Oftedal *et al.*, 1958
Cysteine	1 mg/ml	AFi (human fibrosarcoma)	Mitotic inhibition; outgrowth; survival time	+	Schleich, 1961
Cysteine	2–4 mM	Human kidney strain	Colony formation	+	Vos *et al.*, 1962
Cysteine	50 μg/ml	Human carcinoma strain	Colony formation	+	Kelley and Wheeler, 1961
Cysteine	20 mM	Rabbit thymus lymphocytes	% survival	+	Patt *et al.*, 1952
Cysteine	20 mM	Rat thymus lymphocytes	% survival	+	van Bekkum and de Groot, 1956
Cysteine	1 mM	Rat thymus lymphocytes	% survival	+	Grant and Vos, 1962
Cysteamine	0·06–1·3 mM	Chick fibroblasts	Mitotic inhibition; outgrowth	–	Trabert-van der Maesen, 1957
Cysteamine	1·5 mM	L mouse fibroblasts	Absolute cell survival	–	Therkelsen, 1961
Cysteamine	1 mg/ml	AFi (human fibrosarcoma)	Mitotic inhibition; outgrowth; survival time	+	Schleich, 1961
Cysteamine	2–4 mM	Human kidney strain	Colony formation	+	Vos *et al.*, 1962
Cysteamine	65 mM	Rabbit thymus lymphocytes	% survival	+	Betz *et al.*, 1961
Cysteamine	0·01 mM	Rat thymus lymphocytes	% survival	+	van Bekkum and de Groot, 1956
Cysteamine	0·65 mM	Rat thymus lymphocytes	% survival	+	Grant and Vos, 1962
Cystine	0·5 mM	Human kidney strain	Colony formation	–	Vos *et al.*, 1962
Cystine	0·01 mM	Rat thymus lymphocytes	% survival	–	Grant and Vos, 1962
Cystamine	0·03–0·65 mM	Chick fibroblasts	Mitotic inhibition; outgrowth	–	Trabert-van der Maesen, 1957
Cystamine	0·44 mM	Chick fibroblasts	Mitotic inhibition	–	Oftedal *et al.*, 1958
Cystamine	0·89 mM	Chick fibroblasts	Outgrowth	slight	Oftedal *et al.*, 1958

TABLE V—*continued*

Substance	Concentration[a]	Cells	Assay of radiation effect	Protection	Reference
Cystamine	1·5 mM	L mouse fibroblasts	Absolute cell survival	−	Therkelsen, 1961
Cystamine	2–64 mM	Human kidney strain	Colony formation	−	Vos *et al.*, 1962
Cystamine	33 mM	Rabbit thymus lymphocytes	% survival	+	Betz *et al.*, 1961
Cystamine	0·01 mM	Rat thymus lymphocytes	% survival	−	Grant and Vos, 1962
Glutathione	20 mM	Rat thymus lymphocytes	% survival	+	van Bekkum and de Groot, 1956
Diethyldithiocarbamate	0·01 mM	Rat thymus lymphocytes	% survival	+	van Bekkum and de Groot, 1956
Diethyldithiocarbamate	0·01 mM	Rat thymus lymphocytes	% survival	−	Grant and Vos, 1962
AET	2–4 mM	Human kidney strain	Colony formation	+	Vos *et al.*, 1962
AET	50 μg/ml	Human carcinoma strain	Colony formation	+	Kelley and Wheeler, 1961
AET	0·4 mg/ml	HeLa	Colony formation	+	Morkovin and Puck, 1958
AET	0·4 mM	HeLa	Colony formation	+	Bases, 1959a
AET	0·2 m	Rat thymus lymphocytes	% survival	+	Grant and Vos, 1962
Glycerol	15%	Human kidney strain	Colony formation	+	Vos and Kaalen, 1962
Glycerol	10%	Human bone marrow strain	Colony formation	+	Erikson and Szybalski, 1961
Urethane	0·1%	Chick fibroblasts	Mitotic inhibition; chromosome abnormalities; cell death	+	Paterson and Thompson, 1949
Dimethyl sulphoxide	1–15%	Human kidney strain	Colony formation	+	Vos and Kaalen, 1962
RNA (yeast)	0·2 mg/ml	4 normal human strains	Absolute cell survival	+	Rounds, 1961
RNA (yeast)	0·2 mg/ml	3 malignant human strains	Absolute cell survival	−	Rounds, 1961

[a] In some cases the concentration has been calculated from data given in the reference cited.

were cultured in Rose slide chambers and the number of surviving cells in a standard ruled area was counted at intervals for several days after irradiation. RNA added to the medium protected the cells to some extent, but it was necessary to add it at least 10 h, and preferably 24 h, before irradiation. This is a unique finding: all the other protective substances (listed in Table V) are maximally effective when added just before irradiation. Another remarkable finding was that this RNA did not protect malignant cells. Four different strains of normal cells, derived from human amnion, bone marrow, liver and conjunctiva, were tested and all were protected by RNA; whereas three different strains of malignant cells, derived from various human tumours, were not protected at all. All this suggests that the yeast RNA had to be utilized by the cells in order to confer protection, and that malignant cells, unlike normal ones, do not utilize added RNA. This is in line with some results of Bennett, Skipper, Smithers and Hayes (1959) which indicated that malignant cells do not utilize preformed nucleotides to the same extent as normal cells, presumably because they prefer to synthesize their own. Further work will be required to see if this really is a fundamental metabolic difference between normal and malignant cells. In the past many such differences have proved illusory.

4. *Miscellaneous*

The protective effects recorded for glycerol, urethane and dimethyl sulphoxide are shown in Table V. The action of urethane calls for some comment. Paterson and Thompson (1949) measured the mitotic inhibition and chromosome aberrations produced in chick-fibroblast cultures by 30r of X rays, and also the delayed lethal effect of 6000r. They found that all of these effects could be diminished by adding 0·1% of urethane *after* irradiation, even 40 min after. This appears to be the only known instance of a protective substance being effective post irradiation. It seems unlikely that urethane could facilitate any repair process. The result is therefore very puzzling and it stands in need of confirmation.

The protective effects of hypertonic saline, calcium and agmatine against mitotic inhibition have been described in Section III, A. There is no evidence that they protect against chromosome damage or cell death.

XII. Effects of Radiation on the Culture Medium

We have so far assumed that when a tissue culture is irradiated, the observed effects are due entirely to the action of radiation upon the cells. But this might not be true. Some part of the effect might be due to a noxious action of radiation on the culture medium itself. Radiation might, for instance, destroy some of the growth-promoting components; it might destroy natural radioprotective components such as cysteine or glutathione; or it might generate toxic breakdown products. In theory, therefore, this factor could be of great importance, but in practice, fortunately, it has turned out not to be so.

Strangeways and Fell (1927) showed that embryo extract made from eggs which had been heavily irradiated 24 h beforehand was just as good as normal extract for promoting culture growth and they concluded that growth-promoting substances had not been destroyed, nor had any *stable* toxic products been found. Fischer (1931) claimed that certain toxic products were immediately released from irradiated cells and that these were responsible for the subsequent growth inhibition. He claimed to have demonstrated the effect of these substances on normal cultures, but his published findings were very unconvincing and no one has confirmed them. The work of Goldfeder (1940), discussed in Section VII, A, suggested that cytotoxic products were present in plasma-embryo extract medium irradiated with 30,000r. Osgood (1942) showed that bone-marrow cells survive normally in serum-saline medium which had been exposed to 400r. Levy and Ketchel (1962) measured the migration rate of human neutrophil leucocytes in irradiated plasma and found that 200,000r was needed to produce any deleterious effect.

Peters (1953, 1954) irradiated one half of a hanging-drop fibroblast culture with 500r of X rays, the other half being shielded. A certain amount of mitotic inhibition was detected in the shielded half, and although the author ascribed this to diffusion of a toxic product, it seems questionable whether the possibility of radiation scattering was entirely excluded. In later work, Peters (1959) irradiated the synthetic medium 199 of Morgan, Morton and Parker with doses ranging from 10,000 to 100,000r and then applied the medium to HeLa cell cultures. The irradiated medium inhibited mitosis and the effect was dose-dependent, but it caused no cell death.

Almost all workers came to accept that doses within the ordinary range of interest, say up to 5000r, had no deleterious effect upon the medium, and this seemed a very reasonable assumption. It was assumed of course in all the elaborate studies of the effects of radiation on the cell cycle, on DNA synthesis, and on cell survival kinetics, described in the earlier part of this chapter. But some recent results of Kuyper and Smets (1962), if they can be confirmed, seem to reopen the whole question. These workers cultured a cell strain derived from embryo calf liver in a medium containing inorganic salts, lactalbumen hydrolysate and 5%

of calf serum. Medium was exposed to 500r of X rays and then immediately added to the cultures. One hour later the mitotic index had fallen from 2·18 to 1·6 and the uptake of ^{3}H-thymidine was about 40% depressed. Quantitatively this effect was about the same as that observed after giving 200r to the whole culture. The work of Smith (1962), described in Section V, D, who found that irradiation of the culture medium close to the cell caused inhibition of DNA synthesis, must also be taken into account. It looks as if the whole question of cytological effects resulting from irradiation of the medium will have to be re-examined using the more sensitive indicators of cell damage which are now available.

The rather unusual experiments of Jolles, Remington and Simon-Reuss (1961) may also be relevant to this problem. They exposed a rabbit to 1200r of X rays and 30 min later removed a piece of skin. The piece of skin was perfused interstitially (i.e. through the intercellular spaces, not the blood vessels) and the collected perfusate was placed on hanging-drop cultures of chick fibroblasts, and also on monolayer cultures of rat fibroblasts. The perfusate produced mitotic inhibition and chromosome breakage in the chick cells but not in the rat cells. The results were thought to demonstrate the existence of a diffusible toxic factor ("stromatex") in the irradiated tissue, but it was not explained why only chick cells were affected. More and better-controlled experiments will be required before the stromatex theory can be seriously considered.

XIII. Comparison of *In Vitro* with *In Vivo* Sensitivity

A. Technical Difficulties

It is important to know whether cells really are less sensitive to irradiation *in vitro* than they are in the whole animal, and, if so, by how much, for this measures the "indirect" effect of irradiation. At first sight it would seem that Tissue-Culture experiments should provide a clear-cut answer to this, but there are several facts which conspire to invalidate any strict comparison, and these must now be examined.

If irradiation of the culture medium contributed to the *in vitro* effect, this would invalidate any straight comparison because in the case of localized *in vivo* irradiation the cellular "medium" is rapidly and continuously replaced. In the preceding section it was seen that, even in the biological dose range, an effect of irradiated medium cannot be altogether ruled out. The error from this source is therefore uncertain but it is probably small.

A much greater difficulty arises from the oxygen effect. As shown in Section XI, B, 1, the radiosensitivity of cells can be altered as much as threefold by changing the concentration of oxygen within them. It is obvious therefore that the *in vivo-in vitro* comparison should be made under strictly identical conditions of intracellular oxygen concentration. But since the intracellular oxygen concentration cannot yet be determined with any accuracy either *in vivo* or *in vitro,* this ideal is still rather remote.

Another source of error creeps in when cell strains instead of fresh explants are used for the *in vitro* determination. By the time a strain is established, considerable cell selection has occurred and the more radiosensitive cells may have been either selected or rejected, and this would alter the average sensitivity of the current population.

Recent work has shown that cells may undergo some radical biochemical change at the moment they are removed from the body and that such changes may greatly alter their radiosensitivity. This has been shown in the case of medium and large (proliferating) lymphocytes. One very radiosensitive component of their DNA synthesis is lost within seconds of removing the cells from the body, as has already been described (p. 82), and for this reason they appear to be much less radiosensitive from the word go. It is not yet known whether any other types of cell are also damaged in this way, but the possibility will have to be faced, and it may turn out that most cells *in vitro* are a good deal more abnormal than has hitherto been admitted.

In the ordinary course of events certain cells are irradiated in a whole animal and subsequently assayed for radiation damage in that animal; and this is compared with irradiation of similar cells in tissue culture followed by assay in tissue culture. The weakness of this situation is that the post-irradiation conditions are different in the two cases. Any difference in results might therefore have been due to differences in the post-irradiation conditions or to some technical difference in the method of assay, rather than a real difference in radiosensitivity. In some experiments this difficulty has been avoided by performing the post-irradiation assay *in vitro* in both cases, while in others it was done *in vivo* in both cases. These experiments will be described in B, 3 below.

B. RESULTS

1. *Hanging-drop Cultures*

Strangeways and Fell (1927) exposed 6-day chick embryos to a dose of radiation which, though relatively small, was nevertheless sufficient to produce intravascular clotting in about 80 min and cessation of the heart beat within 24 h. They showed that tissue removed 80 min after irradiation grew quite satisfactorily *in vitro*, whereas left in the animal it of course died. They concluded, rightly, that death of cells in the irradiated embryo was due almost entirely to circulatory arrest. It was in fact an "indirect" effect of irradiation. Heim (1927) also reported that tissues removed immediately from 500r irradiated chick embryos grew normally *in vitro*.

Unfortunately these findings were taken by others as relevant to animal irradiation in general, and for many years it was widely believed that the radiation effects observed in adult mammalian organs were due in part to blood vessel damage. It was not appreciated that the blood vessels of the chick embryo are peculiarly sensitive to radiation. It is now clear that, in the biological range, the acute effects of radiation seen in adult mammalian organs are in no way due to vascular damage; the doses required to produce acute vascular damage are much higher than this. The evidence provided in subsection 3 below, also confirms this conclusion.

In the meantime, however, various workers reported that the doses required to kill cells *in vitro* were appreciably higher than those which sufficed to kill the corresponding cells in the whole animal. This was shown for spleen cells of rat and fowl (Roffo, 1929), mouse sarcoma cells (Sugiura, 1937), and guinea-pig bone-marrow cells (Gregori, 1939). All these observers used rather high doses of radiation and looked for complete cell death.

Lasnitzki used more moderate doses and studied the radiosensitivity of a mouse adenocarcinoma *in vivo* and *vitro*, by adequate quantitative methods. After 198r the percentage of abnormal mitoses was slightly less *in vitro* than *in vivo*, but the amount of mitotic inhibition and delayed cell death was the same in both (Lasnitzki, 1945). After 2000r, full mitotic activity was resumed sooner *in vitro* and the percentage of dead cells was less at all times during the first 10 days (Lasnitzki, 1947).

In ordinary hanging-drop cultures, conditions must be relatively anoxic and the lower radiosensitivity found might be largely due to this.

2. *Organ Cultures*

From experiments on rat lymph nodes in organ culture, which have been described in Vol. 2, Chap. 2, Trowell concluded that small lymphocytes are less sensitive *in vitro* than *in vivo* by a factor of at least 2 (on the worst assumptions about oxygen differences) and possibly as much as 11. Some figures for thymus lymphocytes indicate a difference of the same order. Here the LD_{50} *in vitro* was 114r (Patt, 1955), while the LD_{50} *in vivo* was 16r for the cortex and 54r for the medulla (Trowell, 1961b).

Lucas (1962b) measured the radiosensitivity of the visual cells in organ cultures of guinea-pig retina and found the LD_{50} to be about 2600r as compared with 1900r *in vivo*. This was for culture irradiated 24 h after explantation; cultures irradiated immediately after explantation were more sensitive. This decline of sensitivity during *in vitro* life is very interesting and requires further study.

Borghese (1961a) cultured mouse embryonic lung rudiments and found that 818r completely killed the bronchial epithelium, whereas the same dose to the embryo *in vivo* at the comparable stage of development had no effect. The radiation damage in these lung cultures was more fully described by Alescio and Ladu (1962). This appears to be the only instance of cells being more radiosensitive *in vitro*.

3. *Parallel Assay Experiments*

Ideally, the post-irradiation assay should be carried out in the same way in both cases, and this may be either *in vivo* or *in vitro*.

(*a*) *In vivo assay*. This was first done in a crude sort of way by Wood and Prime (1922). Mouse tumours were irradiated in the whole animal on the one hand, and fragments of extirpated tumour were irradiated *in vitro* on the other. The irradiated material was then implanted into normal mice and its viability assayed by the number of tumour "takes". Wood and Prime decided that the tumour cells were more sensitive when irradiated *in vitro*, but it is probable that their methods of *in vitro* handling inflicted a certain amount of extra damage. Since 1959, relatively accurate assay methods have been developed for leukaemia cells and normal bone-marrow cells in the mouse, and some of these were described on p. 96. This work is not tissue culture of course, but the findings are quite important in the present context. In the case of bone-marrow cells, no difference between *in vivo* and *in vitro* sensitivity could be detected when the viability assay was made by protecting a supralethally irradiated animal (McCulloch and Till, 1960) or by counting cell colonies in the spleen (McCulloch and Till, 1962). Hewitt and Wilson (1961) similarly found no difference in the case of leukaemia cells, where the viability assay was made by leukaemia induction. It must be emphasized that the accuracy of these assay methods is quite high and any worthwhile difference in sensitivity would have been detected. McCulloch and Till (1962), for example, found that the MLD for mouse bone marrow cells was 105 rads *in vitro* and 95 rads *in vivo*, and the difference was not statistically significant.

(*b*) *In vitro assay*. Goldring (1956) exposed the spinal ganglia of chick embryos to 2000r either *in ovo* or *in vitro* and then cultured the material immediately afterwards. She found that fibroblasts and macrophages grew freely from the *in vitro* irradiated ganglia but none grew from those irradiated *in ovo*. She suggested that the observed effect of *in ovo* irradiation was due to blood vessel damage, but it is difficult to see why this should affect the viability of tissues immediately explanted. Philpott, Shaeffer and Tolmach (1962) used the Puck method (p. 92) and determined the dose-survival curve for chick embryo wing bud cells. When irradiated *in vitro* in the ordinary way the MLD was found to be 268r. In further experiments the cells were pre-irradiated *in ovo* and then immediately plated out in the usual way, and in this case the MLD was 323r. These were very accurate and carefully controlled experiments and they probably represent the best *in vivo-in vitro* comparison which has so far been made. Although the difference between 268 and 323 was shown to be statistically significant, the main conclusion was that there was no important difference. Another point about these particular experiments is that differences in cell oxygenation were probably quite small. One may judge that the isolated cells exposed to air on a Puck plate are just about as well oxygenated as they would be in the intact embryo.

C. CONCLUSIONS

In the case of proliferating undifferentiated cells, although the early observers all thought that sensitivity was less *in vitro* than *in vivo,* modern work seems to have established pretty conclusively that there is no difference.

In the case of mature cells, there are still indications of lower sensitivity *in vitro* but the evidence is both scanty and unsatisfactory and no generalization can yet be made.

It may also be remarked that any proven case of lower radiosensitivity *in vitro* would seem to imply the existence of an indirect effect of irradiation in the whole animal, and all the evidence from cross-circulation and parabiosis experiments is against this idea.

XIV. Comparison of Different Sorts of Ionizing Radiation

A. INTRODUCTION

The different forms of ionizing radiation, α particles, β particles, protons, neutrons, γ rays and X rays, have, as the name implies, the common property of ionizing some of the atoms of the material through which they pass. Qualitatively they all have the same effect on cells, but quantitatively they differ in the amount of biological damage produced per unit of physical energy absorbed.

The reasons for these differences in "biological effectiveness", which are partly physical and partly unknown, need not be discussed here.

Conventionally, 250 kV X rays are taken as the standard for comparison, and the "relative biological effectiveness" (RBE) of any other type of radiation is defined as the ratio D_x/D, where D is the dose which produces some arbitrary quantitative effect and D_x is the dose of X rays needed to produce the same effect.

Tissue culture would seem to offer an ideal means of determining RBE at the cellular level. Very accurate methods are available for measuring the biological effect, and complicating "indirect" effects, which might be encountered in the whole animal, are excluded. But, unfortunately, a rather serious difficulty has been encountered and this is a matter of physics. When tissues are exposed to X rays, the dosimetry is valid only on the assumption that each cell is immediately surrounded by other cells, tissue matrix, or bodily fluids. But in hanging-drop and monolayer cultures one surface of the cell is in direct contact with glass, and this makes a difference. As a result of photoelectric emission from the glass the cell receives some additional radiation which is not allowed for in conventional dosimetry. This incidentally is why the original dose figures given by Puck and co-workers had to be corrected by Markovin and Feldman, as noted in the footnote to Table II. For physical reasons, which need not be gone into, the extra irradiation from the glass arises only in the case of X rays, other types of radiation do not produce it. Obviously this greatly complicates the determination of RBE when cells attached to glass are used.

This difficulty was first discovered and eluciated by Paterson (1942). With cells grown on glass she found that X rays were twice as effective as γ rays in producing cell death. But when the cells were grown on paraffin wax or "distrene" (which give rise to no secondary emission) X and γ rays produced equal effects. The true RBE for γ rays was therefore 1·0 and the false value of 0·5 found on glass was due to the error in X ray dosimetry.

In recent years, some further difficulties have been encountered but these are not the fault of Tissue Culture. It has been found that RBE depends on the particular dose level chosen and it also depends on the state of oxygenation under which it is measured. This means that the RBE of a particular type of radiation can no longer be accurately specified by means of a single unqualified figure. For this reason Tissue Culture workers have largely lost interest in the subject, and the following results must be taken for what they are worth.

B. RESULTS

1. *Gamma Radiation*

Gamma radiation is very readily available at high intensity from a radium or ^{60}Cobalt source and it has long been a favourite tool for irradiating Tissue Cultures. In many ways this is more convenient than using an X ray machine and a great deal of the early work, notably that of Canti and Spear, was done with a small radium source.

Lasnitzki and Lea (1940) reported that, for mitotic inhibition in ordinary hanging-drop cultures of chick fibroblasts, the RBE of γ rays was about 0·5. Paterson (1942) measured cell death in similar cultures and found a similar figure. As explained above, Paterson went on to show that the X ray dosimetry in all these experiments was incorrect and she concluded that the true RBE was about 1·0. Modern measurements, with more accurate methods, have proved however that the RBE is less than 1·0. Till and Cunningham (1961) measured the survival of L-strain mouse fibroblasts by the Puck method and found that the RBE for ^{60}Co γ rays was 0·76; and a closely similar figure has been found in many other biological systems.

2. *Beta Rays* (*Electrons*)

Beta radiation is usually obtained from a small radioactive source, which may be radium, ^{32}P or ^{90}Sr. The source has to be placed quite close to the culture on account of the short path of the rays. Lasnitzki (1948) used β rays from Uranium UX_1 (^{232}Thorium) and measured the cell death in fibroblast cultures as compared with that produced by X rays. She found that although cell death occurred much sooner after β irradiation (even before the resumption of mitosis) the overall effect showed an RBE of 1·0, which is higher than expected. Barendsen *et al.* (1960), using a strain of human kidney cells, measured cell survival by the Puck method and found an RBE of 0·85. This figure is in keeping with results obtained in other biological systems.

3. *Fast Electrons*

"Fast electrons", produced by a Betatron generator, are similar to β rays but much more penetrating. Gärtner (1950, 1952, 1953, 1955) compared the effects of fast electrons and X rays on chick fibroblast cultures in respect of mitotic inhibition, mitotic abnormalities and cell death. She described various qualitative as well as quantitative differences between the effects of the two types of radiation, but these are too complicated for description here, and in any case no very clear picture emerged. It was shown however that in respect of mitotic inhibition fast electrons were less effective than ordinary β rays (Gärtner, 1958; Gärtner and Zoeppritz, 1958). The effect of fast electrons on HeLa cell cultures has been described in some detail by Peters (1958). No reliable RBE figures are available.

4. *Alpha Particles*

Uniform irradiation of the cells by α particles is most easily achieved by dissolving radon gas in the culture medium. Lajtha *et al.* (1958) compared the effects of α rays and X rays on DNA synthesis in suspension cultures of bone-marrow cells, and found an RBE of 0·5. Barendsen *et al.* (1960), using the method described in subsection 2 above, found that the RBE of α rays depended on dose; it ranged from 6·0 at the lowest dose used to 2·5 at the highest dose. Barendsen (1962) argued that the results were consistent with the hypothesis that loss of reproductive integrity is brought about by the passage of one single α particle through the nucleus, and this α particle dissipates its energy in a volume 100,000 times less than that of the nucleus. He suggested that the "sensitive site", which so many have sought for in morphological terms, is represented by "a number of essential and unique molecules distributed uniformly through the nucleus", inactivation of a few of these being lethal. When X rays are used however, existing data are more consistent with the idea that several (2–6) highly localized targets have to be hit before the cell is permanently damaged.

Alexander (1962) compared the effects of α rays and X rays on mouse lymphoma cells in suspension culture. Two different cell strains were used and, with X radiation, the MLD was 75r in the one and 200r in the other. But with α rays both strains were equally sensitive. A further difference noticed was that, whereas after X irradiation the cells divided at least once before growing into giant cells, after α radiation they grew into giant cells without any previous division.

These observations have been mentioned because they suggest that perhaps the primary radiobiological lesion produced by α radiation is different from that produced by the other forms of radiation. As yet however they are but straws in the wind.

5. *Fast Neutrons*

"Fast neutrons" are normally obtained from some sort of generator such as a Cyclotron. Gray, Mottram, Read and Spear (1940) compared the effects of fast neutrons and γ rays on chick fibroblast cultures, as measured by mitotic inhibition. The dose-effect curve for γ rays was sigmoid in shape whereas that for fast neutrons was exponential, which seemed to indicate some difference in their mode of action. The RBE for fast neutrons (versus γ rays) varied from 5·0 at low doses to 1·0 at higher doses.

Berry, Hell, Lajtha and Ebert (1961) compared the effects of fast neutrons and X rays on the rate of DNA synthesis in cultures of human bone-marrow cells and mouse ascites-tumour cells. With the cultures in air the RBE was just over 1·0, but when the cultures were irradiated in nitrogen it was 2·5.

C. SUMMARY

These reports on different forms of radiation are sufficient to show that the RBE under certain specified conditions of dose and oxygen concentration can be accurately determined by Tissue-Culture methods. But the experiments are tedious and the results of no great interest.

XV. Effects of Ultraviolet Radiation

In contrast to the types of radiation dealt with above, ultraviolet radiation does not ionize atoms, it only "excites" them. Another important difference is that the excitations produced by ultraviolet are distributed spatially at random, whereas the ionizations produced by ionizing radiations are localized along the tracks of ionizing particles, where they appear as columns or clusters. The idea of a sensitive "target" within the cell which may or may not be "hit" is therefore less appropriate in the case of u.v. radiation. Since ultraviolet rays penetrate living tissue to a depth of 1–2 mm at most, effects in the whole animal are confined to the skin and conjunctiva, and the effects on other cells can be discovered only by the use of Tissue Culture.

It has been found that virtually all of the effects of ionizing radiation on tissue cultures can be exactly reproduced by u.v. radiation. Levaditi and Mutermilch (1913) showed that u.v. completely inhibited the growth of tissue cultures, a year before this was discovered for ionizing radiation. Moppett (1926) studied the cell death produced by u.v. radiation in hanging-drop cultures of a variety of tissues from rats and mice. The epithelial cells from kidney explants were much more sensitive than the fibroblasts from kidney, heart or spleen; the least sensitive cells were macrophages. Cultures of mouse carcinoma and rat sarcoma were more sensitive than any of the aforementioned normal tissues. Mayer (1931) and Mayer and Schreiber (1934) studied in great detail the cell degeneration and inhibition of outgrowth induced in fibroblast cultures, and they established that the optimum wavelength for producing these effects was 230–280 mμ; there was no defined peak.

The effects on mitosis were first described by von Möllendorf and Laqueur (1938) in chick fibroblast cultures. They found that the cells were temporarily restrained from entering mitosis, though those already in mitosis were unaffected, and that cell death first appeared when mitosis was resumed—all exactly as Strangeways and Oakley had described for X rays in 1923. Carlson and Hollaender (1948) found that u.v. irradiation of dividing grasshopper neuroblasts caused severe damage to the mitotic spindle, and Bloom *et al.* (1955) with microbeams showed that the spindle could easily be destroyed by u.v. but not by protons. As noted on p. 87, evidence that ionizing radiation directly damages the mitotic spindle is very scanty. This seems to be the one and only point of difference between the effects of ultraviolet and ionizing radiations.

Chu (1962) cultured embryonic cells from the Chinese hamster and found that u.v. irradiation produced chromosome abnormalitiesi n-distinguishable from those induced by X rays. The optimum wavelength for this effect was 265 mμ. He also showed that subsequent exposure of the cells to visible light reduced the final number of chromosome aberrations. This interesting phenomenon of "photoreactivation" after u.v. irradiation was first discovered in bacteria. It has been shown that a certain enzyme is concerned in the repair of chromosomal DNA and that this enzyme is activated by visible light (Rupert, 1961).

We may note in passing that visible light will also damage cells if it is strong enough. But the only information available is that lymphocytes are more sensitive than other white blood cells (Earle, 1928) and that rat sarcoma cells are more sensitive than chick fibroblasts (Roffo, 1935).

Rubin and Temin (1959) investigated the effect of u.v. radiation on the reproductive integrity of isolated chick fibroblasts by the Puck method. They found that the dose-survival curve was exponential and indistinguishable from that obtained with X rays.

It seems clear therefore that all the cellular effects of ionizing radiation can be produced equally well by u.v. radiation and, bearing in mind that most of them can also be produced by certain radiomimetic chemicals, the conclusion can safely be drawn that none of the radiation effects so far described is specific. Correspondingly, the application of simple "target" theory considerations to biological systems as complex as mammalian cells seems unlikely to be very profitable. This, however, is still a matter of current controversy and the rival views forcibly presented by Alexander and Gray (1961) provide appropriate further reading.

XVI. Conclusion

Most, if not all, radiobiologists assume that radiation directly damages some particular part of the cell. The damage might be to some morphological component, such as chromosomes, nuclear membrane or mitochondria; or it might be to some biochemical component such as a specific enzyme system. But there is as yet no convincing evidence of any such primary and specific lesion: fifty years of Tissue Culture experiment have certainly provided none, and to that extent the results are disappointing. Perhaps, however, there is no primary lesion anyway. It is conceivable that the whole cell is shaken or stressed and that it simply gives way in its weakest parts.

Fortunately there are two sides to every coin. If the use of Tissue Culture to explore radiation has proved dull, the use of radiation to explore Tissue Culture has turned out somewhat brighter, and the dividends here were quite unexpected. Radiation has proved a very useful tool for damaging Tissue Cultures in an easily-controlled and graduated way, and this has been the starting point for various lines of inquiry into the normal processes of survival, growth and metabolism *in vitro,* which have not been unfruitful. It is in this light, their contribution to biology as a whole, that these radiobiological investigations can most favourably be regarded.

References

Alescio, T. and Ladu, M. (1962). Response to gamma-radiation of mouse embryonic lung cultivated *in vitro*. *Int. J. Radiat. Biol.* **5**, 579.

Alexander, P. (1961). Effect of X-rays on mouse lymphoma cells in tissue culture and radiosensitisation by iodoacetate. *Brit. J. Radiol.* **34**, 335.

Alexander, P. (1962). Qualitative differences between the action of α and X rays on lymphoma cells *in vitro*. *Brit. J. Radiol.* **35**, 361.

Alexander, P. and Gray, L. H. (1961). *In* "The Initial Effects of Ionizing Radiation on Cells" (R. J. C. Harris, ed.), pp. 43-44. Academic Press, London.

Alpen, E. L., Cooper, E. H. and Barkley, H. (1960). Effects of ionizing radiation on rat lymphoid tissue *in vivo*. *Int. J. Radiat. Biol.* **2**, 425.

Astaldi, G., Mauri, C. and di Guglielmo, L. (1950). L'effeto dei raggi roentgen sull'ativita proliferativa degli eritroblasti studiato sull midollo osseo umano in cultura. *Haematologica* **34**, 529.

Bacq, Z. M. and Alexander, P. (1961). "Fundamentals of Radiobiology", 2nd. ed., Chap. 10. Pergamon Press, Oxford.

Bagshaw, M. A. (1961). Possible role of potentiators in radiation therapy. *Amer. J. Roentgenol.* **85**, 822.

Barendsen, G. W. (1962). Dose-survival curves of human cells in tissue culture irradiated with alpha-, beta-, 20–kv.X- and 200–kv.X- radiation. *Nature, Lond.* **193**, 1153.

Barendsen, G. W., Beusker, T. L. J., Vergroesen, A. J. and Budke, L. (1960). Effects of different ionizing radiations on human cells in tissue culture. II. Biological experiments. *Radiat. Res.* **13**, 841.

Bases, R. E. (1959a). Some applications of tissue culture methods to radiation research. *Cancer Res.* **19**, 311.

Bases, R. E. (1959b). Modification of the radiation response determined by single cell techniques: actinomycin D. *Cancer Res.* **19**, 1223.

Bender, M. A. (1957). X-ray induced chromosome aberrations in normal diploid human tissue cultures. *Science* **126**, 974.

Bender, M. A. (1960). X-ray induced chromosome aberrations in mammalian cells *in vivo* and *in vitro*. *In* "Immediate and Low Level Effects of Ionizing Radiations" (A. A. Buzzati-Traverso, ed.), pp. 103-118. Taylor and Francis, London.

Bender, M. A. and Gooch, P. C. (1962a). The kinetics of X-ray survival of mammalian cells *in vitro*. *Int. J. Radiat. Biol.* **5**, 133.

Bender, M. A. and Gooch, P. C. (1962b). Types and rates of X-ray-induced chromosome aberrations in human blood irradiated *in vitro*. *Proc. nat. Acad. Sci., Wash.* **48**, 522.

Bender, M. A. and Gooch, P. C. (1962c). Persistent chromosome aberrations in irradiated human subjects. *Radiat. Res.* **16**, 44.

Bender, M. A. and Wolff, S. (1961). X-ray-induced chromosome aberrations and reproductive death in mammalian cells. *Amer. Nat.* **95**, 39.

Bennett, L. L. Jr., Skipper, H. E., Smithers, D. and Hayes, E. E. (1959). Searches for exploitable biochemical differences between normal and cancer cells. IV. Utilization of nucleosides and nucleotides. *Cancer Res.* **19**, 217.

Berry, R. J. and Andrews, J. R. (1961). Quantitative studies of radiation effects on cell reproduction capacity in a mammalian transplantable tumor system *in vivo*. *Ann. N.Y. Acad. Sci.* **95**, 1001.

Berry, R. J., Hell, E., Lajtha, L. G. and Ebert, M. (1961). Further studies on the mechanism of inhibition of DNA-synthesis by ionizing radiation. *Int. J. Radiat. Biol.* **4**, 61.

Betz, E. H., Booz, G. and Lelièvre, P. (1961). Effet protecteur de la cystéamine et de la cystamine sur les thymocytes irradiés *in vitro*. *Rev. franç. Etud. clin. Biol.* **6**, 39.

Bisceglie, V. and Bucciardi, G. (1928). Le modificazioni funzionali e strutturali degli espianti di cuore embrionale di pollo sottoposti all'azione de sostanze radioattive. *Arch. exp. Zellforsch.* **7**, 444.

Bloom, W., Zirkle, R. E. and Uretz, R. B. (1955). Irradiation of parts of individual cells. III. Effects of chromosomal and extrachromosomal irradiation on chromosome movements. *Ann. N.Y. Acad. Sci.* **59**, 503.

Boll, I. (1957). Studien zur Proliferationsaktivität des menschlichen Knochenmarks mittels Einzelzellautoradiographien nach Radiophosphorzusatz *in vitro*. *Acta haemat.* **18**, 390.

Boll, I., Koppe, M., Schaaf, J. and Trautmann, J. (1956). Quantitative und qualitative Veränderungen an röntgenbestrahlten Knochenmarkkulturen. *Strahlentherapie* **100**, 445.

Booz, G. and Betz, E. H. (1961). Action de la tryptamine et de la 5–hydroxytryptamine sur les thymocytes irradiés *in vitro*. *C.R. Soc. Biol., Paris* **155**, 197.

Borghese, E. (1961a). The effect of ionizing radiations on mouse embryonic lungs developing *in vitro*. *Ann. N.Y. Acad. Sci.* **95**, 866.

Borghese, E. (1961b). Die organkultur als Methode der kausalen Embryologie und ihre Anwendung in der Strahlenbiologie. *Embryologia* **6**, 159.

Breitling, G. and Peters, K. (1957). Zur Frage der höchst zulässigen Strahlendosis. *Naturwissenschaften* **44**, 643.

Brues, A. M., Stroud, A. N. and Svihla, G. (1951). Mitotic changes accompanying continuous irradiation. *Anat. Rec.* **109**, 411.

Buchsbaum, R. and Zirkle, R. E. (1949). Shrinking and swelling after alpha irradiation of various parts of large erythrocytes. *Proc. Soc. exp. Biol., N.Y.* **72**, 27.

Buckton, K. E., Jacobs, P. A., Court Brown, W. M. and Doll, R. (1962). A study of the chromosome damage persisting after X-ray therapy for ankylosing spondylitis. *Lancet, ii*, 676.

Canti, R. G. (1928). Cinematograph demonstration of living tissue cells growing *in vitro*. *Arch. exp. Zellforsch.* **6**, 86.

Canti, R. G. (1929). Biological effects of radium irradiation. *Acta radiol., Stockh.* **10**, 320.

Canti, R. G. and Donaldson, M. (1926). The effect of radium on mitosis *in vitro*. *Proc. roy. Soc.* B, **100**, 413.

Canti, R. G. and Spear, F. G. (1927). The effect of gamma irradiation on cell division in tissue culture *in vitro*. *Proc. roy. Soc.* B, **102**, 92.

Canti, R. G. and Spear, F. G. (1929). The effect of gamma irradiation on cell division in tissue culture *in vitro*. Part II. *Proc. roy. Soc.* B, **105**, 93.

Carlson, J. G. (1961). The grasshopper neuroblast culture technique and its value in radiobiological studies. *Ann. N.Y. Acad. Sci.* **95**, 932.

Carlson, J. G. and Hollaender, A. (1948). Mitotic effects of ultraviolet radiation of the 2250 Å region with special reference to the spindle and cleavage. *J. cell. comp. Physiol.* **31**, 149.

Caspersson, T., Klein, E. and Ringertz, N. R. (1958). Cytochemical studies on some effects of X-radiation on three ascites tumours. *Cancer Res.* **18**, 857.

Chambers, R. and Cameron, G. (1941). The reaction of kidney tubules in tissue culture to roentgen rays. *Radiology* **37**, 186.

Chu, E. H. Y. (1962). Photoreactivation and action spectrum of ultraviolet-induced mammalian chromosome aberrations. *Genetics* **47**, 948.

Chu, E. H. Y. and Giles, N. H. (1958). Comparative chromosomal studies on mammalian cells in culture. I. The HeLa strain and its mutant clonal derivatives. *J. nat. Cancer Inst.* **20**, 383.

Clegg, M. D. (1964a). A technique for the microbeam irradiation of single cells in tissue culture. *J. roy. micr. Soc.* **83**, 433.

Clegg, M. D. (1964b). The electron microscopy of cells irradiated with a microbeam of alpha particles. *J. roy. micr. Soc.* **83**, 443.

Cooper, E. H. and Alpen, E. L. (1959). The effects of ionizing radiation on rat thoracic-duct lymphocytes *in vitro*. *Int. J. Radiat. Biol.* **1**, 344.

Cox, S. F. (1931a). Tissue culture and its applications to radiological problems—time and intensity factors in dosage. *Brit. J. Radiol.* **4**, 111.

Cox, S. F. (1931b). Sensitivity to X-rays of cells *in vitro*. *Arch. exp. Zellforsch.* **11**, 121.

Davis, M. and Smith, C. L. (1957). The irradiation of individual parts of single cells in tissue culture with a microbeam of α-particles. I. Apparatus. *Exp. Cell Res.* **12**, 15.

Dendy, P. P. (1962). Studies on nucleic acid synthesis following the irradiation with an ultraviolet microbeam of parts of single cells grown in tissue culture. Second International Congress on Radiation Research, Harrogate, Abstracts p. 25.

Dewey, D. L. (1960). Effect of oxygen and nitric oxide on the radiosensitivity of human cells in tissue culture. *Nature, Lond.* **186**, 780.

Dewey, W. C. and Humphrey, R. M. (1962). Relative radiosensitivity of different phases in the life cycle of L–P59 mouse fibroblasts and ascites tumor cells. *Radiat. Res.* **16**, 503.

Dickson, M., Paul, J. and Davidson, J. N. (1958). The effect of X-irradiation on cultured cells. *Biochem. J.* **70**, 18P.

Dickson, M. S. H. and Paul J. (1961). Some effects of X-irradiation on the metabolism of deoxyribonucleic acid in mammalian cells grown in culture. *Int. J. Radiat. Biol.* **4**, 419.

Doljanski, L. and Goldhaber, G. (1942). Radiobiological studies on tissue cultures. I. The immediate effect of X-rays on cell outgrowth in cultures of fibroblasts. *Growth* **6**, 235.

Doljanski, L., Goldhaber, G. and Halberstaedter, L. (1944). Comparative studies on the radiosensitivity of normal and malignant cells in culture. II. The delayed lethal effect. *Cancer Res.* **4**, 106.

Doljanski, L., Trillat, J. J., Lecomte du Noüy, P. and Rogozinski, A. (1931). L'action des rayons X sur les cultures de tissu *in vitro*. *C. R. Acad. Sci., Paris* **192**, 304.

Drew, R. M. and Painter, R. B. (1959). Action of tritiated thymidine on the clonal growth of mammalian cells. *Radiat. Res.* **11**, 535.

Dubinin, N. P., Kerkis, Yu. Ya. and Lebedeva, L. I. (1961). Experimental analysis of the effect of radiation on cellular nuclei in the culture of embryonal human tissues. *Dokl. Akad. Nauk SSSR, Biol. Sci.* (Eng. Trans.) **138**, 379.

Earle, W. R. (1928). Studies upon the effect of light on blood and tissue cells. I. The action of light on white blood cells *in vitro*. *J. exp. Med.* **48**, 457.

Elkind, M. M. and Sutton, H. (1960). Radiation response of mammalian cells grown in culture. 1. Repair of X-ray damage in surviving Chinese hamster cells. *Radiat. Res.* **13**, 556.

Erikson, R. L. and Szybalski, W. (1961). Molecular radiobiology of human cell lines. 1. Comparative sensitivity to X-rays and ultraviolet light of cells containing halogen-substituted DNA. *Biochem. biophys. Res. Commun.* **4**, 258.

Evans, H. J., Neary, G. J. and Tonkinson, S. M. (1957). The use of colchicine as an indicator of mitotic rate in broad bean root meristems. *J. Genet.* **55**, 487.

Fieschi, A. and Sacchetti, C. (1960). Behaviour of human bone-marrow cells cultured *in vitro* in presence of radioisotopes. Sensitivity to irradiation and biological damage of the bone marrow. *In* "Immediate and Low Level Effects of Ionizing Radiations" (A. A. Buzzati-Traverso, ed.), pp. 125–138. Taylor and Francis, London.

Fischer, A. (1931). Mesothoriumbestrahlung von Gewebezellen *in vitro*. *Strahlentherapie* **40**, 54.

Fogh, J., Biedler, J. L. and Denues, A. R. T. (1961). X-ray effects on cultured human amnion cells. *Ann. N.Y. Acad. Sci.* **95**, 758.

Gärtner, H. (1950). Strahlenbiologische Untersuchungen mit schnellen Electronen und Röntgenstrahlen an Gewebekulturen. *Strahlentherapie* **82**, 539.

Gärtner, H. (1952). Weitere Untersuchungen über die biologische Wirksamkeit schneller Electronen und Röntgenstrahlen an Gewebekulturen. *Strahlentherapie* **86**, 217.

Gärtner, H. (1953). Vergleichende Untersuchungen über den Primäreffekt nach Einwirkung schneller Electronen und Röntgenstrahlen auf Gewebekulturen. *Strahlentherapie* **89**, 26.

Gärtner, H. (1955). Die biologische Wirksamkeit schneller Electronen und ultraharter Röntgenstrahlen einer 15–MeV–Electronenschleuder im Vergleich zu Röntgenstrahlen üblicher Härte. (Untersucht an Gewebekulturen.) *Strahlentherapie* **96**, 201 and 378.

Gärtner, H. (1957). Die Gewebezüchtung als strahlenbiologische Arbeitsmethode. *Strahlentherapie* **103**, 620.

Gärtner, H. (1958). Vergleichende Untersuchungen mit 15–MeV–Elektronen des Betatrons und den Betastrahlen des radioaktiven Strontium an Gewebekulturen. *Fortschr. Röntgenstr.* **88**, 45.

Gärtner, H. and Peters, K. (1953). Einfluss der Dosis und Dosisleistung von Röntgenstrahlen und Schnellen Electronen auf die Mitosenhäufigkeit in Gewebekulturen. *Strahlentherapie* **92**, 555.

Gärtner, H. and Zoeppritz, U. (1958). Strahlenbiologische Untersuchungen mit radioaktiven Strontium (Sr^{90}) an Gewebekulturen. *Fortschr. Röntgenstr.* **88**, 37.

Gaulden, M. E. (1956). Quoted by Hollaender, A. *In* "Ionizing Radiation and Cell Metabolism" (G. E. W. Wolstenholme and C. M. O'Connor, eds.), pp. 206, 207, 303. Churchill, London.

Gaulden, M. E. and Perry, R. P. (1958). Influence of the nucleolus on mitosis as revealed by ultraviolet microbeam irradiation. *Proc. nat. Acad. Sci., Wash.* **44**, 553.

Gilman, R. and Trowell, O. A. (1965). The effect of radiation on the activity of reticuloendothelial cells in organ cultures of lymph node and thymus. *Int. J. Radiat. Biol.* **9**, 313.

Glücksmann, A. (1941). Preliminary observations on the quantitative examination of human biopsy material taken from irradiated carcinomata. *Brit. J. Radiol.* **14**, 187.

Glücksmann, A. (1947). Cell counts in serial biopsies of carcinomata. *In* "Recent Advances in Clinical Pathology" (S. C. Dyke, ed.), pp. 338-349. Churchill, London.

Goldfeder, A. (1938). Studies on the effect of radiation upon growth and respiration of various tissues *in vitro*. *Radiology* **31**, 73.

Goldfeder, A. (1939). Respiratory changes *in vitro* of normal and malignant tissues following irradiation. *Amer. J. Cancer* **36**, 603.

Goldfeder, A. (1940). Further studies on the effects of irradiation on proliferation and metabolic processes of normal and malignant tissues. IV. Effects produced by different dosage rates of X-ray radiation on the proliferation of various tissues grown *in vitro*. *Radiology* **35**, 210.

Goldfeder, A. (1947). Further studies on the relation between radiation effects, cell viability, and induced resistance to malignant growth. IV. Comparison of effects of roentgen rays on mammary tumours autogenous to inbred strains of mice (dba and C3H). *Radiology* **49**, 724.

Goldfeder, A. (1949). Further studies on the radiosensitivity of tumors autogenous to homozygous hosts. *Radiology* **52**, 230.

Goldfeder, A. (1961). Response of neoplastic cells *in vitro* to ionizing radiation. *Ann. N.Y. Acad. Sci.* **95**, 796.

Goldfeder, A. and Fershing, J. L. (1938). The effect of irradiation on cell respiration. I. Respiration and anaerobic glycolysis of mouse kidney *in vitro* following radiation. *Radiology* **31**, 81.

Goldhaber, G. and Back, A. (1941). Studies on radiosensitivity of animal cell *in vitro*. I. Radiosensitivity of muscular and ciliary movement. *Proc. Soc. exp. Biol., N.Y.* **48**, 150.

Goldhaber, G., Doljanski, L. and Halberstaedter, L. (1944). Comparative studies on the radiosensitivity of normal and malignant cells in culture. III. Further studies on the inhibitory effect of X-rays on cell outgrowth. *Cancer Res.* **4**, 110.

Goldring, I. P. (1956). The effects of X-rays on the growth of spinal ganglia from 6- and 12-day chick embryos in tissue culture. *Radiat. Res.* **5**, 390.

Goodheart, C. R. (1961). Radiation dose calculation in cells containing intranuclear tritium. *Radiat. Res.* **15**, 767.

Grant, G. A. and Vos, O. (1962). Chemical protection of rat thymocytes irradiated *in vitro*. *Int. J. Radiat. Biol.* **5**, 413.

Gray, L. H. (1959). Cellular radiobiology. *Radiat. Res.* Suppl. 1, 73.

Gray, L. H., Mottram, J. C., Read, J. and Spear, F. G. (1940). Some experiments upon the biological effects of fast neutrons. *Brit. J. Radiol.* **13**, 371.

Gregori, A. (1939). Wirkung von Röntgenstrahlen auf das Knochenmark *in vivo* und *in vitro*. *Strahlentherapie* **65**, 163.

Halberstaedter, L. and Doljanski, L. (1937). Radiobiologische Untersuchungen an Gewebekulturen. *Arch. exp. Zellforsch.* **19**, 475.

Halberstaedter, L., Goldhaber, G. and Doljanski, L. (1942). Comparative studies on the radiosensitivity of normal and malignant cells in culture. I. The effect of X-rays on cell outgrowth in cultures of normal rat fibroblasts and rat benzpyrene-induced sarcoma. *Cancer Res.* **2**, 28.

Harper, J. Y., Jr., Pomerat, C. M. and Kent, S. P. (1958). Irradiation of cells in tissue culture. IV. The effect of 2000r and 4000r of gamma irradiation from a cobalt^{60} source on cultures of eye tissues. *Z. Zellforsch.* **47**, 392.

Harrington, H. (1960). Effect of irradiation on cell division and nucleic acid synthesis in strain U–12 fibroblasts. *Biochim. biophys. Acta* **41**, 461.

Harrington, H. (1961). The effect of X irradiation on the progress of strain U–12 fibroblasts through the mitotic cycle. *Ann. N.Y. Acad. Sci.* **95**, 901.

Heim, K. (1927). Biologische Röntgenwirkungen, verfolgt beim Huhn vom Ei bis zum Organexplantat. *Strahlentherapie* **27**, 694.

Heine, L. H. (1936). The effect of radiation upon ciliated epithelium. *Ann. Otol., St. Louis* **45**, 60.

Hewitt, H. B. and Wilson, C. W. (1959). A survival curve for mammalian leukaemia cells irradiated *in vivo* (implications for the treatment of mouse leukaemia by whole-body irradiation). *Brit. J. Cancer* **13**, 69.

Hewitt, H. B. and Wilson, C. W. (1961). Survival curves for tumor cells irradiated *in vivo*. *Ann. N.Y. Acad. Sci.* **95**, 818.

Hoffman, R. S. and Wollman, S. H. (1949). Effect of X-rays on the migration of cells from adult tissue explants. *Proc. Soc. exp. Biol., N.Y.* **70**, 38.

Howard, A. (1956). Influence of radiation on DNA metabolism. *In* "Ionizing Radiation and Cell Metabolism" (G. E. W. Wolstenholme and C. M. O'Connor, eds.), pp. 196-211. Churchill, London.

Howard, A. and Pelc, S. R. (1953). Synthesis of desoxyribonucleic acid in normal and irradiated cells and its relation to chromosome breakage. *Heredity* Suppl. **6**, 261.

Hsu, T. C., Dewey, W. C. and Humphrey, R. M. (1962). Radiosensitivity of cells of Chinese hamster *in vitro* in relation to the cell cycle. *Exp. Cell Res.* **27**, 441.

Huntley, G. H. and Lajtha, L. G. (1962). The radiosensitivity of the processes of DNA-synthesis in mouse spleen. *Int. J. Radiat. Biol.* **5**, 447.

Huwer, G. (1933). Zur Histogenese der Riesenzellen in bestrahlten Portiokarzinomen. *Zbl. Gynäk.* **57**, 103.

Jacoby, F., Trowell, O. A. and Willmer, E. N. (1937). Studies on the growth of tissues *in vitro*. V. Further observations on the manner in which cell division of chick fibroblasts is affected by embryo tissue juice. *J. exp. Biol.* **14**, 255.

Jolles, B., Remington, M. and Simon-Reuss, I. (1961). Indirect radiation effects and diffusible factors in irradiated tissues (Stromatex). *Acta Radiol.* **56**, 57.

Juul, J. and Kemp, T. (1933). Ueber den Einfluss von Radium-und Röntgenstrahlen, ultravioletten Licht und Hitze auf die Zellteilung bei warmblütigen Tieren. Studien an Gewebekulturen. *Strahlentherapie* **48**, 457.

Kelley, G. G. and Wheeler, G. P. (1961). The use of mammalian cells to evaluate the effectiveness of agents for preventing radiation damage. Method based on formation of clones and monolayers. *Radiat. Res.* **14**, 174.

Kelly, L. S., Hirsch, J. D., Beach, G. and Petrakis, N. L. (1957). DNA synthesis and incorporation of P^{32} in irradiated Ehrlich ascites cells. *Proc. Soc. exp. Biol., N.Y.* **94**, 83.

Kerkis, Yu. Ya., Lebedeva, L. I. and Osetrova, T. D. (1962). Overall radiosensitivity of organisms and sensitivity of chromosomal apparatus of cells *in vitro*. *Dokl., Biol. Sci. Sect.* **144**, 504.

Kimura, N. (1919). The effects of X-ray irradiation on living carcinoma and sarcoma cells in tissue cultures *in vitro*. *J. Cancer Res.* **4**, 95.

Kohn, H. I. and Fogh, J. E. (1959). Some prompt and delayed effects of X-rays on growth of human amnion cells (strain FL) in tissue culture. *J. nat. Cancer Inst.* **23**, 293.

Koller, P. C. (1947). The effect of radiation on the normal and malignant cell in man. *Brit. J. Radiol.* Suppl. 1, 84.

Kuyper, C. M. A. and Smets, L. A. (1962). Role of the medium in radiation effects on cells cultivated *in vitro*. *Naturwissenschaften* **49**, 21.

Lajtha, L. G. (1961). The effect of ionizing radiations and tumour-chemotherapeutic agents on the bone marrow. *In* "Progress in Biophysics and Biophysical Chemistry" (J. A. V. Butler, B. Katz and R. E. Zirkle, eds.), Vol. 11, pp. 79-109. Pergamon Press, Oxford.

Lajtha, L. G. (1963). The use of radiation in studies of cell proliferation. *In* "Cell Proliferation" (L. F. Lamerton and R. J. M. Fry, eds.), p. 80. Blackwell, Oxford.

Lajtha, L. G., Oliver, R., Berry, R. and Noyes, W. D. (1958). Mechanism of radiation effect on the process of synthesis of deoxyribonucleic acid. *Nature, Lond.* **182**, 1788.

Lajtha, L. G., Oliver, R. and Ellis, F. (1954). Incorporation of ^{32}P and adenine ^{14}C into DNA by human bone marrow cells *in vitro*. *Brit. J. Cancer* **8**, 367.

Lajtha, L. G., Oliver, R., Kumatori, T. and Ellis, F. (1958). On the mechanism of radiation effect on DNA synthesis. *Radiat. Res.* **8**, 1.

Laser, H. (1930). Strahlenbiologische Untersuchungen an Gewebekulturen. *Strahlentherapie* **38**, 391.

Laser, H. and Halberstaedter, L. (1929). Radiosensibilität normaler und bösartiger Gewebe *in vitro*. *Z. Krebsforsch.* **29**, 411.

Lasnitzki, I. (1940). The effect of X-rays on cells cultivated *in vitro*. *Brit. J. Radiol.* **13**, 279.

Lasnitzki, I. (1943a). The effect of X rays on cells cultivated *in vitro*. Part II. Recovery factor. *Brit. J. Radiol.* **16**, 61.

Lasnitzki, I. (1943b). The response of cells *in vitro* to variations in X-ray dosage. *Brit. J. Radiol.* **16**, 137.

Lasnitzki, I. (1945). A quantitative analysis of the effect of gamma radiation on malignant cells *in vitro* and *in vivo*. *Brit. J. Radiol.* **18**, 214.

Lasnitzki, I. (1947). A quantitative analysis of the direct and indirect action of X radiation on malignant cells. *Brit. J. Radiol.* **20**, 240.

Lasnitzki, I. (1948). The effect of beta rays on cells cultivated *in vitro*. *Brit. J. Radiol.* **21**, 265.

Lasnitzki, I. (1961a). The effect of X-rays on cellular differentiation in organ culture. *Ann. N.Y. Acad. Sci.* **95**, 873.

Lasnitzki, I. (1961b). The effect of radiation on the normal and oestrone-treated mouse vagina grown *in vitro*. *Brit. J. Radiol.* **34**, 356.

Lasnitzki, I. and Lea, D. E. (1940). The variation with wavelength of the biological effect of radiation (measured by the inhibition of division in tissue cultures). *Brit. J. Radiol.* **13**, 149.

Levaditi, C. and Mutermilch, St. (1913). Mode d'action des rayons sur la vie et la multiplication des cellules *in vitro* (première note). Rayons ultra-violets. *C.R. Soc. Biol., Paris* **74**, 1180.

Levine, S. and Kritchevsky, D. (1958). Observations on the incorporation of ^{32}P by irradiation-produced giant cells. *Exp. Cell Res.* **15**, 422.

Levis, A. G. and Marin, G. (1963). Induction of multipolar spindles by X-radiation in mammalian cells *in vitro*. *Exp. Cell Res.* **31**, 448.

Levy, C. K. and Ketchel, M. M. (1962). Effects of *in vitro* X-irradiation on the ameboid migration of human leukocytes. *Radiat. Res.* **17**, 608.

Love, W. H. (1931). Some effects of X-radiation on dividing cells in tissue cultures. *Arch. exp. Zellforsch.* **11**, 435.

Lucas, D. R. (1961). The effect of X-radiation on the mouse retina at different stages of development. *Int. J. Radiat. Biol.* **3**, 105.

Lucas, D. R. (1962a). The effect of X-radiation on the visual cells in organ cultures of mature guinea-pig retina. *Int. J. Radiat. Biol.* **5**, 345.

Lucas, D. R. (1962b). Some effects of X-radiation on organ cultures of guinea-pig retina. *Brit. J. Radiol.* **35**, 651.

Luther, W. (1940). Untersuchungen über den Verlauf der Strahlenreaktion im rontgenbestrahlten Mäusekarzinom. *Strahlentherapie* **68**, 669.

Luther, W. (1943). Untersuchungen über die Wirkung von einzeitigen Röntgenbestrahlungen auf ein Impfkarzinom der weissen Ratte. *Strahlentherapie* **72**, 679.

McCulloch, E. A. and Till, J. E. (1960). The radiation sensitivity of normal mouse bone marrow cells, determined by quantitative marrow transplantation into irradiated mice. *Radiat. Res.* **13**, 115.

McCulloch, E. A. and Till, J. E. (1962). The sensitivity of cells from normal mouse bone marrow to gamma radiation *in vitro* and *in vivo*. *Radiat. Res.* **16**, 822.

Marcus, P. I., Cieciura, S. J. and Puck, T. T. (1956). Clonal growth *in vitro* of epithelial cells from normal human tissues. *J. exp. Med.* **104**, 615.

Mayer, E. (1931). Die Wirkung von ultravioletten Strahlengemischen auf Gewebekulturen. *Strahlentherapie* **39**, 148.

Mayer, E. and Schreiber, H. (1934). Die Wellenlängenabhängigkeit der Ultraviolettwirkung auf Gewebekulturen ("Reinkulturen"). *Protoplasma* **21**, 34.

Mitchell, J. S. and Simon-Reuss, I. (1952). Experiments on the mechanism of action of tetra-sodium 2-methyl-1:4-naphthohydroquinone diphosphate as a mitotic inhibitor and radiosensitiser, using the technique of tissue culture. Experimental methods and quantitative results. *Brit. J. Cancer* **6**, 305.

Möllendorff, W. von, and Laqueur, G. (1938). Zur Kenntnis der mitose. Über die Wirkung von ultravioletten Strahlen auf den Wachstumsrhythmus und auf die Zellteilung in Fibrozytenkulturen. *Z. Zellforsch.* **28**, 310.

Montgomery, P. O'B. and Warren, S. (1953). The ultraviolet microscopy of the living cell's response to lethal X-irradiation. *Science* **117**, 589.

Moppett, W. (1926). The lethal effect of ultra-violet light on normal and malignant tissues grown *in vitro*. *Lanceti*, 907.

Morkovin, D. and Feldman, A. (1959). Dosimetry in living cells irradiated on glass: a correction. *Brit. J. Radiol.* **32**, 282.

Morkovin, D. and Feldman, A. (1960). End point of one of the actions of radiations on living tissue important in radiation therapy and in acute radiation syndrome. *Brit. J. Radiol.* **33**, 197.

Morkovin, D. and Puck, T. T. (1958). Single cell techniques in the study of radioprotective action. *Radiat. Res.* **9**, 155.

Munro, T. R. (1958). Alpha irradiation of parts of single cells in tissue cultures. I. Techniques. II. Dosimetry *Exp. Cell Res.* **15**, 529.

Munro, T. R. (1959). Alpha irradiation of parts of single cells in tissue culture. III. Irradiation of chick fibroblasts during metaphase and anaphase. *Exp. Cell Res.* **18**, 76.

Munro, T. R. (1961). Irradiation of selected parts of single cells. *Ann. N.Y. Acad. Sci.* **95**, 920.

Nakanishi, Y. H. and Nakahara, H. (1956). Cytological studies of tumors. XVII. A phase microscopy study on the mitotic process in the MTK-IV tumor and the Watanabe ascites hepatoma. *J. Fac. Sci. Hokkaido Univ. Ser. VI, Zool.* **12**, 456.

Norris, G. and Hood, S. L. (1962). Some problems in the culturing and radiation sensitivity of normal human cells. *Exp. Cell Res.* **27**, 48.

Oakberg, E. F. (1957). Gamma-ray sensitivity of spermatogonia of the mouse. *J. exp. Zool.* **134**, 343.

Oakberg, E. F. (1962). The effect of low radiation doses on spermatogonia and oocytes of the mouse. Strahlenwirkung und Milieu. *Strahlentherapie,* Sonderbände **51**, 103.

Oftedal, P., Oftebro, R. and Eker, R. (1958). Radioprotective properties of cystamine, cysteamine and cysteine when tested with chick fibroblasts *in vitro*. *Nature Lond.* **181**, 344.

Ohnuki, Y., Awa, A. and Pomerat, C. M. (1961). Chromosomal studies on irradiated leukocytes *in vitro*. *Ann. N.Y. Acad. Sci.* **95**, 882.

Ord, M. G. and Stocken, L. A. (1956). The effects of X- and γ-radiation on nucleic acid metabolism in the rat *in vivo* and *in vitro*. *Biochem. J.* **63**, 3.

Ord, M. G. and Stocken, L. A. (1958a). The inhibition by γ-irradiation of incorporation of ^{32}P into rat thymocytes *in vitro*. *Biochem. J.* **68**, 410.

Ord, M. G. and Stocken, L. A. (1958b). Radiobiochemical lesions in animal cells. *Nature, Lond.* **182**, 1787.

Osgood, E. E. (1942). Is the action of roentgen rays direct or indirect? An investigation of this question by the method of human marrow culture. *Amer. J. Roentgenol.* **48**, 214.

Osgood, E. E. and Bracher, G. J. (1939). Culture of human marrow; studies of the effects of roentgen rays. *Ann. intern. Med.* **13**, 563.

Painter, R. B. (1960). Nucleic acid metabolism in HeLa S3 cells after X-ray-induced mitotic delay. *Radiat. Res.* **13**, 726.

Painter, R. B. and Drew, R. M. (1959). Studies on deoxyribonucleic acid metabolism in human cancer cell cultures (HeLa). I. The temporal relationships of deoxyribonucleic acid synthesis to mitosis and turnover time. *Lab. Invest.* **8**, 278.

Painter, R. B. and Hughes, W. L. (1961). Nucleic acid metabolism and the lethal effect of radiation on cultured human cells (HeLa). *Ann. N.Y. Acad. Sci.* **95**, 960.

Painter, R. B. and Robertson, J. S. (1959). Effect of irradiation and theory of role of mitotic delay on the time course of labeling of HeLa S3 cells with tritiated thymidine. *Radiat. Res.* **11**, 206.

Paterson, E. (1942). A comparison of the action of X and gamma radiation on fibroblasts. *Brit. J. Radiol.* **15**, 257 and 302.

Paterson, E. (1944). The time-intensity factor in X-ray irradiation. *Brit. J. Radiol.* **17**, 26.

Paterson, E. and Thompson, M. V. (1949). Effect of urethane combined with X-rays on chick fibroblasts. *Nature, Lond.* **163**, 563.

Patt, H. M. (1955). Factors in the radiosensitivity of mammalian cells. *Ann. N.Y. Acad. Sci.* **59**, 649.

Patt, H. M., Blackford, M. E. and Straube, R. L. (1952). Effect of X-rays on thymocytes and its modification by cysteine. *Proc. Soc. exp. Biol., N.Y.* **80**, 92.

Perry, R. P., Hell, A. and Errera, M. (1961). The role of the nucleolus in ribonucleic acid and protein synthesis. I. Incorporation of cytidine into normal and nucleolar inactivated HeLa cells. *Biochim. biophys. Acta* **49**, 47.

Peters, K. (1953). Stoffwechselbeziehungen zwischen bestrahltem und unbestrahltem Gewebe in ihrem Einfluss auf die Mitosenhäufigkeit *in vitro*. *Z. Zellforsch.* **39**, 203.

Peters, K. (1954). Über die Bedeutung des Mediums für die Wirkung sekundärer Strahlenprodukte auf die Mitosehäufigkeit in halbbestrahlten Gewebekulturen. *Z. Zellforsch.* **40**, 510.

Peters, K. (1958). Untersuchungen über die Einwirkung von Elektronenstrahlen auf Karzinomzellen (Stamm HeLa) in Gewebekulturen. *Fortschr. Röntgenstr.* **88**, 50.

Peters, K. (1959). Über indirekte und direkte Strahlenwirkungen an Krebszellen in Gewebekulturen. *Strahlentherapie*, Sonderbände **43**, 373.

Peters, K. (1962). Untersuchungen über die Wirkung von schwachen Strahlendosen auf Gewebekulturen *in vitro*. *Strahlentherapie* **118**, 481.

Peters, K. and Gärtner, H. (1956). Wirkungssteigerung des Röntgenstrahleneffektes in Gewebekulturen durch Megaphen. *Strahlentherapie* **99**, 387.

Philpott, G. W., Shaeffer, C. W. Jr. and Tolmach, L. J. (1962). Reproductive survival of chick embryos cells irradiated *in ovo* and *in vitro*. *Radiat. Res.* **17**, 508.

Pomerat, C. M. (1958). Cellular changes induced by radiation. *Ann. N.Y. Acad. Sci.* **71**, 1143.

Pomerat, C. M., Fernandes, M. V., Nakanishi, Y. H. and Kent, S. P. (1958). Irradiation of cells in tissue culture. V. The effect of gamma irradiation from a cobalt^{60} source on human amnion cells *in vitro*. *Z. Zellforsch.* **48**, 1.

Pomerat, C. M., Kent, S. P. and Logie, L. C. (1957a). Irradiation of cells in tissue culture. I. Giant cell induction in strain cultures versus elements from primary explants. *Z. Zellforsch.* **47**, 158.

Pomerat, C. M., Kent, S. P. and Logic, L. C. (1957b). Irradiation of cells in tissue culture. II. Cinematographic analyses of cell enlargement and mitotic activity following gamma irradiation at 2000r and 4000r. *Z. Zellforsch.* **47**, 175.

Post, J., Huang, C-Y. and Hoffman, J. (1963). The replication time and pattern of the liver cell in the growing rat. *J. Cell Biol.* **18**, 1.

Price Jones, C. and Mottram, J. C. (1914). A contribution to the study of *in vitro* plasma cultures of mouse carcinoma and rat sarcoma. *Arch. Middx. Hosp.* **33**, 21.

Prime, F. (1917). Observations upon the effects of radium on tissue growth *in vitro*. *J. Cancer Res.* **2**, 105.

Puck, T. T. (1958). Action of radiation on mammalian cells. III. Relationship between reproductive death and induction of chromosome anomalies by X-irradiation of euploid human cells *in vitro*. *Proc. nat. Acad. Sci., Wash.* **44**, 772.

Puck, T. T. (1960). *In vitro* studies of the radiation biology of mammalian cells. *In* "Progress in Biophysics and Biophysical Chemistry" (J. A. V. Butler and B. Katz, eds.), Vol. 10, pp. 237-258. Pergamon Press, Oxford.

Puck, T. T., Cieciura, S. J. and Fisher, H. W. (1957). Clonal growth *in vitro* of human cells with fibroblastic morphology. *J. exp. Med.* **106**, 145.

Puck, T. T. and Marcus, P. I. (1956). Action of X-rays on mammalian cells. *J. exp. Med.* **103**, 653.

Puck, T. T., Marcus, P. I. and Cieciura, S. J. (1956). Clonal growth of mammalian cells *in vitro*. *J. exp. Med.* **103**, 273.

Puck, T. T., Morkovin, D., Marcus, P. I. and Cieciura, S. J. (1957). Action of X-rays on mammalian cells. II. Survival curves of cells from normal human tissues. *J. exp. Med.* **106**, 485.

Rachmilewitz, M., Rosin, A., Goldhaber, G. and Doljanski, L. (1947). Studies on bone marrow *in vitro*. IV. The effect of roentgen rays on explanted bone marrow. *Amer. J. Roentgenol.* **58**, 464.

Reich, E., Franklin, R. M., Shatkin, A. J. and Tatum, E. L. (1961). Effect of Actinomycin D on cellular nucleic acid synthesis and virus production. *Science* **134**, 556.

Reid, T. R. and Gifford, M. P. (1952). A quantitative study of the effects of X radiation on cells *in vitro*. *J. nat. Cancer Inst.* **13**, 431.

Rhynas, P. O. W. and Newcombe, H. B. (1960). A heritable change in radiation resistance of strain L mouse cells. *Exp. Cell Res.* **21**, 326.

Roffo, A. H. (1929). Resistencia del bazo irradiado en el organismo y aislado del mismo. Sur desarrollo en los cultivos *in vitro*. *Bol. Inst. Med. exp. Cáncer., B. Aires* **6**, 400.

Roffo, A. H. (1935). Die Wirkung der Lichtstrahlen auf die Entwicklung normaler und neoplastischer, *in vitro* gezüchteter Zellen. *Strahlentherapie* **52**, 525.

Rounds, D. E. (1961). RNA as a protective agent against irradiation of cell cultures. *Ann. N.Y. Acad. Sci.* **95**, 994.

Rounds, D. E., Pomerat, C. M., Logie, L. C., Nakanishi, Y. H. and Anderson, D. (1959). Irradiation of cells in tissue culture. VI. The influence of oxygen on injury to cells by gamma irradiation from a Cobalt ^{60} source. *Z. Zellforsch.* **50**, 425.

Rubin, H. and Temin, H. M. (1959). A radiological study of cell-virus interaction in the rous sarcoma. *Virology* **7**, 75.

Rupert, C. S. (1961). Repair of ultraviolet damage in cellular DNA. *J. cell. comp. Physiol.* **58**, Suppl. 1, 57.

Sanders, P. C., Peterson, D. F. and Langham, W. H. (1961). The influence of intranuclear irradiation on the growth of HeLa cells in agitated fluid medium. *Ann. N.Y. Acad. Sci.* **95**, 969.

Santesson, L. (1929). Über Röntgenstrahlenwirkung auf *in vitro* gezüchtete Kulturen von Hühnerfibroblasten und Peyton-Rous Hühnersarkom. *Uppsala LäkForen. Förh.* **34**, 591.

Schleich, A. (1961). Studies on radioprotection of various compounds *in vitro* and *in vivo*. *Ann. N.Y. Acad. Sci.* **95**, 1009.

Schleich, A., Gey, M. K. and Gey, G. O. (1961). Attempts at influencing the radiation response of human tumor strains A.Fi. and HeLa in continuous cultures: a test of Synkavit (synthetic vitamin K) as "radiosensitizer". *Ann. N.Y. Acad. Sci.* **95**, 774.

Schrek, R., Leithold, S. L., Friedman, I. A. and Best, W. R. (1962). Clinical evaluation of an *in vitro* test for radiosensitivity of leukemic lymphocytes. *Blood* **20**, 432.

Seed, J. (1960). Inhibition of nucleic acid synthesis caused by X-irradiation of the nucleolus. *Proc. roy. Soc.* B, **152**, 387.

Seed, J. (1962). The synthesis of deoxyribonucleic acid and nuclear protein in normal and tumour strain cells. *Proc. roy. Soc.* B, **156**, 41.

Sheek, M. R., Des Armier, R. M., Sagik, B. P. and Magee, W. E. (1960). Biochemical changes during the formation and growth of giant cells from irradiated HeLa cells. *Exp. Cell Res.* **19**, 549.

Simon-Reuss, I. and Spear, F. G. (1947). The effect of gamma radiation on mitosis *in vitro*. *Brit. J. Radiol.* **20**, 63.

Sinclair, W. K. (1962). Characteristics of mammalian cell populations surviving high doses of X-irradiation *in vitro*. Second International Congress on Radiation Research, Harrogate, Abstracts p. 113.

Sinclair, W. K. and Morton, R. A. (1963). Variations in X-ray response during the division cycle of partially synchronized Chinese hamster cells in culture. *Nature, Lond.* **199**, 1158.

Smith, C. L. (1959). The irradiation of the chromosomes of single cells in metaphase with a microbeam of α-particles 5μ in diameter. *Proc. roy. Soc.* B, **150**, 372.

Smith, C. L. (1962). Effect on nucleic acid synthesis of irradiation of parts of single cells in tissue culture with a microbeam of α–particles. Second International Congress on Radiation Research, Harrogate, Abstracts p. 27.

Smith, L. H. and Vos, O. (1962). Sensitivity and protection of mouse bone-marrow cells X-irradiated *in vitro*. *Int. J. Radiat. Biol.* **5**, 461.

Spear, F. G. (1930). The delayed lethal effect of radium on tissue cultures *in vitro*. *Proc. roy. Soc.* B, **106**, 44.

Spear, F. G. (1931a). The delayed lethal effect of radium on tissue cultures *in vitro* —comparison of continuous and spaced radiation. *Proc. roy. Soc.* B, **108**, 190.

Spear, F. G. (1931b). Immediate and delayed effects of radium (gamma rays) on tissue cultures *in vitro*. *Brit. J. Radiol.* **4**, 146.

Spear, F. G. (1932). The effect of spaced radiation on tissue cultures *in vitro*. *Proc. roy. Soc.* B, **110**, 224.

Spear, F. G. (1935). Tissue culture. Its application to radiological research. *Brit. J. Radiol.* **8**, 68 and 280.

Spear, F. G. and Grimmett, L. G. (1933). The biological response to gamma rays of radium as a function of the intensity of radiation. *Brit. J. Radiol.* **6**, 387.

Stanners, C. P. and Till, J. E. (1960). DNA synthesis in individual L-strain mouse cells. *Biochim. biophys. Acta* **37**, 406.

Strangeways, T. S. P. and Fell, H. B. (1927). A study of the direct and indirect action of X-rays upon the tissues of the embryonic fowl. *Proc. roy. Soc.* B, **102**, 9.

Strangeways, T. S. P. and Hopwood, F. L. (1926). The effects of X-rays upon mitotic cell division in tissue cultures *in vitro*. *Proc. roy. Soc.* B, **100**, 283.

Strangeways, T. S. P. and Oakley, H. E. H. (1923). The immediate changes observed in tissue cells after exposure to soft X-rays while growing *in vitro*. *Proc. roy. Soc.* B, **95**, 373.

Stroud, A. N. (1956). The effects of continuous irradiation by tritium on cells cultivated *in vitro*. *Ann. N.Y. Acad. Sci.* **67**, 11.

Stroud, A. N. and Brues, A. M. (1954). Radiation effects in tissue culture. *Tex. Rep. Biol. Med.* **12**, 931.

Stroud, A. N., Brues, A. M. and Svoboda, B. R. (1961). DNA synthesis in mammalian kidney cells in tissue culture after single and periodic doses of irradiation. *Ann. N.Y. Acad. Sci.* **95**, 942.

Sugiura, K. (1937). Studies on radiosensitivity of mouse sarcoma 180 irradiated *in vivo* and *in vitro*. *Radiology* **29**, 352.

Tansley, K., Spear, F. G. and Glücksmann, A. (1937). The effect of gamma rays on cell division in the developing rat retina. *Brit. J. Ophthal.* **21**, 273.

Taylor, J. H. (1960). Asynchronous duplication of chromosomes in cultured cells of Chinese hamster. *J. Cell Biol.* **7**, 455.

Terasima, T. and Tolmach, L. J. (1963). Variations in several responses of HeLa cells to X-irradiation during the division cycle. *Biophys. J.* **3**, 11.

Therkelsen, A. J. (1961). Protection of cells in tissue culture by means of cysteamine and cystamine against the action of nitrogen mustard and X-rays. *Biochem. Pharmacol.* **8**, 269.

Till, J. E. (1961). Radiation effects on the division cycle of mammalian cells *in vitro*. *Ann. N.Y. Acad. Sci.* **95**, 911.

Till, J. E. and Cunningham, J. R. (1961). *In* "The Physics of Radiology" (H. E. Johns, ed.), p. 672. Thomas, Springfield.

Till, J. E. and McCulloch, E. A. (1961). A direct measurement of the radiation sensitivity of normal mouse bone marrow cells. *Radiat. Res.* **14**, 213.

Till, J. E. and Whitmore, G. F. (1959). Effects of X-rays on mammalian cells in tissue-culture. Proceedings of the Third Canadian Cancer Conference, pp. 415-431.

Tolmach, L. J. (1961). Growth patterns in X-irradiated HeLa cells. *Ann. N.Y. Acad. Sci.* **95**, 743.

Tolmach, L. J. and Marcus, P. I. (1960). Development of X-ray induced giant HeLa cells. *Exp. Cell Res.* **20**, 350.

Trabert-van der Maesen, M. (1957). Etude comparative de la croissance et de la mitose dans des cultures irradiées, avec ou sans traitement préalable à la cystéamine. *C.R. Soc. Biol., Paris* **151**, 1624.

Trowell, O. A. (1958). The lymphocyte. *Int. Rev. Cytol.* **7**, 235.

Trowell, O. A. (1959). The culture of mature organs in a synthetic medium. *Exp. Cell Res.* **16**, 118.

Trowell, O. A. (1961a). Cytocidal effects of radiation on organ cultures. *Ann. N.Y. Acad. Sci.* **95**, 849.

Trowell, O. A. (1961b). Radiosensitivity of the cortical and medullary lymphocytes in the thymus. *Int. J. Radiat. Biol.* **4**, 163.

Umeda, T. (1927). The action of light, X-ray, and radium on the movement of ciliated epithelium (a study in tissue culture method). *Acta derm., Kyoto* **10**, 603.

Van Bekkum, D. W. and de Groot, J. (1956). Observations on chemical protection *in vivo* and *in vitro*. *In* "Progress in Radiobiology" (J. S. Mitchell, B. E. Holmes and C. L. Smith, eds.), pp. 243-246. Oliver and Boyd, Edinburgh.

Vollmar, H. (1939). Wirkung von Röntgenstrahlen auf normale Zellen und auf Tumorzellen. *Arch. exp. Zellforsch.* **22**, 407.

Vollmar, H. and Rajewsky, B. (1937). Mikrokinematographische Studien über die Wirkung von Röntgenstrahlen auf normale und Tumorzellen in Gewebeculturen. *Strahlentherapie* **60**, 524.

Vos, O., Budke, L. and Vergroesen, A. J. (1962). Protection of tissue-culture cells against ionizing radiation. I. The effect of biological amines, disulphide compounds and thiols. *Int. J. Radiat. Biol.* **5**, 543.

Vos, O. and Kaalen, M. C. A. C. (1962). Protection of tissue-culture cells against ionizing radiation. II. The activity of hypoxia, dimethyl sulphoxide, dimethyl sulphone, glycerol and cysteamine at room temperature and at $-196°C$. *Int. J. Radiat. Biol.* **5**, 609.

Wakonig, R. and Ford, D. K. (1960). Chromosome aberrations in irradiated cells of Chinese hamster grown in tissue culture. *Canad. J. Zool.* **38**, 203.

Whitfield, J. F. and Rixon, R. H. (1959). Effects of X-radiation on multiplication and nucleic acid synthesis in cultures of L-strain cells. *Exp. Cell Res.* **18**, 126.

Whitfield, J. F. and Rixon, R. H. (1962). Prevention of postirradiation mitotic delay in cultures of L mouse cells by calcium salts. *Exp. Cell Res.* **27**, 154.

Whitfield, J. F., Rixon, R. H. and Youdale, T. (1962). Prevention of mitotic delay in irradiated suspension cultures of L mouse cells by agmatine. *Exp. Cell Res.* **27**, 143.

Whitman, W. G. (1933). Some observations of the effects of radium irradiation on tissue cultures. *Amer. J. Cancer* **1**, 932.

Whitmore, G. F., Stanners, C. P., Till, J. E. and Gulyas, S. (1961). Nucleic acid synthesis and the division cycle in X-irradiated L-strain mouse cells. *Biochim. biophys. Acta* **47**, 66.

Whitmore, G. F., Till, J. E., Gwatkin, R. B. L., Siminovitch, L. and Graham, A. F. (1958). Increase of cellular constituents in X-irradiated mammalian cells. *Biochim. biophys. Acta* **30**, 583.

Wood, F. C. and Prime, F. (1914). The action of radium on growing cells. *Proc. Soc. exp. Biol., N.Y.* **11**, 140.

Wood, F. C., and Prime, F. (1922). Die tödliche Röntgenstrahlendosis für Krebszellen. *Strahlentherapie* **13**, 628.

Zaroff, L., Sato, G. and Mills, S. E. (1961). Single-cell platings from freshly isolated mammalian tissue. *Exp. Cell Res.* **23**, 565.

Zirkle, R. E. and Bloom, W. (1953). Irradiation of parts of individual cells. *Science* **117**, 487.

CHAPTER 3

Effects of Invading Organisms on Cells and Tissues in Culture

FREDERIK B. BANG

Department of Pathobiology, Johns Hopkins University, School of Hygiene and Public Health, Baltimore, Maryland, U.S.A.

I. Introduction

It may be well at the outset to define the general purpose of a review which attempts to relate the effect of viruses on cells—traditionally the domain of the morphologically oriented virologist—to the study of the growth of viruses in the cell, which has become the domain of the biochemically oriented virologist. Since action and reaction are as inseparable as morphology and function, this discussion will emphasize changes wrought in cells following the introduction of a virus, as well as biochemical changes initiated by virus multiplication.

New information accumulates so fast that important contemporary discoveries are often ignored while basic observations of the past are completely forgotten. For this reason it may be of interest to quote the prophetic words of Carrel (1928), a great proponent and publicist of the value of tissue culture:

> "It is certain that the modern methods, by which pure strains of given cell types are cultivated in flasks in a medium of known composition and maintained in a condition of measurable activity for long periods of time, will help to ascertain the nature and fundamental properties of viruses. A virus may be a very minute organism, or it may be a chemical substance manufactured by the cells themselves. In either case, its multiplication depends upon the activity of a living tissue. Since pure strains of cells are caused to live *in vitro* under such simple conditions that the effects of viruses on cell morphology and reactivity and the relation of the nature and metabolic condition of cells to the viruses may be analyzed, new discoveries will certainly be made."

It should be emphasized also that the fundamental observations recorded in past reviews are supplemented, not superseded, by current ones which substitute the initials DNA for nucleus, RNA for nucleolus and cytoplasm, and "oxydative phosphorylation" for mitochondria. It is still a major task to fit these substances into a picture of the living, reacting cell.

Observation of the effect of virus infection on individual cells remains an indispensable part of research, for as yet no system of animal cells and virus infection has been so sharply synchronized that the events of absorption, penetration, multiplication, and release may be accurately predicted for the entire cell population. Indeed, in several systems, only a fraction of the cells becomes infected.

A primary problem to be faced in reviewing the field of virus-cell interaction is the tremendous variety of known viruses, many of which may have had entirely distinct histories of evolutionary descent from different microbial parasites of cells. A review must also consider the degree of differentiated function which persists in cells studied *in vitro*; the differential behavior of the three major classes of cells (fibroblasts, epithelial cells, and macrophages) in reaction to viruses is beginning to be recognized, but in many cases there are insufficient data on the susceptibility of different cell types grown under the same conditions and similarly exposed to virus.

The great hope of *in vitro* methods is that the study of disease interaction at this level will clarify the processes of disease in the whole animal. While the overwhelming majority of animal viruses are now being studied in cell lines or trypsinized preparations of individual organs, neither type of preparation retains much of its original differentiated function. But to the student of disease, the remarkable specificity of the disease process is one of the greatest puzzles. The study of viruses in organ cultures is one approach to resolution of this dilemma (Bang and Niven, 1958); the scattered literature in this area will be referred to in the appropriate sections.

The increasing number of viruses of man and animals challenges the most ingenious taxonomist, and it is now impossible to review the effects of viruses on cells without separating the different classes of viruses. We have for the most part used Andrewes' (1964) classification for this purpose, but since this review includes some reference to other microbial agents, we have constructed a chart indicating possible evolutionary sequences in the development of the different agents as they became more and more parasitic and dependent upon metabolic processes of the host cell, rather than merely on the end products of metabolism (Fig. 1).

The chief purpose of this chart is to indicate why we have chosen to

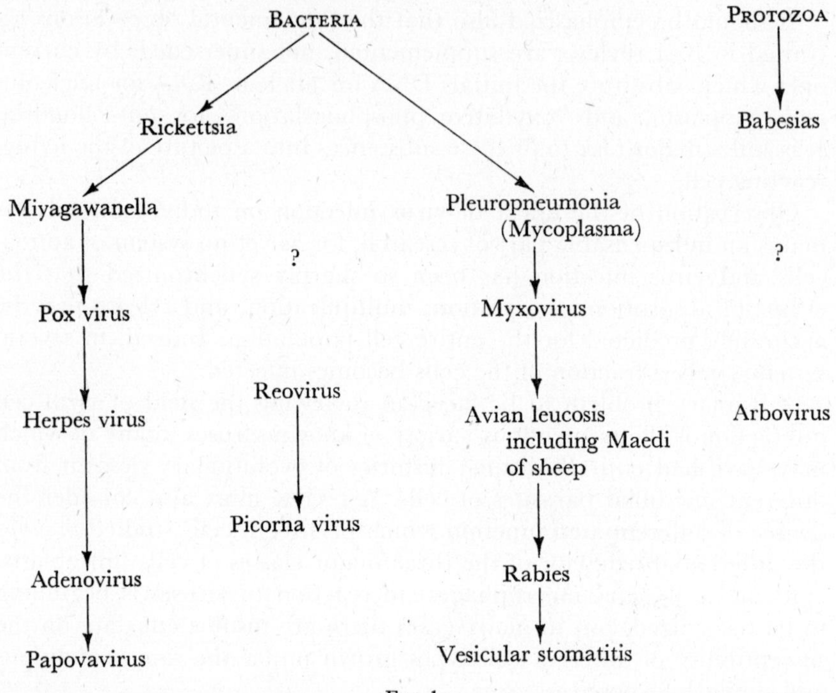

Fig. 1.

follow a particular sequence of presentation. If, as seems likely, DNA and RNA viruses differ in several fundamental ways, then it is necessary to try to follow the linear evolution of the DNA virus line to its most parasitic stage (the papova viruses?) and then return, with a sharp break, to the large RNA viruses. The mycoplasma are treated as an intermediate step in the transition between bacteria and the large RNA viruses, for reasons detailed in the section on mycoplasma (p. 162).

The discussion of the effects of Protozoa on cells in tissue culture is manifestly inadequate for several reasons. Data on the effect of the agent on the host cell, despite the rather extensive descriptions of the growth of various Protozoa in cells, are incomplete. Even more important for our discussion here is the fact that a huge number (particularly of the smaller ones such as *Babesia, Theileria, Pneumocystis* and *Microsporidia*) have, with few exceptions, not been studied in Tissue Culture.

Thus, there is no information available upon which one might base the derivation of arboviruses (or other agents which grow in insects) from such small Protozoa as *Babesia* and *Theileria* which also have a growth stage in insects.

Finally, this review was originally designed to describe the effect of a particular group of agents (bacteria or viruses) on a series of different functions of the living cell (Table I). In many sections, this has proved to be impossible on account of the total absence of information. We have, however, retained the original outline as often as possible, and its absence emphasizes this very defect. Supplemental reviews on the cytopathic effects of viruses are available in articles by Klöne (1957), Pereira (1961) and Bernhard (1964) on fine structure changes. Interferon has been touched on only indirectly in this present report, but has been fully and ably reviewed by Wagner (1963) and Ho (1964).

TABLE I

A. Motion
   1. Migration
   2. Surface movement, microvilli, extrusions
   3. Internal movement, mitochondria, nuclei

B. Reaction to environment
   1. Adherence to substrate
   2. Reaction to other cells
      a. Contact inhibition
      b. Giant cell formation

C. Feeding
   1. Pinocytosis, phagocytosis
   2. Lysosome effects (increased surface activity)
   3. Osmo-regulation in different compartments, vacuolation
   4. Paranuclear hypertrophy (activity of Golgi complex)

D. Growth
   1. Increase in size
   2. Nucleolar size changes (increased metabolism, autoradiography)
   3. Division
      a. Association of virus mass with cell spindle
      b. Direct interference with mitosis
      c. Abnormal mitotic figures with chromosome breaks

E. Pathological Products
   1. Virus colonies
   2. Virus antigens
   3. By-products of virus growth
   4. Cell destruction

F. Response of Entire Culture
   1. Spread through entire culture
   2. Chronic infections as special problems
   3. Organ culture response to infection

II. PROTOZOA

With a few exceptions, only the larger of the numerous intracellular Protozoa have been grown in tissue culture. These include the exoerythrocytic stage of bird *Malaria, Toxoplasma, Leishmania,* and *Trypanosoma cruzi,* and the literature has been summarized by Pipkin and Jensen (1956, 1960). No specific effects on the cell are recorded other than that due to replacement of the host cell's cytoplasm by the parasites as they multiply there. The parasite eventually bursts out, and the host cell disintegrates. In some excellent phase cinematographic studies by Huff, Pipkin, Weathersby and Jensen (1960) the penetration and development of two species of bird malaria plasmodia have been followed in chick fibroblasts. Other than the formation of a vacoule which was essentially filled by the parasites, little effect on the host cell was noted.

Theileria is one of the small Protozoa which causes a febrile disease in cattle, particularly in Africa. It has been grown in tissue cultures of calf spleen or lymph gland (Tchernomoretz, 1945; Brocklesby and Hawking, 1958), and in these cultures has a size ranging from 0·4 to 2μ. No destruction of the host cells is recorded. Recently, Hullinger, Wilde, Brown and Turner (1964) have kept infected cultures going for a period of 4 months and have been unable to detect "cytopathogenic activity." On the other hand, they believe that the parasite is able to maintain infection of cells by dividing with the cells. *Theileria* grew only in bovine cells, and 98–100% of these became infected. Stained preparations of dividing cells showed an average of 14–17 small parasitic particles/cell, and seemed to show parasites attached by a thread to the spindle fibers during the division of the host cell.

It may be suggested that intracellular Protozoa are only partially parasitic and most of the Protozoa attain relatively small numbers within the host cell. However, human exoerythrocytic malaria, which has not been grown in Tissue Culture, attains a population of 10,000–40,000 within individual parenchymal liver cells.

III. Bacteria

In the tradition of Metschnikoff, there developed at the end of the last century and the beginning of this one, a mass of literature dealing with the interaction of a variety of bacteria with an equally bewildering variety of cells. With the introduction of Tissue-Culture methods, a number of further combinations were made to survey the different types of effect which might be obtained. For instance, Smyth (1915) studied the effect of *Micrococcus aureus, Bacterium diphtherium, B. pseudodiphtherium, B. typhosus* and *B. prodigiosus* on cultures of chick-embryo heart fibroblasts. A difference between *B. diphtherium* and *B. pseudodiphtherium* was found in that the first inhibited outgrowth, but *B. pseudodiphtherium* permitted some outgrowth and the fragments sometimes pulsated even when laden with bacteria. Diphtheria toxin had less effect on chick tissues than on those of guinea-pig, and nervous tissue was arrested in its growth by lesser amounts of toxin than spleen or heart. In the fifty years since this work the effect of diphtheria toxin on cells in tissue culture has remained an important subject for study. Suzuki (1918) demonstrated that the effect of toxin might be measured by its capacity to inhibit outgrowth of cells, and that heart and ovary cells from rats (resistant to diphtheria toxin) are resistant *in vitro*. Wadsworth and Hoppe (1931) showed that embryonic guinea-pig cardiac muscle neutralized toxin by binding or destroying it. More recently, it has been shown that the effects of toxin may be demonstrated in cell lines and trypsinized cultures (Placido Sousa and Evans, 1957; Lennox and Kaplan, 1957), and the effect of the toxin on such cells has become the object of intensive biochemical study (Strauss and Hendee, 1959; Strauss, 1960; Kato and Pappenheimer, 1960). Protein synthesis as measured by incorporation of S^{35} methionine is inhibited within 2 h (Strauss and Hendee, 1959), but even before this the incorporation of inorganic phosphorus into ATP is inhibited (Kato and Pappenheimer, 1960). Both of these take place long before cell damage is visible. Both effects are prevented if antitoxin is given within one-half hour of the toxin.

The usual reaction of non-pathogenic bacteria and cells was studied by M. R. Lewis (1923) when she followed the fate of *Bacillus radicicola* (a symbiotic bacterium of plant roots) in chick-embryo fibroblasts. At first the bacteria seemed to be stuck onto the surface of the cell by their flagella, then after entry into the cell, they could be seen moving slowly around in the cell. They gradually decreased in size and faded away without the development of a vacuole. If vacuole formation in the cells was stimulated by omitting dextrose from the medium, the ingested organisms were digested more slowly. The bacilli were arranged along the lines of the spindle fibers during the process of mitosis.

The apparent lack of reaction of the host cell illustrated here may also be found in intracellular infections such as *Brucella abortus*, even when studied with high resolution microscopy. Karlsbad, Kessel, de Petris and Monaco (1964), in an electron-microscopic study, found that *Brucella* in guinea-pig monocytes were found within fairly tight vacuoles surrounded by unit membranes, and that the bacteria appeared much as they did when grown outside the cell.

A great deal might be learned from an analysis of various bacterial infections—perhaps in organ cultures. This is suggested by M. R. Lewis' study (1920) on the effects of *Bacillus typhosus* on cultures of epithelial cells of chick-embryo intestine. When these were exposed to a loopfull of these bacteria, the cells developed large numbers of vacuoles throughout their cytoplasm within 1–2½ h. When the cultures were given neutral red before the addition of the bacteria, the vacuoles became intensely red. A few bacteria could be found within the cells after an hour of exposure. Several other types of bacteria did not cause this effect. This rapid formation of vacuoles had some similarities to the changes seen by Hogue (1919) in cells grown in hypotonic solutions, and to that reported by Yang, Strasser and Pomerat (1965) on reversible drug-induced vacuolation.

A specific study of the effect of a "toxin" from a gram-negative bacillus is that of Vicari, Olitzki and Olitzki (1960) who studied a thermolabile toxin from *Shigella dysenteriae* on KB (human cell line) and "human liver cells." Within 30 min of adding 100 minimal cytopathic doses, some cells developed a transparent cytoplasm, others eosinophilic granules. All the cells were damaged within 3 h, and were destroyed by 6 h. A highly purified preparation of the toxin produced the same effect. Although the toxic effect was neutralized by antiserum, the replacement of toxin by antitoxin in the culture even a few minutes after the addition of the toxin did not prevent subsequent destruction. A similar effect of toxin from gram-negative bacilli on cells of a marine invertebrate (*Limulus*) was reported by Shirodkar, Warwick and Bang (1960).

More specific effects on cells were observed in a study by Felton, Gaggero and Pomerat (1954) who showed that *Hemophilus pertussis* caused vacuolation and nuclear distortion of human and cat brain cells, but did not affect cultures of embryo-chick muscle, skin, or of HeLa cells. The inoculated bacteria were found attached to the surface of nerve cells and within the cytoplasm of the cells. The effect was neutralized by antiserum.

A more remarkable series of continuous records of cell injury by staphylococcus toxin and its reversal by antiserum was made by Felton and Pomerat (1962). Nuclear shrinkage, disappearance of nucleoli, and cytoplasmic vacuolation occurred when human amnion cells were exposed to staphylococcus toxin. Treatment with immune (convalescent) sera after the toxic effect appeared caused a reversal of the process, suggesting that this toxin was not irreversibly fixed to the cell. The antiserum may well have gained entrance to the cell by pinocytosis.

A. ACID-FAST BACTERIA

The study of these bacteria within tissue cells has been of particular interest since *M. leprae* is thought to be host dependent and all mycobacteria cause intracellular infections in mesenchyme cells of their many animal hosts. Three aspects which are more thoroughly reviewed elsewhere (Hanks, 1956; Fell and Brieger, 1947) are briefly surveyed here: (1) the growth of acid-fast bacteria within several cell types and the reaction of these; (2) the formation of giant cells under the stimulus of extracts of acid-fast bacteria; (3) the role of allergy in cell destruction.

Smyth (1916) showed that explants of spleen of 14-day or older chick embryos would, when inoculated with human type tubercle bacilli, react with changes characteristic of early tubercle formation. There was a clustering of lymphocytes, then epithelioid cells, a "multiplication of nuclei in the epithelioid cells," then a fusion of epithelioid cells to form giant cells, and finally a degeneration of cells containing bacteria. The reaction of the cells to the presence of acid-fast bacteria may be minimal (Maximow, 1924). Fibrocytes from non-sensitive hosts, e.g. chick embryonic tissues (Fell and Brieger, 1947) or lepromatous tissues (Hanks, 1941), grow normally, dividing their bacterial content almost equally between the two daughter cells. Mouse macrophages infected with rat leprosy bacilli (Chang, 1961) or avian fibroblasts with avian tubercle bacilli (Fell and Brieger, 1947) contain huge numbers of bacteria within the cytoplasm without apparent disturbance (Fig. 2B). On the other hand, rapid destruction of the cell may take place, as with bovine tubercle bacilli in rabbit lymphoid tissue (Maximow, 1928). Comparisons between macrophages and fibroblasts indicate that the former are more destructive to mycobacteria. Infection of explants of embryonic chick tissue (Fell and Brieger, 1947) offers the avian tubercle bacilli several types of cells which they may infect. Phagocytic cells of the lung were able to control the infection for 2–3 weeks. The tissue seemed unharmed. With subcultivation this protection disappeared since the macrophages died; the lung fibrocytes then became packed with bacteria and eventually died following a bursting of the cytoplasm.

Formation of giant cells was early recognized as part of the response to tubercle bacilli. Giant cells have also been studied, particularly by Roizman (1962a, b), in connection with herpes infection, and he has called them polykaryocytes. He has summarized the conditions under which they occur. They may be stimulated by a variety of foreign bodies, one of the favorites being lycopodium spores (Lambert, 1912). A lipopolysaccharide extract from the tubercle bacilli has been shown to stimulate giant cell formation with macrophages (Frederic and Racadot, 1955), with nuclei far more numerous than in any control preparation. Neutral red was rapidly taken up by the giant cell, but was concentrated in one active area.

Rich and Lewis analyzed by tissue-culture techniques the nature of allergy in tuberculosis in 1932. They found that washed cells obtained from either the buffy coat or the spleen of an animal sensitized to

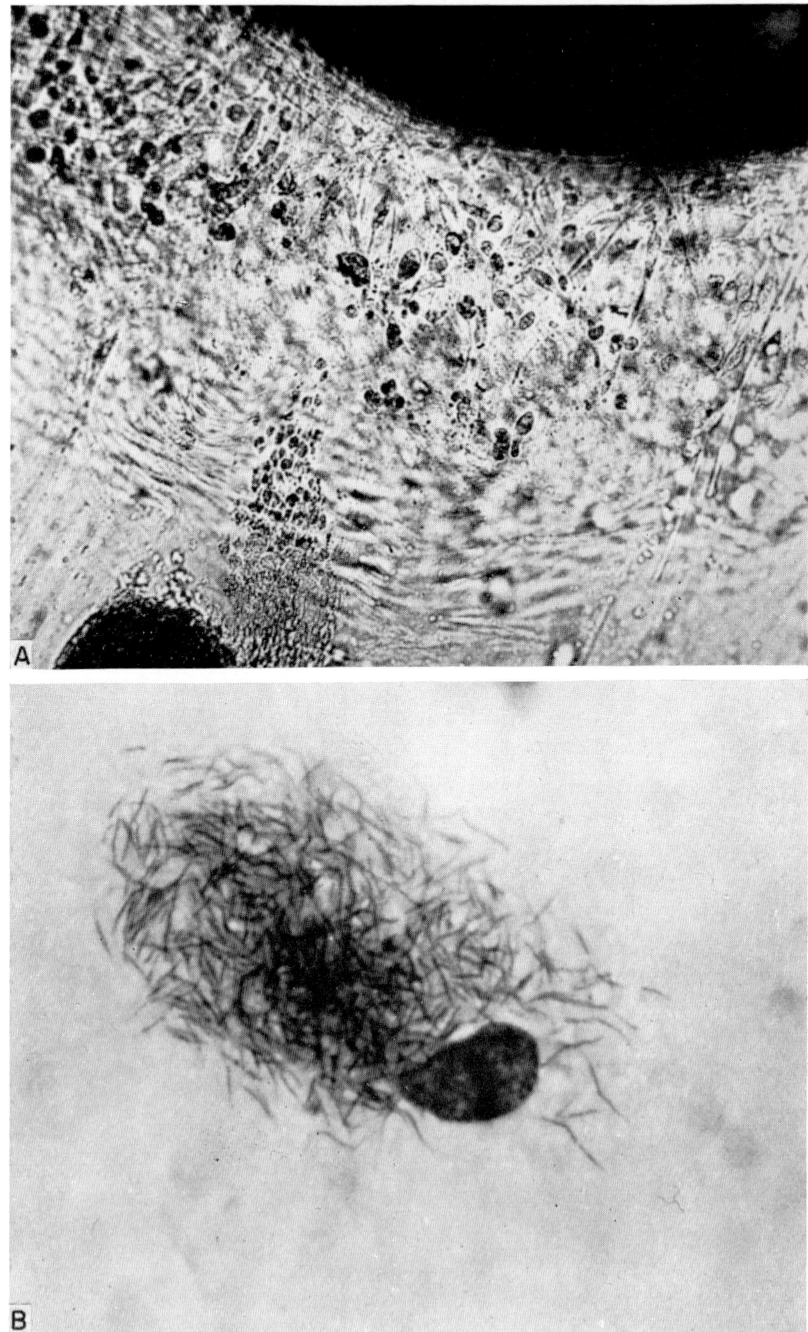

Fig. 2. A. The effect of PPLO on colony of rat cell strain in continuous culture. Courtesy of Dr. G. O. Gey. (A description of this culture appeared in Gey and Gey, 1936.) B. Rat leprosy bacillus in mouse macrophage. Courtesy of Dr. Y. T. Chang.

tuberculin retained their sensitivity to tuberculin *in vitro,* and were rapidly destroyed by a dilution of tuberculin which was harmless to cells from normal guinea-pigs. This work has been confirmed repeatedly and extended to a number of different infections.

B. RICKETTSIA

Although rickettsiae have a remarkable specificity of effect on endothelial cells of the host, there are no studies attempting to analyze this effect. Indeed, there are only a few studies of infected cell cultures under conditions which allow one to determine the sequential growth of rickettsiae in the cells. It is now clear that rickettsiae grow well in actively metabolizing cells and that they do not need static or degenerating cells for growth. *R. burnetti* (Q fever) was grown by Kausche (1952) in chick heart and skeletal muscle fibroblasts. In these they caused large cytoplasmic vacuoles in which long chains of rickettsiae were found. These vacuoles appeared 12 h after infection and were large enough to displace the nucleus. The vacuoles disappeared when aureomycin was added to the culture.

Pinkerton and Hass (1932) found that explants grown at 32°C from the scrotal sac of guinea-pigs in their second or third day of fever, showed large numbers of rickettsiae in the cells. In some cultures the majority of these were found within the nuclei of the infected cell. This was similar to the localization which had been previously determined for this rickettsia in ticks, and is in striking contrast to others such as epidemic typhus and tsutsugamushi disease (scrub typhus). This capacity of *R. rickettsii* to grow not only in the cytoplasm but also in the nucleus was confirmed in cinematographic studies of infection of a rat epithelioid cell strain (14 pf of Gey) (Schaechter, Bozeman and Smadel, 1957), but seems to be partly dependent on the cell type used, for no localization within nuclei was found in any rickettsiae grown in a mouse tumor cell line (MB of de Bruyn) (Bozeman, Hopps, Danauskas, Jackson and Smadel, 1956).

Studies with rickettsiae have shown that the dynamics of entry into cells is not by way of phagocytosis, but depends upon the properties of viable and metabolizing organisms (Cohn, Bozeman, Campell, Humphries and Sawyer, 1959). This penetration is optimal under conditions which enhance the oxidative phosphorylation of rickettsial suspensions and depressed if the rickettsial metabolism is impeded by dinitrophenol, cyanide or azide.

The dynamics of growth within tissue cells have been analyzed by Bozeman *et al.* (1956). They found that the respiration and growth of the MB strain of modified lymphocytes were not modified by infection;

also that the growth of rickettsiae continued even when the growth of host cells had been inhibited by colchicine. Inhibitions of rickettsial growth by chloramphenicol indicated that the rickettsiae conduct an independent synthesis while growing with tissue cells.

Cytologic studies by Schaechter *et al.* (1957) are of interest as one of the first demonstrations that the formation of cell walls by intracellular parasites contributes to the pathogenesis of cell damage. *R. tsutsugamushi* multiplied as small clusters which underwent periodic aggregation and dispersion, and which did not damage heavily infected cells in less than 8 or 9 days. *R. rickettsii* showed much more discrete growth, individual cells undergoing binary fusion, i.e. with more mature walls, and were much more toxic to the 14 pf fibroblasts used as host cells.

IV. Mycoplasma (PPLO)

Bacteriologists have recognized these disease agents for sixty years, but the mycoplasma have recently become targets of interest because of their interaction with mammalian cells. First studied because they were troublesome "contaminants" of cell lines and confused the search for virus–cell reactions, they are receiving serious attention in their own right as intracellular toxic agents.

Bang's (1955a) suggestion that the mycoplasma may have served as the evolutionary origin of the myxovirus group was based on a similarity in morphology, developmental cycle, response to hypertonic saline and a similar place of residence in the respiratory tract. It may now be added that some members of the mycoplasma will agglutinate and hemolyse red cells (Freundt, 1958), that they have an intracellular phase in their "growth" in tissue culture (Hayflick and Stinebring, 1959), and that some recent electron-micrographs of cells infected with mycoplasma show an intimate association, if not joining, of the cell membrane surface with the associated mycoplasma (Edwards and Fogh, 1960). All of these characteristics are well recognized in the myxoviruses. The myxovirus has, of course, lost the independent metabolism of DNA and is smaller. However, the viruses of both the avian leucosis complex and of maedi, a respiratory disease of sheep, are apparently dependent upon the DNA metabolism of their host cells (Thormar, 1965), and there are recent indications that Rous virus may exist in the provirus state as DNA (Temin, 1964).

While most of the mycoplasma probably spend most of their life cycle outside the cell, Nelson (1959) found that some of them grew well not only in tissue cultures, but that they could also grow on heat-killed cells; he has recently studied a murine form of PPLO in living HeLa-cell cultures (Nelson, 1959), and has found that initial multiplication did not effect significant changes in host cell morphology, but that after the second or third replacement of fluid, degenerate cells and a few intracytoplasmic inclusions began to appear in the fluid (Fig. 2A). By the twelfth to fourteenth day of infection, the HeLa cells were almost completely inactivated. The capacity of some (by no means all) of the mycoplasma to destroy cells in tissue culture is now well established (Rovazzo, Luginbuhl and Helmboldt, 1963; Kraemer, Defendi, Hayflick and Manson, 1963; Castrejon-Diez, Fisher and Fisher, 1963). No distinctive cellular changes are recorded, and attention has recently turned to the metabolic changes brought about by the interaction of host cell and parasite.

Chang (1958) studied the variable inositol requirement of different strains of HeLa cells and found no correlation between the presence of contaminating mycoplasmas and the host cell requirement. Powelson (1961) found that host cell metabolism was altered by the addition of mycoplasmas, so that the assimilation and accumulation of several amino acids was changed, presumably independently of the requirements of the mycoplasmas alone. Rouse, Bonifas and Schlesinger (1963) showed that the capacity of adenovirus 2 to produce plaques in tissue culture, which is dependent upon the presence of arginine, could be inhibited by the presence of contaminating mycoplasmas which utilized the arginine. Kraemer (1964) has now found that the lytic activity of several mycoplasmas, including some human strains, for lymphoma cells *in vitro* (Kraemer *et al.*, 1963), is diffusable through porcelain filters and is neutralizable by arginine. Finally, Butler and Leach (1964), in their study of a mycoplasma which originally occurred as a contaminant of HEp 2 cells in a chemostat system, emphasized that parasitism was accompanied by excessive acid production, rounding of cells, and finally degeneration of the cell sheet. When the medium was replaced at 3–4 day intervals, there was no acidity and no apparent effect on the cells.

V. Miyagawanella

A. Life Cycle and Development of Virus Colonies in Vacuoles

Readily visible in the light-microscope as they develop within host cells, these agents were first recognized by Miyagawa, Mitamura, Yaoi, Ishii, Okanishi, Goto and Shimizei (1936). Bland and Canti (1935) followed their development in tissue culture by cinematography.

The concept of a developmental cycle, which had come from studies of smear preparations of infected tissue, was then applied to tissue culture. With increasing sophistication of biochemical techniques, it has become clear that the agents in this group have many of the properties of bacteria. They not only contain both types of nucleic acid, respond to antibiotics, form muramic acid (an amino acid characteristic of bacterial cell walls) (Moulder, 1962), but also have some independent metabolism of glucose, as detected by the formation of radioactive CO_2 from labelled glucose (Weiss, Myers, Dressler and Chun-Hoon, 1964). Thus it is clear that they have evolved to a point of incomplete dependence on host cells. They are not classed as viruses, but are excluded on the basis of arbitrary definitions of viruses and bacteria, definitions which will doubtless be periodically revised. Currently, they may be considered as agents which are clearly dependent upon their host cells, but the nature of the dependence is not known.

Briefly, the sequence of stages involves the following. Shortly after penetration of the cell by the easily recognized elementary body, a large structure, originally called a plaque, develops in the cytoplasm of the host cells. This enlarges and contains both RNA and DNA, and may be clearly shown by fluorochrome staining (Pollard and Starr, 1962) with acridine orange. Thereafter, a large vacuole may develop in the cell; the plaque may then subdivide into a number of elementary bodies which contain DNA (Pollard and Starr, 1962).

The first cinematographic record of this sequence was that of Bland and Canti (1935) who studied the development of psittacosis in tissue culture of chick lung epithelium. Although during the first 8 h of infection they could see elementary bodies outside the cells (Giemsa-stained preparations), it was not until 8–24 h that the homogeneous plaques appeared in the cytoplasm. They were present first at the tip of cell processes, then became more central and larger with time. By 18–24 h there was "colonization" of the larger forms, and by 46 h the elementary bodies were more and more numerous. These authors suggested that a change in viscosity of the matrix in which the elementary bodies develop was responsible for the increase in motility of the particles by 48 h of infection. The nature of this matrix deserves careful study, for trachoma is reported to cause a glycogen matrix in the cells of the conjunctiva *in vivo* (Thygeson, 1959), and there is a brief mention of the occurrence of glycogen-like material in tissue culture-cells infected with trachoma (Lassalle, 1964).

Two simultaneous studies (Manabe, 1939; Gey and Bang, 1939) on the development of lymphogranuloma inguinale showed the same sequence of development in living cells—the formation of vacuoles, then of colonies, and finally the bursting of the cell. In neither of these studies were there any direct effects of the virus on the host cell, except that gradually the entire cytoplasm of the host cell was replaced by the huge amorphous colony of viruses; when the colonies burst, the cells seemed to disintegrate. A series of subsequent electron-microscope studies of meningopneumonitis (Higashi, Tamura and Iwanaga, 1962), trachoma (Armstrong, Valentine and Fildes, 1963), lymphogranuloma venereum (Furness and Csonka, 1963), and other members of the Miyagawanella group (Litwin, Officer, Brown and Moulder, 1961) have all focused attention on the mode of replication of the agent. Armstrong and Reed (1964) changed the method of fixation of the infected cells from one originally designed for animal cells to Kellenberger's method for bacterial cells, and demonstrated that much of the supposed breakdown of virus particles seen early in the course of infection is really an artefact of fixation; and that the appearance of the initial body or plaque in the electron-microscope, when properly preserved, is like a bacterium. The loss of infectivity of the virus during the early stages of development in the host cell (Higashi *et al.*, 1962) is, however, not understood.

B. VARIATION IN EFFECTS ON CELLS

Gey and Bang (1939) found that infection of human fibroblasts with lymphogranuloma venereum was not always manifest by the formation of the typical virus colonies. Infection was apparently latent. Bland and Canti (1935) showed that cells containing motile colonies frequently rounded up and dropped off the glass, but that the virus was contained within the membrane of the vacuole and was not dispersed through the cell. However, Officer and Brown (1960) have shown that a virulent strain of psittacosis, growing either in Chang's liver cell strain or in fetal mouse lung, was dispersed throughout the cytoplasm without preliminary vacuole formation. Virus multiplication followed the usual sequence of initial bodies, then virus colonies, then extensive dispersion through the cytoplasm, then disintegration of the host cell. The apparent cytolytic effects are proposed by Lassalle (1964) as a method of titration of trachoma and of inclusion conjunctivitis. Lysis is of course inherent in the production of plaques, as reported by Higashi *et al.* (1962). These agents are apparently primarily dependent upon the cytoplasm, since they can develop in enucleate fragments of human amnion cells (Crocker and Eastwood, 1963), and in cells disturbed by colchicine (Starr, 1963).

C. PERSISTENT OR CHRONIC INFECTIONS

Gey and Bang (1939) reported that their cultures of human fibroblasts exposed originally to trypsin and infected with lymphogranuloma remained infected for 7 months. Although the mechanism was not investigated, the virus colonies appeared, disappeared and reappeared. Manire and Galasso (1959) have established chronic infections with meningopneumonitis virus, and Officer and Brown (1961) have followed serial changes in Chang's liver cell infected with psittacosis virus for over a year. There was a large variation in the percentage of infected cells, and during the course of infection there was selection for a more virulent virus and for more resistant cells. They suggest, on the basis of stained preparations showing "inclusions" in the cytoplasm of cells in various stages of mitosis, that infection may either persist, or be lost during cell division.

The continued studies of Morgan *et al.* (summarized by Moulder, 1962) on the metabolic factors limiting the growth of this group of agents in the cell in acute experiments, can be expected to explain, at least partially, how such balanced infections are maintained. Pollard and Sharon (1963) produced prolonged latency (4 weeks) by the use of aminopterin. Latency was broken by the addition of folinic acid. Dalen and Morgan (1962) indicate, however, that at least one antimetabolite (2–6 diaminopurine) working on the combined cell-virus system may lose some of its effect on the virus when the host cell also becomes resistant to the drug.

VI. Poxviruses

The poxviruses are now clearly defined as a large group of DNA viruses of a complex structure, having a central nucleoid and a peripheral protein wall, and an intermediate substance between the two. They are ingested into the cell by pinocytotic processes, and shortly after entry into the cytoplasm of the cell lose their protective wall and join the substance of the cytoplasm. Subsequently, a focus of DNA and protein (a virus factory) is formed in this cytoplasm, and within or around this focus complete virus particles are formed. Since the studies of Bland and Robinow (1939), the localization of this virus formation has been clearly recognized, and for this reason the morphological sequences of poxvirus infections are better understood than those of any other viruses. In this section we have arranged the available data under headings which reflect the types of reaction which may be produced in cells.

Among the group are contrasting agents such as fowl-pox virus, which in the natural host has a high affinity for epithelial cells; and fibroma virus of rabbits which causes benign tumors of connective tissue.

A. MOTION

Changes in motion and in reaction to the environment probably develop late in the course of infection. It is not yet possible, however, to describe the various changes in the cell's reaction step by step since poxvirus systems involve a variety of both cells and viruses, and no one system has been sufficiently intensively studied.

Eisenberg-Merling (1940) made careful dark-field observations on living cells infected with vaccinia virus. These were obtained by infecting rabbits on the cornea after scarification. Cells were removed with a thin knife at intervals after infection. The virus was identified in cells as early as 24 h, and at that time the whole surface of many of the cells was studded with elementary bodies which were immobile and adherent to the gel of the cytoplasm. At later stages there seemed to be an oscillatory motion, and in other collections of elementary bodies (virus particles) there was rapid Brownian movement in different parts of the cytoplasm.

In a cinematographic study of trypsinized and Versene-treated embryo fibroblasts infected with ectromelia (mouse pox) after transfer, Habermehl and Diefenthal (1961) found the first morphological changes at 10 h after an infection of a multiplicity of one. At this time there was a decrease in pinocytosis and movement. When individual cells approached each other, there was further decrease of movement (contact inhibition?). Some cells coalesced as early as 13 h, others had incompletely joined at 30 h with a further decrease in movement. There was an increase in elementary bodies in the periphery of the giant cells by 17–27 h, and cytoplasmic strands showed (as in Bland and Robinow (1939) and Robinow's (1950) study of fixed cells) elementary bodies at their tips, which remained when the strand retracted.

B. REACTION TO ENVIRONMENT

A number of authors have noted that various cells exposed to vaccinia or rabbit pox virus are rapidly affected, often rounded, clumped, or agglutinated (Scherer, 1952; Nishmi and Bernkopf, 1958; Bernkopf, Nishmi and Rosin, 1959; Brown, Mayyasi and Officer, 1959a, b; Appleyard, Westwood and Zartouw, 1962). L cells are "agglutinated" by active preparations of virus, a process which begins

7 h after virus is added and is complete by 24 h; u.v.-inactivated preparations also caused agglutination. Clumps of cells were formed in which it was difficult to separate the cytoplasmic portions (Brown *et al.*, 1959a). Only high multiplicities of virus caused this effect, which depended upon temperature and glycolytic cell metabolism, but was not inhibited by azide or amethopterin. The agglutinated cells remained alive for 3 days. Of interest in this connection is the capacity of some of the myxoviruses to form syncytia, apparently due to a resistant portion of the virus. There are also several descriptions of the formation of giant cells in tissue culture during the course of infection by poxviruses (Habermehl and Diefenthal, 1961; Appleyard *et al.* 1962; Plowright, Witcomb and Ferris, 1959; Sokolov and Parfanovich, 1964; Maral, 1957). These, however, do not attain the spectacular size seen in myxovirus and herpes virus infections. Habermehl and Diefenthal (1961) describe the fusion of fibroblasts infected with ectromelia to form such symplasts. In some cases u.v.-irradiated virus killed the cell without multiplying, and could therefore be called "toxic" (Appleyard *et al.*, 1962).

1. *Effect on Macrophages*

Since poxviruses characteristically disseminate through the host, and often multiply in the liver, there has long been an interest in their reaction with macrophages. Beard and Rous (1938) found that vaccinia virus increased in amount when introduced into cultures of Kupffer cells. Florman and Enders (1941) found that vaccinia virus multiplied in roller-tube cultures of rabbit blood macrophages, and Barski, Messore and Lepine (1955) found that vaccine virus destroyed macrophages obtained from the exudate produced by nonspecific irritation of rabbit peritoneum. Finally, Maral (1957) showed that myxoma virus grew well in rabbit peritoneal macrophages and that it caused giant cells to form in these cultures.

2. *Contact Inhibition*

In their study of the effect of u.v.-inactivated vaccinia virus on human amnion cells, Bernkopf *et al.* (1959) commented on the extreme lengthening and thinning of the cytoplasm of these cells after exposure to virus. The homogeneous sheet of cells was transformed into a net-like structure; an illustration shows disoriented cells which today might be interpreted in terms of loss of contact inhibition. Rabbit kidney cells infected with fibroma virus also showed changes in cell morphology when infected with fibroma virus (Hinze and Walker, 1964). Their pattern of growth was altered, and they showed loss of contact inhibition by piling upon each other in a disoriented fashion. Both sheep pox (Plowright and Ferris, 1958) and swine pox (Kasza, Bohl and Jones, 1960) seem to produce similar changes in the orientation of the infected cells, so that an "angular separation" precedes the final rounding up and clumping of the cells.

C. GROWTH

Since Bollinger's description of fowl pox as epithelioma contagiosum (1873), the pox viruses have served as examples of agents which stimulate hyperplasia. Several of them do cause new growths. Fibroma of rabbits and Yaba virus of monkeys (Niven, Armstrong, Andrewes, Pereira and Valentine, 1961) are examples of such benign tumors. Myxomatosis, although causing lumpy swellings, kills primarily through its disseminated destruction of cells. Thus one might ask whether the hyperplasia which is almost a hallmark of the initial lesion may not be reproduced in tissue culture. It was shown that fibroma virus, when infecting rabbit kidney cells, inhibited cell growth for the first 2 days of culture, then the infected cells recovered their growth rate but it did not exceed that of the uninfected controls (Hinze and Walker, 1964). In the various plaque assays which have been developed for determining the titer of pox viruses, a hyperplasia, or rather a piling up of cells at the edge of the plaque is seen (Mayr and Kalcher, 1961; Verna, 1965). The nature of this local increase in cell numbers has not been determined.

Fibroma virus has been reported to form foci of infection on monolayers of rabbit kidney cells under agar, consisting of small piles of cells easily differentiated from the foci of damaged cells produced by myxoma virus (Padgett, Moore and Walker, 1962). Verna (1965) suggests, however, that the type of lesion produced by fibroma virus is dependent upon the cell line used, for he obtained plaques, degeneration and elongation of cells, or foci of cellular aggregates, all with the same strain of virus but with different cell substrates. The simian tumor agent (Yaba) has been grown in cultures of human fetal and adult grivet monkey kidney, and has produced cellular enlargement and intense granulation of the cytoplasm (Niven *et al.*, 1961; Levinthal and Shein, 1964). Continuous transfer of the agent has not been successful.

D. PATHOLOGICAL PRODUCTS

1. *Virus Colonies*

The classic study by Bland and Robinow (1939) on rabbit corneal cells infected *in vitro* with vaccinia clearly showed that the virus particles could be recognized as they developed into colonies within the cell. These authors inoculated small explants of corneal epithelium with purified and concentrated virus for 5 min, then washed away the free virus. The cultures were removed at intervals, fixed with osmic acid vapor, and stained with Giemsa. In the first stage of infection, small homogeneous bodies were found which varied in dimension from the size of an elementary body to that of a staphylococcus. As many as sixty-seven of these were found in one cell. The larger and more distinctly homogeneous bodies appeared later. Small and medium-sized networks then developed within the inclusions and became progressively larger and more numerous during 24 h after infection. Quantitative data on the different types and number of inclusions prevailing at different periods of infection were presented. The elementary bodies, which were readily distinguishable at the start of the infection, disappeared during the middle portion of the cycle and reappeared later, exclusively within the large networks.

Since that time many immunofluorescent, electron-microscopic, autoradiographic and biochemical studies have added much new information but have not changed this basic description. The matrix or inclusion which Bland and Robinow (1939) found to be Feulgen positive is now described as a "virus factory" which contains large amounts of DNA. The individual elementary bodies have been followed as they attach to the cell, are ingested in pinocytotic vacuoles (Dales and Kajuoka, 1964; Nielsen and Peters, 1962) and disappear, to reappear in the virus colony, and the distribution and development of the different antigens within the inclusion have been followed with fluorescent antibody staining. Although the early study of Noyes and Watson (1955) does clearly show viral antigen in the nucleus, the authors emphasize that it occurred only late in the infection, and that at the beginning of infection antigen is limited to the cytoplasm and appears in the area of the inclusion. Subsequent studies confirm this for myxoma (Takahashi, Kato, Kameyama and Kamahora, 1959) and for the different antigens of vaccinia (Loh and Riggs, 1961). In this last study fluorescent antisera were made to three antigens of vaccinia, the LS or soluble antigen, presumed to be on the surface of the virus, the NP (nucleoprotein) and the HA (hemagglutinin). LS antigen appeared in the cytoplasm of HeLa cells 4 h after infection, and was followed 1–2 h later by the NP antigen. The HA antigen appeared finally some 10 h after infection, at a time when mature virus was present.

After ingestion of vaccinia virus into L cells, the following events occur, according to Dales and Kajuoka (1964). The inner core of the virus is released into the cytoplasm by host-cell enzymes. This coincides with the release of the P^{32} labeled phospholipid fraction. Subsequently disruption of the core of the virus, equivalent to the uncoating of the virus (Joklik, 1964), occurs. Kajuoka, Siminovitch and Dales (1964) have then analyzed the formation of the matrix of virus factories by using differential inhibitors of DNA and protein synthesis. Virus damaged by u.v. irradiation before inoculation breaks down, and cores are released into the cytoplasm without provoking new DNA synthesis. Actinomycin (inhibitor of protein synthesis) given to cells during infection allows breakdown, release, and the partial development of viroplasmatic matrices (the Feulgen-positive inclusion of Bland and Robinow), but prevents the formation of complete virus particles. Fluorodeoxyuridine, although preventing DNA synthesis, still allows the formation of the cytoplasmic factories, thus indicating that protein is also formed here. In these, immature forms of vaccinia occur, usually devoid of nucleoids. Mitomycin prevented DNA synthesis and virus formation.

Although this sequence of events now seems well established for the interaction of vaccinia and L cells, and perhaps a few others, this by no means excludes a number of possible variations on the basic theme. For instance, Japanese workers (Kato, Takahashi, Kameyama and Kamahora, 1959a) distinguish two different types of inclusions, designated A and B. Type B inclusions are identified by their positive Feulgen staining and the presence of viral antigen (stained with fluorescent antibody). Type A inclusions are bright red with eosin and, in material fixed in Bouin's fluid and stained in hematoxylin and eosin, surrounded by a clear halo.* Both types of inclusion occur in ectromelia-infected cells, but differ with other poxvirus infections. Kato, Hara, Ogawa, Miyamoto and Kamahora (1963) suggest that different strains of cowpox virus may vary genetically in their capacity to produce virus in association with the inclusions.

Although we have throughout emphasized the limitation of infection to the cytoplasm, there are several clear descriptions of nuclear lesions occurring in cells in tissue culture infected with other poxviruses. Chaproniere (1956) showed that rabbit kidney epithelium infected with myxoma virus develops vacuolated nuclei as well as eosinophilic cytoplasmic masses. Subsequently, empty areas in the nuclei of swine kidney cells infected with swine pox (Kasza *et al.*, 1960), and abnormalities of nuclei of a variety of cells infected with sheep pox, have been clearly demonstrated (Plowright and Ferris, 1958). It is not known whether these areas contain viral antigen, but in the light of Noyes and Watson's (1955) descriptions of vaccinia antigen in the nuclei of HeLa cells, this would be of great interest.

The same general process of the cytoplasmic development of inclusion and virus particles which obtains for vaccinia has been re-

*These inclusions of A type may completely lack virus particles when studied in the electron-microscope, and their nucleoproteins have recently been compared by Ouchterlony methods (Ichihashi and Matsumoto, 1965).

ported for many of the other pox diseases such as ecthyma contagiosum of sheep (Schimmelpfennig and Liess, 1962; Plowright *et al.*, 1959), lumpy skin disease of cattle (Plowright and Witcomb, 1959), ectromelia of mice (Habermehl and Diefenthal, 1961), sheep pox (Plowright and Ferris, 1958) and swine pox (Kasza *et al.*, 1960).

E. SPECIFICITY OF VIRUS EFFECT

There are some indications that pox viruses are adapted to cells of particular animal hosts, and will not grow in cells from "foreign" hosts. For instance, swine pox was carried through five serial passages in swine kidney cells, but failed to grow in kidney cells from several other hosts (Mayr, 1959), and the fowl-pox virus has been grown only in avian tissues. However, myxoma virus has been grown in tissues from resistant hosts such as the squirrel (Chaproniere and Andrewes, 1957), and careful comparative studies are needed before the question of correlation can be determined.

2. *Specificity of Tissue Susceptibility*

Fowl pox, like vaccinia virus, has a special predilection for epithelial tissues. Thus the selective destruction of chick epithelial cells by fowl pox reported by Bang, Levy and Gey (1951), and the selectively rapid destruction of rabbit epithelial cells by vaccinia virus reported by Vieuchange, de Brion and Gruest (1957) come as no surprise. However, throughout this discussion there have been several references to the effect of vaccinia virus on fibroblasts and on L cells (mesodermal) under certain conditions (Spies and Edlinger, 1959). There is good evidence that fowl pox and canary pox can grow in trypsinized chick-embryo fibroblasts (Köhler and Schwöbel, 1956; Mayr and Kalcher, 1959), and plaque methods have been developed for fowl pox (Mayr and Kalcher, 1961) with such trypsinized whole embryo material. This does not contradict the findings of Bang *et al.* (1951) that relatively pure and untrypsinized fibroblasts may be resistant.

A maximum degree of specificity might be apparent in a study of growth in organ cultures. Wolff and de la Forest (1960), in the only report of the production of inclusions by fowl pox virus in tissue culture, have shown that typical fowl pox inclusions are produced in cultures of chick embryo inoculated with the virus; and recently, vaccinia virus has been grown on chick-embryo skin in organ culture (Hodges, 1963; Huang and Bang, 1964). The susceptibility of human embryo skin in organ cultures was tested by Rickenbacher (1964) who found that infection was more successful in cultures from older embryos (60–80 mm in length) than in those from embryos under 60 mm.

The author suggested that vaccinia grew first in the basal layer, which in his cultures developed poorly in the younger embryo preparations.

Inoculation of the scarified cornea of a rabbit with material suspected to be smallpox has been a traditional and favorite method of diagnosis. Kańtoch and Kuczkowska (1964b) have recently shown that organ cultures of rabbit cornea are highly susceptible to smallpox virus, though less so to vaccinia virus. The effect of the virus was readily detected by changes in the transparency, then in the disintegration of the entire culture.

Though one of the original reports of persistent virus infection in tissue culture was that of Feller, Enders and Weller (1940) on the growth of vaccinia in a series of chick embryo roller-tube cultures, relatively few studies are available on persistent or chronic infections with poxviruses. In their study on plasma-clot cultures, Feller *et al.* (1940) showed that despite the presence of vaccinia in high titer over a period of 3 months, there was little apparent effect of the virus on on the growth of the infected chick cardiac cells. These continued to have good lateral diffuse spread and growth, and explants from the infected culture to new tubes grew well. If a large inoculum of virus was used, destruction did follow, but this was replaced by proliferation from the original explant.

In a similar set of cultures of chick fibroblasts, macrophages and epithelium, Bang *et al.* (1951) found persistent infection of the fibroblasts in the absence of cellular destruction or inclusions. Finally, Kato, Takahashi, Kameyama, Morita and Kamahora (1959b) have reported that both rabbit myxoma and fibroma produce "carrier" cultures in the human amnion cell line (FL), and that the growth rate of these trypsinized cultures is somewhat decreased.

VII. Herpes Viruses

Although this classification now includes a large number of different agents such as chicken pox and salivary gland viruses, most experimental work has been done with herpes virus of man, and most of this in turn with epithelial cell cultures. Relatively little has been done with fibroblasts, and none with macrophages. The mode of entry into cells seems to be the same as with poxviruses, through pinocytosis and subsequent digestion of the outer coat of the virus (Epstein, Hummeler and Berkaloff, 1964).

A. Motion

Continuous cinematographic observations with phase contrast of rabbit kidney cells infected with a strain of virus isolated from a case of human stomatitis, but carried in rabbit kidney, were performed by Barski and Robineaux (1959) (Robineaux, film). No changes in the surface activity of cells, or in cytoplasmic movement were noted until late in infection. Mitochondria and cytoplasmic organization remained normal until after nuclear changes (see pp. 178–179) had appeared. In a more detailed study of the same phenomenon, Falke and Richter (1961) showed that nuclear rotation persisted in cultures infected with Herpes B virus (rhesus monkeys) after even the nuclei had been greatly changed and contained crystals, and that in some areas in the giant cell the movement of granules was stopped while in others it seemed to be increased.

B. REACTION TO ENVIRONMENT

Cells infected with this group of viruses have not shown changes in orientation, or lost their adherence to the substrate until the terminal stages of infection.

Although there is no reported loss of contact inhibition as such, one of the most remarkable effects is the loss of cell boundaries by the infected cells as a preamble to the formation of giant cells (Sosa-Martinez, Gutierrez-Villegas and Sosa, 1955). The cinematography mentioned above (Barski and Robineaux, 1959; Robineaux, film; Falke and Richter, 1961) has established that these cells are formed by the fusion of one cell with another, a suggestion previously made by Ross and Orlans (1958) and Stoker (1958) on the basis of stained material. Several authors (Stoker, 1958; Roizman, 1962a, b; Bungay and Watkins, 1964) believe that this is caused by the combination of an infected cell with an uninfected cell. However (see below), this does not exclude effects of the virus on division of nuclei (Wildy, Smith, Newton and Dendy, 1961) or inadequate separation of the cytoplasm as an accessory mechanism of virus effect, phenomena known to occur under slightly different conditions.

Both the type of cell (Crandell, 1959) and the strain of virus may affect the occurrence of giant cells. Herpes simplex infection of mouse fibroblasts produced no giant cells (Felgenhauer and Stammler, 1962). Different strains of virus differ rather markedly, some strains inducing giant cells, other causing pock formation (Gray, Tokumaru and Scott, 1958; Falke, 1961; Nii, 1961; Scott, McLeod and Tokumaru, 1961; Schneweiss, 1962; Wheeler, 1964). Pseudorabies also has been shown to produce rounding degeneration with one strain of virus and giant-cell formation with another (Tokumaru, 1957).

The argument that the fusion which results in a giant cell is fusion of an infected cell with a normal cell is based on indirect evidence.

Giant cells are formed as single foci spreading from the initially infected cell despite the presence of antiserum. They may occur before the release of infectious virus can be detected in the surrounding fluid. The proportion of giant cells to other types of pathological change in a culture is inversely related to the dosage of virus (Roizman, 1962a, b; Bungay and Watkins, 1964). In a cinematographic study of infection of HeLa cells by herpes virus, fusion began 8 h after infection. Addition of a metabolic inhibitor (IDU) to these infected cultures prevented fusion if the IDU was added within 6 h of infection, but at 7 h fusion was not prevented (Bungay and Watkins, 1964).

The argument that an infected cell fuses with a normal cell, however, seems to run counter to the findings with myxoviruses in which (at least Parainfluenza 1—Sendai) a fusion factor present in the virus may cause the fusion of previously normal cells within half an hour after their exposure to high multiplicities of virus.

Since it is clear that herpes virus in one infected cell may be transmitted to uninfected cells despite the presence of antibody, it seems likely that this initial transfer of infection might involve fusion at one spot. Falke and Richter (1961) have in cinematographic studies followed at 30 sec intervals the formation of delicate processes extending from the giant cell to neighboring single, presumably uninfected, cells and the exchange of granules between these cells. According to them, fusion does not take place for several hours after this preliminary granule exchange, which in some cases was followed by temporary reseparation of the two cells. Contact again took place and broader bands formed, then gradually a common pool of cytoplasm was formed. No massive inpouring of material from one cell to another occurred. If these observations are correct, it would seem that the first step is the infection of the normal cell through a narrow, possibly temporary, bridge. The subsequent time interval before real fusion occurs would allow for the receptor cell to change to one whose cell surface has become more like that of the giant cell to which it *subsequently* fuses. These observations then do not support the idea that there is a continuous sequential joining of infected and uninfected cell surface, but at the same time they explain the evidence used to support the idea of a joining together of infected and uninfected cells. They thus fully support Roizman's alternative explanation of giant cell formation, i.e. that the giant cells (polykaryocytes) arise "by fusion . . . of cells differing in time of infection" (Roizman, 1962b).

Shortly after the cells fuse, the nucleus of the new cell may migrate to join the collection of nuclei of the giant cell. The mechanism of this migration has not been investigated. Despite the fact that single particles of virus initiate both effects, cell-killing effects are apparently three times more effective than are focus-forming lesions on HeLa cells (Vantsis and Wildy, 1962), which raises the question whether two populations of virus particles are present or whether the probability of initiating a giant-cell focus is one-third that of killing the cells (Watkins, 1964).

C. FEEDING

No particular changes involving ingestion of fluid or solid material have been recorded, but studies have not been directed to this point. Furthermore, the giant cells, unlike those of measles, have not been described as "red plaques", indicating that there is no increased pinocytotic uptake of neutral red. Finally, there is no large paranuclear mass (hypertrophied Golgi apparatus?) formed during the course of infection, which might indicate a disorder of digestion or secretion.

D. GROWTH

1. *Proliferation*

Among the various strains of herpes that have been studied are some which have been called proliferative (Gray *et al.*, 1958; Scott *et al.*, 1961; Schneweiss, 1962). This effect, apparently first noticed by Gray, Tokumaru and Scott (1958), referred to the formation of a pock in tissue culture which consisted of rounded cells apparently heaped up in one place. It was further shown that there was in such tissue cultures (of HeLa cells) an increase of the number of cells (nuclei?), not however exceeding twice the original number, an increase which did not appear in cultures infected with the other strains of virus, and which did not persist. Hinze and Walker (1961) found that human conjunctival cells and KB cells, after prolonged exposure to herpes virus, developed a new growth pattern. Heaps of cells fifteen to twenty cells thick occurred when these clones of cells were grown in selected human sera, but not in horse sera. A variety of attempts to find persistent virus were negative.

2. *Effect on Mitosis*

Such an effect, though temporary, raises the question of causation, and focuses attention on the relationships of RNA and DNA in the infected cell, and the effect of the virus on nuclear division. Stoker and Newton (1959) have shown by a study of single cells isolated in microdrops from a previously infected suspension of HeLa cells that although almost half of the control cells had divided within 24 h of isolation, only 12% of the cells exposed to a multiplicity of 1·0 had divided and only 5% of those exposed to a multiplicity of 2·7. Thus it would seem that one infectious unit was sufficient to inhibit mitosis. They obtained inhibition of cell division even when virus was first added to cells made parasynchronous in division time by exposure to cold some 90 min before the expected division time. This of course does not exclude the possibility that other strains of virus or cells might permit division. Reissig and Kaplan (1960) have shown that rabbit kidney cells infected with pseudorabies virus and kept isolated from each other were stimulated by infection, so that 40–50% divided amitotically within 10 h of infection. In other experiments with the same virus and cell-strain, cells were shown to fuse and form syncytia when sufficient cells were present to make contact with each other (Kaplan and Vatter, 1959).

Roizman (1961) studied the recruitment of cells in various stages of nuclear division into giant cells. He found that cells treated with colchicine formed smaller and fewer syncytia, and that syncytia were frequently surrounded by numerous cells in mitosis. He concluded that cells may be incorporated into syncytia when the nucleus is in interphase or prophase, and that colchicine prolongs the resistant phase of infection by halting mitosis.

More direct effects of the virus on the mitotic activity of the host cell were obtained by Hampar and Ellison (1963) who showed that the plating efficiency of a line (MGII) of Chinese hamster cells was not reduced by infection with as much as 10^4 infectious particles/cell, if the infected cells were not disturbed. However, if the cell and virus mixture was shaken for 1 h at 37°C, a marked reduction in plating efficiency was obtained. Such shaking did not damage uninfected cells. Chromosome aberrations were apparent during the first division of infected shaken cells. These consisted of multiple breaks and were correlated with the rate of killing. In the unshaken infected clones there was no greater number of abnormal chromosomes than in control cells. Subsequently, they showed (Hampar and Ellison, 1964) that once a cell, infected or uninfected, started to divide, this division proceeded uninterrupted. They believe that cell death produced by virus plus shaking is restricted to the cells which reach division first after infection.

Since herpes virus has this remarkable killing effect and has a special capacity to grow within the nucleus, chromosomal changes with infection might well be expected. That these occur in infected cells was first shown by Hampar and Ellison (1961), and that the changes are not random in distribution was established by Stich, Hsu and Rapp (1964). Human embryonic lung and Chinese hamster lung cells developed chromatid gaps and breaks, particularly in region 3 of the X chromosome and region 7 of chromosome 1 of the hamster cells.

3. *Cytomegalic Viruses* (*Salivary Gland Viruses*)

These agents, which are found chiefly in the salivary glands of mice, guinea-pigs, man and other animals, have recently been included with the herpes viruses because of the presence of intranuclear inclusions, and the similarity of physical and biological properties. However, they have the special characteristic of causing a great increase in the size of the cell which is infected. Both the nucleus and the cytoplasm are involved, and most cells remain with one nucleus (Weller, 1956–57; Smith, 1959). Some may have two or three nuclei, each with a characteristic eosinophilic lesion. Different viruses from different hosts seemed to maintain their specificity in tissue culture, infecting only cells of the appropriate species, but recent isolates of a cytomegalic virus from *Cercopithecus* monkey tissues are able to grow in human cells (Black, Hartley and Rowe, 1963). Salivary gland from 3–5-day-old mice grew in an organoid manner on Maximow slides and developed typical intranuclear lesions by the fifth day and eventually disintegrated (Grand, 1958). The nature of the stimulus which causes the general increase in size of both epithelial cells and fibroblasts when infected with these agents is not known.

4. *Pathological Products*

It is now perfectly clear that the well-known intranuclear lesion of herpes simplex which is common to the entire group of herpes viruses is due to an early selective effect of the virus on the nucleus. Scott, Burgoon, Coriell and Blank (1953) showed that nuclear changes occurred in rabbit corneal cells during the latent period of 2–6 h when infectivity was low, and that these changes later progressed to form the fully developed nuclear lesion. Reissig and Melnick (1955) correlated the appearance of the swelling of the cells, the disappearance of the nucleolus, and the margination and gradual decrease in nuclear chromatin with the growth of the virus. They showed that the nuclear lesion, which consists of a mass of homogeneous eosinophilic material, corresponded to the areas from which the chromatin had disappeared, thus supporting the previous evidence of Gray and Scott (1954) that the virus is intranuclear. The intranuclear concentration of the virus, and its presumptive later appearance in the cytoplasm, is fully supported by the electron-microscope studies of Stoker, Smith and Ross (1958), Reissig and Melnick (1955), Morgan, Rose, Holden and Jones (1959) and Epstein (1962). The latter authors have also shown virus protruding from the surface of the cells, so that virus apparently may be released through microvilli in the manner frequently demonstrated for myxoviruses.

Ross and Orlans (1958) showed that the classical HF strain of herpes virus of man caused a redistribution of nucleic acid and the appearance of specific antigen in the nuclei of HeLa cells along with the complete breakdown of particulate DNA and the deposition of DNA near the membrane. The first abnormality, an irregularity of the nucleoli, appeared at 9 h. Faint intranuclear fluorescence (after staining with fluorescent antibody) appeared at 16 h. The exact sequence of events was difficult to determine since there was technical difficulty in infecting all the cells at once, and obtaining a regular sequence of infection. Suspensions of FL cells treated with varying amounts of *p*-fluorophenylalanine and phenylalanine showed that the external coat formation of the virus was inhibited, so that single membrane particles accumulated within the nucleus (Chitwood and Bracken, 1964). Nucleic acid and viral antigens have also been determined sequentially in cells infected with bovine rhinotracheitis (Armstrong, Pereira and Andrewes, 1961), in horse kidney cells infected with equine rhinopneumonitis (Ishizaki, Shimizu and Matumoto, 1962), and in chick-embryo cells infected with pseudorabies virus (Albrecht, Blaskovic, Jakubik and Lesso, 1963). These confirm the nuclear lesions and apparent early localization of virus in the nucleus. In the study of Ishizaki *et al.* (1962) an additional differentiation of S and V antigens was made, and it was suggested that the S antigen was synthesized in the nucleus, followed by V antigen appearance in the cytoplasm.

Munk and Sauer (1963) did autoradiographic studies with tritiated thymidine on HeLa cells infected with herpes virus of man. In cells receiving the marker before infection, DNA labelling was apparent in the periphery of the nuclear lesion, whereas those given the thymidine at the time of infection or afterwards, showed labelling in the center of the nucleus, again supporting the idea that cell DNA metabolism is interrupted and that viral synthesis takes place in the nucleus.

E. RESPONSE OF ENTIRE CULTURES

The amazing progress of infection through the culture by the formation of syncytia which continue to spread, and at the same time leave behind a central necrotic area, is illustrated in Fig. 3A. The contiguous nature of this spread and the lack of influence of antibody (Hoggan and Roizman, 1959a, b) early suggested that it is due to a phase of virus produced before fully infectious virus is released. The well-known effect of increased temperature on the eruption of fever blisters (herpes simplex) in man has led to a number of studies of the effect of temperature on production of virus and spread from cell to cell. Wheeler (1958) showed that little or no virus was produced at

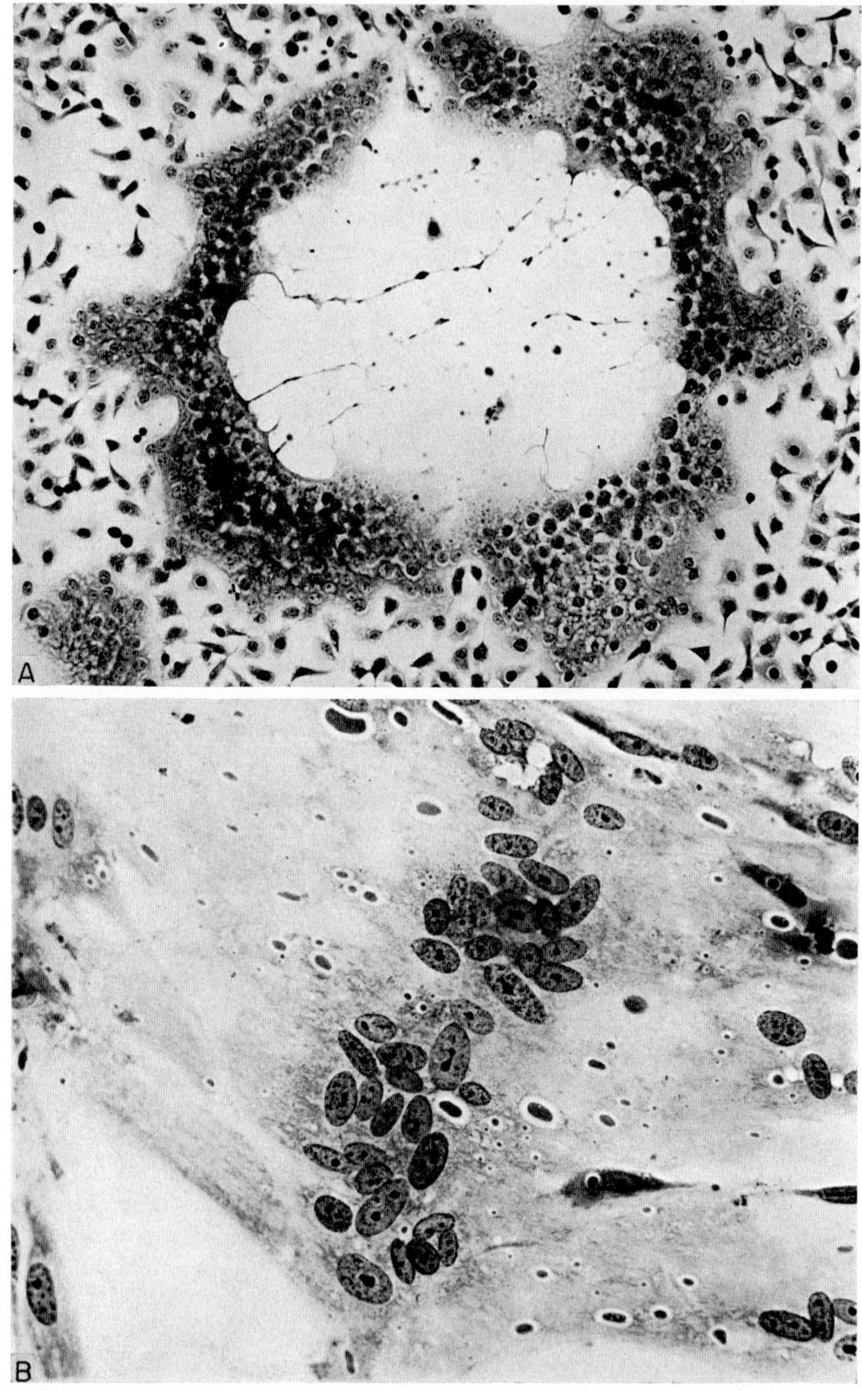

Fig. 3. A. Giant cell formation with central necroses, *Herpes simplex*. Courtesy of Dr. B. Roizman. B. Respiratory syncytial virus on human diploid cells. Courtesy of Mr. W. Ota.

temperatures of 20–27°C, and that the largest amount was produced at 35°C, Hoggan, Roizman and Turner (1960) and Hoggan and Roizman (1959b) used the fact that the plaque grew in size to determine rate of growth and spread of virus, and found that the largest plaques were produced at 37°C 4 days after infection. Hoggan, Roizman and Roane (1961) found antigen stained by fluorescent antibody in the cytoplasmic processes of human amnion cells infected with a large plaque former, but did not detect it in cells infected with a micro-plaque strain of virus. This is further evidence of spread by this mechanism. Persistent infections of HeLa and Detroit 6 cells have been maintained in the presence of antibody (Szanto, 1963).

Herpes simplex has been grown in cultures of human embryonic skin (Bang and Niven, 1958; McGowan and Bang, 1960; McGowan, 1963), and in these forms individual vesicles much like those produced in the intact human were produced. The influence of various environmental factors on such a lesion has not been studied.

Chicken Pox and Herpes Zoster

Since the original work of Weller (1956–57) it has been recognized that this virus can grow readily in a variety of human tissues and in several cell lines. It produces focal lesions which progressively spread from cell to cell and release a minimum amount of virus into the surrounding fluid. The virus (chicken pox and herpes zoster are established as one agent causing different symptoms) causes giant cells and intranuclear lesions identical to those produced by other members of the group (Taylor-Robinson, 1959). Spread is by contiguity, and antiserum has no effect on the spread of the established infections, even though it neutralizes virus obtained directly from human vesicle fluid. Rapp and Vanderslice (1964) followed the spread of infection by determining the number of infected cells (plaque counts) and the amount of immunofluorescence. Eight to sixteen hours were required to infect neighboring cells. IUDR prevented spread of infection from cell to cell, but did not eradicate the infection. With the exception of infection of human thyroid cells (Count, 1963), which can be disrupted ultrasonically to yield neutralizable virus, the virus seems to persist within the cells in an apparently non-infectious condition. No studies of the growth of the agent in differentiated human skin have been reported.

VIII. Adenoviruses

Adenoviruses affect man and a variety of animals. They were first recognized in Tissue Culture, and Tissue Culture is still almost the only means by which they can be studied.

A. MOTION

There are at least five cinematographic or serial photographic studies of cells infected with one or another adenovirus (Balducci and Castelli, 1957; Klöne and Oelrichs, 1958; Klöne, 1958; Pruniéras, Chardonnet and Schier, 1962a; Fonbrune and Reculard, 1963). In all of these the paramount interests were development of the remarkable intranuclear lesion and retraction of the infected cell from the glass. One gleans from these that there are no particular changes of movement of infected cells in relation to each other, nor is there any evident disturbance of internal motion. There seems to be no record in respect to nuclear rotation. One study on canine hepatitis (Fonbrune and Reculard, 1963) calls attention to the intense motion of the nuclear elements which form a chromatin network typical of prophase, but which is not followed by cell division. This may represent one of the earlier stages of the nuclear lesion (see below).

B. REACTION TO ENVIRONMENT

Adherence to Glass Substrate

Subsequent to the recognition of this group of viruses through their generally destructive effect on various human cell lines (Rowe, Huebner, Gilmore, Parrott and Ward, 1953; Hilleman and Werner, 1954), a series of remarkable changes in the nuclei of infected cells was discovered. These changes included the development of crystals visible in the living cells (Leuchtenberger and Boyer, 1957) and Kjellén, Lagermalm, Svedmyr and Thorsson (1955), Lagermalm, Kjellén, Thorsson and Svedmyr (1957), Harford, Hamlin, Parker and van Ravenswaay (1956), Morgan, Howe, Rose and Moore (1956), Boyer, Leuchtenberger and Ginsberg (1957) have made an electron-microscope analysis of these crystals after fixation.

The first recognized "cytopathic effect" consisted of rounding of cells, clumping of groups of cells, then retraction and separation from glass (Rowe, *et al.*, 1953; Hilleman and Werner, 1954). Almost simultaneously three groups of workers (Rowe, Hartley, Roizman and Levy, 1958; Pereira, 1958; Everett and Ginsberg, 1958) recognized that this effect occurred within a few hours after adding large amounts of virus, and that it is due to a protein which is separable from the virus by centrifugation. Since its discovery, there has been little investigation into the details of how and where it produces its primary effect on the cell. The effect is reversible and may directly involve the cell membrane. Presumably the remarkable cytoplasmic retraction, formation of clumps of material, and the apparent disappearance of mitochondria pictured by Klöne (1958) in his sequential studies of adenovirus effect on flattened epithelial cells is due to this associated viral component. If small inocula of virus are used, this effect may not appear until sufficient multiplication of virus has taken place. It is not known whether the stimulating effect of arginine reported by Bonifas and Schlesinger (1959) and confirmed by Ueda, Toyoshima and Seto (1963) has any relation to the production of this early cytopathic protein factor.

C. FEEDING

Ginsberg (1957) states, in a general discussion of adenoviruses, that infected cells reacted to methylene blue, Janus green or neutral red in the same fashion as normal cells despite great changes in their morphology. There are, however, no quantitative studies to determine whether dye intake or phagocytic capacity is changed in infected cells.

D. GROWTH AND TRANSFORMATION

There has, in general, been insufficient investigation of the effects of virus infections on the growth of cells, and this is particularly true of adenoviruses. Since Trentin, Yabe and Taylor (1962) showed that injection of newborn hamsters with adenovirus 12 (and subsequently several others) caused tumors, in much the same way as the papova viruses do, this phase of the virus effect has been under intensive study.

There is an increased rate of growth of infected HeLa cells in comparison with uninfected HeLa cells, if they are initially maintained in human serum (Van Hoosier, Gist, Taylor and Trentin, 1964) (see below). McBride and Wiener (1964) reported the transformation of hamster kidney cells *in vitro* by human adenovirus 12, evinced by a new growth potential and an epithelial pattern of the cells, and the acquisition of adenovirus C.F. antigen despite the loss of infectious virus. A re-examination of "tumor"—or, better, cellular—antigens present in the cell by using antisera from hamsters carrying adeno-induced tumors has yielded new information. Pope and Rowe (1964b) have reported the presence of flecks of antigen in both the nucleus and cytoplasm of hamster and mouse adeno-tumor cells, and in human and hamster cells infected by virus *in vitro,* in which antigen is detected by fluorescent antibody. This antigen appeared as early as 24 h after infection. Thus, as with the papova virus, antibody prepared from tumor-bearing animals revealed a new antigen involved in the early stage of virus growth, and this persisted in the tumor cell which was induced by this virus.

Chromosome structure is disturbed during the process of growth of adenovirus 12 in hamster cells. Stich, Van Hoosier and Trentin (1964) report that these fairly frequent changes involving reduplications and breaks, rather closely resemble those induced by radiation, but differ from the effect of herpes virus on the same cell type.

E. PATHOLOGICAL EFFECTS

The rapid accumulation of knowledge of the remarkable effect of these viruses on the nuclei of cells is well summarized by Dingle and Ginsberg (1959) from whose account much of the next section is taken. As a result of infection, there is an increased synthesis of DNA, increased utilization of glucose, and increased accumulation of organic acids. This causes increased acidity of the cultures, which is in contrast to the effects of other "lytic" viruses but similar to those of Rous virus. Different adenoviruses produce different alterations in the infected cell nuclei of HeLa or human amniotic cells.

One group (types 1, 2, 5, and 6) show multiple well-defined eosinophilic Feulgen-negative inclusions within the nuclei 14–16 h after viral inoculation. These later develop granular Feulgen-positive cores. The outlines of the original inclusions are lost, and basophillic granular clusters are spaced throughout an enlarged nucleus. Infection by some type 5 strains is followed by the formation of Feulgen-negative eosinophilic intranuclear crystals.

The nuclear changes produced by types 3, 4 and 7 are very different. At 14 h there are irregular granular eosinophilic masses and the chromatin is rearranged into a lattice or network pattern. With type 7, well-defined eosinophilic bodies appear. The nucleus becomes larger and distorted. The clear peripheral zone becomes wider and the central area more basophilic. The central mass and the beaded network are Feulgen-positive. Sharp-edged crystal-like masses appear. They may either be Feulgen-positive or negative. Electron-microscopy shows the crystal to consist of virus particles.

Since this summary was written, several other studies have added details of variation of sequence in other strains of adenovirus and in canine hepatitis (Moulton and Frazier, 1961; Chardonnet, Pruniéras and Schier, 1961; Pruniéras, Chardonnet and Schier, 1962a, b; Nosik and Klisenko, 1963). Acid phosphatase was followed histochemically by Chardonnet, Pruniéras and Schier (1962) in renal cells infected by type 1. They found a decrease in staining by the lead precipitate method, particularly as the round cells were formed. There was, however, an increase in staining of the Golgi area during the primary period of infection. Finally, Mayor (1964) has found a labile intranuclear RNA associated with the development of adenoviruses 3 and 7. It was detected by combining the use of specific enzyme digestion with acridine-orange staining (at controlled levels of acidity) for nucleic acids. This labile RNA appeared in the nucleus 16–20 h after infection, and accumulated in greater amounts if viral protein synthesis was inhibited by puromycin. Intranuclear double-stranded DNA continued to form, and thus the labile RNA presumably results from the viral DNA.

F. RESPONSE OF ENTIRE CULTURE

Persistent or chronic infections with adenoviruses were at first possible only in the presence of antisera. However, Van Hoosier *et al.* (1964) have shown that a carrier culture may be established in HeLa cells if an inhibitor in human serum is present at first, but that after a few transfers the cultures maintained infection and viability in the absence of human serum. They showed some cellular loss with the continuous infection, and were resistant to superinfection. The mechanism is not yet understood.

A new method of studying the production of viral antigens by the entire colony has been developed by Mata (1963). In this the virus tissue culture is grown in a well of agar, and the antigens which are produced diffuse through to meet antibody, much as in the Ouchterlony plates. With adenovirus infection, both group- and type-specific antigen-antibody lines were obtained.

Organ Cultures

De LaForest (1961) has studied the lesions produced by the avian adenovirus "Gal" in several tissues of chick embryos grown as organized bits on an agar substrate. Infection was manifested by variable necrosis and cell rounding, basophilic intranuclear inclusions, and a tendency to form cytoplasmic vacuoles. The best lesions were obtained in liver and mesonephros, but were few in gonadal explants. Barski, Kourilsky and Cornefert (1957) report the relative resistance of human and monkey respiratory epithelium to destruction by adenoviruses, but at the same time show a viral lesion with cell destruction 6 days after infection. Hoorn (1964) has also shown that human fetal respiratory mucosa is susceptible to adenovirus when grown in organ culture.

Adenovirus 3 has apparently been grown in less organized cultures of human bronchial epithelium (Maddi, 1963) in Maximow slides. In these cultures it produced intranuclear and intracytoplasmic inclusions in some of the epithelial and ciliated cells. No pictures were published.

IX. Papova Viruses

Interest in this group of agents (Melnick, 1962) has centered on their capacity to cause tumors. *In vitro* preparations of infected cells brought to light the fact that while some infected cells were destroyed, others were altered in their growth patterns, particularly in their relation to each other. This phenomenon of "transformation" has received a major share of attention. Transformation has been defined (Medina and Sachs, 1961) as a stable non-lytic change in the cell produced as as the result of virus infection. While, therefore, most of the recent data on the group concerns cell destructive effects and transformation, a great deal of information will doubtless accumulate in the near future on more general aspects of papova virus cytopathology.

A. Destructive Effects

The simian virus, SV_{40} (vacuolating virus of monkeys), was first recognized when the African Green monkey *Cercopithecus aethiops* was used as a source of kidney cells for studies of poliomyelitis (Melnick, 1962). When fluids from tissue cultures of rhesus monkey kidney cells were inoculated into Green Monkey kidney cells, large cytoplasmic vacuoles appeared in the latter. This effect was not regularly produced in cultures of rhesus kidney cells themselves. The SV_{40} virus was subsequently found as a contaminant in a variety of stocks of different viruses and vaccines (Sweet and Hilleman, 1960).

Hsiung and Gaylord (1961) have described in some detail the effect of this virus on patas monkey cells. They recognized marked nuclear enlargements and nuclear inclusions which preceded the vacuolation of the cytoplasm. The vacuoles varied greatly in size and number, in many instances replacing the entire cytoplasm by a honeycomb effect. Although the nuclear acidophilic and Feulgen-positive inclusions, which contain a great number of virus particles (Gaylord and Hsiung, 1961; Tournier, Granboulan and Bernhard, 1961), seemed to develop independently of the vacuolation, the authors were unable to get any evidence by neutralization, sensitivity to ether, or filtration, that two agents were producing the two effects. The separate effects on nuclei and cytoplasm might be due to the mixed cellular components of cultures of trypsinized monkey kidney.

Mayor, Stinebaugh, Jamison, Jordan and Melnick (1962) have followed changes at hourly intervals in *Cercopithecus* cells inoculated with a multiplicity of 10/cell. The eclipse period was about 20 h; fluorescent antibody showed that diffuse viral antigen first appeared

18 h after inoculation. By 24 h, 4% of the cells had particulate antigen in the nuclei, and there was an occasional stained nucleolus. By 56 h most of the antigen was present in the cytoplasm and no further nuclear fluorescence was detectable. Electron-microscope sections of the vacuolated cells showed virus particles on the membranes of the distended empty vacuoles. None of the authors (Melnick, 1962; Hsiung and Gaylord, 1961; Gaylord and Hsiung, 1961; Mayor *et al.*, 1962) has described stainable material in the vacuoles, and it seems likely that the osmoregulation of the cytoplasm has been grossly disturbed, and that the vacuoles contain little more than fluid and soluble ions. Such an effect might be more apparent in kidney cells than in cells from elsewhere in the body.

In a recent re-examination (Easton, 1964) of the question of the effect of this virus on rhesus monkey cells, a cytopathic effect on primary cell cultures was found. The virus grew slowly, and the infected cells eventually became detached from the glass, so that by day 36 of infection only an occasional cell was still attached to the glass substrate. Syncytial formation and vacuoles were not found, though they are frequently present in primary trypsinyzed rhesus monkey kidney cells, presumably due to another agent.

A variety of viruses may be found in other monkey cells. The lesions produced in Vervet (*Cercopithecus aethiops pygerythrus*) kidney cells have been carefully described by Malherbe and Harwin (1963). They refer to one virus which produced nuclear hypertrophy similar to that of SV_{40}, but the virus did not cause vacuolation and was not significantly neutralized by SV_{40} sera. It is apparent that a great deal more knowledge is needed on the classification of the different monkey agents before an orderly description of their effects on different cells can be given.

B. POLYOMA VIRUS

The demonstration that the viral initiator of parotid tumors in mice may be grown in Tissue Cultures of monkey kidney (Stewart, Eddy, Gochenour, Borgese and Grubbs, 1957) and subsequently in trypsinized mouse-embryo cultures (Eddy, Stewart and Berkeley, 1958) led to a search for cell changes associated with the growth of the virus. Few changes were noted in monkey kidney or in the mouse-embryo cultures at first, but with passage, patches of small dark cells appeared among the sheets of normal cells. The number of pyknotic cells increased for 1–2 weeks, at which time the majority of cells were affected. Other authors (Rabson and Legallais, 1959; Dawe, Law and Dunn, 1959) have subsequently shown that the virus may be carried for long periods in cultures of lymphoma cells, and that in these there may be scattered necrotic cells, and other cells with nuclear enlargement and margination of the chromatin. In Dawe's study (1959), clumping of cells and multinucleated giant cells were also found, but later studies by Love and Rabson (1959) failed to show an increase in giant cells above that found in the uninfected lymphoma cells.

The destructive effect of the virus was used to produce plaques in Tissue Culture by Stewart, Eddy, Stanton and Lee (1959), and subsequently by Winocour and Sachs (1959).

By the use of fluorescent antibody, viral antigen was detected in a few scattered nuclei 2–3 days after infection of mouse-embryo cells with large amounts of virus. By 4 days, most of the cells were infected, and most of the antigen was still in the nuclei (Henle, Deinhardt and Rodriguez, 1959; Malmgren, Rabotti and Rabson, 1960; Bereczky, Dmochowski, and Grey, 1961). By 1 week, many cells showed considerable cytoplasmic antigen, while the nuclei were non-fluorescent, and cell destruction had begun (Henle *et al.*, 1959); reactions reminiscent of those to SV_{40}. Love and Rabson (1959), in a detailed cytochemical study of infection of murine lymphoma cells, showed an alteration in the ribonucleoproteins of the parachromatin of the nucleolus and nucleoplasm, with enlargement of the nuclei, nucleoli, and cytoplasm of infected cells. Vacuoles with abnormal RNP appeared in the nuclei.

Bereczky *et al.* (1961) found two types of lesions in the nuclei. In the one there was a dense homogeneous area surrounded by a clear zone, and in the other, dense strands or scattered dense material. In the electron-microscope, large amounts of polyoma virus were seen in the infected nuclei. By continuous recording (Bereczky and Dmochowski, 1962) by phase-microscopy of infected embryonic mouse cells, the same authors studied the increase in nuclear size, the change of shape of nucleoli and the appearance of the dense bodies. As infection continued, the cytoplasm darkened and retracted, and cells apparently died about 2½ h after the inclusions were first seen. The fibrous type of nuclear lesion was also seen by phase-microscopy, even in binucleate cells, in which one nucleus had a more discrete nuclear body. It is thus clear that attention has focused on the nucleus, but the cytoplasmic changes which also occur need further study.

Beginning with the study of Dawe and Law (1959) on organ cultures of mouse salivary glands infected with polyoma virus, there has been an interesting series of analyses of the effect of the virus on differentiated cells. In this first study, attention was focused on the active proliferation of glandular epithelium induced by the virus. Several Finnish workers, however, using developing organ rudiments to study the differential susceptibility of kidney cells, have shown that the newly formed convoluted tubules are apparently resistant to the effects of the virus, and indeed if the presence of virus is determined by the use of fluorescent antibody, there is evidently a remarkable selection of undifferentiated mesenchyme (Saxén, Vainio and Toivonen, 1962; Vainio, Saxén and Toivonen, 1963a, b). Spinal-cord fragments were used to induce the formation of tubules, and though these became surrounded by infected mesenchyme, the tubules themselves showed no staining with fluorescent antibody.

C. K. VIRUS OF RATS

Although not known to cause tumors, a latent virus of rats found by Kilham and Olivier (1959) has been classified with the papova viruses because of its size, cellular effects (Rabson, Kilham and Kirschstein, 1961) and physical characteristics. Infected hamster or rat-embryo fibroblast cultures showed clumping and rounding of cells, and the nuclei showed Feulgen positive inclusions filled with masses of virus particles (Bernhard, Kasten and Chany, 1963).

D. TRANSFORMATION

1. *Rabbit Papilloma*

The first recognition of transformation produced by the papova group of viruses was probably Coman's (1946) observation that rabbit-papilloma virus stimulated the outgrowth of epithelial cells from explants of rabbit epithelium, and that this sustained, vigorous growth was accompanied by continued tumor-like growth when the infected skin explant was inserted into the liver of the rabbit from which it had been cultured. The growth-stimulating effects have also been noted by de Maeyer (1962) in a preliminary note on the effect of this virus on newborn rabbit skin grown on semi-solid media and under 5% CO_2 in air.

Transformation of cells by other papova viruses suddenly became of great interest when it was shown by Vogt and Dulbecco (1960) and Sachs and Medina (1961), that changes in cell morphology, metabolism and colonial arrangement, which presumably represent loss of contact inhibition, were induced by exposure of rat and hamster cells to the polyoma virus. Stoker and collaborators (Stoker and MacPherson, 1961; Stoker and Abel, 1962), who subsequently showed that a stable hamster cell line might also be transformed, defined transformation as a perpetuated change in one or more properties of the cell, and suggested that oncogenesis may or may not be a part of this transformation. Stoker and MacPherson (1961) stated that individual transformed cells from baby hamster kidney could not be distinguished with certainty from normal cells, but that the pattern of growth of these cells was distinctive, in that they grew across each other in a criss-cross pattern. They found that transformation was a relatively rare event, since about 0·0056% of exposed cells acquired the new characteristic. This may be raised to 5–10% in selected clones, but the limitation is apparently not due to genetic differences in the clones (Black, 1964). The differentiation between transformation and oncogenesis produced by polyoma virus and SV_{40} was carried one step further when Todaro, Nilausen and Green (1963) and Todaro, Green and Goldberg (1964) showed that while early cultures of transformed embryonic hamster cells were evidently unable to cause tumors, tumors were produced by older, further modified (selected?) cells. Vogt and Dulbecco (1962, 1963) studied the chromatid bridges and breaks in the cells during the early phases of exposure of hamster embryo cells to polyoma virus and suggested that the change to malignancy occurred in at least two steps. In addition, morphologically normal hamster cells, growing in an apparently normal pattern, were shown by Defendi, Lehman and Kraemer (1963) to produce tumors in hamsters, and also to be susceptible to the transformation pattern of growth with polyoma virus.

2. *SV_{40}*

Shein and Enders (1962) found that this virus induced in seven of seven experiments a change of some human renal cell cultures from oriented cells to patches of epithelioid cells which frequently grew better. The transformed cells often had nuclei which varied greatly in size and shape, and chromosomal aberrations such as a lack of one of a pair (monosomy), aneuploidy or quasidiploidy were found (Yerganian, Shein and Enders, 1962). In a subsequent study (Shein, Enders, Levinthal and Burket, 1963) it was shown that altered cell morphology, abnormal growth patterns and greatly accelerated growth rate were induced in hamster cell cultures, even though no infectious virus could subsequently be recovered from the affected cells.

The increase in chromosome abnormalities and the conversion to a malignant state of hamster cells has been confirmed by Cooper and Black (1963) and Black and Rowe (1963), who found, as had Shein and Enders, that syncytial formation also appeared during transformation, and that in some cases an aggregation of ten to thirty nuclei showed within the giant cell. The mechanism of formation of syncytia by the virus has not been investigated. Todaro *et al.* (1964) studied the effect of both polyoma and SV_{40} on an established mouse cell line which is essentially fibroblastic in origin, but which in a number of sublines had lost the capacity to synthesize collagen. When these sublines were transformed they regained the capacity to form collagen, as determined by the increase of hydroxyproline in hydrolysates and by the appearance of collagen fibers identified in the electron-microscope. They suggest that the virus, in transforming the cells, released latent but suppressed cellular properties in the established cell line. Finally, Chumakov, Mustafina, Chumakova, Karmysheva, Shestopalova and Reinfold (1964) have found that transformation of human diploid cell lines may be induced by SV_{40} when large amounts of virus are added to cultures of cells derived from "skin muscle". At first, cellular changes consisted of enlarged nuclei, "symplasts" (syncytia) with three to thirty nuclei, the formation of small oxyphilic Feulgen-positive masses in the nuclei, and enlarged and distorted nucleoli. By the twenty-first passage of the culture, the character of the growth suddenly changed, and an area of epithelioid growth appeared. There was a marked shift of pH, and giant nuclei became common; chromosomal aberrations were also noted. A detailed cinematographic study of the effects of SV_{40} on renal cells of the African Green monkey (Pruniéras, Chardonnet and Sohier, 1964), has concentrated on the nuclear changes. An early (20 h) change in the nucleolus was followed by the development of discrete masses in the nucleoplasm, an initial hypertrophy of the nucleolus, then a fragmentation of this structure. The authors suggest that material is transferred from the nucleus to the cytoplasm by small vacuoles, and that the nucleolar changes are related to the transformation.

Through the use of fluorescent sera from hamsters and mice which are carrying "virus free" tumors induced by SV_{40} or polyoma virus, it has been shown that a "tumor" antigen, specific for the virus which originally caused the tumor, is present within the nuclei of these transformed cells (Pope and Rowe, 1964a). This antigen is apparently also present at first during the early and moderate growth of SV_{40} virus in monkey, human and hamster cells (Rapp, Kitahara, Butel and Melnick, 1964). However, this "tumor" antigen disappears as the cytopathic or destructive effect of the virus progresses. The tumor antigen is heat labile (56°C/30 min) in contrast to the viral antigen, and persists in the transformed cells (Sabin and Koch, 1964).

X. Myxoviruses

The myxoviruses were originally differentiated from other viruses on the basis of their size and their affinity for a mucopolysaccharide substrate—a quality most clearly demonstrated *in vitro* by the change in red-cell receptors (Andrewes, Bang and Burnet, 1955). The designation is now applied to an enlarged group of agents (Andrewes, 1964) including those of measles, distemper and rinderpest, and also the respiratory syncytial viruses.

Some of the specific questions which may be asked of this group are:

(1) Why is it that some agents (virulent strains of NDV) are highly destructive, whereas others such as influenza and parainfluenza* are recognized chiefly because of the adherence of red cells to the altered surface of infected cells?

(2) What is the cause of the massive giant cells which are particularly prone to develop in cells infected with respiratory syncytial virus (Fig. 3B), as well as with measles and some members of the parainfluenza group? Does the factor described by Okada and Tadokoro (1962) which causes giant polynuclear cells within 1 h after the addition of large doses of virus have any relation to this?

(3) Is the characteristic modification of the cell surface (leading to altered microvilli which contain large portions of virus and virus products) a basic mechanism of virus release?

(4) What is the mechanism of intranuclear alteration induced by the influenza–fowl plague group, which is in contrast to the mechanism which limits its effects to the cytoplasm in most of the parainfluenza-NDV group?

(5) What part of the virus is responsible for the "toxic" action of large doses of virus on cells *in vitro*? What is the relationship of lysosomes to this action?

(6) In what way is the natural "habitat" or ecological niche of this group of viruses—the respiratory tract of animals—to be explained in terms of their effects on cells *in vitro*? How may this be studied in "organ culture"?

A. MOTION

1. *Migration*

Taylor (1953) reported that when chick-embryo mixed plasma-clot cultures were inoculated with influenza A virus, there was early stimulation of cell growth, followed by later destruction. Mumps virus, on

*Standardization of nomenclature amongst the myxoviruses has been unable to keep pace with the continuing identification of related strains or subgroups. Fowl plague is usually accepted as related to influenza A. Animal analogs of the parainfluenza group, and their designations to date are:

Parainfluenza 1: H.J.V.; Sendai
Parainfluenza 2: SV_5? (see below)
Parainfluenza 3: SF_4 (cattle)
Parainfluenza 4: – – –

in addition, a simian virus usually designated SV_5 may be either an analog of Parainfluenza 2, or may eventually be designated Parainfluenza 5.

the other hand, immediately prevented the appearance of cells, an observation which was interpreted as cell destruction, though it may also represent an inhibitory effect on migration or a unique susceptibility of migrating cells. Subsequently it was reported that mumps virus had no effect on cells after they had been cultured. Gresser and Enders (1961) have, however, shown that trypsinized chick cells are destroyed by mumps virus.

2. *Surface Movement—Microvilli—Extrusions*

There are no sequential studies of living cells infected with myxoviruses in which the microvilli or the surface of infected cells have been directly studied. Phase and dark-field microscopy have been applied to the edge of cells to study filament formation (Hoyle, 1954).

Electron-microscopy of both whole cell mounts grown in tissue culture and sections of infected cells have shown that the cell surfaces, particularly of epithelial cells, may be extensively modified. Though actual movement cannot be observed in these static preparations, the extensive knowledge of the dynamic changes in normal cell surface structure which have been followed by cinematography (Gey, 1954; Pomerat, 1961) demand that these pathological changes also be interpreted dynamically. Normal, short and rather stumpy microvilli are found in Tissue Culture on the surface of chorio-allantoic epithelial cells (Borysko and Bang, 1953) and other cells. These are replaced by masses of long, uniform filaments or spheres, if the cell is infected by influenza virus (Murphy and Bang, 1952; Niven, Armstrong, Balfour, Klemperer and Tyrrell, 1962), or fowl plague (Flewett and Challice, 1951). An eruption of mushrooming, large, stalked spheres and irregular and broken filaments follows infection with NDV (Bang, 1953) or parainfluenza virus (Reczko and Bogel, 1962; Hotchin, Cohen, Ruska and Ruska 1958; Colobert and Berkaloff, 1964). Single cells infected with respiratory syncytial virus may also be covered with elaborately branching cytoplasmic processes containing virus particles. Giant cells have fewer of these (Armstrong, Pereira and Valentine, 1962).

It has, therefore, been assumed that these are greatly altered microvilli, and that the virus has utilized the capacity of the cell to form microvilli as a mechanism of release from the cell. Presumably then the surface of an infected cell is greatly disturbed, continually moving, extruding new filaments and spheres, and these filaments are continually breaking free into the surrounding fluid.

Recently Hoorn (1964) has considerably modified the organ culture method used by Bang and Niven (1958) so that the respiratory mucosa of both human and rabbit fetuses can be kept alive with active cilia for

4–6 weeks in Parker's medium 199 without the addition of serum. He showed that influenza A increased in most of the cultures and frequently, though not always, destroyed the ciliated cells a few days to a week after inoculation. The effect could be followed in the cultures by observing the motion of the cilia. These results have been extended to parainfluenza 1, 2, 3 and 4, respiratory, syncytial and influenza A and B by Hoorn and Tyrell (1965) and Tyrell and Hoorn (1965) on the mucosae of rhesus monkey and of ferret.

3. *Internal Movement—Mitochondria—Nuclei*

The nuclei of the syncytia continue to rotate (Marston, 1958). Klöne and his colleagues (Klöne, Kulemann, Ward and Salk, 1963; Klöne and Kulemann, 1964) have described the formation of a bridge during the process of giant-cell formation in monkey kidney cells infected by measles virus, which pulls the nucleus of the adjoining cell in to join the central mass of nuclei of the giant cell (Fig. 4). This specialized structure of the cytoplasm of the measles giant cell is dependent upon a continuous supply of ATP to do the work of nuclear migration (Kulemann and Klöne, 1964). No disturbance of mitochondria or lipid movement was observed.

B. REACTION TO ENVIRONMENT

1. *Adherence to Substrate*

Although it has been shown that infected, differentiated cells in organ cultures lose their adhesion to other cells and are sloughed out from the mucosa (Bang, 1959; and Fig. 5), this behavior of infected cells has been little studied. As with other virus infections, infected cells frequently lose their adhesion to the glass substrate and float free in the Tissue-Culture fluid. This is probably a terminal stage of infection, and there are few studies of the effects of large amounts of virus (Henle, Girardi and Henle, 1955; Mason and Kaufman, 1960) which would allow for a search for "toxic" factors such as that described for adenoviruses (Pereira, 1958).

2. *Reaction to Other Cells—Contact Inhibition*

Again, though influenza and other members of the myxovirus group may form hyperplastic foci of epithelial cells both on the chorio-allantoic membrane and in mouse lungs, there are no reports on the lack of contact inhibition such as has recently been demonstrated for Rous cultures *in vitro*.

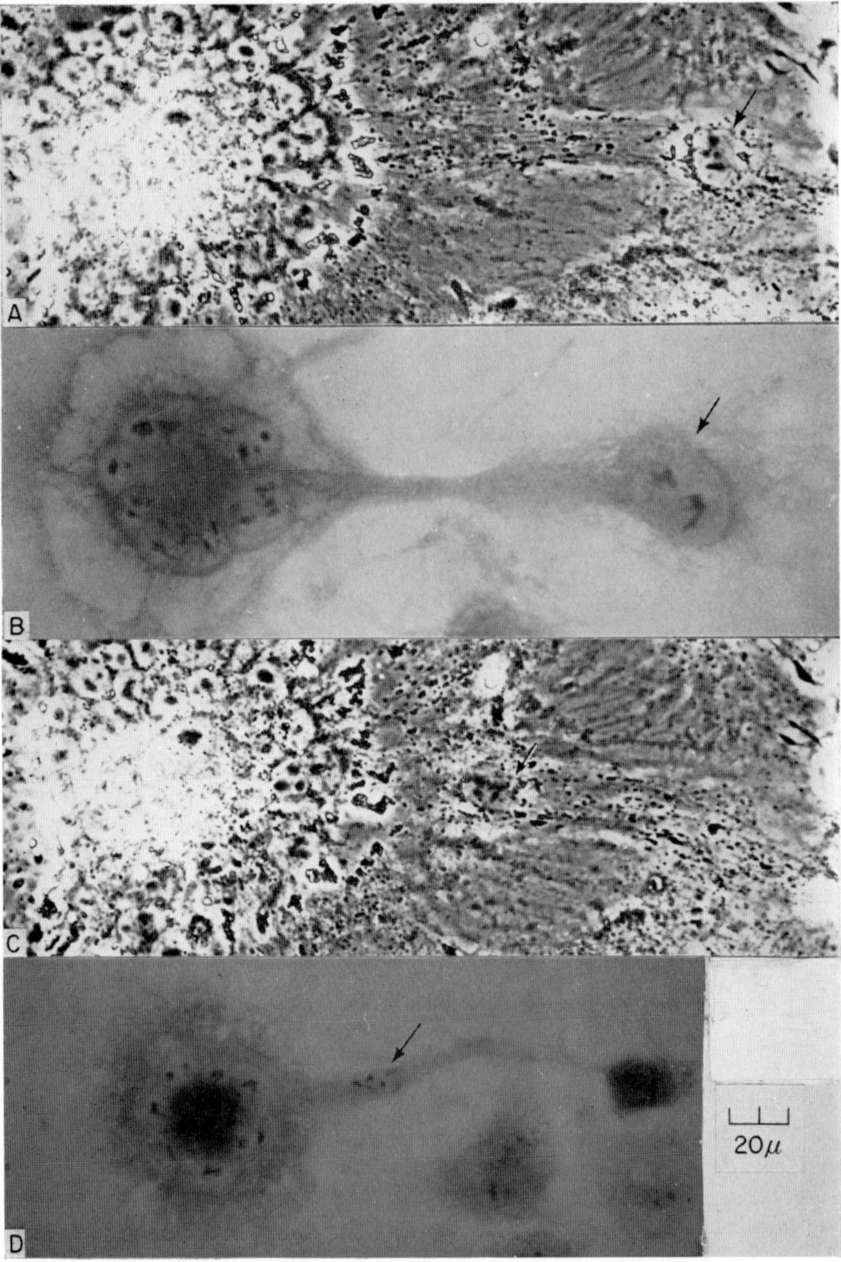

FIG. 4. LLC-MK$_2$ cell strain infected with measles virus (Edmonston strain). Arrows point to nucleus. A. Seven days after infection. Living cell, phase contrast. Bridge formation between nucleus of newly recruited cell and giant cell on left. B. Similar preparation 9 days after infection. Carnoy fixation, Azure B. Note "halo" in cytoplasm around nuclear mass. C. Migration of nucleus within bridge or track formed between cells. 7 days–35 min. D. Similar preparation, 9 days after infection. Carnoy fixation Azure B. The migrating nucleus is within a track where RNA portion is stained both in front of and behind the nucleus. One micrometer marking = 10μ. Courtesy of Dr. W. Klöne.

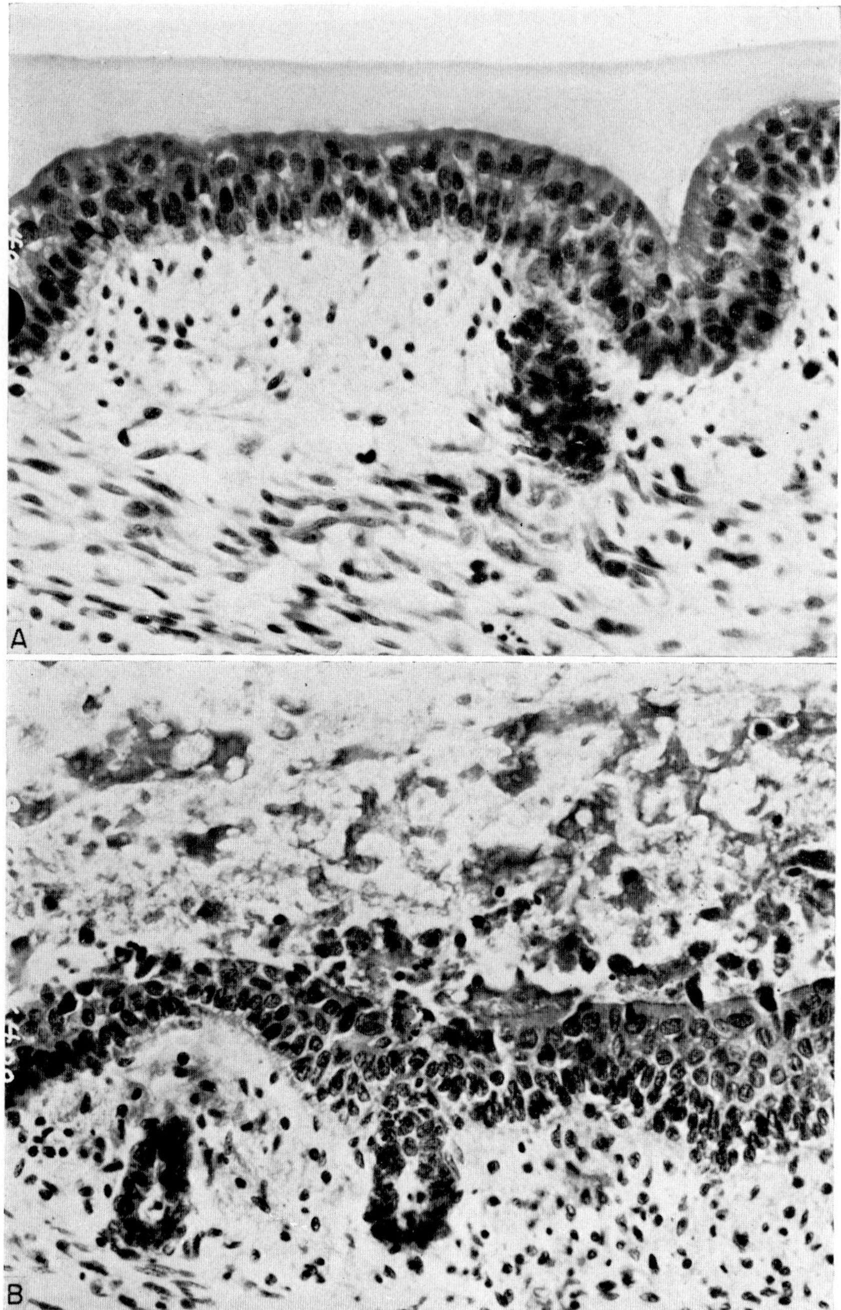

FIG. 5. A. Human embryonic trachea in organ culture, normal. B. Effect of influenza A on human embryonic trachea in organ culture. Note distortion of surface and sloughing of ciliated cells. Original.

3. *Giant-Cell Formation*

Enders and Peebles (1954) who first isolated measles virus from patients, demonstrated the formation of giant cells in cultures of human kidney cells: "Within the sheet-like outgrowth of renal epithelial cells there developed discrete areas with 40 to 100 nuclei. Often the limits of the encompassing cytoplasm were sharply defined, thus contributing to the impression that development of true giant cells has occurred *in vitro*." They commented on the presence of giant cells in lymphoid tissue in cases of measles. Almost simultaneously Henle, Deinhardt and Girardi (1954) showed that when mumps virus was placed on HeLa cells it exerted a "cytolytic effect", in that the borders of the discrete cells were eliminated. This confluence of the cytoplasm caused "false giant cells". The "cytolytic" activity of the virus was neutralized by specific antisera, and the cytolytic activity, like the hemolytic activity of the virus, was relatively resistant to ultraviolet light. Presumably, Henle *et al.* (1954) were studying the same phenomenon which Okada (1962a, b) observed as the effect of parainfluenza virus on mouse ascites cells, and called the "cell fusion factor". Since these first studies by Henle *et al.*, there have been numerous reports of the formation of giant cells by other members of the group of myxoviruses; one caused such marked giant-cell formation in Tissue Culture that it was given the name respiratory syncytial virus (Chanock, Roizman and Myers, 1957; Bennett and Hamre, 1962; Chany, Daniel, Robbe-Fossat, Vialatte, Lepine and Lelong, 1958). The parainfluenza viruses, mumps, Newcastle disease (Bankowski, 1964), measles (Bech and von Magnus, 1957; Sherman and Ruckle, 1958), distemper (Bussell and Karzon, 1962), and rinderpest viruses are now known to cause giant cells. However, influenza (Hinz and Syverton, 1959; Lehmann-Grubé, 1963; Moffat, Holtermann and Hillis, 1960; Niven *et al.*, 1962), fowl plague (Franklin and Breitenfeld, 1959) and Yucaipa virus (Dinter, Hermodsson and Hermodsson, 1964) have as yet not been found to stimulate giant-cell formation in epithelial or fibroblast cells. Fowl plague does, however, stimulate giant-cell formation in chicken macrophages (Franklin, 1958), cells which frequently form giant cells without the addition of virus.

Several studies by cinematography or other methods of sequential recording (Henle *et al.*, 1954; Lepine, Chany, Droz, and Robbe-Fossat, 1959; Thomison, 1962; Marston, 1958) have shown that the giant cells are invariably formed by the loss of the cell boundaries and the joining together of the cytoplasm of different cells so that the nuclei may be associated within one large cytoplasm.

The mechanism of cell fusion produced by parainfluenza 1 (H.J.V.

or Sendai) studied by Okada *et al.* (1962, 1963, 1964) was observed primarily in suspensions of Ehrlich's ascites cells. Although this is not in any sense a tissue culture, the formation of giant cells in suspension by the action of a virus is presumably similar to events in Tissue Culture. Fusion occurred within 30 min at 37°C after agglutination of the cells had been produced by the virus at 4°C. Electron-microscopy showed membrane fusion with some areas of microvilli preserved between the cells. Large inocula of virus were necessary to produce fusion, perhaps more than 10^4 virus particles/cell. Ultrasonic treatment destroyed the fusion factor, but hemolytic and hemagglutinating activity of the virus was retained. Aerobic conditions were essential to produce the fusion reaction. Degenerate cells did not participate in the reaction. Fusion was produced in a variety of established human, monkey, rabbit and mouse cell lines and in human myeloid leukemia cells. It is likely that fusion of the infected cells to form giant cells is produced by a similar factor in other members of the myxovirus complex. For instance, measles virus inactivated by ultraviolet light maintained its capacity to cause fusion of trypsinized cells (Toyoshima, Hata and Miki, 1960), and Chany and Cook, (1960) have shown giant-cell formation preceding virus production. However, leucocytes and freshly cultured fibroblasts from mouse, chick and man had no capacity to fuse (Okada and Tadokoro, 1963).

Measles (Milovanovic, Enders and Mitus, 1957), mumps (Gresser and Enders, 1961) and respiratory syncytial (Chanock *et al.*, 1957; Bennett and Hamre, 1962) viruses have been shown to produce spindle cells and degeneration as well as giant cells. In the case of the first two agents the effect was described for human amniotic cell cultures after trypsinization. It is most unlikely that these cultures contained fibroblasts, and therefore the spindle-cell degeneration may well be an effect which is specific for these viruses. Attempts to select a virus which caused only spindle-cell formation in these mixed cultures failed. As indicated in the illustration (Fig. 3B), however, respiratory syncytial virus produces, in human diploid cells, excellent syncytia which are apparent after fixing and staining.

At the same time, the differential response of different substrains of HeLa cells to measles virus has been noted. A strain adapted to sheep serum yielded large syncytia when infected, whereas a strain adapted to calf serum showed only occasional syncytia with cytopathology delayed and confined to individual cells (Moura, 1961–62).

The significance of giant-cell formation is unknown. However, the common occurrence of this phenomenon among viruses which are transmitted by the respiratory route suggests that it may play a role in the persistence of virus within the respiratory tract, and that spread from cell to cell despite the presence of antibody is thus made possible. Giant cells are frequently found in the respiratory tract during the course of measles (Sherman and Ruckle, 1958).

C. FEEDING

Influenza virus is well known to depress the leucocytic count, and a depression of phagocytosis by leucoytes in the animal has been reported (Kańtoch, 1961). However, there are no direct studies of the effect of any of the myxoviruses, except a parainfluenza virus (SV_5), on phagocytic or pinocytotic activity of cells in tissue culture. This is remarkable since the cell-surface effects of the agents are so well known (see above). If neutral-red intake is taken as a measure of fluid ingestion, stimulation of uptake by epithelial cells, particularly giant cells, has been reported in measles (Moura, 1961–62; Köhn and Yassky, 1962) and in several strains of Newcastle-disease virus (NDV) (Thiry, 1963; Baron, 1964). The depression of neutral-red uptake is of course used routinely in plaque methods, but in these circumstances it is not usually possible to tell whether this depression is merely part of the death of the cells, or whether selective and possibly reversible depression of dye uptake is taking place. Choppin (1964) has ascribed the formation of plaques to inadequate uptake of neutral red by otherwise intact cells infected with SV_5.

1. *Osmoregulation*

Aside from terminal disruption of the cell architecture, again too little attention has been paid to this possible effect. In a Tissue-Culture study of the effects of influenza virus on bovine cell cultures, Niven *et al.* (1962) did show cytoplasmic vacuolation, presumably due to the accumulation of fluid within the endoplasmic reticulum. It would be of interest to determine whether the normal capacity of a cell to osmoregulate within certain limits is altered by the presence of infection, since extensive surface changes are induced by these viruses.

2. *Paranuclear Hypertrophy and the Golgi Complex*

No information is available. Since the lesions produced by other viruses such as poliomyelitis and Rous sarcoma virus in certain cells are so clear and distinct, the absence of any description of lesions produced by the myxoviruses may be taken as an indication that this group of agents rarely induces such lesions.

D. GROWTH

There are no reports of the increase in size of infected cells, other than the formation of syncytia, which is of course not due to an increase of mass, but to an elimination of cell boundaries.

1. *Nucleolar Size, Mitotic Activity*

The metabolic events in the cell which result from infection can occasionally be recognized by morphological means. For instance, an increase in the size of the nucleolus (frequently thought to reflect increased RNA synthesis) has been described in chick-embryo cells infected with fowl-plague virus (*Myxovirus influenza galli*) (Flewett and Challice, 1951), but the fact that nucleoli do not change size is specifically noted in some of the studies on the infection of monkey and human kidney cells with measles (Aoyama, 1959). A change in the size of the nucleolus has been reported with the same virus growing in FL (human amnion) cells (Toyoshima, Hata, Takahashi, Miki and Okuno, 1960).

Using the method of plating described by Puck, Marcus and Ciecura (1956), to determine the capacity of infected cells to produce new colonies, Marcus (1959) showed that HeLa cells infected with Newcastle-disease virus failed to multiply. The one to one ratio of the amount of virus added and the number of cells "killed", suggested that single virus particles were lethal for individual host cells. Wheelock and Tamm (1959) then studied influenza and NDV in HeLa cultures which had been induced by cold treatment to a partial synchronization of division. Infected cells in all stages of mitosis were readily identified by fluorescent antibody staining. Some individual cells immediately after division contained large amounts of viral antigen, amounts so large that they could be accounted for only by multiplication which started in the original cell well before mitosis set in.

Subsequently, Wheelock and Tamm (1961a, b) showed that cultures in which all the HeLa cells were infected with multiplicities of 500:1 and 5: 1of NDV continued to show mitosis for some hours after infection. With the higher multiplicity a decrease in the number of mitoses commenced 5–6 h after infection, and no mitoses were found by 10 h. The lower multiplicity depressed the number of mitoses by 8 h, but some cells were still dividing at 16 h. Thus, it is clear that NDV-infected HeLa cells can divide and even release virus after division. It is entirely possible that the plating procedure used by Marcus (1959), which involves trypsinization and separation of cells, places a greater burden on the cell, and that under these conditions all infected cells fail to multiply.

Cultures of HeLa cells infected with NDV may eventually cease to multiply (Wheelock and Tamm, 1961a) or may continue to multiply indefinitely as chronically infected cultures (Henle, Deinhardt, Bergs and Henle, 1958) (see below). Wheelock and Tamm (1961b) suggest that the inhibition of either protein or RNA synthesis which *precedes* marked morphological changes in the cell, may cause inhibition of mitosis. They emphasize that inhibition of mitosis itself precedes cell breakdown. They present a scheme of changes induced by the virus in the host cell in which it is shown that the earliest changes are marked decreases in the synthesis of protein and DNA (Fig. 6).

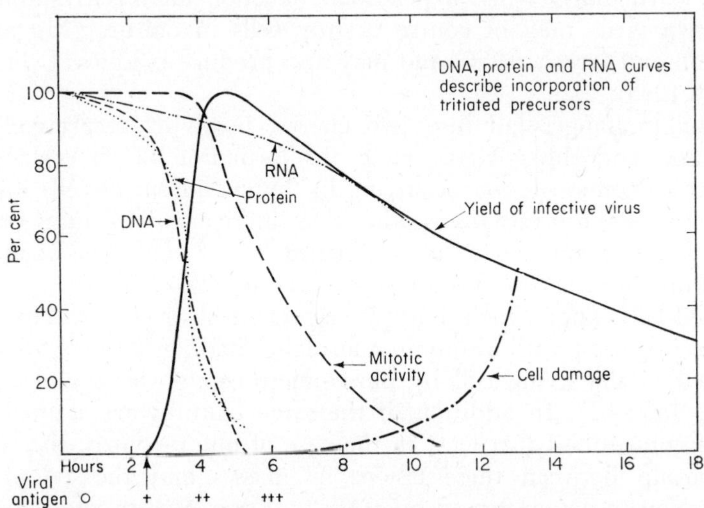

FIG. 6. Temporal relationships between aspects of virus multiplication and cellular response. NVD/HeLa cell multiplicity 500:1. From Wheelock and Tamm (1961b).

Measles virus which, as has been noted, induces giant cells, may also be found in mitotic cells. Roizman and Schluederberg (1961, 1962) found antigen in mitotic cells in anaphase, metaphase and telophase. They further showed that cells blocked by colchicine were nevertheless incorporated into the giant cell. Since many of the changes are like those induced by X-rays, they argued that infection caused aberrant cleavage of the cells. Some confirmation of this type of effect is offered by Nichols, Levan, Hall and Ostergren (1962), who found that cultures of human macrophages from patients with measles may show a high incidence of chromosome breaks. This was, however, not confirmed by Harnden (1964).

E. PATHOLOGICAL CHANGES AND VIRUS LOCALIZATION

These range from an apparently complete lack of change—as in monkey kidney cells grown continuously with a virus natural to the rhesus monkey (SV_5) (Choppin, 1964)—to the acute extensive destruction produced by Newcastle-disease virus on chick fibroblasts (Bang and Warwick, 1957) and other cells (Bankowski, 1964). In several cases, despite the lack of obvious morphological change, large amounts of virus antigen have been demonstrated in the cell by the use of the appropriate fluorescent antibody. This is true of mumps (Walker and Hinze, 1962), measles (Rustigian, 1962), Newcastle-disease virus (Rodriguez and Henle, 1964), and influenza (Deibel and Hotchin, 1959), particularly when a persistent infection has been established. Influenza virus may of course destroy cells in culture (Mogabgab, Simpson and Green, 1956) and may also produce plaques (Lehmann-Grubé, 1963).

Cellular changes fall into two classes, involving respectively the cytoplasm and the nucleus. First, the formation of an eosinophilic mass is a common lesion occurring in the cytoplasm of cells infected with most of the myxoviruses other than influenza. This mass may be large, as in infection with parainfluenza 2 or 3, or much smaller as with mumps virus on certain cells (Brandt, 1961; Mannweiler and Maass, 1959). These "inclusions" are especially clear after acid fixatives, are less apparent with osmium or formalin fixation, and could not be detected in the living cell by phase-microscopy (Maass and Mannweiler, 1960–61). In addition, if the same cultures are stained with fluorescent antibody, at least in the case of mumps virus, there is no relationship between these lesions or masses and the cytoplasmic localization as demonstrated by antisera (Lesso, Szanto and Albrecht, 1963). Similar cytoplasmic lesions are present in measles-infected cells. Takahashi, Miyamoto and Kato (1963) studied them by autoradiography after pulse-labelling with tritiated uridine. Labelling of the cytoplasmic inclusions was less marked than that of the surrounding cytoplasm, suggesting that virus is not being formed in these abnormal areas. Similar inclusions (eosinophilic homogeneous masses in the cytoplasm) were described by Johnson and Goodpasture (1936) in monkeys experimentally infected with mumps. Love and Suskind (1961) point out that cytoplasmic inclusions may also arise in cells infected with parainfluenza 3 virus when, after the ingestion of destroyed cells, pieces of partially digested foreign nuclei remain in the cytoplasm; these can be distinguished from the viral lesion.

Characteristic nuclear changes—again poorly defined masses of eosinophilic material—have also been found in cells infected with measles (Enders and Peebles, 1954; Bech and von Magnus, 1957; Sherman and Ruckle, 1958), parainfluenza 3 (Shipping Fever of cattle) (Reisinger, Heddleston and Manthei, 1959; Churchill, 1963), and even in certain cells (KB-human, and turtle) infected with Newcastle disease virus (Pigoury, Michel and Chabassol, 1962; Fauconnier, 1963). The measles inclusions have been studied by electron-microscopy, and have been shown to consist of randomly arrayed fibers of low density surrounding dense, "highly arrayed" fibers (Kallman, Adams, Williams and Imagawa, 1959; Tawara, Goodman, Imagawa and Adams, 1961). Their size is much below that assigned to the virus (100 μ), and as yet their relation to the virus is unknown.

Viral antigen is found characteristically in the nucleus of cells infected with influenza (Moffat *et al.*, 1960) and fowl plague (Breitenfeld and Schäfer, 1957; Franklin, 1958), but is limited to the cytoplasm of cells infected with mumps, and NDV (Reda, Rott and Schäfer, 1964). In a detailed study of infection of KB cells by parainfluenza 1 (Sendai), Demont, Berkaloff and Colobert (1963) showed that the cytopathologic effect of the virus depended upon the amount of virus inoculated. A low multiplicity of inoculum produced a chronic infection. A moderate inoculum caused cellular degeneration and production of intracellular viral antigen but no infectious virus, whereas a larger inoculum caused the formation of syncytia which subsequently degenerated without the formation of viral antigen. Degeneration of the nucleus was likened to pyknosis. The fusion of cells caused by large inocula occurred about four hours after infection, finally encompassed as many as 100 nuclei, and was followed by degeneration without the formation of any eosinophilic inclusions. From the twelfth hour of infection there was a reduction of mitochondria and an increase in ribosomes and ergastoplasm. If syncytia were lacking, a few nucleoli showed viral antigen, but if syncytia were formed most of the nucleoli became intensely stained. Later, fluorescence developed in the cytoplasm. Parainfluenza 3 in FL (human amnion) cells produced much the same changes. When the syncytia were formed, viral antigen was found throughout the cytoplasm, but was most concentrated at the edge of the cell mass, where virus particles were found when the cells were studied in the electron-microscope (Falke and Schmidt, 1963; Cohen, Bullivant and Edwards, 1961–62).

F. REACTION OF ENTIRE CULTURE

1. *Chronic or Persistent Infections*

The most detailed studies of persistent infection are those of Henle and collaborators (1958) on Newcastle-disease virus. They have shown that only one in fifty HeLa cells became infected with NDV, but that the remaining cells were highly resistant to infection with other viruses. Virus multiplied very slowly. Cultures could be cured by antisera, and these behaved as normal cultures. The resistance of the culture was apparently due to interferon. In extending the study of this infection to L cells, which also may support persistent infections, interferon was again found to play a significant role. Since the important subject of interferon is outside the purview of this review, this extensive series of papers should be consulted for details of the mechanism of this effect.

Another example of a remarkable and persistent myxovirus infection is that of mumps virus in human conjunctival cells (Walker and Hinze, 1962), which was maintained over three years through more than 100 subcultures. The virus had no apparent effect on the growth of the cells, since they grew just as rapidly as the uninfected control cells. Fluorescein-labelled antisera showed that 80–95% of the cells in the culture contained virus antigen which was concentrated in discrete masses in the cytoplasm. Viral infection persisted in the presence of antiserum, even when individual cells were cloned. The presence of virus was also indicated by hemadsorption on the surface of 0·1 to 1% of the cells. Small amounts of virus which was less virulent than the original inoculum were constantly released from the culture. It is clear that, even within the myxovirus group, viral persistence and spread may take a variety of forms.

2. *Organ Cultures*

In the first application of this method of culture to virus study (Bang and Niven, 1958), nasal epithelium of the ferret was shown to be rapidly destroyed by influenza virus, and in a subsequent article (Bang, 1959a) the continuous destructive effect of virulent strains of Newcastle-disease virus on chick tracheal epithelium was shown. Sloughing of ciliated and mucous epithelial cells (Fig. 5B) from human trachea was also clear. In a fairly extensive study of various avian viruses on adult chicken cells in organ cultures and dispersed cultures, Butler (1965) has shown that Newcastle-disease virus produced necrosis of cells of the chick trachea as well as proliferation.

Huang and Bang (1964) showed that when organ cultures of chick embryo skin were converted to mucous-secreting epithelium by the influence of excess vitamin A, the cultures became much more sensitive to the action of influenza virus.

XI. Avian Sarcomas and Lymphomas

A. Introduction

Classification of this group of agents is at present unsatisfactory. It is now known that (1) standard batches of virus contain several agents, some of which are thought to be "helpers" of the others (Rubin, 1960a, b, c); (2) that preparations of virus called Rous sarcoma may produce lymphomas as well, and vice versa (Frederickson, Purchase and Burmester, 1964); and (3) that there is antigenic heterogeneity among the agents called Rous sarcoma (Frederickson *et al.*, 1964; Simons and Dougherty, 1963; Bang and Foard, 1964). This makes it extremely difficult, if not impossible, to know which of the effects produced in Tissue Culture is due to which member of the sarcoma-lymphoma group.

Historically the confusion of classification is based on several things. Since the original discovery of the filterable nature of chicken leucosis (Ellerman and Bang, 1908) and chicken sarcomas (Rous, 1910), tumor viruses were thought to be unique among the viruses, and the cell type affected was thought to represent a fundamental property of the virus. Neither of these assumptions has been sustained. Some members of the leucosis group are clearly related antigenically to the sarcoma agents (Bang and Foard, 1964; Simons and Dougherty, 1963). Despite the work of Duran-Reynals (1947), the host-range of the virus was thought to be narrow. It is now known that members of this group of virus can not only infect a variety of avian tissues, but can cause tumors in rats (Schmitt-Ruppin, 1964; Svoboda, 1964; Ahlstrom, 1964), and monkeys (Munroe, Shipkey, Erlandson and Windle, 1964), and can alter human cells (Jensen, Girardi, Gilden and Koprowski, 1964; Stenkvist and Pontén, 1964). Antigenic studies on the relationship between the different members were almost impossible to carry out since the natural host, the chicken, was spontaneously infected with one or another member of the group of agents, and comparative studies of antigenic relationships could not adequately be determined against this background. With the availability of at least partially clean flocks (Bang and Foard, 1964), it was possible to confirm the antigenic difference of several of the agents. The absence of concentrated virus which is sufficiently free of host antigen to allow for study of antigenic relationships in insusceptible hosts further prevented adequate study.

The recent demonstration (Vogt, 1965) that a standard preparation of Bryan-Rous sarcoma contains two antigenically different agents, each with its "helper" variant, means that much of the work in the past will have to be repeated. Finally, it is clear that the virus-free or "normal" nature of experimental tissue material must be subjected to rigid final proof: for example, the fact that no virus is added to cultures of chicken buffy coat does not exclude the presence of virus; giant-cell formation in such cultures must surely raise the question. Furthermore, since electron-microscopy (Bang, 1958; Zeigel, Burmester and Rauscher, 1964) and interference techniques (Rubin, 1960a) have both indicated the presence of virus in chick tissues, it may be incorrect to consider cultures as "normal" when taken from chickens not infected experimentally.

B. MOTION

The effect of Rous virus on fibroblasts and macrophages was early studied by Borrel (1926), Carrel (1924, 1925), and Fischer (1926), and others. Yet there exists today no analysis of the effect of the virus on the motion of the host cell, whether it has been "transformed" by the virus or has been part of a maintained infection. Such a study would be particularly interesting in relation to the mechanism of interaction of an infected cell with its neighboring homologous or heterologous cell, but there are so far no published cinematographic studies of this virus infection.

C. REACTION TO ENVIRONMENT

The formation of monolayers of normal cells on a glass substrate following trypsinization of the cells is, of course, the reaction of cells following a highly abnormal situation. The failure of Rous-infected cells (Manaker and Groupé, 1956) to respond in the same manner as uninfected cells has been ascribed to a lack of contact inhibition on the part of these cells. Abercrombie and Ambrose (1958) described the phenomenon in which a fibroblast moving ahead on glass with a series of ruffled pseudopods, proceeds no further when it comes in contact with another fibroblast. This inhibition, apparently produced by contact with homologous cells, is clearly part of the contact behavior of cells, but as Abercrombie (1962) makes clear in his discussion of the application of the phenomenon to virus infection and malignancy, it is only one part of the interaction of cells. Loss of adhesiveness occurs whenever a cell is mechanically injured (Kredel, 1927). Normal mouse fibroblasts even under "normal" conditions may vary greatly in the amount of, or lack of, contact inhibition. Some cells normally lack this reaction and climb in a disoriented fashion on top of each other. Macrophages in their normal association of sticking to all kinds of foreign material might be said to lack contact inhibition, yet they also form a monolayer on glass.

The formation of foci of Rous-infected cells which pile on top of each other on a monolayer was first described by Manaker and Groupé (1956). The foci so produced are now used as a routine method of assay of Rous virus (Temin and Rubin, 1958). It is generally ascribed to lack of contact inhibition, yet Abercrombie points out that there may be two kinds of "lack", one dependent upon interaction between homologous cells and another between heterologous cells, and until a detailed study such as that of Abercrombie and Ambrose on normal mouse cells and sarcoma cells, is also done with Rous-infected cells, we cannot assume that we know why the cells behave in this clumped fashion. Indeed, there may be no significant relationship between this altered behavior and the capacity of these cells to produce tumors.

Foci may be suppressed by an excess of calf serum in the agar overlay, or by fetal calf serum, but the mechanism of this suppression is unknown (Rubin, 1960c).

D. FEEDING

Fischer and Laser (1927) pointed out that not only does the ameboid cell found in cultures of the Rous sarcoma phagocytize carmine particles rapidly, but that the fibroblastic type of cell also does this. This was in contrast to normal fibroblasts which, as is well known, are poor phagocytes. Tissue Cultures of Rous sarcomas were accidentally infected by way of chicken plasma with avian tubercle bacilli, and tubercle bacilli were subsequently found in the fibroblastic cells (Fischer, 1927). However, the sarcoma cells did not phagocytize normal connective tissue cells. Incidentally, Fischer pointed out that the tumors which were induced by injection of these cells also contained tubercle bacilli, but that the metastases lost them. Therefore, he concluded that the metastases were due to spread of virus, not to spread of intact cells in this tumor.

Paranuclear hypertrophy. Since this lesion in this infection is associated with the formation of an excess secretory product, it will be discussed in Section G (p. 210).

E. GROWTH

1. *Transformation*

Since Rous virus causes tumors not only in chickens, but in many other birds, as well as mammals, there have been many *in vitro* attempts to understand the nature of this virus effect. One hoped either to see in the isolated cells the essential step which converted normal cells to tumor cells, or at least to induce a conversion of normal cells to malignant cells and then demonstrate the capacity of these converted cells to produce a tumor in the host in the absence of infectious virus. In all of the chicken cultures, new virus has been produced when tumor cells were reinoculated into the new host chicken (Pontén, 1962), so that the conversion of the cells into tumor cells *in vitro* is not proven. Indeed, most new tumor cells in a transfer of Rous tumors are newly *infected* cells (Pontén, 1962). Underlying the use of the word "transformation" has been the inference that the transformed cell is equivalent to a tumor cell. This is incorrect historically, for the word has been used to mean little more than "changed". It is incorrect also in a literal sense, for cells may be altered in their *in vitro* growth characteristics without being malignant in the host animal. Historically, Carrel and Ebeling (1926) wrote of the "transformation of monocytes into fibroblasts through the action of Rous virus", and stated that the inoculation of cultures of monocytes from the blood with a filtered extract of Rous sarcoma frequently caused fibroblasts to appear in the cultures. Although this early work has not since been repeated, and indeed has been denied by Sanford, Likely, Bryan and Earle (1952), the variety of viruses now included in the category of "Rous virus" at present prevents fair evaluation of the original claim.

Baluda (1962), in a series of interesting studies on avian myeloblastosis, which is related antigenically to the Bryan strain of Rous virus, showed that certain cells in the hemopoietic tissues of the chick were converted *in vitro* into small round cells which, when inoculated into chickens, induced myeloblastosis. These cells grew exponentially, divided about every 2–2½ days, and had a diploid set of chromosomes. The target cells for the virus were found in cultures of spleen, yolk sac, liver, bone marrow, and kidney at certain stages of development. In his summary of these studies, Baluda (1962) is careful to speak only of "conversion", a term apparently fully justified by the facts. However, the paper is listed with others on virus infections under the title of "Cellular Transformation by Viruses" in the Cold Spring Harbor Symposium (1962), and in a subsequent paper Rubin discusses the phenomenon as "Virus Defectiveness and Cell Transformation in the Rous Sarcoma" (1964). This is regrettable in view of the fact that it is not possible at present to determine whether the morphological and behavioral changes seen in tissue culture (see below) are necessary for the production of malignancy in the chicken *in vivo*. It may be objected that morphological changes have been fully demonstrated to occur *in vitro* in the absence of detectable infectious virus, yet that these cells produce tumors when inoculated into chickens (Temin, 1962). However, the cells do later spontaneously release virus, even in the absence of helper virus, and although some of the tumors lack detectable infectious virus, here, too, new virus frequently appears. Thus, there is plenty of opportunity for cell-to-cell infection to take place in the animal in a manner analogous to the spread of herpes virus in Tissue Culture.

2. In vitro *Growth Stimulus*

Ting (1964) studied two variants of the H_3Cl strain of Rous virus, derived originally from Bryan's standard strain. One grew well on duck cells, the other did not. In this way he was able to show that the resistance induced by one against the other was effective as early as 4 h after the initial infection. He also found that infection with the virus apparently induced a delay in division of one or two cycles, which was not seen in established infections. He interpreted the delay as associated with the latent period of infection. Rous-infected cells seemed to grow at a slightly greater rate than normal fibroblasts.

3. *Chromosome Structure*

Although the large number and small size of individual chromosomes in chick tissues make analysis difficult (Schmid, 1962), Pontén (1963) has shown that both the Rous sarcoma and an erythroleukemia had the normal mode of 78 chromosomes and did not show any visible aberrations. One exceptional Rous sarcoma, however, and the transplantable RPL 12 lymphoid tumor, were hyperdiploid. Evidence of consistent chromosomal changes is lacking.

Since it has been shown that simian and human cells may be infected with the Schmitt-Ruppin strain of sarcoma virus, evidenced by the production of vacuolated cells (Jensen *et al.*, 1964; Stenkvist and Pontén, 1964) containing enlarged nuclei with large and abnormal nucleoli, attention has been focused on the effect of this strain on chromosome structure. Nichols (1963) has shown a progression of chromosomal changes in rat-embryo cells infected with this strain, both *in vitro* and *in vivo,* and further (Nichols, 1964) has claimed that —in contrast to the Bryan strain—it inhibits mitosis in human leucocyte cultures. In somewhat lower dilutions it causes the appearance of increased percentages of abnormal metaphase plates and chromosome breaks.

F. RESPONSE OF ENTIRE CULTURE

Developing limb buds of chick embryos have been inoculated with the Bryan strain (Dunkel and Groupé, 1965). Hemorrhage and tumors were found by the ninth day. Limb buds have also been grown in organ cultures, and in these Rous virus produced degeneration and destruction, but no real tumors (Bang, unpublished). Rabin (unpublished) has inoculated a variety of types of differentiated chick-embryo cells with the virus, but observed no changes in the differentiated cells, except for the characteristic vesicular changes in fibroblastic cells.

Vogt (1964), in a fluorescent-antibody analysis of single plaques occurring on plates of fibroblasts, supports the idea of helper-virus induction, since Rous-virus antigen was detected only in the area of foci. However, the general reaction of the culture to infection, other than acid production (Lo, Gey and Shapras, 1955) has not been studied.

G. PATHOLOGICAL PRODUCTS

Apparently the first direct inoculation of tissue cultures with a virus was that of Carrel (1924) who showed that macrophages inoculated with filtered extracts of the Rous sarcoma produced round, dark, and agglomerated cells in the middle of normal-appearing monocytes. Later there was a mass of necrotic tissue from which fibroblast-like cells escaped. In his studies of infected fibroblasts a year later, Carrel (1925) noted that the cells *in vitro* often took on the appearance of the primary sarcoma; that is, they developed a voluminous cytoplasm full of vacuoles, granulations, and multiple nuclei, and occasionally had nuclei united by a bridge. Borrel (1926) studied Tissue Cultures of the sarcoma, and noted the presence of plasmodial cells which attained dimensions of 500–600μ. His illustrations showed fibroblastic cells heaped on top of each other. The mitochondria of the macrophages and the fibroblasts were normal.

The most detailed studies of Rous sarcomas cultivated *in vitro* have been those of Doljanski and co-workers (Doljanski and Tenenbaum, 1942; Doljanski and Pikorski, 1942; Tenenbaum and Doljanski, 1943). They maintained a culture of Rous sarcoma for eighteen years by constantly adding fragments of normal chick tissue to the culture which was maintained in chicken plasma clotted by diluted embryo extract. Two types of cell were seen—spindle and round cells. The spindle cells appeared as fibroblasts, while the round cells were basophilic and had eccentric nuclei. The round cells picked up carmine from the media, and turned into carmine-containing spindle cells when placed in new media. The nuclei of the basophilic cells (Tenenbaum and Doljanski, 1943) were vesicular; the nucleoli were large and in many cases pushed to one side. A Feulgen-negative inclusion was frequently found in the nucleus. The cytoplasm of the sarcoma cells underwent a separation of the central region from the peripheral part so that two zones appeared. In the central mass there were many eosinophilic granules and even crystal-like structures.

In contrast to these changes, Doljanski and Pikorski (1942) found that the agent of fowl leucosis was maintained on explants of fibroblasts from bone marrow and myocardium of normal adult chickens without detectable changes in the cells. They used the hematocytoblastic strain of Engelbredth-Holm and maintained the agent for 178 days in culture. Intramuscular injection of the cultures did not yield sarcomas.

In a phase-microscopic study of the cellular lesion of Rous virus, Lo *et al.* (1955) found that apparently normal adult chick fibroblast cultures first (8–14 days) showed degeneration and necrosis when exposed to filtrates of the sarcoma or to Bryan's purified suspension. Serial subcultures of these degenerating cultures yielded vigorously growing, apparently healthy colonies, but, within these, there appeared hypertrophied multinucleated giant cells loaded with inclusion droplets. These altered cells eventually disintegrated. There was no evidence of increased proliferation.

As with other viruses, different strains of the agent used produce different morphological effects. Temin (1960) described three variants of the original Bryan passage: one that produced round refractile cells as had been reported in the original studies of Temin and Rubin (1958); one which produced long fusiform cells on the plate of fibroblasts; and one which produced short fusiform cells. These agents were cloned and continuously produced these effects on particular cell types, but the effect was varied by growth on other cells such as duck-embryo fibroblasts. However, both the long fusiform type and the variant which produced round refractile cells were able to convert pigmented iris epithelium into fusiform cells (Ephrussi and Temin, 1960) or round cells respectively.

1. *Mucopolysaccharides*

Borrel in 1926 noted that a viscous eosinophilic substance was uniformly present in the Rous sarcoma. He cultured the cells. By staining the cultures with Giemsa he showed that this substance was present in the macrophages, but that it showed even more clearly in the fibroblasts in which it was found in masses associated with vacuoles. Erichsen, Eng and Morgan (1961) studied the formation of a mucopolysaccharide as detected by histochemical means (colloidal iron, alcian blue, and periodic acid-Schiff (PAS)) in the infected cells. They found that transformed cells were filled with small blue granules (alcian blue) by 5 days of infection, and by the ninth day the substance was found between cells.

Salido-Rengell (1965) has determined that this diastase-resistant material could be found in the cytoplasm of converted cells in the paranuclear area and also close to the surface of the cell. It would then seem that an additional factor in some of the effects of some strains of the virus is the production of an excess of mucopolysaccharide. Whether this material is normal or abnormal is not known.

2. *Biochemical Changes*

Goldé (1962) showed that fibroblasts infected with Bryan "high titer" virus produced an increased amount of RNA, reaching a 75% greater amount per cell by the seventh day of infection. The quantity of DNA per infected cell remained constant. This does not agree with the finding by others of enlarged nuclei, but may be explicable on the basis of different cultural conditions. Hampton and Eidinoff (1962) found that infected and transformed cells took up radioactive uridine into the RNA of the nucleoli at a rate of 2–4 × normal, and that there was an 8 × increase in the thymidine uptake of the nuclei by 14 days. Their results were dependent upon a comparison of the "transformed" cells in the midst of the foci with the unaltered cells in between the foci. They also found that the "transformed" cells yielded a greater precipitate of dinitroformazan when tested for lactic dehydrogenase, than did the normal cells. Salido-Rengell (1966) also found that there was an increased amount of staining with DPN and succinic dehydrogenase systems, staining which localized in a pattern similar to that of the mitochondria.

H. VIRUS GROWTH

1. *By Electron-microscopy*

Although a number of authors have described the appearance of the virus since Claude, Porter and Pickels (1947) first found it in cultures of tumors, Bernhard, Dontcheff, Oberling and Vigier (1953) after some difficulty found it in degenerating cells. However, since normal cultures of embryos often show identical particles (Bang, 1958), and since the demonstration of the blocking effect by Rous interfering factor (RIF) in "normal" cultures (Rubin, 1960a), it is not possible to say which of the various members—of the present complex—were seen in any of the electron-microscope studies.

2. *By Fluorescent Antibody*

Somewhat the same difficulty applies to the identification of antigen in the infected cell. Vogt and Rubin (1961) and Vogt and Luykx (1963) studied the surface of cells for the presence of antigen in unfixed cells, feeling that this method allowed them to detect smaller amounts of antigen. They followed the attachment of viral antigen at 3 h, its disappearance by 18 h, and the reappearance at the cell surface by 70 h. They considered that viral antigen could be detected at the cell surface 25 h earlier in unfixed than in fixed preparations.

XII. Picorna Viruses

Recently poliomyelitis has not only been classified with the enteroviruses, but in turn, the whole group including the new rhinoviruses has been subsumed under the category of Picorna viruses. This group is defined as very small ether-resistant RNA viruses, and includes, among the animal viruses, foot-and-mouth disease and encephalomyocarditis. However, since the studies on cell pathology concentrate on poliomyelitis, studies of the effects of this virus in tissue cultures will dominate the review. Variations in cell susceptibility—related primarily to host of origin, degree of differentiation, temperature of growth—are recognized.

Very little information about the effect of this group of viruses on motion, reaction to environment, and feeding and digestion by the cells is available. The large paranuclear mass (Barski, 1962) which develops in many cells infected with the enteroviruses might be considered under the heading of feeding (and digestion), since Lewis (1919) studied the same lesion in degenerating chick-embryo fibroblasts and suggested that the accumulation of granules and vacuoles which appeared around a giant "centrosphere" may represent waste products of the cell. This work, in combination with the observations of Terni and Allara (1962), makes it clear that even though no virus is added to a culture, this lesion may be produced in "degenerating" or "aging" cells. The mechanism of production of the lesion is unknown.

The general outline of the effects of viruses on motion, feeding, etc., which has been followed in the other sections cannot be adhered to in discussing Picorna viruses because of lack of information on these points. Discussion of this group of agents will then be limited to (1) the *direct pathological effects of the virus on the cell,* the so-called "cytopathic effect", a term coined by Robbins, Enders and Weller (1950) to describe the effect of poliomyelitis on human cell cultures, and (2) *the variation in susceptibility of cells, with particular reference to differentiation.*

A. Cytopathic Effects

After Enders, Weller and Robbins (1949) had found that poliomyelitis grows in cultures of various human tissues suspended in a serum medium, they turned to an analysis of the effects of the virus on cells (Robbins *et al.,* 1950). They first showed that tissue fragments from the suspension cultures lost their typical staining properties when infected and developed nuclear pyknosis and fragmentation. They then determined that such fragments, when explanted on glass, sent out few or no cells from the explant, and that the few cells that did migrate soon degenerated. Finally, they studied the direct inoculation of cultures of cell fragments explanted into roller tubes in which the cells had already migrated. In these they showed that poliomyelitis "rapidly destroys the cells growing out from human skin-muscle." This article (Robbins *et al.,* 1950) was entitled "Cytopathogenic Effect of Poliomyelitis Viruses *in vitro* on Human Embryonic Tissues". Thus was created the term "cytopathogenic", later shortened to "cytopathic". It has now come to mean all kinds of effects on cells, and is familiarly shortened to the initials "CPE", so that it has lost most of its original meaning. We will therefore, here attempt to describe the specific effect of the virus wherever possible, and avoid the more general term, CPE. The early history of the discovery of the general susceptibility of many primate tissues, of the use of trypsinized monkey kidney cultures and the development of techniques for plaque formation have been well summarized by Klöne (1958). It may be added, however, that human fetal respiratory mucosa in organ culture has been destroyed by echovirus and rhinovirus (Hoorn and Tyrell, 1965).

1. *Destruction*

The initial reaction of an infected cell to the growth of poliomyelitis is not localized to any one area. Several phase-microscope studies of this have shown that retraction of the cytoplasmic granules from the edge of a cell, leaving a fractured transparent cytoplasmic edge, is accompanied, practically simultaneously, by a decrease in size of the nucleus and collapse of the nuclear membrane (Klöne, 1955a, 1957, 1958; Stoler and Gey, 1953; Reissig, Howes and Melnick, 1956). The irregular bubbling protrusions at the site seem to be remnants of the ectoplasm, rather than newly extruded material. In a detailed study by phase-microscopy of the infection of monkey kidney cells by Coxsackie A9 virus, Klöne (1957) has shown that the early phase of infection is accompanied by enlargement of the nucleolus and simultaneous swelling and increase in optical density of the mitochondria. In later stages of cytoplasmic retraction, the number of mitochondria is reduced (Fig. 7). Otherwise, the changes are like those of poliomyelitis.

Changes in the cell membrane potential of HeLa cells infected by poliomyelitis have been measured by electrophoretic mobility determinations (Sachtleben and Luyken, 1962) which may reflect these early changes in morphology. In many, but not all, cell strains, the morphological changes are accompanied by the formation of a large dense paranuclear mass (Barski *et al.,* 1955) (see below).

Lwoff, Dulbecco, Vogt and Lwoff (1955) have followed the se-

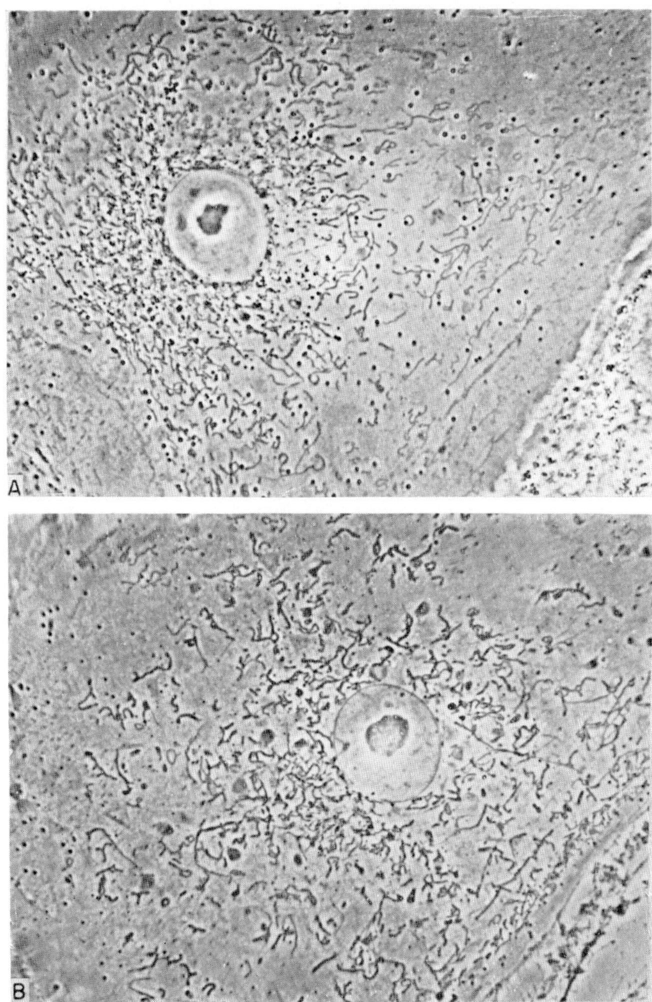

Fig. 7. Coxsackie. A. Tissue culture of living rhesus monkey kidney epithelium infected with Group A Type 7 Coxsackie Virus. The cell shows no morphological changes. Positive phase contrast; 6 h after infection. × 800. B. The same cell 15 h after infection. Enlargement and beginning loosening of nucleolus. Swelling of mitochondria and increase of optical thickness of these.

quence of destruction of individual infected HeLa and monkey kidney cells maintained in droplets on glass under oil. Although such cells were under somewhat abnormal conditions, many of them became attached to the glass and spread on this surface. The first visible reaction to virus was a contraction of the whole cell about an hour before virus was released. At contraction, granular material tended to con-

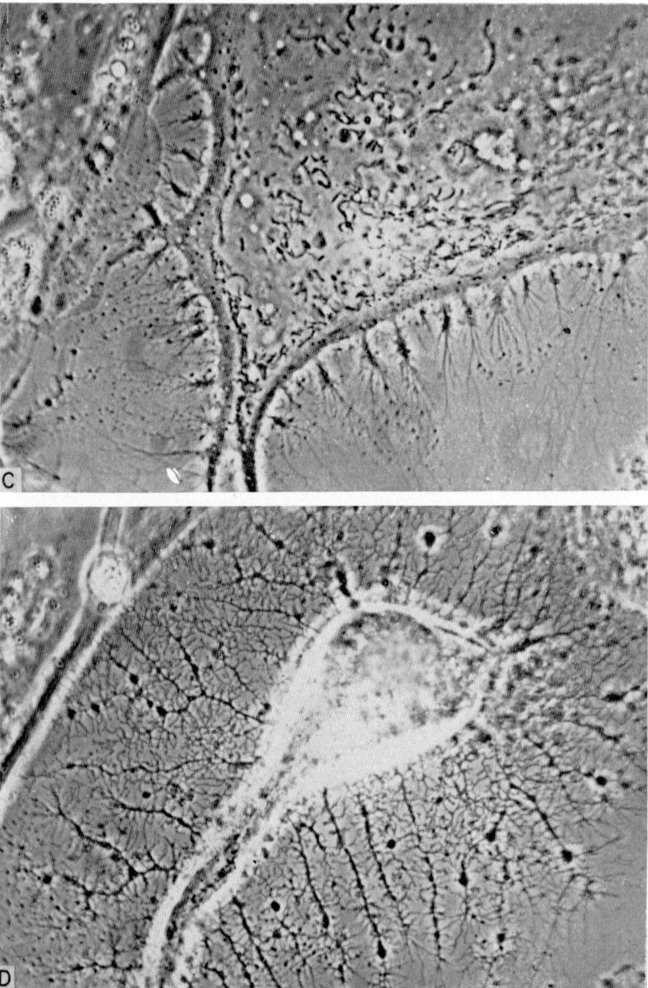

FIG. 7. C. 18⅓ hours after infection of the culture. Same visual field. Formation of protoplasmic extensions. D. 21 h after infection of culture. Same visual field. Continued cell retraction. Courtesy of Dr. W. Klöne.

centrate in the central portion of the cell, leaving a peripheral hyaline zone. After the first virus was released, the hyaline zone underwent profound changes, and in less than a half hour it became vacuolated, developed an irregular outline and was lysed (Fig. 8). One of the difficulties of the study of virus release in this system is that events do not occur synchronously; there may be early releasers which continue to release virus, and other cells which only release virus late in infection (Dunnebacke and Williams, 1961).

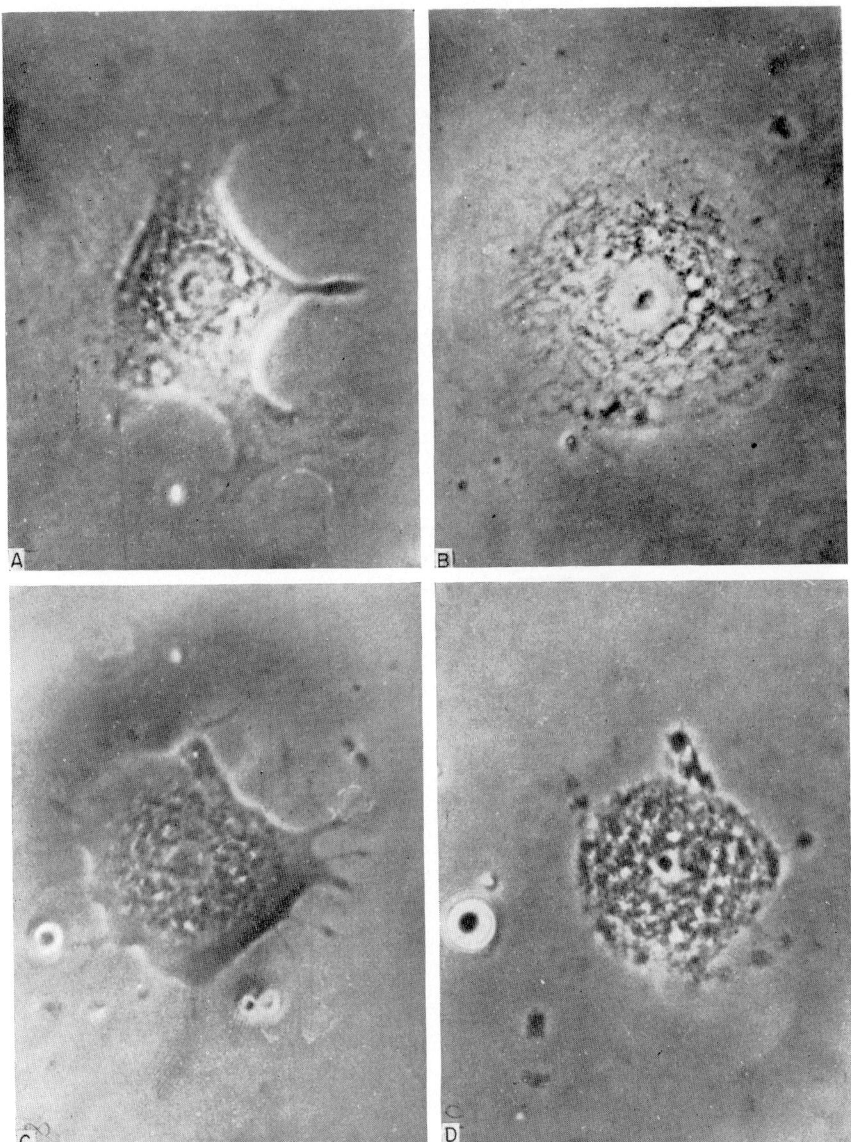

FIG. 8. Sequential destruction of a HeLa cell in a microdrop by poliovirus. Phase microscopy. Courtesy of Dr. A. Lwoff.

In an attempt to localize the infection within the cells, Dunnebacke (1962) studied both poliomyelitis and Coxsackie A9 viruses in individual monkey, FL, and primary human amnion cells. When the latter cells were bisected with a microdissecting needle $4\frac{1}{2}$ h after infection, virus was found in the portion of the cell containing both cytoplasm and nucleus, and not in the purely cytoplasmic portion. There were early nucleolar changes. The same viruses did not localize in the FL and monkey kidney cells.

2. *Nuclear Changes*

These are present. Aside from the distortion produced by pressure, and the shrinkage of the membrane, there may be variable numbers of small nuclear granules. These have been reported in monkey kidney cells infected with polio, Coxsackie, and Echo viruses (Shaver, Barron and Karzon, 1958) (Fig. 9). However, two members of the Echo virus series, Echo 22 and 23, have been shown to produce unique changes in the nucleus (Shaver *et al.*, 1961). In addition to the usual changes produced by enteroviruses in monkey kidney cells, the nucleolus first loses its staining characteristics, then disappears. The chromatin becomes beaded and also disappears, leaving an "empty" nucleus. This is reminiscent of the much less extensive change in the nucleolus of human amnion cells produced by poliomyelitis (Dunnebacke, 1956).

An interesting attempt was made by Klöne (1955b) to determine whether infection of monkey kidney cells had any direct effect on mitotic activity. No increase or decrease in mitotic rate was observed, but certain findings suggested that cells might be infected before mitosis set in, and that division would then proceed though both daughter cells eventually died. By following individual cells for a number of hours, he was able to show that both daughter cells were destroyed at similar but not identical times. In one case, a cell was followed through to an abnormal telophase, from which the cell did not recover but fell apart.

3. *Paranuclear Lesions*

Barski, Robineaux and Endo (1955) early emphasized the development of a large paranuclear mass in the cytoplasm of fibroblasts infected with two strains of poliomyelitis as a distinctive lesion of this virus. He would include the capacity to produce this lesion as one of the characteristics of the enteroviruses in any general description (Barski, 1962. In Barski's original study the lesion developed about 20 h after the culture had been incubated at 30–31°C. The infected cells remained motile, and filamentous mitochondria persisted. Such lesions have now been repeatedly demonstrated in several differ-

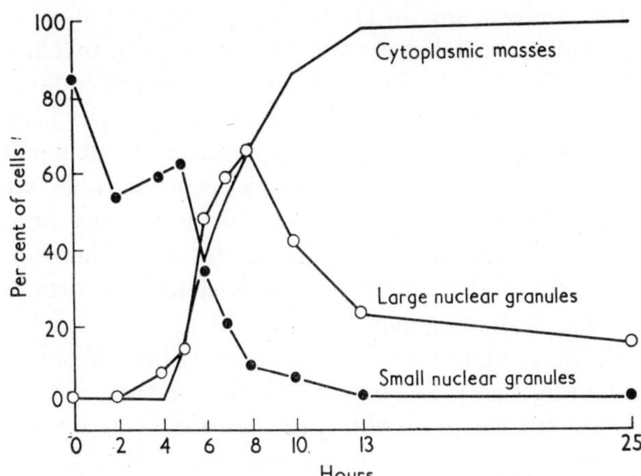

FIG. 9. Quantitative analysis of cytoplasmic and nuclear changes in monkey kidney cells infected with type 1 poliomyelitis (Shaver *et al.*, 1958).

ent cell systems including monkey kidney (Reissig *et al.*, 1956; Beale, Stevens, Davis, Stackiw and Rhodes, 1956; Rifkind, Godman, Howe, Morgan and Rose, 1960), human amnion cells (Endo, Aoyama, Hayashida and Kamimura, 1959), K.B. cells (Terni and Allara, 1962), and HeLa cells (Dunnebacke, 1956), but Klöne failed to find them in living monkey kidney cells (Klöne, 1955, 1958), and Dunnebacke did not see them in human amnion (Dunnebacke, 1956). It might well be, then, that this lesion, common as it is in enterovirus infections, is not an essential step in the destruction of an infected cell by enteroviruses.

4. *Cytochemistry of Paranuclear Mass*

Monkey kidney cells, when developing the characteristic lesion, have at first a mass of tiny granules which stain with Sudan black, PAS, and pyronin, thus suggestive that the Golgi area is a complex lipoprotein structure (Rovescalli and Campanella, 1962). KB cells similarly infected with poliomyelitis have paranuclear masses which are PAS positive, and contain small granules. The Schiff reaction is elicited only after the cell is treated with periodic acid, and is not eliminated by diastase; the mass does not stain metachromatically with toluidine blue, thus it may be a "neutral" polysaccharide.

5. *Similarity to "Aging" Changes or Other Cellular Lesions*

We have pointed out previously (Bang, 1955b, 1959b) that lesions closely resembling paranuclear masses are present in Rous-virus infection, and that W. H. Lewis (1920) pointed them out many years ago amongst the various abnormalities present in some tumor cells grown in Tissue Culture. Indeed, one of Gey's rat tumors, which was derived *in vitro* from normal rat cells, has constantly a large paranuclear mass (Gey, 1954). Since Lewis' (1919) pioneer work is neglected today, it may be worth reviewing, and stating the conditions under which the changes were seen. Cells were of course not trypsinized, and small explants were taken from the legs of 6–8-day chick embryos. They were placed directly on glass in a medium which would not today be considered adequate. Cells were examined directly under oil immersion and were often stained with vital dyes to determine details of structure. Lewis pointed out that both degeneration granules and vacuoles accumulated around the centriole or centrosphere. These granules took up neutral red avidly, and Lewis suggested that they represent waste products. As the culture grew older, the centriole was surrounded by a more or less clear area, and the centrosphere might attain an area and thickness equal to that of the nucleus. Terni and Borghi (1964) took up the problem again, without apparent knowledge of Lewis's work, studied the changes produced by aging, and followed the cytochemistry of the lesion. They showed that 7-day untreated cultures of KB cells developed the same changes seen in poliovirus infected cells at two days. Aggregated in the cytoplasm was an accumulation of RNA, lipids, protein-bound SS and SH groups, alkaline and acid phosphatases. They point to the recent suggestion that cell changes may be due in part to a release of hydrolytic enzymes from lysosomes. It would seem apparent that the characteristic lesion of poliomyelitis is indeed common and reproducible. It is not non-specific, for few changes are, but until more detailed studies are done, it cannot be demonstrated to be specific in the sense that it is uniquely produced by enteroviruses.

6. *Presence of Virus*

(*a*) *Localization of antigen.* The localization of poliomyelitis-virus antigen as determined by fluorescent antibody shows that antigen may be detected as a diffuse cytoplasmic material as early as 2 h after infection, and that it remains in the cytoplasm for these first hours (Buckley, 1955, 1957; Lebrun, 1957). It has also been found in the peripheral portions of the cell as the cell breaks down, particularly in the beaded and bulbous processes of the cell which are left behind as the cell contracts (Buckley, 1957). Later (5 h in Lebrun's study (1957)), spots of fluorescence appear in the nuclei, then, as cell breakdown proceeds, the remnants of cells, including nuclei, have the characteristic antigen. It seems likely, then, that poliomyelitis protein is made primarily in the cytoplasm. The virus of mouse encephalomyelitis (once known as mouse poliomyelitis) and Echo 4 virus, produce similar destruction of mouse L cells, and fluorescent antibody shows that these viruses also localize in the cytoplasm (Henry and Franklin, 1959; Jamison, Mayer and Melnick, 1963).

(*b*) *Virus particles*. Small particles have been seen in cells infected with poliomyelitis in Tissue Culture (Braunsteiner, Fiala, Pakesch and Auerswald, 1958; Ruska, Stuart and Winsser, 1955). These are believed to be the virus. In some cases they have been found in a crystalline array (Stuart and Fogh, 1959; Mayor and Jordan, 1962). Echo viruses were also seen in the cytoplasm of cells, arrayed in parallel rows (Rifkind *et al.*, 1960; Núñez-Montiel, Weibel and Vitelli-Flores, 1961), and Coxsackie virus formed excellent crystals in HeLa cells (Morgan, Howe and Rose, 1959).

(*c*) *Nucleic acid changes*. A review of the biosynthesis of poliomyelitis virus in cells (Darnell and Eagle, 1960) should be consulted for the biochemical aspects. Acridine-orange staining, which differentiates the nucleic acids of the infected cells, shows that 3 h after infection, the nucleus in monkey kidney cells develops a hazy greenish fluorescence which becomes bright green at 4 h, as the cytoplasm becomes reddish. At 5 h a bright green paranuclear spherical body appears concomitant with the disappearance from the nucleus of the bright green fluorescence. This brief report by Tenenbaum (1957) indicates that the earliest change occurs in the nucleus; the observation must be extended to other cell types and other members of the Picorna group before its general application is inferred. Jamison, Mayer and Melnick (1963) followed the cytoplasmic RNA of two strains of Echo 4 virus, one readily neutralized by homologous anti-sera, the other not. They found that the readily neutralized virus produced detectable increase in cytoplasmic RNA 2 h earlier than the one in which the virus was not easily neutralized by its own serum.

Mouse poliomyelitis (GD VII) was first grown in suspended chopped cultures of mouse brain (Parker and Hollender, 1945). Since it will also grow in a mouse cell line, L cells (Henry and Franklin, 1959), which in turn may grow in cell suspension, this virus and a related agent, encephalomyocarditis or Mengo, have been used for extensive studies of the biochemistry of infection, with particular reference to the type and time of formation of virus RNA (Homma and Graham, 1963; Baltimore and Franklin, 1963; Tobey, 1964). These extensive and important studies are, however, outside the purpose of this review. In this connection, it is of interest that Barski emphasizes the lack of development of a paranuclear mass in cells infected with Mengo virus (Barski and Kishida, 1961).

B. VARIATION IN CELL SUSCEPTIBILITY

1. *Effect of Temperature*

This important subject is treated elsewhere in the text and in Pereira's review on "The Cytopathic Effect of Animal Viruses" (1961). It is clear that different mutants of poliomyelitis have different optimum temperatures of growth. The mechanism of the effect is not understood.

2. *Differentiation of Cells*

Central to the problems of pathogenesis of virus diseases lies the problem of specificity. Poliomyelitis posed this in a unique way from the start, for here is a disease in which the motor nerve cells of the spinal cord are selectively destroyed, and yet the virus is now known to multiply in a variety of tissues. It was the very specificity of the viral effect in the human and monkey which prevented researchers for many years from realizing that this virus can be grown on and destroy many primate cells if they have adequate receptors (see below). On the other hand, the current ready availability of susceptible cells has inhibited a study of the phenomenon of specificity in Tissue Culture. The present development of methods for the culture of uniquely differentiated nerve cells should re-awaken interest. Hogue, McAllister, Greene and Coriell (1955, 1958) did study the effect of poliomyelitis 1, 2 and 3 on human brain cells in Tissue Culture. The most marked effect was the early contraction of the tips of the long filamentous nerve cell processes, which was sometimes followed by a withdrawal of the processes into the cell body. The cells continued to contract and finally fragmented into separate masses. The specificity of this effect, which occurred within a few hours of adding virus, was demonstrated by the lack of effect of heated virus and by the neutralization by specific antisera. The effects of other enteroviruses which are not neurotropic would be of considerable interest.

Macrophages from peritoneal exudate of monkeys, plasmacytoma cells and macrophages from human bone marrow-cultures from myeloma patients are not destroyed by poliomyelitis virus (Barski and Robbe-Fossat, 1957; Cramer and Franzen, 1957). Barski and Robbe-Fossat (1957) found that the virus grew in the monkey macrophages, but that the cells were evidently not destroyed. It is, if course, possible that a small portion of fibroblasts present in their cultures might have been responsible for virus growth. In addition, Barski *et al.* (1957) point to the resistance of monkey or human ciliated epithelium *in vitro* to the action of both poliomyelitis and adenovirus. Recently, Gresser, Chany and Enders (1965) studied the continued production of poliomyelitis virus by cultures of strips of human amniotic membrane in suspension. At intervals the strips were removed from the culture, mounted and stained. Despite the continued production of virus no "obvious difference" between the infected and control cultures was observed. However, in both preparations there were foci devoid of amniotic cells, and thus a destructive effect of the virus cannot be ruled out. In this connection the studies of Ackermann, Rabsin and Kurtz (1954) on the lack of parallelism between cell injury and poliomyelitis-virus growth in HeLa cells are of interest. After administration of fluorophenylalanine, virus multiplication proceeded but was markedly inhibited. This may be related to the recent proposal that cell destruction is often produced by the release of lysosomal material into the cell by virus infection (Allison and Mallucci, 1965).

3. *Cell Receptors and Susceptibility*

In addition to the variation in susceptibility of differentiated cells, there is a variation in cell lines. This is summarized by Melnick and Rapp in the following chapter, and it is of interest here merely to point out that although much of the variation in cell and tissue susceptibility may be explained by the presence or absence of appropriate cell receptors (Holland and McLaren, 1961; Holland, 1961; Darnell and Sawyer, 1960; Kunin, 1964), it does not explain the specificity of the destruction of anterior horn cells by poliovirus.

4. *Embryonic and Adult*

Coxsackie viruses were first isolated by the inoculation of baby mice and subsequent localization of the infection in muscle tissues. Adult mice are not susceptible unless pregnant or treated with cortisone. Kańtoch and Kuczkowska (1964a) showed that muscle explants of newborn uninfected mice on collagen substrate yielded an excellent outgrowth of long spindly cells, whereas none migrated from adult mice. Similar cultures made from baby mice infected *in vivo* failed to produce an outgrowth. The authors suggest that this Tissue-Culture method on collagen has indicated the higher susceptibility of the undifferentiated muscle cells. It is of course possible that many other factors are responsible, among them hormones, as the authors point out. In this connection the report that prednisolone increases the susceptibility of connective tissue *in vitro* is interesting (Hovel, 1963).

XIII. Arboviruses

The arbovirus group includes an assortment of viruses, some of which are known to have RNA and cubical symmetry and all of which are believed to be transmitted by—and multiply in—insects (Andrewes, 1964). This characteristic, along with the necessity for producing viremia in their vertebrate hosts, has doubtless been a selective evolutionary force which has tended to keep them set apart, and may have produced some degree of convergent evolution. The degree of homogeneity within the arbovirus group has not been worked out. The fact that some of them localize in the central nervous system (encephalitis), some in the liver (yellow fever, Rift Valley fever), and some presumably in the skin (dengue), is probably of secondary importance, and may not be associated with any basic difference in viral structure or function. The tissue specificity, though, must represent differential "tropisms", and these have not yet been investigated in Tissue Culture.

A. MOTION

Most of the arboviruses have direct destructive effects on the cells, do not produce distinctive cellular lesions, and seem to produce chronic infections in cultures by destroying a percentage of the cells, inducing thereby the production of interferon which in turn protects cells which have not yet been attacked by virus. The principal affected area of the cell is evidently the cytoplasm. Although yellow-fever virus was the first arbovirus to be grown in Tissue Culture (Haagen and Theiler, 1932), in this and in subsequent extensive studies which led to the development of a vaccine (Lloyd, Theiler and Ricci, 1935–36) no attempt was made to determine the effects of the virus on the cultures in which the virus was growing.

The destructive effect of these viruses upon cells was observed quite early in Tissue Culture and was used as a method of titration on Western equine encephalomyelitis by Huang (1943), who showed that transplants of infected Tissue Cultures failed to grow. Later it was shown that selected cell lines from the same original host might have differing susceptibility to Eastern equine encephalomyelitis (Bang and Gey, 1952), and that persistent or chronic infections could be established in cell cultures with this same virus (Bang, Gey, Foard and Minnegan, 1957). The high yield of virus in cell culture allowed relatively easy visualization with the electron-microscope (Bang and Gey, 1949). It was the destructive effect of this group of viruses which was used by Dulbecco and Vogt (1954) to establish the plaque-counting method of titrating encephalitis which has since been extensively used for titrations of many agents. In spite of the long history of the study of arboviruses in Tissue Culture, the literature on stepwise changes effected in cells by the viruses is very scanty, and little attempt has been made to correlate morphological and biochemical events in infected cells.

B. REACTION TO ENVIRONMENT

Despite the early interest in the effects of this group of viruses on cells, and the subsequent continued practical use of some cell strains and cultures in the isolation of viruses in the field, both from infected vertebrates and mosquitoes, relatively little is known about potential or real differential cellular susceptibility. Although it is clear (Table II) that all of the viruses of group A destroy both epithelial and fibroblast cells, there are no published reports of the effect of group A viruses on macrophages.* This is particularly startling when one considers that all of these agents are dependent upon a viremia for their continued survival, and that the large amounts of virus in the blood presumably result from growth of the virus either in circulating leucocytes (including macrophages) or in the endothelial cells lining the liver, spleen, etc. This lack of information is particularly striking for yellow fever, since it is known that the pathogenesis of yellow fever involves extensive destruction of the Kupffer-cell system (Smetana, 1962).

The virus of Eastern equine encephalomyelitis grows readily in laboratory rats, and occasionally kills by infection of the central nervous system. Cell lines which have been maintained in tissue cultures for some years differ markedly in their susceptibility to this virus. A line of normal rat fibroblasts was found highly resistant to the effect, whereas a tumor cell derivative of this linc was found highly susceptible when cultivated in identical media. Other rat cell lines were found to have intermediate degrees of susceptibility (Bang and Gey, 1952).

C. PATHOLOGICAL EFFECTS

Buckley (1961) and Buckley and Shope (1961) have systematically studied the effect of a large number of arboviruses on one cell type (HeLa) and found that the great majority of them are destructive, but that an occasional strain of virus (even within group A) does not grow in or destroy these cells. No pattern of relationships among the viruses emerged. Although Henderson and Taylor (1960), in testing the susceptibility of cells kept under agar, found that the three groups did have some differential effect on different types of primary trypsinized cells, the variety of effects produced by altering the overlay (Georgiades, Stern, McCollum and Henderson, 1965; Porterfield, 1959) at present prevents one from making a valid generalization. In addition, following the demonstration by Miles and Austin (1963) that the hamster

*One member of group B, West Nile virus, has been shown to grow well in macrophage cultures from genetically susceptible mice (Goodman and Koprowski, 1962).

TABLE II

Authors	Virus	Cell system	Effects of viruses on cells
1. Buckley, 1962	Group A, B, C	HeLa	Marked through moderate destruction
2. Henderson and Taylor, 1960	Group A, B, C	Chick embryo, duck embryo membrane and kidney, rhesus monkey kidney trypsinized	Differential destruction under agar
3. Rapp and Buckley, 1962	Junin virus	HeLa	Antigen in cytoplasm (fluorescent antibody) basophilic inclusions cytopathology: destruction or chronic infection
Mettler *et al.*, 1961	Junin virus	HeLa	Cytopathic after 10 serial passages
4. Huang, 1943	Western Equine Encephalitis (A)	Chick embryo	Destruction
5. Bang and Gey, 1952	Eastern Equine Encephalitis (A)	Several types rat fibroblasts; human tumor strains	Differential destruction or chronicity, type-related
Bang *et al.*, 1957	E E E (A)	Chick fibroblasts	Destruction of entire cell
6. Chambers, 1957	W E E (A)	L strain fibroblasts	Destruction
7. Mussgay and Weibel, 1962	W E E (A)	KB cells, trypinized	Virus in membranes (electron microscope)
8. Eiring and Scherer, 1960	W E E (A)	Mouse fibroblasts	"Cytonecrosis" after passage
9. Noyes, 1955	Egypt 101 (B)	Human carcinoma Epidermal carcinoma	Viral antigen diffuse in cytoplasm
10. Hotta, 1959	Dengue (B)	Rhesus kidney trypsinized	Slender strands; juxtanuclear hypertrophy
Hotta *et al.*, 1962, 1964	Jap B (B)	Puppy cerebellar explant	Destruction
	Yellow fever (B)	(Several species) kidney trypsinized	Degeneration

TABLE II (*continued*)

Authors	Virus	Cell system	Effects of viruses on cells
11. Sokolov *et al.*, 1963	Russian Spring-Summer tick-borne encephalitis (B)	Sheep embryo kidney	Perinuclear mass; stains with fluorescent antibody; nucleoli swollen; no destruction
12. Doherty, 1958	Yellow fever (B) West Nile (B)	Conjunctiva Appendix	No destruction Destruction and regeneration both Yellow fever and West Nile
13. Kovac *et al.*, 1961–62	Russian Spring-Summer tick-borne encephalitis (B)	HeLa	Hypertrophy of Golgi vesicles
14. Zalkind *et al.*, 1963	Russian Spring-Summer tick-borne encephalitis (B)	Hep-2	Heterogeneity, giant cells; no destruction
15. Buckley and Shope, 1961	Group (C)	Detroit 6 Hep-1; Hep-2 Human intestine	Destruction
16. Coackley, 1963	Rift Valley fever (C)	Lamb testis trypsinized	Eosinophilia; filaments in nucleus; rapid cell death

kidney cell line BHK 21 is highly susceptible to a number of arboviruses, N. Karabatsos and S. Buckley (personal communication) have found that this cell line is susceptible to more than 120 different arboviruses, including A, B, C, and other groups.

XIV. Miscellaneous Viruses

Four other viruses which have not yet been adequately classified deserve discussion, because in each case unique effects on cells have been discovered or unique experiments have been done with them. These are rabies, reoviruses, vesicular stomatitis, and mouse hepatitis.

A. Rabies

This virus has long been recognized as a neurotrope because of its remarkable dissemination in the nervous system and apparent entry through peripheral nerves, yet its excretion from the salivary glands raised doubts that growth was limited to the central nervous system. It has been grown in a variety of mixed Tissue Cultures (Klöne, 1958), but the data on the effect of the virus on the cells in which it grew have been scanty until recently. The virus destroys cells from the cerebellum and Ammon's horn *in vitro* (Fernandes and Pomerat, 1961). Two recent advances have changed this picture. First, it has been identified by electron-microscopy in the central nervous system (Matsumoto, 1962, 1963) and subsequently in infected Tissue Cultures of chick embryos (Davies, Englert, Sharpless and Cabasso, 1963; Atanasiu, Lepine and Dragonas, 1963) as a short or elongated rod of complex structure occurring both at the surface of the cell and within the cytoplasm. Secondly, fluorescent-antibody techniques have shown that large amounts of antigen are present in infected cells without extensive cell destruction (Atanasiu *et al.*, 1963; Nadel and Orsi, 1964; Allen, Sims and Sulkin, 1964; Fernandes, Wiktor and Koprowski, 1964; Atanasiu, Favre and Collombier, 1961). The dissemination of rabies virus was not apparent in standard microscopic preparations, but recent techniques have shown clearly that rabies virus occurs in a variety of cell types and that, like poliomyelitis virus, it is not dependent upon nervous tissue for growth *in vitro*.

Allen *et al.* (1964) have shown that virus may grow in cultures of brown fat of bats at 37·5°C without producing degenerative changes, but that cytoplasmic inclusions are seen in cells. When the temperature is lowered to 8°C (mimicking hibernation of the bat) virus is no longer produced, though fluorescent antibody shows that viral antigen is still present in the cytoplasm. When the temperature is returned to 37·5°C, virus again appears in the cells and medium, and large cytoplasmic inclusions are often seen. These studies are of interest in relation to the capacity of the virus to grow in brown fat of infected bats *in vivo*. Salivary gland cells may also support the growth of virus in culture (Depoux, 1963). The 2017th rabbit brain passage of virus originally isolated by Louis Pasteur grew on dispersed cells obtained from puppies, preferably newborn. No apparent specific degeneration of infected cells was produced even in cultures which were kept for 15 weeks with constant fluid renewal. Infected cells which were allowed to degenerate because of lack of fluid renewal also showed no specific changes. The lack of virus effect on these two cell types (dog salivary gland and bat brown fat) may have no special meaning for pathogenic studies, however, since neither chick embryo (Nadel and Orsi, 1964) nor rabbit endothelial cells (Fernandes, Wiktor and Koprowski, 1963) are destroyed by the virus either, even when large amounts are present.

The most remarkable instance of a symbiotic relationship between host cell and rabies virus is that reported by Fernandes *et al.* (1964). They showed that no cytopathic effect was produced by virus in rabbit endothelial cells through some ninety-three transfers, and yet virus was continually demonstrated by fluorescent antibody staining. During the initial phase of infection of this cell line a low percentage of cells carried antigen, but by the fourth subculture 100% of the cells showed excellent fluorescent cytoplasmic granules and inclusions. All cells undergoing division showed viral antigen throughout the mitotic process. The growth rate, plating efficiency, and morphological characteristics of the infected and control cultures were identical. Antiserum failed to stop the continuous production of virus and its dispersion to daughter cells during mitosis. The infected system was resistant to super-infection with homologous and heterologous viruses. In the above respects it most closely resembles the infection of human conjunctival cells by mumps virus (Walker and Hinze, 1962).

B. REOVIRUSES

This group of agents was originally recognized as a cause of hepatoencephalomyelitis in mice, and has subsequently been found among various enteric and respiratory agents recovered from man. They are now defined as ether-stable RNA viruses having a cubical symmetry of about 60–90 mμ. They deserve special attention because of the peculiar accumulation and distribution of virus-containing material in the cytoplasm of cells which they infect (Drouhet, 1958), and because of the association of this inclusion with the mitotic spindle (Spendlove, Lennette and John, 1963a).

Drouhet (1960) demonstrated that this remarkable mass, which surrounds the nucleus without seeming to affect the appearance of either the nucleus or other areas of the cytoplasm, is Feulgen-negative but stains intensely red with methyl-green pyronin. This latter staining is prevented by digestion with RNAase. Virus is found within such "inclusions" in variable amounts, sometimes in apparent crystalline array (Tournier and Plissier, 1960). Rhim, Jordan and Mayor (1962) then extended these findings, following the development of cellular lesions in a one step growth infection of monkey kidney cells by phase-microscopy, acridine-orange staining, and electron-microscopy. They found that a small inclusion of irregular shape first appeared in the cytoplasm 6 h after infection. By 12–24 h, 20% of the cells had cytoplasmic changes. The first increase of RNA occurred at 16 h; both RNA and antigen, detected by fluorescent antibody, reached their maximum by 54 h, at which time the entire nucleus was surrounded by an irregular, often filamentous, material which broke up and rejoined at different places to form a reticulum (Fig. 10). This matrix

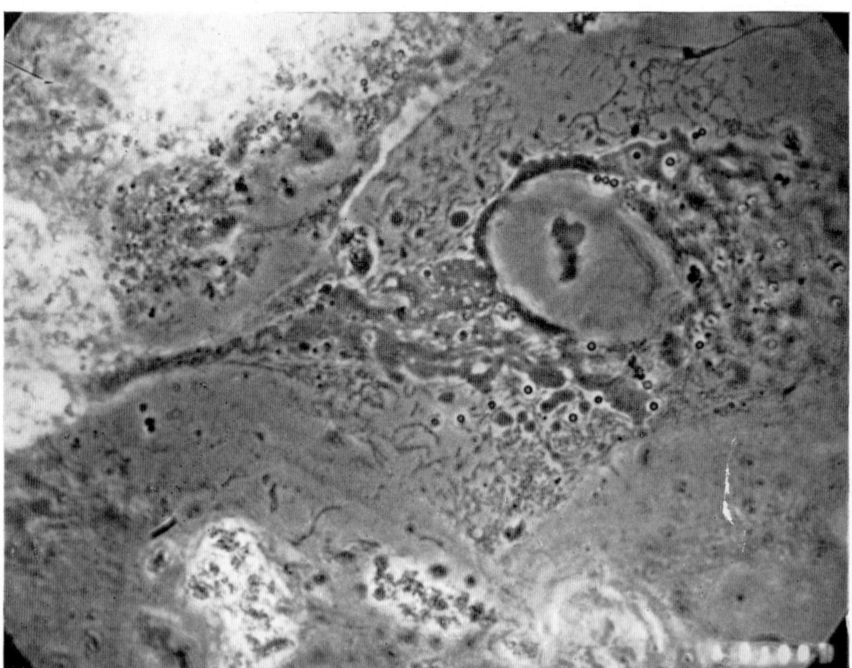

FIG. 10. Monkey kidney cell in culture infected with SV_{12} (Reovirus); inclusion in cytoplasm consists of virus colonies surrounding nucleus. Phase microscopy. Courtesy of Dr. H. G. du Buy.

contained 70 μ virus particles. A similar developmental sequence has been described in HeLa cells (Spendlove, Lennette, Knight and Chin, 1963b).

Spendlove *et al.* (1963a) discovered that this reticulated mass of virus material is associated with the mitotic apparatus, and that this may be demonstrated in human amnion cells made parasynchronous in their division by exposure to temperatures of 4°C for 30 min followed by incubation at 35°C. Staining with fluorescent antibody showed that the antigen in its reticular formation shifts to the perinuclear region as infection progresses, and that it localizes in the centriole region and among the spindle fibers during the process of division. Various mitotic inhibitors such as mercaptoethanol, colchicine, podophyllin and vincaleucoblastine prevented the reticulum formation and caused the antigen to localize in small and large spheres scattered throughout the cytoplasm, but did not seem to decrease the total antigen.

Dales (1963) and Dales and Gomatos (1965) have followed the same series of events with the electron-microscope and have obtained striking pictures in L cells, showing virus particles directly adherent to the individual spindle tubules. Colchicine caused the spindle tubules to disappear, but virus particles measured by both morphological appearance and titer were not affected. A recent examination of the infected cell (Dales and Gomatos, 1965) with a combination of autoradiography and ferritin-tagged antibody indicates that a close association of mitotic spindle tubules and a cytoplasmic filamentous component are involved in virus synthesis.

C. VESICULAR STOMATITIS

This rod-shaped RNA virus, which is the cause of disease in cattle and a variety of other animals, matures at the membrane surfaces of the infected cell. It has been observed attached to cytoplasmic membranes, and within, and attached to the membranes of, vacuoles, Spherical particles are also found (Mussgay and Weibel, 1963). Although it is reported to be smaller than rabies virus, much of its morphological development is similar to rabies. It has been of particular interest in Tissue-Culture studies because of the production of interferon (Hackett, 1964). Its specific importance in this review relates to studies by Saxén, Vainio and Toivonen (1963) on the selective destruction of cells in embryonic organ cultures. Mouse kidney rudiments when infected *in vitro* with this virus have certain stages of development which determine viral susceptibility. The condensed areas of metanephrogenic mesenchyme suffer first; subsequently the destructive effect spreads throughout the kidney rudiment. When virus multiplication and localization were determined by fluorescent antibody, the following results were obtained: (1) the mesenchyme supported the growth of both polyoma virus (see Section IX) and vesicular stomatitis, whereas renal tubules were resistant to both; (2) mesenchymal condensations, which represented the first detectable step in tubulogenesis, resisted polyoma but were highly susceptible to vesicular stomatitis, and large amounts of virus were found in them (Vainio, Saxén and Toivonen, 1963 a, b, c). Since vesicular stomatitis both produces interferon and is susceptible to its action (Hackett, 1964), it is possible that a portion of this variation in cell susceptibility within the organizing rudiment is related to variation in the capacity of the cells to produce interferon.

D. MOUSE HEPATITIS

Acute, often fatal, destruction of the liver is produced by members of this group of agents. Some strains of virus are dependent upon an associated protozoon (*Epierythrozoon coccoides*), while other strains cause destruction without the associated protozoon. Tissue-Culture interest relates to the selective destruction of macrophages by virus which is unadapted to Tissue Culture (Bang and Warwick, 1959), the association of genetic susceptibility with cell susceptibility (Bang and Warwick, 1960), the possible damage of cells by release of lysosomes (Allison and Mallucci, 1965), and the protection against cytotoxic effects by antihistamine drugs (Vainio *et al.,* 1962a, b). A strain of virus which is pathogenic for weanling mice produces giant cells in cultures of macrophages (Mallucci, 1965).

Explants of embryonic mouse liver when placed on a collagen substrate yield a mixed growth of parenchymal liver cells, fibroblasts, and a large population of macrophages which migrate away from the collagen substrate. Destruction of these macrophages as well as those in the explant takes place within two to three days of addition of virus. Despite this, the parenchymal liver cells and fibroblasts remain undamaged (Bang and Warwick, 1959). After serial passage the virus becomes adapted and destroys other cells (Bang and Warwick, 1960; Mosely, 1961). However, when virus has been taken directly from an infected mouse, the selective destruction of macrophages has remained constant. Two inbred lines of mice were shown to differ in susceptibility to the strain of virus used. PRI mice were highly susceptible and C_3H mice resistant. Hybridization and cross-breeding tests have shown the genetic factor to be unifactorial and autosomal. Tests of peritoneal macrophages for susceptibility reflect the same results as obtained with adult mice (Kańtoch, Warwick and Bang, 1963); the resistant cells were destroyed only by amounts of virus 10^4 to 10^6 times that needed to initiate infection in susceptible cells. Destruction of susceptible cells by the virus has been obtained in monolayers under agar, thus forming excellent plaques (Shif and Bang, 1966).

Macrophage cultures infected with MHV_3 (a strain pathogenic for weanling mice) form giant cells which may also be used to titrate the virus in Tissue Culture (Mallucci, 1965). Such macrophages, when infected, show a greater amount of acid phosphatase in the cell than do normal macrophages (Allison and Mallucci, 1965). The relation between this possible mechanism of cell effect, and the partial prevention of cell destruction by an antihistamine, diphenhydramine, when MHV_3 is growing in spleen macrophages (Vainio *et al.,* 1962) needs investigation.

XV. Apologia and Epilogue

The volume of new literature on the effects of viruses and other living agents on cells in Tissue Culture has been so great, even since Klöne's (1958) review, that it has been necessary to limit this present survey in order to keep it manageable. Some important areas have been omitted, especially the insect viruses, interferon production, detection of certain viruses or strains of virus by the interference phenomenon, and the biochemical effects of viruses on cells. These were conscious omissions in the face of the rapid output of increasingly specialized literature which should be analyzed by someone specifically qualified. No attempt has been made to chart the formidably full list of agents which have been grown in Tissue Culture, nor have significant studies on mammary tumor inciter, frog carcinoma, and several unclassified viruses been described. There may have been other omissions through oversight or ignorance.

Nonetheless, a large literature has been surveyed. It is a surprisingly biased literature. In the introduction, the types of essential information for analyzing the effects of living agents on cells was outlined. When the currently available information for each group of agents is pooled, it is clear that very little is known about their effects on cell motion and feeding. The cell has to be able to regulate the type and number of internal ions. Hogue (1919) showed that normal cells in hypotonic solutions would develop vacuoles, M. R. Lewis (1920) that intestinal epithelial cells would develop vacuoles when infected with typhoid bacteria, and it is known that kidney cells develop large vacuoles when infected with the Papova virus SV_{40}. It is not known whether these developments are related.

Once it was recognized that transformed cells showed disoriented growth and apparently lost contact inhibition, the phenomenon has been intensely studied. It is now clear, from Abercrombie's (1962) warning that the phenomenon has limited application, and Stoker's (1964a, b) demonstration that transformed cells do interact with normal cells, that investigation of this fruitful area has just begun.

Quantitative virology has correctly emphasized the need to infect a large proportion of standardized cells—usually trypsinized (Cold Spring Harbor Symposium, 1962). Yet most of the differentiated functions of cells are depressed or lost in cell lines or trypsinized suspensions, so it is not surprising that very little is known concerning the effect of living agents on such things as mucous secretion, endocrine production, or collagen formation. Rous-infected cells, however, have been shown to secrete an excess of mucopolysaccharide (Erichsen *et al.*, 1961), and transformed mouse cells to regain the capacity to make collagen (Todaro *et al.*, 1964). Organ cultures, which preserve a much larger degree of differentiated function, are being used more frequently for virus studies, and it is possible that disturbances of function, rather than cell death, may be more explicitly detailed in the future.

A major task has been to arrange the available knowledge in some comprehensible fashion. The classification of different viruses is just now reaching an acceptible state, but will no doubt continue to be revised. Predicated on the theory of increasing parasitism in the evolution of viruses (the Green-Laidlaw hypothesis, ably defended by Sir Christopher Andrewes, 1965), the material covered in this review has been arranged in a chart which proceeds from larger to smaller agents, and shows the multiple origins of these small intracellular parasites. While classification today is based on the nature of the nucleic acid, morphology, and serological relationships of the agents (Andrewes, 1964), it is clear that certain classes of viruses have very similar effects on the cell. The smaller DNA viruses (adeno and papova viruses) are the only ones so far known to complete their formation inside the nucleus. Herpes (the next larger DNA virus) causes major changes in the nucleus where a large portion of its growth takes place. However, the growth of rickettsia in the nuclei, the increase of myxovirus antigen (influenza and fowl plague), and the production of nuclear lesions by measles and bovine parainfluenza 3 make it clear that other agents can both have a direct effect on the nucleus and derive part of their vitality from it. The localization and huge amount of adeno and papova viruses in the nuclei of the infected cells is so striking that it seems likely that it represents a fundamental step in the biochemical dependence of this group of agents, particularly since increasing dependence on the host accompanies decreasing size. Most parasites acquire new characteristics as they lose others. The specialized mechanisms which the myxoviruses have developed to use the cell surface for release, or the production of giant syncytia by these and the herpes agents, may represent the acquisition or accentuation of such properties. Penetration into new cells by pinocytosis is followed by induced active changes in the cell. Agents which spread from cell to cell despite the presence of antibody may have skipped the step of pinocytosis, and the formation of syncytia may be related to this.

The forces of natural selection (almost by definition) favor those agents which can persist and reproduce. There are then mechanisms for continued association of viruses in cells and specialized mechanisms for progression from cell to cell. Chronic infections without the presence of antibody have been found in Tissue Culture in most if not all of the groups. Increasing study of chronic or persistent infections of cultures has shown that there may be a variety of mechanisms involved, one of which is clearly the production of interferon. On the other hand, in mumps (Hinze and Walker, 1961) and rabies (Fernandes *et al.*, 1964) cultures, the virus has evidently adapted its growth almost perfectly to that of the host cell. Whether these cultured cell systems are able to respond to unfavorable conditions as well as the uninfected cells in the living host has not been determined. Finally, virus antigen may persist in the adeno and papova systems, presumably through some association with host DNA replications.

References

Abercrombie, M. (1962). Contact-dependent behavior of normal cells and the possible significance of surface changes in virus-induced transformation. *Cold Spr. Harb. Symp. quant. Biol.* **27**, 427.

Abercrombie, M. and Ambrose, E. J. (1958). Interference microscope studies of cell contacts in tissue culture. *Exp. Cell Res.* **15**, 332.

Ackermann, W. W., Rabsin, A. and Kurtz, H. (1954). Growth characteristics of poliomyelitis virus in HeLa cell cultures. Lack of parallelism in cellular injury and virus increase. *J. exp. Med.* **100**, 437.

Ahlstrom, C. G. (1964). Neoplasm in mammals induced by Rous chicken sarcoma material. International Conference on Avian Tumor Viruses. *Nat. Cancer Inst. Monogr.* **17**, 299.

Albrecht, P., Blaskovic, D., Jakubik, J. and Lesso, J. (1963). Demonstrations of pseudorabies virus in chick embryo cell cultures and infected animals by the fluorescent antibody technique. *Acta virol.* **7**, 289.

Allen, R., Sims, R. A. and Sulkin, S. E. (1964). Studies with cultured brown adipose tissue. I. Persistence of rabies virus in bat brown fat. *Amer. J. Hyg.* **80**, 11.

Allison, A. C. and Mallucci, L. (1965). Histochemical studies of lysosomes and lysosomal enzymes in virus-infected cell cultures. *J. exp. Med.* **121**, 463.

Andrewes, C. H. (1964). Arboviruses. *In* "Viruses of Vertebrates", pp. 49–103. Williams and Wilkins, Baltimore.

Andrewes, C. H. (1965). Viruses and Noah's Ark. *Bact. Rev.* **29**, 1.

Andrewes, C. H., Bang, F. B. and Burnet, F. M. (1955). A short description of the *Myxovirus* group (influenza and related viruses). *Virology* **1**, 176.

Aoyama, Y. (1959). Changes of cultured cells infected with measles virus. *Jap. J. exp. Med.* **29**, 535.

Appleyard, G., Westwood, J. C. N. and Zartouw, H. T. (1962). The toxic effect of rabbit-pox virus in tissue culture. *Virology* **18**, 159.

Armstrong, J. A., Pereira, H. G. and Andrewes, C. H. (1961). Observation on the virus of infectious bovine rhinotracheitis and its affinity with the herpesvirus group. *Virology* **14**, 276.

Armstrong, J. A., Pereira, H. G. and Valentine, R. C. (1962). Morphology and development of respiratory syncytial virus in cell cultures. *Nature, Lond.* **196**, 1179.

Armstrong, J. A. and Reed, S. E. (1964). Nature and origin of initial bodies in lymphogranuloma venereum. *Nature, Lond.* **201**, 371.

Armstrong, J. A., Valentine, R. C. and Fildes, C. (1963). Structure and replication of the trachoma agent in cell cultures, as shown by electron microscopy. *J. gen. Microbiol.* **30**, 59.

Atanasiu, P., Favre, S. and Collombier, M. (1961). Multiplication du virus de la rage fixe sur cellules gliales en culture et apparition d'inclusions spécifiques intracytoplasmiques. Application au diagnostic de la rage. *C.R. Acad. Sci., Paris* **252**, 2029.

Atanasiu, P., Lepine, P. and Dragonas, P. (1963). Étude cinetique du virus rabique en culture de tissus à l'aide des anticorps fluorescents et des coupes ultra-fines. *Ann. Inst. Pasteur* **105**, 813.

Balducci, D. and Castelli, L. (1957). Confronto dei fenomeni citopatogeni da virus poliomelitici e virus adenoidei in cellule HeLa. Osservazioni in contrasto di fase riprese con cinematografica a colori. *R.C. 1st sup. Sanit.* **20**, 865.

Baltimore, D. and Franklin, R. M. (1963). A new ribonucleic acid polymerase appearing after mengovirus infection of L-cells. *J. biol. Chem.* **238**, 3395.

Baluda, M. A. (1962). Properties of cells infected with avian myeloblastosis. *Cold Spr. Harb. Symp. quant. Biol.* **27**, 415.

Bang, F. B. (1953). The development of the virus of Newcastle disease in epithelial and fibroblast cells in tissue culture. *Johns Hopk. Hosp. Bull.* **92**, 291.

Bang, F. B. (1955a). Morphology of viruses. *In* "Annual Review of Microbiology" (C. E. Clifton, S. Raffel and R. Y. Stanier, eds.), Vol. 9, pp. 21–44. George Banta Publishing Co., Stanford, California.

Bang, F. B. (1955b). Pathology of the cell infected with viruses—morphological and biochemical aspects. *Fed. Proc.* **14**, 619.

Bang, F. B. (1958). Three dilemmas in the study of viruses and tumor cells. *Cancer Res.* **18** (9), 1004.

Bang, F. B. (1959a). Physiologic and structural aspects of viral cell pathology. *Lab. Invest.* **8**, 557.

Bang, F. B. (1959b). The morphological approach. *In* "The Viruses" (F. M. Burnet and W. M. Stanley, eds.), Vol. 3, pp. 63–110. Academic Press, New York and London.

Bang, F. B. and Foard, M. (1964). Use of Rous-free flock of chickens in study of antigenic relationships to avian tumor viruses. *Nat. Cancer Inst. Monogr.* **17**, 495.

Bang, F. B. and Gey, G. O. (1949). Electron microscopy of tissue cultures infected with the virus of Eastern equine encephalomyelitis. *Proc. Soc. exp. Biol., N.Y.* **71**, 78.

Bang, F. B. and Gey, G. O. (1952). Comparative susceptibility of cultured cell strains to the virus of Eastern equine encephalomyelitis. *Johns Hopk. Hosp. Bull.* **91**, 427.

Bang, F. B., Gey, G. O., Foard, M. and Minnegan, D. (1957). Chronic infections produced in cultured cell strains by the virus of Eastern equine encephalomyelitis. *Virology* **4**, 404.

Bang, F. B., Levy, E. and Gey, G. O. (1951). Some observations on host-cell-virus relationship in fowl pox. I. Growth in tissue cultures. *J. Immunol.* **66**, 329.

Bang, F. B. and Niven, J. S. F. (1958). A study of infection in organized tissue cultures. *Brit. J. exp. Path.* **39**, 317.

Bang, F. B. and Warwick, A. (1957). The effect of an avirulent and a virulent strain of Newcastle virus (*Myxovirus multiforme*) on cells in tissue culture. *J. Path. Bact.* **73** (2), 321.

Bang, F. B. and Warwick, A. (1959). Macrophages and mouse hepatitis. *Virology* **9**, 715.

Bang, F. B. and Warwick, A. (1960). Mouse macrophages as host cells for the mouse hepatitis virus and the genetic basis of their susceptibility. *Proc. nat. Acad. Sci.* **46**, 1065.

Bankowski, R. A. (1964). Cytopathogenicity of Newcastle disease virus. *In* "Newcastle Disease Virus, an Evolving Pathogen" (R. P. Hanson, ed.), pp. 231–246. University of Wisconsin Press, Madison, Wisconsin.

Baron, S. (1964). Relationship of interferon and temperature to virulence of Newcastle disease virus. *In* "Newcastle Disease Virus, an Evolving Pathogen" (R. P. Hansson, ed.), pp. 205–220. University of Wisconsin Press, Madison, Wisconsin.

Barski, G. (1962). The significance of *in vitro* cellular lesions for classification of enteroviruses. *Virology* **18**, 152.

Barski, G. and Kishida, T. (1961). Continuous phase contrast observation of cells infected with mengo-EMC viruses. *Virology* **14**, 299.

Barski, G., Kourilsky, R. and Cornefert, F. (1957). Resistance of respiratory ciliated epithelium to action of polio and adenoviruses *in vitro*. *Proc. Soc. exp. Biol., N.Y.* **96**, 386.

Barski, G., Messore, G. and Lepine, P. (1955). L'exsudat péritonéal artificiel source de cellules pour la culture des virus *in vitro*. *Ann. Inst. Pasteur* **89**, 366.

Barski, G. and Robbe-Fossat, F. (1957). Multiplication du virus poliomyélitique dans les cultures *in vitro* de cellules exsudatives de singe sans effet cytopathogène généralisé. *Ann. Inst. Pasteur* **92**, 301.

Barski, G. and Robineaux, R. (1959). Evolution of herpes simplex cellular lesions observed *in vitro* by phase contrast microcinematography. *Proc. Soc. exp. Biol., N.Y.* **101**, 632.

Barski, G., Robineaux, R. and Endo, M. (1955). Phase contrast cinematography of cellular lesion produced by poliomyelitis virus *in vitro*. *Proc. Soc. exp. Biol., N.Y.* **88**, 57.

Beale, A. J., Stevens, P. F., Davis, N., Stackiw, W. and Rhodes, A. J. (1956). The development of inclusions in tissue cultures of monkey kidney epithelial cells infected with poliomyelitis virus. *Canad. J. Microbiol.* **2**, 298.

Beard, J. W. and Rous, P. (1938). The fate of vaccinia virus on cultivation *in vitro* with Kupffer cells (reticulo-endothelial cells). *J. exp. Med.* **67**, 883.

Bech, V. and von Magnus, P. (1957). Studies on measles virus in monkey kidney tissue cultures. *Acta path. microbiol. scand.* **42**, 75.

Bennett, C. R., Jr. and Hamre, D. (1962). Growth and serological characteristics of respiratory syncytial virus. *J. infect. Dis.* **110**, 9.

Bereczky, E. and Dmochowski, L. (1962). Continuous phase contrast cinemicrophotography of polyoma-infected mouse embryo cells. *Virology* **18**, 320.

Bereczky, E., Dmochowski, L. and Grey, C. E. (1961). Study of host-virus relationship. 1. Light, phase, and fluorescence microscopy of mouse-embryo cells infected with polyoma virus. *J. nat. Cancer Inst.* **27**, 99.

Bernhard, W. (1964). Fine structural lesions induced by viruses. *In* "Cellular Injury" (A. V. S. de Reuck and J. Knight, ed.), pp. 209–247. Little Brown and Co., Boston.

Bernhard, W., Dontcheff, A., Oberling, C. and Vigier, P. (1953). Corpuscules d'aspect virusal dans les cellules du sarcome de Rous. *Bull. Cancer* **40**, 311.

Bernhard, W., Kasten, F. H. and Chany, C. (1963). Étude cytochimique et ultrastructurale de cellules infectées par le virus K du rat et le virus H. *C.R. Acad. Sci., Paris* **257**, 1566.

Bernkopf, H., Nishmi, M. and Rosin, A. (1959). Effect of active and inactive vaccinia virus preparations on human amnion cell cultures. *J. Immunol.* **83**, 635.

Black, P. H. (1964). Studies on the genetic susceptibility of cells to polyoma virus transformation. *Virology* **24**, 179.

Black, P. H., Hartley, J. W. and Rowe, W. P. (1963). Isolation of a cytomegalovirus from African green monkey. *Proc. Soc. exp. Biol., N.Y.* **112**, 601.

Black, P. H. and Rowe, W. P. (1963). Transformation in hamster kidney monolayers by vacuolating virus, SV-40. *Virology* **19**, 107.

Bland, J. O. W. and Canti, R. G. (1935). The growth and development of Psittacosis virus in tissue cultures. *J. Path. Bact.* **40**, 231.

Bland, J. O. W. and Robinow, C. F. (1939). The inclusion bodies of vaccinia and their relationship to the elementary bodies studied in cultures of the rabbit's cornea. *J. Path. Bact.* **48**, 381.

Bollinger, O. (1873). Ueber Epithelioma contagiosum beim Haushuhn und die sogenannten Pocken des Geflügels. *Arch. path. Anat.* **58**, 349.

Bonifas, V. and Schlesinger, R. W. (1959). Nutritional requirements for plaque production. *Fed. Proc.* **18**, 560.

Borrel, A. (1926). Cytologie du sarcome de Peyton Rous et substance spécifique. *C.R. Soc. Biol., Paris* **94**, 500.

Borysko, E. and Bang, F. B. (1953). The fine structure of the chorio-allantoic membrane of the normal chick embryo. A control study for virus work. *Johns Hopk. Hosp. Bull.* **92**, 257.

Boyer, G. S., Leuchtenberger, C. and Ginsberg, H. S. (1957). Cytological and cytochemical studies of HeLa cells infected with adenoviruses. *J. exp. Med.* **105**, 195.

Bozeman, F. M., Hopps, H. E., Danauskas, J. X., Jackson, E. B. and Smadel, J. E. (1956). Study on the growth of rickettsiae. *J. Immunol.* **76**, 475.

Brandt, C. (1961). Cytopathic action of myxoviruses on cultivated mammalian cells. *Virology* **14**, 1.

Braunsteiner, H., Fiala, Y., Pakesch, F. and Auerswald, W. (1958). Uber das intracellulare Verhalten des Poliomyelitisvirus nach Infektion von Zellkulturen. *Klin. Wschr.* **36**, 1128.

Breitenfeld, P. M. and Schäfer, W. (1957). The formation of fowl plague virus antigens in infected cells, as studied with fluorescent antibodies. *Virology* **4**, 328.

Brocklesby, D. W. and Hawking, F. (1958). Growth of *Theileria annulata* and *T. parva* in tissue. *Trans. R. Soc. trop. Med. Hyg.* **52**, 414.

Brown, A., Mayyasi, S. and Officer, J. E. (1959a). The agglutination of L-cells by vaccinia virus. II. The cell virus interaction related to the agglutination reaction. *J. Immunol.* **83**, 521.

Brown, A., Mayyasi, S. and Officer, J. E. (1959b). The "toxic" activity of vaccinia virus in tissue cultures. *J. infect. Dis.* **104**, 193.

Buckley, S. M. (1955). Visualization of poliomyelitis virus by fluorescent antibody. *Arch. ges. Virusforsch.* **6**, 388.

Buckley, S. M. (1957). Cytopathology of poliomyelitis virus in tissue culture. Fluorescent antibody and tinctorial studies. *Amer. J. Path.* **33**, 691.

Buckley, S. M. (1961). Serial propagation of types 1, 2, 3 and 4 dengue virus in HeLa cells with concomitant cytopathic effect. *Nature, Lond.* **192**, 778.

Buckley, S. M. (1962). Application of tissue culture methods to the study of the arthropod-borne group of animal viruses. (With special reference to the HeLa (Gey) strain of human malignant epithelial cell). *Int. Kongr. Ent., Wien* 1960, **9**, 762.

Buckley, S. M. and Shope, R. E. (1961). Comparative assay of arthropod-borne group C virus antibodies by tissue culture neutralization and hemagglutination-inhibition tests. *Amer. J. trop. Med. Hyg.* **10**, 53.

Bungay, C. and Watkins, J. F. (1964). Observations in polykaryocytosis in HeLa cells infected with herpes simplex virus. *Brit. J. exp. Path.* **45**, 48.

Bussell, R. H. and Karzon, D. T. (1962). Canine distemper virus in chick embryo cell culture. Plaque assay, growth, and stability. *Virology* **18**, 589.

Butler, M. P. (1965). Avian viruses in adult cells *in vitro*. A comparison of fowlpox, bronchitis, laryngotracheitis, and Newcastle disease viruses in tissue cultures of embryonic and adult fowl cells. *Virology* **25**, 454.

Butler, M. and Leach, R. H. (1964). A mycoplasma which induces acidity and cytopathic effect in tissue culture. *J. gen. Microbiol.* **34**, 285.

Carrel, A. (1924). Action de l'extrait filtré du sarcome de Rous sur les macrophages du sang. *C.R. Soc. Biol., Paris* **91**, 1069.

Carrel, A. (1925). Effets de l'extrait de sarcomes fusocellulaires sur des cultures pures de fibroblastes. *C.R. Soc. Biol., Paris* **92**, 477.

Carrel, A. (1928). Tissue cultures in the study of viruses. *In* "Filterable Viruses" (T. M. Rivers, ed.), pp. 97–109. Baillière, Tindall and Cox, London.

Carrel, A. and Ebeling, A. (1926). The transformation of monocytes into fibroblasts through the action of Rous virus. *J. exp. Med.* **43**, 461.

Castrejon-Diez, J., Fisher, T. N. and Fisher, E., Jr. (1963). Experimental infection of tissue cultures with certain mycoplasma (PPLO). *Proc. Soc. exp. Biol., N.Y.* **112**, 643.

Chambers, V. C. (1957). The prolonged resistance of Western equine encephalomyelitis virus in cultures of strain L-cells. *Virology* **3**, 62.

Chang, R. S. (1958). Differences in inositol requirements of several strains of HeLa, conjunctival, and amnion cells. *Proc. Soc. exp. Biol., N.Y.* **99**, 99.

Chang, Y. T. (1961). The mouse macrophage as host cell for *Mycobacterium lepraemurium*. Symposium on Research in Leprosy, pp. 118–129.

Chanock, R., Roizman, B. and Myers, M. (1957). Recovery from infants with respiratory illness of a virus related to chimpanzee coryza agent (CCA). I. Isolation, properties and characterization. *Amer. J. Hyg.* **66**, 281.

Chany, C. and Cook, M. K. (1960). Sur un facteur induit par le virus entrainant la formation de syncytium en culture cellulaire. *Ann. Inst. Pasteur* **98**, 920.

Chany, C., Daniel, P., Robbe-Fossat, F., Vialatte, J., Lepine, P. and Lelong, M. (1958). Isolement et étude d'un virus syncytial non-identifié associé à des affections respiratoires aigues du nourrisson. *Ann. Inst. Pasteur* **95**, 721.

Chaproniere, D. M. (1956). The effect of myxoma virus on cultures of rabbit tissues. *Virology* **2**, 599.

Chaproniere, D. M. and Andrewes, C. H. (1957). Cultivation of rabbit myxoma and fibroma viruses in tissues of nonsusceptible hosts. *Virology* **4**, 351.

Chardonnet, Y., Pruniéras, M. and Schier, R. (1961). Effets cytopathogènes des adénovirus type 5. I. Aspects morphologiques. *Ann. Inst. Pasteur* **100**, 777.

Chardonnet, Y., Pruniéras, M. and Schier, R. (1962). Effets cytopathogènes des adénovirus type 5. III. Les phosphatases acides. *Ann. Inst. Pasteur* **102**, 129.

Chitwood, L. A. and Bracken, E. C. (1964). Replication of herpes simplex virus in a metabolically imbalanced system. *Virology* **24**, 116.

Choppin, P. (1964). Multiplication of a myxovirus (SV 5) with minimal cytopathic effects and without interference. *Virology* **23**, 224.

Chumakov, M. P., Mustafina, A. N., Chumakova, V., Karmysheva, Ya., Shestopalova, N. M. and Reinfold, V. N. (1964). Cultivation of Simian Virus SV 40 in continuous human diploid cells. *Acta virol.* **8**, 217.

Churchill, A. E. (1963). Intranuclear inclusions produced by bovine parainfluenza. *Nature, Lond.* **197**, 409.

Claude, A., Porter, K. R. and Pickels, E. G. (1947). Electron microscope study of chicken tumor cells. *Cancer Res.* **7**, 421.

Coackley, W. (1963). The effect of recently isolated strains of Rift Valley Fever virus on lamb testis cell cultures. *J. Path. Bact.* **86**, 530.

Cohen, S. M., Bullivant, S. and Edwards, G. A. (1961–62). Morphologic study of FL cells infected with parainfluenza 3 virus. *Arch. ges. Virusforsch.* **11**, 493.

Cohn, Z. A., Bozeman, F. M., Campell, J. M., Humphries, J. W. and Sawyer, T. K. (1959). Study on growth of Rickettsiae. V. Penetration of Rickettsiae tsutsugamushi into mammalian cells *in vitro*. *J. exp. Med.* 271.

Cold Spring Harbor Symposia on Quantitative Biology (1962). Basic Mechanisms in Animal Virus Biology. Vol. 27. Long Island Biological Association, Cold Spring Harbor, Long Island, New York.

Colobert, L. and Berkaloff, A. (1964). Libération du virus sendai par des cellules porteuses d'une infection chronique. *Ann. Inst. Pasteur* **106**, 581.

Coman, D. R. (1946). Induction of neoplasia *in vitro* with a virus. Experiments with rabbit skin grown in tissue culture and treated with Shope papilloma virus. *Cancer Res.* **6**, 602.

Cooper, H. L. and Black, P. H. (1963). Cytogenetic studies of hamster kidney cell cultures transformed by the Simian vacuolating virus (SV40). *J. nat. Cancer Inst.* **30**, 1015.

Count, A. E. (1963). Growth of *Varicella-zoster* virus in human thyroid tissue cultures. *Lancet ii*, 982.

Cramer, R. and Franzen, S. (1957). On the absence of a cytopathogenic effect of the three poliovirus types on plasmocytoma cells and macrophages in bone marrow cultures. *Arch. ges. Virusforsch.* **7**, 461.

Crandell, R. A. (1959). Multiplication and cytopathogenicity of herpes simplex virus in cultures of feline renal cells. *Proc. Soc. exp. Biol., N.Y.* **102**, 508.

Crocker, T. T. and Eastwood, J. M. (1963). Subcellular cultivation of a virus. Growth of ornithosis virus in nonnucleate cytoplasm. *Virology* **19**, 23.

Dalen, A. B. and Morgan, H. R. (1962). Factors related to the growth of Psittacosis agent. VI. Host cell purine nucleotide pyrophosphorylases. *Proc. Soc. exp. Biol., N.Y.* **110**, 251.

Dales, S. (1963). Association between the spindle apparatus and reovirus. *Proc. nat. Acad. Sci., Wash.* **50**, 268.

Dales, S. and Gomatos, P. J. (1965). The uptake and development of reovirus in strain L cells followed with labeled viral ribonucleic acid and ferritin antibody conjugates. *Virology* **25**, 193.

Dales, S. and Kajuoka, R. (1964). The cycle of multiplication of vaccinia virus in Earle's strain L cells. I. Uptake and penetration. *Virology* **24**, 278.

Darnell, J. E., Jr. and Eagle, H. (1960). The biosynthesis of poliovirus in cell cultures. *In* "Advances in Virus Research" (K. M. Smith and M. A. Lauffer, eds.), Vol. 7, pp. 1–26. Academic Press, New York and London.

Darnell, J. E., Jr. and Sawyer, T. K. (1960). The basis for variation in susceptibility to poliovirus in HeLa cells. *Virology* **11**, 665.

Davies, M. C., Englert, M. E., Sharpless, G. R. and Cabasso, V. J. (1963). The electron microscopy of rabies virus in cultures of chicken embryo tissues. *Virology* **21**, 642.

Dawe, C. J. and Law, L. W. (1959). Morphologic changes in salivary-gland tissue of the newborn mouse exposed to parotid-tumor agent *in vitro*. *J. nat. Cancer Inst.* **23**, 1157.

Dawe, C. J., Law, L. W. and Dunn, T. B. (1959). Studies of parotid tumor agent in cultures of leukemic tissues of mice. *J. nat. Cancer Inst.* **23**, 717.

Defendi, V., Lehman, J. and Kraemer, P. (1963). Morphologically normal hamster cells with malignant properties. *Virology* **19**, 592.

Deibel, R. and Hotchin, J. E. (1959). Quantitative application of fluorescent antibody technique to influenza-virus-infected cell cultures. *Virology* **8**, 367.

De LaForest, G. (1961). Étude histologique des lesions produites par le virus "Gal" dans des cultures d'organes embryonnaires de poulet. *Ann. Inst. Pasteur* **101**, 834.

de Maeyer, E. (1962). Organ culture of newborn rabbit skin affected by rabbit papilloma virus. *Science* **136**, 985.

Demont, G., Berkaloff, A. and Colobert, L. (1963). Manifestations cytologiques de l'infection des cellules KB par myxovirus parainfluenzae 1 (Virus Sendai). *Ann. Inst. Pasteur* **104**, 26.

Depoux, R. (1963). Multiplication du virus rabique fixe dans les cellules de glandes salivaires de chien cultivées *in vitro*. *C.R. Acad. Sci., Paris* **257**, 2757.

Dingle, J. H. and Ginsberg, H. S. (1959). The adenovirus group. *In* "Viral and Rickettsial Infections of Man" (T. M. Rivers and F. L. Horsfall, eds.), pp. 613–632. Lippincott, Philadelphia.

Dinter, Z., Hermodsson, S. and Hermodsson, L. (1964). Studies on myxovirus Yucaipa: its classification as a member of the paramyxovirus group. *Virology* **22**, 297.

Doherty, R. L. (1958). Effects of Yellow Fever (17D) and West Nile viruses on the reactions of human appendix and conjunctiva cells to several other viruses. *Virology* **6**, 575.

Doljanski, L. and Pikorski, M. (1942). Agent of fowl leucosis in tissue cultures. *Cancer Res.* **2**, 626.

Doljanski, L. and Tenenbaum, E. (1942). Studies on Rous sarcoma cells cultivated *in vitro*. *Cancer Res.* **2**, 776.

Drouhet, V. (1958). Sur l'effet cytopathogène du virus Echo 10. *Ann. Inst. Pasteur* **95**, 781.

Drouhet, V. (1960). Lésions cellulaires provoquées par les réovirus (Virus Echo 10), anticorps fluorescents et étude cytochimique. *Ann. Inst. Pasteur* **98**, 618.

Dulbecco, R. and Vogt, M. (1954). Plaque formation and isolation of pure lines with poliomyelitis viruses. *J. exp. Med.* **99**, 167.

Dunkel, V. C. and Groupé, V. (1965). Effects of Rous Sarcoma virus on chicken-embryo limb buds grafted onto the chorioallantoic membrane. *J. nat. Cancer Inst.* **34**, 201.

Dunnebacke, T. H. (1956). Cytopathic changes associated with poliomyelitis infections in human amnion cells. *Virology* **2**, 811.

Dunnebacke, T. H. (1962). Amounts of polio and coxsackie viruses within the separate portions of bisected cultured cells. *Virology* **16**, 392.

Dunnebacke, T. H. and Williams, R. C. (1961). The maturation and release of infectious polio and coxsackie viruses in individual tissue cultured cells. *Arch. ges. Virusforsch.* **11**, 583.

Duran-Reynals, G. (1947). A study of three new duck variants of the Rous chicken sarcoma. *Cancer Res.* **7**, 99.

Easton, J. M. (1964). Cytopathic effect of Simian virus 40 on primary cell cultures of rhesus monkey kidney. *J. Immunol.* **93**, 716.

Eddy, B. E., Stewart, S. E. and Berkeley, W. (1958). Cytopathogenicity in tissue culture by a tumor virus from mice. *Proc. Soc. exp. Biol., N.Y.* **98**, 848.

Edwards, G. A. and Fogh, J. (1960). Fine structure of pleuropneumonia-like organisms in pure culture and in infected tissue culture cells. *J. Bact.* **79**, 267.

Eiring, A. and Scherer, W. F. (1960). Appearance of persistently cytopathic Eastern and Western encephalitis viruses after blind passage in cultures of L mouse fibroblasts. *J. Immunol.* **87**, 96.

Eisenberg-Merling, K. B. (1940). Observations on living vaccinia virus in the corneal cells of the rabbit. *J. Path. Bact.* **50**, 279.

Ellermann, V. and Bang, O. (1908). Experimentelle Leukämie bei Hühnern. *Zbl. Bakt. I. Abt. Orig.* **46** (9), 595.

Enders, J. F. and Peebles, T. C. (1954). Propagation in tissue cultures of cytopathogenic agents from patients with measles. *Proc. Soc. exp. Biol., N.Y.* **86**, 277.

Enders, J. F., Weller, T. H. and Robbins, F. C. (1949). Cultivation of the Lansing strain of poliomyelitis virus in cultures of various human embryonic tissues. *Science* **109**, 85.

Endo, M., Aoyama, Y., Hayashida, T. and Kamimura, T. (1959). Sur les lesions des cellules epitheliales d'amnion humain causées par le virus poliomyelitique *in vitro*. *Jap. J. exp. Med.* **29**, 547.

Ephrussi, B. and Temin, H. M. (1960). Infection of chick iris epithelium with the Rous sarcoma virus *in vitro*. *Virology* **11**, 547.

Epstein, M. A. (1962). Observations on the fine structure of mature herpes simplex virus and on the composition of its nucleoid. *J. exp. Med.* **115**, 1.

Epstein, M. A., Hummeler, K. and Berkaloff, A. (1964). The entry and distribution of herpes virus and colloidal gold in HeLa cells after contact in suspension. *J. exp. Med.* **119**, 291.

Erichsen, S., Eng, J. and Morgan, H. R. (1961). Comparative studies on Rous sarcoma with virus tumor cells and chick embryo cells transformed *in vitro* by virus. *J. exp. Med.* **114**, 435.

Everett, S. F. and Ginsberg, H. S. (1958). A toxinlike material separable from type 5 adenovirus particles. *Virology* **6**, 770.

Falke, D. (1961). Isolation of two variants with different cytopathic properties from a strain of herpes B virus. *Virology* **14**, 492.

Falke, D. and Richter, I. E. (1961). Mikrokinematographische Studien über die Entstehung von Riesenzellen durch Herpes B virus in Zellkulturen. *Arch. ges. Virusforsch.* **11**, 73.

Falke, D. and Schmidt, G. (1963). Riesenzelltypen durch Parainfluenzavirus 3 in Kulturzellen. *Zbl. Bakt. I. Abt. Ref.* **188**, 149.

Fauconnier, B. (1963). Inclusions nucleaires eosinophiles provoquées par la multiplication du virus de la maladie de Newcastle dans les cellules de rein de tortue (*Testudo graeca*). *Ann. Inst. Pasteur* **105**, 444.

Felgenhauer, K. and Stammler, A. (1962). Die histochemisch nachweisbaren Veranderungen in der mit dem Virus des Herpes simplex inokulierten Zellkultur. *Arch. ges. Virusforsch.* **12**, 222.

Fell, H. B. and Brieger, E. M. (1947). The effect of phagocytosis on the growth and survival of avian tubercle bacilli in embryonic chicken tissue cultivated *in vitro. J. Hyg., Camb.* **45**, 359.

Feller, A. E., Enders, J. F. and Weller, T. H. (1940). The prolonged co-existence of vaccinia virus in high titre and living cells in roller tube cultures of chick embryonic tissue. *J. exp. Med.* **72**, 367.

Felton, H. M., Gaggero, A. and Pomerat, C. M. (1954). Reactions of cells in tissue culture to *Hemophilus pertussis. Tex. Rep. Biol. Med.* **12**, 960.

Felton, H. M. and Pomerat, C. M. (1962). Cell injury and repair following staphyloccus toxin and antiserum. *Exp. Cell Res.* **27**, 280.

Fernandes, M. V. and Pomerat, C. M. (1961). Cytopathogenic effects of rabies virus on nervous tissue *in vitro. Z. Zellforsch.* **53**, 431.

Fernandes, M. V., Wiktor, T. J. and Koprowski, H. (1963). Mechanism of the cytopathic effect of rabies virus on tissue culture. *Virology* **21**, 128.

Fernandes, M. V., Wiktor, T. J. and Koprowski, H. (1964). Endosymbiotic relationship between animal viruses and host cells. A study of rabies virus in tissue culture. *J. exp. Med.* **120**, 1099.

Fischer, A. (1926). Transformation des cellules normales en cellules malignes *in vitro. C.R. Soc. Biol., Paris* **94**, 1217.

Fischer, A. (1927). Sarkomzellen und Tuberkelbazillen *in vitro. Arch. exp. Zellforsch.* **3**, 389.

Fischer, A. and Laser, H. (1927). Studien uber Sarkomzellen *in vitro.* V. Uber Phagocytose von Zellen des Rous sarkom und von Fibroblasten *in vitro. Arch. exp. Zellforsch.* **3**, 363.

Flewett, T. H. and Challice, C. E. (1951). The intracellular growth of fowl-plague virus. A phase-contrast and electron microscopical study of infected tissue cultures. *J. gen. Microbiol.* **5**, 279.

Florman, A. E. and Enders, J. F. (1941). The effect of homologous antiserum and complement on the multiplication of vaccinia virus in roller-tube cultures of blood-mononuclear cells. *J. Immunol.* **43**, 159.

Fonbrune, P. and Reculard, P. (1963). Étude cinematographique des effets cytopathogenes du virus de Rubarth en "microcultures" cellulaires spéciales. *Ann. Inst. Pasteur* **104**, 335.

Franklin, R. M. (1958). The growth of fowl plague virus in tissue cultures of chick macrophages and giant cells. *Virology* **6**, 81.

Franklin, R. M. and Breitenfeld, P. M. (1959). The abortive infection of Earle's L-cells by fowl plague virus. *Virology* **8**, 293.

Frederic, J. and Racadot, J. (1955). Transformation de cellules cultivées *in vitro* en cellules épithéliodes et géantes, sous l'action d'un extrait de bacilles tuberculeux. *Arch. Anat. micr. Morph. exp.* **44**, 56.

Frederickson, T. N., Purchase, H. G. and Burmester, B. R. (1964). Transmission of virus from field cases of avian lymphomatosis. III. Variation in the oncogenic spectra of passaged virus isolates. International Conference on Avian Tumor Viruses. *Nat. Cancer Inst. Monog.* **17**, 1.

Freundt, E. A. (1958). "The Mycoplasmataceae. (The Pleuropneumonia Group of Organisms)." Munksgaard, Copenhagen.

Furness, G. and Csonka, G. W. (1963). A study by fluorescence microscopy of the replication of lymphogranuloma venereum virus in HeLa cell monolayers. *J. gen. Microbiol.* **31**, 161.

Gaylord, W. H., Jr. and Hsiung, G. D. (1961). The vacuolating virus of monkeys. II. Virus morphology and intranuclear distribution with some histochemical observations. *J. exp. Med.* **114**, 987.

Georgiades, J., Stern, T. B., McCollum, R. W. and Henderson, J. R. (1965). Dengue virus plaque formation in rhesus monkey kidney cultures. *Proc. Soc. exp. Biol., N.Y.* **118**, 385.

Gey, G. O. (1954). Some aspects of constitution and behavior of normal and malignant cells maintained in continuous culture. *Harvey Lect.* **50**, 200.

Gey, G. O. and Bang, F. B. (1939). Experimental studies on the cultural behavior and the infectivity of lymphopathia venerea virus maintained in tissue culture. *Johns Hopk. Hosp. Bull.* **65**, 393.

Gey, G. O. and Gey, M. K. (1936). The maintenance of pure strains of human and animal normal and tumor cells in tissue culture. Report of the International Cancer Research Foundation, pp. 36–39.

Ginsberg, H. S. (1957). Biological and physical properties of the adenoviruses. *Ann. N.Y. Acad. Sci.* **67**, 383.

Goldé, A. (1962). Chemical changes in chick embryo cells infected with Rous sarcoma virus *in vitro*. *Virology* **16**, 9.

Goodman, G. T. and Koprowski, H. (1962). Study of the mechanisms of innate resistance to virus infections. *J. cell. comp. Physiol.* **59**, 333.

Grand, N. G. (1958). Production of salivary gland virus inclusions in cultures of mouse salivary gland. *Amer. J. Path.* **34**, 775.

Gray, A. and Scott, T. F. M. (1954). Some observations on the intracellular localization of the virus of herpes simplex in the chick embryo liver. *J. exp. Med.* **100**, 473.

Gray, A., Tokumaru, T. and Scott, T. F. M. (1958). Different cytopathogenic effects observed in HeLa cells infected with herpes simplex virus. *Arch. ges. Virusforsch.* **8**, 59.

Gresser, I., Chany, C. and Enders, J. F. (1965). Persistent polioviral infection of intact human amniotic membrane without apparent cytopathic effect. *J. Bact.* **89**, 470.

Gresser, I. and Enders, J. F. (1961). Cytopathogenicity of mumps virus in cultures of chick embryo and human amnion cells. *Proc. Soc. exp. Biol., N.Y.* **107**, 804.

Haagen, E. M. and Theiler, M. (1932). Studies of yellow fever in tissue culture. *Proc. Soc. exp. Biol. Med., N.Y.* **29**, 435.

Habermehl, K. O. and Diefenthal, W. (1961). Kinematographische Untersuchungen an Fibroblasten nach Infektion mit Ektromelievirus (Mause pocken). *Arch. ges. Virusforsch.* **11**, 629.

Hackett, A. J. (1964). Possible morphological basis for the auto-interference phenomenon in vesicular stomatitis virus. *Virology* **24**, 51.

Hampar, B. and Ellison, S. A. (1961). Chromosomal aberrations induced by an animal virus. *Nature, Lond.* **192**, 145.

Hampar, B. and Ellison, S. A. (1963). Cellular alterations in the MCH line of Chinese hamster cells following infection with herpes simplex virus. *Proc. nat. Acad. Sci., Wash.* **49**, 474.

Hampar, B. and Ellison, S. A. (1964). Infection of MCH Chinese hamster cells with herpes simplex virus. Relation of cell killing to time of division. *Virology* **24**, 654.

Hampton, E. G. and Eidinoff, M. L. (1962). Transformation of chick embryo cells in culture by Rous sarcoma virus—cytochemical studies. *Cancer Res.* **22**, 1061.

Hanks, J. H. (1941). Behavior of leprosy bacilli in complex liquid media with highly available sources of nutrient and accessory substances. *Int. J. Leprosy* **9**, 275.

Hanks, J. H. (1956). Competitive aspects of tissue cell and bacterial physiology. *In* "Host-Parasite Relationships in Living Cells" (McLaughlin Symposium), pp. 63–76. Charles C. Thomas, Springfield, Ill.

Harford, C. G., Hamlin, A., Parker, E. and van Ravenswaay, T. (1956). Electron microscopy of HeLa cells infected with adenovirus. *J. exp. Med.* **104**, 443.

Harnden, D. G. (1964). Cytogenetic studies on patients with virus infections and subjects vaccinated against yellow fever. *Amer. J. hum. Genet.* **16**, 204.

Hayflick, L. and Stinebring, W. R. (1959). Intracellular growth of pleuropneumonia-like organisms in tissue culture and *in ovo*. *Ann. N.Y. Acad. Sci.* **79**, 433.

Henderson, J. R. and Taylor, R. M. (1960). Propagation of certain arthropod-borne viruses in avian and primate cell cultures. *J. Immunol.* **84**, 590.

Henle, G., Deinhardt, F., Bergs, V. V. and Henle, W. (1958). Studies on persistent infections of tissue cultures. I. General aspects of the system. *J. exp. Med.* **108**, 537.

Henle, G., Deinhardt, F. and Girardi, A. (1954). Cytolytic effects of mumps virus in tissue cultures of epithelial cells. *Proc. Soc. exp. Biol., N.Y.* **87**, 386.

Henle, G., Deinhardt, F. and Rodriguez, J. (1959). The development of polyoma virus in mouse embryo cells as revealed by fluorescent antibody. *Virology* **8**, 388.

Henle, G., Girardi, A. and Henle, W. (1955). A non-transmissible cytopathogenic effect of influenza virus in tissue culture accompanied by formation of non-infectious hemagglutinins. *J. exp. Med.* **101**, 25.

Henry, C. and Franklin, R. M. (1959). Growth of mouse encephalomyelitis virus in Earle's L-cells. *Virology* **9**, 84.

Higashi, N., Tamura, A. and Iwanaga, M. (1962). Developmental cycle and reproductive mechanisms of the meningo-pneumonitis virus in strain L-cells. *Ann. N.Y. Acad. Sci.* **98**, 100.

Hilleman, M. R. and Werner, J. H. (1954). Recovery of new agent from patients with acute respiratory illness. *Proc. Soc. exp. Biol., N.Y.* **85**, 183.

Hinz, R. W. and Syverton, J. T. (1959). Mammalian cell cultures for study of influenza virus. II. Virus propagation. *Proc. Soc. exp. Biol., N.Y.* **101**, 22.

Hinze, H. C. and Walker, D. L. (1961). Occurrence of focal three-dimensional proliferation in cultured human cells after prolonged infection with herpes simplex virus. *J. exp. Med.* **113**, 885.

Hinze, H. C. and Walker, D. L. (1964). Response of cultured rabbit cells to infection with the Shope fibroma virus. I. Proliferation and morphological alteration of the infected cells. *J. Bact.* **88**, 1185.

Ho, M. (1964). Identification and "induction" of interferon. *Bact. Rev.* **28**, 367.

Hodges, G. M. (1963). La vaccine en culture organotypique. *Ann. Inst. Pasteur* **106**, 311.

Hoggan, M. D. and Roizman, B. (1959a). The isolation and properties of a variant of herpes simplex producing multinucleated giant cells in monolayer cultures in the presence of antibody. *Amer. J. Hyg.* **70**, 208.

Hoggan, M. D. and Roizman, B. (1959b). The effect of the temperature of incubation on the formation and release of herpes simplex virus in infected FL cells. *Virology* **8**, 508.

Hoggan, M. D., Roizman, B. and Roane, P. B., Jr. (1961). Further studies of variants of herpes simplex virus that produce syncytia or pocklike lesions in cell cultures. *Amer. J. Hyg.* **73**, 114.

Hoggan, M. D., Roizman, B. and Turner, T. B. (1960). The effect of the temperature of incubation on the spread of herpes simplex virus in an immune environment in cell culture. *J. Immunol.* **84**, 152.

Hogue, M. J. (1919). The effect of hypotonic and hypertonic solutions on fibroblasts of the embryonic chick heart *in vitro*. *J. exp. Med.* **30**, 617.

Hogue, M. J., McAllister, R., Greene, A. E. and Coriell, L. L. (1955). The effect of poliomyelitis virus on human brain cells in tissue culture. *J. exp. Med.* **102**, 29.

Hogue, M. J., McAllister, R., Greene, A. E. and Coriell, L. L. (1958). A comparative study of the effect of the poliomyelitis virus types 1, 2 and 3 on human brain cells grown in tissue cultures. *Amer. J. Hyg.* **67**, 267.

Holland, J. J. (1961). Receptor affinities as major determinants of enterovirus tissue tropisms in humans. *Virology* **15**, 312.

Holland, J. J. and McLaren, L. C. (1961). The location and nature of enterovirus receptors in susceptible cells. *J. exp. Med.* **114**, 161.

Homma, M. and Graham, A. F. (1963). Synthesis of RNA in L cells infected with mengo virus. *J. cell. comp. Physiol.* **62**, 179.

Hoorn, B. (1964). Respiratory viruses in model experiments. Transactions of the 15th Congress of the Scandinavian Oto-laryngological Society 1963. *Acta Oto-laryng.* Suppl. **188**, 138.

Hoorn, B. and Tyrell, D. A. J. (1965). On the growth of certain "newer" respiratory viruses in organ cultures. *Brit. J. exp. Path.* **46**, 109–118.

Hotchin, J. E., Cohen, S. M., Ruska, H. and Ruska, G. (1958). Electron microscopical aspects of hemadsorption in tissue cultures infected with influenza virus. *Virology* **6**, 689.

Hotta, S. (1959). Propagation of Dengue virus in tissue culture. *Acta trop., Basel* **16**, 108.

Hotta, S., Kuromaru, S. and Funasaka, K. (1964). Experimental infection of dogs with Japanese B encephalomyelitis virus. *Acta Neuropath., Berlin* **3**, 494.

Hotta, S., Ohyama, A., Fujita, N. and Yamada, T. (1962). Propagation of yellow fever virus (17 D strain) in primary trypsinized cell cultures. *Amer. J. trop. Med.* **11**, 811.

Hovel, H. (1963). Uber den Einfluss von Prednisolon auf die Empfindlichkeit von Strumagewebekulturen gegenuber dem Poliovirus type III (Saukett). *Z. Naturforsch.* **18b**, 374.

Hoyle, L. (1954). The release of influenza virus from the infected cell. *J. Hyg., Camb.* **52**, 180.

Hsiung, G. D. and Gaylord, W. H., Jr. (1961). The vacuolating virus of monkeys. I. Isolation, growth characteristics, and inclusion body formation. *J. exp. Med.* **114**, 975.

Huang, C. H. (1943). Further studies on the titration and neutralization of the Western strain of equine encephalomyelitis virus in tissue cultures. *J. exp. Med.* **78**, 111.

Huang, J. S. and Bang, F. B. (1964). The susceptibility of chick embryo skin organ cultures to influenza virus following excess vitamin A. *J. exp. Med.* **120**, 129.

Huff, C. G., Pipkin, A. C., Weathersby, A. B. and Jensen, D. V. (1960). The morphology and behavior of living exo-erythrocytic stages of *Plasmodium gallinaceum* and *P. fallax* and their host cells. *J. biochem. biophys. Cytol.* **7**, 93.

Hullinger, L., Wilde, J. K. H., Brown, C. G. D. and Turner, L. (1964). Mode of multiplication of *Theileria* in cultures of bovine lymphocytic cells. *Nature, Lond.* **203**, 728.

Ichihashi, and Matsumoto, S. (1965). Studies of Marchal body. *Rep. Inst. Virus Res. Kyoto* **8**.

Ishizaki, R., Shimizu, T. and Matumoto, M. (1962). Sequential development of antigens of equine rhinopneumonitis virus in cultured horse kidney cells as studied with fluorescent antibody. *Arch. ges. Virusforsch.* **12**, 346.

Jamison, R. M., Mayor, H. D. and Melnick, J. L. (1963). Studies in Echo 4 virus (Picorna virus group) and its intracellular development. *Exp. molec. Path.* **2**, 188.

Jensen, F. C., Girardi, A. J., Gilden, R. V. and Koprowski, H. (1964). Infection of human and simian tissue cultures with Rous sarcoma virus. *Proc. nat. Acad. Sci., Wash.* **52**, 53.

Johnson, C. D. and Goodpasture, E. W. (1936). The histopathology of experimental mumps in the monkey, *Macacus rhesus*. *Amer. J. Path.* **12**, 495.

Joklik, W. K. (1964). The intracellular uncoating of poxvirus: DNA, the molecular basis of the uncoating process. *J. molec. Biol.* **8**, 277.

Kajuoka, R., Siminovitch, L. and Dales, S. (1964). The cycle of multiplication of vaccinia virus in Earle's strain L-cells. II. Initiation of DNA synthesis and morphogenesis. *Virology* **24**, 295.

Kallman, F., Adams, J. M., Williams, R. C. and Imagawa, D. T. (1959). Fine structure of cellular inclusions in measles virus infections. *J. biochem. biophys. Cytol.* **6**, 379.

Kańtoch, M. (1961). The role of phagocytes in virus infections. *Arch. Immunol. i Terapii Doswiadczalncj*

Kańtoch, M. and Kuczkowska, B. (1964a). Studies on susceptibility of mouse muscle cells to Coxsackie A4 virus infection. *Arch. Immunol. Ther. exp.* **12**, 358.

Kańtoch, M. and Kuczkowska, B. (1964b). A new method of cultivating vaccinia and variola viruses in organ cultures of rabbit corneae. *Arch. Immunol. Ther. exp.* **12**, 709.

Kańtoch, M., Warwick, A. and Bang, F. B. (1963). The cellular nature of genetic susceptibility to a virus. *J. exp. Med.* **117**, 781.

Kaplan, A. S. and Vatter, A. E. (1959). A comparison of herpes simplex and pseudorabies viruses. *Virology* **7**, 394.

Karlsbad, G., Kessel, R. W. I., de Petris, S. and Monaco, L. (1964). Electron microscope observations of *Brucella abortus* grown within monocytes *in vitro*. *J. gen. Microbiol.* **35**, 383.

Kasza, L., Bohl, E. H. and Jones, D. O. (1960). Isolation and cultivation of swine pox virus in primary cell cultures of swine origin. *Amer. J. Vet. Res.* **21**, 269.

Kato, S., Hara, J., Ogawa, M., Miyamoto, H. and Kamahora, J. (1963). Inclusion markers of cowpox virus and alastrim virus. *Biken's J.* **6**, 233.

Kato, I. and Pappenheimer, A. M., Jr. (1960). An early effect of diphtheria toxin on the metabolism of mammalian cells growing in culture. *J. exp. Med.* **112**, 329.

Kato, S., Takahashi, M., Kameyama, S. and Kamahora, J. (1959a). A study on the morphological and cyto-immunological relationship between the inclusions of variola, cowpox, rabbitpox, vaccinia (Variola origin) and vaccinia IHD and a consideration of the term "Guarnieri body". *Biken's J.* **2**, 353.

Kato, S., Takahashi, M., Kameyama, S., Morita, K. and Kamahora, J. (1959b). Studies on the carrier culture of rabbit fibroma and myxoma virus. *Biken's J.* **2**, 30.

Kausche, G. A. (1952). Uber das Verhalten der *Rickettsia* (Coxiella) *burnetti* auf der Fibroblastenkultur. *Z. Naturforsch.* **7b**, 243.

Kilham, L. and Olivier, L. J. (1959). A latent virus of rats isolated in tissue culture. *Virology* **7**, 428.

Kjellén, L., Lagermalm, G., Svedmyr, A. and Thorsson, K. G. (1955). Crystalline-like patterns in the nuclei of cells infected with an animal virus. *Nature, Lond.* **175**, 505.

Klöne, W. (1955a). Untersuchungen zur Cytopathogenitat des Poliomyelitisvirus (Typ Leon). *Arch. ges. Virusforsch.* **6**, 36.

Klöne, W. (1955b). Untersuchungen über den Einfluss der Poliomyelitisvirus-infektion auf die Teilung von Gewebekulturzellen. *Exp. Cell Res.* **9**, 541.

Klöne, W. (1957). Untersuchungen zur Cytopathogenitat des Coxsackievirus Gruppe A Typ 9 in kulturen von Affennierenepithel. *Behringwerk Mitteilungen* **33**, 3.

Klöne, W. (1958). Der Nachweis menschenpathogener Virusarten mittels der Gewebkultur. *In* "Handbuch für Virusforschung" (C. Hallauer and K. F. Meyer, eds.), pp. 203–299. Springer-Verlag, Vienna.

Klöne, W. and Kulemann, H. (1964). Directed migration in measles induced giant cells. *Bull. Inst. P.G. med. Educ. Res.* **6** (2), 31.

Klöne, W., Kulemann, H., Ward, E. N. and Salk, J. E. (1963). Some observations on measles induced giant cell formation. *Exp. Cell Res.* **31**, 438.

Klöne, W. and Oelrichs, L. (1958). Untersuchungen zur Cytopathogenitat des Adenovirus type 3 Gewebekulturen. I. Phasekontrastmikroskopische Beobachtungen. *Zbl. Bakt. I Abt. Orig.* **172**, 376.

Köhler, H. and Schwöbel, W. (1956). Uber die Vermehrung von Huhnerpockenvirus in der gewebekultur. *Zbl. Bakt. I Abt. Orig.* **166**, 454.

Kohn, A. and Yassky, D. (1962). Growth of measles virus in KB cells. *Virology* **17**, 157.

Kovac, W., Kunz, C. and Stockinger, L. (1961–62). Die elektronenmikroskopische Darstellung des Virus du Fruhsommer-meningoencephalitis (FSME) in HeLa-zellen. *Arch. ges. Virusforsch.* **11**, 544.

Kraemer, P. M. (1964). Interaction of mycoplasma (PPLO) and murine lymphoma cell cultures. *Proc. Soc. exp. Biol., N.Y.* **115**, 206.

Kraemer, P. M., Defendi, V., Hayflick, L. and Manson, L. A. (1963). Mycoplasma (PPLO) strains with lytic activity for murine lymphoma cells in vitro. *Proc. Soc. exp. Biol., N.Y.* **112**, 381.

Kredel, F. (1927). The physical relations of cells in tissue cultures. *Johns Hopk. Hosp. Bull.* **40**, 216.

Kulemann, H. and Klöne, W. (1964). Effect of respiratory inhibitors on nuclear migration in measles-induced giant cells. *Bull. Inst. P.G. med. Educ. Res.* **6** (4), 119.

Kunin, C. M. (1964). Cellular susceptibility to enteroviruses. *Bact. Rev.* **28**, 382.

Lagermalm, G., Kjellén, L., Thorsson, K. G. and Svedmyr, A. (1957). Electron microscopy of HeLa cells infected with agents of the adenovirus (APC-RI-ARD) group. *Arch. ges. Virusforsch.* **7**, 221.

Lambert, R. A. (1912). The production of foreign body giant cells *in vitro*. *J. exp. Med.* **15**, 510.

Lassalle, J. (1964). Étude sur cultures cellulaires de l'effet cytolytique des agents du trachome et de la conjunctivité à inclusions. *Ann. Inst. Pasteur* **106**, 752.

Lebrun, J. (1957). L'Antigène poliomyêlitique au cours du développement intra-cellulaire du virus. *Ann. Inst. Pasteur* **93**, 225.

Lehmann-Grubé, F. (1963). Influenza viruses in cell cultures. I. Preparation and use of fetal pig lung cells for quantal assay. *Arch. ges. Virusforsch.* **14**, 1.

Lennox, E. S. and Kaplan, A. S. (1957). Action of diphtheria toxin on cells cultivated *in vitro*. *Proc. Soc. exp. Biol., N.Y.* **95**, 700.

Lepine, P., Chany, C., Droz, B. and Robbe-Fossat, F. (1959). Cytopathogenic effect of two newly recognized myxovirus strains. Mechanism of syncytial formation. *Ann. N.Y. Acad. Sci.* **81**, 62.

Lesso, J., Szanto, J. and Albrecht, P. (1963). Mumps virus infection of HeLa cells studied by the fluorescent antibody method. *Acta virol.* **7**, 37.

Leuchtenberger, C. and Boyer, G. S. (1957). The occurrence of intranuclear crystals in living HeLa cells infected with adenovirus. *J. biochem. biophys. Cytol.* **3**, 323.

Levinthal, J. M. and Shein, H. M. (1964). Propagation of a simian tumor agent (Yaba Virus) in cultures of human and simian renal cells, as detected by immunofluorescence. *Virology* **23**, 268.

Lewis, M. R. (1920). The formation of vacuoles due to *Bacillus typhosus* in the cells of tissue cultures of the intestine of the chick embryo. *J. exp. Med.* **31**, 293.

Lewis, M. R. (1923). The destruction of *Bacillus radicicola* by the connective-tissue cells of the chick embryo *in vitro*. *Johns Hopk. Hosp. Bull.* **34**, 223.

Lewis, W. H. (1919). Degeneration granules and vacuoles in the fibroblasts of chick embryos cultivated *in vitro*. *Johns Hopk. Hosp. Bull.* **30**, 81.

Lewis, W. H. (1920). Giant centrospheres in degenerating mesenchyme cells of tissue culture. *J. exp. Med.* **31**, 275.

Litwin, J., Officer, J. E., Brown, A. and Moulder, J. W. (1961). A comparative study of the growth cycles of different members of the Psittacosis group in different host cells. *J. infect. Dis.* **109**, 251.

Lloyd, W., Theiler, M. and Ricci, N. T. (1935–6). Modification of the virulence of yellow fever virus by cultivation in tissues *in vitro*. *Trans. R. Soc. trop. Med. Hyg.* **29**, 481.

Lo, W., Gey, G. O. and Shapras, P. (1955). The cytopathogenic effect of the Rous sarcoma virus on chicken fibroblasts in tissue cultures. *Johns Hopk. Hosp. Bull.* **97**, 248.

Loh, P. C. and Riggs, J. L. (1961). Demonstration of the sequential development of vaccinial antigens and virus in infected cells. Observations with cytochemical and differential fluorescent procedures. *J. exp. Med.* **114**, 149.

Love, R. and Rabson, A. S. (1959). Cytochemical studies of milk-adapted murine lymphoma cells (strains P 388 D_1) infected with polyoma virus. *J. nat. Cancer Inst.* **23**, 875.

Love, R. and Suskind, R. G. (1961). Cytopathology of parainfluenza type 3 virus infection in HeLa and monkey kidney cells *in vitro*. *Exp. Cell Res.* **24**, 521.

Lwoff, A., Dulbecco, R., Vogt, M. and Lwoff, M. (1955). Kinetics of the release of poliomyelitis virus from single cells. *Virology* **1**, 128.

Maass, G. and Mannweiler, K. (1960–61). Cytologische und biologische Untersuchungen uber das Verhalten des Mumps-virus in Affennierenepithelkulturen. *Arch. ges. Virusforsch.* **10**, 195.

Maddi, F. V. (1963). The effect of adenovirus 3 on human bronchial epithelium in tissue culture. *Ann. Inst. Pasteur* **104**, 43.

Malherbe, H. and Harwin, R. (1963). The cytopathic effects of vervet monkey viruses. *S. Afr. med. J.* **37**, 407.

Mallucci, L. (1965). Observations on the growth of mouse hepatitis virus (MHV-3) in mouse macrophages. *Virology* **25**, 30.

Malmgren, R. A., Rabotti, G. and Rabson, A. S. (1960). Intracellular localization of polyoma virus antigen demonstrated with fluorescein-labeled antiserums. *J. nat. Cancer Inst.* **24**, 581.

Manabe, K. (1939). Uber Lymphogranuloma inguinale Virus gewonnen durch Gewebekultur. II. Uber den entwicklunges Prozess in der Zelle und die Morphologie des Virus. *Jap. J. exp. Med.* **17**, 355.

Manaker, R. A. and Groupé, V. (1956). Discrete foci of altered chicken embryo cells associated with Rous sarcoma virus in tissue culture. *Virology* **2**, 838.

Manire, G. P. and Galasso, G. J. (1959). Persistent infection of HeLa cells with meningopneumonitis virus. *J. Immunol.* **83**, 529.

Mannweiler, K. and Maass, G. (1959). Untersuchungen cytologischer Veränderungen von Affennierengewebekulturen nach Infektion mit Mumpsviren. *Zbl. Bakt. I Abt. Ref.* **176**, 357.

Maral, R. (1957). Étude du développement du virus de la myxomatose en cultures de tissus. *Ann. Inst. Pasteur* **92**, 742.

Marcus, P. I. (1959). Symposium on the biology of cells modified by viruses or antigens. IV. Single-cell techniques in tracing virus-host interactions. *Bact. Rev.* **23** (4), 232.

Marston, R. Q. (1958). Cytopathogenic effects of hemadsorption virus, type I. *Proc. Soc. exp. Biol., N.Y.* **98**, 853.

Mason, E. J. and Kaufman, N. (1960). The relationship between viral reproduction and cytotoxicity of Newcastle disease virus and influenza virus (PR-8) in three cell strains. *J. infect. Dis.* **107**, 245.

Mata, L. J. (1963). The agar cell culture precipitation test: its application to the study of vaccinia virus, adenoviruses and herpes simplex virus. *J. Immunol.* **91**, 151.

Matsumoto, S. (1962). Electron microscopy of nerve cells infected with street rabies virus. *Virology* **17**, 198.

Matsumoto, S. (1963). Electron microscope studies of rabies virus in mouse brain. *J. Cell Biol.* **19**, 565.

Maximow, A. (1924). Tuberculosis of mammalian tissue *in vitro*. *J. infect. Dis.* **34**, 549.

Maximow, A. (1928). Étude comparative des cultures de tissus inoculées soit avec le bacille tuberculeux du type bovin soit avec le bacille BCG de Calmette-Guérin. *Ann. Inst. Pasteur* **42**, 225.

Mayor, H. D. (1964). A labile intranuclear RNA associated with the development of adenoviruses. *J. exp. Med.* **119**, 433.

Mayor, H. D. and Jordan, L. E. (1962). Formation of poliovirus in monkey kidney tissue culture cells. *Virology* **16**, 325.

Mayor, H. D., Stinebaugh, S. E., Jamison, R. M., Jordan, L. E. and Melnick, J. L. (1962). Immunofluorescent, cytochemical, and microcytological studies on the growth of the simian vacuolating virus (SV-40) in tissue culture. *Exp. molec. Path.* **1**, 397.

Mayr, A. (1959). Experimentelle Untersuchungen über das Virus der originären Schweinepocken. *Arch. ges. Virusforsch.* **9**, 156.

Mayr, A. and Kalcher, K. (1959). Vergleichende Studien uber die Züchtung von Geflügelpockenviren in der Zellkultur. *Arch. ges. Virusforsch.* **10**, 72.

Mayr, A. and Kalcher, K. (1961). Plaque-bildung bei den Geflügelpockenviren. *Arch. ges. Virusforsch.* **11**, 307.

McBride, W. D. and Wiener, A. (1964). *In vitro* transformation of hamster kidney cells by human adenovirus 12. *Proc. Soc. exp. Biol., N.Y.* **115**, 870.

McGowan, T. R. (1963). Long-term support of intact skin in organ cultures, with application to study of virus infection. *Nat. Cancer Inst. Monogr.* **11**, 95.

McGowan, T. R. and Bang, F. B. (1960). Organ cultures of human fetal skin for the study of skin diseases. *Johns Hopk. Hosp. Bull.* **107**, 63.

Medina, D. and Sachs, L. (1961). Cell-virus interactions with the polyoma virus. The induction of cell transformation and malignancy *in vitro*. *Brit. J. Cancer* **15**, 885.

Melnick, J. L. (1962). Papova virus group. *Science* **135**, 1128.

Mettler, N., Buckley, S. M. and Casals, J. (1961). Propagation of Junin virus, the etiological agent of Argentinian hemorrhagic fever, in HeLa cell cultures. *Proc. Soc. exp. Biol., N.Y.* **107**, 684.

Miles, J. A. R. and Austin, F. J. (1963). Growth of arboviruses in B.H.K.-21 cells. *Aust. J. Sci.* **25**, 466.

Milovanovic, M. V., Enders, J. F. and Mitus, A. (1957). Cultivation of measles virus in human amnion cells and in developing chick embryo. *Proc. Soc. exp. Biol., N.Y.* **95**, 120.

Miyagawa, Y., Mitamura, T., Yaoi, H., Ishii, N., Okanishi, J., Goto, T. and Shimizei, S. (1936). Studies on the virus of lymphogranuloma inguinale, *Nicolas, Favre,* and *Durand.* VII. Cultivation of the virus by tissue culture method. *Jap. J. exp. Med.* **14**, 207.

Moffat, M. A. J., Holtermann, O. A. and Hillis, W. D. (1960). The development of Soluble (S) and Viral (V) antigens of influenza A virus in tissue culture as studied by the fluorescent antibody technique. II. Studies employing a high multiplicity of infection in beef embryo kidney cells. *Acta path. microbiol. scand.* **50**, 409.

Mogabgab, W. J., Simpson, G. I. and Green, I. J. (1956). Growth characteristics and cytopathogenic effects of influenza A and B in cultures of human embryo tissues. *J. Immunol.* **76**, 314.

Morgan, C., Howe, C. and Rose, H. M. (1959). Intracellular crystals of coxsackie virus viewed in the electron microscope. *Virology* **9**, 145.

Morgan, C., Howe, C., Rose, H. M. and Moore, D. H. (1956). Structure and development of viruses observed in the electron microscope. IV. Viruses of the RI-APC group. *J. biophys. biochem. Cytol.* **2**, 351.

Morgan, C., Rose, H. M., Holden, M. and Jones, E. P. (1959). Electron microscopic observations on the development of herpes simplex virus. *J. exp. Med.* **110**, 643.

Mosely, J. W. (1961). Multiplication and cytopathogenicity of mouse hepatitis virus in mouse cell cultures. *Proc. Soc. exp. Biol., N.Y.* **108**, 524.

Moulder, J. W. (1962). "The Biochemistry of Intracellular Parasitisim", p. 171. University of Chicago Press.

Moulton, J. E. and Frazier, L. M. (1961). Desoxyribonucleic acid and protein changes in dog kidney cells infected with infectious canine hepatitis virus. *Virology* **15**, 91.

Moura, R. A. (1961–62). The influence of serum on the cytopathic effect of measles virus. *Arch. ges. Virusforsch.* **11**, 487.

Munk, V. K. and Sauer, G. (1963). Autoradiographische Untersuchungen uber das Verhalten der Desoxyribonucleinsaüre in Herpes-virus infizierten Zellen. *Z. Naturforsch.* **18b**, 211.

Munroe, J. S., Shipkey, F., Erlandson, R. A. and Windle, W. F. (1964). Tumors induced in juvenile and adult primates by chicken sarcoma virus. International Conference on Avian Tumor Viruses. *Nat. Cancer Inst. Monogr.* **17**, 365.

Murphy, J. S. and Bang, F. B. (1952). Observations with the electron microscope on cells of the chick chorio-allantoic membrane infected with influenza virus. *J. exp. Med.* **95**, 259.

Mussgay, M. and Weibel, J. (1962). Electron microscope and biological studies on the growth of Venezuelan equine encephalitis virus in KB cells. *Virology* **16**, 52.

Mussgay, M. and Weibel, J. (1963). Electron microscopic studies on the development of vesicular stomatitis virus in KB cells. *J. Cell Biol.* **16**, 119.

Nadel, M. K. and Orsi, E. V. (1964). Immunofluorescence of non-cytopathic tissue culture adapted fixed rabies. *Amer. J. med. Tech.* **30**, 173.

Nelson, J. B. (1959). The behavior of murine PPLO in HeLa cell cultures. *Ann. N.Y. Acad. Sci.* **79**, 450.

Nichols, W. W. (1963). Relationships of viruses, chromosomes and carcinogenesis. *Hereditas* **50**, 53.

Nichols, W. W. (1964). Chromosome abnormalities *in vitro* in human leucocytes associated with Schmidt-Ruppin Rous sarcoma virus. *Science* **146**, 248.

Nichols, W. W., Levan, A., Hall, B. and Ostergren, G. (1962). Measles-associated chromosome breakage. Preliminary communication. *Hereditas* **48**, 367.

Nielsen, G. and Peters, D. (1962). Elektronenmikroskopische Untersuchungen über die Initialstadien der Vaccine-Virusinfektion von HeLa-Zellen. *Arch. ges. Virusforsch.* **12**, 496.

Nii, S. (1961). The difference in the cytopathic changes in FL cells infected with different strains of herpes simplex virus. *Biken's J.* **4**, 215.

Nishmi, M. and Bernkopf, H. (1958). The toxic effect of vaccinia virus on leucocytes *in vitro*. *J. Immunol.* **81**, 460.

Niven, J. S. F., Armstrong, J. A., Andrewes, C. H., Pereira, H. G. and Valentine, R. C. (1961). Subcutaneous growths in monkeys produced by a poxvirus. *J. Path. Bact.* **81**, 1.

Niven, J. S. F., Armstrong, J. A., Balfour, B. M., Klemperer, H. G. and Tyrrell, D. A. J. (1962). Cellular changes accompanying the growth of influenza virus in bovine cell cultures. *J. Path. Bact.* **84**, 1.

Nosik, N. N. and Klisenko, G. A. (1963). Cytochemical studies on nucleic acids in cells from tissue cultures infected with type 5 adenovirus. *Acta virol.* **7**, 42.

Noyes, W. F. (1955). Visualization of Egypt 101 virus in the mouse's brain and in cultured human carcinoma cells by means of fluorescent antibody. *J. exp. Med.* **102**, 243.

Noyes, W. F. and Watson, B. K. (1955). Studies on the increase of vaccine virus in cultured human cells by means of the fluorescent antibody technique. *J. exp. Med.* **102**, 237.

Núñez-Montiel, O., Weibel, J. and Vitelli-Flores, J. (1961). Electron microscopic study of the cytopathology of Echo virus infection in cultivated cells. *J. Cell Biol.* **11**, 457.

Officer, J. E. and Brown, A. (1960). Growth of Psittacosis virus in tissue culture. *J. infect. Dis.* **107**, 283.

Officer, J. E. and Brown, A. (1961). Serial changes in virus and cells in cultures chronically infected with Psittacosis virus. *Virology* **14**, 88.

Okada, Y. (1962a). Analysis of giant polynuclear cell formation caused by HJV virus from Ehrlich's ascites tumor cells. I. Microscopic observation of giant polynuclear cell formation. *Exp. Cell Res.* **26**, 98.

Okada, Y. (1962b). Analysis of giant polynuclear cell formation caused by HJV virus from Ehrlich's ascites tumor cells. III. Relationship between cell condition and fusion reaction or cell degeneration reaction. *Exp. Cell Res.* **26**, 119.

Okada, Y. and Tadokoro, J. (1962). Analysis of giant polynuclear cell formation caused by HJV virus from Ehrlich's ascites tumor cells. II. Quantitative analysis of giant polynuclear cell formation. *Exp. Cell Res.* **26**, 108.

Okada, Y. and Tadokoro, J. (1963). The distribution of cell fusion capacity among several cell strains or cells caused by HJV. *Exp. Cell Res.* **32**, 417.

Okada, Y., Yamada, K. and Tadokoro, J. (1964). Effect of antiserum on the cell fusion reaction caused by HJV. *Virology* **22**, 397.

Padgett, B. L., Moore, M. S. and Walker, D. L. (1962). Plaque assays for myxoma and fibroma viruses and differentiation of the viruses by plaque form. *Virology* **17**, 462.

Parker, R. C. and Hollender, A. J. (1945). Propagation of Theiler's GD-VII mouse virus in tissue culture. *Proc. Soc. exp. Biol., N.Y.* **60**, 88.

Pereira, H. G. (1958). A protein factor responsible for the early cytopathic effect of adenoviruses. *Virology* **6**, 601.

Pereira, H. G. (1961). The cytopathic effect of animal viruses. *In* "Advances in Virus Research" (K. M. Smith and M. A. Lauffer, eds.), chap. 8. Academic Press, New York and London.

Pigoury, L., Michel, C. and Chabassol, C. (1962). Note sur le pouvoir cytopathogène du virus de la maladie de Newcastle cultivé sur cellules KB. *Ann. Inst. Pasteur* **103**, 443.

Pinkerton, H. and Hass, G. M. (1932). Intranuclear Rickettsiae in spotted fever studied in tissue culture. *J. exp. Med.* **56**, 151.

Pipkin, A. C. and Jensen, D. V. (1956). Avian embryos and tissue culture in the study of parasitic protozoa. I. Malarial parasites. *Exp. Parasit.* **7**, 491.

Pipkin, A. C. and Jensen, D. V. (1960). Avian embryos and tissue culture in the study of parasitic protozoa. II. Protozoa other than *Plasmodium*. *Exp. Parasit.* **9**, 167.

Placido Sousa, G. and Evans, D. G. (1957). The action of diphtheria toxin on tissue cultures and its neutralization by antitoxin. *Brit. J. exp. Path.* **38**, 644.

Plowright, W. and Ferris, R. D. (1958). The growth and cytopathogenicity of sheep-pox virus in tissue cultures. *Brit. J. exp. Path.* **39**, 424.

Plowright, W. and Witcomb, M. A. (1959). The growth in tissue cultures of a virus derived from lumpy-skin disease of cattle. *J. Path. Bact.* **78**, 397.

Plowright, W., Witcomb, M. A. and Ferris, R. D. (1959). Studies with a strain of contagious pustular dermatitis virus in tissue culture. *Arch. ges. Virusforsch.* **9**, 214.

Pollard, M. and Sharon, N. (1963). Induction of prolonged latency in Psittacosis infected cells by aminopterin. *Proc. Soc. exp. Biol., N.Y.* **112**, 51.

Pollard, M. and Starr, T. J. (1962). Study of intracellular virus with acridine orange fluorochrome. *Progr. med. Virol.* **4**, 54.

Pomerat, C. M. (1961). Cinematography, indispensable tool for cytology. *In* "International Review of Cytology" (G. H. Bourne and J. F. Danielli, eds.), Vol 2, pp. 307–334. Academic Press, New York and London.

Pontén, J. (1962). Homologous transfer of Rous sarcoma by cells. *J. nat. Cancer Inst.* **29**, 1147.

Pontén, J. (1963). Chromosome analysis of three virus-associated chicken tumors: Rous sarcoma, erythroleukemia, and RPL-12 lymphoid tumor. *J. nat. Cancer Inst.* **30**, 897.

Pope, J. H. and Rowe, W. P. (1964a). Detection of specific antigen in SV_{40}-transformed cells by immunofluorescence. *J. exp. Med.* **120**, 121.

Pope, J. H. and Rowe, W. P. (1964b). Immunofluorescent studies of adenovirus 12 tumors and of cells transformed or infected by adenoviruses. *J. exp. Med.* **120**, 577.

Porterfield, J. S. (1959). Plaque production with yellow fever and related arthropod-borne viruses. *Nature, Lond.* **183**, 1069.

Powelson, D. M. (1961). Metabolism of animal cells infected with mycoplasma. *J. Bact.* **82**, 288.

Pruniéras, M., Chardonnet, Y. and Schier, R. (1962a). Effets cytopathogènes des adénovirus type 5. *Ann. Inst. Pasteur* **103**, 484.

Pruniéras, M., Chardonnet, Y. and Schier, R. (1962b). Effets cytopathogènes des adénovirus type 5. II. Étude cytochimique. *Ann. Inst. Pasteur* **102**, 24.

Pruniéras, M., Chardonnet, Y. and Schier, R. (1964). Étude microcinematographique de l'effet cytopathogène du virus vacuolisant (SV 40) sur cellules rénales de *Cercopithecus aethiops*. *Ann. Inst. Pasteur* **106**, 1.

Puck, T. T., Marcus, P. I. and Ciecura, S. J. (1956). Clonal growth of mammalian cells *in vitro*. *J. exp. Med.* **103**, 273.

Rabson, A. S., Kilham, L. and Kirschstein, R. L. (1961). Intranuclear inclusions in *Rattus* (*Mastomys*) *natalensis* infected with rat virus. *J. nat. Cancer Inst.* **27**, 1217.

Rabson, A. S. and Legallais, F. Y. (1959). Cytopathogenic effect produced by polyoma virus in cultures of milk-adapted murine lymphoma cells. (Strain P 388 D_1). *Proc. Soc. exp. Biol., N.Y.* **100**, 229.

Rapp, F. and Buckley, S. M. (1962). Studies with the etiologic agent of Argentinian epidemic hemorrhagic fever (Junin virus). *Amer. J. Path.* **40**, 63.

Rapp, F., Kitahara, T., Butel, J. S. and Melnick, J. L. (1964). Synthesis of SV 40 tumor antigen during replication of Simian Papovavirus (SV 40). *Proc. nat. Acad. Sci., Wash.* **52**, 1138.

Rapp, F. and Vanderslice, D. (1964). Spread of zoster virus in human embryonic lung cells and the inhibitory effect of iododeoxyuridine. *Virology* **22**, 321.

Reczko, E. and Bogel, K. (1962). Elektronenmikroskopische Untersuchungen uber das Verhalten eines vom Kalb isolierten Parainfluenza 3 Virus in Kalbernierenzellkulturen. *Arch. ges. Virusforsch.* **12**, 404.

Reda, I. M., Rott, R. and Schäfer, W. (1964). Fluorescent antibody studies with NDV-infected cell systems. *Virology* **22**, 422.

Reisinger, R. C., Heddleston, K. L. and Manthei, C. A. (1959). A myxovirus (SF-4) associated with shipping fever of cattle. *J. Amer. vet. med. Ass.* **135**, 147.

Reissig, M., Howes, D. W. and Melnick, J. L. (1956). Sequences of morphological changes in epithelial cell cultures infected with poliovirus. *J. exp. Med.* **104**, 289.

Reissig, M. and Kaplan, A. S. (1960). The induction of amitotic nuclear division by pseudorabies virus multiplying in single rabbit kidney cells. *Virology* **11**, 1.

Reissig, M. and Melnick, J. L. (1955). The cellular changes produced in tissue cultures by herpes B virus correlated with the concurrent multiplication of the virus. *J. exp. Med.* **101**, 341.

Rhim, J. S., Jordan, L. E. and Mayor, H. D. (1962). Cytochemical, fluorescent-antibody and electron microscopic studies on the growth of reovirus (Echo 10) in tissue culture. *Virology* **17**, 342.

Rich, A. R., and Lewis, M. R. (1932). The nature of allergy in tuberculosis as revealed by tissue culture studies. *Johns Hopk. Hosp. Bull.* **50**, 115.

Rickenbacher, J. (1964). Infektionsversuche mit Vakzinevirus an menschlicher embryonaler Haut *in vitro*. *Path. Microbiol.* **27**, 624.

Rifkind, R. A., Godman, G. C., Howe, C., Morgan, C. and Rose, H. M. (1960). Echo 9 virus in tissue culture observed by light and electron microscopy. *Virology* **12** 331.

Robbins, F. C., Enders, J. F. and Weller, T. H. (1950). Cytopathogenic effect of poliomyelitis viruses *in vitro* on human embryonic tissues. *Proc. Soc. exp. Biol., N.Y.* **75**, 370.

Robineaux, R. (film). Évolution des lesions herpetiques en culture de tissu. Service du Film de Recherche Scientifique, Paris.

Robinow, C. F. (1950). A note on stalked forms of viruses. *J. gen. Microbiol.* **4**, 242.

Rodriguez, J. E. and Henle, W. (1964). Studies on persistent infections of tissue cultures. V. The initial stages of infection of L (MCN) cells by Newcastle disease virus. *J. exp. Med.* **119**, 895.

Roizman, B. (1961). Virus infection of cells in mitosis. *Virology* **13**, 387.

Roizman, B. (1962a). Polykaryocytosis induced by viruses. *Proc. nat. Acad. Sci., Wash.* **48** (2), 228.

Roizman, B. (1962b). Polykaryocytosis. *Cold Spr. Harb. Symp. quant. Biol.* **27**, 327.

Roizman, B. and Schluederberg, A. (1961). Virus infection of cells in mitosis. II. Measles virus infection of mitotic HEp-2 cells. *Proc. Soc. exp. Biol., N.Y.* **106**, 320.

Roizman, B. and Schluederberg, A. (1962). Virus infection of cells in mitosis. III. Cytology of mitotic and amitotic HEp-2 cells infected with measles virus. *J. nat. Cancer Inst.* **28**, 35.

Ross, R. W. and Orlans, E. (1958). The redistribution of nucleic acid and the appearance of specific antigen in the HeLa cells infected with herpes virus. *J. Path. Bact.* **76**, 393.

Rous, P. (1910). A transmissible avian neoplasm. Sarcoma of the common fowl. *J. exp. Med.* **12**, 696.

Rouse, H. C., Bonifas, V. H. and Schlesinger, R. W. (1963). Dependence of adenovirus replication on arginine and inhibition of plaque formation by pleuropneumonia-like organisms. *Virology* **20**, 357.

Rovazzo, G. C., Luginbuhl, R. E. and Helmboldt, C. F. (1963). A mycoplasma from a bovine causing cytopathogenic effects in calf kidney tissue culture. *Cornell Vet.* **53**, 560.

Rovescalli, A. and Campanella, F. (1962). Cytopathologie der durch Poliomyelitisvirus bedingten Zellinfektion. *Zbl. Bakt. I Abt. Ref.* **186**, 423.

Rowe, W. P., Hartley, J. W., Roizman, B. and Levy, H. B. (1958). Characterization of a factor formed in the course of adenovirus infection of tissue cultures, causing detachment of cells from glass. *J. exp. Med.* **108**, 713.

Rowe, W. P., Huebner, R. J., Gilmore, L. K., Parrott, R. H. and Ward, T. G. (1953). Isolation of a cytopathogenic agent from human adenoids undergoing spontaneous degeneration in tissue culture. *Proc. Soc. exp. Biol., N.Y.* **84**, 570.

Rubin, H. (1960a). A virus in chick embryos which induces resistance *in vitro* to infection with Rous sarcoma virus. *Proc. nat. Acad. Sci., Wash.* **46**, 1105.

Rubin, H. (1960b). An analysis of the assay of Rous sarcoma cells *in vitro* by the infective center technique. *Virology* **10**, 29.

Rubin, H. (1960c). The suppression of morphological alterations in cells infected with Rous sarcoma virus. *Virology* **12**, 14.

Rubin, H. (1964). Virus defectiveness and cell transformation in the Rous sarcoma. *J. cell. comp. Physiol.* **64**, (Suppl. 1), 173.

Ruska, H., Stuart, D. C., Jr. and Winsser, J. (1955). Electron microscopic visualization of intranuclear virus-like bodies in epithelial cells infected with poliomyelitis virus. *Arch. ges. Virusforsch.* **6**, 379.

Rustigian, R. (1962). A carrier state in HeLa cells with measles virus (Edmonston strain), apparently associated with non-infectious virus. A preliminary report. *Virology* **16**, 101.

Sabin, A. B. and Koch, M. A. (1964). Source of genetic information for specific complement-fixing antigens in SV 40 virus-induced tumors. *Proc. nat. Acad. Sci., Wash.* **52**, 1131.

Sachs, L. and Medina, D. (1961). *In vitro* transformation of normal cells by polyoma virus. *Nature, Lond.* **189**, 457.

Sachtleben, P. and Luyken, R. (1962). Veranderungen des elektrokinetischen Potentials von HeLa-Zellen nach Infektion mit Poliomyelitisvirus. *Arch. ges. Virusforsch.* **11**, 732.

Salido-Rengell, F. (1966). Cytochemical studies in cell cultures infected with Rous sarcoma virus. *Cancer Res.* **26**, 1031.

Sanford, K. K., Likely, G. D., Bryan, W. R. and Earle, W. R. (1952). The infection of cells in tissue culture with Rous sarcoma virus. *J. nat. Cancer Inst.* **12**, 1317.

Saxén, L., Vainio, T. and Toivonen, S. (1962). Effect of polyoma virus on mouse kidney rudiment *in vitro*. *J. nat. Cancer Inst.* **29**, 597.

Saxén, L., Vainio, T., and Toivonen, S. (1963). Viral susceptibility and embryonic differentiation: I. The histopathology of mouse kidney rudiments infected with polyoma and vesicular stomatitis viruses *in vitro*. *Acta path. microbiol. scand.* **58**, 191.

Schaechter, M., Bozeman, F. M. and Smadel, J. E. (1957). Morphologic observations of living rickettsiae in tissue culture cells. *Virology* **3**, 160.

Scherer, W. F. (1952). Agglutination of a pure strain of mammalian cells (L strain, Earle) by suspensions of vaccinia virus. *Proc. Soc. exp. Biol., N.Y.* **80**, 598.

Schimmelpfennig, H. and Liess, B. (1962). Histologische Untersuchungen an Schafen und an Kalberhodenzellkulturen nach Infektion mit dem Virus des Lippengrindes (*Ecthyma contagiosum*) oviner und humaner Herkunft. *Zbl. Bakt. I Abt. Orig.* **187**, 421.

Schmid, W. (1962). DNA replication patterns of the heterochromosomes in *Gallus domesticus*. *Cytogenetics* **1**, 344.

Schmitt-Ruppin, K. H. (1964). Heterotransplantation of Rous sarcoma and Rous sarcoma virus to mammals. *Oncologia* **17**, 247.

Schneweiss, K. E. (1962). Der cytopathische Effekt des Herpes simplex Virus (stammdifferenzen, Stabilität, Einfluss von Immunserum und Beziehungen zur Pockengrosse). *Zbl. Bakt. I Abt. Orig.* **186**, 467.

Scott, T. F. McN., Burgoon, C. F., Coriell, L. L. and Blank, H. (1953). The growth curve of the virus of herpes simplex in rabbit corneal cells grown in tissue culture with parallel observations on the development of the intranuclear inclusion body. *J. Immunol.* **71**, 385.

Scott, T. F. McN., McLeod, D. L. and Tokumaru, T. (1961). A biologic comparison of two strains of herpesvirus hominis. *J. Immunol.* **86**, 1.

Shaver, D. N., Barron, A. L. and Karzon, D. T. (1958). Cytopathology of human enteric viruses in tissue culture. *Amer. J. Path.* **34**, 943.

Shaver, D. N., Barron, A. L. and Karzon, D. T. (1961). Distinctive cytopathology of Echo viruses type 22 and 23. *Proc. Soc. exp. Biol., N.Y.* **106**, 648.

Shein, H. M. and Enders, J. F. (1962). Transformation induced by Simian Virus 40 in human renal cell cultures. I. Morphology and growth characteristics. *Proc. nat. Acad. Sci., Wash.* **48**, 1164.

Shein, H. M., Enders, J. F., Levinthal, J. D. and Burket, A. E. (1963). Transformation induced by Simian Virus 40 in newborn Syrian hamster renal cell cultures. *Proc. nat. Acad. Sci., Wash.* **49**, 28.

Sherman, F. E. and Ruckle, G. (1958). *In vivo* and *in vitro* cellular changes specific for measles. *Arch. Path., Chicago* **65**, 587.

Shif, I. and Bang, F. B. (1966). *Proc. Soc. exp. Biol., N.Y.* (in press).

Shirodkar, M. V., Warwick, A. and Bang, F. B. (1960). The *in vitro* reactions of *Limulus* amebocytes to bacteria. *Biol. Bull.* **118**, 324.

Simons, P. J. and Dougherty, R. M. (1963). Antigenic characteristics of three variants of Rous sarcoma virus. *J. nat. Cancer Inst.* **31**, 1275.

Smetana, H. F. (1962). The histopathology of experimental yellow fever. *Virchows Arch. path. Anat.* **335**, 411.

Smith, M. G. (1959). The salivary gland viruses of man and animals (Cytomegalic inclusion disease). *Progr. med. Virol.* **2**, 171.

Smyth, H. F. (1915). The reactions between bacteria and animal tissues under conditions of artificial cultivation. *J. exp. Med.* **21**, 103.

Smyth, H. F. (1916). The reaction between bacteria and animal tissues under conditions of artificial cultivation. *J. exp. Med.* **23**, 283.

Sokolov, N. N. and Parfanovich, M. I. (1964). Character of the accumulation and localization of specific antigen and nucleic acids in the course of vaccinia virus infection of tissue cultures as revealed by fluorescence microscopy. *Acta virol.* **8**, 30.

Sokolov, N. N., Parfanovich, M. I. and Mekler, L. B. (1963). On the nature of tick-borne encephalitis virus. I. A comparative study of nucleic acids and specific antigen in sheep embryo kidney cultures infected with tick-borne encephalitis virus by fluorescent microscopy. *Acta virol.* **7**, 209.

Sosa-Martinez, J., Gutierrez-Villegas, L. and Sosa, R. M. (1955). Propagation of herpes simplex virus in tissue cultures of rabbit kidney. *J. Bact.* **70**, 391.

Spendlove, R. S., Lennette, E. H. and John, A. C. (1963a). The role of the mitotic apparatus in the intracellular location of reovirus antigen. *J. Immunol.* **90**, 554.

Spendlove, R. S., Lennette, E. H., Knight, C. O. and Chin, J. N. (1963b). Development of viral antigen and infectious virus in HeLa cells infected with reovirus. *J. Immunol.* **90**, 548.

Spies, K. and Edlinger, E. (1959). Vermehrung und Weiterzüchtung eines dermotropen bovinen Vacinne-stammes in mesodermalen Zellen (L-Stamm, Earle) *in vitro*. *Zbl. Bakt. I Abt. Ref.* **174**, 29.

Starr, T. J. (1963). Morphological and biochemical integrity of colchicine-induced, Psittacosis-infected micronucleated cells. *Tex. Rep. Biol. Med.* **21**, 412.

Stenkvist, B. and Pontén, J. (1964). Morphological changes in bovine and human fibroblasts exposed to two strains of Rous sarcoma virus *in vitro*. *Acta path. microbiol. scand.* **62**, 315.

Stewart, S. E., Eddy, B. E., Gochenour, A. M., Borgese, N. G. and Grubbs, G. E. (1957). The induction of neoplasms with a substance released from mouse tumors by tissue culture. *Virology* **3**, 380.

Stewart, S. E., Eddy, B. E., Stanton, M. F. and Lee, S. L. (1959). Tissue culture plaques of SE Polyoma virus. *Proc. Amer. Cancer Res.* **3**, 67.

Stich, H. F., Hsu, T. C. and Rapp, F. (1964). Viruses and mammalian chromosomes. I. Localization of chromosome aberrations after infection with *Herpes simplex*. *Virology* **22**, 439.

Stich, H. F., Van Hoosier, G. L. and Trentin, J. J. (1964). Viruses and mammalian chromosomes: Chromosome aberrations by human adenovirus type 12. *Exp. Cell Res.* **34**, 400.

Stoker, M. G. P. (1958). Mode of intercellular transfer of herpes virus. *Nature, Lond.* **182**, 1525.

Stoker, M. G. P. (1964a). A simple marker technique for cells in culture. *Exp. Cell Res.* **35**, 429.

Stoker, M. G. P. (1964b). Regulation of growth and orientation in hamster cells transformed by polyoma virus. *Virology* **24**, 165.

Stoker, M. G. P. and Abel, P. (1962). Conditions affecting transformation by polyoma virus. *Cold Spr. Harb. Symp. quant. Biol.* **14**, 375.

Stoker, M. G. P. and MacPherson, I. (1961). Studies of transformation of hamster cells by polyoma virus *in vitro*. *Virology* **14**, 359.

Stoker, M. G. P. and Newton, A. (1959). Mitotic inhibition in HeLa cells caused by herpes virus. *Ann. N.Y. Acad. Sci.* **81**, 129.

Stoker, M. G. P., Smith, K. M. and Ross, R. W. (1958). Electron microscope studies of HeLa cells infected with herpes virus. *J. gen. Microbiol.* **19**, 244.

Stoler, M. and Gey, M. K. (1953). Destruction of a human fibrosarcoma strain (A.Fi.) in tissue cultures following the growth of poliomyelitis viruses. A preliminary report. *Johns Hopk. Hosp. Bull* **92**, 385.

Strauss, N. (1960). The effect of diphtheria toxin on the metabolism of HeLa cells. II. Effect on nucleic acid metabolism. *J. exp. Med.* **112**, 351.

Strauss, N. and Hendee, E. D. (1959). The effect of diphtheria toxin in the metabolism of HeLa cells. *J. exp. Med.* **109**, 145.

Stuart, D. C., Jr. and Fogh, J. (1959). Electron microscopic demonstration of intracellular poliovirus crystals. *Exp. Cell Res.* **18**, 378.

Suzuki, Y. (1918). The study of problems of immunity by the tissue culture method. *J. Immunol.* **3**, 238.

Svoboda, J. (1964). Malignant interaction of Rous virus with mammalian cells *in vivo* and *in vitro*. Int. Conf. Avian Tumor Viruses. *Nat. Cancer Inst. Monogr.* **17**, 277.

Sweet, B. H. and Hilleman, M. R. (1960). The vacuolating virus, SV-40. *Proc. Soc. exp. Biol., N.Y.* **105**, 420.

Szanto, J. (1963). Course of persistent infection of HeLa and Detroit 6 cells with herpes simplex virus. *Acta virol.* **7**, 385.

Takahashi, M., Kato, S., Kameyama, S. and Kamahora, J. (1959). A study on the multiplication of rabbit myxoma virus with the fluorescent antibody technique. *Biken's J.* **2**, 333.

Takahashi, M., Miyamoto, H. and Kato, S. (1963). Localization of RNA and DNA synthesis in measles virus-infected cells. *Biken's J.* **6**, 215.

Tawara, J., Goodman, J. R., Imagawa, D. T. and Adams, J. M. (1961). Fine structure of cellular inclusions in experimental measles. *Virology* **14**, 410.

Taylor, C. E. (1953). Interference between influenza and equine encephalitis viruses in tissue culture. *J. Immunol.* **71**, 125.

Taylor-Robinson, D. (1959). Chickenpox and herpes zoster. III. Tissue culture studies. *Brit. J. exp. Path.* **40**, 521.

Tchernomoretz, I. (1945). Multiplication *in vitro* of Koch bodies of *Theileria annulata*. *Nature, Lond.* **156**, 391.

Temin, H. M. (1960). The control of cellular morphology in embryonic cells infected with Rous sarcoma virus *in vitro*. *Virology* **10**, 182.

Temin, H. M. (1962). Separation of morphological conversion and virus production in Rous sarcoma virus infection. *Cold. Spr. Harb. Symp. quant. Biol.* **27**, 407.

Temin, H. M. (1964). Nature of the provirus of Rous sarcoma. International Conference on Avian Tumor Viruses. *Nat. Cancer Inst. Monogr.* **17**, 557.

Temin, H. M. and Rubin, H. (1958). Characteristics of an assay for Rous sarcoma virus and Rous sarcoma cells in tissue culture. *Virology* **6**, 669.

Tenenbaum, E. (1957). Changes in cellular nucleic acids during infection with poliomyelitis virus as studied by fluorescence microscopy. *Nature, Lond.* **180**, 1044.

Tenenbaum, E. and Doljanski, L. (1943). Studies on Rous sarcoma cells cultivated *in vitro*. II. Morphologic properties of Rous sarcoma cells. *Cancer Res.* **3**, 585.

Terni, M. and Allara, E. (1962). Lesioni da virus poliomielitico e modificazioni citochimiche spontanée in cellule KB. *Sperimentale* **112**, 28.

Terni, M. and Borghi, M. M. (1964). Ulteriori osservazioni citochimiche sulle alterazioni da infezione con poliovirus e da invecchiamento di cellule umane del ceppo KB. *Sperimentale* **114**, 32.

Thiry, L. (1963). Chemical mutagenesis of Newcastle disease virus. *Virology* **19**, 225.

Thomison, J. B. (1962). Evolution of measles giant cells in tissue culture: analysis by time-lapse microcinematography. *Lab. Invest.* **11**, 211.

Thormar, H. (1965). Effect of 5-bromodeoxyuridine and actinomycin D on the growth of Visna virus in cell cultures. *Virology* **26**, 36.

Thygeson, P. (1959). Trachoma and inclusion conjunctivitis. *In* "Viral and Rickettsial Infections of Man" (T. M. Rivers and F. L. Horsfall, eds.), pp. 729–740. Lippincott, Philadelphia.

Ting, R. C. (1964). Studies of the early stages of Rous sarcoma virus infection *in vitro*. *Virology* **22**, 568.

Tobey, R. A. (1964). Mengovirus replication. I. Conservation of virus RNA. *Virology* **23**, 10.

Todaro, G. J., Green, H. and Goldberg, B. D. (1964). Transformation of properties of an established cell line by SV 40 and polyoma virus. *Proc. nat. Acad. Sci., Wash.* **51**, 66.

Todaro, G. J., Nilausen, K. and Green, H. (1963). Growth properties of polyoma virus-induced hamster tumor cells. *Cancer Res.* **23**, 825.

Tokumaru, T. (1957). Pseudorabies virus in tissue culture. Differentiation of two distinct strains of virus by cytopathogenic pattern induced. *Proc. Soc. exp. Biol., N.Y.* **96**, 55.

Tournier, P., Granboulan, N. and Bernhard, W. (1961). Examen au microscope électronique des cellules de rein de Cercopithèque infectées *in vitro* par virus SV 40. *C.R.Acad. Sci., Paris* **253**, 2283.

Tournier, P. and Plissier, M. (1960). Étude au microscope électronique des lesions cellulaires provoquées *in vitro* par le virus Echo 10 (Reovirus). *C.R. Acad. Sci., Paris* **250**, 630.

Toyoshima, K., Hata, S. and Miki, T. (1960). Virological studies on measles virus. IV. The effect of active and inactivated measles virus on cultured cells. *Biken's J.* **3**, 281.

Toyoshima, K., Hata, S., Takahashi, M., Miki, T. and Okuno, Y. (1960). Virological studies on measles virus. III. Morphological changes and virus growth in FL cultures. *Biken's J.* **3**, 241.

Trentin, J. J., Yabe, Y. and Taylor, G. (1962). The quest for human cancer viruses. *Science* **137**, 835.

Tyrell, D. A. J. and Hoorn, B. (1965). The growth of some myxoviruses in organ cultures. *Brit. J. exp. Path.* **46**, 514.

Ueda, T., Toyoshima, S. and Seto, Y. (1963). Accelerating effect of arginine on the development of cytopathic effect of adenovirus. *Keio J. Med.* **12**, 139.

Vainio, T. and Judah, J. D. (1962a). Mechanism of cellular damage by virus. A study of antihistamine drugs. II. Murine hepatitis virus and mouse macrophages. *Exp. Molec. Path.* **1**, 27.

Vainio, T., Judah, J. D. and Bjotvedt, G. (1962b). Mechanism of cellular damage by virus. A study of antihistamine drugs. I. Murine hepatitis virus and liver explant cultures. *Exp. Molec. Path.* **1**, 15.

Vainio, T., Saxén, L. and Toivonen, S. (1963a). The acquisition of cellular resistance to polyoma virus during embryonic differentiation. *Virology* **20**, 381.

Vainio, T., Saxén, L. and Toivonen, S. (1963b). Viral susceptibility and embryonic differentiation: II. Immunofluorescence studies of viral infection in the developing mouse kidney *in vitro*. *Acta path. microbiol. scand.* **58**, 205.

Vainio, T., Saxén, L. and Toivonen, S. (1963c). Viral susceptibility and embryonic differentiation. III. Correlation between an inductive tissue interaction and the onset of viral resistance. *J. nat. Cancer Inst.* **31**, 1533.

Van Hoosier, G. L. Jr., Gist, C., Taylor, G. and Trentin, J. J. (1964). Persistent infection of human cells (HeLa) with adenovirus type 12. *Proc. Soc. exp. Biol., N.Y.* **115**, 591.

Vantsis, J. T. and Wildy, P. (1962). Interaction of herpes virus and HeLa cells. Comparison of cell killing and infective center formation. *Virology* **17**, 225.

Verna, J. E. (1965). Cell-culture response to fibroma virus. *J. Bact.* **89** (2), 524.

Vicari, G., Olitzki, A. L. and Olitzki, Z. (1960). The action of the thermolabile toxin of *Shigella dysenteriae* in cells cultivated *in vitro*. *Brit. J. exp. Path.* **41**, 179.

Vieuchange, J., de Brion, G. and Gruest, J. (1957). De l'action cytopathogène du virus vaccinal en culture de tissus et de l'hypothèse d'un effet cytotoxique. *Ann. Inst. Pasteur* **93**, 218.

Vogt, M. and Dulbecco, R. (1960). Virus-cell interaction with a tumor-producing virus. *Proc. nat. Acad. Sci., Wash.* **46**, 365.

Vogt, M. and Dulbecco, R. (1962). Properties of cells transformed by polyoma virus. *Cold Spr. Harb. Symp. quant. Biol.* **27**, 367.

Vogt, M. and Dulbecco, R. (1963). Steps in the neoplastic transformation of hamster embryo cells by polyoma virus. *Proc. nat. Acad. Sci., Wash.* **49**, 171.

Vogt, P. K. (1964). Fluorescence microscopic observations on the defectiveness of the Rous sarcoma virus. International Conference on Avian Tumor Viruses. *Nat. Cancer Inst. Monogr.* **17**, 523.

Vogt, P. K. (1965). A heterogeneity of Rous sarcoma virus revealed by selectively resistant chick embryo cells. *Virology* **25**, 237.

Vogt, P. K. and Luykx, N. (1963). Observations on the surface of cells infected with Rous sarcoma virus. *Virology* **20**, 75.

Vogt, P. K. and Rubin, H. (1961). Localization of infectious virus and viral antigen in chicken fibroblasts during successive stages of infection with Rous virus. *Virology* **13**, 528.

Wadsworth, A. and Hoppe, E. N. (1931). The neutralization or destruction of diphtheria toxin by tissue. *J. exp. Med.* **53**, 821.

Wagner, R. R. (1963). Cellular resistance to viral infection, with particular reference to endogenous interferon. *Bact. Rev.* **27**, 72.

Walker, D. L. and Hinze, H. C. (1962). A carrier state of mumps virus in human conjunctiva cells. I. General characteristics. II. Observations on intercellular transfer of virus and virus release. *J. exp. Med.* **116**, 739.

Watkins, J. F. (1964). Inhibition of spreading of HeLa cells after infection with herpes simplex virus. *Virology* **23**, 436.

Weiss, E., Myers, W. F., Dressler, H. R. and Chun-Hoon, H. (1964). Glucose metabolism by agents of the Psittacosis-Trachoma group. *Virology* **22**, 551.

Weller, T. (1956–57). Observations on the behavior of certain viruses that produce intranuclear inclusion bodies in man. *Harvey Lect.*, 228.

Wheeler, C. E., Jr. (1958). The effect of temperature upon the production of herpes simplex virus in tissue culture. *J. Immunol.* **81**, 98.

Wheeler, C. E., Jr. (1964). Biological comparison of a syncytial and a small giant cell-forming strain of herpes simplex. *J. Immunol.* **93**, 749.

Wheelock, E. F. and Tamm, I. (1959). Mitosis and division in HeLa cells infected with influenza or Newcastle disease virus. *Virology* **8**, 532.

Wheelock, E. F. and Tamm, I. (1961a). The effect of multiplicity of infection on Newcastle disease virus—HeLa cell interaction. *J. exp. Med.* **113**, 317.

Wheelock, E. F. and Tamm, I. (1961b). Biochemical basis for alterations in structure and function of HeLa cells infected with Newcastle disease virus. *J. exp. Med.* **114**, 617.

Wildy, P., Smith, C., Newton, A. A. and Dendy, P. (1961). Quantitative cytological studies on HeLa cells infected with herpes virus. *Virology* **15**, 486.

Winocour, E. and Sachs, L. (1959). A plaque assay for the polyoma virus. *Virology* **8**, 397.

Wolff, E. and de la Forest, P. G. (1960). Sur les lésions histopathologiques spécifiques provoquées par le virus de la variole aviaire dans des explants de peau embryonnaire de poulet en culture d'organe *in vitro*. *Ann. Inst. Pasteur* **98**, 325.

Yang, W. C. T., Strasser, F. F. and Pomerat, C. M. (1965). Mechanism of drug-induced vacuolization in tissue culture. *Exp. Cell Res.* **38**, 495.

Yerganian, G., Shein, H. M. and Enders, J. F. (1962). Chromosomal disturbances observed in human fetal renal cells transformed *in vitro* by Simian Virus 40 and carried in culture. *Cytogenetics* **1**, 314.

Zalkind, S. Y., Andzhaparedze, O. G., Bogomolova, N. N. and Folina, A. M. (1963). Morphological and cytochemical study of HeP_2 cultures persistently infected with tick-borne encephalitis virus. *Acta virol.* **7**, 48.

Zeigel, R. F., Burmester, B. R. and Rauscher, F. J. (1964). Comparative morphologic and biologic studies of natural and experimental transmission of avian tumor viruses. International Conference on Avian Tumor Viruses. *Nat. Cancer Inst. Monogr*, **17**, 711.

CHAPTER 4

Cell, Tissue and Organ Cultures in Virus Research

FRED RAPP and JOSEPH L. MELNICK

Department of Virology and Epidemiology, Baylor University College of Medicine, Houston, Texas, U.S.A.

I. Introduction

The pioneering work by Harrison (1907) who demonstrated that fragments of tissue could be maintained *in vitro* led to attempts to utilize this method for the multiplication and study of viruses. Steinhardt,

Israeli and Lambert (1913) were able to cultivate vaccinia virus in fragments of rabbit and guinea-pig cornea. Although a number of such studies were carried out during the next three decades, the use of Tissue Cultures* in virus research did not gain wide acceptance partly because of the difficulties in observing the effects of the viruses in the tissue fragments and partly because of lack of knowledge concerning the maintenance of the cells in the cultures. The discovery that the replication of poliovirus in Tissue Culture could be readily followed by the cytopathic effect produced (Robbins, Enders and Weller, 1950) led to the recent developments in virology.

During the past fifteen years, Tissue Culture has been widely employed in virology. The cultures most often used consist of monolayers of cells in either bottles, tubes, or Petri dishes, and some workers have effectively used cells in suspension. Organ cultures, though useful for special purposes, have not yet found wide acceptance. The preparation of cultures has been facilitated by recently developed methods for dispersal of cells without damage to their viability. The use of the enzyme trypsin for this purpose, first described by Rous and Jones (1916) and introduced to virology by Dulbecco (1952) has made it possible to grow a variety of cells in culture. Different culture media have been developed and the incorporation of antibiotics to prevent bacterial contamination has facilitated progress. Although many media have been introduced, medium 199 (Morgan, Morton and Parker, 1950), Eagle's basal medium (Eagle, 1959) and Melnick's lactalbumin hydrolysate medium (Melnick, 1955) are most often used by virologists. These media are often fortified with serum (human, horse, calf, or fetal calf) and sometimes with various embryonic or yeast extracts or tryptose phosphate broth. The reader is referred to the chapter by Waymouth (Vol. 1, Chap. 3) for detailed description of the media available for the growth of cells in culture.

The use of Tissue-Culture systems has greatly facilitated the isolation of viruses and their identification. The availability of quantitative techniques has enabled investigators to study the properties of many viruses, including viral replication and viral genetics. In addition, various cell systems are widely employed in the production of virus vaccines. A recent development has been the demonstration that viruses with oncogenic properties can transform normal cells growing in culture into those with neoplastic properties. These latter studies are enabling investigators to study in greater detail the mechanisms by which tumor viruses carry out their oncogenic functions.

*Most virus work is carried out in *cell*, rather than *tissue*, culture. However, Tissue Culture has become an accepted term even though referring to cultures of undifferentiated cells and will be used synonymously with cell culture in this chapter.

The following sections of this chapter have been designed to explore these aspects more fully. No attempt has been made to cover completely the various fields and the reader will be referred to recent reviews. This chapter was completed and submitted in August 1963; minor revisions were made in January 1964.

II. Isolation of Viruses in Tissue Culture

The isolation of viruses can be attempted from any material, although cytotoxicity of the inoculum is sometimes a problem. Material from which viruses have been isolated includes stool, rectal swabs, throat washings, blood, urine, tissue biopsies, autopsy tissue, and specimens taken from lesions of various types. The material to be tested is generally made into a homogeneous suspension, clarified by low speed centrifugation, and inoculated into tubes or bottles containing monolayers of cells. The type of cell culture chosen is usually one which is sensitive to the virus being sought; isolation of viruses from human material is generally carried out in primary monkey kidney cells (epithelial), human amnion cells (epithelial), continuous human cell lines like HeLa (epithelial), or human embryonic lung strains (diploid fibroblastic) although other types may also be used when desirable. The suspensions to be inoculated are generally treated with large amounts of antibiotics (penicillin, streptomycin, neomycin, mycostatin). The methods used to isolate the specific viruses have been thoroughly reviewed in the 3rd edition of "Diagnostic Procedures for Viral and Rickettsial Diseases" (1964).

Most commonly, the cultures are observed daily for cytopathic effects. When these occur, a second passage into fresh cells is usually carried out and the virus is further identified after that passage by serologic techniques. Viral replication, in the absence of cytopathic effects, can be detected by a number of indirect means. Portions of the cell culture can be stained with hematoxylin and eosin or with Giemsa and typical intranuclear or intracytoplasmic inclusions can sometimes be observed. Other methods, such as hemadsorption, metabolic effects, interference, and electron-microscopy will be reviewed in the next section on identification of viruses.

If no effects are seen on first passage in the cell system employed, after a suitable period of time (which often depends upon ability to maintain the cultures in a healthy state), the cells may be disrupted by rapid freezing and thawing or by treatment in a sonic oscillator and passed into fresh cells. This procedure is especially useful for viruses that replicate slowly and in cases where the initial inoculum proves to be toxic to the cells. A number of such blind passages may be made, although one or two passages are usually sufficient. Prolonged maintenance of the primary cultures or cells obtained directly from biopsy or autopsy material sometimes results in a slow build-up of virus in the culture until cytopathic effects can be noted. The changes of fluid medium in the active cell culture serves to remove antibodies carried over with the original tissue, and this may be the chief factor in allowing an occult virus to proliferate in the culture. This technique has proved especially useful for the isolation of adenovirus (Rowe, Huebner, Gilmore, Parrott and Ward, 1953), cytomegalovirus (Rowe, Hartley, Waterman, Turner and Huebner, 1956; Smith, 1956), and the SV40 papovavirus (Ashkenazi and Melnick, 1962).

The isolation of a virus is relatively easy when compared to the steps necessary to identify the isolated agent. Knowledge of the properties of the various virus groups is extremely helpful and availability of standardized antisera is essential for this purpose.

III. Identification of Viruses

A. Cytopathic Effects

The morphological changes induced by the replication of viruses in susceptible cells in Tissue Culture detectable in the ordinary microscope are called cytopathic effects. They are discussed in more detail in Chapter 3. While many viruses cause cytopathic changes in cultured cells, the rapidity of development and nature of the change seen often furnish a clue to the type of virus and greatly facilitate subsequent identification. In addition, identification can also be aided by ability of viruses to cause cytopathic effects in certain cells but not in others.

The most dramatic changes are induced when replication of the virus results in cell lysis. For example, many enteroviruses (Reissig, Howes and Melnick, 1956; Melnick, Wenner and Rosen, 1964) cause such lysis. Human strains of these viruses, with the exception of some coxsackievirus types, multiply readily in primary cultures of human and monkey tissues producing degenerative changes that result in destruction of the cells (Figs. 1–4). These cytopathic changes usually occur within 8 h after infection of the cells (Fig. 5). When most of the cells are initially infected, the cultures are totally destroyed within 12–24 h post-inoculation. The morphologic changes seen in monkey kidney cells infected with poliovirus appear to be related to release of the virus from the cell (Lwoff, Dulbecco, Vogt and Lwoff, 1955).

The differential susceptibility of cells from rhesus and patas monkeys

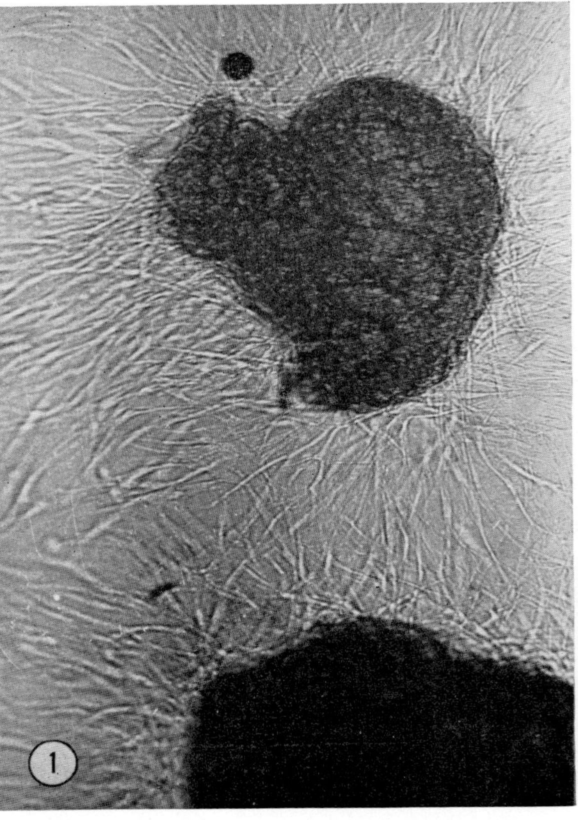

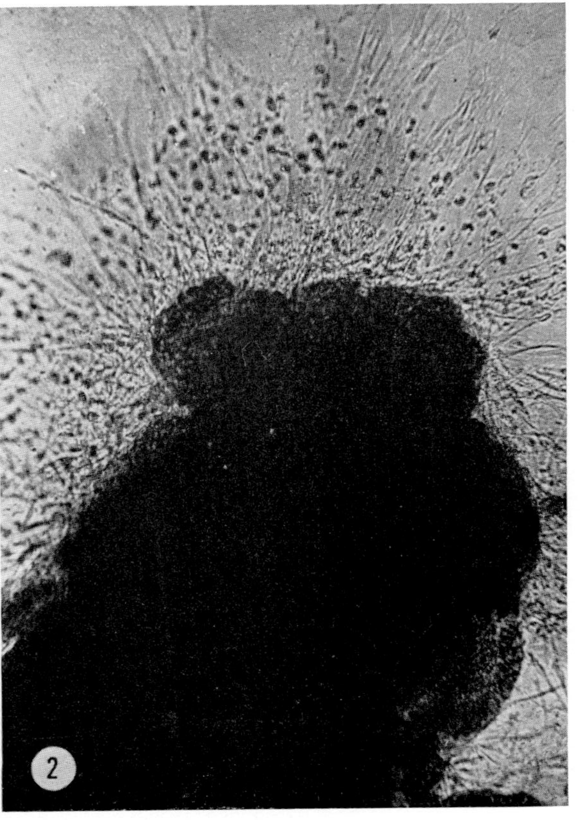

FIG. 1. Fragments of monkey testis grown in plasma clot culture. Areas of fibroblastic growth radiate out from fragments. Unstained.

FIG. 2. Fragments of the same monkey testis as in Fig. 1. Note destruction of fibroblastic growth 5 days after inoculation of the cultures with poliovirus type 1. Unstained.

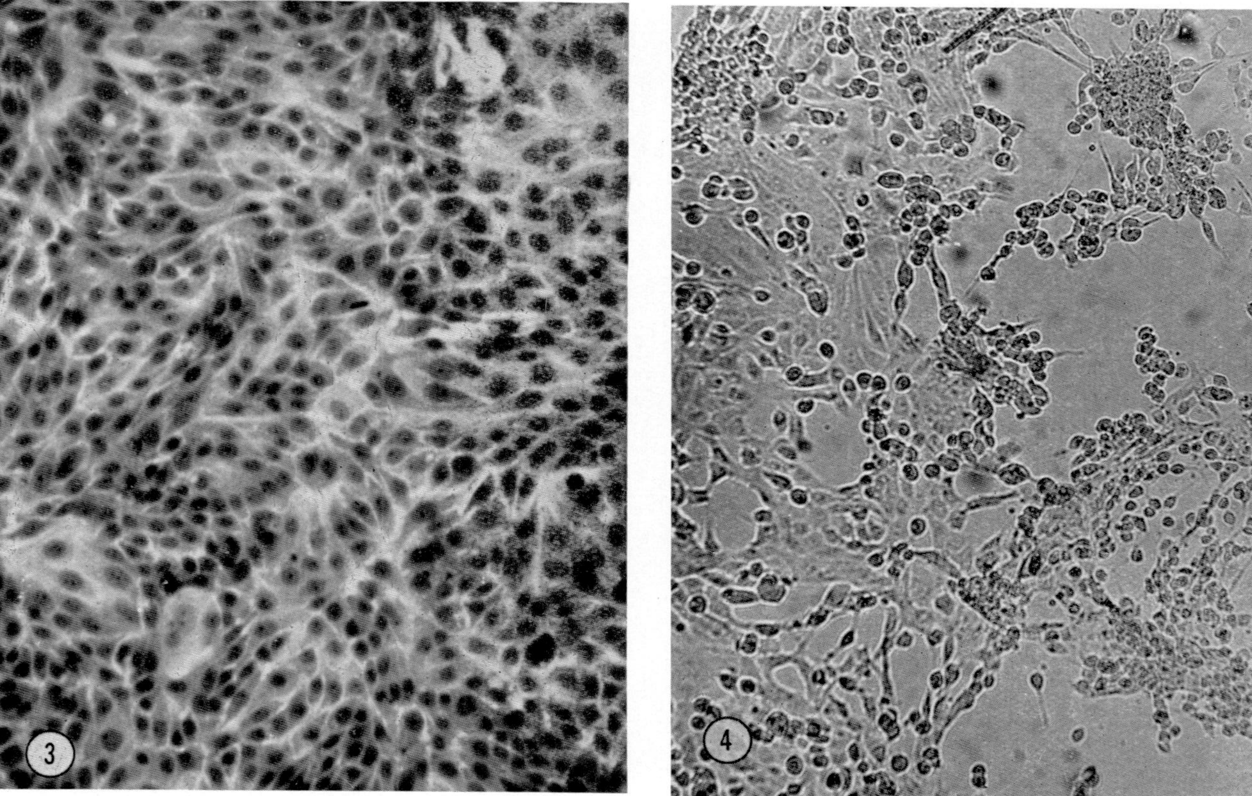

FIG. 3. Monolayer of uninoculated monkey kidney cells. Stained with hematoxylin and eosin.
FIG. 4. Monolayer of monkey kidney cells following inoculation with poliovirus type 1. Extensive destruction and cytopathic effects are evident in about 50% of the culture. Unstained.

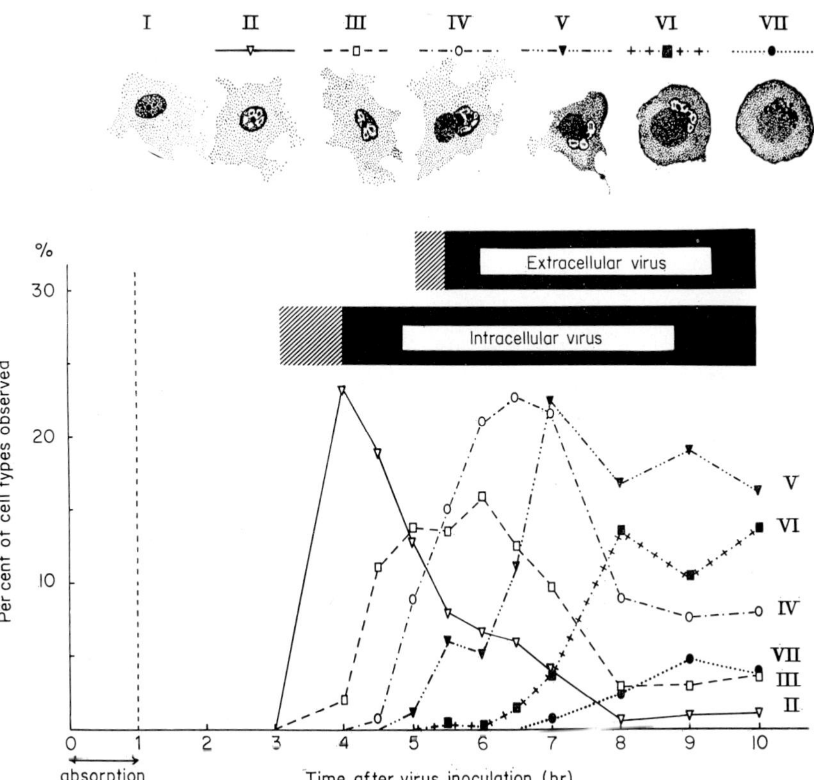

FIG. 5. Cytopathic changes seen in monkey kidney cells after infection with poliovirus. Note correlation of changes with detection of intra- and extracellular virus. In order to evaluate the morphological data on a more quantitative basis, the cells were classified into seven different types (I-VII above) depending on the degree of cytopathic change, and differential cell counts were made on a number of areas in each culture. The results of differential cell counts are plotted above. The appearance of infective virus within the cells occurred approximately at the same time as the first nuclear alterations were observed, usually coincident with the time of appearance of type II cells. Virus release occurred at variable times, always before the rounded type VI cells appeared. (Reissig *et al.*, 1956.)

to echoviruses has been used to subdivide this group (Hsiung and Melnick, 1957). Similar differences in ability to multiply in some cells are also useful in identification of coxsackie A and B viruses (Dalldorf, Melnick and Curnen, 1959). However, animal or cell pathology is inadequate to classify enteroviruses, as seen from Table I, which indicates the overlap in the subgrouping of these agents.

Arboviruses (arthropod-borne viruses) often cause marked cytopathic effects in susceptible cells, although moderate changes and carrier states in which the virus multiplies without apparent injury to

TABLE I

Enteroviruses: growth in monkey kidney and human cell cultures and pathogenicity for animals

	Monkey kidney cells	HeLa and other human cells	Pathogenicity Mice	Pathogenicity Monkeys
Polio	+	+	0[1]	+[2]
Coxsackie A	0[3]	0[4]	+[3]	0[5]
Coxsackie B	+	+	+[3]	0[5]
Echo	+[7]	0[4]	0[6]	0[5]

[1]Some strains of each type have been adapted to mice.

[2]Attenuated strains used for oral vaccine produce mild localized lesions when inoculated intraspinally and almost no lesions when inoculated intracerebrally.

[3]Coxsackie A9 and B strains grow readily in monkey kidney cells; some strains grow poorly in mice and fail to produce disease in them.

[4]Some strains grow preferentially in or have been adapted to human cell cultures. Coxsackie A11, 13, 15, 18, 20, 21 may be isolated directly in human cells.

[5]Coxsackie A7 produces a severe polioencephalomyelitis in monkeys; other coxsackie and echo strains produce *mild* lesions in the central nervous system that resemble mild poliomyelitis.

[6]Whereas the prototype and other strains of echovirus 9 are not pathogenic for mice, a number of other strains, especially after passage in monkey kidney cells, produce paralysis in mice (severe coxsackievirus type of myositis).

[7]Echovirus 21 is cytopathogenic for human epithelial cells but not for monkey cells.

the cell are known. The affected cells usually contract, become rounded, and granularity of the cytoplasm is often evident. Most arboviruses multiply readily in mammalian and chick-embryo Tissue Cultures (Buckley, 1959). Hamster kidney cultures seem to be peculiarly susceptible to some strains (Diercks and Hammon, 1958).

The type of cellular change produced by adenoviruses is characteristic (Boyer, Leuchtenberger and Ginsberg, 1957). The infected cell enlarges and becomes round and refractile; affected cells tend to cluster. These viruses are generally cytopathic for epithelial cells derived from a closely related species; they lack pathogenicity for cells of distantly related animals and are most virulent for cells from the species from which they were originally isolated (Rowe and Hartley, 1962).

Many viruses cause the formation of multinucleated giant cells in Tissue Cultures (Fig. 6). These include poxvirus (Pereira, 1961), herpesviruses (Reissig and Melnick, 1955; Hoggan and Roizman, 1959), varicella-zoster (Weller, Witton and Bell, 1958), measles virus (Enders and Peebles, 1954; Seligman and Rapp, 1959), and the related canine distemper (Rockborn, 1958) and rinderpest viruses (Plowright, 1962), and the myxoviruses including mumps (Henle, Deinhardt and Girardi, 1954), parainfluenza (Marston, 1958), and respiratory

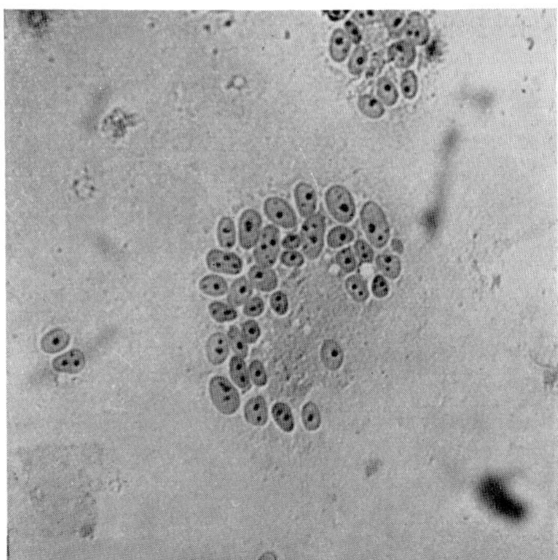

FIG. 6. Culture of Hep-2 cells 10 days after inoculation with measles virus. Note multinucleated giant cell.

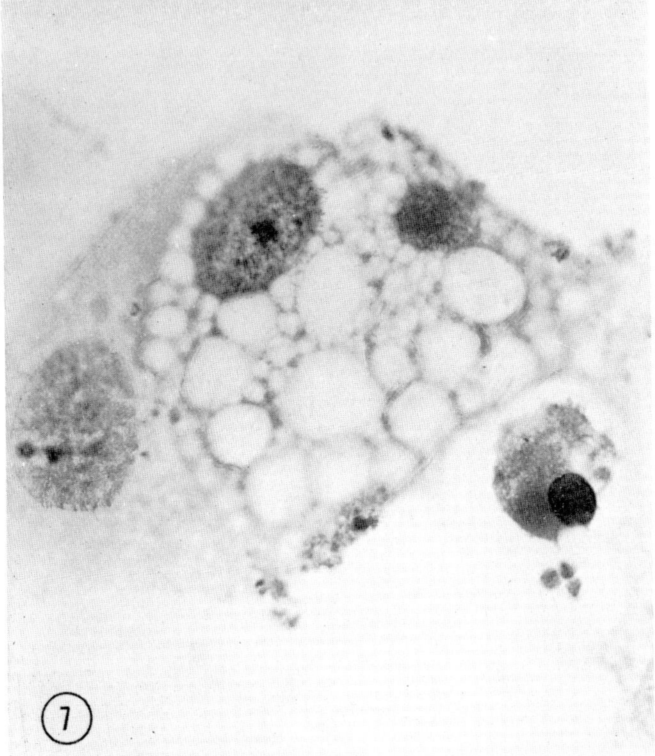

FIG. 7. Culture of cercopithecus monkey kidney cells 72 h following inoculation with SV40 virus. Extensive cytoplasmic vacuolation can be seen. × 640.

syncytial virus (Chanock and Finberg, 1957). These viruses often cause other effects as well. It is noteworthy that some of the changes seen in culture resemble those seen *in vivo*; perhaps the best example is the formation *in vivo* of giant cells during measles (Warthin, 1931).

A peculiar effect caused by a virus is cytoplasmic vacuolation (Fig. 7). The simian papovavirus SV40 causes extensive vacuolation in cercopithecus monkey kidney cells, and led to the agent being named the vacuolating virus (Sweet and Hilleman, 1960). While the virus also produces intranuclear changes in cells of other species (rhesus, baboon, human), vacuolation is usually absent.

The effect of a virus on a cell can therefore be suggestive of its identity, but it is by no means pathognomonic. This is especially true since uninoculated cells in cultures often show aberrations (Fig. 8) similar to those seen in virus-infected cultures (Kleinfeld and Melnick, 1958). In conjunction with cytopathic observations on living cultures, it is often useful to fix and stain cells for further information concerning the identity of viruses.

FIG. 8. Variety of abnormal cell types seen in *uninoculated* primary cultures of rhesus kidney. All cultures were stained with hematoxylin-eosin. (Kleinfeld and Melnick, 1958.) × 700.

(1) Two normal metaphase figures: A, polar view; B, side view. (2) A tripolar anaphase figure. (3) A tetrapolar metaphase figure. (4) A tetrapolar metaphase with one group of chromosomes oriented in a plane perpendicular to another group. The metaphase plate seen from polar view contains only 12 chromosomes. (5) Late anaphase of a tetrapolar division. Note the unequal distribution of chromosomes to the four daughter cells. (6) Unequal distribution of chromosomes and cytoplasm in a bipolar division. (7) A hypohaploid cell in mitosis. The chromosomes appear thinner than typical metaphase chromosomes. (8) A polyploid cell in metaphase. Note the chromosome fragments which have failed to become oriented on the metaphase plate. (9) A cell in mitosis showing precocious movement of chromosomes. (10 and 11) Cells in anaphase with chromosome bridges. (12) A tripolar anaphase division figure with lagging chromosomes. (13) A cell with an anomolous spindle. The chromosomes are scattered about in a disorganized fashion. (14) A multinucleate cell with four polyploid (or aneuploid) nuclei. The two nuclei on the left have a common bridge between them and may be in the process of fusing. Note the knob-like protrusion coming from the uppermost nucleus. This is probably the manner in which most micronuclei, frequently seen in these cultures, are formed. (15) A giant binucleate cell with extensive lobation of the nuclei. There appears to be some interaction or connections between the two nuclei suggestive of fusion. (16) A large nucleus containing a commonly seen inclusion. The inclusion appears to have been formed by an invagination of the nuclear membrane encircling cytoplasmic material. (17) A cell showing a prominent nuclear inclusion bounded by a dense basophilic membrane. (18 and 19) Nuclear inclusions which appear to form in association with an invaginated surface of the nuclear membrane. Note the intricate system of radiations. The nucleoli of cells having such inclusions are pale and highly vacuolated. (20) Phagocytosis in a dividing cell. The phagocytized cell is a pycnotic, dying cell and has been completely engulfed by the dividing cell. (21, 22 and 23) Phagocytosis with nuclear involvement. (21 and 22) The nucleus is encircling the phagocytized pycnotic cell. (23) The nucleus has completely engulfed the phagocytized cell ("nuclear phagocytosis"). The nucleoli (N) can readily be distinguished from the phagocytized cell (I).

B. TINCTORIAL PROPERTIES

Cultured cells infected with viruses and stained with either hematoxylin and eosin or Giemsa, after fixation with Bouin's fluid, or a comparable fixative, often yield specific staining patterns which are useful for virus identification. For this purpose, cells are generally cultivated on slides or on coverglasses placed in Petri dishes and grown in a nutrient medium exposed to 5% CO_2 or on coverglasses in Leighton

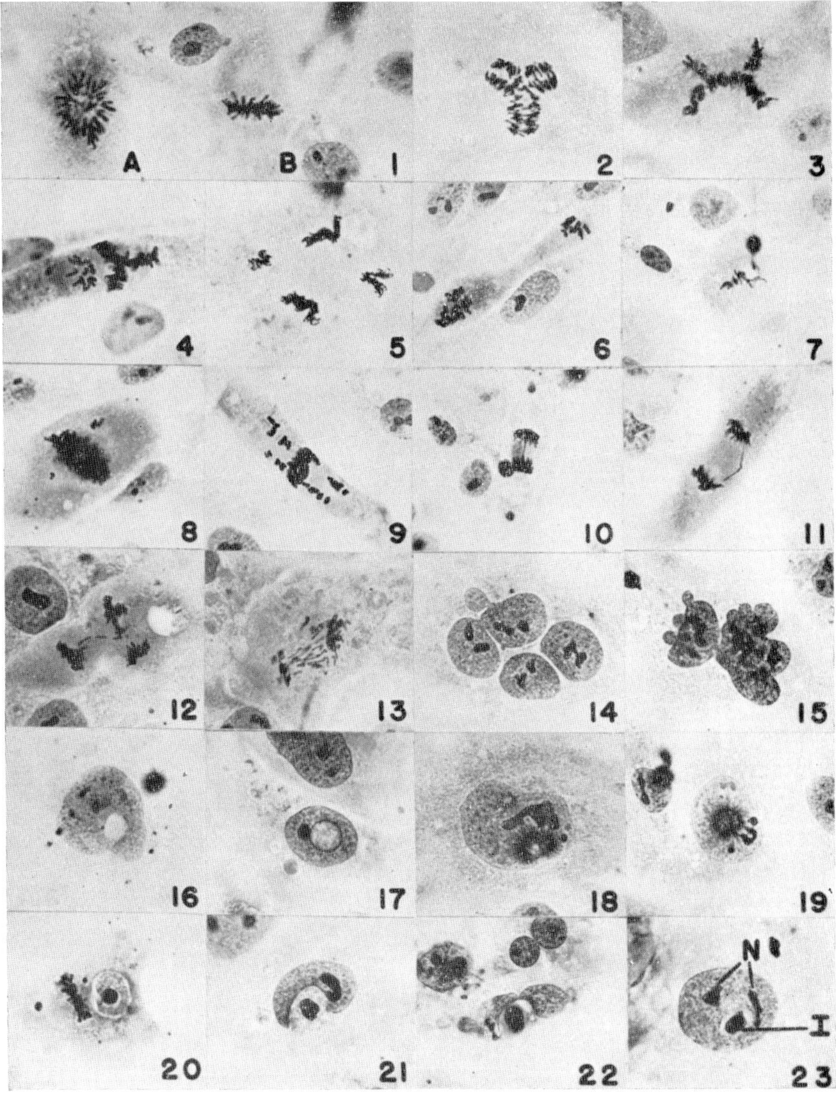

tubes (Leighton, 1954). The staining characteristics of many virus-cell systems have been reviewed by various authors (Whitelock, 1959; Pereira, 1961).

Viruses can be grouped by their ability to cause formation of intranuclear eosinophilic or basophilic inclusions, cytoplasmic eosinophilic or basophilic inclusions, or combinations of these (Fig. 9). Table II summarizes the inclusion patterns of the major virus groups.

The use of the fluorochrome, acridine orange, to study the replication of viruses and to determine the type of nucleic acid of viruses has received wide attention. Cells are treated as for conventional staining except that an acid fixative is used. Deoxyribonucleic acid (DNA) gives a green color when the DNA is in the double-stranded form.

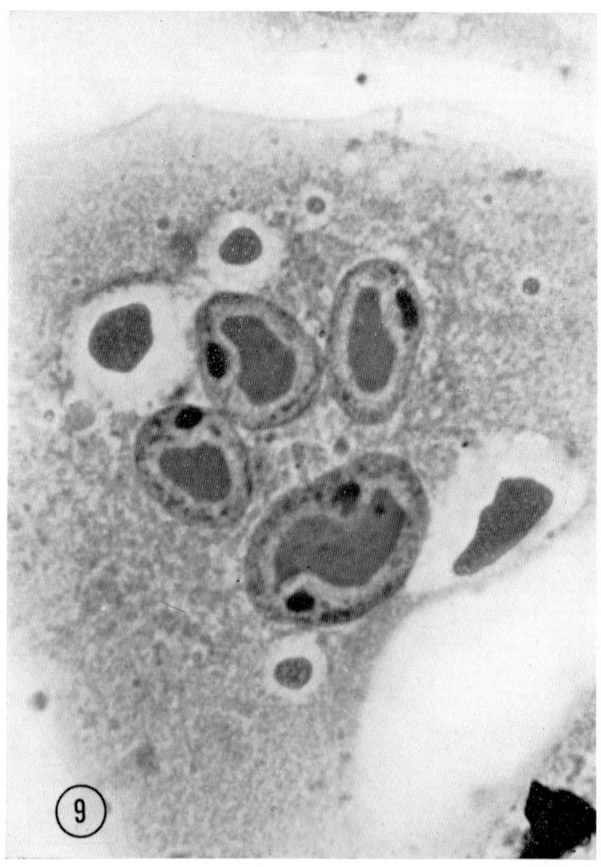

Fig. 9. Multinucleated cell typical of measles virus infection in monkey kidney cultures. Both cytoplasmic and intranuclear eosinophilic inclusions are present. Hemotoxylin and eosin. × 1000.

TABLE II

Staining pattern of viruses in susceptible cells

Viruses	Inclusion bodies Nuclear	Cytoplasmic
DNA viruses		
Poxvirus	None	Basophilic and eosinophilic
Adenovirus	Basophilic[1]	None
Herpesvirus[5]	Eosinophilic[3]	None[2]
Papovavirus	Basophilic	None
RNA viruses		
Myxoviruses		
(a) Influenza	None	None
(b) Mumps, NDV, RS, parainfluenza	None	Eosinophilic
(c) Measles, distemper, rinderpest	Eosinophilic	Eosinophilic
Reoviruses	None	Eosinophilic
Arboviruses	None	None
Picornaviruses		
(a) Enterovirus	None[4]	None[4]
(b) Rhinovirus	None	None

[1]Occasionally, small eosinophilic bodies are seen.
[2]Cytomegalovirus causes formation of eosinophilic bodies.
[3]Basophilic if examined early (i.e. before the virus has left the nucleus).
[4]Early eosinophilic intranuclear inclusions are seen in poliovirus infection and perinuclear eosinophilic masses are present in the cytoplasm before virus is released.
[5]Includes varicella-zoster, equine abortion, cytomegalovirus, avian laryngotracheitis, pseudorabies and B virus.

Single-stranded DNA (φX174 bacteriophage) and ribonucleic acid (RNA) appear red when viewed by fluorescence microscopy after staining with acridine orange. Current knowledge gained by the use of this technique has been summarized by Mayor (1963) in a recent review.

C. PLAQUES

The size and shape of virus-induced plaques are important characteristics that aid in identifying a virus. A plaque is a clear area in a sheet of cells resulting from destruction of the cells in that area by a virus. This phenomenon, well studied for bacterial viruses, was adapted to the study of animal viruses by Dulbecco (1952). The ability of a virus to cause plaque formation in a cell system is often directly proportional to the intensity of the cytopathic changes in that system. A virus that does not induce cell destruction is not likely to cause the formation of plaques.

Cells are grown in either bottles or Petri dishes and, after a monolayer has formed, virus is seeded onto the cell sheet. After a suitable period of adsorption, a viscous overlay containing nutrients is added to prevent infection of distant cells by virus liberated into the nutrient medium. Under these conditions, one infectious virus particle usually gives rise to one plaque. Agar is the substance most widely used to prevent secondary spread but other materials, especially methyl cellulose (Hotchin, 1955), have been employed especially since the observations that agar inhibits plaque formation by poliovirus (Takemori and Nomura, 1960), encephalomyocarditis virus (Takemoto and Liebhaber, 1961), dengue virus (Schulze and Schlesinger, 1963), and herpes simplex virus (Rapp, 1963; Tytell and Neuman, 1963). Neutral red is usually added after a suitable period of incubation to facilitate reading of the clear areas. However, if proper precautions are taken (using suitable agar, filtering instead of autoclaving neutral red), agar may be used and neutral red incorporated in the overlay (Wallis, Melnick and Bianchi, 1962). In this way, plaques have been obtained with certain echoviruses which had previously failed to yield them.

Fig. 10. Plaques produced by echoviruses 12 and 13 in monolayers of monkey kidney cells 7 days after inoculation of the cultures. Note large, circular (echo 12) and small irregular (echo 13) plaques produced.

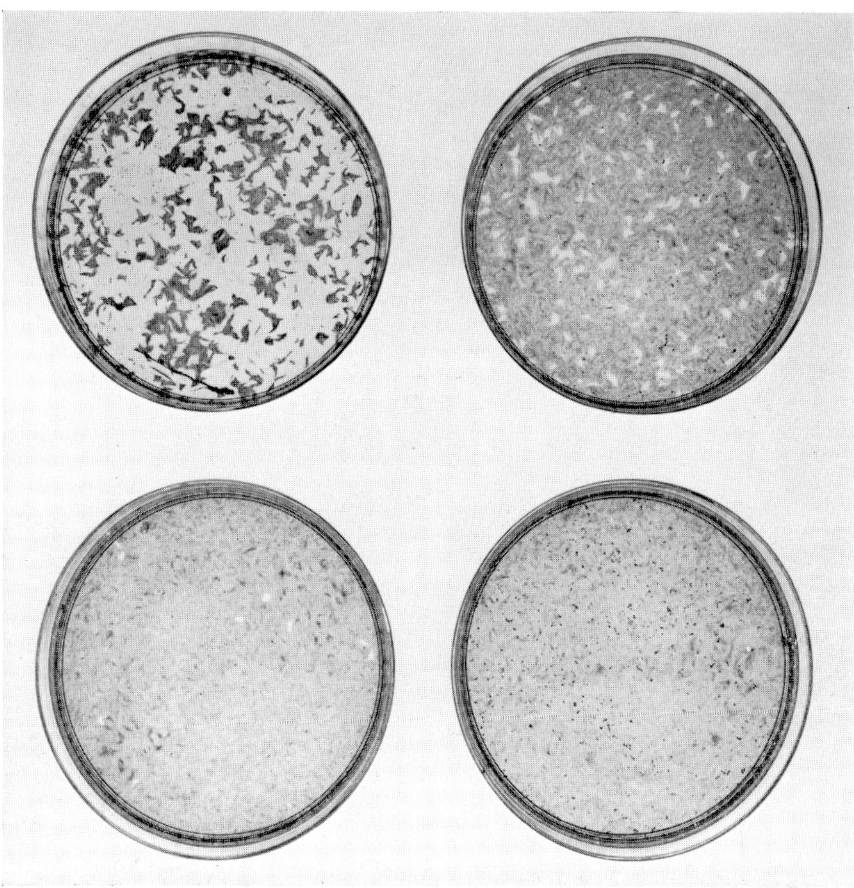

FIG. 11. Plaques formed in embryonic human lung cells 7 days after cells infected with zoster virus were seeded onto the monolayers. Upper left: destruction almost confluent because large number of infected cells were seeded. Upper right: approximately 100 plaques when infected suspension was diluted 10-fold. Lower left: 10 plaques when infected cells were diluted 100-fold. Lower right: no plaques in uninoculated control.

The shape and size of the plaques in various cells under differing environmental conditions may be a useful marker for virus identification, and even for distinguishing virulent from attenuated strains of virus. The best studied examples are the enteroviruses, which can often be differentiated by plaque morphology (Melnick *et al.,* 1964) (Fig. 10). Thus, mixtures of enteroviruses can be separated by picking virus from different types of plaques. This method is also useful for purifying viruses genetically, since all progeny in a plaque area result from infection induced by a single virus particle. Care must be taken to pick only from widely separated plaques. Mosley and Enders (1961) have reported the spread of virus through overlays containing agar, and serial plaque isolations are therefore necessary to establish genetic purity of viruses.

The plating of cells infected with viruses onto fresh monolayers can also lead to plaque formation (Fig. 11). Zoster virus, which loses infectivity when released from infected cells in culture can, however, induce plaques when viable infected cells are plated onto fresh cells (Rapp and Benyesh-Melnick, 1963). Cytomegalovirus, a closely related virus, apparently does not have this property and this method can therefore distinguish fresh isolates of these viruses.

D. HEMAGGLUTINATION AND HEMADSORPTION

A number of viruses can agglutinate erythrocytes. Replication of such viruses in Tissue Culture can often be checked by mixing the extracellular Tissue-Culture fluids with red blood cells and observing the mixture for hemagglutination. When viruses capable of agglutinating red cells are formed at the surface of the cell in culture, they can be detected by hemadsorption (Vogel and Shelokov, 1957). Erythrocytes added to an infected culture will adhere to the cells and resist elution by washing. Since hemadsorbing viruses often multiply in cells without manifesting detectable cellular alterations, and sometimes do so without producing detectable hemagglutinins in the extracellular fluids, hemadsorption makes it possible to detect and identify such viruses (Chanock, Parrott, Cook, Andrews, Bell, Reichelderfer, Kapikian, Mastrota and Huebner, 1958). This method is especially useful for the demonstration of myxoviruses (Hilleman, 1962) and of measles virus (Rosanoff, 1961).

E. METABOLIC EFFECTS

The multiplication of viruses usually causes profound changes in the metabolism of the infected cell. This is especially true where viral replication is accompanied by cytopathic change. During glycolytic activity, the normal cell forms acids which are liberated into the nutrient medium, and lower its hydrion concentration. This change in the pH of the fluid is usually observed by incorporation of phenol red into the growth fluids; the color of the medium as it progresses from red to orange to yellow is therefore a good indication of lowering of pH.

Cytopathic viruses stop cellular metabolism and the pH of the medium may therefore remain static or even rise. It is therefore possible to view cultures macroscopically for signs of virus infection. It is important to realize, however, that degenerative changes in cell cultures unaccompanied by viral replication will also cause a rise in the pH of the culture medium and adequate controls must be included in each test.

The multiplication of adenoviruses is a noteworthy exception. Replication of these viruses is accompanied by increased glycolysis and the accumulation of lactic acid (Fisher and Ginsberg, 1957). This causes a marked drop in pH of the medium; this fall usually exceeds that seen in normal cells and is therefore a useful criterion for presumptive identification of adenoviruses.

F. INTERFERENCE

Infection of cells with one virus may prevent multiplication of a second virus subsequently added to the culture. The mechanism by which this interference becomes operative is not well understood; various theories have been reviewed by Wagner (1960). Some interfering viruses cause the cells to produce a small protein, interferon, which protects the cells against subsequent viral infection. For recent developments relating to the production and action of interferon, the reader is referred to a review by Isaacs (1962).

Interference has recently proven useful in the isolation and detection of rubella virus (Weller and Neva, 1962; Parkman, Buescher and Artenstein, 1962). Rubella virus was initially detected by failure of echovirus type 11 to induce cytopathic effects in cultures infected with rubella virus. The ability of rubella virus to interfere with a number of other viruses has continued on subpassage, and this method may become an important one for the recognition of other viruses which have thus far not yielded to attempts at their isolation.

G. ANTIGENIC CHARACTERIZATION

The most useful and definitive methods for identifying viruses are serologic. The procedures used involve combination of virus material with specific antibody and that combination is then measured by the techniques to be described below. Viruses for these procedures are most often grown in cell culture and some of the tests are also performed on cultured cells.

1. *Neutralization*

Combination of a virus with its specific antibody neutralizes the virus and renders it non-infective. Therefore, when a cytopathic virus is mixed with serum containing homologous antibody to the virus and the mixture is then inoculated into a susceptible Tissue-Culture system, cytopathic changes do not occur. This test can be used to measure the amount of antibody in a serum (Fig. 12). In practice, serial dilutions of serum are mixed with a standardized virus preparation, and the highest dilution which neutralizes the virus is referred to as the serum endpoint or titer. Since lack of infection allows the cells

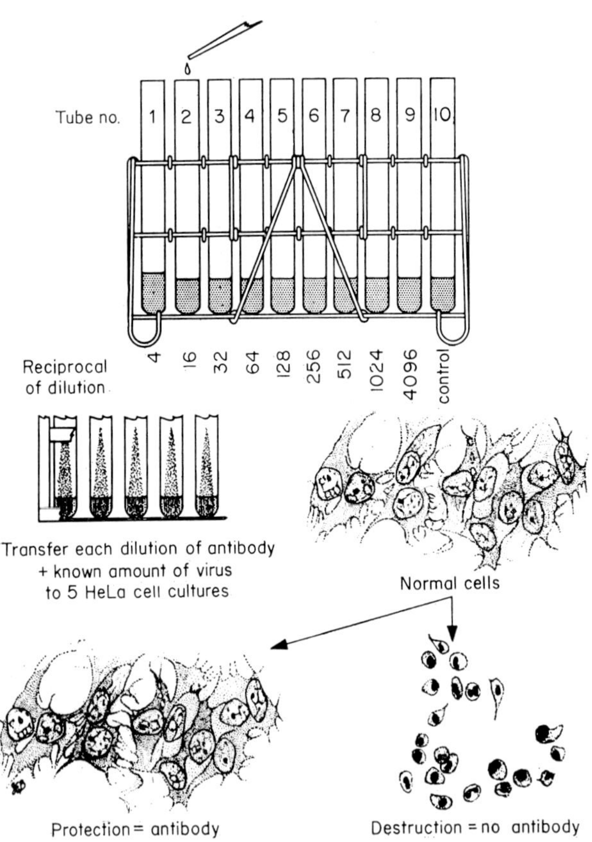

FIG. 12. Schematic drawing to illustrate the procedures and results of the technique employed for estimation of antibody or other virus inhibitor. The first set of tubes with known amount of diluent permits dilution of the test unknown serum within a known range for mixture with a constant amount of virus; the second set of tubes illustrates the five cellular cultures employed to test each successive decrement of antiserum for its ability to neutralize the virus in mixture; the drawings of cells depict the change from normal cells at the start to dead cells (lower right) when free virus persists, that is, unneutralized virus, or to the persistence of unaltered cells (lower left) to illustrate protection from the cytopathogenic effect of free virus. (Syverton and Scherer, 1954.)

to metabolize normally, a pH-color test can be used to detect the presence or absence of antibody (Salk, Youngner and Ward, 1954). The test is readily carried out in disposable plastic panels (Melnick and Opton, 1956). Pools of known antiserum are often used in combination to reduce the number of tests required for the identification of viruses (Lim and Benyesh-Melnick, 1960; Casals, 1961; Schmidt and Lennette, 1961). A variation of this technique is to study the reduction in plaques after mixing a virus with antibody (Dulbecco, Vogt and Strickland, 1956). Quantitative data on the amount of antibody present in a serum can be obtained in this manner.

2. *Complement-fixation*

The combination of antigen and antibody is measured by the ability of the complex to combine with complement. The utilization of complement is detected by its failure to combine with the indicator system (sheep erythrocytes and specific antibody). Hemolysis occurs only if complement is not utilized by the virus-antibody system under test. The complement-fixation test is widely used. Many of the complement-fixing viral antigens are grown in Tissue Culture ("Diagnostic Procedures for Viral and Rickettsial Diseases" (1964)). Such antigens are more easily prepared and tend to be less anticomplementary than extracts of infected organs from animals.

3. *Hemagglutination-inhibition*

Hemagglutination of erythrocytes by viruses having this property can be prevented by antibody against the virus or its hemagglutinins. The presence of such antibody can therefore be detected by mixing virus and serum (often serially diluted) and after suitable incubation, adding red blood cells to the mixture. Lack of agglutination reveals the presence of antibody. The serum dilution preventing agglutination when mixed with a standardized suspension of virus and erythrocytes is approximately proportional to the amount of antibody present.

4. *Immunofluorescence*

The fluorescent antibody method is also used to locate and to identify virus antigens in infected cultured cells (Coons and Kaplan, 1950; Weller and Coons, 1954). A fluorescent compound, fluorescein isocyanate or isothiocyanate, or rhodamine, is coupled either to antibody against the virus or to a globulin which will react with the antiviral globulin. Specific details of this method have recently been reviewed by Beutner (1961). Reaction of antibody with virus antigen is then detected by viewing the cells in a fluorescence-microscope; localization of the fluorescent dye suggests coupling of antibody with virus antigen, but controls must be included to rule out non-specific reactions. This method can therefore be used to detect viruses when standardized antisera are available, and it can also be used to detect antibody against known viruses.

5. *Flocculation, Agglutination and Precipitation*

Application of these techniques to study the antigenic make-up of viruses is possible if enough virus antigen is available. In practice, relatively few studies using this method have been carried out (W. Smith, 1958; Schmidt and Lennette, 1961). In the gel diffusion technique, antigen and antibody are allowed to move through the agar toward each other and, when they meet, a band of precipitate results. The number of bands formed is a minimum estimate of the number of antigen-antibody reactions occurring. Le Bouvier (1957) has employed this method to study the antigens of poliovirus, and the technique has been adapted to a micro-method utilizing ordinary microscope slides (Grasset, Bonifas and Pongratz, 1958).

Recently, Mata and Weller (1962) have described a method for cultivation of viruses in cell cultures in small wells in an agar medium. Placement of various sera in peripheral wells permits study of virus antigens without prior concentration of the virus. The method may also prove useful for virus identification.

H. ELECTRON-MICROSCOPY

The evolution of techniques for the study of viruses with the electron-microscope has been very rapid, and is still continuing. Much of the early work concerned the location of viruses in cultured cells and numerous studies were carried out to determine the morphologic basis of viral replication and the site of formation of virus components (Gaylord and Melnick, 1953; Morgan, Rose and Moore, 1958).

Recently, newer methods of staining virus particles have enabled electron-microscopists to define the substructure of viruses more clearly (Wildy and Horne, 1963). Viruses for this method are usually grown in a suitable cell system, and particles are either harvested from the fluid (if they are liberated spontaneously) or after disruption of the cells.

Negative staining with phosphotungstic acid (PTA) renders virus particles light against a dark background of PTA (actually the particles are infiltrated by a cloud of heavy metal salt) (Fig. 13) and allows calculations of the number of capsomeres in viruses having cubic symmetry (Horne and Wildy, 1962). Capsomeres are structural subunits of viruses and are usually arranged in a symmetrical array (see

Fig. 13). This technique has led to important contributions on the mechanisms of assembly of virus particles (Caspar and Klug, 1962) and on the functions of these particles (Wildy and Watson, 1962). The introduction of uranyl acetate as a positive stain for viruses by Valentine (1958) has yielded a method by which the nucleic acid content of viruses can be readily determined since DNA viruses (Fig. 13), but not RNA viruses, stain intensely when treated with this compound in dilute solution (Smith and Melnick, 1962a).

A method for specific identification of virus particles even within cells involves staining with ferritin-labeled antibody (Singer, 1959) before their examination in the electron-microscope. The iron core of ferritin is readily visible in the electron-microscope and viruses which have reacted with ferritin-antibody are surrounded by the electron-dense molecules of iron. A number of viruses and viral precursors have been studied and identified by this method (Morgan, Rifkind and Rose, 1962).

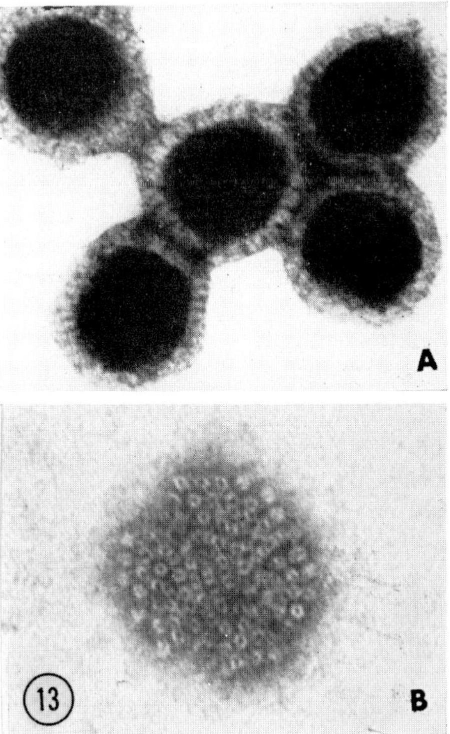

Fig. 13. Electron-micrographs of herpes simplex virus (× 230,000). A. Stained with uranyl acetate, and showing five virus particles. B. A single virus particle, stained with phosphotungstic acid, and showing the individual capsomeres (Smith and Melnick, 1962b.)

IV. Titration of Viruses

Wherever possible, Tissue Cultures have completely supplanted animals for titration of viruses, except for special studies where virulence or tumorigenic properties of viruses are under investigation. The use of cultured cells surmounts the complex factors operative in animals which often cause large variations in susceptibility. In addition, large numbers of cultures can be stored in a small space at low cost and can be repeatedly viewed in a short time span. In all methods, serial dilutions of virus are introduced into replicate cultures in order to determine the concentration of infective virus.

A. Cytopathic Effects in Tube Cultures

This is perhaps the most common method used to titrate viruses although in many instances it is being superseded by plaque methods (see Section IV, C). Based on the early observations of Robbins *et al.* (1950), that poliovirus can cause cytopathic changes in Tissue Cultures, this method involves the microscopic determination of such changes in a series of replicate cultures inoculated with varying dilutions of virus (Fig. 14). From the results of these observations, the titer of the virus can be calculated by a number of methods (Karber, 1931; Reed and Muench, 1938; Chang, Berg, Busch, Stevenson, Clarke and Kabler, 1958). The titer is usually expressed as the reciprocal of the dilution of virus per ml of the original suspension capable of causing cytopathic effects in 50% of the cultures (TCD_{50}). For purposes of calculation, it is desirable to include in the series a dilution of virus which will yield cytopathic changes in all tubes inoculated and one which will not cause destruction in any of the cultures.

B. Metabolic Inhibition Method

This method is similar to the one described previously except that readings are done macroscopically. The inhibition by viruses of the normal lowering of the pH of cultures, as measured by lack of color changes, has been described in Section III, E. Titers are calculated and expressed as in Section IV, A. This method is useful only with virus-cell systems in which rapid cell death is obtained. Slowly replicating viruses, or those which produce only partial cytopathic changes, cannot be titrated by this method.

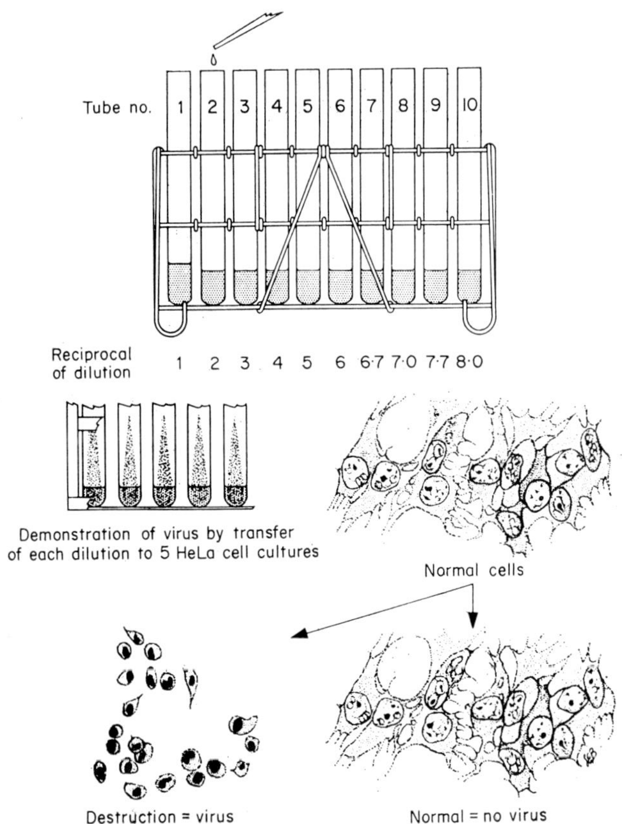

FIG. 14. Schematic drawing to illustrate the methodology for virus assay and the results of a test. The first set of tubes contains diluent to effect dilutions of the test virus suspension within a known range; the second set of five cellular tube cultures of strain HeLa are for detection of virus; the normal HeLa cells upon infection by virus are destroyed (lower left) or remain unchanged (lower right) in the absence of virus. (Syverton and Scherer, 1954.)

C. PLAQUE METHODS

The observations by Dulbecco (1952) that animal viruses can cause the formation of plaques in mammalian cells has greatly facilitated the titration of viruses that give rise to plaques. The plaque assay is based on the assumption that one plaque-forming particle gives rise to one plaque. This has been confirmed in many studies with many virus-cell systems. Virus titers are calculated directly by multiplying the number of plaques by the dilution plated; the figure obtained represents the number of plaque-forming units (PFU) in the original suspension per volume plated (Figs. 11 and 15). Generally, two to four plates or bottles are used per dilution. Dulbecco and Vogt (1954) have calculated that a single 60 mm Petri dish containing from 40 to 50 plaques is statistically equivalent to 80 tube cultures in a virus assay. It is important to recognize that only the particles capable of plaque formation are included in the titers derived by this method.

Some tumor viruses can be titrated by similar methods but instead of plaques, foci of altered cells are counted. The counting of such foci as a means of measuring the concentration of virus has been used by Temin and Rubin (1958) for Rous sarcoma virus and by Baluda and Goetz (1961) for avian myeloblastosis virus.

D. PARTICLE COUNTS

Suspensions of viruses can be assayed by counting the virus particles in an electron-microscope. Virus grown in Tissue Cultures can be assayed either as released virus, as cell-associated virus, or as the total yield of the culture. Early workers utilized a spray droplet method and shadow casting to aid in counting the particles (Backus and Williams, 1950; Donald and Isaacs, 1954; Crocker, 1954) but the newer studies use sedimentation from a known volume onto a known area (Sharp, 1960) and uranyl acetate or phosphotungstic acid stains to aid in differentiating debris from virus particles (Smith and Melnick, 1962a). Direct calculations of virus particles, in a fashion similar to the counting of blood cells in a hemocytometer, are then carried out.

Particle counts obtained by these methods represent total counts, and as such, they are always higher than the titers obtained by biologic assays. This presumably reflects incorporation in the particle count of non-infectious virus particles; these particles are thought to be non-infective because of incomplete or deficient nucleic acid cores, or because of abnormalities of the protein comprising the capsomeres (Rhim, Smith and Melnick, 1961).

E. IMMUNOFLUORESCENT FOCI

Viruses that do not cause cytopathic changes (and therefore do not form plaques) in a particular cell system can, nevertheless, be titrated by the fluorescent antibody technique (see Section III, G, 4). This method was first applied to the quantitation of measles virus (Rapp, Seligman, Jaross and Gordon, 1959) and has since been used for influenza virus (Deibel and Hotchin, 1959), Newcastle-disease virus (Wheelock and Tamm, 1961), vaccinia virus (Spendlove and Lennette, 1962), avian myeloblastosis virus (Vogt and Rubin, 1963) and cyto-

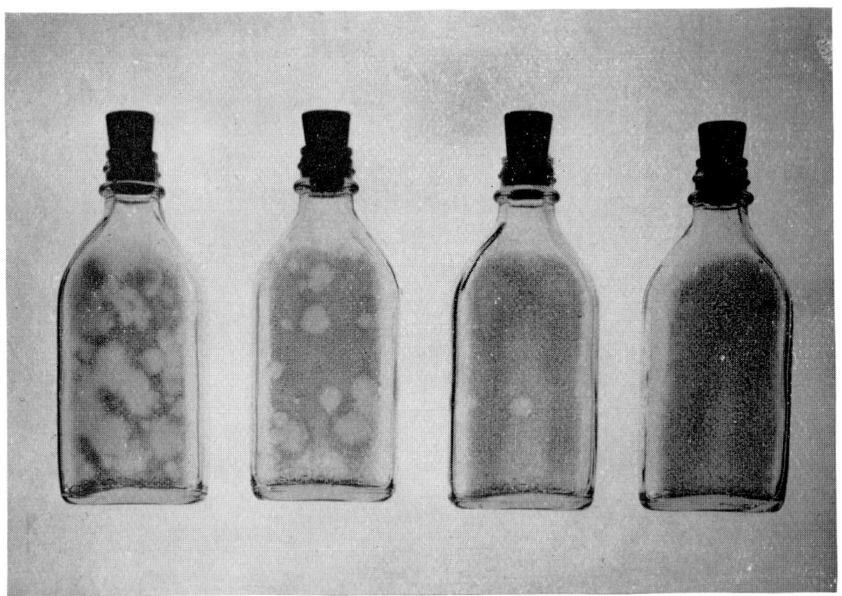

FIG. 15. Plaque assay of poliovirus type 3 in monkey kidney cell cultures. Left to right: serial tenfold dilution of the virus was added to the cultures. Note corresponding decrease in number of plaques.

megalovirus (Rapp, Rasmussen and Benyesh-Melnick, 1963). These studies have demonstrated that one infectious unit of virus yields one immunofluorescent focus (Fig. 16). Secondary spread of the virus is inhibited by methyl cellulose (Rapp *et al.*, 1959) which is then removed (after chilling) before the application of the immunologic reagents. Viruses, such as cytomegalovirus, that are not released from the cell can be titrated in the absence of an overlay (Rapp *et al.*, 1963).

V. Replication of Viruses

The development of Tissue Culture and related methods coupled with advances in precise quantitation of viruses has led to new insights into the mechanism of virus replication. Studies of virus-cell interaction are now being carried out almost exclusively in cultured cell systems. The following sections cover various aspects of virus-cell interaction: (1) adsorption of virus to the cell surface; (2) penetration of the cell; (3) induction of new enzymes; (4) synthesis of viral proteins and nucleic acid; (5) chromosome response; (6) virus maturation; (7) virus release from the cell, and (8) spread of virus to susceptible cells.

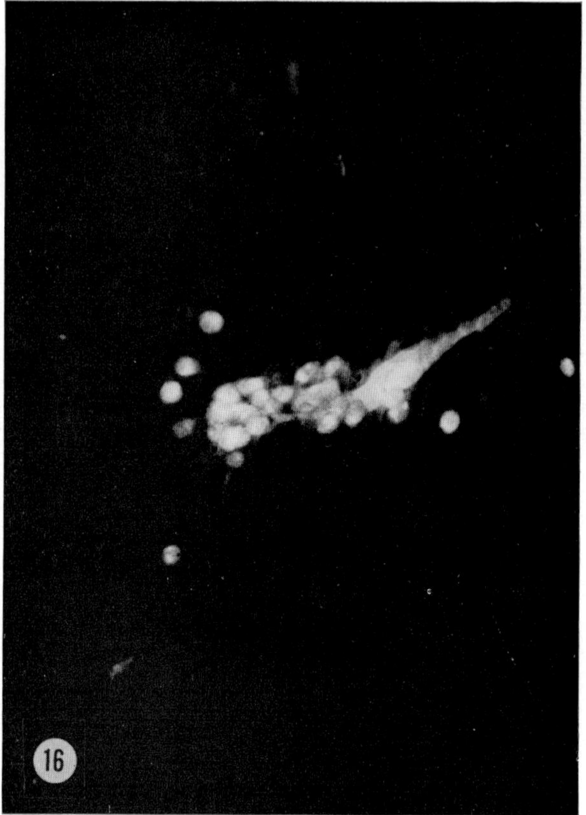

FIG. 16. Immunofluorescent focus of cytomegalovirus in human embryonic lung cells. White area represents the infected cells.

A. ADSORPTION

A prerequisite for the replication of viruses is adsorption or attachment to the cells. This can be measured either by loss of virus from the suspension placed on the cells, or by direct analysis of the number of plaques formed after a given period of contact between virus and cell under carefully defined conditions. The latter method of analysis requires extensive washing of the cells to remove unadsorbed virus.

Recently Holland (1961) showed that the susceptibility of non-neural human tissue in cell culture to poliovirus is due to the development *in vitro* of receptor material which is not present in cells growing *in vivo*. Even the conditions under which cells are kept *in vitro* greatly influence whether or not receptor substance appears. For example, when human amnion cells were left on the amniotic membrane in

Tissue Culture they were resistant to poliovirus and contained no receptor substance. However, when these cells were removed from the membrane by trypsinization and cultivated directly on the glass they then produced receptor substance and became susceptible to poliovirus within a week.

Attachment is generally regarded as having a reversible and then an irreversible stage. Using poliovirus labeled with P^{32}, Joklik and Darnell (1961) were able to follow the adsorption and early fate of the virus in susceptible HeLa cells. Virtually all the virus particles attach to susceptible cells. Once adsorbed, the fate of the virus particles varies. Over 50% of the particles elute from the cells. Such virus particles are different from the original ones, for they now are unable to adsorb and to initiate infection. However, functional infective RNA can be extracted from such damaged virus particles. Smith and Sharp (1960) have also reported the elution of vaccinia virus from L cells. This early attachment appears to be electrostatic and is therefore influenced by the concentration of salts and hydrogen ions (Allison and Valentine, 1960).

Steps leading to irreversible attachment are poorly understood since it is difficult to separate the reversible and irreversible events. It appears that salts do not influence the irreversible attachment of poliovirus to HeLa cells but that temperature does influence this step (Holland, 1962; Mandel, 1962). Philipson (1963) has thoroughly reviewed the events concerned with the attachment of viruses to cells and the reader is referred to his review for a detailed analysis of the phenomenon.

B. PENETRATION

Penetration of cells by animal viruses appears to involve decoating of the virus, which occurs soon after the virus enters the cell. The site of decoating is not well known and may not be the same for all virus-cell systems (Philipson, 1963).

Joklik and Darnell (1961) found that almost all the adsorbed poliovirus which does not elute is rapidly broken down within the cell and appears in acid-soluble material. It is well known in poliovirus infections that cells produce far more viral particles than can be accounted for by the number of infectious particles. It would appear from the studies of Joklik and Darnell that all virus particles are capable of adsorbing to cells, and thus contain viral protein in a functional form. Also, eluted virus particles contain as much infectious RNA as particles which have never been exposed to susceptible cells. The authors believe that it is a matter of chance whether or not some particles are inactivated and eluted, while others enter the cell and initiate infection, and that the ability to cause infection is not restricted to a small fraction of the total virus population.

Early in the breakdown of intracellular poliovirus there is a conversion of the virus to a state in which it is susceptible to RNAase. The mechanism of this step or the extent of removal of the protein coat is not known. However, it all takes place relatively quickly, for it is 50% completed within 15–20 min after virus adsorption and is largely complete within the first hour after infection. The next hour or two is a true eclipse period, for the formation of viral RNA and protein does not begin until at least $2\frac{1}{2}$ h after infection.

One of the most exciting recent observations in virology has been that infectious viral nucleic acid, free of protein coat, can infect cells that are resistant to infection with the complete virus particle (Holland, McLaren and Syverton, 1959; Mountain and Alexander, 1959). For example, after exposure to RNA isolated from poliovirus, the normally resistant cells from rabbit, mouse, guinea-pig, hamster, or chick, yield complete poliovirus. The new virus is precisely the same as the original poliovirus which yielded the nucleic acid, in that it also cannot infect rodent cells but can infect primate cells. Thus, all the data presented strengthen the widely held view that the protein coat, or capsid, of viruses does not function merely as a protective mechanism for the nucleic acid, but plays an important role in determining which cells are susceptible to the virus. The protein coat provides specific means for the efficient attachment to and penetration of the cells in which the virus can replicate. Since viral nucleic acid by itself lacks the antigenic component imparted by the protein capsid, it cannot be inactivated by specific antibodies. Thus the possibility has been raised by several investigators that viral nucleic acids may be one means by which viral infections may continue to smolder even in the presence of circulating antibodies. To curtail this phase of viral infection one would have to call upon the enzymes, the nucleases, which are present in sera to a varying degree.

Cell variants of a single line have also been obtained and show differences in their susceptibility to a virus. For example, Vogt and Dulbecco (1958) by exposing a HeLa-cell culture to poliovirus and then curing the infection in surviving cells with antiserum, obtained a variant which adsorbed virus equally as well as the parent cell line and even had the same latent period. However, there was such a low efficiency of infection after adsorption that the over-all susceptibility of the variant cell line was only about 7% that of the parent. This type of relative resistance, in which cells adsorb virus equally well but only one genetic variant produces large amounts of infectious virus, is due to an inherited property of the cells which decreases the ability of adsorbed virus to enter the cell and multiply therein. This is a different form of resistance from that caused by lack of receptor substances on the cell surface.

The resistant line described by Vogt and Dulbecco was composed of "fibroblastic" cells. By cloning HeLa cells, Darnell and Sawyer (1959, 1960) obtained epithelial sublines which showed the same type of post-adsorption block. However, they found that while the cell lines differed fifteenfold in their susceptibility to whole virus, they were equally susceptible to free viral nucleic acid. It would appear that the block was caused by a failure of the infected cells to deproteinize the whole virus and liberate the free nucleic acid within the cell.

C. INDUCTION OF ENZYMES

While it has long been recognized that infection by a virus causes a reorientation of the metabolism of the cell towards the production of viral components, few definitive studies have been carried out to determine the specific changes that occur. The selection of cells with certain genetic properties has recently yielded the first data on how some viruses can induce the cell to produce the enzymes required for viral multiplication. By growing L cells in the presence of 5-bromodeoxyuridine, a strain of cells was selected which lacked thymidine kinase activity. Both herpes simplex and vaccinia viruses (Kit, Piekarski and Dubbs, 1963) can induce these cells to produce this enzyme which is vital for the production of the viral DNA. This approach should yield insight into other enzyme systems required for viral replication and perhaps lead to a greater understanding of the enzymes involved.

D. PRODUCTION OF VIRAL NUCLEIC ACIDS

It has been well established that viruses contain either deoxyribose or ribose nucleic acid and that the nucleic acid is essential for infectivity and subsequent replication of complete virus particles. Using modifications of methods developed for tobacco mosaic virus by Gierer and Schramm (1956) and for some animal viruses by Colter (1958) and Wecker (1959), the nucleic acids of a number of RNA- and DNA-containing viruses have been extracted. These nucleic acids have been infectious when placed in contact with cells in Tissue Culture. The respective nuclease (deoxyribo- or ribo-) destroys the infectivity, but antibody against the virus has no effect. It is interesting that among the DNA viruses, the only successful isolations of infectious nucleic acid have been from the tumorigenic papovaviruses (Di Mayorca, Eddy, Stewart,

Hunter, Friend and Bendich, 1959; Ito and Evans, 1961; Gerber, 1962).

The production of viral RNA and DNA in cultured cells can be measured by a variety of techniques. Incorporation in the nutrient fluid of (1) specific inhibitors of protein synthesis (such as puromycin or parafluorophenylalanine), (2) specific inhibitors of DNA (i.e. 5-fluorouracil or 5-iodo-2-deoxyuridine) or (3) specific inhibitors of RNA synthesis (i.e. actinomycin) are often used to accumulate virus precursors or to study the importance of the nucleic acids or proteins in continuing viral synthesis. These studies have demonstrated that synthesis of virus nucleic acid may slightly precede that of viral protein although the two events are often closely related. The biochemical events associated with the production of various viral nucleic acids have been recently reviewed (Wecker and Richter, 1962; Darnell, 1962; Franklin and Baltimore, 1962; Joklik, 1962; Green, 1962).

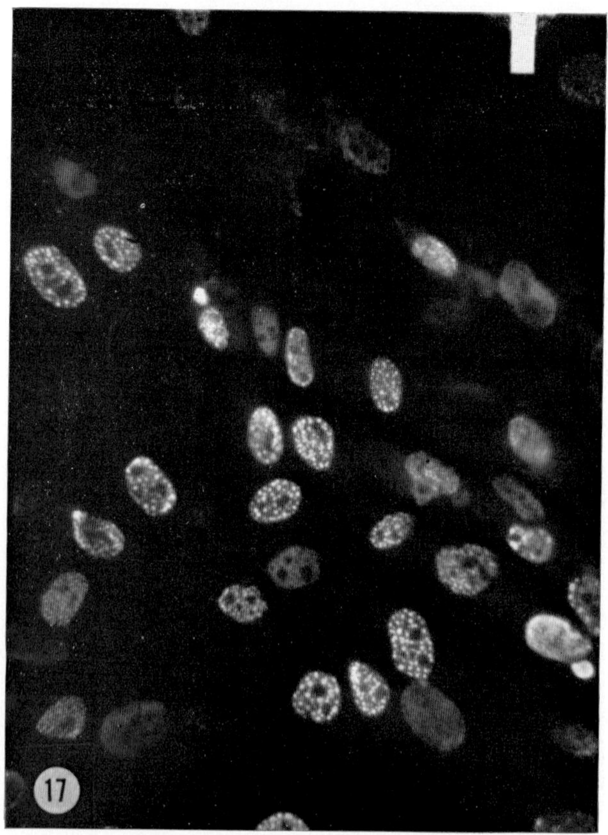

FIG. 17. Immunofluorescent photomicrograph of cercopithecus monkey kidney cells infected 72 h previously with SV40 virus. Note granular viral antigen in nuclei and absence of SV40 antigen in cytoplasm.

E. PRODUCTION OF VIRAL PROTEINS

The replication of viral nucleic acid is accompanied or followed by production of virus proteins, and these events can be investigated much more readily in Tissue Culture than in infected animal hosts. Viral proteins can be found either in the nucleus (Fig. 17), in the cytoplasm (Figs. 18–20), or in both the nucleus and cytoplasm (Fig. 21). It is important to differentiate between the initial site of protein formation and its subsequent spread to other parts of the cell.

The immunofluorescent technique (see Sections III, G, 4 and IV, E), isotope methods, and electron-microscopy (see Sections III, H and IV, D) have proved to be especially useful for detection and localization of viral proteins in cultured cells. A classic study by Breitenfeld and Schäfer (1957) using the fluorescent technique demonstrated that the nucleoprotein of fowl plague virus is formed in the nucleus but that the coat protein is produced in the cytoplasm (Scholtissek, Rott, Hausen, Hausen and Schäfer, 1962). The protein, as well as the deoxyribonucleic acid, of vaccinia virus appears to be produced exclusively in the cytoplasm (Cairns, 1960; Loh and Riggs, 1961).

The protein of many viruses, especially DNA-containing viruses (with

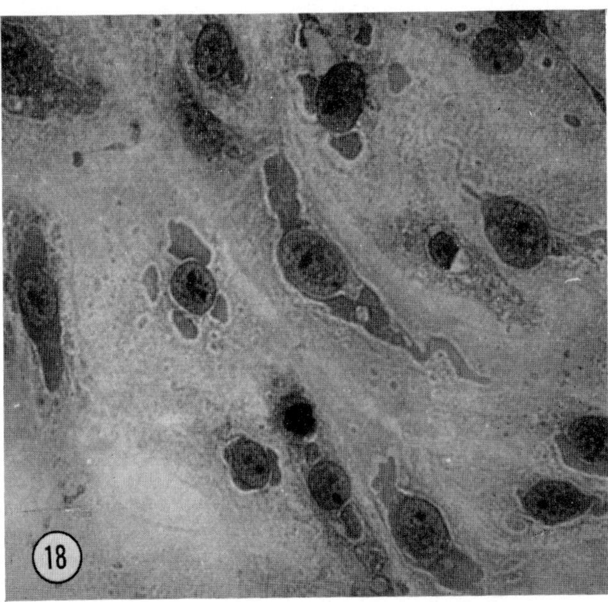

FIG. 18. Photomicrograph of rhesus monkey kidney cells infected with reovirus and stained with hematoxylin and eosin. Inclusions are in the cytoplasm sometimes completely surrounding the nucleus. (Rhim, Jordan and Mayor, 1962.)

the exception of the aforementioned vaccinia virus) is formed in the nucleus. This has been well documented for the papovaviruses, polyoma (Bereczky, Dmochowski and Grey, 1961) and SV40 (Mayor, Stinebaugh, Jamison, Jordan and Melnick, 1962) and for adenoviruses (Harford, Hamlin, Parker and Van Ravenswaay, 1956; Morgan, Howe, Rose and Moore, 1956; Denny and Ginsberg, 1959). Protein can be detected in the nucleus and cytoplasm early in the reproductive cycle of herpesviruses but it appears likely that the protein in the cytoplasm represents migration of virus from the nucleus (Morgan, Rose, Holden and Jones, 1959).

Myxoviruses (Morgan, Rose and Moore, 1956), including the leukemia viruses (de Harven and Friend, 1960; Heine, de Thé, Beard and Beard, 1963) and Rous sarcoma virus (Vogt and Rubin, 1961) acquire their coat constituents near or at the cell membrane. These may include lipids as well as protein (Kates, Allison, Tyrrell and James,

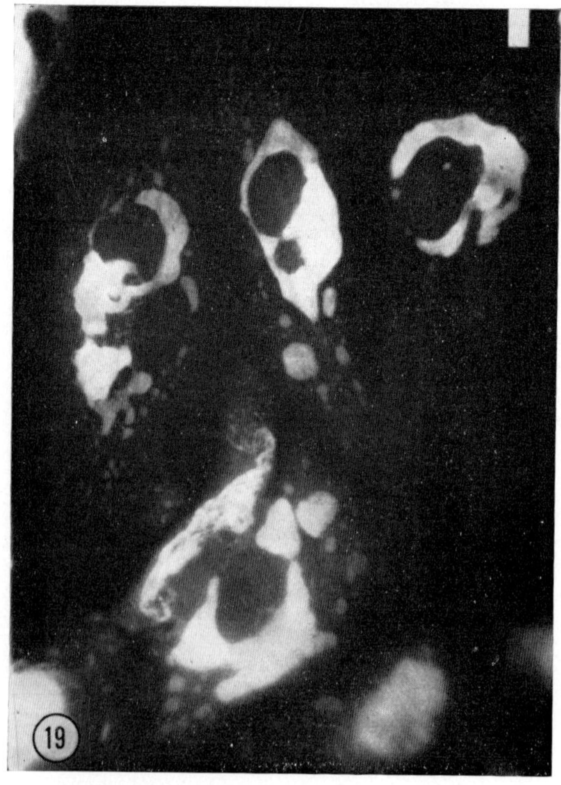

Fig. 19. Immunofluorescent photomicrograph of rhesus monkey kidney cells infected with reovirus. White areas in cytoplasm represent sites of virus antigen. Dark centers are nuclei. Compare with Fig. 18. (Rhim *et al.*, 1962.)

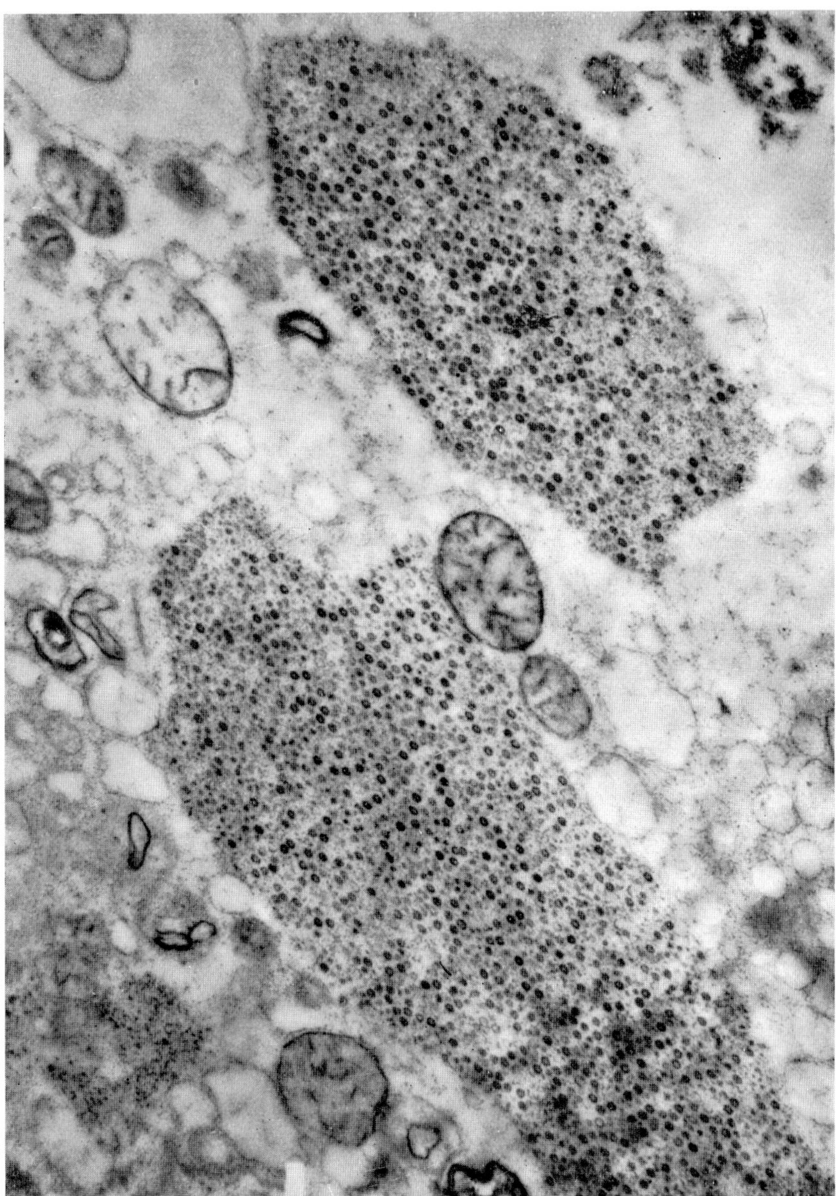

Fig. 20. Electron-micrograph of rhesus monkey kidney cells infected with reovirus. Virus particles are concentrated in the cytoplasmic inclusions. (Rhim *et al.*, 1962.) × 20 000.

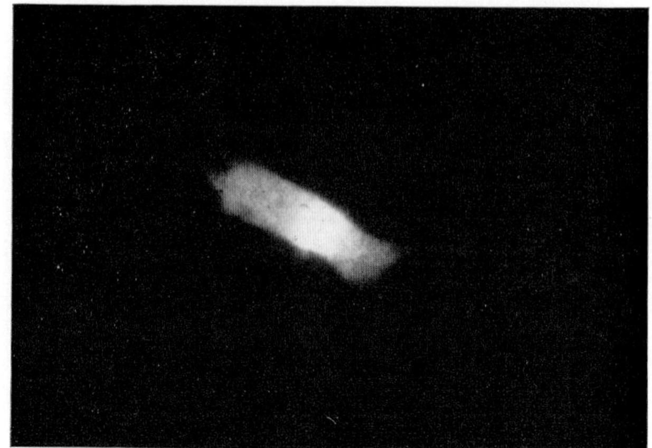

FIG. 21. Immunofluorescent photomicrograph of human embryonic lung cells infected with cytomegalovirus 5 days previously. A single cell in center contains virus antigen in both nucleus and cytoplasm. Surrounding dark areas contain uninfected cells that did not react with the immunofluorescent reagents.

1962). It has not yet been possible to study some of the leukemia viruses in Tissue Culture and careful analysis of their growth cycle awaits this development. Dmochowski (1963) has reviewed information obtained with the electron-microscope in studies of the replication of these viruses.

Inhibitors of nucleic-acid synthesis have facilitated studies concerned with production of viral protein. Studies carried out in Tissue Culture have revealed that virus protein continues to form in the presence of inhibitor, but infectious virus is not produced (Reissig and Kaplan, 1962; Salzman, Shatkin and Sebring, 1963; Melnick, Stinebaugh and Rapp, 1964).

F. EFFECT OF VIRUSES ON CHROMOSOMES (see also Chapter 3)

Advances in cytogenetics coupled with greater precision in the quantitation of viruses has led to a number of studies concerned with the effects of viruses on the chromosomes of cells in culture. The first reported changes were produced by herpes simplex virus (Hampar and Ellison, 1961, 1963). This virus has now been shown to cause selective aberrations in the number 1 and X (but not Y) chromosomes of Chinese hamster diploid cells (Stich, Hsu and Rapp, 1964). SV40 virus has also been reported to cause breaks, translocations, and deletions in the chromosomes of cells exposed and transformed by the virus (Koprowski, Pontén, Jensen, Ravdin, Moorhead and Saksela, 1962;

Shein and Enders, 1962; Yerganian, Shein and Enders, 1963; Cooper and Black, 1963) and it appears that these aberrations develop rapidly after exposure to the virus (Rapp and Hsu, 1965). Herpes zoster virus affects the chromosomes of embryonic lung cells and arrests mitosis at metaphase, thus resembling colchicine in its effects. This results in the formation of micronuclei (Benyesh-Melnick, Stich, Rapp and Hsu, 1964).

A recent report (Spendlove, Lennette and John, 1963) noted that reovirus antigen is localized in areas occupied by spindles and centrioles and that this antigen is oriented by the spindle into a network-like structure.

G. MATURATION OF VIRUSES

The production of virus nucleic acid and virus protein must be followed by assembly of the two components (maturation) if infectious virus is to appear. The biochemical events mediating this step are not known. When the components are produced in different sites in the cell, as they are in the case of fowl plague virus, inability of one component to migrate to the site of the second will result in abortive infection (Franklin and Breitenfeld, 1959). A number of DNA viruses mature in the nucleus although some, like herpes simplex virus, may acquire constituents at the nuclear membrane (Morgan *et al.*, 1959). The myxoviruses mature in the cytoplasm (Breitenfeld and Schäfer, 1957) and also receive constituents from the cell membrane (Kates *et al.*, 1962). The final viral population produced by the cell includes virus particles in all stages of formation, but only those particles having biologic activity can be readily measured (Smith, 1963a).

H. RELEASE OF VIRUSES

The production of viruses is followed by their release. This can be rapid for those viruses capable of lysing the cell like poliovirus (Lwoff *et al.*, 1955; Howes and Melnick, 1957) or viruses can be released slowly in small amounts over a long period of time (Temin and Rubin, 1959). The mechanism of liberation is dependent on the virus-cell system. Myxoviruses and leukemia viruses are released by a process analogous to budding from the cell membrane (Morgan *et al.*, 1956; Dmochowski, 1963). In Tissue-Culture systems some viruses have not been detected as free extracellular virus (Weller *et al.*, 1958); however, they may be followed quantitatively by assaying for infected cells (Rapp and Benyesh-Melnick, 1963).

I. SPREAD OF VIRUSES

The most common mechanism for the spread of virus is via liberation into the extracellular fluid and infection of other cells in the culture at a close or distant site. This type of spread is operative in all cases where virus is released into the fluid unless such spread is inhibited by either a semi-solid overlay or antibody against the virus. Studies using antibody in the extracellular fluid have demonstrated the continued spread of certain viruses throughout the culture (Black and Melnick, 1955; Rapp, Gordon and Baker, 1960; Nishmi and Keller, 1962). The virus migrates to cells contiguous with the infected cell and this process continues until the whole culture is infected and shows cytopathic changes. Viral replication in some cells is not accompanied by release of the virus and spread is by contiguity only (Weller *et al.*, 1958; Rapp *et al.*, 1963; Rapp and Vanderslice, 1964).

VI. Viral Genetics

Early investigations on viral genetics were carried out in animals. Few such studies were fruitful, but Berry and Dedrick (1936) were able to transform rabbit fibroma virus to myxomatosis virus using heat-killed myxoma and active fibroma virus. These experiments were repeated in Tissue Culture by Kilham (1957) who also demonstrated that it is the DNA of myxoma virus that is responsible for the transformation (Shack and Kilham, 1959). Transformation and recombination among various poxviruses using Tissue-Culture techniques appears to be a reproducible phenomenon (Hanafusa, Hanafusa and Kamahora, 1959a, b, c; Fenner and Comben, 1958). However, "transformation" now appears to be a non-genetic event in which the inability of heat-inactivated virus to uncoat is compensated by the induction of uncoating enzyme (Joklik, 1964) by a second poxvirus. This enables the original viral DNA to uncoat and become active.

The well-known variation of influenza viruses has led to many studies designed to explore the possible recombination of different strains. The early work was reviewed comprehensively by Burnet (1959). Because most strains of influenza virus grow poorly, if at all, in Tissue Culture, much of this work has continued to be done in animals or in the developing chick embryo. Recombination in influenza viruses was first described by Burnet (1951) and many studies since then have illustrated the ease of obtaining such recombinations with influenza viruses. Hirst (1962) and Kilbourne (1963) have recently reviewed these studies and the possible reasons for the ready recombination of these viruses.

Influenza viruses vary considerably in physical and biological properties. The latter include content of RNA and marked antigenic differences. The virus apparently mutates readily and does so under natural, as well as laboratory, environments. It is relatively simple to measure infectious and non-infectious components of the virus and to detect antigenic variation. These properties have, therefore, been used to advantage in studying recombination with these viruses.

Enterovirus particles obtained from mixed infections in Tissue Culture may sometimes be neutralized by the antiserum to either parent. This has been found within the polioviruses (Sprunt, Mountain, Redman and Alexander, 1955) and even with two different enteroviruses (echovirus type 7 and coxsackievirus A9) (Itoh and Melnick, 1959). The method for carrying out such experiments, utilizing single-

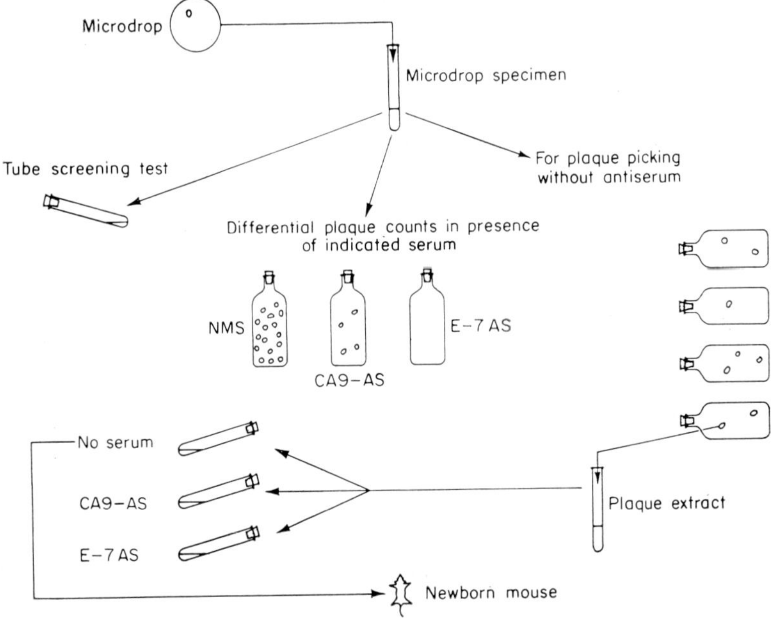

FIG. 22. Methods used for characterization of viruses in a single cell yield and the plaque progeny of such virus particles. A microdrop containing a single infected cell under oil is harvested. The harvest is tested for viral activity in the tube screening test. Positive fluids are then tested for doubly neutralizable particles by means of differential plaque counts in the presence of each parent antiserum (AS) and normal monkey serum (NMS). To obtain plaque-purified progeny, the microdrop specimen is plated under agar at a dilution calculated to yield about two to three plaques per bottle and the progeny identified by neutraliization in a tube test. Progeny can also be examined for mouse virulence. In the absence of any interaction of the two viruses in the microdrop, the sum of numbers of plaques in the CA 9 serum bottle and the E7 serum bottle should equal the number of plaques in the control bottle. If particles with doubly antigenic characters existed, the plaque number in the two bottles with antisera would be less than in the control bottle. (Itoh and Melnick, 1959.)

cell yields and plaque progeny of single virus particles, is illustrated in Fig. 22. The doubly antigenic particles on passage segregated into parental types. Phenotypic but not genotypic mixing is considered the most probable explanation of these results.

These studies are made possible by plaque variation and development of selective markers which allow analysis of the viral progeny of cells infected with two related viruses. Variation in virulence (Sabin, 1957; Rapp, 1963), resistance to serum inhibitors (Takemori, Nomura, Nakano, Morioka, Henmi and Kitaoka, 1958), resistance to chemical inhibitors (Melnick, Crowther and Barrera-Oro, 1961; Eggers and Tamm, 1961), ability to form plaques under certain conditions (Figs. 23 and 24) (Vogt, Dulbecco and Wenner, 1957; Hsiung and Melnick, 1958), resistance to thermal inactivation (Lwoff, 1962) and other properties (McBride, 1962; Melnick, 1962; K. O. Smith, 1963b) can be used in genetic studies. In practice, the difficulties encountered in analyzing large virus populations have greatly restricted genetic studies with animal viruses. Recently, however, Ledinko

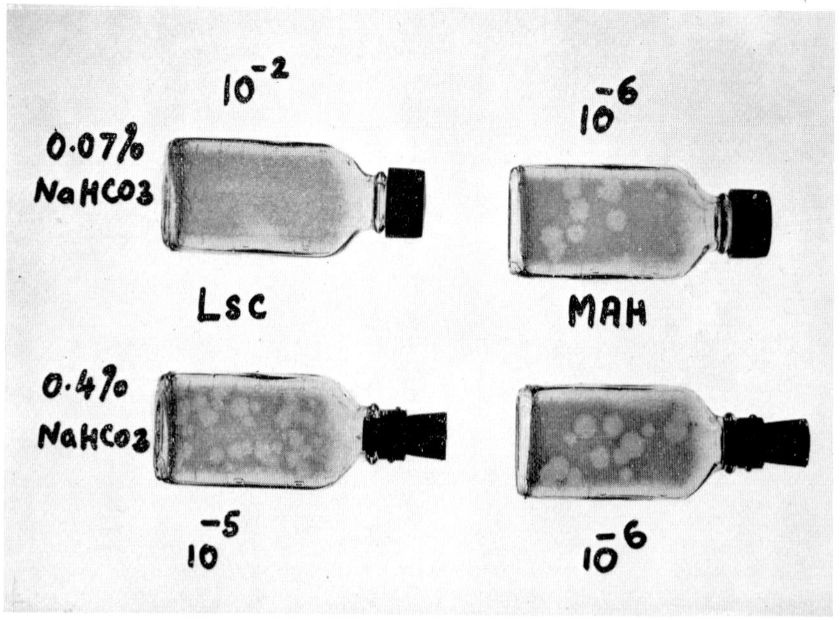

FIG. 23. Differentiation of attenuated and virulent poliovirus by plaque formation in tissue culture. Attenuated LSc poliovirus failed to produce plaques at low concentrations of bicarbonate even with 1000 times larger inoculum than in the control with 0·4% bicarbonate. As shown at the right, the virulent Mahoney strain is unaffected by the concentration of bicarbonate in the agar overlay. At the same virus dose (10^{-6}) approximately the same number of plaques were present with low and high concentrations of bicarbonate.

(1963) demonstrated a poliovirus mutant combining two of the markers listed above, which were stable on passage and seemed to be a true genetic recombinant.

FIG. 24. Plaque formation by a constant dose of poliovirus in the presence of various molar concentrations of glycine. The number of plaques and plaque size is considerably reduced in the two middle bottles and somewhat less reduced in the bottle on the right (compare with control bottle, containing no glycine, on the left).

It is important to recognize that replication of viruses can be influenced by the cell (Murphy and Landau, 1962) so that cloning of the cells (Puck, Marcus and Cieciura, 1956) is often desirable. Vogt and Dulbecco (1958) and Darnell and Sawyer (1959, 1960) demonstrated that strains of HeLa cells differed in susceptibility to poliovirus. This difference was apparently a reflection of the inability of the cells to deproteinize the virus, since virus adsorbed equally well to the resistant and susceptible cells. Sublines of Hep-2 cells differing in susceptibility to measles virus have also been developed (Rapp, 1960). The generation time of the cells, the time required for cytopathic response, and the amount of measles virus produced appeared to be correlated.

VII. Production of Virus Vaccines

One of the most practical applications of Tissue Cultures to virology has been their use for the production of virus vaccines. Though many experimental vaccines have been produced in Tissue Cultures and animals, the widely used vaccines against poliomyelitis, measles and adenoviruses are produced exclusively in cultured cells.

Poliovirus grown in primary monkey kidney cell cultures can be inactivated by formalin and ultraviolet irradiation; this procedure is used in the production of the Salk inactivated vaccine (McLean and Taylor, 1958). Vaccine of increased potency has been obtained by inactivating the nucleic acid component in the presence of $MgCl_2$, a stabilizer of the protein antigen (Ozaki and Melnick, 1963).

Potency tests for viral vaccines are usually carried out by determining the capacity of the vaccine to produce antibodies in animals. For polio vaccine, an *in vitro* test for the quantitative determination of the antigenic potency has been described (Benyesh-Melnick and Melnick, 1959). This test—termed the neutralizing-antibody-combining (NAC) test—is based on the measurement of the capacity of an inactivated virus in Tissue Culture to bind neutralizing antibody. Details of the experimental design and technique are given in the paper cited above, the authors stressing the importance of using small and precisely known dosages of virus and antiserum and of incubating the test mixtures for a sufficiently long period. In preparing the test mixtures, it is essential to incubate first the vaccine + antiserum, and then add the virus. No vaccine activity will be demonstrable if the test is set in the reverse order.

Experiments carried out with the NAC test have shown that: (a) the test is reproducible and type-specific; (b) the antigen-antibody union in the system is irreversible; (c) the results of the NAC test did not always agree with those obtained in animal potency tests, because of vagaries in the latter; (d) dried vaccines retain their complement-fixing activity, but lose their power to combine with neutralizing antibody *in vitro* and to produce neutralizing antibodies *in vivo*—a finding which suggests that the NAC test measures *in vitro* the same antigen as that responsible for neutralizing-antibody production *in vivo*.

Attenuated strains of poliovirus that have been genetically plaque-purified are also grown in monkey kidney cells to produce a live vaccine, which can then be administered orally (Sabin, 1957; Pan Am. Hlth. Org., 1959, 1960). The safety and potency tests required for each lot of the inactivated as well as the live virus vaccines are carried out in Tissue Cultures as well as in monkeys. The efficacy of the vaccines and persistence of virus in the community after vaccination are also largely checked in Tissue-Culture systems.

As with polioviruses, both inactivated and live measles virus vaccines are now available. The attenuated virus is grown in cultures of chicken embryo fibroblasts (Enders, Katz, Milovanovic and Holloway, 1960) and the virus for the inactivated vaccine is propagated in monkey kidney cultures (Warren and Gallian, 1962). Again, safety and potency tests are carried out with the help of Tissue Cultures.

Adenovirus vaccines are also prepared in monkey kidney cell cultures (Hilleman, Stallones, Gauld, Warfield and Anderson, 1956). The virus is inactivated with formalin. Vaccine prepared by thermal inactivation of the viral nucleic acid may offer a method of preparing more potent material (Yang, Tai, Wallis and Melnick, 1963).

Tissues may be infected latently with viruses and when cells from such tissue are grown in culture, virus spontaneously appears in them (Rowe *et al.*, 1953, 1956; Sweet and Hilleman, 1960; Ashkenazi and Melnick, 1962). For example, adenovirus harvests in monkey kidney cultures have been found to have a higher concentration of simian papovavirus SV40 than of the adenovirus (Yang and Melnick, 1963).

With enteroviruses, the virus seeds used for preparing the immunizing antigen, or the immunizing antigen itself, can be treated by hot (50°) molar $MgCl_2$ to eliminate a large number of potential contaminating viruses (Wallis and Melnick, 1961). Only the picornaviruses and reoviruses are known to survive the treatment (Wallis and Melnick, 1962a).

Another method for curtailing contamination of seed and immunizing virus is to prepare harvests in cultures grown in low concentrations of $AlCl_3$ (Wallis and Melnick, 1962b). In such a medium, adventitious agents do not flourish as readily as they do in an $AlCl_3$-free medium, and the seeds are more readily maintained free of viral and perhaps mycoplasmal impurities.

VIII. Transformation of Cells by Viruses

It has been known since the early part of the century that viruses can cause neoplasia in animals and the work on demonstrating the viral etiology of a variety of neoplasias in various species of animals has been reviewed (Rapp, 1962). The use of Tissue Cultures for the study of the tumorigenic properties of viruses has been a recent development (see also Chapter 3).

The demonstration that Rous sarcoma virus could alter the morphology of chicken embryo fibroblasts in culture (Manaker and Groupé, 1956; Temin and Rubin, 1958) represents the first of a series of investigations describing transformation of cells in culture by viruses. The changes seen in the cultured chicken cells resemble those obtained *in vivo* after injection of the virus. The virus apparently induces changes at the cell surface (Vogt and Rubin, 1962) which lead to a tendency to unrestricted growth resulting in piling up of cells. These cells are thought to have lost contact inhibition (Abercrombie, 1962), a property of cells that normally prevents cells from growing over each other. Baluda and Goetz (1961) have also transformed cultured chicken cells with avian myeloblastosis virus. The transformed cells resemble those seen in myeloblastotic chickens (Baluda, 1962). Similar spontaneous transformations of human bone-marrow cultures from fibroblastic to lymphoblastoid cells have been observed in cultures obtained from children with leukemia and other hematological diseases (Benyesh-Melnick, Fernbach and Lewis, 1963).

The papovaviruses can also transform cells in culture. With SV40, both human cells (Shein and Enders, 1962; Koprowski *et al.*, 1962; Ashkenazi and Melnick, 1963) and hamster cells (Black and Rowe, 1963; Ashkenazi and Melnick, 1963) have been transformed *in vitro* (Figs. 25 and 26). Hamster cells transformed by polyoma or SV40 virus can induce tumors when inoculated into hamsters (Vogt and Dulbecco, 1960; Rabson and Kirschstein, 1962; Ashkenazi and Melnick, 1963); the tumors can then be removed and grown again in Tissue Culture. The transformed human cells have thus far failed to produce tumors when inoculated into hamsters.

These studies have yielded evidence for the production of a new cellular antigen by the transformed cells (Sjögren, Hellström and Klein, 1961; Habel, 1961, 1962). This antigen is specific for polyoma and for SV40-cell systems (Habel and Eddy, 1963; Koch and Sabin, 1963; Defendi, 1963; Khera, Ashkenazi, Rapp and Melnick, 1963) when measured by a protection test in hamsters, but some degree of cross-reaction may exist between papovaviruses, SV40, human wart and rabbit papilloma viruses (Khera *et al.*, 1963). More information is needed to clarify the steps by which viruses can transform cells, and Tissue Cultures will play a vital role in these studies. These problems are further discussed in Chapter 3, and the induction and role of specific tumor antigens induced by viruses are thoroughly reviewed by Rapp and Melnick (1966).

IX. Virus Studies in Organ Cultures

A number of studies concerned with viral replication have been carried out in organ cultures. These studies however, though interesting, represent only preliminary utilization of organ cultures for the study of viral effects. References to them will be found in Chapter 3.

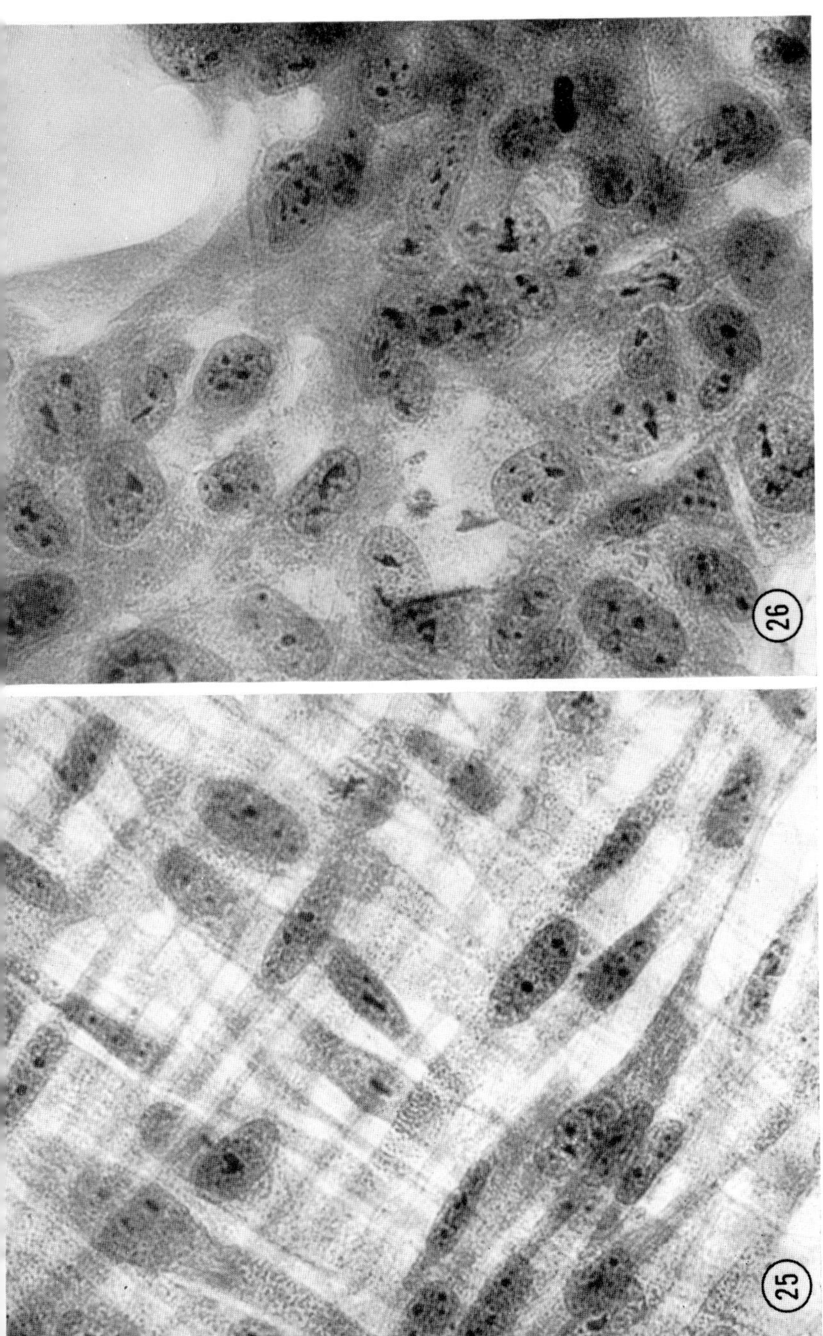

FIG. 25. Normal embryonic human lung cells. Cells are fibroblastic.
FIG. 26. Embryonic human lung cells transformed by SV40 virus. Cells are epithelioid.

References

Abercrombie, M. (1962). Contact-dependent behavior of normal cells and the possible significance of surface changes in virus-induced transformation. *Cold Spr. Harb. Symp. quant. Biol.* **27**, 427.

Allison, A. C. and Valentine, R. C. (1960). Virus particle adsorption. III. Adsorption of viruses by cell monolayers and effects of some variables on adsorption. *Biochim. biophys. Acta* **40**, 400.

Ashkenazi, A. and Melnick, J. L. (1962). Induced latent infection of monkeys with vacuolating SV-40 papova virus. Virus in kidneys and urine. *Proc. Soc. exp. Biol., N.Y.* **111**, 367.

Ashkenazi, A. and Melnick, J. L. (1963). Tumorigenicity of simian papovavirus SV40 and of virus-transformed cells. *J. nat. Cancer Inst.* **30**, 1227.

Backus, R. C. and Williams, R. C. (1950). The use of spraying methods and of volatile suspending media in the preparation of specimens for electron microscopy. *J. appl. Phys.* **21**, 11.

Baluda, M. A. (1962). Properties of cells infected with avian myeloblastosis virus. *Cold Spr. Harb. Symp. quant. Biol.* **27**, 415.

Baluda, M. A. and Goetz, I. E. (1961). Morphological conversion of cell cultures by avian myeloblastosis virus. *Virology* **15**, 185.

Benyesh-Melnick, M., Fernbach, D. J. and Lewis, R. T. (1963). Studies on human leukemia. I. Spontaneous lymphoblastoid transformation of fibroblastic bone marrow cultures derived from leukemic and nonleukemic children. *J. nat. Cancer Inst.* **31**, 1311.

Benyesh-Melnick, M. and Melnick, J. L. (1959). Neutralizing-antibody-combining (NAC) test for measuring antigenic potency of poliomyelitis vaccine. *Bull. World Hlth Org.* **20**, 1075.

Benyesh-Melnick, M., Stich, H. F., Rapp, F. and Hsu, T. C. (1964). Viruses and mammalian chromosomes. III. Effect of herpes zoster virus on human embryonal lung cultures. *Proc. Soc. exp. Biol., N.Y.* **117**, 546.

Bereczky, E., Dmochowski, L. and Grey, C. E. (1961). Study of host-virus relationship. I. Light, phase, and fluorescence microscopy of mouse-embryo cells infected with polyoma virus. *J. nat. Cancer Inst.* **27**, 99.

Berry, G. P. and Dedrick, H. M. (1936). A method for changing the virus of rabbit fibroma (Shope) into that of infectious myxomatosis (Sanarelli). *J. Bact.* **31**, 50.

Beutner, E. H. (1961). Immunofluorescent staining: The fluorescent antibody method. *Bact. Rev.* **25**, 49.

Black, F. L. and Melnick, J. L. (1955). Micro-epidemiology of poliomyelitis and herpes-B infections. Spread of the viruses within tissue cultures. *J. Immunol.* **74**, 236.

Black, P. H. and Rowe, W. P. (1963). Transformation in hamster kidney monolayers by vacuolating virus, SV-40. *Virology* **19**, 107.

Boyer, G. S., Leuchtenberger, C. and Ginsberg, H. S. (1957). Cytological and cytochemical studies of HeLa cells infected with adenoviruses. *J. exp. Med.* **105**, 195.

Breitenfeld, P. M. and Schäfer, W. (1957). The formation of fowl plague virus antigens in infected cells, as studied with fluorescent antibodies. *Virology* **4**, 328.

Buckley, S. M. (1959). Propagation, cytopathogenicity, and hemagglutination-hemadsorption of some arthropod-borne viruses in tissue culture. *Ann. N.Y. Acad. Sci.* **81**, 172.

Burnet, F. M. (1951). A genetic approach to variation in influenza viruses. I-III. *J. gen. Microbiol.* **5**, 46.

Burnet, F. M. (1959). Genetic interactions between animal viruses. *In* "The Viruses" (F. M. Burnet and W. M. Stanley, ed.), Vol. 3, p. 275. Academic Press, New York.

Cairns, J. (1960). The initiation of vaccinia infection. *Virology* **11**, 603.

Casals, J. (1961). Procedures for identification of arthropod-borne viruses. *Bull. World Hlth Org.* **24**, 723.

Caspar, D. L. D. and Klug, A. (1962). Physical principles in the construction of regular viruses. *Cold Spr. Harb. Symp. quant. Biol.* **27**, 1.

Chang, S. L., Berg, G., Busch, K. A., Stevenson, R. E., Clarke, N. A. and Kabler, P. W. (1958). Application of the "most probable number" method for estimating concentrations of animal viruses by the tissue culture technique. *Virology* **6**, 27.

Chanock, R. and Finberg, L. (1957). Recovery from infants with respiratory illness of a virus related to chimpanzee coryza agent (CCA). II. Epidemiologic aspects of infection in infants and young children. *Amer. J. Hyg.* **66**, 291.

Chanock, R. M., Parrott, R. H., Cook, M. K., Andrews, B. E., Bell, J. A., Reichelderfer, T., Kapikian, A. Z., Mastrota, F. M. and Huebner, R. J. (1958). Newly recognized myxoviruses from children with respiratory disease. *New Engl. J. Med.* **258**, 207.

Colter, J. S. (1958). Nucleic acid as the carrier of viral activity. *Progr. med. Virol.* **1**, 1.

Coons, A. H. and Kaplan, M. H. (1950). Localization of antigen in tissue cells. II. Improvements in a method for the detection of antigen by means of fluorescent antibody. *J. exp. Med.* **91**, 1.

Cooper, H. L. and Black, P. H. (1963). Cytogenetic studies of hamster kidney cell cultures transformed by the simian vacuolating virus (SV40). *J. nat. Cancer Inst.* **30**, 1015.

Crocker, T. T. (1954). The number of elementary bodies per 50% lethal dose of meningo-pneumonitis virus as determined by electron microscopic counting. *J. Immunol.* **73**, 1.

Dalldorf, G., Melnick, J. L. and Curnen, E. C. (1959). The Coxsackie virus group. *In* "Viral and Rickettsial Infections of Man," 3rd ed., (T. M. Rivers and F. L. Horsfall, Jr., eds.), p. 519. Lippincott, Philadelphia.

Darnell, J. E., Jr. (1962). Early events in poliovirus infection. *Cold Spr. Harb. Symp. quant. Biol.* **27**, 149.

Darnell, J. E., Jr. and Sawyer, T. K. (1959). Variation in plaque-forming ability among parental and clonal strains of HeLa cells. *Virology* **8**, 223.

Darnell, J. E., Jr. and Sawyer, T. K. (1960). The basis for variation in susceptibility to poliovirus in HeLa cells. *Virology* **11**, 665.

Defendi, V. (1963). Effect of SV_{40} virus immunization on growth of transplantable SV_{40} and polyoma virus tumors in hamsters. *Proc. Soc. exp. Biol., N.Y.* **113**, 12.

De Harven, E. and Friend, C. (1960). Further electron microscope studies of a mouse leukemia induced by cell-free filtrates. *J. biophys. biochem. Cytol.* **7**, 747.

Deibel, R. and Hotchin, J. E. (1959). Quantitative application of fluorescent antibody technique to influenza-virus-infected cell cultures. *Virology* **8**, 367.

Denny, F. W., Jr. and Ginsberg, H. S. (1959). Intracellular localization of type 4 adenovirus. I. Cellular fractionation studies. *J. exp. Med.* **109**, 69.

"Diagnostic Procedures for Viral and Rickettsial Diseases." (1964). 3rd ed. (E. H. Lennette and N. J. Schmidt, eds.). American Public Health Association, New York.

Diercks, F. H. and Hammon, W. McD. (1958). Hamster kidney cell tissue cultures for propagation of Japanese B encephalitis virus. *Proc. Soc. exp. Biol., N.Y.* **97**, 627.

Di Mayorca, G. A., Eddy, B. E., Stewart, S. E., Hunter, W. S., Friend, C. and Bendich, A. (1959). Isolation of infectious deoxyribonucleic acid from SE polyoma-infected tissue cultures. *Proc. nat. Acad. Sci., Wash.* **45**, 1805.

Dmochowski, L. (1963). The electron microscopic view of virus-host relationship in neoplasia. *Progr. exp. Tumor Res.* **3**, 35.

Donald, H. B. and Isaacs, A. (1954). Counts of influenza virus particles. *J. gen. Microbiol.* **10**, 457.

Dulbecco, R. (1952). Production of plaques in monolayer tissue cultures by single particles of an animal virus. *Proc. nat. Acad. Sci., Wash.* **38**, 747.

Dulbecco, R. and Vogt, M. (1954). Plaque formation and isolation of pure lines with poliomyelitis viruses. *J. exp. Med.* **99**, 167.

Dulbecco, R., Vogt, M. and Strickland, A. G. R. (1956). A study of the basic aspects of neutralization of two animal viruses, Western equine encephalitis virus and poliomyelitis virus. *Virology* **2**, 162.

Eagle, H. (1959). Amino acid metabolism in mammalian cell cultures. *Science* **130**, 432.

Eggers, H. J. and Tamm, I. (1961). Spectrum and characteristics of the virus inhibitory action of 2-(α-hydroxybenzyl)-benzimidazole. *J. exp. Med.* **113**, 657.

Enders, J. F., Katz, S. L., Milovanovic, M. V. and Holloway, A. (1960). Studies on an attenuated measles-virus vaccine. I. Development and preparation of the vaccine: technics for assay of effects of vaccination. *New Engl. J. Med.* **263**, 153.

Enders, J. F. and Peebles, T. C. (1954). Propagation in tissue cultures of cytopathogenic agents from patients with measles. *Proc. Soc. exp. Biol., N.Y.* **86**, 277.

Fenner, F. and Comben, B. M. (1958). Genetic studies with mammalian poxviruses. I. Demonstration of recombination between two strains of vaccinia virus. *Virology* **5**, 530.

Fisher, T. N. and Ginsberg, H. S. (1957). Accumulation of organic acids by HeLa cells infected with type 4 adenovirus. *Proc. Soc. exp. Biol., N.Y.* **95**, 47.

Franklin, R. M. and Baltimore, D. (1962). Patterns of macromolecular synthesis in normal and virus-infected mammalian cells. *Cold Spr. Harb. Symp. quant. Biol.* **27**, 175.

Franklin, R. M. and Breitenfeld, P. M. (1959). The abortive infection of Earle's L-cells by fowl plague virus. *Virology* **8**, 293.

Gaylord, W. H., Jr. and Melnick, J. L. (1953). Intracellular forms of poxviruses as shown by the electron microscope (vaccinia, ectromelia, molluscum contagiosum). *J. exp. Med.* **98**, 157.

Gerber, P. (1962). An infectious deoxyribonucleic acid derived from vacuolating virus (SV_{40}). *Virology* **16**, 96.

Gierer, A. and Schramm, G. (1956). Infectivity of ribonucleic acid from tobacco mosaic virus. *Nature, Lond.* **177**, 702.

Grasset, E., Bonifas, V. and Pongratz, E. (1958). Rapid slide precipitin microreaction of poliomyelitis antigens and antisera in agar. *Proc. Soc. exp. Biol., N.Y.* **97**, 72.

Green, M. (1962). Studies on the biosynthesis of viral DNA. *Cold Spr. Harb. Symp. quant. Biol.* **27**, 219.

Habel, K. (1961). Resistance of polyoma virus immune animals to transplanted polyoma tumors. *Proc. Soc. exp. Biol., N.Y.* **106**, 722.

Habel, K. (1962). Antigenic properties of cells transformed by polyoma virus. *Cold Spr. Harb. Symp. quant. Biol.* **27**, 433.

Habel, K. and Eddy, B. E. (1963). Specificity of resistance to tumor challenge of polyoma and SV_{40} virus-immune hamsters. *Proc. Soc. exp. Biol., N.Y.* **113**, 1.

Hampar, B. and Ellison, S. A. (1961). Chromosomal aberrations induced by an animal virus. *Nature, Lond.* **192**, 145.

Hampar, B. and Ellison, S. A. (1963). Cellular alterations in the MCH line of Chinese hamster cells following infection with herpes simplex virus. *Proc. nat. Acad. Sci., Wash.* **49**, 474.

Hanafusa, T., Hanafusa, H. and Kamahora, J. (1959a). Transformation phenomena in the pox group viruses. I. Transformation of ectromelia into vaccinia virus in tissue culture. *Biken's J.* **2**, 77.

Hanafusa, H., Hanafusa, T. and Kamahora, J. (1959b). Transformation phenomena in the pox group viruses. II. Transformation between several members of pox group. *Biken's J.* **2**, 85.

Hanafusa, T., Hanafusa, H. and Kamahora, J. (1959c). Transformation of ectromelia into vaccinia virus in tissue culture. *Virology* **8**, 525.

Harford, C. G., Hamlin, A., Parker, E. and van Ravenswaay, T. (1956). Electron microscopy of HeLa cells infected with adenoviruses. *J. exp. Med.* **104**, 443.

Harrison, R. G. (1907). Observations on the living developing nerve fiber. *Proc. Soc. exp. Biol., N.Y.* **4**, 140.

Heine, U., de Thé, G., Beard, D. and Beard, J. W. (1963). Multiplicity of cell response to the BAI strain A (myeloblastosis) avian tumor virus. V. Elaboration of virus by pancreas of chickens inoculated with the agent. *J. nat. Cancer Inst.* **30**, 817.

Henle, G., Deinhardt, F. and Girardi, A. (1954). Cytolytic effects of mumps virus in tissue cultures of epithelial cells. *Proc. Soc. exp. Biol., N.Y.* **87**, 386.

Hilleman, M. R. (1962). The parainfluenza viruses of man. *Ann. N.Y. Acad. Sci.* **101**, 564.

Hilleman, M. R., Stallones, R. A., Gauld, R. L., Warfield, M. S. and Anderson, S. A. (1956). Prevention of acute respiratory illness in recruits by adenovirus (RI-APC-ARD) vaccine. *Proc. Soc. exp. Biol., N.Y.* **92**, 377.

Hirst, G. K. (1962). Genetic recombination with Newcastle disease virus, polioviruses, and influenza. *Cold Spr. Harb. Symp. quant. Biol.* **27**, 303.

Hoggan, M. D. and Roizman, B. (1959). The isolation and properties of a variant of *herpes simplex* producing multinucleated giant cells in monolayer cultures in the presence of antibody. *Amer. J. Hyg.* **70**, 208.

Holland, J. J. (1961). Receptor affinities as major determinants of enterovirus tissue tropisms in humans. *Virology* **15**, 312.

Holland, J. J. (1962). Irreversible eclipse of poliovirus by HeLa cells. *Virology* **16**, 163.

Holland, J. J., McLaren, L. C. and Syverton, J. T. (1959). The mammalian cell virus relationship. IV. Infection of naturally insusceptible cells with enterovirus ribonucleic acid. *J. exp. Med.* **110**, 65.

Horne, R. W. and Wildy, P. (1962). Recent studies on the fine structure of viruses by electron microscopy using negative staining techniques. *Brit. med. Bull.* **18**, 199.

Hotchin, J. E. (1955). Use of methyl cellulose gel as a substitute for agar in tissue culture overlays. *Nature, Lond.* **175**, 352.

Howes, D. W. and Melnick, J. L. (1957). The growth cycle of poliovirus in monkey kidney cells. I. Maturation and release of virus in monolayer cultures. *Virology* **4**, 97.

Hsiung, G. D. and Melnick, J. L. (1957). Morphologic characteristics of plaques produced on monkey kidney monolayer cultures by enteric viruses (poliomyelitis, coxsackie, and echo groups). *J. Immunol.* **78**, 128.

Hsiung, G. D. and Melnick, J. L. (1958). Effect of sodium bicarbonate concentration on plaque formation of virulent and attenuated polioviruses. *J. Immunol.* **80**, 282.

Isaacs, A. (1962). Production and action of interferon. *Cold Spr. Harb. Symp. quant. Biol.* **27**, 343.

Ito, Y. and Evans, C. A. (1961). Induction of tumors in domestic rabbits with nucleic acid preparations from partially purified Shope papilloma virus and from extracts of the papillomas of domestic and cottontail rabbits. *J. exp. Med.* **114**, 485.

Itoh, H. and Melnick, J. L. (1959). Double infections of single cells with ECHO 7 and coxsackie A9 viruses. *J. exp. Med.* **109**, 393.

Joklik, W. K. (1962). The multiplication of poxvirus DNA. *Cold Spr. Harb. Symp. quant. Biol.* **27**, 199.

Joklik, W. K. (1964). The intracellular uncoating of poxvirus DNA. II. The molecular basis of the uncoating process. *J. mol. Biol.* **8**, 277.

Joklik, W. K. and Darnell, J. E., Jr. (1961). The adsorption and early fate of purified poliovirus in HeLa cells. *Virology* **13**, 439.

Karber, G. (1931). Beitrag zur kollecktiven behandlung pharmakologischer reihenversuche. *Arch. exp. Path. Pharmak.* **162**, 480.

Kates, M., Allison, A. C., Tyrrell, D. A. J. and James, A. T. (1962). Origin of lipids in influenza virus. *Cold Spr. Harb. Symp. quant. Biol.* **27**, 293.

Khera, K. S., Ashkenazi, A. S., Rapp, F. and Melnick, J. L. (1963). Immunity in hamsters to cells transformed *in vitro* and *in vivo* by SV_{40}. Tests for antigenic relationship among the papovaviruses. *J. Immunol.* **91**, 604.

Kilbourne, E. D. (1963). Influenza virus genetics. *Progr. med. Virol.* **5**, 79.

Kilham, L. (1957). Transformation of fibroma into myxoma virus in tissue culture. *Proc. Soc. exp. Biol., N.Y.* **95**, 59.

Kit, S., Piekarski, L. J. and Dubbs, D. R. (1963). Induction of thymidine kinase by vaccinia-infected mouse fibroblasts. *J. mol. Biol.* **6**, 22.

Kleinfeld, R. and Melnick, J. L. (1958). Cytological aberrations in cultures of "normal" monkey kidney epithelial cells. *J. exp. Med.* **107**, 599.

Koch, M. A. and Sabin, A. B. (1963). Specificity of virus-induced resistance to transplantation of polyoma and SV_{40} tumors in adult hamsters. *Proc. Soc. exp. Biol., N.Y.* **113**, 4.

Koprowski, H., Pontén, J., Jensen, F., Ravdin, R., Moorhead, P. and Saksela, E. (1962). Transformation of cultures of human tissue infected with simian virus SV-40. *J. cell comp. Physiol.* **59**, 281.

Le Bouvier, G. L. (1957). Poliovirus precipitins. A study by means of diffusion in agar. *J. exp. Med.* **106**, 661.

Ledinko, N. (1963). Genetic recombination with poliovirus type I. Studies of crosses between a normal horse serum-resistant mutant and several guanidine-resistant mutants of the same strain. *Virology* **20**, 107.

Leighton, J. (1954). The growth patterns of some transplantable animal tumors in sponge matrix tissue culture. *J. nat. Cancer Inst.* **15**, 275.

Lim, K. A. and Benyesh-Melnick, M. (1960). Typing of viruses by combinations of antiserum pools. Application to typing of enteroviruses (Coxsackie and Echo). *J. Immunol.* **84**, 309.

Loh, P. C. and Riggs, J. L. (1961). Demonstration of the sequential development of vaccinial antigens and virus in infected cells: observations with cytochemical and differential fluorescent procedures. *J. exp. Med.* **114**, 149.

Lwoff, A. (1962). The thermosensitive critical event of the viral cycle. *Cold Spr. Harb. Symp. quant. Biol.* **27**, 159.

Lwoff, A., Dulbecco, R., Vogt, M. and Lwoff, M. (1955). Kinetics of the release of poliomyelitis virus from single cells. *Virology* **1**, 128.

Manaker, R. A. and Groupé, V. (1956). Discrete foci of altered chicken embryo cells associated with Rous sarcoma virus in tissue culture. *Virology* **2**, 838.

Mandel, B. (1962). The use of sodium dodecyl sulfate in studies on the interaction of poliovirus and HeLa cells. *Virology* **17**, 288.

Marston, R. Q. (1958). Cytopathogenic effects of hemadsorption virus type I. *Proc. Soc. exp. Biol., N.Y.* **98**, 853.

Mata, L. J. and Weller, T. H. (1962). A cell culture system of agar permitting direct investigation of viral antigens by immunodiffusion. *Proc. Soc. exp. Biol., N.Y.* **109**, 705.

Mayor, H. D. (1963). The nucleic acids of viruses as revealed by their reactions with fluorochrome acridine orange. *In* "International Review of Experimental Pathology" (G. W. Richter and M. A. Epstein, eds.), Vol. 2, p. 1. Academic Press, New York and London.

Mayor, H. D., Stinebaugh, S. E., Jamison, R. M., Jordan, L. E. and Melnick, J. L. (1962). Immunofluorescent, cytochemical, and microcytological studies on the growth of the simian vacuolating virus (SV-40) in tissue culture. *Exp. mol. Path.* **1**, 397.

McBride, W. D. (1962). Biological significance of poliovirus mutants of altered cystine requirement. *Virology* **18**, 118.

McLean, I. W. and Taylor, A. R. (1958). Experiences in the production of poliovirus vaccines. *Progr. med. Virol.* **1**, 122.

Melnick, J. L. (1955). Tissue culture techniques and their application to original isolation, growth, and assay of poliomyelitis and orphan viruses. *Ann. N.Y. Acad. Sci.* **61**, 754.

Melnick, J. L. (1962). Population genetics applied to live poliovirus vaccine. *Amer. J. publ. Hlth* **52**, 472.

Melnick, J. L., Crowther, D. and Barrera-Oro, J. (1961). Rapid development of drug-resistant mutants of poliovirus. *Science* **134**, 557.

Melnick, J. L. and Opton, E. M. (1956). Assay of poliomyelitis neutralizing antibody in disposable plastic panels. *Bull. World Hlth Org.* **14**, 129.

Melnick, J. L., Stinebaugh, S. E. and Rapp, F. (1964). Incomplete simian papovavirus SV40. Formation of non-infectious viral antigen in the presence of fluorouracil. *J. exp. Med.* **119**, 313.

Melnick, J. L., Wenner, H. A. and Rosen, L. (1964). Enteroviruses. *In* "Diagnostic Procedures for Viral and Rickettsial Diseases," 3rd ed. (E. H. Lennette and N. J. Schmidt, eds.). American Public Health Association, New York.

Morgan, C., Howe, C., Rose, H. M. and Moore, D. H. (1956). Structure and development of viruses observed in the electron microscope. IV. Viruses of the RI-APC group. *J. biophys. biochem. Cytol.* **2**, 351.

Morgan, C., Rifkind, R. A. and Rose, H. M. (1962). The use of ferritin conjugated antibodies in electron microscopic studies of influenza and vaccinia viruses. *Cold Spr. Harb. Symp. quant. Biol.* **27**, 57.

Morgan, C., Rose, H. M., Holden, M. and Jones, E. (1959). Electron microscopic observations on the development of herpes simplex virus. *J. exp. Med.* **110**, 643.

Morgan, C., Rose, H. M. and Moore, D. H. (1956). Structure and development of viruses observed in the electron microscope. III. Influenza virus. *J. exp. Med.* **104**, 171.

Morgan, C., Rose, H. M. and Moore, D. H. (1958). Use of the electron microscope in the study of intracellular virus. *Bull. N.Y. Acad. Sci.* **34**, 85.

Morgan, J. F., Morton, H. J. and Parker, R. C. (1950). Nutrition of animal cells in tissue culture. I. Initial studies on a synthetic medium. *Proc. Soc. exp. Biol., N.Y.* **73**, 1.

Mosley, J. W. and Enders, J. F. (1961). A critique of the plaque assay technique in bottle cultures. *Proc. Soc. exp. Biol., N.Y.* **108**, 406.

Mountain, I. M. and Alexander, H. E. (1959). Infectivity of ribonucleic acid (RNA) from type I poliovirus in embryonated egg. *Proc. Soc. exp. Biol., N.Y.* **101**, 527.

Murphy, W. H. and Landau, B. J. (1962). Clonal variation and interaction of cells with viruses. *Nat. Cancer Inst. Monograph* No. 7, 249.

Nishmi, M. and Keller, R. (1962). The microepidemiology of vaccinial infection as studied in HeLa cell stationary cultures. *Virology* **18**, 109.

Ozaki, Y. and Melnick, J. L. (1963). Reaction of poliovirus and formaldehyde in magnesium chloride solution to enhance potency of killed-virus vaccine. *J. Immunol.* **90**, 429.

Pan American Health Organization and World Health Organization (1959). Live Poliovirus Vaccines. Papers presented and discussions held at 1st International Conference on Live Poliovirus Vaccines. Scientific Publication No. 44. Pan American Sanitary Bureau, Washington.

Pan American Health Organization and World Health Organization (1960). Live Poliovirus Vaccines. Papers presented and discussions held at 2nd International Conference on Live Poliovirus Vaccines. Scientific Publication No. 50. Pan American Sanitary Bureau, Washington.

Parkman, P. D., Buescher, E. L. and Artenstein, M. S. (1962). Recovery of rubella virus from army recruits. *Proc. Soc. exp. Biol., N.Y.* **111**, 225.

Pereira, H. G. (1961). The cytopathic effect of animal viruses. *In* "Advances in Virus Research " (K. M. Smith, ed.), Vol. 8, p. 245. Academic Press, New York.

Philipson, L. (1963). The early interaction of animal viruses and cells. *Progr. med. Virol.* **5**, 43.

Plowright, W. (1962). Rinderpest virus. *Ann. N.Y. Acad. Sci.* **101**, 548.

Puck, T. T., Marcus, P. I. and Cieciura, S. J. (1956). Clonal growth of mammalian cells *in vitro*. Growth characteristics of colonies from single HeLa cells with and without a "feeder" layer. *J. exp. Med.* **103**, 273.

Rabson, A. S. and Kirschstein, R. L. (1962). Induction of malignancy *in vitro* in newborn hamster kidney tissue infected with simian vacuolating virus (SV_{40}). *Proc. Soc. exp. Biol., N.Y.* **111**, 323.

Rapp, F. (1960). Observations of measles virus infection of human cells. III. Correlation of properties of clones of H.Ep.-2 cells with their susceptibility to infection. *Virology* **10**, 86.

Rapp, F. (1962). The virologist's approach to the cancer problem. *Trans. Amer. Acad. Ophthal. Otolaryng.* **66**, 736.

Rapp, F. (1963). Variants of herpes simplex virus: isolation, characterization, and factors influencing plaque formation. *J. Bact.* **86**, 985.

Rapp, F. and Benyesh-Melnick, M. (1963). Plaque assay for measurement of cells infected with zoster virus. *Science* **141**, 433.

Rapp, F., Gordon, I. and Baker, R. F. (1960). Observations of measles virus infection of cultured human cells. I. A study of development and spread of virus antigen by means of immunofluorescence. *J. biophys. biochem. Cytol.* **7**, 43.

Rapp, F. and Hsu, T. C. (1965). Viruses and mammalian chromosomes. IV. Replication of herpes simplex virus in diploid Chinese hamster cells. *Virology* **25**, 401.

Rapp, F. and Melnick, J. L. (1966). Papovavirus SV40, adenovirus and their hybrids: Transformation, complementation, and transcapsidation. *Progr. med. Virol.* **8**, (in press).

Rapp, F., Rasmussen, L. E. and Benyesh-Melnick, M. (1963). The immunofluorescent focus technique in studying the replication of cytomegalovirus. *J. Immunol.* **91**, 709.

Rapp, F., Seligman, S. J., Jaross, L. B. and Gordon, I. (1959). Quantitative determination of infectious units of measles virus by counts of immunofluorescent foci. *Proc. Soc. exp. Biol., N.Y.* **101**, 289.

Rapp, F. and Vanderslice, D. (1964). Spread of zoster virus in human embryonic lung cells and the inhibitory effect of iododeoxyuridine. *Virology* **22**, 321.

Reed, L. J. and Muench, H. (1938). A simple method of estimating fifty per cent endpoints. *Amer. J. Hyg.* **27**, 493.

Reissig, M., Howes, D. W. and Melnick, J. L. (1956). Sequence of morphological changes in epithelial cell cultures infected with poliovirus. *J. exp. Med.* **104**, 289.

Reissig, M. and Kaplan, A. S. (1962). The morphology of noninfective pseudorabies virus produced by cells treated with 5-fluorouracil. *Virology* **16**, 1.

Reissig, M. and Melnick, J. L. (1955). The cellular changes produced in tissue cultures by herpes B virus correlated with the concurrent multiplication of the virus. *J. exp. Med.* **101**, 341.

Rhim, J. S., Jordan, L. E. and Mayor, H. D. (1962). Cytochemical, fluorescent-antibody and electron microscopic studies on the growth of reovirus (ECHO 10) in tissue culture. *Virology* **17**, 342.

Rhim, J. S., Smith, K. O. and Melnick, J. L. (1961). Complete and coreless forms of reovirus (ECHO 10). Ratio of number of virus particles to infective units in the one-step growth cycle. *Virology* **15**, 428.

Robbins, F. C., Enders, J. F. and Weller, T. H. (1950). Cytopathogenic effect of poliomyelitis viruses *in vitro* on human embryonic tissues. *Proc. Soc. exp. Biol., N.Y.* **75**, 370.

Rockborn, G. (1958). Canine distemper virus in tissue culture. *Arch. ges Virusforsch.* **8**, 485.

Rosanoff, E. I. (1961). Hemagglutination and hemadsorption of measles virus. *Proc. Soc. exp. Biol., N.Y.* **106**, 563.

Rous, P. and Jones, F. S. (1916). A method for obtaining suspensions of living cells from the fixed tissues, and for the plating out of individual cells. *J. exp. Med.* **23**, 549.

Rowe, W. P. and Hartley, J. W. (1962). A general review of the adenoviruses. *Ann. N.Y. Acad. Sci.* **101**, 466.

Rowe, W. P., Hartley, J. W., Waterman, S., Turner, H. C. and Huebner, R. J. (1956). Cytopathogenic agent resembling human salivary gland virus recovered from tissue cultures of human adenoids. *Proc. Soc. exp. Biol., N.Y.* **92**, 418.

Rowe, W. P., Huebner, R. J., Gilmore, L. K., Parrott, R. H. and Ward, T. G. (1953). Isolation of a cytopathogenic agent from human adenoids undergoing spontaneous degeneration in tissue culture. *Proc. Soc. exp. Biol., N.Y.* **84**, 570.

Sabin, A. B. (1957). Properties and behavior of orally administered attenuated poliovirus vaccine. *J. Amer. med Ass.* **164**, 1216.

Salk, J. E., Younger, J. S. and Ward, E. N. (1954). Use of color change of phenol red as the indicator in titrating poliomyelitis virus or its antibody in a tissue-culture system. *Amer. J. Hyg.* **60**, 214.

Salzman, N. P., Shatkin, A. J. and Sebring, E. D. (1963). Viral protein and DNA synthesis in vaccinia virus-infected HeLa cell cultures. *Virology* **19**, 542.

Schmidt, N. J. and Lennette, E. H. (1961). Recent advances in the serodiagnosis of virus infections. *Progr. med. Virol.* **3**, 1.

Scholtissek, C., Rott, R., Hausen, P., Hausen, H. and Schäfer, W. (1962). Comparative studies of RNA and protein synthesis with a myxovirus and a small polyhedral virus. *Cold Spr. Harb. Symp. quant. Biol.* **27**, 245.

Schulze, I. T. and Schlesinger, R. W. (1963). Inhibition of infectious and hemagglutinating properties of type 2 dengue virus by aqueous agar extracts. *Virology* **19**, 49.

Seligman, S. J. and Rapp, F. (1959). A variant of measles virus in which giant cell formation appears to be genetically determined. *Virology* **9**, 143.

Shack, J. and Kilham, L. (1959). Relation of myxoma deoxyribonucleic acid (DNA) to fibroma-myxoma virus transformation. *Proc. Soc. exp. Biol., N.Y.* **100**, 726.

Sharp, D. G. (1960). Sedimentation counting of particles via electron microscopy. Fourth International Conference on Electron Microscopy 1958, p. 542. Springer-Verlag, Berlin.

Shein, M. H. and Enders, J. F. (1962). Transformation induced by simian virus 40 in human renal cell cultures. I. Morphology and growth characteristics. *Proc. nat. Acad. Sci., Wash.* **48**, 1164.

Singer, S. J. (1959). Preparation of an electron dense antibody conjugate. *Nature, Lond.* **183**, 1523.

Sjögren, H. O., Hellström, I. and Klein, G. (1961). Transplantation of polyoma virus-induced tumors in mice. *Cancer Res.* **21**, 329.

Smith, K. O. (1963a). Physical and biological observations on herpesvirus. *J. Bact.* **86**, 999.

Smith, K. O. (1963b). Some biologic aspects of herpesvirus-cell interactions in the presence of 5-iodo, 2-desoxyuridine (IDU). Demonstration of a cytotoxic effect by herpesvirus. *J. Immunol.* **91**, 582.

Smith, K. O. and Melnick, J. L. (1962a). A method for staining virus particles and identifying their nucleic type in the electron microscope. *Virology* **17**, 480.

Smith, K. O. and Melnick, J. L. (1962b). Recognition and quantitation of herpesvirus particles in human vesicular lesions. *Science* **137**, 543.

Smith, K. O. and Sharp, D. G. (1960). Interaction of virus with cells in tissue cultures. I. Adsorption on and growth of vaccinia virus in L cells. *Virology* **11**, 519.

Smith, M. G. (1956). Propagation in tissue cultures of a cytopathogenic virus from human salivary gland virus (SGV) disease. *Proc. Soc. exp. Biol., N.Y.* **92**, 424.

Smith, W. (1958). Direct virus antibody flocculation reactions. *Progr. med. Virol.* **1**, 280.

Spendlove, R. S. and Lennette, E. H. (1962). A simplified immunofluorescent plaque method. *J. Immunol.* **89**, 106.

Spendlove, R. S., Lennette, E. H. and John, A. C. (1963). The role of the mitotic apparatus in the intracellular location of reovirus antigen. *J. Immunol.* **90**, 554.

Sprunt, K., Mountain, I. M., Redman, W. M. and Alexander, H. E. (1955). Production of poliomyelitis virus with combined antigenic characteristics of type I and type II. *Virology* **1**, 236.

Steinhardt, E., Israeli, C. and Lambert, R. A. (1913). Studies on the cultivation of the virus of vaccinia. *J. infect. Dis.* **13**, 294.

Stich, H. F., Hsu, T. C. and Rapp, F. (1964). Viruses and mammalian chromosomes. I. Localization of chromosome aberrations after infection with herpes simplex virus. *Virology* **22**, 439.

Sweet, B. H. and Hilleman, M. R. (1960). The vacuolating virus, S.V.40. *Proc. Soc. exp. Biol., N.Y.* **105**, 420.

Syverton, J. T. and Scherer, W. F. (1954). The application of mammalian cells in continuous culture for assays in virology. *Ann. N.Y. Acad. Sci.* **58**, 1056.

Takemori, N. and Nomura, S. (1960). Mutation of polioviruses with respect to size of plaque. II. Reverse mutation of minute plaque mutant. *Virology* **12**, 171.

Takemori, N., Nomura, S., Nakano, M., Morioka, Y., Henmi, M. and Kitaoka, M. (1958). Mutation of polioviruses to resistance to neutralizing substances in normal bovine sera. *Virology* **5**, 30.

Takemoto, K. K. and Liebhaber, H. (1961). Virus-polysaccharide interactions. I. An agar polysaccharide determining plaque morphology of EMC virus. *Virology* **14**, 456.

Temin, H. M. and Rubin, H. (1958). Characteristics of an assay for Rous sarcoma virus and Rous sarcoma cells in tissue culture. *Virology* **6**, 669.

Temin, H. M. and Rubin, H. (1959). A kinetic study of infection of chick embryo cells *in vitro* by Rous sarcoma virus. *Virology* **8**, 209.

Tytell, A. A. and Neuman, R. E. (1963). A medium free of agar, serum and peptone for plaque assay of herpes simplex virus. *Proc. Soc. exp. Biol., N.Y.* **113**, 343.

Valentine, R. C. (1958). Quantitative electron staining of virus particles. *J. roy. micr. Soc.* **78**, 26.

Vogel, J. and Shelokov, A. (1957). Adsorption-hemagglutination test for influenza virus in monkey kidney tissue culture. *Science* **126**, 358.

Vogt, M. and Dulbecco, R. (1958). Properties of a HeLa cell culture with increased resistance to poliomyelitis virus. *Virology* **5**, 425.

Vogt, M. and Dulbecco, R. (1960). Virus-cell interaction with a tumor-producing virus. *Proc. nat. Acad. Sci., Wash.* **46**, 365.

Vogt, M., Dulbecco, R. and Wenner, H. A. (1957). Mutants of poliomyelitis viruses with reduced efficiency of plating in acid medium and reduced neuropathogenicity. *Virology* **4**, 141.

Vogt, P. K. and Rubin, H. (1961). Localization of infectious virus and viral antigen in chick fibroblasts during successive stages of infection with Rous sarcoma virus. *Virology* **13**, 528.

Vogt, P. K. and Rubin, H. (1962). The cytology of Rous sarcoma virus infection. *Cold Spr. Harb. Symp. quant. Biol.* **27**, 395.

Vogt, P. K. and Rubin, H. (1963). Studies on the assay and multiplication of avian myeloblastosis virus. *Virology* **19**, 92.

Wagner, R. R. (1960). Viral interference. Some considerations of basic mechanisms and their potential relationship to host resistance. *Bact. Rev.* **24**, 151.

Wallis, C. and Melnick, J. L. (1961). Stabilization of poliovirus by cations. *Tex. Rep. Biol. Med.* **19**, 683.

Wallis, C. and Melnick, J. L. (1962a). Magnesium chloride enhancement of cell susceptibility to poliovirus. *Virology* **16**, 122.

Wallis, C. and Melnick, J. L. (1962b). Suppression of adventitious agents in monkey kidney cultures. *Tex. Rep. Biol. Med.* **20**, 465.

Wallis, C., Melnick, J. L. and Bianchi, M. (1962). Factors influencing enterovirus and reovirus growth and plaque formation. *Tex. Rep. Biol. Med.* **20**, 693.

Warren, J. and Gallian, M. J. (1962). Concentrated inactivated measles virus vaccine. I. Preparation and antigenic potency. *Amer. J. Dis. Child.* **103**, 418.

Warthin, A. S. (1931). Occurrence of numerous large giant cells in the tonsils and pharyngeal mucosa in the prodromal stage of measles. *Arch. Path.* **11**, 864.

Wecker, E. (1959). The extraction of infectious virus nucleic acid with hot phenol. *Virology* **7**, 241.

Wecker, E. and Richter, A. (1962). Conditions for the replication of infectious viral RNA. *Cold Spr. Harb. Symp. quant. Biol.* **27**, 137.

Weller, T. H. and Coons, A. H. (1954). Fluorescent antibody studies with agents of varicella and herpes zoster propagated *in vitro*. *Proc. Soc. exp. Biol., N.Y.* **86**, 789.

Weller, T. H. and Neva, F. A. (1962). Propagation in tissue culture of cytopathic agents from patients with rubella-like illness. *Proc. Soc. exp. Biol., N.Y.* **111**, 215.

Weller, T. H., Witton, H. M. and Bell, E. J. (1958). The etiologic agents of varicella and herpes zoster. Isolation, propagation, and cultural characteristics *in vitro*. *J. exp. Med.* **108**, 843.

Wheelock, E. F. and Tamm, I. (1961). Enumeration of cell-infecting particles of Newcastle disease virus by the fluorescent antibody technique. *J. exp. Med.* **113**, 301.

Whitelock, O. v. St. (Ed.). (1959). The cytopathology of virus infection. *Ann. N.Y. Acad. Sci.* **81**, 1.

Wildy, P. and Horne, R. W. (1963). Structure of animal virus particles. *Progr. med. Virol.* **5**, 1.

Wildy, P. and Watson, D. H. (1962). Electron microscopic studies on the architecture of animal viruses. *Cold Spr. Harb. Symp. quant. Biol.* **27**, 25.

Yang, C. and Melnick, J. L. (1963). Contamination of adenovirus stocks with SV40 (papovavirus group). *Proc. Soc. exp. Biol., N.Y.* **113**, 339.

Yang, C., Tai, F., Wallis, C. and Melnick, J. L. (1963). Adenovirus vaccine prepared by thermal inactivation of the infective moiety of the virus in magnesium ions. *J. Immunol.* **91**, 283.

Yerganian, G., Shein, H. M. and Enders, J. F. (1963). Chromosomal disturbances observed in human fetal renal cells transformed *in vitro* by simian virus 40 and carried in culture. *Cytogenetics* **1**, 314.

CHAPTER 5

Antibody Production in Tissue Culture

G. J. V. NOSSAL*

The Walter and Eliza Hall Institute and Department of Medical Biology, University of Melbourne, Melbourne, Australia

I. Introduction

The main purpose of Tissue Culture is to allow the biologist to study cellular behaviour and function under conditions at once much simpler and much more easily controlled than those obtaining in the whole animal. A mammal's defence against infection, of which antibody formation is a vital part, involves a collaborative effort by many types of cells, the detailed functions of each being only incompletely understood. Antibody formation shares with adaptive enzyme synthesis and virus infection the distinction of being one of the few model systems of protein synthesis where a cell assumes *apparently* new synthetic capacities following an inductive stimulus. Dissection of the molecular events involved is thus of intense interest both to the biochemist and to the molecular geneticist. Moreover, the inductive phase of antibody formation is accompanied by a dramatic change in cellular proliferation in lymphoid tissues, with the creation of a specialized cell family, the

*Supported by Grant No. AI–O–3958 from the Institute for Allergy and Infectious Diseases, U.S. Public Health Service, Bethesda, Md., U.S.A.; and by a grant from the National Health and Medical Research Council, Canberra, Australia.

plasma-cell series, the sole duty of which appears at present to be antibody synthesis. It is thus a fascinating example of cellular differentiation and of the assumption of specialized cell function. Study of either the biological or the biochemical components of the process in the intact animal are rendered especially difficult by the fact that antibody formation is not the duty of any one organ, but is diffused throughout the whole lymphoid system. Moreover, in any one lymph node at any one time, only a small minority of the cells in the node are engaged in the synthesis of the particular antibody under study, so that many issues are clouded by the proliferation and metabolic activity of other cells engaged in other tasks. These considerations would seem to make an *in vitro* approach to antibody synthesis particularly desirable.

Though some notable advances in knowledge have been gained in recent years through study of antibody synthesis in Tissue Culture, the field remains fraught with serious difficulties and limitations. Lymphoid cells are notoriously difficult to maintain and grow in tissue culture; they adhere poorly to glass, and resent being forcibly separated from their fellows by teasing or trypsinization. Moreover, the investigator is not yet as clever as the body in controlling the cells' environment so as to ensure optimal conditions for induction and maintenance of maximal synthesis. Induction *ab initio* of antibody formation in an entirely *in vitro* system is difficult, if not, as some investigators claim, impossible. The synthetic rates obtained *in vitro* compare unfavourably with the estimated *in vivo* performance of the same cells. Therefore, at the moment, antibody formation in Tissue Culture is at an interesting threshold; enough background information is available to ensure that further study, along sufficiently ingenious lines to overcome the obstacles mentioned, will be productive; and enough key issues remain unsolved to constitute an exciting challenge.

The present brief review makes no pretensions to be exhaustive, as an extremely meticulous survey of the field has been made quite recently (Stavitsky, 1961). I have selected some aspects which deal with important problems, tread on controversial ground or seem to me to be at the centre of the advancing edge of the field. It is hoped that any reader wanting to probe more deeply will thus be guided to an interesting literature.

II. Early Attempts at *In Vitro* Studies

The history of attempts at the induction of antibody formation in Tissue Culture is almost as long as that of Tissue Culture itself. After the demonstration by Pfeiffer and Marx (1898) that certain tissues from immunized animals, notably spleen, lymph nodes and bone marrow, contained antibody more quickly after immunization than did the serum, Carrel and Ingebrigsten (1912) claimed to have shown antibody production in tissue culture by guinea-pig cells. They took fragments of lymph node and bone marrow from normal adult guinea-pigs, mixed them with goat erythrocytes, and placed them in tissue culture. After 3–5 days, they prepared extracts of the cultured tissue, and demonstrated a "hemolytic effect" greater than that of control tissues, but no actual antibody titres were given. Kuczynski, Tenenbaum and Werthemann (1925) attempted a very similar experiment, culturing rabbit spleen cells in the presence of sheep erythrocytes, but failed completely to get detectable haemolysing antibodies from extracts of the cultured cells. Fearing that the antigen may not have diffused adequately into the cells, they injected the antigen into the rabbits shortly before killing, but again negative results were obtained. Salle and McOmie (1937) have reviewed early Japanese work along similar lines, which also, in the main, failed to substantiate Carrel and Ingebrigsten's claims.

Ludke (1912) produced more convincing evidence of antibody formation. He immunized rabbits or guinea-pigs *in vivo* with killed *Salmonella* or *Shigella* bacteria, and killed the animals some days after the last of several injections of antigen. Fragments of spleen or bone marrow were then cultured, and extracts of the tissues, prepared after 5 days of incubation, contained agglutinating antibody up to a titre of 1:160. Meyer and Loewenthal (1928) were the first to claim actual secretion of antibody into the tissue-culture medium. Using rabbit spleen from animals immunized *in vivo* with a *Salmonella typhi* vaccine, they reported titres of agglutinins as high as 1:320 in the supernatant tissue-culture fluid. They commented on the importance of cellular proliferation in antibody formation. When they poisoned the culture fluid by the use of an excess of manganese ions, tissue growth and antibody formation were simultaneously inhibited. Salle and McOmie (1937) criticized these and similar experiments on the grounds that the apparent increase of antibody titre after incubation *in vitro* might merely be due to the gradual autolysis of cells and consequent release of intracellular antibody which had actually been formed while the animal was still alive. They conducted an extensive series of experiments in which both embryonic and adult cells, from spleen and other organs, cultured under conditions adequate for cellular proliferation, failed completely to produce precipitins, agglutinins or haemolysins when mixed with antigen *in vitro*. Reviewing the literature up till 1936, they concluded that the evidence for the actual synthesis of antibody *in vitro* up till that time was not convincing.

III. RECENT *IN VITRO* STUDIES

A. METHODOLOGY

1. *Tissue Culture*

Since these early attempts, the methodology of Tissue Culture, as regards both the handling of cells and the nature of the culture medium, has received increasing attention. In another chapter (Vol. 2, Chap. 2) Trowell has outlined the conditions of culture which allow healthy survival of lymphoid tissue. In 1955, he showed that amino acids and vitamins were helpful in the maintenance of normal histology and differentiation (Trowell, 1955). He described a technique in which small fragments of lymphoid tissue were supported on fine tantalum mesh. However, though good histological appearance was preserved, little mitotic activity was noted. Steiner and Anker (1956) have described an ingenious chamber for the maintenance of lymphoid cell viability, and claimed that antibody production was greatly enhanced by its use. The chamber consists essentially of a cellophane membrane, below which there is a fluid reservoir, which is constantly agitated and changed to remove products of cell metabolism and renew the supply of nutrients. Isolated lymphoid cells are placed on the membrane, together with a minimal quantity of a complete tissue-culture medium. Above this, there is a system of gas circulation which preserves the desired carbon dioxide and oxygen saturation. This device has been modified by Ainis, who claims to be able to maintain a high level of antibody-producing capacity for upwards of 3 weeks by isolated cells (Ainis, unpublished). However, unless these special procedures are used, most workers agree that single-cell suspensions are less viable than fragments of tissue of about 5–20 mg in weight. In most successful experiments, the tissues have been from lymph nodes, spleen or bone marrow. Care was taken not to subject the cells to rough handling, as any treatment which interfered with the viability of cells, such as mechanical disruption or lysis in distilled water, abolished their capacity to synthesize antibody *in vitro* (Stavitsky, 1955). The tissue was generally diced into small squares with scissors or scalpel, and on occasions embedded in agar to prevent cells from migrating out and to preserve structural organization (Grabar and Corvazier, 1960). Whereas antibody synthesis by isolated cells generally stops after a few days, the tissue fragments kept under ideal conditions continued to produce antibody for up to 4 weeks (Michaelides, 1957; Stavitsky, 1958). Though a large variety of media have been used for these studies, there is little evidence to suggest that the nutritional requirements of antibody forming cells are any different from those of other cells cultured *in vitro* and synthesizing large amounts of protein. Mountain (1955) has shown an optimal concentration of amino acids for antibody synthesis, and that excessive amounts of cysteine and cystine proved deleterious. Most workers have been content to use well-known tissue-culture media, such as full Eagle's medium, with or without minor modifications. Kern and Eisen (1959) have described a medium which is particularly useful if maintenance of a carbon dioxide containing environment is not convenient. In their balanced salt solution, the bicarbonate buffering system of most media is replaced with a phosphate buffering system, and 0·005–0·01 M "Tris" (tris-hydroxymethyl-amino-methane) is added to give extra buffering capacity. Most published reports of successful antibody synthesis *in vitro* have included the use of normal serum as a supplement to the medium. As in so many fields of tissue culture, each investigator finds that a particular medium works in his hands, and is subsequently loth to change it. While this is a very understandable attitude, results would be much easier to compare and repeat if a standard synthetic medium were used. Perhaps the very fact that no one medium has become outstandingly popular is evidence of the one great deficiency of all media yet tried, namely that none allow convincing and continued proliferation of antibody-forming cells.

2. *Antibody Assay*

As the titre of antibody formed in Tissue Culture is generally less than that formed by an intact animal, it has been necessary to use sensitive assay methods in this work. Whereas many conventional assays, such as the estimation of phage-neutralizing ability, bacterial H-agglutination, and neutralization of diphtheria toxin, are sufficiently sensitive to be used, two ingenious new techniques have become particularly popular in recent years.

Boyden (1951) has developed the technique of tanned cell haemagglutination, which is suitable for the detection of antibodies against nearly any soluble protein antigen. Sheep erythrocytes are treated with tannic acid, which adheres to them, and then with a dilute solution of the antigen. The antigen "sticks" to the tannic acid on the red cells, and the subsequent addition of antiserum agglutinates the tanned and antigen-coated cells, presumably by the formation of a lattice. Complement is not required for the reaction. The antisera employed should first have all natural antibodies capable of agglutinating *untanned and uncoated* sheep erythrocytes removed by absorption. If a pattern method is used for observing the agglutination, the test is extremely sensitive, being capable of detecting less than 0·01 μg of antibody, but many precautions must be taken and control tests performed to ensure the specificity of the reaction (Stavitsky, 1961).

Ranney and London (1951) were the first to describe a technique which is just as sensitive, but which can also differentiate passive antibody release from active antibody synthesis. They took slices of tissue from rabbits immunized against pneumococci, and incubated them in a medium consisting purely of inorganic salts. They added a small quantity of ^{14}C-labelled glycine, incubated for 4 h, precipitated out any antibody present with the relevant pneumococci, and counted the radioactivity in the precipitate. With slices from immunized spleen (but not from unimmunized) high counts were obtained, presumably indicating net synthesis of antibody and incorporation of the labelled amino acid. They found less activity in immunized liver slices, and none in immunized kidney slices. Their medium was, by present standards, quite an unsatisfactory one, and the basic technique has subsequently been considerably modified (Askonas and Humphrey, 1958; Stavitsky and Wolf, 1958; Helmreich, Kern and Eisen, 1960, 1961). The most satisfactory procedure is to incubate lymph node cells in a serum-supplemented tissue-culture medium, together with the labelled amino acid or acids, and after incubation for several hours to treat the tissue-culture medium with a heterologous antigen-antibody aggregate to remove non-specific factors, and then to isolate the antibody either by precipitation with the antigen, or by co-precipitation on a homologous antigen-antibody aggregate (Stavitsky, 1961). With this method, it is quite clear that cells taken from immunized animals and kept under good conditions not only release antibody in tissue culture, but actually synthesize it *de novo* from the amino-acid pool of the medium, and in fact continue to do so for days or weeks.

B. INDUCTION OF ANTIBODY SYNTHESIS

When an antigen is introduced into an adult animal, after some days an antibody is poured out into the serum which had not been detectably present before the antigenic stimulus. Antibody formation then proceeds for some weeks or months, and eventually stops or reaches a very low level. If the antigen is re-introduced, a more intense response, the so-called "booster response" ensues. Thus the problem of the induction of antibody synthesis deals with two related questions: how does the cell get the information for the synthesis of this new specific substance, and how does the animal, having once formed a specific antibody "remember" the fact and react in a more intense fashion after a second stimulation? There are two main groups of theories to explain these and other facets of the immune response, namely the "instructive" and the "selective" theories (Lederberg, 1959). The instructive theories have as their central tenet the concept that the antigen imprints its pattern on the synthetic machinery of the cell, so that the cell turns out a molecule with one or more reactive sites complementary to the antigenic determinant groupings on the foreign molecule. The "direct template" hypothesis, as outlined by Pauling (1940), Mudd (1932) and Haurowitz (1953), proposes simply that the antigen enters the antibody-forming cell, and that a globulin polypeptide chain folds itself in steric contact with an antigen template, till it reaches the required shape. Our modern view of protein synthesis (Crick, 1958) postulates a "chain of command", originating in the genome of the cell where the basic information for protein synthesis is coded in the sequence of nucleotides in nuclear deoxyribonucleic acid (DNA); a translation of the code into ribonucleic acid (RNA), possibly an unstable "messenger" RNA formed in the nucleus and transported to the cytoplasmic ribosomes (Brenner, Jacob and Meselson, 1961); and finally transmission of the coded information into protein, the sequence of amino acids in the polypeptide chain being the final reflection of gene activity. In order to bring antibody synthesis into line with this "dogma", Karush (1961) has postulated that the sequence of amino acids in all γ-globulins is either immaterial or identical, and that specificity of reactive sites rests solely on the pattern of folding of the molecule. This is a somewhat heretical concept, as many protein chemists believe that the tertiary folding is already inherent in and at least partly dependent on the primary sequential structure of the protein (Anfinsen, 1961). According to Karush's view, the globulin chain is held in contact with the antigen template for long enough to allow the formation of cross-linking disulphide bonds to stabilize the structure. There are sufficient half-cysteine residues in globulin to allow for quite considerable variation, with the creation of perhaps 10^5 or 10^6 different types of antibody. In the "indirect template" versions of the instructive hypotheses (Burnet and Fenner, 1949; Burnet, 1956; Schweet and Owen, 1957), it is postulated that antigen enters the nucleus of the cell, and actually causes or directs a change in the cell's genetic machinery, with the production of a secondary template, coded in nucleic acids. This "genocopy" of the antigen, it is postulated (Burnet, 1956), may even infect other cells and transfer the capacity to form antibody. As the property of being able to form specific antibody is now a part of the cell's genetic complement, it is not necessary to demand the continuing physical presence of the antigen in the cell to account for immunological memory.

The "selective" theories of antibody formation (Burnet, 1957, 1959; Talmage, 1957; Lederberg, 1959; Jerne, 1955, 1960) deny the possibility that an exogenous protein can "force" a cell to do something new; unlike a virus, antigen brings in no nucleic acid "instructions" to divert the normal pattern of gene function. The common feature of all selective hypotheses is the postulate that the number of possible types of antibody is not infinite, and that the information for the synthesis of *all* the types of antibody which a given animal can produce is already present in the adult, unstimulated animal. The antigen, rather than "instructing" the cell, merely catalyses the emergence of a synthetic capacity that had been lying latent in the cell. Jerne (1955, 1960) has postulated that antigen acts by linking to "natural antibody" (randomly synthesized by the lymphoid system), with the formation of an antigen-antibody complex which is then taken up by reticulo-endothelial cells, the antibody then acting as a template for the synthesis of more of itself. Burnet (1957, 1959) and Talmage (1957) chose to regard the self-replicating entity not as a globulin molecule, but as a cell, genetically pre-adapted to form one or a small number of types of globulin only. The differentiation process is presumed to have ensured, in some way, that the total immunological potential of the animal is represented by a large number of clones, each with a much more limited potential than the whole animal. When antigen is introduced in adult life, the cells of the clone or clones specifically reactive to that antigen proliferate and differentiate, causing the elaboration of a readily detectable amount of antibody. When the stimulus is repeated some weeks later, there are more cells of the "right" clone present ready to react, and more intense antibody formation ensues. Lederberg (1959) pointed out that the same principle could apply equally readily if the self-replicating entity were subcellular, each cell perhaps possessing the genetic potential for the formation of all antibodies, and the antigenic stimulus calling forth the emergence of the corresponding potential. Such "subcellular selective" mechanisms would be very difficult to differentiate experimentally from instructive ones.

This theoretical introduction has been included to emphasize that the induction of antibody formation is a complex and poorly understood process, there being as yet no critical experiment which can decide even between the two major (instructive and selective) groups of hypotheses. It is perhaps but little wonder, then, that the field we are about to review in this section contains conflicting reports, including partial success and total failure in the induction of antibody formation *in vitro*.

1. *Induction of the Primary Response* in vitro

Apart from the occasional reports in the early literature, cited in Section II, most attempts to induce the primary immune response *in vitro* have been entirely unsuccessful. However, two recent approaches to the problem have claimed some degree of success.

(*a*) *Pre-incubation of macrophages and antigen.* There seems little doubt that the reticulo-endothelial system, and particularly the macrophage, plays some role in antibody formation, though macrophages do not appear to form antibody themselves (Nossal, 1959b; McMaster, 1961). Several investigators have suggested that the macrophage takes up antigen and elaborates something which is then passed on to the plasma-cell precursors and stimulates antibody formation; this could be a "genocopy" of the antigen (Burnet and Fenner, 1949; Burnet, 1956), or a diluted (Burnet, 1959) or digested (Harris and Ehrich, 1946) antigen which might be more palatable to the ancestors of antibody-forming cells. Fishman (1959, 1961) has infused new life into the "two-cell" approach to antibody formation in recent experiments. He took macrophages from rat peritoneal exudate and incubated them *in vitro* with an antigen, namely bacteriophage virus particles, under conditions suitable for phagocytosis. After 30 min incubation, he washed excess antigen away from the macrophages and homogenized the latter in a tissue grinder. The macrophage extract, which still contained about one-tenth of the phage infectivity originally added, was then added to a serum-supplemented Eagle's tissue-culture medium. Normal lymph-node cells from young adult rats were then added, and the mixture incubated for up to 12 days. At various intervals, the medium was removed, globulin-like proteins concentrated by ammonium sulphate fractionation, and tested for their phage-neutralizing ability. In about one experiment in five, the tissue-culture supernatants were found to contain significant phage-neutralizing activity. In no case, including those experiments discarded as negative, did control cultures have any such activity. The activity was inhibited by rabbit anti-rat globulin, and was presumably due to antibody synthesized in the entirely *in vitro* system. When heterologous (rabbit) macrophages were used, no antibody formation was obtained. The extract of phage-treated homologous macrophages was heat-stable and sensitive to RNAase. In an attempt to find a more uniformly positive test system, Fishman also injected lymph-node cells, pre-treated with the extract, into chick embryos. He was thus able to obtain evidence of antibody (phage-neutralizing activity and the immunologically identified presence of rat serum proteins) in the circulation of the newly hatched chick some days later. Recent experiments, preliminarily described by Fishman (1961), showed that when the extract-treated lymphoid cells were placed in diffusion chambers and incubated in the peritoneal cavities of homologous, X-irradiated rats, considerable antibody formation followed.

Fishman (1961) has suggested that his macrophages manufacture an RNA moiety or an antigen–RNA complex which, on transfer to lymphoid precursors of plasma cells, stimulates the induction of antibody formation. When RNAase was added to the culture medium in his *in vitro* induction experiments, the macrophage extract could not exert its effects. Also, Fishman, Hammerstrom and Bond (1963) found that under certain culture conditions, a low molecular weight RNA from macrophages could be passed to lymph-node cells *in vitro*, but the specificity or biological activity of this transfer has not yet been shown.

A recent line of investigation from our own laboratory, though not involving tissue-culture techniques, may be relevant here. We have noted that a specialized population of macrophages exists in the primary lymphoid follicles of rat lymph nodes, which actively takes up any antigen, but fails to take up isotopically-labelled "self" proteins (Nossal, Ada and Austin, 1963, 1964; Ada, Nossal and Austin, 1964). Around these dendritic macrophages, primitive lymphoid cells collect, proliferate and finally form a germinal centre. These germinal-centre cells may represent the ancestors of the antibody-forming plasma cells. When critically small amounts of antigen were used, and when the antigen was labelled with carrier-free ^{125}I in a manner which allowed the detection of small numbers of antigen molecules by autoradiography, it was found that the antibody-forming plasma cells were themselves unlabelled. The conclusion reached was that, if antigen or antigen-derived peptide fragments had been passed from macrophage to primitive lymphoid cells, the amounts must have been very small indeed. Perhaps immune induction *in vivo* was due to the passage of RNA from antigen-containing macrophages to germinal centre lymphoid blast cells, as Fishman has suggested; alternatively, minute amounts of processed antigen may have acted as an inducer. In any case, the experiments provided strong arguments against the direct template hypothesis of antibody formation or its variants. There was unlikely to be enough antigen in the antibody-forming cell to make a template mechanism feasible.

(*b*) *Pre-injection of donor animals with endotoxin.* The other recent claim to have produced antibody formation in an entirely *in vitro* system is that of Stevens and McKenna (1958). They injected adult rabbits intravenously with *Salmonella typhi* endotoxin to stimulate the reticulo-endothelial system non-specifically, and killed them 24 h later. The spleen was diced into small fragments, which were exposed to bovine γ-globulin, washed free of excess antigen, and placed in tissue culture. After as little as 1 h, material claimed to be antibody was detected in the medium by Boyden's tanned cell technique. Stavitsky (1961) has reported extensive attempts to repeat these experiments, with interesting results. In several experiments, substances which agglutinated tanned and antigen-coated red cells appeared in titres as high as 1:80, but the reactions were not specific, and could not be inhibited by the antigen. Moreover, the media also contained material capable of co-precipitating with a heterologous antigen-antibody system. Stavitsky is careful to point out that the relationship of this material, which could be a complement-like agent, to that of the material agglutinating tanned cells in the experiments of Stevens and McKenna (1958) has not been established. Several features of the Stevens and McKenna experiments are distinctly unusual for *in vitro* antibody synthesis. First, the material is very labile, for example it loses activity even at —20°C in a few days. Most antibodies are stable to heat as high as 56°C. Moreover, the kinetics of appearance of the substance are extraordinary. Some activity is already present at the first testing at 1 h; though the haemagglutinating titre rises over the next day, the rate of production is not nearly as fast as the initial burst of release would lead one to expect. This raises the probability that the haemagglutinating material found at 1 h might have been pre-formed in the spleen, and not actually synthesized *in vitro*. On the balance of the evidence, it seems unlikely that the haemagglutinating material observed by Stevens and McKenna was classical antibody.

2. *Induction of the Secondary Response* in vitro

Very much less work dealing with the induction of the secondary response *in vitro* has been reported in the literature. In a brief communication, Michaelides (1957) reported experiments with rabbit lymph nodes, primarily immunized against diphtheria toxoid *in vivo*, allowed to rest, and then cultured *in vitro* in Eagle's medium, after stimulation with the antigen *in vitro*. When the supernatant fluid after incubation was titrated for antibody by the Boyden technique, some stimulation of antibody production as a result of the *in vitro* stimulus was reported, but the total antibody production was much less than when the secondary stimulus had been given *in vivo*. A somewhat similar partially successful experiment, utilizing spleen fragments and an isotope-incorporation assay, has been reported by Stavitsky (1960). A fuller description of their technique and analysis of results of secondary stimulation *in vitro* has recently been published by Michaelides and Coons (1963). The conclusion reached was that specific anamnestic responses could be induced *in vitro*, and that the system represented a helpful tool for qualitative analyses, but that it was not sufficiently reliable for quantitative studies. Great variations from experiment to experiment were reported. Whereas suitable tissue fragments gave generally good results, cell suspensions failed to respond. With diphtheria toxoid as the antigen, lymph-node fragments maintained their capacity to react anamnestically for 4 days after the beginning of culture. With bovine serum albumin, responsiveness lasted for about 8 days. Once an anamnestic response had begun, antibody formation *in vitro* continued for 4 weeks or more. The morphological changes taking place in the explanted, anamnestically stimulated fragments have been observed by means of immunofluorescent techniques (O'Brien, Michaelides and Coons, 1963). Two days after *in vitro* stimulation, no antibody-containing cells could be found. By day 3, a few cells with fluorescent cytoplasm could be seen, and by 4 days many antibody-containing plasma cells, immature as well as mature, were widely and irregularly distributed throughout the fragment. By the eighth day and thereafter, most of the positive cells were mature plasma cells. Most of the cells responsible for antibody production remained in the explant, although a few could be found in the outgrowing sheet of cells.

Michaelides and Coons (1963) suggested that their experiments emphasized an apparently qualitative difference between primary and secondary responses, since they could induce the latter, but not the former, in their *in vitro* system. However, they warn that "large quantitative differences may masquerade as qualitative ones", and conclude that failure in the primary response may simply mean that not enough active cells could accumulate *in vitro* to bring the level of antibody above the threshold of the tests used.

3. *Induction of the Transition of the Small Lymphocyte to Lymphoid Blast Cell* in vitro

It has recently been demonstrated that small lymphocytes taking part in a graft-versus-host immunological reaction dedifferentiate into large lymphoid blast cells with pyroninophilic cytoplasm (Gowans, 1962) which then presumably proliferate and form immunologically active small lymphocytes. There has been much speculation as to whether such a process is also involved in the early stages of the primary response to non-living antigens. It appears that a change morphologically similar to that reported by Gowans can occur *in vitro*. Hungerford, Donnelly, Nowell and Beck (1959) noted that certain human leucocytes prepared from peripheral blood and incubated *in vitro* could transform into large, rapidly dividing mononuclear blast cells. This happened only when the red cells had been removed by agglutination with phytohaemagglutinin (PHA). The exact chemical nature of the factor in PHA which stimulates this change is not known. Careful studies were performed by Marshall and Roberts (1963) which clearly demonstrated that the cell type which transformed was the small lymphocyte. The changed lymphocytes were pyroninophilic, and a proportion of them were morphologically similar to plasma cells. However, electron-microscopic observation showed that the cells had only scanty endoplasmic reticulum, and in this respect differed from plasma cells. More recently, it has been preliminarily reported (Elves, Roath, Taylor and Israels, 1963) that lymphocytes from individuals who had been pre-immunized with diphtheria toxoid or tetanus toxoid could undergo a similar transformation *in vitro* when incubated with the antigen. Moreover, these authors claimed that the transformed lymphocytes produced antibody, as judged by immunofluorescent methods, and concluded that a secondary response had been initiated *in vitro*. They postulated that small lymphocytes had the intrinsic ability to "remember" a previous experience with an antigen, and could respond to it years after the antigen injection. Needless to say, these experiments, if confirmed, would have great bearing on current theories of antibody formation. There is an apparent paradox in the relative ease with which it has been possible to demonstrate this change in human peripheral blood lymphocytes and the great difficulty that workers have had in producing clear-cut secondary responses *in vitro* using lymph-node or splenic cell suspensions from experimental animals. Unfortunately, it is too early to assess the experiments in detail, but obviously this could become an extremely important area of *in vitro* immunobiology.

4. *Transfer of Mitosis-stimulating Factor between Cells in the Spleen*

It has recently been shown (Dutton and Pearce, 1962) that low concentrations of antigen can stimulate DNA synthesis *in vitro* by spleen fragments from pre-immunized rabbits. This again emphasizes the importance of cell division as an early phenomenon in the induction of the secondary response. Dutton and Harris (1963) went on to report the intriguing finding that cells "primed" by brief contact with antigen are able to transfer the ability to divide more rapidly to other, fresh, non-antigen treated cells from the same spleen as measured by ^{3}H-thymidine incorporation rate. The effect could not have been due simply to the transfer of antigen, as very little antigen had actually been taken up by the primed cells. Irradiation or freezing and thawing of the primed cells did not destroy the mitosis-stimulating factor. Three possible explanations were proposed by the authors to explain this effect. Firstly, the minute quantities of antigen taken up by the primed cells may have represented an extremely potent fraction of the original antigen preparation. Secondly, the antigen may have had its immunogenicity greatly enhanced immediately after uptake. Thirdly, the cells which take up the antigen may have handed on some material other than antigen which is capable of stimulating cell division in cells from suitably pre-immunized animals. This factor need not necessarily itself transfer information or retain antigen specificity. The relationship, if any, between Dutton's and Fishman's factors remains to be established, as does the relationship of Dutton's work to the PHA or antigen-induced proliferation of human small lymphocytes *in vitro*.

C. MAINTENANCE OF ANTIBODY SYNTHESIS

There has been much work done recently on the continuation *in vitro* of antibody formation begun *in vivo,* and it is not possible to cite every experiment in this field. Most workers have taken spleen or lymph-node fragments at a stage when the donor animal was synthesizing antibody at a maximal rate, or just before this time, generally during a secondary or hyperimmune response. They have placed the tissue under standard culture conditions and have investigated factors such as the kinetics of antibody appearance, the nutritional requirements of the cells, the effects of various inhibitory agents, the biochemical processes occurring in the cultured antibody-forming cells and the progressive morphological alteration of the cell population. A few of the key findings are discussed below.

1. *Antibody Production by Cell Populations*

Though it is of course quite arbitrary to separate the earlier from the current studies, one of the first of the "newer" *in vitro* approaches to antibody formation was that of Fagraeus (1948). She studied the histological changes in the spleens of rabbits immunized with various antigens, and found an association between antibody formation and the development of plasma cells in the splenic red pulp. When she separated red pulp (containing predominantly plasma cells) and white pulp (consisting mainly of lymphocytes) by microdissection under a low-power microscope, and placed both fractions in tissue culture, she found far more antibody production by red than by white pulp. The difference was greatest some 4 days after antigenic stimulation, when the red pulp was particularly rich in immature plasma cells. Keuning and van der Slikke (1950) and Thorbecke and Keuning (1953) confirmed and extended these findings. Ranney and London (1951) were the first to show that antibody was actually synthesized, and not merely released, *in vitro*. Wesslen (1952) found that thoracic-duct lymphocytes, containing few or no typical plasma cells, could form some antibody during 24 h incubation *in vitro*. More extensive experiments by Stavitsky (1958) showed that the lymph nodes of rabbits, immunized with a variety of antigens (diphtheria toxoid, bovine γ-globulin, bovine serum albumin or ovalbumin), could synthesize antibody for some days, and that the process was an active one, requiring an available amino-acid pool, energy, and the presence of viable cells. No one, so far, has been able to produce antibody-formation in a cell-free system, though Kern, Helmreich and Eisen (1959) found a specific and firm association between intracellular antibody and ribosomes. The achievement of the production of antibody in a system, somewhat analogous to the one used by Bishop, Favelukes, Schweet and Russell (1961) for *in vitro* haemoglobin synthesis, using isolated ribosomes, or perhaps intact polysomes, cannot be too far away. Askonas and Humphrey (1958) immunized rabbits heavily with pneumococci or ovalbumin and, in careful kinetic studies, investigated the relative antibody-forming potentials of different organs by tissue-culture methods. They found that the following organs formed antibody (in decreasing order of intensity): lymph nodes, spleen, bone marrow and lung. Liver and kidney had no demonstrable activity. When radioactively labelled amino acids were fed to the cultures, there was incorporation into intracellular antibody commencing immediately, without any lag as judged by a precipitin assay. Incorporation of label into the antibody released into the medium commenced after a lag of about 1 h. When the radioactivity in intra- and extracellular antibody was summed, it was shown that the amount incorporated rose linearly while the isotope was freely available. The results were consistent with the view that antibody is synthesized from the amino-acid pool available to the cells; it then enters an intracellular pool, but is only held there for a short time, about 1 h, and is then promptly released into the medium. The results are not consistent with the theory put forward by Schooley (1961) that antibody is produced in immature plasma cells, stored, and then released when the plasma cells have reached morphological maturity. Eisen and his collaborators (Kern and Eisen, 1959; Kern *et al.*, 1959; Helmreich *et al.*, 1960, 1961) have independently been developing a similar careful approach to the kinetics of antibody release, with essentially comparable results. Dutton, Dutton and Vaughan (1960), in some particularly interesting experiments which we will cite again (Section III, D), have shown that when lymphoid cells are removed from a rabbit 3 days after a secondary stimulus and placed in single cell culture in an Eagle's type medium, the rate of antibody synthesis is constant over the first 24 h. However, when cells were removed at 2 days after secondary stimulation, the rate of synthesis rose progressively over the first 24 h of culture. It appears that at least some of the events of differentiation normally occurring within the animal, can also occur under tissue-culture conditions. Grabar and Corvazier (1960) studied lymph nodes and spleens removed shortly after primary immunization *in vivo*; under their conditions of culture, in which the cell fragments were embedded in an agar plug to prevent cell emigration, the rate of antibody production by the cellular population cultured *in vitro* appeared to rise and then fall with the progress of time in very much the same fashion as it would have done in the intact animal. Histological study showed that the normal architecture and health were maintained much better by lymph-node than by spleen fragments; this may account in part for the common experience that lymph-nodes "work" better than spleen in this type of study.

In our own laboratory, we have been interested in the rates of synthesis of RNA and protein by antibody-forming cells *in vitro,* as measured by autoradiography (Mitchell and Nossal, 1963; Nossal and Mitchell, 1963; Mitchell, 1964a, b). We have shown that, as might have been expected, mature antibody-forming plasma cells exhibit a high level of protein-synthesis as judged by ^{3}H-leucine incorporation, but a surprisingly low level of RNA metabolism. This was true both in single cell tissue culture in Eisen's medium and *in vivo*. By contrast, their plasmablast* ancestors show extremely rapid RNA synthesis. This emphasizes the specialized nature of the non-dividing mature plasma cell. Apparently it utilizes messenger RNA, synthesized by its more primitive ancestors, and thus resembles in some ways the reticulocyte, which no longer synthesizes RNA but produces a highly specialized protein, haemoglobin. Pulse-labelling experiments with 30 sec exposure to ^{3}H-uridine *in vitro* emphasized the relative stability of macromolecular RNA in lymphoid blast cells, providing support for the notion that much of the high RNA synthesis in blasts is directed towards the manufacture of ribosomes and messenger templates for use by the progeny cells.

It is therefore obvious that the chain of events set in motion in the body when an animal is immunized can be continued quite efficiently by cells cultured under satisfactory nutritional conditions. This should enable considerable progress to be made, particularly in the biochemistry of antibody synthesis, since an *in vitro* system is so much easier to control and characterize. Production of antibody by isolated ribosomes, for example, would of course speed progress even more. However it is the inductive events leading up to antibody formation that are perhaps the most interesting from the biologist's point of view, and in this area, tissue culture has been of but little help. The findings of Fishman (Section III, B, 1), if confirmed, should provide a considerable stimulus here, and any discovery which facilitated the proliferation and function of antibody-forming cells *in vitro* would undoubtedly open up a whole new chapter.

2. *Antibody Production by Single Cells*

In view of the heterogeneous nature of lymphoid cells, two groups of workers have recently attempted to extend knowledge of antibody

*The following terms are here used synonymously, without further implications: blasts, plasmablasts, lymphoid blasts; lymphoblasts and stem cells.

production by studying individual lymph-node cells isolated from an immunized animal and incubated singly in microdrops of synthetic media supplemented by whole serum, and maintained under paraffin oil (reviewed by Nossal and Mäkelä, 1962b). Nossal, Mäkelä and Lederberg (Nossal and Lederberg, 1958; Nossal, 1958, 1959a, b, 1960a; Mäkelä and Nossal, 1961a, b, 1962; Nossal and Mäkelä, 1962b, c) have immunized rats with various *Salmonella* antigens, isolated lymph-node cells by micromanipulation, and after 3–4 h incubation in Eisen's medium have observed microscopically the behaviour of a small number of bacteria, antigenically related to the immunizing strains, instilled into the microdrops. Agglutination, immobilization, abnormal growth characteristics or specific adherence of bacteria to the cell were used as indicators for the presence of various sorts of antibodies. Attardi, Cohn, Horibata and Lennox (1959) immunized rabbits with whole phage particles, and then isolated lymph-node cells by freehand manipulation, incubated them in a serum-supplemented medium for 48 h, and tested the droplets for their content of phage-neutralizing antibody. In both cases, evaporation was prevented by surrounding the microdrops with paraffin oil. Though the experimental designs were rather similar, the results of the two groups differed in some important respects. The key findings are summarized below.

Our own group has concluded that:

(a) Most antibody-producing cells belong to a specialized family of cells, the plasma-cell series, characterized by RNA-rich cytoplasm and eccentric nucleus. Occasional weakly-positive cells appear to be lymphocytes, but most probably these are an unusual variety, which appear as a specific result of antigenic stimulation and may represent an aberrant type of plasma cell. They have more abundant cytoplasm than the typical small lymphocytes.

(b) The chief difference between a primary and a secondary response is a greater proportion and absolute number of antibody-forming plasma cells proliferating in the lymph-nodes after the secondary stimulation. Although our assay is not strictly quantitative, we also formed the impression that cells isolated during the secondary response were somewhat "stronger" antibody-producers. This may be because they form more antibody, or because they form antibody of higher specificity and avidity.

(c) Plasma cells are highly specialized in what they can do. With rare exceptions, antibody-producing cells from animals immunized with three or more antigens, can each form one type of antibody only, though the animal as a whole is forming roughly equal amounts of three or more antibodies. Less than 2% of cells are demonstrably positive for the production of two antibodies simultaneously, though because of certain methodological limitations the true figure of double-producers may be slightly higher (Nossal and Mäkelä, 1962b). Moreover, most double producers exhibit weak reactivity against one of the two test antigens, as though they were producing large or typical amounts of one antibody, and only small, barely detectable amounts of the second. Neither the duration nor the intensity of immunization had any effect on the observed incidence of doubly-active cells (Nossal and Mäkelä, 1962c).

(d) Antibody-forming plasma cells are the descendants of primitive lymphocytes which proliferate rapidly even in the unstimulated animal. Antigenic induction apparently is a signal for some of these cells to undergo "clonal expansion" and differentiation towards the plasma cell. This is accomplished by some acceleration of the mitotic rate, but the main factor leading to clonal expansion is the enlargement of the primitive pool, presumably because *both* daughters of each mitotic division in stem cells remain primitive for some 6–10 mitotic divisions after antigenic stimulation (Nossal and Mäkelä, 1962a).

(e) The duration of antibody formation by most plasma cells in a lymph-node is short—probably somewhat more than 2 days, though a small but possibly very important proportion of the population live much longer than this.

(f) The most active plasma cells can probably form over 1000 molecules of antibody per second *in vitro* (Nossal and Mäkelä, 1962b). However, plasma cells do not readily tolerate the conditions obtaining in paraffin-bounded microdrops, and survive for some hours only, probably considerably less than the 48 h utilized in the experiments of Attardi *et al.* (1959).

By contrast, Attardi *et al.* (1959) find that:

(a) Antibody production is by no means confined to the plasma-cell family. Though a greater proportion of plasma cells than lymphocytes can be shown to be active antibody-producers, the absolute number of lymphocytes (typical small lymphocytes) forming antibody is greater than the absolute number of plasma cells. Each lymphocyte appears to form approximately as much antibody as each plasma cell.

(b) Some 15–22% of plasma cells obtained from rabbit popliteal lymph-nodes following immunization with two unrelated phages appear to be capable of forming roughly equal quantities of two different sorts of antibody. If one makes certain calculations (Nossal and Mäkelä, 1962b) based on the assumption that most ostensibly-negative plasma cells are yet forming some sort of antibody which is not detectable by the assay procedure used, it seems likely that many more, in fact most, of the active cells in the experiments of Attardi *et al.* were bi- or perhaps multi-potent.

These important differences have caused us much concern, and we have been at some pains to devise experiments in which the proportion of double-producers might be raised (Nossal and Mäkelä, 1962c), but without success. It is of interest to note that no one has yet described a cell which can form three antibodies simultaneously.

The results of single-cell study must therefore be regarded as consistent with the view expressed by Lederberg (1959), writing in support of Burnet's (1957) clonal selection hypothesis of antibody formation, that there is a single "gene for globulin synthesis" within each immunologically competent cell which genetically defines and limits its antibody-producing potential. If this gene locus in a diploid somatic mammalian cell were occupied by two heterozygous alleles, each cell could form two different antibodies. However, the phenotypic restriction of antibody-forming potential described in our experiments is amenable to many other types of explanation, and cannot be construed as evidence for any theory of antibody formation. Until the discrepancies between our results and those of Attardi *et al.* can be explained by further experimentation, we are holding firm to the view that plasma cells, for the most part, form only a single antibody at a time, and that the extreme heterogeneity of antibody-globulin molecules constituting an antiserum is a consequence of extensive heterogeneity amongst the antibody-forming cells, each of which may be secreting an essentially homogeneous product, perhaps even a single molecular species.

In recent experiments, we have turned our attention to the problem of the production of macroglobulin (19S) antibody, using *in vitro* single-cell analysis (Nossal, Szenberg, Ada and Austin, 1964). Most species of animals so far investigated, when immunized for the first time with a particulate or aggregated antigen, form only 19S macroglobulin antibody during the very early stages of the primary response. This 19S antibody is short-lived, and frequently is replaced by the more customary 7S γ-globulin antibody of similar specificity. There has been considerable discussion in the literature about the cellular origin of 19S antibody. Accordingly, we prepared cell suspensions from the popliteal lymph node of rats at various times after immunization with *Salmonella* flagella, and identified cells with antibody on their surface by the method of bacterial adherence. By micromanipulation, such cells were washed, placed into microdroplets, examined under high-power phase contrast and broken to release intracellular antibody. These droplets were then studied in one of two ways. In the first, each drop was halved and one half treated with 0·1 M 2-mercaptoethanol. This reagent for splitting disulphide bonds has the capacity to destroy 19S antibody activity under conditions which leave 7S antibody activity virtually unaltered. Then both half-droplets were titrated for immobilizing antibody through serial twofold dilutions of the half-microdroplets. Droplets showing destruction of antibody by mercaptoethanol were classified as 19S; those showing no reduction in titre as 7S; and those showing significant reduction as double-producers, i.e. cells containing both 19S and 7S antibody of similar specificity. In the second method, droplets were divided into quarters, for testing after treatment with either mercaptoethanol, or with a specific rabbit anti-rat 7S γ-globulin serum, or both. In these experiments, cells showing some remaining antibody after treatment with either reagent, but not after treatment with both reagents, were classified as double producers.

Of 144 cells tested, 123 contained readily detectable amounts of antibody. These comprised 42 19S-cells, 64 7S-cells and 17 double-producers. The double-producers were frequent at times when the switchover from 19S to 7S antibody production was occurring. All except four of the cells in the study could clearly be identified as members of the plasma-cell family. Many of the 19S cells were plasmablasts, but many were fully mature plasma cells. Cells producing 19S antibody could not be distinguished on morphological grounds from those producing 7S.

These results suggested that many cells or cell clones go through a sequence whereby each forms first 19S and later 7S antibody, with identical or very similar combining sites, there being a short period in the life history of the cell when the two functions overlap. This type of "double-producer" must be sharply distinguished from the aberrant double-producers discussed in the previous section, which formed two different types of combining site. The biological purpose of the transition, which does not appear to occur after the injection of a soluble antigen such as flagellin, is not yet clear.

3. *Plaque Technique for Detecting Antibody-producing Cells*

Since the first draft of this review was prepared, an exciting new analytical tool utilizing *in vitro* techniques has appeared. This is the development by Jerne and Nordin (1963) of a plaque technique for the detection of antibody-producing cells. The principle underlying the method is the use of complement to develop lysis in antibody-sensitized sheep erythrocytes. The cell suspension, e.g. from the spleen of immunized mice, containing an unknown number of antibody-producing cells is mixed with the antigen, sheep red cells, and a suitable concentration of agar, and a thin plate is poured. After a short period of incubation, complement is poured on to the plate. Any sheep erythrocytes which had been lying in the vicinity of an antibody-producing cell became coated with antibody, and when the complement was added, they underwent lysis. Thus tiny clear plaques of lysis developed, and these always exhibited a nucleated cell at the exact centre. Interestingly, normal mouse spleens contained a small number of active cells. After primary immunization, the number rose exponentially, and during secondary immunization, much greater numbers still of antibody-producing cells appeared. This work is still in its preliminary stages at the time of writing, but promises to be a most fruitful area for future investigation.

D. INHIBITION OF ANTIBODY SYNTHESIS

Quite a number of agents have been shown to be inhibitory to antibody formation *in vitro*. Obviously, lack of amino-acid building blocks in the tissue-culture medium or other inadequacies of the growth conditions will be inhibitory. Respiratory poisons such as sodium cyanide or general cytotoxic agents such as salts of heavy metals are potent inhibitors (Mountain, 1955). A number of inhibitors of normal protein synthesis, such as DL-ethionine, *p*-fluorophenylalanine, and γ-ethylamidoglutamic acid, have been implicated (Stavitsky and Wolf, 1958). A wide variety of agents have been shown to be specifically toxic for lymphoid cells cultured *in vitro,* including barbiturates, colchicine and cortisone (Trowell, 1958), and considerable work has been done on the effects of cortisone on antibody formation *in vitro*. Though the effects seem to be somewhat less dramatic than the effects *in vivo,* there seems no doubt that cortisone can inhibit antibody formation *in vitro* (Trowell, 1952; Mountain, 1955). Until the biochemical events leading to antibody formation are better characterized, the exact site of action of these inhibitors will remain poorly understoood.

Of special interest is the inhibitory action of certain purine and pyrimidine analogues on antibody formation (Stavitsky, 1961). It appears that agents interfering with normal RNA and DNA synthesis inhibit antibody formation at concentrations lower than those needed to kill the cells. Dutton *et al.* (1960) studied the effects of 5-bromouracil deoxyriboside on antibody formation of lymphoid cells removed from a rabbit 2 days after an anamnestic stimulus with alum-precipitated human serum albumin. Careful kinetic studies showed that two phases of synthesis could be discerned *in vitro,* only one of which was sensitive to the inhibitor. They constructed the hypothesis that the main effect on the inhibitor was on the phase of cellular multiplication occurring *in vitro* between the second and third day. Inhibition of orderly mitosis by the analogue resulted in a 30–80% inhibition of the *in vitro* synthesis. More direct evidence for the importance of cellular division in *in vitro* antibody production has recently been presented by Dutton (1961). Tritiated thymidine of very high specific activity was added to the culture medium. The dividing cells took up the DNA precursor, thereby absorbing a very significant dose of radiation. Non-dividing cells received only little irradiation owing to the short path length of the β particles emitted by tritium. It was found that up to 70% inhibition of antibody formation could be achieved in this way, and the inhibition was antagonized by an excess of non-radioactive thymidine, and could not be mimicked by equivalent amounts of tritiated water in the culture medium. It was calculated that the radiation received by each nucleus of dividing cells was of the order of 50–170 rads per h. By comparison, 200–500 rads of X-irradiation given to the cells at the beginning of the incubation period were required to reduce the antibody synthesis to half of the control level. Autoradiographs of smears of cells from the culture showed that 2–3% had very high levels of incorporation in the nuclei. Apparently specific radiation damage to these cells was the cause of the reduction of *in vitro* synthesis.

Conflicting results have been obtained by Sterzl (1961). Working *in vivo,* he found that mitotic poisons such as colchicine and actinomycin C did not affect the antibody response. However, purine analogues were effective, much more so than pyrimidine derivatives. Sterzl interprets his data as indicating that the purine derivatives must act by interfering directly with adaptive metabolic processes taking place during the inductive phase, and not by inhibiting cell division. On the other hand, we (Nossal and Mäkelä, 1962a; Mäkelä and Nossal, 1962) have shown that every plasma cell is the result of a recent mitotic division, and that it appears to be impossible to create plasma cells from other cell types merely by differentiation without division. These results are in agreement with recent reports by Baney, Vazquez and Dixon (1962) and by Urso and Makinodan (1963) so that the balance of the evidence now indicates that both intracellular adaptations and extensive cell division are integral parts of every immune response.

Studies on the effects of metabolic inhibitors on the induction of the secondary response *in vitro* have recently been reported from Coons' laboratory (O'Brien and Coons, 1963; Ambrose and Coons, 1963). Studies with 5-bromodeoxyuridine (BUDR) showed that the observed development of antibody production *in vitro* depended on cell multiplication between the second and fourth day after antigenic stimulation, and suggested that the progenitive cells capable of responding to the antigen were either resting, or dividing at a relatively slow rate, before antigenic stimulation and for about 1 day thereafter. The most interesting results were obtained when rabbits had been immunized *in vivo* with two unrelated antigens, A and B. When cells from these rabbits were exposed to antigen A in the presence of BUDR for 2·5 days, very little antibody was produced. When the BUDR was removed, and the culture re-stimulated, this time with antigens A and B, it made good antibody to B, but very little to A. It thus appeared that one had two populations of progenitive cells, or, to use our term, "memory" cells. That capable of responding to A had been stimulated to divide, and had thus been damaged by the BUDR, and was not available to respond later on. The cells capable of reacting to B had been unstimulated during the incubation with BUDR, did not divide over this time, and thus remained undamaged. The experiments strongly suggested that, in the secondary response at least, different cells exhibited different capacities to respond to the two antigens. In that sense, the secondary response might be considered as a clonal phenomenon. The experiments, of course, do not answer the vital question of whether the original cells mediating the primary response were members of pre-adapted clones.

By contrast with BUDR, which had its main effect on antibody production over a limited period, low concentrations of chloramphenicol inhibited antibody production *in vitro* at all stages (Ambrose and Coons, 1963). However, the degree of inhibition was much greater when the drug was present from days 0 to 6 than when it was present from days 9 to 15. It was suggested that chloramphenicol interfered predominantly with an early phase of antibody production, and the possibility that it interfered with messenger RNA formation or function was raised. Uhr (1963) has recently studied the effect of actinomycin D on the induction of the secondary response *in vitro*. This drug is widely believed to inhibit DNA-dependent RNA synthesis. Using phage as the antigen, Uhr was able to demonstrate slight continuing primary antibody synthesis in lymph-node fragments cultured without antigen or actinomycin D. This continuing synthesis could be partially inhibited by 0·3 μg/ml of the drug. When cultures were re-stimulated by the presence of phage in the nutrient medium, greatly accelerated antibody synthesis followed. This was dramatically inhibited by the continuous presence of actinomycin D, and partially inhibited when the drug was added 4 days after the re-stimulation. When the animals were secondarily immunized *in vivo*, and the nodes placed into culture 4 days later, only partial suppression of antibody synthesis was achieved with actinomycin D. Mitchell (1964b) has investigated the effects of actinomycin D on RNA and protein synthesis by antibody-forming cells of various categories. She has found that 60–70% of the protein synthesis occurring in mature plasma cells is resistant to concentrations of actinomycin D which abolish all detectable RNA synthesis in all types of cells. Putting this result together with those quoted above, one might conclude that synthesis of antibody by mature plasma cells does not depend on the continued production of messenger units of short half-life made on the DNA template. All the inhibition studies could be explained on the concept that actinomycin D prevents the formation of messenger RNA, and probably of other forms of RNA such as ribosomal RNA, in the plasmablasts. When the drug is exhibited early during incubation, most of the active cells are in the blast form, and the effect is profound. When the drug is introduced later, many cells are already mature, and thus little affected by the drug. However, most plasma cells formed in the secondary response have quite a short life span, and continued antibody production both *in vivo* and *in vitro* must depend at least in part on continued recruitment of new plasma cells from ancestral blast lines. Presumably it is RNA synthesis in this population which is inhibited when the drug is introduced late, and reduction but not abolition of antibody formation follows.

IV. Combined *in vitro-in vivo* Studies

A. Cell-transfer Studies

Because of some of the limitations of tissue culture, a large number of workers have turned to a combination of *in vitro* and *in vivo* studies to delineate the cellular mechanisms of antibody formation. The first to transfer antibody-producing capacity by means of cells was Deutsch (1899) who showed that spleen cells from animals infected with typhoid organisms could be transferred to recipients with the subsequent development of agglutinins in their serum. Landsteiner and Chase (1942) transferred from one animal to another, by means of peritoneal exudate cells, a hypersensitivity to simple chemicals, and these experiments have been greatly extended by Chase (reviewed by Chase, 1953). There seems no doubt as a result of these studies that it was intact living cells which effected the transfer, and not antigen. This type of study entered a new phase of usefulness and precision as a result of the studies of Harris and his collaborators, who took normal lymph-node cells, stimulated them by incubation with soluble *Shigella* antigen *in vitro*, and transferred them to immunologically-neutral recipient hosts, such as heavily irradiated animals (Harris, Harris and Farber, 1955). They showed that lymph-node cells, 95–99% of which were large, medium and small lymphocytes, were the most efficient in mediating this type of transfer, and that peritoneal exudates consisting primarily of monocytic cells were also effective, while granulocytic exudates were not. Circulating blood leucocytes did transfer some activity, but much less (cell for cell) than the lymph-nodes. The transferred cells were capable of undergoing secondary responses, and were effectively inhibited by antiserum prepared against them in homologous rabbits (reviewed by Harris and Harris, 1960). These studies suggested that only healthy, living cells, and not subcellular fractions, could transfer antibody-producing capacity. By contrast, Sterzl and Hrubesova (1956) claimed that nucleic-acid fractions prepared from immunized rabbit spleens could transfer antibody-producing capacity in the absence of viable cells. These claims have been somewhat difficult to substantiate by further study (Hrubesova, Askonas and Humphrey, 1959; Nester, Mäkelä and Nossal, 1961). An interesting discovery was made by Dixon and Weigle (1957a, b) in their transfer studies in rabbits. Adult cells appeared to be incapable of initiating antibody formation in newborn rabbits, while the cells from newborn rabbits, themselves not yet capable of forming antibody in the environment of their own body, could form antibody when transferred to X-irradiated adult recipients. There thus seemed to be a factor inimical to the initiation of antibody formation in the newborn animals. As newborn animals were adequate hosts for cells already engaged in antibody production, the postulate was made that the factor inhibited one of the first steps in the induction process. I was able partially to confirm and extend these results (Nossal, 1959c). In these experiments, initiation of a *primary* response by *in vitro* stimulation of normal cells and transfer to newborn recipients proved impossible, but when cells from an animal primarily immunized *in vivo* some weeks previously were taken, re-stimulated *in vitro*, and transferred to newborn recipients, a typical secondary response with extremely high resulting antibody titres was initiated in the recipient, presumably mediated by the transferred cells. The existence of the Dixon and Weigle effect has been denied (Trnka, 1958; Harris, Harris and Farber, 1959), and much further work must be done before the issue can be regarded as settled one way or the other. However, until specific flaws can be detected in the experiments of Dixon and Weigle, and in my confirmatory ones, the extremely important possibility remains that the immunological incompetence of the newborn is not an inherent property of his lymphoid cells, but rather an environmental effect. It could represent the lack of a certain entity, or the existence of a specific inhibitor which prevents the initiation of a primary immune response. The postulated factor must be present in normal or X-irradiated adult animals, and not concerned in secondary responses or the maintenance of established antibody production.

Cell-transfer studies have also helped in elucidating the mechanism of immunological tolerance. It has been shown that immunological tolerance of mice, both to homograft antigens and soluble antigens, can be broken down by "adoptive immunization" with non-tolerant cells

(Medawar, 1956; Mitchison, 1957). Isologous lymphoid cells, either normal or pre-immunized to the relevant antigen, are transferred to the tolerant recipient, and within some days the graft is rejected or specific antibody formation begins. This shows that immunological tolerance is a "central failure" of the immune response, rather than "mopping up" of antibody by antigen excess.

Repeated alternate *in vitro* stimulations and *in vivo* transfers of spleen cells from immunized mice have given some information relevant to the antibody-producing capacities of lymphoid cells (Nossal, 1960a, b, 1962). When cells are taken from mice immunized with antigens A and B, and transferred through a series of immunologically neutral isologous hosts every 4 weeks, being stimulated *in vitro* prior to each transfer with antigen A but not with antigen B, they soon lose the capacity to form antibody B, while remaining capable of forming anti-A antibody for up to 10 months. While certain technical factors make these experiments difficult to interpret, they are consistent with the notion that once a cell has begun to form a certain antibody, it and its progeny are "committed" to the continued production of that antibody, i.e. that it is genotypically as well as phenotypically restricted in its antibody-producing capacity. However, in view of the incompleteness of the data, this must still be regarded as a highly speculative point.

I have picked out here only a fraction of the extensive data obtained by transfer of immunologically competent cells, using the recipient animal essentially as a sophisticated tissue-culture medium. Readers interested in this aspect should avail themselves of the excellent and comprehensive review published recently by Cochrane and Dixon (1962).

B. DIFFUSION CHAMBER STUDIES

Another useful approach is to take a population of potential antibody-forming cells and to transfer them to a host animal in a Millipore diffusion chamber. This method has the advantage that the cellular population transferred is a captive one, and histological differentiation can readily be observed. Holub and Riha (1960) took lymphoid cells from the cisterna chyli or lymph-nodes of rabbits, added a small quantity of a soluble protein antigen, and placed the mixture in a diffusion chamber permeable to macromolecules but not to cells. On transplantation of the chamber into newborn homologous rabbits, antibody appeared in the serum of these animals, and also could be detected in the chambers themselves, using the Boyden technique of tanned cell haemagglutination. In these experiments, Holub and Riha combined the chamber technique with the Coons (1956) immunofluorescent technique. They detected antigen in the large lymphocytes and phagocytic cells on the first 2 days within the chambers, and subsequently detected antibody in plasma cells and the abnormal small lymphocytes which we have already mentioned as antibody producers (Section III, C, 2). They commented on the infrequent occurrence of mitotic figures in the chambers, and concluded that at least some antibody-forming cells must have been derived from lymphocytes without intervening mitosis.

The experiments of Holub (1962) showed very different results when normal thoracic-duct lymphocytes were transplanted back into the donor rabbit, together with human serum albumin (HSA) as an antigen; and when they were transferred homologously into baby rabbit hosts. In the former situation, only a very small proportion changed into large cells resembling blasts. Most of these eventually turned into histiocytes. In the latter case, the total number of plasma cells formed amounted to 3·5% of the original cell inoculum in the chamber. About half of the plasma cells could be shown to contain anti-HSA by immunofluorescence. Apparently, the extra antigenic stimulation to which cells placed in a homologous environment were subjected, in some way enhanced the anti-HSA response. Holub has not really produced any evidence that the anti-HSA plasma cells arose by direct transformation without intervening mitoses, and his conclusions seem to be in conflict with many data which deny this possibility. Several aspects of this work remain in need of confirmation. For example, an opposite conclusion has been reported by Schooley and Berman (1960). They found that when diffusion-chamber techniques were combined with autoradiography, the plasma cells appearing in the chambers during the first 5 days after transplantation were the derivatives of rapidly dividing cells. Our own *in vivo* work described above (Sections III, C, 2, and III, D) would make the latter view more likely.

V. Conclusions

Both *in vitro* and *in vivo* studies lead us to the conclusion that antibody formation depends on a sequence of elaborate morphological and functional intracellular changes occurring *pari passu* with a series of mitoses in the differentiating cells. In some way, antigen acts as the inductive stimulus setting these events in motion, but the mechanisms remain obscure. Quite possibly, a delicately controlled intercellular collaboration is needed, and the progress of Fishman's (1961) studies will be watched with interest. So far, *in vitro* studies have contributed mainly to our knowledge of the end results of the cellular changes. They have helped to show that lymph nodes, spleen and bone marrow are the organs synthesizing most of the antibody appearing in the serum of immunized animals, and that the plasma cell is the chief antibody-former. They have revealed the conditions under which synthesis can proceed *in vitro* (though it seems likely that no Tissue-Culture approach yet reported fully mirrors the tremendous synthetic capacities of plasma cells *in vivo*), and some factors which, fairly specifically, inhibit the process. Some progress has been made in the biochemical analysis of the synthetic steps, though, by analogy with other aspects of biochemistry, it seems unlikely that real insight will be obtained until synthesis can be carried out at the subcellular level. What all immunologists really hope for is the day when *in vitro* conditions can be found which will allow the induction, maintenance, and physiological decline of antibody formation according to the kinetics observed *in vivo,* and accompanied by the cell differentiation and division characteristic of every immune response in the whole animal. Then detailed biological and biochemical analysis would become immeasurably easier.

It is idle to speculate whether and when this Utopian goal can be achieved, but I believe that many investigators desirous of reaching it are seeking it in quite the wrong way. They try to achieve continuing antibody production *in vitro* by taking tissues from animals hyper-immunized by many injections and already synthesizing antibody at maximal rate *in vivo*; and evince surprise or disappointment when the process stops *in vitro* after a few days or weeks. This disregards the fact that such tissues initially contain mainly small lymphocytes and mature plasma cells, and neither of these types are capable of further division *in vivo*. Though some plasma cells are long-lived, most of them have a short life span *in vivo,* and they seem particularly prone to degeneration after explantation into tissue culture. Little wonder, then, that antibody formation does not readily proceed under such conditions. It would be unreasonable to expect the antibody-forming cells to behave *in vitro* in a way that is contrary to their behaviour *in vivo*. Continued antibody synthesis *in vivo* appears to be dependent, at least in part, on the continued proliferative activity of a relatively small number of blast cells, presumably resident in the germinal centres (Nossal and Mäkelä, 1962a). This, in turn, appears to depend on the continued presence of antigenic depots in dendritic macrophages lying in close and presumably highly organized contact with germinal centre and medullary blast cells. Many workers have observed that relatively greater success in *in vitro* antibody production can be achieved with tissue fragments rather than cell suspensions. Perhaps this is because at least a part of the complicated micro-environmental anatomy of the antibody-forming tissue would be preserved in the fragment. However, there must be many subtle homeostatic mechanisms ensuring an orderly balance between cell birth and cell death in the whole animal, which it would be extremely difficult to achieve *in vitro*.

It is dangerous to predict in which direction a particular science is going to move, but two areas of investigation would seem to offer prospects of spectacular progress. Firstly, it is clear that something vital happens in the body between follicular antigen-containing macrophages and the surrounding lymphoid blasts. Much of the work that we have reviewed (Fishman's, Dutton's, our own, and that of many others) is examining different facets of this interrelationship using a combined *in vivo* and *in vitro* approach. The body is allowed to do some of the difficult and mysterious things; the investigator is content to crystallize his knowledge of one aspect or another with the aid of his sharp *in vitro* tools. Sooner or later, the various issues raised independently by these studies will begin to fit together, and the synthesis should be extremely revealing. Secondly, many as yet fragmentary pieces of evidence are drawing attention to the small lymphocyte to blast transformation. The small lymphocyte had previously been considered to be an end cell. The transformation may thus serve both as an interesting model of somatic dedifferentiation and as an important process in immunity. Our own work (Nossal, Mitchell and McDonald, 1963) has failed to detect such a transformation as the initial step in the induction of a primary immune response. However, the evidence presented by Gowans (1962) is compelling, and the overall concept of the small lymphocyte as a larval cell capable of transforming itself into a rapidly dividing cell which then gives rise to effector progeny is biologically very attractive. Thus it might be wise to continue to search for this event in the early primary response. For reasons that we have discussed extensively elsewhere (Mitchell, Nossal and McDonald, 1963), autoradiographic analysis may never give the answer. Perhaps the *in vitro* approach will again come to our rescue, and all developments in the field opened by Marshall and Roberts (1963), Elves *et al.* (1963), and Hirshhorn, Bach, Kolodny, Firschein and Hashem (1963) (see Section III, B, 3) will be watched with great interest.

While we have stressed the potential of the *in vitro* approach to immunology in this review, it is chastening to note that some spectacular prizes such as Miller's (1961) demonstration of the effect of neonatal thymectomy are still lurking within the whole animal; while the rush for new techniques, elaborate media and sophisticated analyses is both desirable and inevitable, one has the feeling that in the field of antibody formation there is still much room for old-fashioned ingenuity and original ideas.

References

Ada, G. L., Nossal, G. J. V. and Austin, C. M. (1964). The ability of cells in lymphoid follicles to recognize foreignness. *Aust. J. exp. Biol.* **42**, 331.

Ambrose, C. T. and Coons, A. H. (1963). Studies on antibody production. VIII. The inhibitory effect of chloramphenicol on the synthesis of antibody in tissue culture. *J. exp. Med.* **117**, 1075.

Anfinsen, C. B. (1961). Points of current interest in protein chemistry. *Lab. Invest.* **10**, 987.

Askonas, B. A. and Humphrey, J. H. (1958). Formation of specific antibodies and γ–globulin *in vitro*. A study of the synthetic ability of various tissues from rabbits immunized by different methods. *Biochem. J.* **68**, 252.

Attardi, G., Cohn, M., Horibata, K. and Lennox, E. S. (1959). Symposium on the biology of cells modified by viruses or antigens. II. On the analysis of antibody synthesis at the cellular level. *Bact. Rev.* **23**, 213.

Baney, R. N., Vazquez, J. J. and Dixon, F. J. (1962). Cellular proliferation in relation to antibody synthesis. *Proc. Soc. exp. Biol., N.Y.* **109**, 1.

Bishop, J., Favelukes, G., Schweet, R. and Russell, E. (1961). Control of specificity in haemoglobin synthesis. *Nature, Lond.* **191**, 1365.

Boyden, S. V. (1951). The adsorption of proteins on erythrocytes treated with tannic acid and subsequent haemagglutination by antiprotein sera. *J. exp. Med.* **93**, 107.

Brenner, S., Jacob, F. and Meselson, M. (1961). An unstable intermediate carrying information from genes to ribosomes for protein synthesis. *Nature, Lond.* **190**, 576.

Burnet, F. M. (1956). "Enzyme, Antigen and Virus". Cambridge University Press.

Burnet, F. M. (1957). A modification of Jerne's theory of antibody production using the concept of clonal selection. *Aust. J. Sci.* **20**, 67.

Burnet, F. M. (1959). "The Clonal Selection Theory of Acquired Immunity". Cambridge University Press, London, and Vanderbilt University Press, New York.

Burnet, F. M. and Fenner, F. (1949). "The Production of Antibodies", 2nd ed. Macmillan, London.

Carrel, A. and Ingebrigsten, R. (1912). The production of antibodies by tissues living outside of the organism. *J. exp. Med.* **15**, 287.

Chase, M. W. (1953). *In* "The Nature and Significance of the Antibody Response" (A. M. Pappenheimer, Jr., ed.), p. 156. Columbia University Press, New York.

Cochrane, C. G. and Dixon, F. J. (1962). Antibody production by transferred cells. *Advanc. Immunol.* **2**, 205.

Coons, A. H. (1956). Histochemistry with labeled antibody. *Int. Rev. Cytol.* **5**, 1.

Crick, F. H. C. (1958). The Biological Replication of Macromolecules. *Symp. Soc. exp. Biol.* p. 153.

Deutsch, L. (1899). Contribution à l'étude de l'origine des anticorps typhiques. *Ann. Inst. Pasteur* **13**, 689.

Dixon, F. J. and Weigle, W. O. (1957a). The nature of the immunologic inadequacy of neonatal rabbits as revealed by cell transfer studies. *J. exp. Med.* **105**, 75.

Dixon, F. J. and Weigle, W. O. (1957b). Antibody production by cells of the neonatal rabbit. *Fed. Proc.* **16**, 411.

Dutton, R. W. (1961). Importance of cell division for antibody production in an *in vitro* system. *Nature, Lond.* **192**, 462.

Dutton, R. W., Dutton, A. H. and Vaughan, J. H. (1960). The effect of 5–bromouracil deoxyriboside on the synthesis of antibody *in vitro*. *Biochem. J.* **75**, 230.

Dutton, R. W. and Harris, G. (1963). Transfer of stimulation of deoxyribonucleic acid synthesis in antigen-stimulated rabbit spleen cell cultures. *Nature, Lond.* **197**, 608.

Dutton, R. W. and Pearce, J. D. (1962). Antigen-dependent stimulation of synthesis of deoxyribonucleic acid in spleen cells from immunized rabbits. *Nature, Lond.* **194**, 93.

Elves, M. E., Roath, S., Taylor, G. and Israels, M. C. G. (1963). The *in vitro* production of antibody lymphocytes. *Lancet i,* 1292.

Fagraeus, A. (1948). Antibody production in relation to development of plasma cells; *in vivo* and *in vitro* experiments. *Acta med. scand.* Suppl. 204.

Fishman, M. (1959). Antibody formation in tissue cultures. *Nature, Lond.* **183**, 1200.

Fishman, M. (1961). Antibody formation *in vitro*. *J. exp. Med.* **114**, 837.

Fishman, M., Hammerstrom, R. A. and Bond, V. P. (1963). *In vitro* transfer of macrophage RNA to lymph node cells. *Nature, Lond.* **198**, 549.

Gowans, J. L. (1962). The fate of parental strain small lymphocytes in Fl hybrid rats. *Ann. N.Y. Acad. Sci.* **99**, 432.

Grabar, P. and Corvazier, P. (1960). *In* "Ciba Foundation Symposium: Cellular Aspects of Immunity" (G. E. W. Wolstenholme and C. M. O'Connor, eds.), pp. 198-206. Churchill, London.

Harris, T. N. and Ehrich, W. E. (1946). The fate of injected particulate antigens in relation to the formation of antibodies. *J. exp. Med.* **84**, 157.

Harris, T. N. and Harris, S. (1960). *In* "Ciba Foundation Symposium: Cellular Aspects of Immunity" (G. E. W. Wolstenholme and C. M. O'Connor, eds.), p. 172. Churchill, London.

Harris, T. N., Harris, S. and Farber, M. B. (1955). Studies on the transfer of lymph node cells. VI. Transfer of cells incubated *in vitro* with *Shigella*-treated rabbit serum. *J. Immunol.* **75**, 112.

Harris, T. N., Harris, S. and Farber, M. B. (1959). Effect of injection of rabbit leucocytes into neonatal rabbits on subsequent lymph node cell transfer. *Proc. Soc. exp. Biol., N.Y.* **102**, 495.

Haurowitz, F. (1953). *In* "The Nature and Significance of the Antibody Response" (A. M. Pappenheimer, Jr., ed.), p. 3. Columbia University Press, New York.

Helmreich, E., Kern, M. and Eisen, H. N. (1960). Synthesis and release of antibody by isolated lymph node cells. *Fed. Proc.* **19**, 200.

Helmreich, E., Kern, M. and Eisen, H. N. (1961). The secretion of antibody by isolated lymph node cells. *J. biol. Chem.* **236**, 464.

Hirschhorn, K., Bach, F., Kolodny, R. L., Firschein, I. L. and Hashem, I. L. (1963). Immune response and mitosis of human peripheral blood lymphocytes *in vitro*. *Science* **142**, 1185.

Holub, M. (1962). Potentialities of the small lymphocyte as revealed by homotransplantation and autotransplantation experiments in diffusion chambers. *Ann. N.Y. Acad. Sci.* **99**, 477.

Holub, M. and Riha, I. (1960). *In* "Mechanisms of Antibody Formation" (M. Holub and L. Jarošková, eds.), pp. 39-50. Academic Press, New York.

Hrubesova, M., Askonas, B. A. and Humphrey, J. H. (1959). Serum antibody and γ-globulin in baby rabbits after transfer of ribonucleoprotein from adult rabbits. *Nature, Lond.* **183**, 97.

Hungerford, D. A., Donnelly, A. J., Nowell, P. C. and Beck, S. (1959). The chromosome constitution of a human phenotypic intersex. *Amer. J. hum. Genet.* **11**, 215.

Jerne, N. K. (1955). The natural-selection theory of antibody formation. *Proc. nat. Acad. Sci., Wash.* **41**, 849.

Jerne, N. K. (1960). Immunological speculations. *Annu. Rev. Microbiol.* **14**, 341.

Jerne, N. K. and Nordin, A. A. (1963). Plaque formation in agar by single antibody-producing cells. *Science* **140**, 405.

Karush, F. (1961). *In* "Immunochemical Approaches to Problems in Microbiology" (M. Heidelberger and O. Plescia, eds.), p. 368. Rutgers University Press, New Jersey.

Kern, M. and Eisen, H. N. (1959). The effect of antigenic stimulation on incorporation of phosphate and methionine into proteins of isolated lymph node cells. *J. exp. Med.* **110**, 207.

Kern, M., Helmreich, E. and Eisen, H. N. (1959). A demonstration of antibody activity on microsomes. *Proc. nat. Acad. Sci. Wash.* **45**, 862.

Keuning, F. J. and van der Slikke, L. B. (1950). Role of immature plasma cells, lymphoblasts, and lymphocytes in formation of antibodies, as established in tissue culture experiments. *J. Lab. clin. Med.* **36**, 167.

Kucynski, M. A., Tenenbaum, E. and Werthemann, A. (1925). Untersuchungen über Ernährung und Wachstum der Zellen erwachsener Säugetiere in Plasma under Verwendung wohlcharakterisiertes Tusätze an Stelle von Gewebsauszügen. *Virchow's Arch.* **258**, 687.

Landsteiner, K. and Chase, M. W. (1942). Experiments on transfer of cutaneous sensitivity to simple compounds. *Proc. Soc. exp. Biol., N.Y.* **49**, 688.

Lederberg, J. (1959). Genes and antibodies. *Science* **129**, 1649.

Ludke, H. (1912). Über Antikörpersbildung in Kulturen lebender Körperzellen. *Berl. Klin. Wschr.* **49**, 1034.

McMaster, P. D. (1961). *In* "The Cell" (J. Brachet and A. E. Mirsky, eds.), Vol. 5. p. 323. Academic Press, New York.

Mäkelä, O. and Nossal, G. J. V. (1961a). Bacterial adherence: a method for detecting antibody production by single cells. *J. Immunol.* **87**, 447.

Mäkelä, O. and Nossal, G. J. V. (1961b). Study of antibody-producing capacity of single cells by bacterial adherence and immobilization. *J. Immunol.* **87**, 457.

Mäkelä, O. and Nossal, G. J. V. (1962). Autoradiographic studies on the immune response. II. DNA synthesis amongst single antibody-producing cells. *J. exp. Med.* **115**, 231.

Marshall, W. H. and Roberts, K. B. (1963). The growth and mitosis of human small lymphocytes after incubation with a phytohaemagglutinin. *Quart. J. exp. Physiol.* **48**, 146.

Medawar, P. B. (1956). A discussion on immunological tolerance. *Proc. R. Soc.* B, **146**, 1.

Meyer, K. and Loewenthal, H. (1928). Untersuchungen über Antikörperbildung in Gewebekulturen. *Z. ImmunForsch.* **54**, 420.

Michaelides, M. C. (1957). Antibody production in tissue culture. *Fed. Proc.* **16**, 426.

Michaelides, M. C. and Coons, A. H. (1963). Studies on antibody production. V. The secondary response *in vitro*. *J. exp. Med.* **117**, 1035.

Miller, J. F. A. P. (1961). Immunological function of the thymus. *Lancet ii*, 748.

Mitchell, J. (1964a). Autoradiographic studies of nucleic acid and protein metabolism in lymphoid cells. I. Differences amongst members of the plasma cell sequence. *Aust. J. exp. Biol.* **42**, 347.

Mitchell, J. (1964b). Autoradiographic studies of nucleic acid and protein metabolism in lymphoid cells. II. The stability and actinomycin sensitivity of rapidly formed RNA and protein. *Aust. J. exp. Biol.* **42**, 363.

Mitchell, J. and Nossal, G. J. V. (1963). Ribonucleic acid metabolism in the plasma cell sequence. *Nature, Lond.* **197**, 1121.

Mitchell, J., Nossal, G. J. V. and McDonald (1963). Autoradiographic studies on the immune response. III. Differential lymphopoiesis in various organs. *Aust. J. exp. Biol.* **41**, 411.

Mitchison, N. A. (1957). Adoptive transfer of immune reactions by cells. *J. cell. comp. Physiol.* **50**, Suppl. 1, 247.

Mountain, I. M. (1955). Antibody production by spleen *in vitro*; influence of cortisone and other chemicals. *J. Immunol.* **74**, 270.

Mudd, S. (1932). A hypothetical mechanism of antibody formation. *J. Immunol.* **23**, 423.

Nester, M., Mäkelä, O. and Nossal, G. J. V. (1961). Studies on the transfer of nucleoprotein fractions from immunized spleens. *Transplant. Bull.* **28**, 478.

Nossal, G. J. V. (1958). Antibody production by single cells. *Brit. J. exp. Path.* **39**, 544.

Nossal, G. J. V. (1959a). Antibody production by single cells. II. The difference between primary and secondary response. *Brit. J. exp. Path.* **40**, 118.

Nossal, G. J. V. (1959b). Antibody production by single cells. III. The histology of antibody production. *Brit. J. exp. Path.* **40**, 301.

Nossal, G. J. V. (1959c). Studies on the transfer of antibody-producing capacity. I. The transfer of antibody-producing cells to young animals. *Immunology* **2**, 137.

Nossal, G. J. V. (1960a). Antibody production by single cells. IV. Further studies on multiply immunized animals. *Brit. J. exp. Path.* **41**, 89.

Nossal, G. J. V. (1960b). Studies on the transfer of antibody-producing capacity. II. The serial transfer of antibody-producing cells. *Immunology* **3**, 109.

Nossal, G. J. V. (1962). Genetic studies on immunologically competent cells. *Advanc. Immunol.* **2**, 163.

Nossal, G. J. V., Ada, G. L. and Austin, C. M. (1963). The behaviour of active bacterial antigens during the induction of the immune response. II. The cellular distribution of I^{131}-labelled flagella. *Nature, Lond.* **199**, 1259.

Nossal, G. J. V., Ada, G. L. and Austin, C. M. (1964). Antigens in immunity. IV. Cellular localization of ^{125}I- and ^{131}I-labelled flagella in lymph nodes. *Aust. J. exp. Biol.* **42**, 311.

Nossal, G. J. V. and Lederberg, J. (1958). Antibody production by single cells. *Nature, Lond.* **181**, 1419.

Nossal, G. J. V. and Mäkelä, O. (1962a). Autoradiographic studies on the immune response. I. The kinetics of plasma cell proliferation. *J. exp. Med.* **115**, 209.

Nossal, G. J. V. and Mäkelä, O. (1962b). Elaboration of antibodies by single cells. *Annu. Rev. Microbiol.* **16**, 53.

Nossal, G. J. V. and Mäkelä, O. (1962c). Kinetic studies on the incidence of cells appearing to form two antibodies. *J. Immunol.* **88**, 604.

Nossal, G. J. V. and Mitchell, J. (1963). *In* "Proceedings of the Third International Symposium on Immunopathology" (F. J. Dixon, ed.), p. 113. Karger, Basle.

Nossal, G. J. V., Mitchell, J. and McDonald, W. (1963). Autoradiographic studies on the immune response. IV. Single cell studies on the primary response. *Aust. J. exp. Biol.* **41**, 423.

Nossal, G. J. V., Szenberg, A., Ada, G. L. and Austin, C. M. (1964). Single cell studies on 19S antibody producing cells. *J. exp. Med.* **119**, 485.

O'Brien, T. F. and Coons, A. H. (1963). Studies on antibody production. VII. The effect of 5–bromodeoxyuridine on the *in vitro* anamnestic antibody response. *J. exp. Med.* **117**, 1063.

O'Brien, T. F., Michaelides, M. C. and Coons, A. H. (1963). Studies on antibody production. VI. The course, sensitivity, and histology of the secondary response *in vitro*. *J. exp. Med.* **117**, 1053.

Pauling, L. (1940). Theory of structure and process of formation of antibodies. *J. Amer. chem. Soc.* **62**, 2643.

Pfeiffer, R. and Marx, Z. (1898). Die Bildungsstätte der Choleraschutzstoffe. *Z. Hyg.* **27**, 272.

Ranney, H. M. and London, I. M. (1951). Antibody formation in surviving tissues. *Fed. Proc.* **10**, 562.

Salle, A. J. and McOmie, W. A. (1937). Immunological responses of tissues cultivated *in vitro*. *J. Immunol.* **32**, 157.

Schooley, J. C. (1961). Autoradiographic observations of plasma cell formation. *J. Immunol.* **86**, 331.

Schooley, J. C. and Berman, I. (1960). Morphologic and autoradiographic observations of H^3-thymidine-labelled thoracic duct lymphocytes cultured *in vivo*. *Blood* **16**, 1133.

Schweet, R. S. and Owen, R. D. (1957). Concepts of protein synthesis in relation to antibody formation. *J. cell comp. Physiol.* **50**, Suppl. 1, 199.

Stavitsky, A. B. (1955). *In vitro* production of diphtheria antitoxin by tissues of immunized animals. *J. Immunol.* **75**, 214.

Stavitsky, A. B. (1958). *In vitro* production of diphtheria antitoxin by tissues of immunized animals. III. Incorporation of amino acids into antibody; relationship to antibody synthesis and sensitivity relative to other methods. *Brit. J. exp. Path.* **39**, 661.

Stavitsky, A. B. (1960). *In* "Mechanisms of Antibody Formation" (M. Holub and L. Jarošková, eds.), p. 295. Academic Press, New York.

Stavitsky, A. B. (1961). *In vitro* studies of the antibody response. *Advanc. Immunol.* **1**, 211.

Stavitsky, A. B. and Wolf, B. (1958). Mechanisms of antibody globulin synthesis by lymphoid tissue *in vitro*. *Biochim. biophys. Acta* **27**, 4.

Steiner, D. F. and Anker, H. S. (1956). On the synthesis of antibody protein *in vitro*. *Proc. nat. Acad. Sci., Wash.* **42**, 580.

Stevens, K. M. and McKenna, J. M. (1958). Studies on antibody synthesis initiated *in vitro*. *J. exp. Med.* **107**, 537.

Sterzl, J. (1961). Effect of some metabolic inhibitors on antibody formation. *Nature, Lond.* **189**, 1022.

Sterzl, J. and Hrubesova, M. (1956). The transfer of antibody formation by means of nucleoprotein fractions to non-immunized recipients. *Folia Biol.* **2**, 21.

Talmage, D. W. (1957). Allergy and immunology. *Annu. Rev. Med.* **8**, 239.

Thorbecke, G. J. and Keuning, F. J. (1953). Antibody formation *in vitro* by haemopoietic organs after subcutaneous and intravenous immunization. *J. Immunol.* **70**, 129.

Trnka, Z. (1958). Antibody formation by isolated cells of hen spleen after mixing with antigen *in vitro* and transfer to chicks. *Nature, Lond.* **181**, 55.

Trowell, O. A. (1952). The culture of lymph nodes *in vitro*. *Exp. Cell Res.* **3**, 79.

Trowell, O. A. (1955). The culture of lymph nodes in synthetic media. *Exp. Cell Res.* **9**, 258.

Trowell, O. A. (1958). The cytocidal action of barbiturates on lymphocytes *in vitro*. *Biochem. Pharmacol.* **1**, 288.

Uhr, J. W. (1963). Actinomycin D: its effect on antibody formation *in vitro*. *Science*, **142**, 1476.

Urso, P. and Makinodan, T. (1963). The roles of cellular division and maturation in the formation of precipitating antibody. *J. Immunol.* **90**, 897.

Wesslen, T. (1952). Studies on the role of lymphocytes in antibody production. *Acta derm.-venereol., Stockh.* **32**, 265.

CHAPTER 6

Tissue Culture in Pharmacology

V. M. ROSENOER

Medical Unit and Department of Pharmacology, Royal Free Hospital, London, England

and

W. JACOBSON

Sir Halley Stewart Research Fellow, Strangeways Research Laboratory, Cambridge, England

I. Introduction

Pharmacology has been defined as "the study of the manner in which the function of living organisms can be modified by chemical substances" (Wilson and Schild, 1959) and the object of this chapter is to discuss how the techniques of Tissue Culture may aid in such studies.

The advantage of Tissue Culture in the analysis of drug action is clear, viz. it provides a method for the investigation of the direct action of drugs on cells and tissues in the absence of the complex metabolic interactions which apply in the whole animal. However, the limitations of this approach must also be stressed. Most of the studies of the action of pharmacologically active agents in Tissue Culture which have so far been made relate to the metabolic processes associated with cell survival and growth, for, with few exceptions, the highly diversified functions of differentiated cells in the intact animal have not been reproduced in serially propagated dispersed cell cultures. Neoplastic mast cells in culture continue to synthesize histamine and 5-hydroxytryptamine (Schindler, Day and Fischer, 1959) and cultures of anterior pituitary gland cells have been reported to elaborate growth hormone (Thompson, Vincent, Jensen, Price and Schapiro, 1959), but most reports of functioning cells in Tissue Culture concern freshly isolated cells in primary culture which are either not multiplying or have gone through, at most, a few divisions. Thus, dissociated rat heart-muscle cells in primary culture have continued to pulsate for many days, but this property was lost on subculture (Harary and Farley, 1960). The study of the factors responsible for the maintenance of function in dispersed cell cultures is a major prerequisite to pharmacological studies. The possible importance of humoral and substrate factors in the culture media has been reviewed by Levintow and Eagle (1961) (see also Vol. 1, Chaps. 8, 16 and 17).

From a pharmacological standpoint, the retention of normal function is of prime importance. The majority of reports of sustained function in Tissue Culture deal with primary cultures of organized tissues—"organ cultures"—which preserve the normal parenchymal-stromal relationships and specific synthetic activities. Thus organ culture of cartilage and bone have been used to study the effects of vitamin A (Fell and Thomas, 1960), hydrocortisone (Fell and Thomas, 1961), thyroxine (Fell and Mellanby, 1956), triiodothyronine (Lawson, 1961a, b), insulin (Chen, 1954), parathormone (Gaillard, 1961) and antisera (Fell and Weiss, 1965).

These studies, reviewed in earlier chapters (Vol. 1, Chaps. 16 and 17; Vol. 2, Chap. 4), merge methodologically with classical pharmacological studies on surviving tissues in organ baths, but the degree of sophistication in the system of tissue maintenance is far higher. Unfortunately, in most cases the quantitation of the tissue response has yet to reach the degree of precision possible in organ-bath systems.

To illustrate this point, the following example has been selected. Raisz (1963a, b, 1965) has developed a technique for the study of the action of parathyroid hormone on embryonic rat bone maintained in organ culture, measuring bone resorption in terms of the release of ^{45}Ca previously incorporated *in vivo* in the embryonic bone. By this method, parallel line 4 or 6-point dilution assays may be carried out, the effect of parathyroid hormone being expressed as the ratio of ^{45}Ca released from treated bones to that released from paired controls. The sensitivity of this assay is greater than that of the usual rat assay (Munson, 1961) in terms of the amount of hormone required, and the method has been of value in detecting the small amounts of bone-resorbing activity produced by single rat parathyroids in Tissue Culture (Raisz, 1963b). However, the precision of the assay is low, the index of precision (L) (see discussion by Gaddum, 1953) for the Tissue-Culture assays being only 2·9–3·6 compared with 3·6–5·6 for standard rat assays and 5·9–12·5 for immunoassays by complement fixation. An accurate assay for histamine using the isolated guinea-pig ileum has an L value of 30 (Schild, 1942).

The results of pharmacological studies in organ culture have both broadened and deepened our understanding of organogenesis and provide a model for the study of the effects of new drugs upon foetal development. Thus Mulherkar (1960) has studied the production of malformations in the chick embryo *in vitro* by trypan blue. Chick embryos at the primitive streak, or early head-process, and at the neural plate stages were treated with trypan blue. Many abnormalities were produced including malformation of the somites, shortening of the axis, the formation of large blisters on the embryo and delayed heart flexure. In some specimens the notochord failed to form and a median somite strand was found.

More recently, Jainchill, Saxén and Vainio (1964) have studied the effect of the polypeptide antibiotic, actinomycin D, on the induction of tubulogenesis in mouse metanephrogenic mesenchyme by dorsal spinal cord fragments *in vitro*, using a culture system similar to that described by Trowell (1954). Treatment of the mesenchyme with actinomycin D (0·05 μg/ml) inhibited tubulogenesis. Treatment of the spinal cord inducer alone, before recombination with the mesenchyme, had no effect. Differentiation could no longer be inhibited if 24 or more hours elapsed between recombination of the two tissues and treatment with the drug. Wessells (1964) studied the temporal characteristics of actinomycin D sensitivity of developing mouse pancreas explants maintained in Tissue Culture. He cultured pieces of 11-day mouse pancreatic epithelium separated by millipore filters from embryonic mouse salivary-gland mesenchyme and recorded differentiation in terms of the formation of zymogen granules. Actinomycin D insensitive cells first appeared between 48 and 72 h of culture and the numbers of such resistant cells which form zymogen granules increased during longer culturing. 8-Azaguanidine, however, inhibited cell differentiation at times after actinomycin insensitivity had developed. Autoradiographic studies showed that actinomycin D did not, in the relatively low concentrations used (0·015 μg/ml), alter the patterns of tritiated uridine incorporation into nuclear regions nor the subsequent appearance of the radioactive label in the cytoplasm. In interpreting these interesting results, it must be remembered that the differentiated pancreatic cells may well have affected the integrity of actinomycin D.

Studies in tissue and organ culture closely approach the classical biochemical studies with tissue slices and brei. Only the duration of study distinguishes them, and no fundamental distinction can be made. For example, Day and Green (1962b) studied the effects of monoamine oxidase inhibitors and Carlini, Fischer and Giarman (1964) the effects of reserpine and chlorpromazine on the 5-hydroxytryptamine content of neoplastic mast cells in culture. Reserpine was several times more potent than chlorpromazine in depleting mast cells of 5-hydroxytryptamine but the time course of the depletion was slower. It is of basic interest that at a time when the cells were maximally depleted of 5-hydroxytryptamine, they continued to reproduce with no change in the doubling time. Storage of the amine would appear to be unnecessary for normal cell proliferation. Monoamine oxidase inhibitors failed to produce a significant increase in 5-hydroxytryptamine in the mast cells—a finding consistent with the absence of appreciable monoamine oxidase activity in these cells (Day and Green, 1962a). However, the inhibitors of monoamine oxidase studied could block reserpine-induced release of 5-hydroxytryptamine, strongly suggesting that the property responsible for this is dissociable from their effect on monoamine oxidase. Day and Green (1962b) also studied the effects of imipramine and α-methyldopa on the uptake of ^{14}C histamine, ^{14}C-5-hydroxytryptamine, ^{14}C-histidine and ^{14}C-hydroxytryptophane by cultured mast cells. α-Methyldopa inhibited the uptake of 5-hydroxytryptophane without influencing the uptake of 5-hydroxytryptamine, histidine or histamine. Imipramine inhibited uptake of both amines but not of the amino acids. The authors conclude that the mechanism of uptake of the amines and their precursor amino acids must differ.

Leslie and Sinclair (1959) in their investigation of the action of thyroxine and triiodothyronine on cultured human cells, followed both cell growth in terms of protein nitrogen, lipid phosphorus, RNA phosphorus and DNA phosphorus, and metabolic activity in terms of glucose and amino-acid utilization and lactic acid, α-keto acid and ammonia production. They found that the growth of freshly explanted foetal lung cultures was inhibited by 10^{-4}M thyroxine and triiodothyronine, but the same concentrations did not affect the proliferation of human foetal liver and kidney cells nor that of Hep-1 and Hep-2 carcinoma cells which had been maintained in Tissue Culture for some years. No change in cell composition was detected after hormone treatment. All the cell types tested showed increased glycolysis after exposure to 10^{-4}M concentrations of the hormones, although no effects were detectable at the more physiological concentration of

10^{-7}M. The authors concluded that thyroxine and triiodothyronine cannot uncouple oxidative phosphorylation in the mitochondria of long established strains of foetal cells which have lost most of their initial oxidative activity. This result emphasizes that differential responses which may be observed in Tissue Culture do not necessarily depend upon whether the cells studied are derived from normal or malignant cells. Changes in enzyme patterns during prolonged cultivation *in vitro* cannot be ignored.

The examples presented in this chapter have been selected to emphasize two aspects of the subject under discussion: firstly that pharmacology embraces the study of the biological mode of action of chemical substances irrespective of their origin, and secondly that in pharmacological studies, the techniques applied are derived from all the biological sciences. In this context Tissue Culture is but one of those techniques.

II. Methods of Assessment of Drug Activity

The action of drugs on cells in Tissue Culture may be studied cytologically or biochemically by following modifications in cell form and structure, growth rate, differentiation and migration, and by applying micro-chemical techniques and those using isotopes.

Growth in monolayer and suspension cultures may be estimated by relatively simple procedures. Monolayer cultures can be suspended after removing the cells from the glass by treatment with trypsin or Versene, and the suspension counted in a haemocytometer chamber or with a Coulter electronic counter. Aliquots of suspension cultures may be counted directly. It is, of course, essential that such suspensions are well dispersed; gross inaccuracies can arise from counts of poorly dispersed or badly clumped cells. Neutral-red staining of viable cells or trypan-blue staining of damaged cells (Girardi, McMichael and Henle, 1956) may assist in differentiating living from dead cells, although this is not usually required. Moreover, the dye-exclusion tests for cell viability are not infallible. High stain concentrations and low concentrations of serum tend to increase the stained cell counts when eosin is used, irrespective of whether the cell suspensions are initially damaged or not (Black and Berenbaum, 1964). The plating procedures that have recently been developed now make it possible to determine the number of cells in a population that are capable of division (Gwatkin, Till, Whitmore, Siminovitch and Graham, 1957) and to determine the rate of growth of clones derived from single cells (Puck, Marcus and Cieciura, 1956).

Measurements of dry weight or of packed cell volume or turbidimetric methods may be used in estimating cell growth. However, as Kuchler and Merchant (1958) demonstrated, an increase in cell size during the lag phase of growth may account for an increase in packed cell volume without an increase in cell number. Youngner (1954) found that the measured relation between optical density and cell numbers in suspensions of monkey-kidney cells deviated from the theoretical relationship expected in a uniform suspension of single cells. Inadequate dispersion with clumping of cells could account for these discrepancies.

The chemical determination of one of the cell constituents may be preferred in the assessment of cell growth in replicate cultures. Cell protein is most conveniently measured by Oyama and Eagle's (1956) modification of the phenol method of Lowry, Rosebrough, Farr and Randall (1951) which is adapted for direct use in monolayer cultures. The phenol reagent develops a blue colour on reaction with the phenylalanine, tyrosine and tryptophane residues of the protein. Suspension cultures must be centrifuged and well washed before this method is used, because constituents of the medium, especially tyrosine, interfere with the colour reaction. Szybalski and Smith (1959) used bromophenol blue to determine cell protein. Grady, Lummis and Smith (1960a) compared three simplified methods for the determination of the growth of human carcinoma cells in monolayer culture—determination of colour intensity in lysates of cells stained with crystal violet, determination of the reduction of 2,6-dichlorophenolindophenol and the determination of total organic solids using a modified dichromate method (Johnson, 1949). The three methods gave comparable measurements of relative cell growth and the correlation with protein assays by Oyama and Eagle's method was good. The crystal-violet method appeared to be especially suitable for assaying large numbers of samples in large-scale drug screening.

Cell DNA may be measured directly by the method of McIntyre and Sproull (1957) in which the DNA is precipitated by salmine. The purines and pyrimidines are extracted from the precipitate by a hot acid-salt solution and measured by the ultraviolet absorption of the extract at 268 mμ.

It should be noted that these chemical procedures are all subject to the limitation that the cell constituent measured may not parallel other cell constituents or cell number. This concerns particularly DNA estimates applied to rapidly growing cells in view of the known dissociation of cell growth and cell division.

The development of improved methods of light-microscopy, e.g. phase-contrast and interference-microscopy, and of electron-microscopy has extended the scope of morphological studies. Thus, Fell and Allsopp (1948) described the cytopathological changes and the profound disturbances of the mitotic process in cells exposed to mustard gas, whilst Hughes and Fell (1949) extended these studies by phase-contrast cinematography in living cells. Pomerat, Lefeber and Smith (1954) discussed the use of this technique in the quantitative analysis of the activity of cells and their organelles—including nuclear rotation, muscular contraction, pulsatile activity of oligodendroglia, pinocytosis and mitotic activity. However, the difficulties inherent in the quantitative analysis of the results obtained by these techniques have, so far, limited their application in analytical pharmacological studies. For example, Nakazawa (1960) studied the effects of chlorpromazine and 5-hydroxytryptamine on the behaviour of oligodendrocytes from the chick brain stem and spinal cord and from the thalamus of newborn kittens and puppies, using the perfusion-chamber technique and the phase-contrast, time-lapse cinematographic recording methods described by Pomerat (1951). The contraction rates of the oligodendrocytes increased after treatment with both drugs, the response to chlorpromazine being rapid, dose-dependent and reversible, that to 5-hydroxytryptamine being delayed and not reversible. Simultaneous treatment with chlorpromazine and 5-hydroxytryptamine appeared to antagonize the effects produced by these drugs when perfused separately.

Harary and Farley (1960) examined the effects of drugs on the rate of rhythmic contraction of rat heart cells, separated by treatment with trypsin and grown attached to glass in a liquid medium. Acetylcholine (10^{-6}M) produced a marked reversible decrease in the rate. Eserine (10^{-5}M) appeared to prolong the acetylcholine inhibition while ouabain (10^{-6}M) increased the rate of contraction. Various metabolic inhibitors were also studied. Dinitrophenol (5×10^{-5}M) produced a transient stimulation followed by inhibition. ATP (5×10^{-6}M) reversed this inhibition. Monofluoracetate (10^{-6}M) inhibited contractions completely, as did iodoacetamide (10^{-3}M).

Wollenberger and Halle (1960) have described the effects of cardiac glycosides on contractions of single cultured embryonic chick heart-muscle cells. They observed with known cardio-active glycosides an increase in the rate of beat in concentrations as low as 10^{-9}M. At concentrations of 10^{-7}M and above, the acceleration was accompanied by, or soon followed by, disturbances of automaticity and of co-ordinated contraction. Such phenomena as partial and complete block of propagation of the contraction wave, bigeminal rhythm, ectopic beats and "fibrillation" could all be observed in single isolated ventricle cells. Cardio-inactive glycosides were without significant chronotropic action, did not induce rhythmic contraction in quiescent cells and produced no irregularities of beat. The authors concluded that the structural requirements for the display of biological activity by these drugs are as stringent in the cultured embryonic heart cell as in the inact adult vertebrate heart.

Murray (Vol. 2, Chap. 8) has briefly reviewed the action of drugs on the rhythmical contractions of cardiac and skeletal muscle cells in Tissue Culture. She points out that rhythmically contracting cultures of skeletal muscle cells, which are entirely devoid of neural connections and endplates, provide an important technique for studying the direct effects of chemical agents both on the cell membrane and on the contractile system itself. However, the sporadic and non-uniform nature of the contractions in this type of preparation limits the precision possible in quantitating the results. Using a numerical rating system, based on the number of fibres contracting spontaneously and on the apparent strength of these contractions, Murray found that foetal rat somatic muscle without innervation or endplates was inhibited by procaine, veratrine, ryanodine and d-tubocurarine, although at very low concentrations (0·01 μg/ml) tubocurarine appeared to stimulate, ATP and acetylcholine were without effect, or were inhibitory, whilst caffeine and mapharsen appeared to activate contraction.

Crain (Vol. 2, Chap. 8) has reviewed the electrophysiological studies of cardiac and skeletal muscle cells in culture and discussed studies with long-term cultures of myotomes explanted from 12-day-old mouse embryos (Crain, 1964) onto collagen-coated coverslips, fed with a serum-saline nutrient medium and maintained for months in the Maximow slide assembly. Muscle contractions could be elicited by electrical stimulation of strictly localized areas of the spinal cord or of the ventral nerve roots. d-Tubocurarine (0·5–5 μg/ml) selectively and rapidly blocked the neurally evoked contractions although the muscles still responded to direct stimulation. Strychnine (10 μg/ml) increased the duration and amplitude of cord "after-discharges" and vigorous, repetitive muscle contractions were associated with this augmented neural activity. Eserine (0·1–0·5 μg/ml) produced repetitive muscle twitches after a single cord stimulus, but the bioelectric activity of the cord tissue was unaltered.

The technique described by Willmer (1933) and by Willmer and Jacoby (1936) for recording mitotic activity and cell-movement in fibroblast colonies, was adopted by Jacoby, Medawar and Willmer (1941) in a study of the toxicity of sulphonamides to cells *in vitro*. In principle they used time-lapse photomicrography of a sample of cells from the peripheral part of a colony of fibroblasts growing in Carrel flasks to which an optically flat glass base had been fitted. For freshly explanted tissues they determined the threshold concentration of drug which inhibited all outgrowth from a standard explant maintained for 24 h at 37°C. Pomerat (1942), Pomerat, Capouya and Greenleaf (1944) and Pomerat, Drager and Painter (1946) used similar techniques in studies on the effects of tyrothricin, allantoin, sulphonamides and barbiturates on tissues *in vitro*.

Mitotic counts of cells in culture made on fixed and stained preparations, may be of value in assessing cell multiplication. The use of colchicine, which arrests mitosis in metaphase, often enables a higher mitotic index to be obtained and may help in the analysis of the multiplication potential of different cell types in culture. Jacobson (1954a, b) studied the direct action of folic acid antagonists on cells *in vitro* and, from quantitative analyses of the different phases of mitosis, established the function of folinic acid during the mitotic process. The relative durations of the various phases of mitosis and of the intermitotic interval may be measured directly or calculated from autoradiographic studies of cultures (Lajtha, 1959; see also Vol. 1, Chap. 6).

Another approach to the study of the action of drugs on cells is to measure the cellular utilization of glucose and amino acids and the production of lactic and α-keto acids, or the incorporation of variously labelled precursors may be followed. For example, the incorporation into RNA of ^{32}P from ^{32}P-labelled phosphate, of ^{14}C from ^{14}C-adenine and of ^{3}H from tritiated thymidine may be demonstrated autoradiographically or determined by measuring the radioactivity after chemical extraction. Thus Yarnell, Ambrose, Shepley and Tchao (1964) assayed the effects of alkylating agents on human tumour explants maintained in organ culture by determining ^{32}P uptake into the cellular nucleic acids. Changes in the glycolytic respiratory activities of cell cultures may be followed, oxygen uptake being measured by Warburg manometry, by the Cartesian diver (Paul and Danes, 1961) or electrochemically (Woodliff and Davis, 1960).

Caspersson, Farber, Foley and Killander (1963) have developed cytochemical techniques for the quantitative determination of the DNA, RNA, and dry mass of individual cells in large cell populations. The biophysical instruments used were an ultramicrospectrophotometer for use in the ultraviolet and visible ranges, a corresponding high resolution instrument designed for Feulgen spectrophotometry, an ultramicro-interferometer, a rapid microplanimeter for nucleolar measurements and instrumentation for the rapid determination of mass by X-ray absorption. Using these methods they studied the effects of nitrogen mustard and actinomycin D on the nucleolar system of Ehrlich ascites cells *in vivo* and a line of normal mouse fibroblasts maintained in cell culture. Nitrogen mustard added in appropriate concentrations to the cell cultures blocked mitosis but did not block DNA synthesis, as adjudged by the accumulation of DNA to pre-mitotic levels in non-dividing cells. Concurrently, the total cellular RNA and the total cell mass of these cells increased well beyond normal values, with an over-development of the nucleolar apparatus. Actinomycin D in doses which blocked mitotic activity (0·075 μg/ml) appeared to block almost all synthetic activities; in lower doses which permitted a 90% increase in cell number following 48 h exposure to the drug (0·0375 μg/ml) the average DNA content of each cell was very close to that of the control population while the mass value and the RNA value were significantly diminished, indicating marked inhibition of the synthesis of RNA and proteins. The inhibition of the synthesis of RNA and proteins by actinomycin D was even more evident in cell populations treated with nitrogen mustard. In all the experiments discussed, inhibition of RNA synthesis appeared to be the primary effect of actinomycin D, with a consequent inhibition of protein synthesis. Parallel studies on the nucleoli of individual cells with ultraviolet-microscopy and spectrophotometry supported the concept that the nucleolus-associated chromatin is concerned primarily with the synthesis of ribosomal RNA—either directly, or by the mediation of a "messenger" fraction of RNA.

III. Tissue Culture in Screening Systems in Cancer Chemotherapy

Drug screening refers to the initial testing of chemical compounds and other substances for some specific form of pharmacological activity, the immediate goal being to provide "leads" for a further and more intensive study of compounds which show promise and indications for the design of others structurally related to them. The main function of a screening procedure is to limit the number of potentially useful compounds by rejecting inactive substances with a minimum of testing and retaining active ones for further study. A major problem is to devise laboratory tests which reflect the type of activity desired in man, and a minimum requirement is that the laboratory test should reveal any compound which would be active in man.

Screening tests in cancer chemotherapy are usually carried out using either spontaneous or induced and generally transplantable neoplasms of laboratory animals, but as screening tools these are expensive. Further, there is a wide variability of response among experimental neoplasms to chemotherapeutic agents and, because of the relative paucity of reliable clinical data, comparisons of studies of antitumour activity in experimental and human neoplasms are hazardous (Gellhorn and Hirschberg, 1955).

Tissue-Culture systems have recently been introduced into screening programmes for cancer chemotherapeutic agents, the principal rationale for their use being based upon the fact that the tissue used is a human cancer.

A. CELL-CULTURE SYSTEMS

1. *Introduction*

In 1948, Ormsbee and Cornman established a procedure for the systematic testing *in vitro* of substances with possible antitumoral activity. Since 1955 cell-culture screening systems have been investigated intensively. Eagle and Foley (1956) reported that of a number of agents known to have antitumour effects in animals or man, a large proportion were highly cytotoxic against several human and animal cells cultured *in vitro,* whilst several compounds without antitumour activity did not show significant cytotoxicity against these cells. These observations have been extended to a series of two hundred compounds (Eagle and Foley, 1958a, b), selected to include known antitumour compounds as well as agents highly active in other biological systems but not known to possess antitumour activity. No systematic difference in susceptibility of cell lines derived from normal and from malignant tissues to the various agents was found. The tumour-active compounds of the series were significantly more cytotoxic than the tumour-inactive compounds. Of the sixty-eight compounds with known *in vivo* antitumour activity, studied in two or more experimental systems, 79% inhibited cell growth by 50% or more at a concentration of $1{\cdot}0 \times 10^{-4}$ g/ml. Of the ninety-one compounds in the series with no reported antitumour activity, nineteen were cytotoxic at $1{\cdot}0 \times 10^{-4}$ g/ml or less. This correlation between cytotoxicity in cell culture and antitumour activity *in vivo* has been the basis for an *in vitro* screening trial in cell culture by the Cancer Chemotherapy National Service Center (CCNSC) using randomly selected compounds which were also being evaluated for anti-cancer activity in experimental animals. The results of this comparative study on almost 2000 compounds (Schepartz, Macdonald and Leiter, 1961) confirmed that a correlation existed and that this correlation improved with an increasing degree of cytotoxicity.

On this basis cell-culture testing has been introduced into the CCNSC screening programme for all synthetic compounds. The role of cell cultures as a primary screen cannot yet be accurately defined. However, there is little doubt that Tissue Culture can be used as a bioassay in the purification of tumour-active substances in the crude filtrates from bacterial and fungal cultures.

2. *Assay Methods*

Several methods have been reported for the detection and assay of cytotoxic agents *in vitro*. Biesele (1951) has described an assay procedure, based upon the comparison of the toxicities of a given agent to embryonic and sarcomatous cells of the mouse, in which 24-h established roller-tube cultures are dosed with a series of concentrations of the agents to be tested. After a further 24-h incubation each culture is examined under the low power of the microscope, and the damage to the cells assessed on the basis of rounding up, granularity, cellular degeneration and the inhibition of outgrowth beyond that attained before the agent was administered. A more elaborate assessment of cellular damage can be made by oil-immersion phase-contrast microscopy if the cells are cultured on coverslips inserted into the roller tubes and applied to flattened regions of the tube wall with a plasma clot. Further information may be obtained by determining the proportions of mitotic cells and of pyknotic nuclei in the outgrowth.

The tube dilution or broth assay introduced by Eagle and Foley (1956) is better adapted to a large scale screening programme. In this procedure, Eagle's KB strain of human epidermoid carcinoma cells are removed from glass by trypsin, Versene or mechanical scraping and the dispersed cells centrifuged and resuspended in complete medium or diluted to an inactive concentration of dispersing agent. About 50,000 cells in 1 ml medium are then implanted in a series of replicate 15 mm screwcap culture tubes and incubated at a 10° angle at 37°C. After 24 h the original medium is removed and fresh medium containing the drug is added. The cultures are re-fed at 72 h and the cell-protein content is determined 1 or 2 days later. Smith, Lummis and Grady (1959) have simplified this assay by using a cell suspension diluted to a concentration of 10–20 μg cell-protein per ml. 3·9 ml of this suspension are added to each culture tube to which 0·1 ml drug or suitable control material has already been added. The test is terminated after 72 h, and thus provides a more rapid test by eliminating the need for re-feeding the cultures. A modification in which the cells are incubated for 24 h before the addition of the drug, together with fresh medium, may also be found useful. The determination of cytotoxicity is based on measuring the inhibition of cell-protein synthesis. The initial cell-protein per tube (C_0) in an aliquot of inoculum or in a sample of control tubes at the time of drug addition, and the final cell-protein per tube in control (C) and treated (T) tubes are estimated using the Folin-Ciocalteu phenol reagent (Oyama and Eagle, 1956).

The estimation of protein in tubes containing medium but no cells is essential as it has been found that up to 30 μg protein from the medium adheres to the glass of each tube. The inhibition of cell-protein production may be calculated for each dose from $\frac{T - C_0}{C - C_0}$. The critical factor in these assays is the degree of cell multiplication and a satisfactory experiment provides at least a sixfold increase in the final cell-protein of the control tubes.

Rightsel, Schultz, Muething and McLean (1956) described a simple, rapid and inexpensive method for virus and drug assays in Tissue-Culture systems using a moulded vinyl plastic panel containing a series of depressions. The optical properties of the plastic permitted the microscopic examination of each chamber in the plate. This technique has been used by Toplin (1959a, b). Standardized inocula of HeLa or other serially propagated cell lines are exposed to the drug under test for 5 days at 37°C, the inhibitory activity being measured in terms of the concentrations required to produce cytopathic changes in the cells and to produce complete cell destruction. Despite the more stringent end-point, i.e. overt morphological damage, the results reported for a series of compounds tested in this system correlate, in general, qualitatively with the results reported by Eagle and Foley (1956, 1958a, b) in growth inhibitory assays. However, certain drugs, e.g. 6-mercaptopurine, were found to inhibit cell growth at concentrations far below those that resulted in cytopathic effects. The cell cultures appeared "frozen" on the plastic surface although cell growth and metabolism, as indicated by acid production, had ceased. More recently, Toplin (1961) has described the results of a comparative study of 17,000 antibiotic beers and filtrates tested in this system and in three mouse-tumour systems (S 180, Ca 755 and L 1210). The correlation of *in vitro* activity, at a dilution of 1:32 or greater, with *in vivo* activity (S 180, 49%; Ca 755, 64%; L 1210, 68%) suggests that increasing *in vitro* activity does increase the probability of activity *in vivo* and that this type of *in vitro* method might be used profitably to "enrich" the number of active filtrates submitted for *in vivo* screening and to follow the activity during fractionation and purification of antibiotic beers.

Jacquez (1962), also using the plastic panel technique described by Rightsel *et al.* (1956), determined the "differential toxicity index" of a series of compounds of known biological activity for HeLa cells and for primary explants of mouse bone-marrow cells. Although there was considerable variation in the ID_{50} values (the dose inhibiting growth to 50% of control growth) on repeated testing, there was, in general, far less variation in the "differential toxicity index" which was calculated as the log ID_{50} for bone-marrow cells minus log ID_{50} for HeLa cells. Of the nineteen compounds studied, six were more toxic for marrow cells than HeLa cells, seven were essentially equitoxic for both cell lines, while three had an ID_{50} for HeLa cells which was less by one log unit or more than the ID_{50} for mouse bone-marrow cells. The results for Methotrexate were inconclusive because of the considerable variation observed in repeated assays, whilst two compounds were of such low toxicity that the differential toxicity index could not be determined.

McAllister, Grunmeier, Coriell and Blakemore (1959) have used a modification of the cytotoxic metabolic inhibition test for the assay of inhibitory agents, in which serial dilutions of the test substances are incubated at 37°C for 14 days with known numbers of HeLa cells in suspension culture under a seal of mineral oil. The substrate contains phenol red and the results are measured in terms of pH changes as judged by the colour changes of the indicator dye. Tubes containing more than 2000 HeLa cells in normal control diluent change colour from red (pH 7·6) to yellow (pH 7·0). Tubes in which antitumour agents prevent the metabolism of HeLa cells gradually change from red to purple (pH 8·0 +). End-points of cytotoxicity are read as any pH greater than 7·0 and the results can be expressed in terms of the number of cells killed per mg of antitumour agent. Kääriäinen (1962) has used a similar metabolic inhibition test with the plastic panel technique.

Miyamura (1956) has described a disc-plate method for the assay of cytotoxic agents in which the cytotoxic activity is indicated by the inhibition of methylene-blue reduction by Ehrlich ascites cells suspended in an agar medium and incubated at 37°C for 8 h. This method has been confirmed and extended by Yamazaki, Nitta, Hikiji, Nogi, Takeuchi, Yamamoto and Umezawa (1956) and Di Paolo and Moore (1957), whilst Miyamura and Niwayama (1959) have adapted it for use with agar suspensions of HeLa cells. Schuurmans, Duncan and Olson (1960) have further modified the procedure for use with S 180 cells to allow for growth of the cells during the assay period.

Grady, Lummis and Smith (1960a) and Siminoff and Hursky (1960a) have used a system which differs from the agar-suspension methods described in that the cells are grown on glass and the resultant monolayers are overlaid with an agar maintenance medium. Samples of the material under test are placed on the agar surface and the zones of cytotoxicity produced can be detected after incubation overnight, or for up to 4 days if a second layer of overlay agar is added. The cells are fixed and stained after washing off the agar overlay. This method depends upon the removal of injured and dead cells from the glass from within the zone of inhibition. Unfortunately the trauma of the removal of the agar layer is superimposed on that of the action of the drug and may confuse the results. Renis, Johnson and Bhuyan (1962) have recently described a disc-plate method using Eagle's KB cells grown on a collagen gel. A suspension of KB cells (5×10^6 cells per ml) in Eagle's medium is placed on the collagen gel and, after incubation for 2–3 h to allow the cells to become attached, the fluid medium is removed and paper discs containing the cytotoxic agents are placed on the collagen gel. After overnight incubation, neutral red is applied to the plates. The healthy live cells remain attached to the collagen and are stained, while the injured cells within the toxic zones are washed away, leaving a clear unstained zone. The diameters of these cytotoxic zones are measured. Renis *et al.* have reported a linear log dose-response relation for the antibiotics tested.

Bhuyan, Renis and Smith (1962) have compared the cytotoxic activities of various antibiotics, metabolic inhibitors and miscellaneous chemicals against Eagle's KB cells in broth dilution assays, in agar suspension disc-plate assays and in collagen-plate assays. No direct relationship was observed between the inhibitory activities of agents as determined by the three assay methods which measure different aspects of cell inhibition—inhibition of growth and protein production in the broth assay, inhibition of dye-reducing ability in the agar-disc-plate assay and removal of cells from the gel surface in the collagen-plate assay. When there is a discrepancy between the assays, a compound being active in the broth tubes on the one hand and inactive in collagen or agar plates on the other hand, three explanations may be considered: either the agent prevents the attachment of KB cells to glass, or it is most active against cells during their rapid growth phase, or it does not diffuse through collagen or agar. A drug which specifically inhibits the dehydrogenase system would produce a large zone of inhibition in the agar plate assay without necessarily showing comparable activity in the broth dilution or collagen-plate assays.

The choice of *in vitro* assay procedure in the comparative assessment of cytotoxic agents must, at present, be regarded as arbitrary. The broth dilution assay, in which the criterion of activity is inhibition of cell growth and protein production, would appear to be the most relevant to the problems of primary drug screening. However, although the method is highly sensitive and reproducible, it is still somewhat cumbersome and time consuming. The various disc-plate methods appear to be of greatest value in the purification of tumour-active substances in crude fermentation filtrates. They are simple, rapid, and easily adapted to bioautography in which the fermentation filtrates are chromatographed on paper in various solvent systems, the developed paper strips being applied to suitably prepared mammalian cells in agar- or collagen-plate cultures (Miyamura, 1956; Di Paolo and Moore, 1957; Grady *et al.*, 1960b; Siminoff and Hursky, 1960b; Renis *et al.*, 1962; Schuurmans *et al.*, 1964). Oda and Yamamoto (1959) have described a one-step bioautograph procedure in which chromatographic and electrophoretic paper strips are sprayed with a suspension of Ehrlich ascites cells. After incubation, the strips are sprayed with 2, 6-dichlorophenolindophenol, utilizing the inhibition of cellular dehydrogenase activity as the indicator of cytotoxicity. Such procedures have proved to be powerful tools in an antibiotic screening programme (Peterson and Reineke, 1950), providing early characterization of the antibiotic activity, determining whether single or multiple activities are present and giving early information regarding the solubility characteristics and possible extraction behaviour of the active substances.

3. *Design of the Screening Procedure*

The design of the screening procedure adopted by the CCNSC is of interest. The tube-dilution assay introduced by Eagle and Foley (1956) and simplified by Smith, Lummis and Grady (1959) is used. Three to five logarithmically spaced dose levels are used for each test substance (e.g. 1, 10 and 100 μg/ml for synthetic compounds) with two tubes per dose level. About 50–75 materials are evaluated at one time using a common set of controls. The number of baseline and control tubes (N) is calculated from the formula $N = 2\sqrt{n}$ where n is the number of materials to be tested. This procedure ensures optimal use of the cell cultures (Finney, 1952). A positive control compound is included with alternate control groups. The ED_{50} is the calculated dose which inhibits growth, measured in terms of cell-protein synthesis, to 50% of control growth in 3 days after drug addition. An estimate of the reproducibility of the ED_{50} has been made from the results of repeated tests with positive control compounds. The ED_{50} estimates are log-normally distributed with a standard deviation of 0·208 (giving a 2·61 error ratio, $P = 0{\cdot}95$). As expected, reproducibility is better when 5 dose levels, spaced at 0·3 log units are used than when 3 dose levels at 1·0 log units are used (Leiter, Abbott, Macdonald and Schepartz, 1964).

It is clear that the precision of a single estimate of the ED_{50} is insufficient to determine the acceptance or rejection of a compound in a mass screening programme. Davies (1958), Armitage and Schneiderman (1958), Litchfield (1958) and Dunnett (1961) have shown that inactive compounds can be eliminated most efficiently by sequential procedures—a series of repetitive tests with prescribed criteria for acceptance or rejection. The choice of criteria involves balancing the risk of missing a good drug against the risk of accepting a poor one. The operating characteristic curve, which gives the theoretical relationship between the probability of acceptance and the activity of the drug under consideration, may be compared with the experimental results on repeated tests with known positive and negative agents, to ascertain whether the procedure is achieving the desired object.

In developing the CCNSC screening procedure, Armitage and Schneiderman (1958) first specified the level of drug activity they wished to accept, the probability of its acceptance and the form of the operating characteristic curve. They then calculated the acceptance and rejection rules required for these specifications. A two stage sequential test has been introduced for the KB-cell tube-dilution assay, the criteria for rejection or acceptance of synthetic compounds being shown in Table I.

TABLE I

Test number	Critical value for average ED_{50} (μg/ml)	Action if critical value is Exceeded	Not exceeded
1	6	Reject	Test again
2	4	Reject	Accept

Clearly inactive materials are rejected after one test, borderline materials after two tests, whilst truly active materials are tested at least twice before undergoing confirmatory tests in an independent laboratory.

The degree of cytotoxicity required in cell-culture testing depends upon the purpose for which the information will be used. For correlation with *in vivo* antitumour activity the criterion of positive effect for synthetic compounds is 50% or more inhibition of growth at 100 μg/ml (the critical ED_{50}). For selecting materials for re-synthesis and further evaluation *in vivo,* the critical ED_{50} is 4 μg/ml—a value chosen to select 10% of the compounds tested. For selecting materials for clinical evaluation, without regard to their activity in animal tumour systems, a critical ED_{50} of 1 μg/ml has been chosen in order to select 1–2% of the compounds tested.

A major criticism of the use of cell-culture screening in cancer chemotherapy arises from the lack of methods by which chemotherapeutic indices of Tissue-Culture positive compounds can be calculated and the relative merits of these compounds compared. No systematic differences in susceptibility of cell lines derived from normal and from malignant tissues to various agents was found in the study reported by Eagle and Foley (1958b). It is therefore possible that the cell-culture screening systems will select highly cytotoxic agents of little therapeutic value. The comparative study of almost 2000 compounds by Schepartz *et al.* (1961) confirming that a correlation existed between the degree of cytotoxicity in cell culture and antitumour activity *in vivo* gives some hope that this will not prove to be correct.

4. *Effect of Assay Conditions*

As with other pharmacological systems, the precise conditions of assay in cell culture may modify the results obtained. Levintow and Eagle (1961) have reviewed the role of serum supplements in cell-culture media (see also Vol. 1, Chaps. 8, 16 and 17). The evidence indicates that both the growth-promoting activity of serum protein and its action in enhancing the attachment of cells to glass may be related to small molecular weight compounds contributed to the substrate by the serum protein. However, the precise biochemical nature of most of these factors is uncertain. Wrba (1962) has reviewed the growth-stimulating and growth-inhibitory factors described in sera and tissues. The studies of Saxén and Penttinen (1961) indicate that permanent differences exist between fresh human sera in their growth controlling capacity and that these differences may be related to low density proteins. Fedoroff and Doerr (1962) have reported a natural cytotoxic system in human sera which can be demonstrated in cell culture, whilst Björklund (1960) has described a cytotoxic factor which occurs in human serum in combination with an inhibitor. The "nerve growth factor" is discussed later in this chapter.

The presence of these factors in serum supplements may influcnce the results obtained in cell-culture assays. Further, it should be stressed that in any study of the action of inhibitors of cell growth, substrate competition must be considered. Giuffre, Perlman and Jackson (1961) found that the sensitivity of Earle's strain L–929 mouse fibroblasts to the cytotoxic effects of several actinomycins varied in different media, the cells being less sensitive when grown in media supplemented with calf serum than when grown in media containing proteose peptone in place of the serum or in Waymouth's synthetic medium MB 752/1. The observation on the decreased sensitivity of cells growing rapidly in response to the usual serum supplement, in contrast to the greater sensitivity in cells growing more slowly in serum-free media, may explain differences observed in the inhibitory activity of actinomycin D. Bennett, Brindle, Giuffre, Jackson, Kowald, Pansy, Perlman and Trejo (1962) have made similar observations with another antibiotic, SQ 15, 859. Cobb and Walker (1961), in a study of the effects of heterologous, homologous and autologous sera on cells *in vitro,* have reported that the sensitivity of explants of human tumours to a number of anticancer agents is greater in media supplemented with horse serum or pooled human serum than with autologous serum.

The effect of temperature on cells *in vitro* exposed to the action of drugs has been studied by Schmähl and Druckrey (1956), using Yoshida ascites cells, Walker carcinoma 256 cells and Jensen sarcoma cells, incubated for short periods *in vitro* with alkylating agents and subsequently implanted *in vivo*. To produce the same degree of inhibition of subsequent tumour growth after incubating Yoshida cells *in vitro* with nitrogen mustard (HN2) at 5°C, five to six times the drug concentration effective at 37°C was required. HN2 oxide was apparently completely inactive at 5°C since a 3000-fold increase in the concentration active at 37°C was still ineffective at 5°C. Mahaley and Woodhall (1961), using cell-clump suspensions in Ringer's solution of VX2 rabbit carcinoma, found a marked increase in inactivation of neoplastic cells after *in vitro* incubation with drugs at 37°C compared with incubation at 20°C, the inactivation being measured in terms of the weights of tumours produced in host animals inoculated with the incubated cells. Incubation at 42°C produced an even greater inactivation of tumour cells.

Takaki, Sugi, Katsuta, Takahashi, Kamiya and Takahashi (1960), in studying the effect of chromomycin on HeLa-cell cultures, observed that the time in the growth cycle at which the drug is added may affect the results obtained, the growth-inhibiting effect being greater at the time of inoculation than on the fourth day of cultivation.

Lichter, Wellham and Sigel (1964) have demonstrated marked differences in the rate of action of inhibiting agents in KB-cell culture. Some compounds, highly potent when allowed to remain in contact with the cells for 72 h, show no effect on short contact, whilst others, relatively less potent in the standard 72-h exposure test, do destroy or damage cells in a matter of minutes. The potential usefulness of such rapidly acting agents in local or regional perfusion therapy is emphasized.

5. *Cell-line Sensitivity to Inhibitory Agents*

The concept of differential sensitivities of cell lines to inhibitory agents, reviewed recently by Foley and Epstein (1964), has led to sensitivity assays with individual tumour specimens—an attractive study—and of direct application to the selection of specific chemotherapeutic agents for the treatment of individual patients. Preliminary studies by Wright, Cobb, Gumport, Golomb and Safadi (1957) on the relationship between inhibitory activity in cell cultures and clinical response to chemotherapeutic agents gave encouraging results, and later studies (Golomb, Cobb, Walker and Wright, 1962) showed a positive correlation between *in vitro* and *in vivo* results in thirteen of sixteen cases treated by regional perfusion.

The *in vitro* methods used have varied widely. McDonald and Cole (1959) used primary explant cultures of human tumours grown for 14 days in roller tubes and assessed the effects of the anticancer compounds tested (nitrogen mustards, thio-tepa, triethylene melamine and actinomycin D) in terms of cytopathological changes and inhibition of growth. The results obtained with individual compounds were reproducible in replicate cultures of the same tumours but varied when other tumours were used. Golomb *et al.* (1962) used a similar culture system—primary plasma-clot cultures rotated in Porter flasks—and assessed the effects of the compounds tested according to the rate and extent of cellular migration. Di Paolo and Dowd (1961) used the inhibition of dehydrogenase activity in agar suspensions of homogenized human tumour biopsies to permit the simultaneous *in vitro* assay of several potential chemotherapeutic agents against the same tumour specimen. On the basis of this method, forty-two patients received the selected drug, but only ten showed improvement. Ambrose, Andrews, Easty, Field and Wylie (1962) used monolayer cultures of primary explants of human tumours and kept them in chambers which permitted microscopic examination and cell counting *in situ*. The *in vitro* results were encouraging, but more extensive studies should be undertaken. It must be stressed that the therapeutic value of sensitivity in explant cultures has yet to be established by well-designed and controlled clinical correlative studies.

B. ORGAN-CULTURE SYSTEMS

Organ culture of embryonic tissues which are subject to invasion by neoplastic cells offers interesting possibilities for the development of screening systems for cancer chemotherapy which might assess tumour invasiveness and, at the same time, provide methods for the determination *in vitro* of chemotherapeutic indices of the agents studied. Active invasion of embryonic fragments of mesonephros from 6–9-day-old chick embryos results when they are grown in juxtaposition with explants of mouse or human tumours (Wolff, 1956; Wolff and Wolff, 1961, 1963). The malignant cells adapt rapidly to their new environment, but retain the cytological and histological characteristics of the original tumour, despite the rapid growth of the tumour mass and the invasion of the embryonic chick kidney.

More recently Easty and Easty (1963) have described an organ-culture system for the study of tumour invasiveness, in which the infrequency of mitosis makes possible such investigations in the absence of extensive tumour growth. They use a modification of Trowell's (1954) technique in which small fragments of tissue are placed on a rayon strip laid on a stainless steel grid, the underside of which is in contact with the medium, usually of Eagle's HeLa medium with 10% calf serum. The normal tissues (mouse kidney, liver, lung or skin) and tumour tissues (Harding-Passey melanoma, Sarcoma 180 or a solid transplantable mouse myeloma) are placed in apposition (side by side, overlapping or on top of each other) and are maintained in an atmosphere of 95% oxygen and 5% carbon dioxide at 37°C for 7 days. Fusion of the normal and tumour tissues occurs in a few days and examination of sections after 7 days in culture reveals infiltration of tumour cells into the adjacent normal organized tissues, either singly or in small groups.

These types of culture offer exceptionally favourable conditions for the study of tumour invasiveness, as the two tissues—normal and cancerous—are directly apposed in a simplified system, thus avoiding the complex considerations which exist in the whole animal. However, there is as yet no method for measuring the inhibitory action of drugs in these assay systems which is of sufficient simplicity to permit application to large-scale studies.

Leighton (1960) has suggested an assay system utilizing aggregates of neoplastic cells maintained on the surface of a plasma clot and overlaid with nutrient medium. The inhibitory activity of a compound can then be measured by alterations in the pattern of the outgrowth of cells emerging from the original implant on to the surface of the clot. Leighton suggested that this system might lead to the identification of new classes of inhibitory compounds. Kline and Acker (1960) have described the comparative assay of compounds against the same cell lines cultured on coverslips, on the surface of plasma clots and within fragments of human umbilical cord. In all three methods inhibitory activity is demonstrable but the umbilical-cord method requires culturing the cells for about 3 weeks and evaluation by histological section.

More recently Yarnell *et al.* (1964) have reported a method for the study of the responses of human tumour explants to potential anti-tumour agents. The explants are supported on siliconed lens paper and bathed by diffusion from the fluid medium. For assay purposes, nucleic acid synthesis is estimated in control and treated cultures by determining the uptake of ^{32}P into nucleic acids. The results reported are sufficiently encouraging to warrant a larger scale study of the method.

Algard (1963) has compared the responses to hormones of three experimentally induced sex-hormone dependent tumours in cell- and in organ-culture systems. The cell cultures were uninfluenced by the presence or absence of the hormones, although when reimplanted into animals they grew only in the presence of the appropriate exogenous hormones. The organ cultures, on the other hand, all showed enhanced survival and the occurrence of mitoses in the presence of hormones. Algard concludes that the capacity of these neoplasms to respond to hormonal excitation is related to tissue integrity.

C. CELL-VIRUS SYSTEMS

The accumulating evidence for the viral aetiology of a number of mammalian tumours together with recent evidence for the differential inhibition of cellular and viral nucleic acid synthesis has re-awakened interest in cell-virus assay systems in cancer chemotherapy. However, the problems discussed in relation to screening compounds for cytotoxic activity apply with equal force to screening systems for anti-viral drugs. The choice of virus for the screen is analogous to the choice of tumour cell for the anticancer screen. There is no reason to suppose that the RNA viruses will have the same chemotherapeutic sensitivities as the DNA viruses. The attractiveness of using known tumorigenic viruses—for example, the Rous (RNA) virus and the polyoma (DNA) virus—for these studies is evident, but recent work by Trentin, Yabe and Taylor (1962), Huebner, Rowe and Lane (1962) and Girardi, Hilleman and Zwickey (1964) on the oncogenicity of other viruses suggest that useful information may be derived from the study of inhibitory agents in such other cell-virus systems.

Several methods are available for the screening of anti-viral agents in Tissue Culture. Virucidal activity may be determined by incubating the virus with various concentrations of the drug and subsequent titration of the virus-drug suspensions in Tissue Culture. Virustatic activity may be determined by adding the agent in various concentrations to cell cultures a few hours after infection and incubating the cultures for a further 24 h. The active virus present may then be assayed, after cell disruption by freezing at $-70°C$, by titration in fresh cell cultures. In the first case, the drug acts on resting viruses, in the second upon multiplying viruses. The presence of the tissue cells in the virustatic assays adds an additional factor—the cell-drug interaction—which may be of major importance in interpreting the results.

The virus titrations may be carried out by assessing cytopathological changes by low-power microscopy and estimating the dose required to infect 50% of the culture cells; by the lytic plaque technique in Tissue Cultures under agar, using the technique developed by Dulbecco (1952), in which the cytopathology of the virus can be demonstrated by the appearance of macroscopic areas of lysis in the cell sheets; by the Salk colorimetric test (Salk, Youngner and Ward, 1954) which is based upon the viral inhibition of acid production by cells grown in an alkaline medium; or by a haemadsorption test based upon the observation that cells infected with viruses of the influenza or para-influenzal group are)fixed to the surface of red cells. (See Chapter 4.)

Using these methods, an estimate may be made of the virucidal or virustatic ED_{50} of the agents under consideration. The toxicity of the drugs to the cell cultures can be estimated by methods discussed in the section on cell-culture screening systems (pp. 369–370) and, from the information obtained, a therapeutic index may be calculated and a basis established for the acceptance or rejection of the drugs under study.

Herrman, Gabliks, Engle and Perlman (1960), Siminoff (1961) and Rada and Závada (1962) have described modifications of the plaque method for the assay of anti-viral and anti-cell activity using virus-infected cell cultures. The method consists essentially of an agar overlay on monolayers of chick embryo cells, paper discs or cups containing the compounds to be assayed being placed on the surface of the infected agar overlay and incubated for 4 days. The monolayers are stained—with iodonitrotetrazolium chloride, with neutral red or with toluidine blue following fixation with Bouin's solution—to reveal plaque formation and zones of plaque inhibition. Siminoff (1961) also described the application of agar-cell suspensions to the study of anti-viral compounds.

These agar-diffusion methods can be used both qualitatively and quantitatively and are suitable for the direct assay of paper chromatograms of antibiotic beers. Cytotoxic effects of the substances used may be distinguished and it may be possible by paper chromatography to separate toxic impurities from the compounds of interest.

IV. Tissue Culture in the Study of Pharmacologically Active Agents

In the preceding sections we have discussed the general scope and limitations of Tissue-Culture procedures as applied to the study of pharmacologically active agents. In this section we propose to discuss five types of problem in more detail: the problems associated with the mode of action and development of resistance to the antifolate drugs Methotrexate and aminopterin; the actions of lathyrogens on constituents of connective tissue and its derivatives, model experiments on the induction of acute porphyria, drug-induced cytoplasmic vacuolation in Tissue Culture and lastly the role of Tissue Culture in the isolation and purification of the "nerve growth factor".

A. ANTIFOLATE DRUGS

Folic acid and its natural metabolites, the 5,6,7,8-tetrahydro derivatives (Fig. 1), are primarily concerned in biochemical reactions which involve the transfer of single carbon units at the oxidation level of methyl formate or formaldehyde. The labile carbon atom may be attached to the pteridine moiety in position 5, or to the nitrogen atom 10 of the *p*-aminobenzoyl moiety, or it may be arranged as a methylene bridge ($-CH_2-$) between positions 5 and 10. The different forms are probably interconvertible and carry out the following important coenzymatic functions: (1) the methylation of deoxyuridylate to thymidylate; (2) supplying carbon 8 and then carbon 2 in the *de novo* synthesis of the purine ring; (3) the interconversion of the following three pairs of amino acids—homocysteine and methionine, serine and glycine, and histidine and glutamate. Another important function of folinic acid (the 5-formyltetrahydrofolate) was established by Jacobson (1954a, b, c), who demonstrated that it was essential for cell division and particularly for the step from metaphase to anaphase when the two longitudinal halves of each chromosome (the chromatids) part.

Jacobson, using the principle of "inhibition analysis", demonstrated that when the function of folinic acid was blocked by aminopterin (the

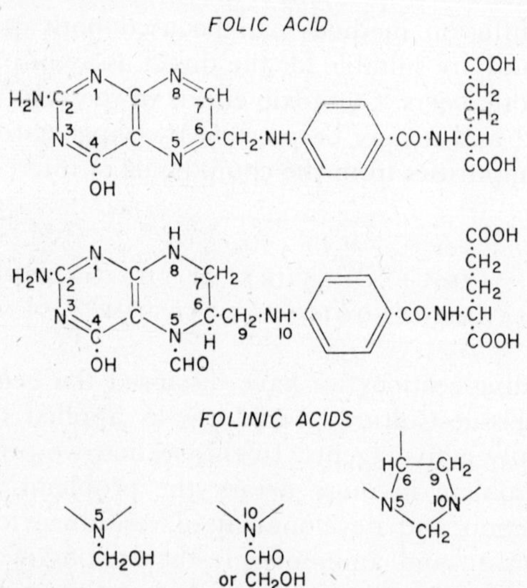

FIG. 1. Formulae of folic acid (top) and the members of the folinic acid group; all 5,6,7,8-tetrahydro derivatives of folic acid. The 5-formyl derivative of folinic acid is shown in the middle, and below are 5-hydroxymethyl, 10-formyl, 10-hydroxy methyl and 5,10-methylene derivatives.

4-amino analogue of folic acid; Fig. 2), cells would continue entering mitosis for some time and proceed through prophase and metaphase, but could not enter into anaphase. Thus within 15 min after the direct application of the antagonist to cultures of fast-growing chick embryo osteoblasts or fibroblasts the percentage distribution of the mitotic phases was characteristically altered: instead of 35–40% of all dividing cells being in metaphase and 15–20% in anaphase, 15 min after the application of the antagonist 60–70% of all dividing cells were in metaphase and 0–5% in anaphase. Those cells which had reached the anaphase stage of mitosis at the moment of direct application of the antagonist continued through anaphase to telophase and thus completed division.

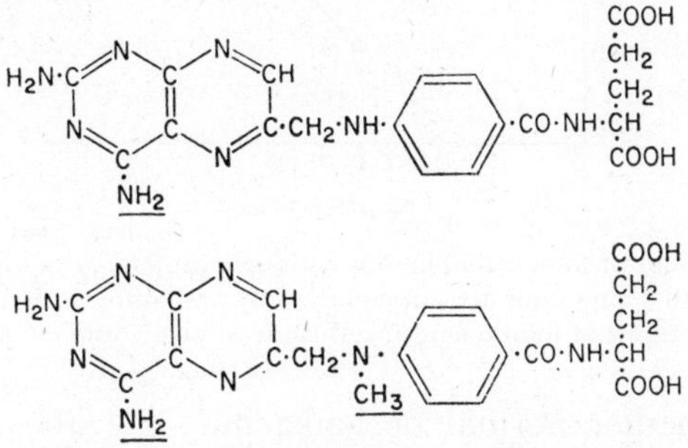

FIG. 2. Formulae of two folic acid antagonists: aminopterin (top) = 4-aminofolic acid; methotrexate (Amethopterin) (below) = 4-amino-10-methylfolic acid.

When both antagonist and folinic acid were applied simultaneously and directly to the cells, a complete protection from the action of aminopterin could be achieved, provided folinic acid was given in excess. The specificity of folinic acid to protect cells, almost instantaneously, from the action of the inhibitor (aminopterin) was demonstrated by the complete failure of folic acid to counteract the effect of the inhibitor. When cells were pre-incubated for 1–48 h with folic acid no protection could be shown. These cells were apparently unable to convert folic to folinic acid. The concentrations of folinic acid required to protect cells completely from the inhibitory action of aminopterin were determined for five levels of the antagonist and are illustrated in Fig. 3. Aronow (1959), using L-strain mouse fibroblasts, showed that Amethopterin (methotrexate, the 4-amino-10-methyl derivative of folic acid; Fig. 2) operates also as a competitive antagonist of folinic acid.

As folic acid antagonists were shown to arrest dividing cells in metaphase in a wide range of tissues, from embryonic cells to mouse and human intestinal epithelial cells and human and mouse bone-

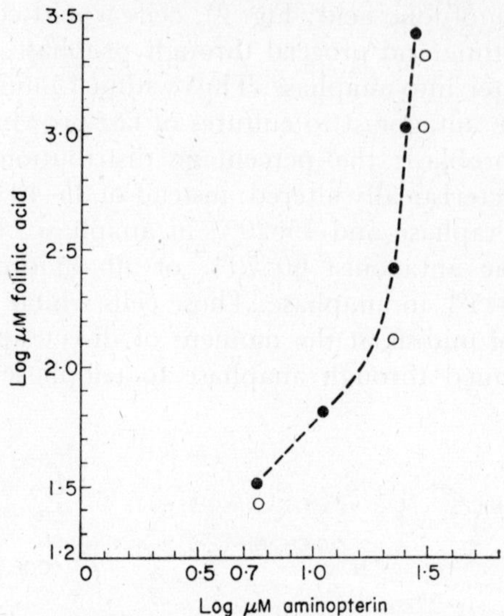

FIG. 3. ●, Concentrations of folinic acid giving complete protection to dividing cells against aminopterin when both compounds are applied directly and simultaneously to cells in tissue cultures. ○, Concentrations of folinic acid insufficient to give complete protection.

marrow cells whether normal or leukaemic, the above observations may be taken to indicate that folinic acid is a compound essential for the step from metaphase to anaphase.

The study of the effect of folic acid antagonists on cells growing *in vitro* led to another interesting observation which contributed to the understanding of a perplexing phenomenon, namely the "resistance" of cells to folic acid antagonists, as illustrated in the following example. Cultures of chick-embryo osteoblasts or fibroblasts showed the striking arrest of dividing cells by aminopterin within 15 min. When such cultures were observed after 24 h they had almost completely overcome the inhibition caused by aminopterin and were indistinguishable from control cultures.

However, these cells were not independent of folinic acid. A second application of aminopterin after 24 h caused the same metaphase arrest within 15 min as had the first application. It appeared that the cells had inactivated aminopterin since the culture medium containing the aminopterin had no inhibitory effect on dividing cells of other cultures. Aminopterin solutions, kept under sterile conditions at 37°C as controls for 24 or 48 h, without contact with cells, retained their full inhibitory effect on dividing cells. It was found that chick-embryo osteoblasts and fibrobasts converted aminopterin into an inactive compound by an intramolecular rearrangement (Fig. 4); the cells did

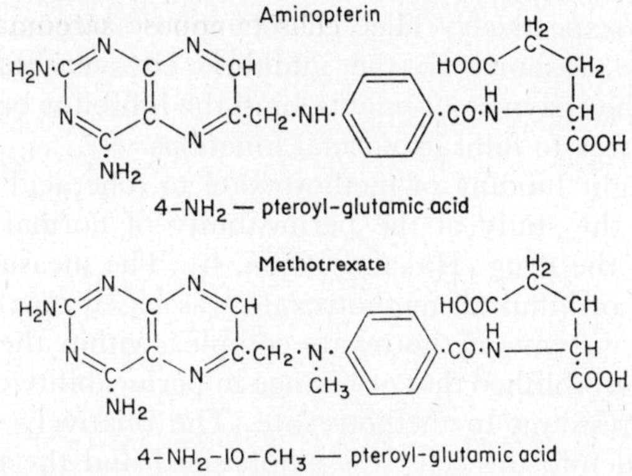

Aminopterin

4-NH_2 — pteroyl-glutamic acid

Methotrexate

4-NH_2-10-CH_3 — pteroyl-glutamic acid

FIG. 4. Formulae of the two folic acid antagonists, aminopterin and methotrexate, redrawn to illustrate the hypothesis of extracellular inactivation of these compounds by ring closure of the terminal glutamic acid (see Jacobson and Cathie, 1960b).

not break down the aminopterin. The inactive form of the inhibitor, prepared in a pure form, can be re-converted to its active form by exposure to very mild acid or alkali at room temperature for 15–20 min (Jacobson and Cathie, 1960a).

The extracellular inactivation of aminopterin and methotrexate is an important mechanism by which cells become resistant to these compounds. Several normal tissues and leukaemic cells (of the acute form of childhood leukaemia) share this quality with embryonic cells grown *in vitro*.

Thus the principle of inhibition analysis applied to cells growing *in vitro* has led to two interesting observations: the function of folinic acid during mitosis and a new extracellular mechanism for the development of drug resistance (Jacobson, 1965).

Another mechanism of resistance to folic acid antagonists has been studied by Hakala, Zakrzewski and Nichol (1961). This concerns an intracellular process. Methotrexate (Amethopterin) forms a complex with the enzyme folate reductase. This enzyme normally operates by converting folate or dihydrofolate to the biologically active form of the coenzyme, i.e. tetrahydrofolate. The function of folate reductase is essential, as in the transfer of the methylene group of folinic acid to deoxyuridylate (to form thymidylate) folinic acid is oxidized to the dihydro form. Hakala *et al.* found that cells of the mouse sarcoma 180, growing *in vitro* in the presence of methotrexate, became resistant to the drug. This resistance was associated with an increase of the enzyme folate reductase. The resistant cells contained 65–155 times more of this enzyme than the methotrexate-sensitive control cells, depending on whether the cells were grown in a medium containing hypoxanthine or thymidine respectively. The cells of mouse sarcoma 180 grown *in vitro* achieved resistance to the inhibitor by synthesizing sufficient quantities of the enzyme not only to bind the inhibitor but also to leave some enzyme free to fulfil its normal functions.

The very tight binding of methotrexate to folic acid reductase has been used in the study of the permeability of normal and resistant S 180 cells to the drug (Hakala, 1965a, b). The measurement of the apparent rate of influx of methotrexate was based on the rate of formation of the enzyme-methotrexate complex within the cells. By this method it was established that no change in permeability occurred when cells became resistant to methotrexate. The relatively slow influx of this compound into the cells was emphasized and the net influx was shown to be dependent on at least four processes: a slow influx, apparently by diffusion; a rapid, energy-dependent efflux; the very rapid binding of inhibitor to intracellular folic acid reductase, and the slow dissociation of the latter complex. The dissociation of the enzyme-methotrexate complex appeared to be of importance in determining the degree of resistance of cells to this inhibitor. The net rate of influx of methotrexate could be increased by raised temperatures, lowered pH, by calcium ions, 2, 4-dinitrophenol and depletion of riboflavin. It might be possible to increase the growth-inhibitory potency several-fold by a combination of these factors.

B. LATHYROGENS

Tissue Culture methods have been used in the study of experimental lathyrism, a condition giving, *in vivo,* deformed bones, fragile connective tissue and aortic rupture (Geiger, Steenbock and Parsons, 1933; Ponseti and Baird, 1952). Since the aortic rupture is preceded by changes in the elastic laminae, McCallum and Paul (1961) tested the effect of lathyrogens on the formation of elastic fibres in chick-embryo heart cultures. They found that lathyrogens, as for example β-aminopropionitrile, inhibited the production of these fibres, while chemically related non-lathyrogens did not. From this they concluded that the changes in the elastic laminae constitute a block in synthesis rather than a degeneration (McCallum, 1965).

Burzynski (1963) and Bickley and Orbison (1964) tested the effect of adding a lathyrogen to fibroblast cell-cultures and reported an increased synthesis of protein-bound hexose and an increased uptake of sulphate, respectively. Schryver and Biggers (1963) produced the changes of lathyrism in chick-embryo tibiotarsi grown in organ culture by adding methylene-aminoacetonitrile or aminoacetonitrile to the chemically defined medium. Growth in length was inhibited and the structure of the matrix was altered, there being a loss of metachromasia and an increase in water content, some of the explants becoming extremely hydropic. Martin and Goldhaber (1963) using 5-day mouse calvaria cultured in the presence of aminoacetonitrile and L-(^{14}C) proline showed that the salt-soluble collagen from lathyric bones was labelled equally with that from controls grown without aminoacetonitrile, but that the insoluble residue was less strongly labelled in the lathyric bones. From this they deduced that, in collagenous tissues, lathyrogens act by blocking the conversion of the newly synthesized soluble collagen to the mature insoluble form. (See also Vol. 2, Chap. 4.)

C. DRUG-INDUCED ACUTE PORPHYRIA

Granick (1965) used Tissue Cultures as a model to study drug-induced acute porphyria. Suspensions of trypsinized liver cells from 16–17-day-old chick embryos were grown on a coverslip. After 1 day *in vitro* the compounds known to induce acute porphyria were added to the culture medium which consisted of Eagle's basal medium, supplemented with glutamine, 10% foetal bovine serum and penicillin, streptomycin and mycostatin. Within 3–7 h after the addition of the compounds an increased synthesis of porphyrin could be demonstrated by the pink u.v. fluorescence of the liver cells. The maximum fluorescence was reached within 24 h after the application of the drugs. Allylisopropylacetamide was one of the best inducers, but griseofulvin, hexachlorobenzene, sulphonal, sodium phenobarbitone, aminopyrine, methyprylon, glutethimide, mephentoin, sodium diphenylhydantoin, meprobamate and several other drugs also caused a demonstrable increase in porphyrin synthesis in the liver cells. Biochemical analysis showed that all these compounds led to an increase in δ-aminolevulinic acid synthetase activity. That this increase was due not merely to activation of this enzyme, but to its *de novo* synthesis was shown by the blocking effect of the inhibitors of protein synthesis, puromycin (5 μg/ml), mitomycin C (2 μg/ml) and actinomycin D (0·25 μg/ml). Further, the experiments with mitomycin C and actinomycin D indicated that intact DNA was required for the synthesis of δ-aminolevulinic acid synthetase and porphyrin formation (via δ-aminolevulinate and porphobilinogen).

Granick proposes the following normal control mechanism for the synthesis of δ-aminolevulinic acid synthetase (Fig. 5). A regulator gene (RG) synthesizes an apoprotein (Ap) which combines with haem to form a repressor of the operator gene (Op). Haem is known to exert a negative feedback effect on the synthesis of δ-aminolevulinate in *Rhodopseudomonas spheroides* (Burnham and Lascelles, 1963) and

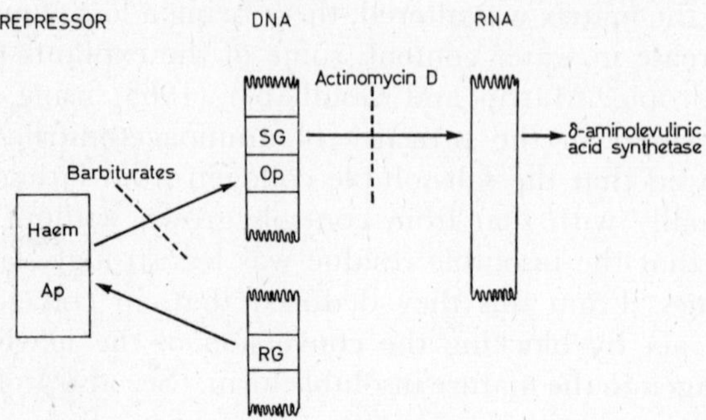

FIG. 5. Proposed control mechanism for the synthesis of δ-aminolevulinic acid synthetase (Granick, 1965).

probably also in rabbit reticulocytes (Karibian and London, 1965). Drugs like barbiturates and griseofulvin which induce chemical porphyria may interact with haem or prevent it combining with the aporepressor to form the repressor. Thus, the operator gene (Op) is no longer inhibited and the structural gene (SG) in the DNA will form the specific messenger RNA required for the increased synthesis of δ-aminolevulinic acid synthetase.

D. DRUG-INDUCED CYTOPLASMIC VACUOLATION IN TISSUE CULTURE

Drug-induced cytoplasmic vacuolation was first reported by Lettré and Albrecht (1941, 1943, 1951) who noted that a number of β-phenyl ethylamines and a variety of other amines, including tyramine (100 μg/ml), ephedrine (150 μg/ml), histamine (200 μg/ml), piperidine (40 μg/ml), isopropylamine (60 μg/ml) and ammonia (15 μg/ml), produced cytoplasmic "aqueous vacuoles" in chick fibroblasts cultured *in vitro*. A number of alkaloids, including aconitine (70 μg/ml) also elicited this phenomenon.

Pomerat and Emerson (1944–5) described vacuolation induced *in vitro* in chick-heart fibroblasts, epithelial cells of chick intestine and lung and in leucocytes from splenic explants after exposure to phenylephrine and naphazoline. Buchsbaum and Kuntz (1954) reported that the vacuolation was reversible. Chick-embryo fibroblasts, treated in a perfusion chamber with appropriate concentrations of morphine sulphate (0·25–3·3 mg/ml), codeine sulphate (3·7 mg/ml), amphetamine sulphate (0·4–1·0 mg/ml) and strychnine (0·5–3·8 mg/ml) produced vacuoles of a size dependent on the concentration and length of exposure to the drug. Complete recovery took place in 1–2 h after removal of the drug.

Belkin, Hardy, Orr and Lachman (1962) have tested a number of autonomic drugs to investigate the mechanism of intracellular vacuole formation by such chemical agents. The experiments were performed *in vitro* at room temperature on mouse ascites-tumour cells (sarcoma 37, Ehrlich carcinoma, hepatoma 129 P and leukaemia L 1210). They found that fourteen of thirty-six drugs, belonging to various autonomic groups, induced vacuoles in concentrations of 1–4mM, the maximum effect appearing in about 3 h. When the vacuolating cells were washed free of the drug and placed in normal balanced salt solution, reversal of the phenomenon was observed, the vacuoles progressively disappearing in 3–4 h. Of the adrenergic drugs tested, amphetamine phosphate, ephedrine hydrochloride and methoxyphenamine hydrochloride produced vacuolation whilst adrenaline and l-noradrenaline did not. Of the sympatholytic drugs tested tolazoline hydrochloride produced a marked vacuolar response. Pilocarpine hydrochloride induced marked cytoplasmic vacuolation in all the cell cultures, but the other parasympathomimetic drugs tested, including acetylcholine chloride and carbachol, were without effect. Physostigmine sulphate produced a marked response although another cholinesterase inhibitor, prostigmine bromide, produced no effect. Of the anticholinergic drugs tested, atropine sulphate, homatropine hydrochloride, hyoscyamine sulphate and hyoscine hydrobromide produced consistent vacuolation although propantheline bromide produced inconsistent responses. Mecamylamine hydrochloride, alone of the ganglionic blocking agents tested, produced marked vacuolation of all the cell cultures.

Experiments with pilocarpine, methoxyphenamine hydrochloride, hyoscine and physostigmine at 37°C on cells of the four mouse ascites tumours showed that there was a marked increase in the rate of formation and number of the vacuoles induced in three of the tumours compared to the response at room temperature.

Human malignant cell lines, HeLa and D189, when treated with pilocarpine (4mM) produced marked vacuolation. However, cultured normal cells of human lung, kidney, skin and muscle and mouse embryo showed a far less pronounced effect, whilst normal mouse-cell suspensions obtained by passing spleen, liver, kidney or testes through a tissue press did not show any vacuole formation after treatment with pilocarpine.

The authors were unable to correlate the structure of the drugs studied or their pharmacological properties with their ability to produce vacuoles, nor could they explain the apparent difference between malignant and normal cells in the vacuolation response to autonomic drugs.

More recently, Yang, Strasser and Pomerat (1965) have used phase contrast time-lapse cinematography in the study of drug-induced vacuolation in primary cultures of chick heart fibroblasts, HeLa cells, an amnion cell line and primary cultures of foetal rat heart. Procaine hydrochloride, procaine amide, cocaine hydrochloride, pilocarpine and ephedrine sulphate (3·7 mM) and atropine sulphate (1 mM) all produced marked cytoplasmic vacuolation, the vacuoles usually starting in the perinuclear area. The vacuoles gradually increased in size and by 12–14 h each cell had developed one or more large central vacuoles which might displace the nucleus or nuclei to the periphery. The vacuoles often coalesced to form a large one and such enlargements were sometimes followed by the expulsion of the vacuole from the cell. At the site of the expulsion a small clear area remained which rapidly grew in size to form a new vacuole. The accumulation of vacuoles did not affect the motility or mitosis of the cells. After the drug had been removed by washing, the vacuoles eventually disappeared completely. Ammonium chloride (1 mM) produced essentially the same phenomenon as the other drugs tested.

The influence of the pH of the external medium on the process of drug induced vacuolation was also examined. In media, adjusted to an acid pH, where the undissociated base was in relatively low concentration, vacuolation was reduced. The authors concluded that penetration of weak bases into the cells may be the factor responsible for vacuole formation which in turn might be a means of counteracting cellular pH changes. Further studies, to determine the vacuolar composition and pH, are needed in order to test this hypothesis.

The study of reversible cytoplasmic vacuolation may help to elucidate the normal processes by which cells cope with deleterious conditions. The capacity of cells to withstand a great deal of chemical and physical stress has been emphasized by these studies, for the concentrations of the drugs used were enormous. For example, the concentration of morphine sulphate used by Buchsbaum and Kuntz (1954)—0·25 mg/ml—would be equivalent to a dose of 17·5 g given to an adult man!

In view of the recent developments in the study of lysosomes (de Reuck and Cameron, 1963) and cytoplasmic vacuolation it would be interesting to correlate these results with the effects of the drugs used on the lysosomal membranes and the related enzymic activity.

E. NERVE GROWTH FACTOR

Tissue-Culture methods have provided a simple and rapid bioassay system for the isolation and identification of nerve growth factor. In 1948, Bueker reported that heterotransplants of mouse sarcoma 180 in chick embryos produced hypertrophy and hyperplasia of the lumbo-dorsal ganglia. Levi-Montalcini (1952) postulated that these effects were due to a diffusable agent released by the tumour into the circulation of the embryo, and tested this hypothesis by implanting the tumour into the chorioallantois of 4-day-old chicks. Although no direct contact was possible between the neoplastic and embryonic tissues, the growth and differentiation of the sympathetic ganglia were selectively enhanced. Levi-Montalcini, Meyer and Hamburger (1954) found that small fragments of sarcomas 180 or 37 placed 1–2 mm from spinal or sympathetic ganglia of chick embryos maintained in hanging-drop Tissue Culture induced within 24 h the precocious production of an excessive number of nerve fibres growing radially in all directions to form a "halo" around the ganglion (Fig. 6). The density of the outgrowth decreased and the length increased with increasing distance from the sarcoma. The authors concluded that the same diffusible agent was responsible for both the *in vitro* and *in vivo* effects on spinal and sympathetic ganglia.

The availability of this clear and rapid *in vitro* assay method (12–18 h) has contributed greatly to the study of the nerve growth factor. Cohen, Levi-Montalcini and Hamburger (1954) localized the factor in the microsomal fraction of the tumour and in the course of further studies Cohen and Levi-Montalcini (1956) isolated it from snake venom and later from the salivary glands of the mouse, rat and hamster (Cohen, 1958), while Levi-Montalcini and Booker (1960a) have demonstrated that it is also present in the serum of adult and weanling mice. Maximal effects were obtained from the serum of adult male mice, the serum of female mice being less effective. The authors pointed out that this sex difference paralleled the sex difference in the size of adult sympathetic nerve cells. Levi-Montalcini and Angeletti (1961) have also demonstrated the presence of nerve growth factor in human serum.

The mouse salivary nerve growth factor has been purified (Cohen, 1960) and is a heat-labile, non-dialysable, antigenically-active protein with a molecular weight of 44,000, completely destroyed by pepsin and chymotrypsin and less completely by trypsin. It is resistant to 0·1 N alkali and destroyed by 0·1 N acid solutions. The snake venom factor appears to differ from the mouse salivary factor despite the similarity in biological properties. The ultracentrifugation pattern of the venom protein showed a single peak with a sedimentation coefficient (S_{20}) of 2·2S, whereas that of the mouse protein was found to be 4·33S. Antigenic difference were also noted. Schenkein and Bueker (1964) have demonstrated the presence of two essential components in the mouse salivary nerve growth factor, one of which is dialysable. The

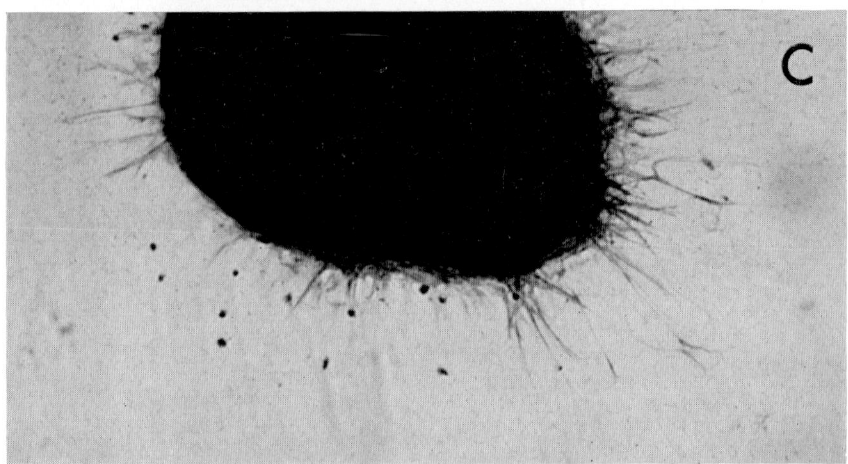

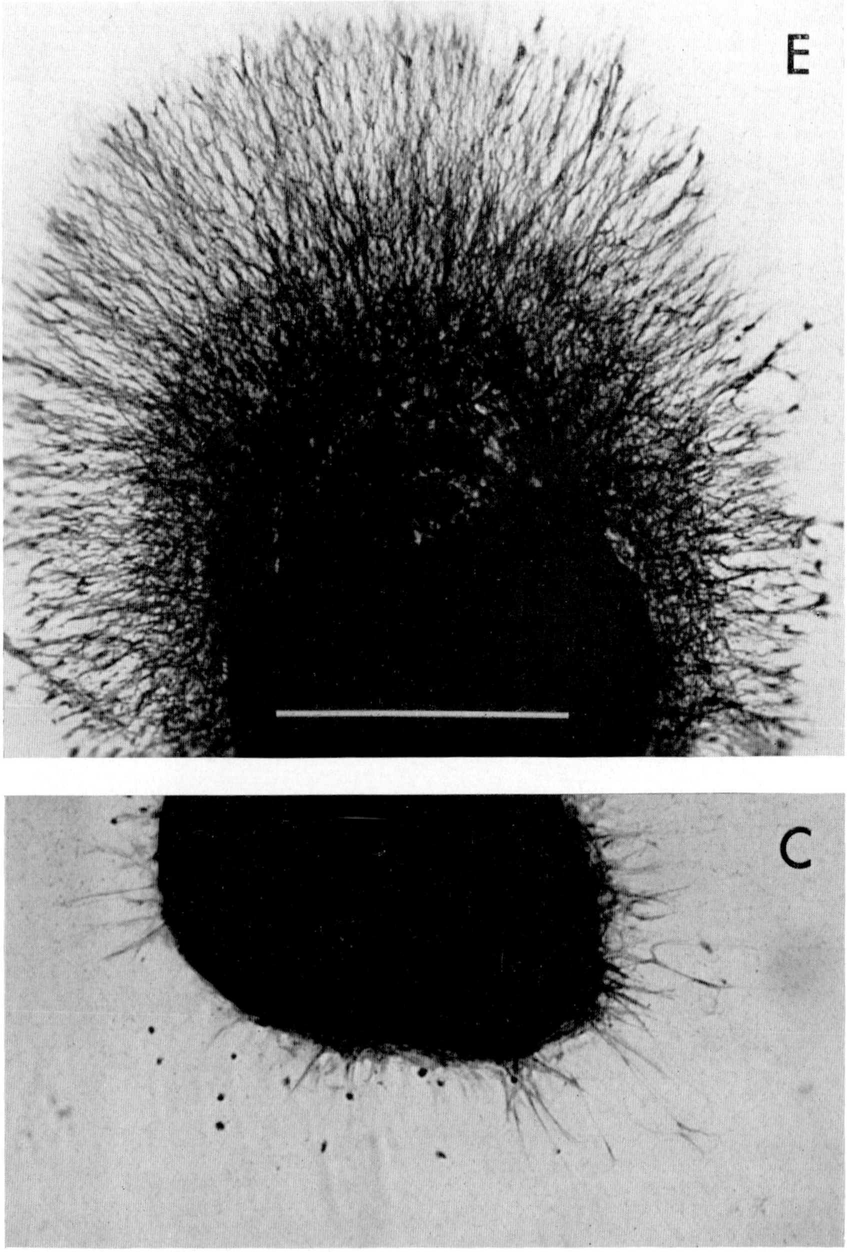

FIG. 6. Profuse outgrowth of nerve fibres from 8-day chick embryo dorsal root ganglion after 1 day of incubation in culture medium containing 2 NGF units/ml (E), as compared with sparse neuritic outgrowth in control medium (C). Scale: 1 mm. (From Crain *et al.* 1964.)

relation between these findings and those of Cohen (1960) awaits further clarification.

The peripheral mode of action of nerve growth factor has recently been studied by electron-microscopy of short-term cultures of chick embryo dorsal root ganglia (Crain, Benitez and Vatter, 1964). The most striking observation was the development of cytoplasmic crystalline structures in cultures treated with nerve growth factor consisting of granules, 100–180 Å in diameter with as many as 100 lined up, 200–300 Å apart, in relatively straight paired rows (Figs. 7 and 8). These arrays were observed in regions of the cytoplasm which were densely packed with ribosomes. The authors concluded that they were dealing with an extremely rapid development of cell organelles from cytoplasmic granules, augmented by nerve growth factor and beginning well before neuritic outgrowth could be detected.

Preliminary studies by Cohen (1959) on the effect of the nerve growth factor on the metabolism of sensory nerve cells *in vitro* showed that the growth effect required a source of energy which could be supplied by glucose or mannose. The growth effect was accompanied by a marked increase in the oxidation of glucose to CO_2. The presence of inhibitors, such as cyanide or fluoride, did not prevent the outgrowth of nerve fibres nor the increased oxidation of (1–^{14}C) glucose to $^{14}CO_2$, suggesting that there was, in embryonic sensory nerve cells, a direct oxidative pathway of glucose metabolism which was specifically stimulated by the nerve growth factor.

Angeletti, Liuzzi, Levi-Montalcini and Attardi (1964) have extended these observations using short-term cultures of embryonic chick and neonatal mouse sensory and sympathetic ganglia in Warburg flasks. From experiments with (6–^{14}C) glucose and (1–^{14}C) glucose, it appeared that the increased oxidation of glucose to CO_2 following the addition of mouse salivary nerve growth factor (0·05 μg/ml) to the incubation medium was due mainly to the oxidation of (1–^{14}C) glucose. The ratio of the radioactivity recovered as $^{14}CO_2$ from 1–C over that from 6–C was found to be approximately 1·3 in control ganglia and approximately 2 in the nerve growth factor-treated ganglia. These findings suggested an activation of the hexose monophosphate pathway in the nerve cells under the influence of the nerve growth factor.

Toschi, Attardi and Angeletti (1964) have studied the effect of the nerve growth factor on RNA metabolism by cultured chick-embryo sensory ganglia using the uptake of tritiated uridine and (1–^{14}C) leucine to follow the effects on RNA and protein synthesis. The results indicated that the nerve growth factor stimulated RNA synthesis and that this effect preceded the stimulation of protein synthesis. Experiments with the inhibitors actinomycin D and puromycin suggested that the

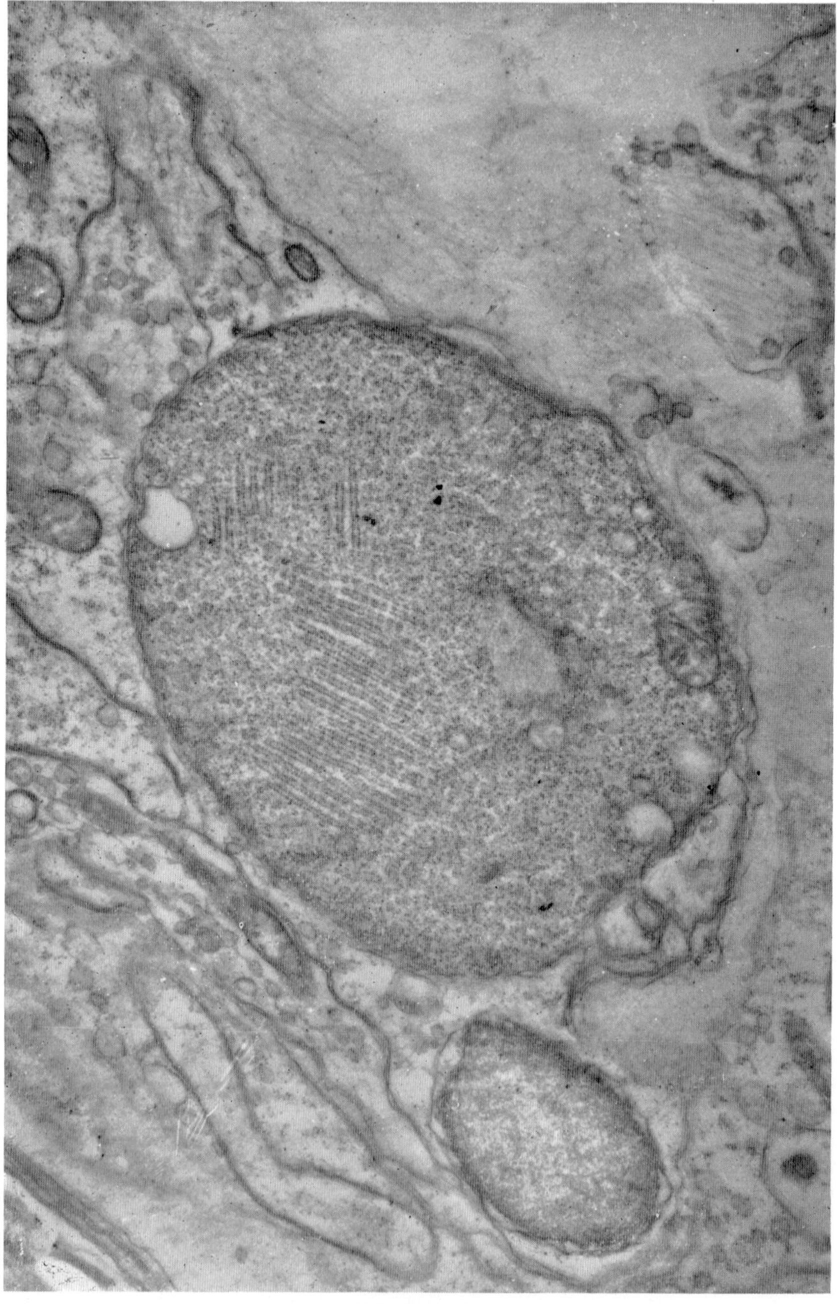

FIG. 7. Electron-micrograph of a section through a dorsal-root ganglion explant after 2 days of incubation in culture medium containing 2 NGF units/ml. Note paired rows of granules forming crystalline array. Scale: 1μ. (From Crain *et al.*, 1964.)

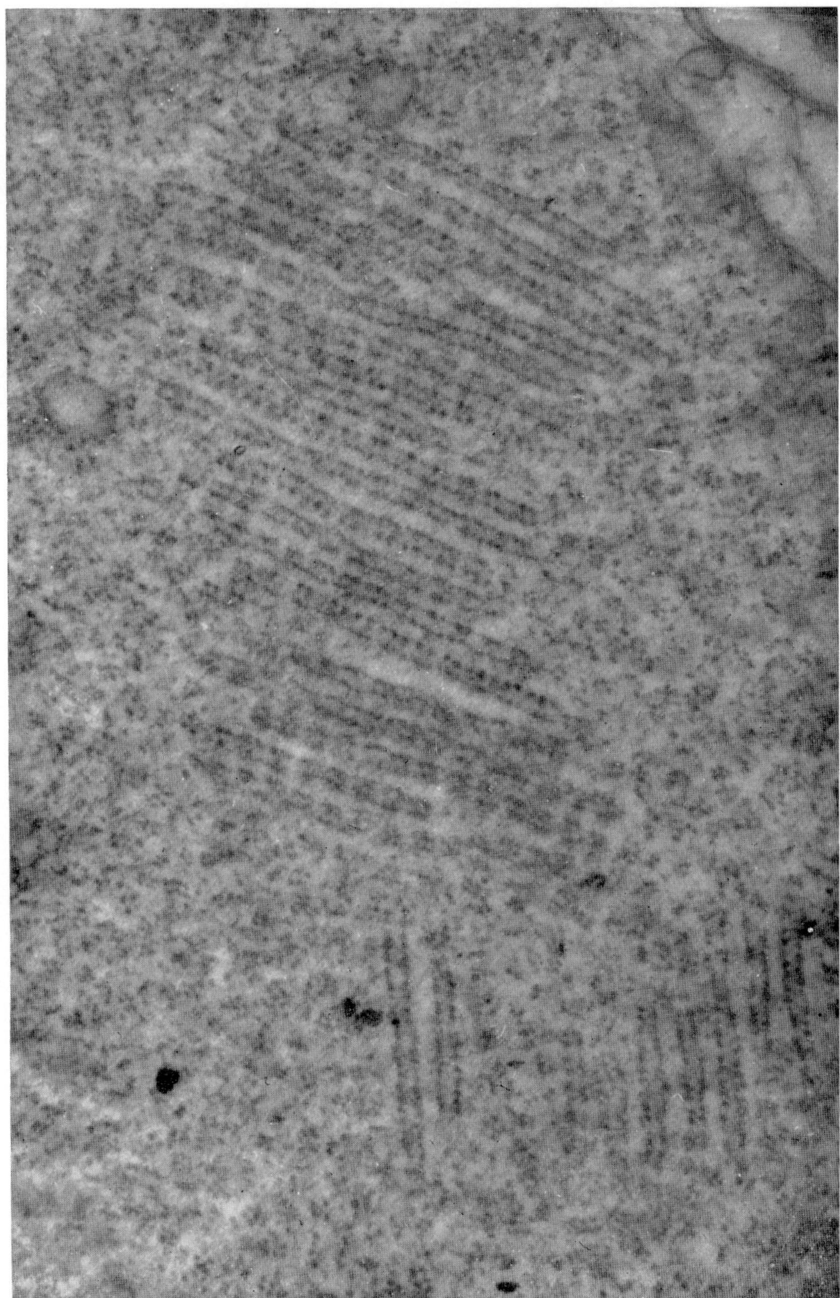

FIG. 8. Higher magnification of a portion of section shown in Fig. 7. Scale: 1μ. (From Crain *et al.*, 1964.)

stimulation of protein synthesis by the nerve growth factor depends on a primary effect on nuclear RNA synthesis.

The importance of the nerve growth factor in the life of its target cells was indicated by experiments demonstrating that isolated sympathetic nerve cells could survive and grow in Tissue Culture only in its presence (Levi-Montalcini and Angeletti, 1963). However, the dramatic effects elicited by the antiserum to nerve growth factor, developed by injecting the purified factor with Freund's adjuvant into the pads of rabbits (Cohen, 1960), have demonstrated that this factor is also essential for the *in vivo* subsistence of sympathetic cells and of sensory cells, at least during the early phase of their differentiation. Levi-Montalcini and Booker (1960b) showed that the injection of minute amounts of this antiserum into newborn mammals immediately blocked the growth and differentiation of developing sympathetic nerve cells and killed already differentiated neurones. The sympathetic ganglia underwent almost total atrophy. The physiological and pharmacological implications of this "immunosympathectomy" is now the subject of intensive investigation (Zaimis, Berk and Callingham, 1965; Iversen, Glowinski and Axelrod, 1965).

References

Algard, F. T. (1963). Action of sex hormones on dependent tumors in cell and organ-culture systems. *Nat. Cancer Inst. Monogr.* **11**, 215.

Ambrose, E. J., Andrews, R. D., Easty, D. M., Field, E. O. and Wylie, J. A. H. (1962). Drug assays on cultures of human tumour biopsies. *Lancet i*, 24.

Angeletti, P. U., Liuzzi, A., Levi-Montalcini, R. and Attardi, D. G. (1964). Effect of a nerve growth factor on glucose metabolism by sympathetic and sensory nerve cells. *Biochim. biophys. Acta* **90**, 445.

Armitage, P. and Schneiderman, M. A. (1958). Statistical problems in a mass screening programme. *Ann. N.Y. Acad. Sci.* **76**, 896.

Aronow, L. (1959). Studies on drug resistance in mammalian cells. I. Amethopterin resistance in mouse fibroblasts. *J. Pharmacol. exp. Therap.* **127**, 116.

Belkin, M., Hardy, W. G., Orr, H. C. and Lachman, A. B. (1962). Induction *in vitro* by autonomic drugs of cytoplasmic vacuoles in ascites tumor cells. *J. nat. Cancer Inst.* **28**, 187.

Bennett, R. E., Brindle, S. A., Giuffre, N. A., Jackson, P. W., Kowald, J., Pansy, F. E., Perlman, D. and Trejo, W. H. (1962). Production of a novel cytotoxic agent SQ. 15,859 by *Streptomyces chrysomallus*. *In* "Antimicrobial agents and Chemotherapy 1961" (M. Finland and G. M. Savage, eds.), pp. 169–172. Braun-Brumfield, Ann Arbor, Michigan.

Bhuyan, B. K., Renis, H. E. and Smith, C. G. (1962). A collagen plate assay for cytotoxic agents. II. Biological studies. *Cancer Res.* **22**, 1131.

Bickley, H. C. and Orbison, J. L. (1964). The effect of a lathyrogen on sulfate metabolism in cultures of the strain L fibroblast. *Lab. Invest.* **13**, 172.

Biesele, J. J. (1951). Tissue culture screening of agents in experimental cancer chemotherapy. *In* "Methods in Medical Research" (M. B. Visscher, ed.), Vol. 4, pp. 272–274. Year Book Publishers, Chicago.

Björklund, B. (1960). A serum cytolytic factor active against HeLa and other established cell strains. *Proc. Soc. exp. Biol., N.Y.* **103**, 1.

Black, L. and Berenbaum, M. C. (1964). Factors affecting the dye exclusion test for cell viability. *Exp. Cell Res.* **35**, 9.

Buchsbaum, R. and Kuntz, J. A. (1954). The effects of certain stimulants and depressants on individual fibroblasts in a perfusion chamber. *Ann. N.Y. Acad. Sci.* **58**, 1303.

Bueker, E. D. (1948). Implantation of tumors in the hind limb field of the embryonic chick and the developmental response of the lumbo-sacral nervous system. *Anat. Rec.* **102**, 369.

Burnham, B. F. and Lascelles, J. (1963). Control of porphyrin biosynthesis through a negative-feedback mechanism. *Biochem. J.* **87**, 462.

Burzynski, N. J. (1963). Effect of β-aminopropionitrile on cultured cells. *Lab. Invest.* **12**, 816.

Carlini, G. R. S., Fischer, G. A. and Giarman, N. J. (1964). Differences in characteristics of release of serotonin from neoplastic mast cells in culture by reserpine and chlorpromazine. *J. Pharmacol. exp. Therap.* **146**, 74.

Caspersson, T., Farber, S., Foley, G. E. and Killander, D. (1963). Cytochemical observations on the nucleolus-ribosome system. Effects of actinomycin D and nitrogen mustard. *Exp. Cell Res.* **32**, 529.

Chen, J. M. (1954). The effect of insulin on embryonic limb-bones cultivated *in vitro*. *J. Physiol.* **125**, 148.

Cobb, J. P. and Walker, D. G. (1961). Effect of heterologous, homologous and autologous serums on human normal and malignant cells *in vitro*. *J. nat. Cancer Inst.* **27**, 1.

Cohen, S. (1958). A nerve growth-promoting protein. *In* "Chemical Basis of Development" (W. D. McElroy and B. Glass, eds.), pp. 665–679. John Hopkins Press, Baltimore.

Cohen, S. (1959). Purification and metabolic effects of a nerve growth promoting protein from snake venom. *J. biol. Chem.* **234**, 1129.

Cohen, S. (1960). Purification of a nerve growth promoting protein from the mouse salivary gland and its neurocytotoxic antiserum. *Proc. nat. Acad. Sci. Wash.* **46**, 302.

Cohen, S. and Levi-Montalcini, R. (1956). A nerve growth-stimulating factor isolated from snake venom. *Proc. nat. Acad. Sci. Wash.* **42**, 571.

Cohen, S., Levi-Montalcini, R. and Hamburger, V. (1954). A nerve growth-stimulating factor isolated from sarcomas 37 and 180. *Proc. nat. Acad. Sci. Wash.* **40**, 1014.

Crain, S. M. (1964). Electrophysiological studies of cord-innervated skeletal muscle in long-term tissue cultures of mouse embryo myotomes. *Anat. Rec.* **148**, 273.

Crain, S. M., Benitez, H. and Vatter, A. E. (1964). Some cytological effects of salivary nerve-growth factor on tissue cultures of peripheral ganglia. *Ann. N.Y. Acad. Sci.* **118**, 206.

Davies, O. L. (1958). The design of screening tests in the pharmaceutical industry. *Bull. int. Stat. Inst.* **36**, 226.

Day, M. and Green, J. P. (1962a). The uptake of amino acids and the synthesis of amines by neoplastic mast cells in culture. *J. Physiol.* **164**, 210.

Day, M. and Green, J. P. (1962b). The uptake of biogenic amines by neoplastic mast cells in culture. *J. Physiol.* **164**, 227.

de Reuck, A. V. S. and Cameron, M. P. (Eds.). (1963). "Lysosomes." Ciba Foundation Symposium. Churchill, London.

Di Paolo, J. A. and Dowd, J. E. (1961). Evaluation of inhibition of human tumor tissue by cancer chemotherapeutic drugs with an *in vitro* test. *J. nat. Cancer. Inst.* **27**, 807.

Di Paolo, J. A. and Moore, G. E. (1957). An evaluation of ascites tumor cell plating for screening chemotherapeutic agents. *Antibiot. Chemother.* **7**, 465.

Dulbecco, R. (1952). Production of plaques in monolayer tissue cultures by single particles of an animal virus. *Proc. nat. Acad. Sci. Wash.* **38**, 747.

Dunnett, C. W. (1961). Statistical theory of drug screening. *In* "Quantitative Methods in Pharmacology" (H. de Jonge, ed.), pp. 212–231. North Holland Publishing Co., Amsterdam.

Eagle, H. and Foley, G. E. (1956). The cytotoxic action of carcinolytic agents in tissue culture. *Amer. J. Med.* **21**, 739.

Eagle, H. and Foley, G. E. (1958a). Cytotoxicity in human cell cultures as a primary screen for the detection of anti-tumor agents. *Cancer Res.* **18**, 1017.

Eagle, H. and Foley, G. E. (1958b). Susceptibility of cultured human cells to anti-tumor agents. *Ann. N.Y. Acad. Sci.* **76**, 534.

Easty, G. C. and Easty, D. M. (1963). An organ culture system for examination of tumour invasion. *Nature, Lond.* **199**, 1104.

Fedoroff, S. and Doerr, J. (1962). Effect of human blood serum on Tissue Cultures. III. A natural cytotoxic system in human blood serum. *J. nat. Cancer Inst.* **29**, 331.

Fell, H. B. and Allsopp, C. B. (1948). The action of mustard gas (ββ′dichloro-diethyl sulphide) on living cells *in vitro*. I. The immediate cytological effects of mustard gas and of its hydrolysis products. II. The effect on cell growth of adding small concentrations of mustard gas to the culture medium. *Cancer Res.* **8**, 145.

Fell, H. B. and Mellanby, E. (1956). The effect of L-triiodothyronine on the growth and development of embryonic chick limb-bones in tissue culture. *J. Physiol.* **133**, 89.

Fell, H. B. and Thomas, L. (1960). Comparison of the effects of papain and vitamin A on cartilage. II. The effects on organ cultures of embryonic skeletal tissue. *J. exp. Med.* **111**, 719.

Fell, H. B. and Thomas, L. (1961). The influence of hydrocortisone on the action of excess vitamin A on limb bone rudiments in culture. *J. exp. Med.* **114**, 343.

Fell, H. B. and Weiss, L. (1965). The effect of antiserum, alone and with hydrocortisone, on foetal mouse bones in culture. *J. exp. Med.* **121**, 551.

Finney, D. J. (1952). "Statistical Method in Biological Assay." Charles Griffin, London.

Foley, G. E. and Epstein, S. S. (1964). Cell culture and cancer chemotherapy. *In* "Advances in Chemotherapy" (A. Goldin and F. Hawking, eds.), Vol. 1, pp. 175–353. Academic Press, New York.

Gaddum, J. H. (1953). Bioassays and mathematics. *Pharmacol. Rev.* **5**, 87.

Gaillard, P. J. (1961). Parathyroid and bone in tissue culture. *In* "The Parathyroids" (R. O. Greep and R. V. Talmage, eds.), p. 20. Thomas, Springfield.

Geiger, B. J., Steenbock, H. and Parsons, H. T. (1933). Lathyrism in the rat. *J. Nutr.* **6**, 427.

Gellhorn, A. and Hirschberg, E. (Eds.). (1955). Investigation of diverse systems for cancer chemotherapy screening. *Cancer Res. Suppl.* **3**.

Girardi, A. J., Hilleman, M. R. and Zwickey, R. E. (1964). Tests in hamsters for oncogenic quality of ordinary viruses including Adenovirus Type 7. *Proc. Soc. exp. Biol., N.Y.* **115**, 1141.

Girardi, A. J., McMichael, H., Jr., and Henle, W. (1956). The use of HeLa cells in suspension for the quantitative study of virus propagation. *Virology* **2**, 532.

Giuffre, N. A., Perlman, D. and Jackson, P. W. (1961). Effect of medium composition on sensitivity in suspension culture of Earle's L-929 mouse fibroblasts to antibiotics. *Cancer Chemother. Rep.* **11**, 57.

Golomb, F. M., Cobb, J. P., Walker, D. G. and Wright, J. C. (1962). *In vitro* selection of chemotherapeutic agents for perfusion therapy of human cancer. *Surgery* **51**, 639.

Grady, J. E., Lummis, W. L. and Smith, C. G. (1960a). An improved tissue culture assay. III. Alternate methods for measuring cell growth. *Cancer Res.* **20**, 1114.

Grady, J. E., Lummis, W. L. and Smith, C. G. (1960b). Tissue culture bioautographic system. *Proc. Soc. exp. Biol., N.Y.* **103**, 727.

Granick, S. (1965). Hepatic porphyria and drug-induced or chemical porphyria. *Ann. N.Y. Acad. Sci.* **123**, 188.

Gwatkin, R. B. L., Till, J. E., Whitmore, G. F., Siminovitch, L. and Graham, A. F. (1957). Multiplication of animal cells in suspension measured by colony counts. *Proc. nat. Acad. Sci. Wash.* **43**, 451.

Hakala, M. T. (1965a). On the role of drug penetration in Amethopterin resistance of sarcoma-180 cells *in vitro*. *Biochim. biophys. Acta* **102**, 198.

Hakala, M. T. (1965b). On the nature of permeability of sarcoma-180 cells to Amethopterin *in vitro*. *Biochim. biophys. Acta* **102**, 210.

Hakala, M. T., Zakrzewski, S. F. and Nichol, C. A. (1961). Relation of folic acid reductase to Amethopterin resistance in cultured mammalian cells. *J. biol. Chem.* **236**, 952.

Harary, I. and Farley, B. (1960). *In vitro* studies of single isolated beating heart cells. *Science* **131**, 1674.

Herrman, E. C. Jr., Gabliks, J., Engle, C. and Perlman, P. L. (1960). Agar diffusion method for detection and bioassay of antiviral antibiotics. *Proc. Soc. exp. Biol., N.Y.* **103**, 625.

Huebner, R. J., Rowe, W. P. and Lane, W. T. (1962). Oncogenic effects in hamsters of human adenovirus types 12 and 18. *Proc. nat. Acad. Sci. Wash.* **48**, 2051.

Hughes, A. F.W. and Fell, H. B. (1949). Studies on abnormal mitosis induced in chick tissue cultures by mustard gas ($\beta\beta'$-dichlordiethyl sulphide). *Quart. J. micr. Sci.* **90**, 37.

Iversen, L. L., Glowinski, J. and Axelrod, J. (1965). Reduced uptake of tritiated noradrenaline in tissues of immunosympathectomized animals. *Nature, Lond.* **206**, 1222.

Jacobson, W. (1954a). The mode of action of folic acid antagonists on cells. *J. Physiol.* **123**, 603.

Jacobson, W. (1954b). The function of the *Leuconostoc citrovorum* factor in cell division and the inactivation of aminopterin. *J. Physiol.* **123**, 618.

Jacobson, W. (1954c). The mode of action of folic acid antagonists and the function of the *Leuconostoc citrovorum* factor. *In* "The Chemistry and Biology of Pteridines", pp. 329–355. Ciba Foundation Symposium, Churchill, London.

Jacobson, W. (1965). The basis of chemotherapy with folic acid antagonists in acute leukaemia of children. *In* "The Treatment of Cancer" (J. S. Mitchell, ed.), pp. 30–51. Cambridge University Press.

Jacobson, W. and Cathie, I. A. B. (1960a). The inactivation of folic acid antagonists by normal and leukaemic cells. *Biochem. Pharmacol.* **5**, 130.

Jacobson, W. and Cathie, I. A. B. (1960b). The nature of aminopterin inactivated by normal and leukaemic tissues. *Biochem. Pharmacol.* **5**, 143.

Jacoby, F., Medawar, P. B. and Willmer, E. N. (1941). The toxity of sulphonamide drugs to cells *in vitro*. *Brit. med. J.* **2**, 149.

Jacquez, J. A. (1962). Tissue culture screening. *Cancer Res.* **22**, pt. 2, 81.

Jainchill, J., Saxén, L. and Vainio, T. (1964). Studies on kidney tubulogenesis. I. The effect of actinomycin D on tubulogenesis *in vitro*. *J. Embryol. exp. Morph.* **12**, 597.

Johnson, M. J. (1949). A rapid micromethod for estimation of non-volatile organic matter. *J. biol. Chem.* **181**, 707.

Kääriäinen, L. (1962). Metabolic inhibition test on a plastic panel. *Acta path. microbiol. scand. Suppl.* **154**, 352.

Karibian, D. and London, I. M. (1965). Control of heme synthesis by feedback inhibition. *Biochem. biophys. Res. Commun.* **18**, 243.

Kline, I. and Acker, R. F. (1960). The effects of chemical agents on cells propagated in tissue culture systems. *Cancer Chemother. Rep.* **9**, 73.

Kuchler, R. J. and Merchant, D. J. (1958). Growth of tissue cells in suspension. *Univ. Michigan med. Bull.* **24**, 200.

Lajtha, L. G. (1959). On DNA labelling in the study of the dynamics of bone marrow cell populations. *In* "Kinetics of Cellular Proliferation" (F. Stohlman, Jr., ed.), pp. 173–182. Grune and Stratton, New York.

Lawson, K. (1961a). The differential growth response of embryonic chick limb bone rudiments to triiodothyronine *in vitro*. I. Stage of development and organ size. *J. Embryol. exp. Morph.* **9**, 42.

Lawson, K. (1961b). The differential growth response of embryonic chick limb bone rudiments to triiodothyronine *in vitro*. 2. Growth rate. *J. Embryol. exp. Morph.* **9**, 534.

Leighton, J. (1960). The propagation of aggregates of cancer cells; implications for therapy and a simple method of study. *Cancer Chemother. Rep.* **9**, 71.

Leiter, J., Abbott, B. J., Macdonald, M. M. and Schepartz, S. A. (1964). Screening data from the Cancer Chemotherapy National Service Center Screening Laboratories XX. *Cancer Res.* **24**, pt. 2, 880.

Leslie, I. and Sinclair, R. (1959). The action of thyroxine and triiodothyronine on human cells growing in tissue culture. *Exp. Cell Res.* **17**, 272.

Lettré, H. and Albrecht, M. (1941). Zur Wirkung von β-Phenyläthyläminen auf *in vitro* gezüchtete Zellen. *Hoppe-Seyl. Z. physiol. Chem.* **271**, 200.

Lettré, H. and Albrecht, M. (1943). Zur Wirkung von Aminen auf *in vitro* gezüchtete Zellen. *Hoppe-Seyl. Z. physiol. Chem.* **279**, 206.

Lettré, H. and Albrecht, M. (1951). Weitere Untersuchungen über eine Mitosegiftwirkung von Alkaloiden. *Hoppe-Seyl. Z. physiol. Chem.* **287**, 58.

Levi-Montalcini, R. (1952). Effects of mouse tumor transplantation on the nervous system. *Ann. N.Y. Acad. Sci.* **55**, 330.

Levi-Montalcini, R. and Angeletti, P. U. (1961). Growth control of the sympathetic nervous system by a specific protein factor. *Quart. Rev. Biol.* **36**, 99.

Levi-Montalcini, R. and Angeletti, P. U. (1963). Essential role of the nerve growth factor in the survival and maintenance of dissociated sensory and sympathetic embryonic nerve cells *in vitro*. *Devl. Biol.* **7**, 653.

Levi-Montalcini, R. and Booker, B. (1960a). Excessive growth of the sympathetic ganglia by a protein isolated from the salivary gland. *Proc. nat. Acad. Sci. Wash.* **46**, 373.

Levi-Montalcini, R. and Booker, B. (1960b). Destruction of the sympathetic ganglia in mammals by an antiserum to the nerve-growth protein. *Proc. nat. Acad. Sci. Wash.* **46**, 384.

Levi-Montalcini, R., Meyer, H. and Hamburger, V. (1954). *In vitro* experiments on the effects of mouse sarcomas 180 and 37 on the spinal and sympathetic ganglia of the chick embryo. *Cancer Res.* **14**, 49.

Levintow, L. and Eagle, H. (1961). Biochemistry of cultured mammalian cells. *Ann. Rev. Biochem.* **30**, 605.

Lichter, W., Wellham, L. and Sigel, M. M. (1964). Use of cell culture for study of rate of drug action. A search for drugs for local therapy. *Cancer Chemother. Rep.* **38**, 1.

Litchfield, J. T. (1958). Determination of efficacy and safety of new drugs. *In* "A Symposium on the Evaluation of Drug Toxicity" (A. L. Walpole and A. Spinks, eds.), p. 36–47. Churchill, London.

Lowry, O. H., Rosebrough, N. J., Farr, A. L. and Randall, R. J. (1951). Protein measurement with the Folin phenol reagent. *J. biol. Chem.* **193**, 265.

McAllister, R. M., Grunmeier, P. W., Coriell, L. L. and Blakemore, W. S. (1959). A quantitative technique for the measurement of *in vitro* cytotoxicity of 5-fluoro-2-deoxyuridine (FUDR), nitrogen mustard (HN2) and other antitumor agents. *Cancer* **12**, 938.

McCallum, H. M. (1965). Experimental lathyrism in tissue culture. *J. Path. Bact.* **89**, 637.

McCallum, H. M. and Paul, J. (1961). Lathyrogenic activity *in vitro*. *Nature, Lond.* **192**, 273.

McDonald, G. O. and Cole, W. H. (1959). The use of human tumors in primary culture for testing anticancer compounds. *Surg. Forum* **10**, 67.

McIntyre, F. C. and Sproull, M. F. (1957). A simple method for determination of desoxypentose nucleic acid in tissue cultures. *Proc. Soc. exp. Biol., N.Y.* **95**, 458.

Mahaley, M. S., Jr. and Woodhall, B. (1961). Effect of temperature upon the *in vitro* action of anticancer agents on VX2 carcinoma. *J. Neurosurg.* **18**, 269.

Martin, G. R. and Goldhaber, P. (1963). Action of aminoacetonitrile on bone collagen in tissue culture. *Biochim. biophys. Acta* **69**, 568.

Miyamura, S. (1956). A determination method for anticancer action of antibiotics by the agar plate diffusion technique. *Antibiot. Chemother.* **6**, 280.

Miyamura, S. and Niwayama, S. (1959). An agar plate diffusion method using HeLa cells for antitumor screening. *Antibiot. Chemother.* **9**, 497.

Mulherkar, L. (1960). The effects of trypan blue on chick embryos cultured *in vitro*. *J. Embryol. exp. Morph.* **8**, 1.

Munson, P. L. (1961). Biological assay of parathyroid hormone. *In* "The Parathyroids" (R. O. Greep and R. V. Talmage, eds.), p. 94. Thomas, Springfield.

Nakazawa, T. (1960). Effects of chlorpromazine and serotonin on the contractility of oligodendrocytes. *Tex. Rep. Biol. Med.* **18**, 52.

Oda, A. and Yamamoto, T. (1959). A rapid *in vitro* screening test for antitumor substance on the filter paper. *Jap. J. exp. Med.* **29**, 87.

Ormsbee, R. A. and Cornman, I. (1948). The place of tissue culture in a cancer chemotherapy screening programme. *Cancer Res.* **8**, 384.

Oyama, V. I. and Eagle, H. (1956). Measurement of cell growth in tissue culture with a phenol reagent (Folin-Ciocalteu). *Proc. Soc. exp. Biol., N.Y.* **91**, 305.

Paul, J. and Danes, B. S. (1961). A modified Cartesian diver method permitting measurement of oxygen uptake in the presence of carbon dioxide. *Analyt. Biochem.* **2**, 470.

Peterson, D. H. and Reineke, L. M. (1950). A paper chromatographic technique and its application to the study of new antibiotics. *J. Amer. chem. Soc.* **72**, 3598.

Pomerat, C. M. (1942). Effect of direct application of tyrothrycin and allantoin to cells *in vitro*. *Proc. Soc. exp. Biol., N.Y.* **51**, 345.

Pomerat, C. M. (1951). Tissue Culture Methods. *In* "Methods in Medical Research" (M. B. Visscher, ed.), Vol. 4, p. 198. Year Book Publishers, Chicago.

Pomerat, C. M., Capouya, M. and Greenleaf, F. I. (1944). Sulfonamide crystals applied directly to fibroblasts and leucocytes *in vitro*. *Texas Rep. Biol. Med.* **2**, 97.

Pomerat, C. M., Drager, G. A. and Painter, J. T. (1946). Effect of some barbiturates on tissues *in vitro*. *Proc. Soc. exp. Biol., N.Y.* **63**, 322.

Pomerat, C. M. and Emerson, G. A. (1944–5). Induction of aqueous vacuolization in cells grown in tissue culture by various agents. *Proc. Trans. Texas Acad. Sci.* **28**, 91.

Pomerat, C. M., Lefeber, C. G. and Smith, McD. (1954). Quantitative cine analysis of cell organoid activity. *Ann. N.Y. Acad. Sci.* **58**, 1311.

Ponseti, I. V. and Baird, W. A. (1952). Scoliosis and dissecting aneurysm of the aorta in rats fed with *Lathyrus odoratus* seeds. *Amer. J. Path.* **28**, 1059.

Puck, T. T., Marcus, P. I. and Cieciura, S. J. (1956). Clonal growth of mammalian cells *in vitro*. Growth characteristics of colonies from single HeLa cells with and without a "feeder" layer. *J. exp. Med.* **103**, 273.

Rada, B. and Závada, J. (1962). Screening test for cytostatic and virustatic substances. *Neoplasma* **9**, 57.

Raisz, L. G. (1963a). Stimulation of bone resorption by parathyroid hormone in tissue culture. *Nature, Lond.* **197**, 1015.

Raisz, L. G. (1963b). Regulation by calcium of parathyroid growth and secretion *in vitro*. *Nature, Lond.* **197**, 1115.

Raisz, L. G. (1965). Bone resorption in tissue culture. Factors influencing the response to parathyroid hormone. *J. clin. Invest.* **44**, 103.

Renis, H. E., Johnson, H. G. and Bhuyan, B. K. (1962). A collagen plate assay for cytotoxic agents. I. Methods. *Cancer Res.* **22**, 1126.

Rightsel, W. A., Schultz, P., Muething, D. and McLean, I. W., Jr. (1956). Use of vinyl plastic containers in tissue cultures for virus assays. *J. Immunol.* **76**, 464.

Salk, J. E., Youngner, J. S. and Ward, E. N. (1954). Use of color change of phenol red as the indicator in titrating poliomyelitis virus or its antibody in a tissue-culture system. *Amer. J. Hyg.* **60**, 214.

Saxén, E. and Penttinen, K. (1961). Host factors in cell culture: further studies on the growth-controlling action of fresh human serum. *J. nat. Cancer Inst.* **26**, 1367.

Schenkein, I. and Bueker, E. D. (1964). The nerve growth factor as two essential components. *Ann. N.Y. Acad. Sci.* **118**, 171.

Schepartz, S. A., Macdonald, M. M. and Leiter, J. (1961). The use of cell culture as a presumptive screen for antitumor agents. *Proc. Amer. Ass. Cancer Res.* **3**, 265.

Schild, H. O. (1942). A method of conducting a biological assay on a preparation giving repeated graded responses illustrated by the estimation of histamine. *J. Physiol.* **101**, 115.

Schindler, R., Day, M. and Fischer, G. A. (1959). Culture of neoplastic mast cells and their synthesis of 5-hydroxytryptamine and histamine *in vitro*. *Cancer Res.* **19**, 47.

Schmähl, D. and Druckrey, H. (1956). Beiträge zum Wirkungsmechanismus von N-Oxyd-Lost. *Naturwissenschaften* **43**, 199.

Schryver, H. F. and Biggers, J. D. (1963). The effect of lathyrogenic agents on embryonic chick tibiotarsi *in vitro*. *J. exp. Zool.* **154**, 339.

Schuurmans, D. M., Duncan, D. T. and Olson, B. H. (1960). An agar plate assay for anti-cancer agents utilising serially cultured sarcoma 180 (Foley). *Antibiot. Chemother.* **10**, 535.

Schuurmans, D. M., Duncan, D. T. and Olson, B. H. (1964). A bioautographic system employing mammalian cell strains and its application to antitumor antibiotics. *Cancer Res.* **24**, 83.

Siminoff, P. (1961). A plaque suppression method for the study of antiviral compounds. *Appl. Microbiol.* **9**, 66.

Siminoff, P. and Hursky, V. S. (1960a). Determination of mammalian cell (strain HeLa) inhibition by an agar diffusion technic. I. Quantitative assay methods. *Cancer Res.* **20**, 615.

Siminoff, P. and Hursky, V. S. (1960b). Determination of mammalian cells (strain HeLa) inhibition by an agar diffusion technic. II. Paper chromatographic methods. *Cancer Res.* **20**, 618.

Smith, C. G., Lummis, W. L. and Grady, J. E. (1959). An improved tissue culture assay. I. Methodology and cytotoxicity of antitumor agents. *Cancer Res.* **19**, 843.

Szybalski, W. and Smith, M. J. (1959). Genetics of human cell lines. I. 8-azaguanine resistance, a selective "single-step" marker. *Proc. Soc. exp. Biol., N.Y.* **101**, 662.

Takaki, R., Sugi, Y., Katsuta, K., Takahashi, T., Kamiya, T. and Takahashi, T. (1960). Effect of chromomycin on the strain cells in tissue culture. *Kyushu J. med. Sci.* **11**, 225.

Thompson, K. W., Vincent, M. M., Jensen, F. C., Price, R. T. and Schapiro, E. (1959). Production of hormones by human anterior pituitary cells in serial culture. *Proc. Soc. exp. Biol., N.Y.* **102**, 403.

Toplin, I. (1959a). Preliminary report on a tissue culture cytoxicity test for large-scale cancer chemotherapy screening. *Cancer Chemother. Rep.* **3**, 12.

Toplin, I. (1959b). A tissue culture cytoxicity test for large-scale cancer chemotherapy screening. *Cancer Res.* **19**, 959.

Toplin, I. (1961). Experiences with the tissue culture system in large-scale cancer chemotherapy screening. *Cancer Res.* **21**, 1042.

Toschi, G., Gandini, D. A. and Angeletti, P.U. (1964). Effect of a specific neuronal growth factor on RNA metabolism by sensory ganglia from chick embryo. *Biochem. Biophys. Res. Commun.* **16**, 111.

Trentin, J. J., Yabe, Y. and Taylor, G. (1962). The quest for human cancer viruses. *Science* **137**, 835.

Trowell, O. A. (1954). A modified technique for organ culture *in vitro*. *Exp. Cell Res.* **6**, 246.

Wessells, N. K. (1964). Acquisition of actinomycin D insensitivity during differentiation of pancreas exocrine cells. *Devl. Biol.* **9**, 92.

Willmer, E. N. (1933). Studies on the growth of tissues *in vitro*. II. An analysis of the growth of chick heart fibroblasts in a hanging drop of fluid medium. *J. exp. Biol.* **10**, 323.

Willmer, E. N. and Jacoby, F. (1936). Studies on the growth of tissues *in vitro*. IV. On the manner in which growth is stimulated by extracts of embryo tissues. *J. exp. Biol.* **13**, 237.

Wilson, A. and Schild, H. O. (1959). "Applied Pharmacology," 9th ed. Churchill, London.

Wolff, E. (1956). La culture de cellules tumorales sur des explants d'organes *in vitro*. *Experientia* **12**, 321.

Wolff, Et. and Wolff, Em. (1961). Le comportement en culture *in vitro* de cancers humains associés à des explants de rein embryonnaire de Poulet. *C. R. Soc. Biol., Paris* **155**, 441.

Wolff, Et. and Wolff, Em. (1963). Carcinologie expérimentale. Sur la culture de longue durée d'un cancer humain *in vitro*. *C. R. Acad. Sci., Paris* **256**, 1173.

Wollenberger, A. and Halle, W. (1960). Specificity of the effects of cardiac glycosides on the rhythmic contractions of single cultured cardiac muscle cells. *Nature, Lond.* **188**, 1114.

Woodliff, H. J. and Davis, J. M. G. (1960). Effect of Amethopterin and 6-mercaptopurine on the pattern of oxygen tension measurements in the fluid phase of serum cultures of bone marrow flecks. *Nature, Lond.* **185**, 477.

Wrba, H. (1962). Wachstumsfördernde Stoffe und Hemmfaktoren in Warmblütlergeweben (Unidentifizierte humorale Regulationsstoffe). *Naturwissenschaften* **49**, 97.

Wright, J. C., Cobb, J. P., Gumport, S. L., Golomb, R. M. and Safadi, D. (1957). Investigation of the relation between clinical and tissue culture response to chemotherapeutic agents on human cancers. *New Engl. J. Med.* **257**, 1207.

Yamazaki, S., Nitta, K., Hikiji, T., Nogi, M., Takeuchi, T., Yamamoto, T. and Umezawa, H. (1956). Cylinder plate method of testing the anti-cell effect. Studies on antitumor substance produced by Actinomycetes. XII. *J. Antibiotics, Tokyo* **A9**, 135.

Yang, W. C., Strasser, F. F. and Pomerat, C. M. (1965). Mechanism of drug induced vacuolization in tissue culture. *Exp. Cell Res.* **38**, 495.

Yarnell, M., Ambrose, E. J., Shepley, K. and Tchao, R. (1964). Drug assays on organ cultures of biopsies from human tumours. *Brit. med. J.* **2**, 490.

Youngner, J. S. (1954). Monolayer tissue cultures. I. Preparation and standardization of suspensions of trypsin-dispersed monkey kidney cells. *Proc. Soc. exp. Biol., N.Y.* **85**, 202.

Zaimis, E., Berk, L. and Callingham, B. A. (1965). Morphological, biochemical and functional changes in the sympathetic nervous system of rats treated with nerve growth factor-antiserum. *Nature, Lond.* **206**, 1220.

CHAPTER 7

Invertebrate Tissue and Organ Culture in Cell Research

BRYN M. JONES

Department of Zoology, University College of Wales, Aberystwyth, Wales

I. Introduction

The present study is essentially an analysis of the contribution that has been made by investigations on the cells, tissues, organs, and embryos of invertebrates *in vitro* to the general background of cytological knowledge.

In tracing the development of invertebrate tissue and cell culture from its beginnings, one can discern trends that are closely linked with particular problems of experimental cell research. These are largely centred within the subjects of cell adhesion in aggregates and tissue synthesis, cell growth and differentiation, cell irradiation and of virus multiplication and pathology, and one of the main aims has been to show how advances in these subjects in particular have been aided by *in vitro* studies on invertebrate tissues and cells.

No great difficulty has ever been experienced in maintaining invertebrate tissue cells *in vitro* long enough for the cells to display significant changes in behaviour. Neither has it been necessary in the case of many kinds of invertebrate tissue cells to design special media. Cells derived from sponges and the embryos of many marine invertebrates, for example, will survive for long periods in filtered sea-water. For this reason investigators were able, around the turn of the century, to study the behaviour of cells *in vitro* and make observations which focused attention on a number of biological problems upon which cytologists have been intensively engaged ever since.

One of the most remarkable things that emerges from a scrutiny of the literature on the subject of the behaviour of invertebrate tissue cells *in vitro*, is how much we are indebted to the results of early work carried out long before it became possible to maintain and grow vertebrate tissues *in vitro* successfully. It was Herbst (1900) who first discovered that sea-urchin embryos dissociated into separate cells in sea-water depleted of Ca, and, what was even more remarkable, that these same cells adhered to each other when the Ca was restored. He thus demonstrated the importance of Ca on the binding activity of these cells, and he foresaw the presence of an adhesive mechanism at the cell surface. There is now abundant proof that the adhesive mechanism of cells is Ca-dependent. But it was Wilson (1907) in his classical experiments on sponge cells who showed that the cell-binding activity could be selective. He demonstrated this in the following way. He mixed isolated cells obtained by mechanically dissociating the tissues of two different species of sponges in sea-water, and found that when the cells formed aggregates, these were composed entirely of either one or the other species of sponge.

In the period between the wars, very important observations were made on the aggregation and subsequent development of dissociated sponge tissues by Galtsoff (1923, 1925a, b), Huxley (1911, 1921), de Laubenfels (1932) and Fauré-Fremiet (1932). The last-named author was among the first to call attention to the properties and behaviour of four main types of cell which he could identify in his cell suspensions and cultures. His studies were, indeed, essentially tissue and cell cultures, and as such they have not received the attention that they deserve.

It is significant that sponge cells are still regarded as being an excellent experimental material for studying the problem of cell contact and adhesion, as illustrated by the recent investigations of Curtis (1962b) and Moscona (1963) on sponge cell recombinations. This ability of cells to recombine *in vitro* after dissociation has an important bearing on the adhesion and de-adhesion of cells in relation to their movements from one place to another within the organism, particularly during embryogenesis. But when vertebrate tissues are employed to supply separated cells for aggregation studies, they can only be dispersed into separate cells by chemical means. It is generally agreed that this is a disadvantage, for when mammalian or avian embryonic tissues are treated with low concentrations of trypsin, intercellular substances are disrupted, and if chemical bonds do exist to hold the cells together, they too must be broken in the process which seems to be necessary to dissociate the tissues into separate cells. Moreover, there is the possibility of molecular changes and an accompanying alteration in the adhesive properties being brought about at the cell surface by the action of trypsin. Since sponge tissues and many other kinds of invertebrate embryonic tissues can be mechanically dissociated, one may assume that the amount of disorganization at the surfaces of cells obtained in this way is far less than it is after treatment with tryptic enzymes.

Although Herbst (1900) and Wilson (1907) had drawn attention to the binding activity of cells obtained from mechanically dissociated tissues, it was Loeb (1927) who first put forward the view that the way cells combined with each other *in vitro* gave an insight into how tissues were synthesized, and furthermore that tissue formation depended on radical changes taking place at the surface. This conviction was held by Loeb (1927) after he had observed that the blood cells of *Limulus*, the King crab, "agglutinated" in hanging-drops of plasma withdrawn from the same animal, to form "amoebocytic tissue". He preferred to believe that adsorption of plasma proteins at the surfaces of the cells did not promote the aggregation observed, and that in the plasma the actual surface properties of the cells were altered sufficiently to render the cells adhesive. The possibility that factors in the plasma could influence the aggregating ability of the cells cannot, however, be dismissed. Indeed it is difficult to imagine from studies so far carried out on the cohesion, grouping and selective association of cells, which are aspects of the transition from single cells to the multicellular system, that environmental factors do not have a role in the binding of cells.

If Herbst (1900) and Wilson (1907) at the turn of the century in their *in vitro* studies on the reaggregation behaviour of the cells of invertebrates pointed to the depth of the problem of cell adhesion, then it was Goldschmidt (1915), in stimulating silkmoth spermatocytes to display maturation division by using the hanging-drop method of Harrison (1906), who first indicated that the cultivation of invertebrate tissues *in vitro* was possible.

This early success of Goldschmidt (1915) in initiating the division of spermatocytes by placing them in a medium composed simply of salts and silkmoth haemolymph created considerable interest in the use of insect material as a medium for studying the problem of gametogenesis, and it led to a great deal of further work on the subject (Lewis, 1916; Lewis and Robertson, 1916; Takakuson, 1924; Chambers, 1925; Bělăr, 1929; Baumgartner and Payne, 1930; Stern, 1940; Ris, 1949).

Since Goldschmidt (1915) demonstrated that these sex cells were capable of dividing *in vitro*, it suggested that other kinds of invertebrate tissue cells might do the same. But the early attempts to culture insect cells, whether of gut tissues (Collier, 1920), of blood (Glaser, 1917; Lazarenko, 1925; Taylor, 1935; Millara, 1946; Arvy and Gabe, 1946), imaginal discs (Frew, 1928), muscle tissue (Schmidtmann, 1925), or silkmoth ovaries (Trager, 1935), were disappointing in so far that the cells did not proliferate. Equally disappointing in this respect during the same period were the results of attempts to cultivate mollusc tissues (Gatenby, 1931, 1932; Gatenby and Duthie, 1932; Hill and Gatenby, 1934; Bevelander and Martin, 1949), planarian tissue (Murray, 1931), and crustacean tissues (Fischer-Piette, 1929, 1931, 1933).

Since invertebrate animals possess remarkable powers of regeneration, the inability of their tissues to grow *in vitro* must have been puzzling to these pioneer workers. Their methods of approach were not, however, as meticulous as they might have been and the precautions taken to prevent contamination of their materials may have been inadequate in many cases. Notwithstanding this, cells emerged from the explanted tissues and migrated some distance over the surface of the coverglass in the successful cultures. But mitosis was not with any certainty detected in them. Descriptions of these exploratory preparations also suggest that there was some confusion over the precise meaning of such terms as "cell multiplication" or "cell growth" in the minds of early workers when they applied them to the cultures they obtained. For, as often as not, the terms were used to describe the extent of the cellular outgrowths from the explant tissue. As more cells emigrate from the explant the outgrowth enlarges, but this need not be synonymous with a proliferation of cells by cell division, which is now the accepted definition of "cell multiplication" or "cell growth" in Tissue Culture.

Curiously enough, to design media which threw the cells and tissues of invertebrates into a proliferating phase *in vitro* was an unexpectedly difficult problem, and it is only within the last ten years that it has been resolved. But even so, this success has been largely confined to insect Tissue Culture (review by Jones, 1962). The reason for this is that the approach to the problem of inducing insect cells to proliferate by cell division in culture was more carefully planned than hitherto, as knowledge of the biochemistry and physiology of insects increased (Buck, 1953; Wyatt, 1961). It was Trager (1935) who first indicated the suitability of silkmoth ovarian tissue for cultivation *in vitro*, and Wyatt (1956), Grace (1958a, b) and Jones and Cunningham (1960, 1961) established successful methods of growing this ovarian tissue in primary cultures, while Grace (1962a) took the work a stage further by establishing cell lines obtained from the same tissue.

It is significant that Trager (1935) produced his cultures of silkmoth ovarian tissue primarily to investigate the polyhedral viruses, which occur naturally and multiply in silkmoth tissues. That insect tissue culture is a valuable research tool in virology and pathology is now fully recognized, and tick Tissue Culture is equally important in this respect.

A further trend within which is centred the use of techniques for culturing invertebrate organs and embryos, or fragments of these, has stemmed from the early *in vitro* studies on insect gonads, which were largely concerned with investigations on the problem of gametogenesis. The application of organ-culture techniques has been extended considerably since these early studies were made, and investigations on cell irradiation and on cell growth and differentiation are now possible.

It will be apparent from the above considerations that the application of invertebrate tissue and organ culture to cell research is many-sided. It is therefore to be expected that I have overlooked much that could have been included. However the aim has been to cover the subject sufficiently to establish points that will possibly be of general interest, and if this has come out in the present study, then its purpose will have been achieved.

II. Design of Culture Media

Tissue-Culture work is still characterized by the design of media being circumscribed by the concept that the optimum environment for tissues *in vitro* is one which imitates the composition of blood (Waymouth, 1957). Yet, curiously enough, there is ample evidence from the results of work on the cultivation of vertebrate tissues, that plasma and similar biological fluids are inadequate for the survival of many types of cells, as well as for the growth of most cells (Waymouth, 1957). Furthermore, there is no evidence that the blood and body fluids of invertebrates are superior in providing the chemical requirements for the growth of invertebrate tissues *in vitro*. Indeed the blood of haemolymph of insects in particular, although it directly bathes the tissues and may be looked upon as the universal provider of the cells, is exceptionally toxic in a culture medium unless it is specially treated beforehand. For the blood and coelomic fluids of invertebrates are certainly the "sink" as well as the "source" for a wide array of cell products and metabolites.

Nevertheless, the view that the optimum environment for the growth of cells should be one that resembles plasma and body fluids has been widely held. Thus workers concerned with the problem of invertebrate Tissue Culture have in general believed that the nutritional requirements of invertebrate tissue cells *in vitro* were to be found in the composition of plasma and coelomic fluids.

Thus a great deal of attention has been focused on the part that the "growth and differentiation hormone" derived from the thoracic gland of insects might play in initiating the growth of insect cells *in vitro*. Since Schmidt and Williams (1953) demonstrated that progress in the development of silkmoth spermatocytes *in vitro* was dependent on the amount of the prothoracic gland hormone present in the haemolymph, it has puzzled insect physiologists that the presence of this hormone in a suitable medium fails to initiate the growth of insect tissue cells. Yet there is no evidence that the growth of most kinds of cells *in vitro* requires the presence of any particular hormone. The growth of vertebrate cell strains, for example, is completely independent of hormones (Paul, 1959).

When Trager (1938) succeeded in maintaining the imaginal discs, ovaries and pieces of the mid-gut of mosquitoes for long periods in a medium which contained ingredients known to favour the growth of vertebrate tissues *in vitro*, it led to a wave of enthusiasm over the possibility that the use of vertebrate Tissue-Culture media provided the answer. Trager's medium (1938) consisted of equal parts of heparinized guinea-pig or chick plasma diluted with one-half its volume of distilled water, and a nutrient solution of the following composition:

ml	
33	0·3 M glucose
4·5	0·3 M NaCl
0·4	0·2 M KCl
0·7	0·2 M $CaCl_2$
2·1	0·2 M phosphate buffer of pH 7·2
10	peptic digest of egg albumen
49	distilled water

The phosphate buffer was prepared by mixing two parts of previously autoclaved 0·2 M NaH_2PO_4, H_2O and seven parts of 0·2 M K_2HPO_4. Apparently this nutrient solution supported the mosquito tissues "fairly well, but not as well as when mixed with plasma". Since so little was known about the composition of insect haemolymph, the design of suitable culture media was a most difficult problem, and when attempts were made to cultivate the nerve tissue (Pfeiffer, 1937, 1939, 1943; Carlson, 1946), salivary glands and gut (Gavrilov and Cowez, 1941) of the mosquito as well as the imaginal discs of *Drosophila* (Gottschewski and Fischer, 1939) in media similar to Trager's, the results were unsuccessful. A certain amount of success, however, was claimed by Glaser (1917) in inducing haemocytes to multiply *in vitro*, and Lazarenko (1925), Taylor (1935) and Arvy and Gabe (1946) maintained that haemocytes displayed mitosis in their cultures. Goodchild (1954) and Grace (1954) attempted to grow haemocytes under the same conditions as those described by these earlier workers but without the success they claimed. In my own laboratory we have never obtained evidence that insect haemocytes are capable of proliferating *in vitro*.

The tendency to believe that the natural blood, coelomic fluids, and tissue extracts of invertebrates, as well as ingredients known to favour the growth of vertebrate tissues *in vitro*, ought to contain the nutritional requirements for the growth of invertebrate tissue *in vitro* is also reflected in attempts that were made to culture the cells and tissues of flat worms, annelids, molluscs, and crustaceans.

Murray (1931) kept the parenchyma tissue of planarian worms in an apparently viable state for 2 weeks in a solution containing 0·5 g NaCl, 0·01 g KCl, 0·07 g $CaCl_2 2H_2O$, and 0·01 g $NaHCO_3$ in distilled water. But it was found that the tissues could be maintained for 4 weeks after the addition of an extract of planarian tissues to the medium. Murray (1927) also tested the effect of the tissue extracts of tapeworms, clams, isopods and sheep on cultures of planarian tissues and "found them harmful". When dextran and peptone were added to the solution of salts, the life of the cultures was prolonged and cell division was stimulated. Glycogen, leucine and tyrosine were found to be not unfavourable, but arginine had a distinctly toxic effect on the planarian tissues.

The media used to culture mollusc tissues were usually composed of tissue extracts in a suitable physiological solution. Bohuslav (1932) cultured tissues derived from different organs of a variety of species of molluscs, for example *Helix pomatia, H. obvia, H. austriaca* and *Arion empiricorum* in the following medium:

g	
0·74	NaCl
0·045	KCl
0·5	$CaCl_2$
0·002	$MgCl_2$
0·015	$NaHCO_3$
0·005	Na_2HPO_4
0·06	glucose
3·1	extract of the explant tissue
	in 100 ml distilled water

Gatenby and Hill (1933) kept their cultures of mollusc tissues "alive" for several weeks in a salt solution at pH 8·8 and containing 0·8% snail blood. The incorporation of snail blood in the salt solution, according to Gatenby (1931), stimulated the migration of cells from pieces of snail tissue and caused "cell multiplication" more successfully than extracts of albumen gland and ovo-testis. It is not made clear what Gatenby (1931) meant by "cell multiplication". But since he himself (1932) stated that although they believed cell multiplication took place in their cultures of small pieces of the wall of the pulmonary cavity, they did not detect cells displaying mitosis, then one may presume that "cell multiplication" simply describes the increase in size of the cellular outgrowths. This of course may be achieved simply by more cells emigrating from the explant tissue.

However, Flandre and Vago (1963) claim to have produced cultures of tissues of the foot, heart and mantle of *Helix aspersa* superior to those described by earlier workers, for example Gatenby (1931, 1932), Gatenby and Duthie (1932), Gatenby and Hill (1933), Bohuslav (1932, 1933), Konicek (1933) and Bevelander and Martin (1949). The salt solution used by Flandre and Vago (1963) was as follows:

	g
$NaCl$	0·72
KCl	0·74
$CaCl_2$	0·03
NaH_2PO_4	0·02
$MgSO_4$	0·02
$NaHCO_3$	0·55
Distilled water to 100 ml	

To ensure the "multiplication of cells" they added the following:

	g
Snail blood	0·1
Lactalbumin hydrolysate	0·01
Glucose	0·05

The medium was adjusted to pH 7·6 with a solution of 5% sodium bicarbonate and then sterilized by filtration. The medium was also varied by adding chick-embryo extract in the proportion of 2 parts to 3 of the medium. This mixture in turn was also used after adding chick plasma in the ratio of 1 part of plasma to 20 parts of the mixture.

In these media, which were semi-solid, the explant tissues produced cellular outgrowths in which it was stated "continuous mitosis" was observed "during numerous subcultures". It would, however, have been useful if the illustrations in the paper had shown cells displaying different stages of mitosis, in view of the negative results of the earlier workers. The different kinds of cells that were obtained in the cultures had obviously assumed peculiar shapes, judging by the formation of the processes extending from the cells. It would be interesting to learn whether the nature of the media used had a modulating effect on the shape of the cells.

Fauré-Fremiet (1934) pointed out that the amoebocytes of annelids survived in the coelomic fluids of the organisms concerned, Fauré-Fremiet (1925) had also previously observed that the amoebocytes of *Arenicola* agglutinated in coelomic fluid, and Loeb (1927) found that the haemocytes of *Limulus,* the King crab, behaved similarly in haemolymph *in vitro.* Fischer-Piette (1931) placed fragments of the "lymph gland" of *Homarus,* the lobster, in hanging-drops of coagulated plasma, and observed that whereas cells within the fragments displayed mitosis, those which were liberated into the plasma did not. The gland tissue and cells were maintained for 10–15 days, although it is not made clear whether the fresh plasma, which was added every two days, was cell-free.

It is evident from the literature that workers often experienced difficulty in preventing contamination of their cultures. Although precautions were taken, it is difficult to assess whether or not the tissues were naturally infected. When this occurs the tissues are likely to be unsuitable for culturing purposes, because the infective agents cannot always be destroyed by antibiotics.

Ever since Wilson (1907) discovered that studies on the aggregative behaviour of sponge cells in sea-water gave an insight into the problem of cellular adhesiveness, a considerable number of workers have employed the same cell system to investigate the same problem further and to make important contributions to the subject. It is significant that although mouse and chick embryonic tissues can be dissociated into separate cells and therefore made suitable for studies on cell aggregation (Moscona and Moscona, 1952), the merits of sponge cells for studying this problem are still appreciated (Curtis, 1962b; Moscona, 1963). The cells of *Hydra* have been cultured in fresh-water (Papenfuss and Bokenham, 1939) and studies have been made on the behaviour of the dissociated cells of the hydroids, *Pennaria tiarella* and *Eudendrium carneum,* and of *Alcyonaria* and of *Asterias* (Wilson, 1911).

There still remained, however, the problem of designing media which would throw invertebrate tissue cells into a growth phase comparable with that associated with primary cultures of vertebrate cells. Although a profound knowledge of the chemical composition of the blood and coelomic fluids of invertebrates would not of itself necessarily lead to the design of such media, it could nevertheless serve as a valuable guide for the design of suitable physiological solutions upon which to base the composition of favourable media.

This has been substantially borne out by the way analyses of the physical and chemical properties of insect blood (Buck, 1953; Wyatt, 1961) have enabled physiologists to devise successful methods of insect Tissue Culture.

The purpose of a balanced salt solution is to maintain the pH and osmotic pressure and to provide the proper balance of essential inorganic ions as well. In insects, the mole ratio of sodium to potassium in blood ranges from 0·1 to 25, with the ratio for phytophagous insects less than 1, for zoophagous greater than 1, and for omnivorous ones, in between (Buck, 1953). These ratios seem to be genetically fixed since they are unaffected by a change in diet, insects being able to maintain them through regulation of the ion content of their blood

(Martignoni, 1960; Wyatt, 1961). In the tissues of the few insects studied, the ratio is 0·3 to 0·4, a range similar to that for man. Potassium is therefore relatively high and it apparently remains so even when it happens to be low in the blood. This implies that insect tissues *in vitro* should be highly tolerant to varied ion ratios in the medium, and judging by the results of measuring the rhythmical beating of isolated hearts in solutions in which the ion ratios were varied (Barsa, 1954), this would seem to be the case. Trager (1935), for example, used a balanced salt solution with a high content of sodium chloride in his medium for culturing the ovarian tissue of *Bombyx mori*. When it was shown later that the content of potassium was high compared with sodium in silkworm blood (Tobias, 1948), Wyatt (1956) looked into the possibility of improving Trager's cultures by reversing the ratio of potassium to sodium in his original medium. However, changing the ratio did not produce the effect expected. Wyatt (1956) also tested a salt solution in which sodium, potassium, calcium, and magnesium were present at the relatively high concentrations found to occur naturally in silkworm blood (Bialaszewicz and Landau, 1938), and Versene was at the same time used to chelate excess calcium and magnesium in order to eliminate possible toxic effects of these ions. However, Wyatt again found that this modified version of Trager's medium led to no improvement in the cultures, thus indicating that the sodium to potassium ratio was not in itself critical for these tissues.

The hydrogen ion concentration of the blood of insects varies within the range pH 6·0–7·5 and in the same insect it is liable to vary up to 0·7 pH units, which is considerably greater than the 0·1 variation in man (Martignoni, 1960).

The buffering of insect blood depends mainly on bicarbonate, inorganic phosphates, organic phosphates and histidine. The presence of organic phosphates in insect blood is one of its unusual and characteristic features, because in vertebrates, for example, organic phosphates occur only within the cells. The buffer capacity of these compounds in insect blood is high, being sufficient to balance 30–40% of cations present (Wyatt, 1961). It is also probable that the carboxyl groups of amino acids and other organic acids act as buffers on the acid side, and the imino groups of the amino acids on the alkaline side. Insect blood also contains a high concentration of proteins and these too could act as a buffer over a wide range.

Correct adjustment of osmotic pressure in a culture medium is important and it is significant that in insect blood the high content of amino acids accounts for about 40% of the total osmotic pressure, whereas in vertebrate plasma amino acids account for only 1%, while 92% is due to inorganic ions (Martignoni, 1960).

Monosaccharides are present in small amounts in insect blood, and when this was first realized it posed the question of what happened to the sugars. The long-standing mystery was cleared up when it was discovered that the non-reducing disaccharide, trehalose, is the principal sugar in insect blood (Wyatt and Kalf, 1956; Howden and Kilby, 1956; Evans and Dethier, 1957), being commonly present at concentrations of 1000 mg/100 ml (Duchateau, Florkin and Gromadska, 1958). It has been suggested that conversion of sugars to trehalose aids their diffusion through the gut wall (Treherne, 1958a, b, c).

The way in which insect tissues utilize trehalose is little understood. They do not seem capable of using it *in vitro*. But as in the case of vertebrate tissues, they can utilize simple sugars *in vitro* as a source of energy. It is likely that simple sugars could serve adequately as an energy source for the maintenance of most, if not all kinds of invertebrate tissues.

Glycogen (Buck, 1953), free glycerol (Wyatt and Meyer, 1959) and cholesterol (Heller, 1932; Heller and Moklowska, 1930) are all present in insect blood. Their presence in culture media, however, does not seem to be essential. Cholesterol, for example, is an important requirement for the growth of insects, but it does not appear to be so for isolated tissues *in vitro* (Grace, 1958a).

One of the most distinguishing features of insect blood is the high concentration of amino acids (Sarlet, Duchateau and Florkin, 1952a, b.) In silkworms, for example, it can be about fifty times higher than it is in human plasma, in which amino acids are present at 3·5 mg/100 ml (Table I). All the known twenty-one amino acids have been shown to be present in the blood of insects, although the actual number varies from insect to insect (Wyatt, 1961). But high concentrations of glutamine, proline, arginine, lysine and histidine seem to be common (Wyatt, 1961).

So far information on the organic acids in insect blood is fragmentary, but malate (Nossal, 1952), citrate and lactate (Levenbook, 1950) and α-ketoglutarate (Levenbook, 1951) have been detected in *Gasterophilus* larvae. Wyatt (1961) has also demonstrated the presence of citrate, malate, succinate, fumarate, α-ketoglutarate, pyruvate and several unknowns in a total amount of 25–35 mEq/l of organic acids in the silkworm, *Hyalophora cecropia*. Buck (1953) has suggested that these organic acids are probably widespread in insect blood and serve to bind cations in weakly ionized form.

It will therefore be apparent from the above considerations that the composition of the blood of insects differs profoundly in many respects from that of vertebrates. Although our information on the chemical content of insect blood is based on analysing the blood of about a dozen

TABLE I

Composition of free amino acids in biological and synthetic solutions (mg/100 ml)
(From Jones, 1962.)

	Human plasma*	Lactalbumin hydrolysate†		Blood‡		Wyatt's physiological solution §	Vertebrate synthetic medium M. 199‖
		0·4%	1·0%	*Bombyx mori*	*Galleria mellonella*		
Alanine	3·41	10·8	27	50	225	45	5
Arginine	1·51	12·5	31	28	39	—	7
Arginine HCl	—	—	—	—	—	70	—
Aspartic	0·03	3·8	9·5	10	38	35	6
Asparagine	0·58	—	—	59	13	35	—
Cysteine + cystine	1·18	8·7	21·5	0	0	2·5	2
Glutamic acid	0·70	15·9	40	10	22	60	15
Glutamine	8·30	(10)	25	143	369	60	10
Glycine	1·54	1·8	4·5	73	51	65	5
Histidine	1·15	1·5	4	273	136	250	2
Isoleucine	0·89	12·4	31 }	29	42	{10	4
Leucine	1·69	37	92·5}			{15	12
Lysine	2·72	17·8	45	164	168	—	7
Lysine HCl	—	—	—	—	—	125	—
Methionine	0·38	6·7	16·5	14	27	10	3
Phenylalanine	0·84	14·3	35·5	11	11	15	5
Proline	2·36	4·1	10	36	520	35	4
Serine	1·12	9·2	23	111	47	110	5
Threonine	1·39	6·5	16·5	36	62	35	6
Tyrosine	1·03	10·8	27	31	76	5	4
Tryptophane	1·11	4·3	10·8	—	—	10	2
Valine	2·88	15·8	40	23	29	20	5
Total of above	34·8	203	470·3	1101	1875	1012	109
Peptide bound	—	101	250	—	—	—	—
Overall total	34·8	304	720	—	—	1012	—

*Stein and Moore (1954). †Kagawa *et al.* (1960). ‡Wyatt *et al.* (1956). §Wyatt (1956). ‖Morgan *et al.* (1950).

insects (Martignoni, 1960), there is no reason to suppose that it does not reflect the characteristics of insect blood in general. Table II shows the proportions of the main components of the blood of two species of silkmoth, each in a different stage of development (Wyatt, 1961).

TABLE II

Components of the blood of two insects
(From Wyatt, 1961.)

	Bombyx mori larva (mg/100 ml)	*Hyalophora cecropia* diapause pupa (mg/100 ml)
Na, K, Ca, Mg, Cl	400	400*
Phosphates	1100	600
Citrate	600	200
Trehalose	400	500
Glycerol	0	2800
Amino acids	1200	900
Other non-protein N	1900	2000
Protein	1900	7000
Total of above	7500	14,500
Total non-volatile matter	7800	15,800

*From values of *Antheraea polyphemus*.

On the assumption that a physiological solution whose composition resembled the natural composition of insect blood would be the most favourable one for maintaining *in vitro* the tissues of the insect concerned, first Levenbook (1950) and then Wyatt (1956) designed such solutions to serve as a basis for culture media. Levenbook (1950) found that his cultures of *Gastrophilus* larval tissue were not improved by following this procedure. But Wyatt (1956), on the other hand, obtained cultures of silkmoth ovarian tissue which were far superior to those obtained earlier by Trager (1935) by designing a physiological solution composed of ingredients in proportions similar to those which were known to occur in silkmoth blood (Table III). Grace (1958a) added nine components of the vitamin-B complex as well as cholesterol to Wyatt's medium, and claimed that they were beneficial to the cultures. Thiamine, riboflavine, Ca pantothenate, pyridoxine, nicotinic acid, biotin, folic acid, and choline, were added at a concentration of 0·001 mg/100 ml, and m-inositol at 0·2 mg/100 ml.

Jones and Cunningham (1960, 1961) incorporated as supplements hydrolysate of lactalbumin and T.C. yeastolate into the medium used to stimulate cell growth in their cultures of silkmoth ovarian tissue (see Table IV). For the cultivation of mammalian cells, 0·4% of lactalbumin hydrolysate is incorporated to provide about 300 mg of amino

TABLE III

Physiological solution for *Bombyx mori*
(From Wyatt, 1956.)

	mg/100 ml		mg/100 ml
NaH_2PO_4	110	DL-Alanine	45
$MgCl_2.6H_2O$	304	β-Alanine	20
$MgSO_4.7H_2O$	370	L-Proline	35
KCl	298	L-Tyrosine	5
$CaCl_2$	81	DL-Threonine	35
		DL-Methionine	10
Glucose	70	L-Phenylalanine	15
Fructose	40	DL-Valine	20
Sucrose	40	DL-Isoleucine	10
		DL-Leucine	15
L-Arginine HCl	70	L-Tryptophane	10
DL-Lysine HCl	125	L-Cystine	2·5
L-Histidine	250	Cysteine HCl	8
L-Aspartic acid	35		
L-Asparagine	35	Malic acid	67
L-Glutamic acid	60	α-Ketoglutaric acid	37
L-Glutamine	60	Succinic acid	6
Glycine	65	Fumaric acid	5·5
DL-Serine	110		
		Antibiotics (as necessary)	

pH = 6·35

TABLE IV

Medium for *Samia advena*
(From Jones and Cunningham, 1961.)

	mg/100 ml		mg/100 ml
NaH_2PO_4	110	Lactalbumin hydrolysate	1000
$MgCl_2.6H_2O$	300		
$MgSO_4.7H_2O$	370	Yeast extract (yeastolate)	100
KCl	300		
$CaCl_2$	80	Malic acid	60
		α-Ketoglutaric acid	35
Glucose	70	Succinic acid	6
Fructose	40	Fumaric acid	5·5
Sucrose	40		
		Antibiotics (as necessary)	

pH = 6·35

Supplements: LD-Lysine (100 mg/100 ml), L-histidine (200 mg) and DL-serine (100 mg) may be substituted for 300 mg lactalbumin hydrolysate; heat-treated haemolymph (10%).

acids per 100 ml. Since the concentration of amino acids in a 100 ml of insect blood is much higher, the amount of lactalbumin hydrolysate added to the medium must be proportionally increased (see Table I). Jones and Cunningham (1960) also added T.C. yeastolate, and although this supplement of bacteriological media seemed to improve the appearance of the cultures, it did not particularly enhance cell growth. Trager (1959a, b) employed the same supplements to cultivate trypanosomes *in vitro* in the presence of various tissues of the tsetse-fly pupa.

The large-molecule fraction in media for culturing invertebrate tissues has been provided by adding the blood of the animal from which the tissues were derived. In the case of insects, the blood should not be added to a culture medium unless it is pretreated to prevent the deposition of toxic phenolic compounds. Indeed there is nothing more toxic to insect tissues *in vitro* than untreated insect blood. Since the production of the toxic compounds is medicated by a phenol-oxidase, blocking this enzyme can prevent the deposition of the compounds concerned. Glutathione and phenylcarbamide are well known blocking agents of phenol-oxidase, but Wyatt (1956) reported that they were unsatisfactory when used in culture media. Bodine, Tahmisian and Hill (1944), however, demonstrated how the activity of phenol-oxidase could be completely inhibited by heating the blood at 60°C for about 5 min, and it has been the practice to heat the insect blood before adding it to the medium (Wyatt, 1956). It is of interest, however, that when Cunningham (1961) replaced blood with either methyl-cellulose or polyvinylpyrrolidone in her cultures of silkmoth ovarian tissue, cells migrated to form substantial outgrowths. This suggests that the main role of the treated blood in encouraging cell migration is simply to provide a large-molecule fraction. Cunningham (1961) also succeeded in inducing the cells of *Drosophila* tissues to migrate in a medium containing lactalbumin hydrolysate and T.C. yeastolate. In view of this it is tempting to suggest that culture media which have been successfully used to stimulate the growth of one kind of insect tissue *in vitro* could with appropriate modification be made suitable for culturing a wide array of insect tissues and indeed many other kinds of invertebrate tissues.

Any modification that may be necessary would largely involve altering the composition of the physiological saline, because an important requirement in designing a medium to suit a particular invertebrate tissue is a favourable physiological solution to which growth-promoting supplements and serum may be added. Lockwood (1961) has outlined some of the biologically important properties of inorganic ions and of the part played by different ion species in the metabolism of cells. He has also given the composition of about 100 physiological salt solutions which favour the maintenance of tissues of different kinds of animals, including annelids, crustaceans, insects and molluscs. In addition to this he has provided information on the ion composition of the blood of a number of invertebrate animals. Indeed any investigator contemplating the design of culture media for invertebrate tissues will find Lockwood's comprehensive survey of "Ringer" solutions most useful.

It is curious, however, that in the case of tick Tissue-Culture work, the design of the media used to cultivate tick tissues successfully has been based on that of media which favours the growth of mammalian cells. Martin and Vidler (1962) found that explanted tissues of the tick, *Rhipicephalus appendiculatus* produced outgrowths, in which cells displayed mitosis, in a medium that consisted of Hank's balanced salt solution to which were added the amino acids and vitamins of Eagle's (1955) basal medium and 20% ox serum. Řeháček (1962) also incorporated the ingredients of Eagle's medium, as well as 3% dextran and 0·1% dried calf serum in his medium for cultivating the trypsin-dissociated cells of the tissues of *Dermacentor marginatus* and *Hyalomma asiaticum*.

The failure of early workers to stimulate the growth of invertebrate tissues in media which contained ingredients known to favour the growth of vertebrate tissues *in vitro*, has obviously not deterred other workers from persevering with this procedure. It is significant that, in organ-culture work in particular, media which contain chicken plasma, or horse serum or chick-embryo extract have been successfully used to stimulate the development of invertebrate organs *in vitro*. Lender and Duveau-Hagege (1962, 1963) found that the male and female gonads of the Bee moth, *Galleria mellonella*, progressed in their development in a medium containing chick-embryo extract and horse serum. An important observation was that the addition of the blood of the moth did not enhance the development of the gonads. Thus the concept of the presence of the blood or tissue fluids of invertebrates being necessary in the culture medium to stimulate the growth of the cells and tissues of invertebrates does not seem to hold in this case. Demal and Leloup (1963) found that a simple salt solution containing chick-embryo extract was more favourable to the growth of the organs of dipterous insects than media containing insect blood as normally utilized in insect Tissue Culture. Maintenance of the fragments of the organs of *Limulus*, the King crab, *in vitro* was best achieved in media which were composed essentially of 7 vol of Gey's salt solution (0·8% NaCl; 0·03% KCl; 0·027% $CaCl_2$; 0·02% $MgCl_2.6H_2O$; 0·015% $Na_2HPO_4.2H_2O$; 0·002% KH_2PO_4; 0·02% glucose; 0·025% $NaHCO_3$) containing 1% gelatine; 5 vol of filtered sea-water; and 1 vol of either *Limulus* blood, or chick-embryo extract, or chicken plasma, or horse serum. There were other modifications, but in all the media devised, fragments of the heart, the liver, and the nervous system were apparently maintained in a "healthy" state for up to 12 days. Fragments of the earthworm, *Lumbricus herculeus*, have also been kept in a medium consisting of Tyrode's solution containing seventeen amino acids, long enough for significant histological changes to take place in the tissues (Gay, 1963).

Carlson (1961) has successfully used cultures of fragments of grasshopper embryos of *Chortophaga* in radiobiological studies on the effects of ionizing radiations on the neuroblast cells. Fragments composed of the abdominal region extending from the 1st to the 4th segment were cultured in the following media made up from stock solutions.

Stock solutions: (1) 7% NaCl, 0·2% KCl, 0·2% $CaCl_2$, 0·1% $MgCl_2$, 0·2% NaH_2PO_4;

(2) 0·05% $NaHCO_3$ (which can be autoclaved)

(3) 8% dextrose.

One part of each of these three solutions is added to 7 parts of Pyrex-distilled H_2O.

Shaw's medium (1956) is an improvement, since in its design it brings the sodium to potassium ratio and the concentrations of chlorides and organic anions in closer agreement with those existing in the insect.

Stock solutions: (1) 0·5M potassium glutamate plus 0·5M glycine (7·35 g glutamic acid, and 3·75 g glycine adjusted to pH 7·3 by the addition of concentrated KOH free of bicarbonate, and diluted with Pyrex-distilled water to make 100 ml of solution);

(2) 0·5M sodium glutamate plus 0·5M glycine (prepared as in (1) except that the pH is adjusted with NaOH);

(3) 0·2 g $CaCl_2.2H_2O$, 0·1 g $MgCl_2.6H_2O$, Pyrex-distilled H_2O to make up to 100 ml;

(4) 0·8 g NaH_2PO_4, 0·5 g $NaHCO_3$, Pyrex-distilled H_2O to make up to 100 ml;

(5) 7·0 g anhydrous glucose (or 7·7 g glucose.H_2O); Pyrex-distilled water to make up to 100 ml.

The culture medium is prepared by mixing 0·75 ml of (1), 1·25 ml of (2), 1·0 each of (3), (4) and (5), and approximately 5·0 ml of Pyrex-distilled water. A small amount of grasshopper egg yolk is placed in the hanging-drop (Gaulden and Kokomoor, 1955).

Braeman (unpublished) has found that both Carlson's and Shaw's media are favourable to the development of axons in the dissociated nerve cells of locust embryos, *Schistocerca*, but the presence of yolk in the hanging-drop appears to be an essential requirement for these cells to differentiate.

Li, Baker and Andrew (1963) have recommended a medium for culturing the dissociated cells of *Hydra* based on a mixture of Eagle's saline medium, horse serum, and modified Earle's medium with the addition of Fumidil B to eliminate infections with microsporidia, as well as the antibiotics, neomycin, streptomycin and penicillin.

The modified Earle's saline medium was made up as follows:

	mg/100 ml
NaCl	5·8
$MgSO_4.7H_2O$	100·0
$NaHCO_3$	168·0
KCl	7·5
$CaCl_2$	111·0
Dextrose	1000·0
Phenol red	10·0
Streptomycin	12·5

The medium employed to culture the *Hydra* cells was as follows:

Eagle's saline medium	100 ml
Horse serum	100 ml
Penicillin	200 units
Fumidil B	500 units
Earle's saline medium	100 ml
Triple distilled water	700 ml

0·15M Phosphate buffer to maintain the pH at 6·8.

The *Hydra* cells were cultured in the above medium at 22°C, and it is likely that this medium is superior to filtered pond water for general studies on the behaviour of *Hydra* cells *in vitro* (Papenfuss and Bokenham, 1939).

The recent successes in maintaining and growing invertebrate tissues in media containing ingredients that favour the growth of vertebrate tissues *in vitro* are interesting, for they lead one to suspect that the disappointing results obtained by early workers when they incorporated the same ingredients in their media were largely due to too little attention being paid to the need for aseptic conditions, and the fact that effective antibiotics such as streptomycin and penicillin were not then available.

III. Preparation of Materials and Techniques

One of the chief hazards in Tissue Culture work is contamination of media with bacteria and toxic chemical substances. But the introduction of antibiotics, for example streptomycin and penicillin, into media has greatly reduced contamination in cultures, and a scrutiny of the literature would seem to suggest that the recent establishment of successful methods of invertebrate Tissue Culture probably owes a great deal to the use of antibiotics.

The hanging-drop method, originally devised by Harrison (1906), has considerable advantages in exploratory Tissue Culture work on invertebrates, particularly if the explants tend to be small, as they often are when obtained from invertebrate animals. But when invertebrate tissues can be dissociated by tryptic enzymes into separate cells, the primary cultures may then be seeded with large numbers of cells derived, if need be, from tissues supplied by several animals. The dissociated cells in suspension can then be introduced into roller tubes or Carrel flasks for culturing.

A clear account of how to prepare materials for Tissue Culture in general has been given by Paul (1959) and the main methods of culture have been discussed in Vol. 1, Chap. 2. Nevertheless it might be appropriate here to consider some of the main points in the preparation of materials that have been used in successful insect Tissue-Culture methods, and we might take as our example the preparation of materials for culturing silkmoth ovarian tissue.

All glassware is cleaned with soap and water, and then rinsed thoroughly with tap water and distilled water, before being finally sterilized by heat or autoclaving.

To ensure that no bacteria contaminate the preparation, the extraction of blood and the removal of the tissues should be done inside a u.v. sterilized glass or perspex hood. Since the ovaries in question are small, it is also essential to place a stereo-microscope inside the hood, but with the eyepieces conveniently protruding through a hole in the sloping front panel.

For obtaining blood from the silkmoth larva it is preferable to anaesthetize the larva with CO_2. This relaxes the larva, which is surface sterilized with 96% ethanol before an incision is made in the head region to release the blood. If the pupa is used, it is only necessary to surface-sterilize the integument before making the incision in the head region. The blood is squeezed out of the aperture into a centrifuge tube kept chilled in a beaker of ice. This precaution halts the deposition of the toxic phenolic substances. The blood is next heated at 60°C for 5 min to precipitate out the phenol-oxidase, and then kept in deep freeze for about 12 h; it is afterwards centrifuged at 6000 *g* for 10 min, the clear supernatant fluid being decanted off for storage at −30°C until required.

After extraction of the blood, the ovarioles are removed in the following way. In the case of the pupa the dorsal half of the abdominal wall is first cut away to expose the underlying fat-body. In this, in the region of the 5th segment, reside the translucent globular shaped caps, or outer sheaths, which enclose the coiled-up distal portions of the ovarioles. A little patient searching may be needed at first until one becomes familiar with the material. The cap is held with a watchmaker's forceps and lifted out of the fat-body with the uncovered ovarioles, which tend to break off from the oviduct. In the process, the other cap is often pulled out of its natural position, so that one should allow for this when searching for it. The ovarioles are transferred to a Petri dish containing a sterile physiological solution. This is prepared by dissolving 7·5 g NaCl, 0·2 g KCl, 0·2 g $CaCl_2$, 2 g glucose and 0·02 g phenol red in 900 ml distilled water, and autoclaving this solution before adding to it 0·2 g $NaHCO_3$ in 100 ml which has been separately sterilized through a Seitz filter. Streptomycin and penicillin are added to a concentration in the final solution of 100 i.u. per ml. While in this solution in the Petri dish the ovarioles are cleaned of fat-body and cut into two or three pieces to serve as explants.

In preparing the culture medium shown in Table IV, the ingredients were dissolved in water redistilled in a Pyrex glass still, but the lactalbumin (polypeptides and amino acids) is dissolved separately by autoclaving the solution at 10 lb pressure for 10 min. The solutions are mixed, the $CaCl_2$ being added last. At this stage the pH is adjusted to 6·35 with 10% KOH, the blood being added afterwards at a final concentration of 10%. The final solution is then sterilized through a Seitz filter. Streptomycin and penicillin are added last at 100 i.u. per ml, and 50 i.u. per ml, respectively. This medium can be stored at 5°C, but it is advisable to make it up fresh from stock solutions about every 4 weeks, or even more frequently.

In preparing the cultures, the explants are placed in a drop of the medium spread on a standard square coverglass and left for about 10 min to settle against the surface. The coverglass is then inverted over a chamber, formed by sticking four thin glass strips to a slide with Araldite, and sealed with a mixture of wax and vaseline. The preparations are best kept in Petri dishes containing moist filter paper and incubated at 25°C, the medium being changed every fifth day.

When the explants and cellular outgrowths are firmly adhering to the coverglass, they can be fixed and stained *in situ*. A recommended fixative is 33% acetic acid in 80% ethanol. After careful fixation, the preparation can then be stained.

By examining a series of stained preparations of cultures of different ages and making cell counts to estimate the percentage of mitotic figures in each, it has been possible to measure the rate of cell growth in cultures of silkmoth ovarian tissue (Jones and Cunningham, 1960, 1961) (Fig. 12).

If the above procedures were adapted to culturing the tissues of other groups of invertebrates, it is likely that it would result in a much greater measure of success in the cultivation of invertebrate tissues.

There is certainly room for improvement in the design of methods for culturing the tissues of flatworms, annelids, molluscs and crustaceans. It is also likely that the cells of these tissues might be more successfully cultured if they were introduced in large numbers as free cells into the medium. This could be achieved easily enough if the tissues could be dispersed into separate cells by a proteolytic enzyme such as trypsin.

It is of interest that Martignoni, Zitcer and Wagner (1958) successfully dissociated the tissues of the cutworm, *Peridroma margaritosa* into separate cells by using hydrolytic enzymes obtained from the hepatopancreas and crop of the snail *Helix aspersa*. However, a clue to future possibilities was provided by St. Amand and Tipton (1954) when they succeeded in separating grasshopper neuroblasts with both trypsin and hyaluronidase without apparent harm to the cells. But in this laboratory Braeman (unpublished) has found that the prospective nerve tissue of locust embryos can be mechanically dissociated into separate cells in saline at room temperature. Grace (1962a), however, found that silkmoth ovarian tissue could only be dissociated into separate cells in a trypsin solution, and it is likely that many kinds of invertebrate tissues require to be chemically dissociated, when separate cells are needed to seed cultures.

Hydra has been dissociated successfully with trypsin into separate cells (Li, Baker and Andrew, 1963), but we have found in this laboratory that Versene will also dissociate *Hydra*. The *Hydra* were starved for 2 days before being trypsinized for 15 min, and the filtrate was centrifuged at 700 r.p.m. for 10 min to get rid of the nematocysts. *Hydra* cells were ultimately suspended in the culture medium (see p. 414) at a density of 64×10^3 cells per ml. It was observed that only the interstitial cells seemed capable of displaying mitotic division in the cultures obtained.

The aim of organ culture as is generally known is to maintain organs or fragments of organs as well as whole embryos in an intact condition *in vitro,* and at the same time to stimulate their growth and development in directions that they would be expected to go *in vivo*.

An important requirement in the preparation of explants for organ culture is to avoid any disruption or damage to the boundary cell layers. If this occurs, there is a tendency for cells to de-adhere and emerge from the damaged sites to form outgrowths over the glass surface.

A thick plasma clot containing tissue extract is the traditional semi-solid medium that is employed. But nowadays synthetic or semi-synthetic media are also commonly used, and have proved to be extremely satisfactory. The techniques of organ culture can be divided into those employing a semi-solid medium and those employing a fluid one (Paul, 1959). These same two techniques have already been used to culture fragments of invertebrate organs and embryos.

IV. Sources of Cells and Tissues

Tissues and cells may, of course, be obtained from any source, but it is well known that it is more difficult to initiate the growth of adult tissues of vertebrates *in vitro*. Yet these same tissues will grow at the same rate as embryonic tissues once they are thrown into a proliferating phase.

It is therefore reasonable to assume that the adult tissues of invertebrates are also suitable for cultivating *in vitro* provided that media can be devised to initiate their growth. So far, however, those invertebrate tissues which have been grown successfully *in vitro* have been derived from immature stages, for example the immature ovary and the imaginal buds residing in the larval and pupal stages of insects.

There are, however, sources of adult invertebrate tissue cells which provide excellent material for studying the adhesiveness, aggregation and differentiation of cells. Sponge cells, as already mentioned, are excellent for studying these problems. *Hydra* is also a good source of material for *in vitro* studies on the regeneration of tissues (Papenfuss and Bokenham, 1939) and the reorganization of cell layers (Roudabush, 1933). The shapes assumed by the parenchyma cells of planarians *in vitro* (Murray, 1931) suggest their suitability for studying plasticity in cells.

The amoebocytes of the annelids, *Arenicola* and *Nephthys* (Fauré-Fremiet, 1925, 1934) and the blood cells of *Limulus,* the King crab, will form aggregates in plasma in hanging-drop preparations (Loeb, 1927). The haemocytes of silkmoths will also rapidly form aggregates in citrated plasma (Fig. 14), and there is reason to believe that this cell system is admirably suitable for investigating the possibility of cell-aggregation-promoting factors being present in the plasma.

A great deal of the early exploratory work in invertebrate Tissue Culture is centred on attempts to grow mollusc tissues *in vitro*. Tissues from the wall of the pulmonary cavity (Gatenby and Duthie, 1932), the receptaculum seminis (Bohuslav, 1932, 1933) and the mantle (Bevelander and Martin, 1949) have been kept for several weeks in balanced salt solutions, with cells emigrating from the explants to form outgrowths. Flandre and Vago (1963) have succeeded in culturing tissues of the foot, the heart and the mantle of *Helix aspersa* in a semi-solid medium (see p. 404); they reported that mitosis occurred and that it was possible to subculture the cells.

It was Trager (1935) who first pioneered the culture of silkmoth ovarian tissue. Different kinds of cells emerge from pieces of silk-moth ovaries *in vitro,* and in a culture medium which favours cell growth certain of these cell-types proliferate by cell division (see

Jones, 1962). So far only silkmoth ovarian tissue has provided cells that can be propagated by continuous subculture as cell strains (Grace, 1962a). Another most promising source of cells for seeding cultures is the white-body tissue of *Octopus vulgaris* (Rocca and Martin, 1963).

The cells of silkmoth ovarian tissue have been successfully used, since Trager first used them (1935) to study the origin and multiplication of the polyhedral virus (Smith and Xeros, 1953; Grace, 1958c, 1962b), but silkmoth blood cells can also be successfully infected with the same virus (Martignoni and Scallion, 1961). Cultures of mosquito tissues (Trager, 1938), and leafhopper tissues (Hirumi and Maramorosch, 1964) have been employed to support the multiplication of different kinds of viruses *in vitro* and the scope in the study of viruses in natural vectors has now been extended by the successful cultivation of tick tissues (Řeháček, 1962; Martin and Vidler, 1962) (see p. 227.) Trypanosomes have also been stimulated to develop to the infective stage *in vitro* in cultures of tsetse-fly tissues (Trager, 1959a, b).

Geneticists and embryologists have for many years been interested in the possibility of culturing the tissues and organs of the fruit-fly, *Drosophila.* Cunningham (1961) and Castiglioni and Raimondi (1961) have succeeded in maintaining *Drosophila* tissues and imaginal buds *in vitro* for long periods and in stimulating them to produce cellular outgrowths. Cunningham (1961) also succeeded in separating nurse cells and ova, and in maintaining them *in vitro.* It is likely that this is of interest to those concerned with investigating the effect of various metabolites on the nurse cells, which are particularly active sites of ribonucleic acid and protein synthesis (Zalokar, 1960).

Successful organ cultures have been obtained by using the immature male gonads of the Cecropia silkmoth (Schmidt and Williams, 1953), the immature male and female gonads of the Bee moth, *Galleria mellonella* (Lender and Duveau-Hagege, 1962, 1963), and the immature hermaphrodite gonads of the ascidian, *Molgula manhattensis* (Sengel and Kieny, 1963) in developmental studies. Locust embryos also provide excellent material for *in vitro* studies on the growth and development of experimental organisms which have been ligatured at different levels to divide the body into separate compartments to interfere with the distribution of humoral growth factors (Jones, 1956a, b) (Fig. 17).

Carlson (1961) has also strongly recommended the use of the neuroblasts of the grasshopper embryo to study the effects of cell irradiation. The neuroblasts form a ventrally placed monolayer of cells in the prospective nervous system, which in the young embryo is subjacent to the hypodermis (Fig. 18). The young embryo (14 days old at 26°C incubation) resides near the posterior end of the egg, recognized by the presence of the sieve-like hydropyle disc.

The embryo may be removed as follows. First the outer chorion is removed by immersing the egg in 50% bleach solution (calcium hypochlorite) for 3–5 min to expose the transparent serosal cuticle, through which can be seen the embryo relative to the yolk system. The egg is washed with water and transferred to an insect Ringer's solution. The end furthest away from the embryo is cut off, and the embryo is then gently pressed out of the open end into the solution. The yolk is removed, and the amniotic membrane is broken to release the appendages. The region of the abdomen extending from the 1st to about the 4th segment is separated off from the rest of the embryo by simply making the two necessary transverse cuts. This part of the embryo is finally placed ventral surface against a coverglass in a thin film of the culture medium (see p. 413).

Braeman (unpublished) has succeeded in stimulating the nerve cells of the prospective ventral nerve cord of young locust embryos to produce long axons *in vitro*. The nerve cord is removed with part of the hypodermis attached, and is mechanically dissociated. The separate nerve cells may survive *in vitro* long enough to differentiate and assume the appearance of a typical neurone with its axon. The axon grows out from a site at the surface of the cell as a thin cytoplasmic strand with an exploratory fan-shaped distal tip. At the end of 48 h, the cells, which are about 10 μ in diameter, have produced axons about 100–150 μ in length (Fig. 20).

V. Growth by Cell Division in Tissue Cultures

It could be argued that the difference between conditions for the survival as opposed to the growth (proliferation) of cells *in vitro* is centred on the presence or absence of one or more growth-promoting compounds in the medium. Such compounds were thought to be endowed with special stimulatory growth effects which could be exerted when they were incorporated in a physiological solution.

Waymouth (1957) pointed out the pitfalls of accepting too readily the concept of the "growth-promoting factor". The mistake has been to confer upon this obscure factor the ability to trigger off cell proliferation as if it were some kind of endocrine substance. Hence there has been a tendency to believe that the growth-promoting factors ought to reside in the blood and in tissue extracts of invertebrates. Such factors are certainly present in chick-embryo extract. In this, however, it is likely that there are a multiplicity of components and nutrient substances. These are presumably balanced sufficiently well for the chick-embryo cells to utilize them for nuclear synthesis which favours cell division. By implication the metabolism of these cells can adjust itself to the *in vitro* conditions sufficiently to enable the cells to multiply.

It seems, therefore, that an important criterion for cell growth in culture is whether the cells chosen to seed the cultures are able to utilize the nutrient components in the medium for both their survival and growth. It is probably just as essential for the cells to alter the given set of conditions to let their metabolism get under way, as it is for the experimenter to design them in the first place. This is reflected in the way cells pass through an initial lag phase, or phase of non-growth while they are adapting themselves to the environment, and conversely the environment to themselves.

It is likely that when the tissues of invertebrates are maintained for long periods in culture they utilize the components in the medium. However, it is, so far, only the immature tissues of insects and in particular the immature ovarian tissue of a silkmoth that seem to possess a metabolism capable of an adjustment that leads to the cells proliferating *in vitro* at a rate that bears comparison with that recorded for primary cultures of vertebrate tissues (Jones, 1962).

The immature silkmoth ovary is a relatively simple organ consisting of two sets of four ovarioles attached at their proximities to stalk regions which are connected to the oviduct. The distal portions of the four ovarioles are coiled up within a sheath or outer cap referred to in a previous section of this article. Each ovariole has its own sheath composed of a few layers of flattened cells, and a subjacent layer (the intermediate layer) of loosely connected cells. These cells are separated from the inner layer of follicle cells by a membrane.

Evidence for growth by cell division taking place in cultures of silkmoth ovarian tissue has been furnished by Jones and Cunningham (1960, 1961), and this contribution to insect Tissue Culture was made possible by the excellent pioneer work of many investigators, particularly Trager (1935), Wyatt (1956) and Grace (1958a).

Martignoni (1960) questioned whether growth occurred in cultures of insect tissues. The evidence was certainly fragmentary and tissue culturists in general found it unacceptable. Indeed, it in no way detracts from the excellent work of Wyatt (1956) and Grace (1958a) to state that progress in the design of methods to stimulate the actual growth of insect tissues in culture was regarded as being no further forward than the design of those associated with other invertebrate tissues. The crucial requirement was to present acceptable evidence that cell proliferation could be obtained in cultures of insect tissues.

This evidence was provided by Jones and Cunningham (1960, 1961) as follows. The medium was prepared by incorporating "lactalbumin hydrolysate" and "T.C. yeastolate" in Wyatt's physiological solution

(1956) (Table IV). In this medium there emerged from explants of silkmoth ovarian tissue, obtained from diapausing pupae, large numbers of cells which formed extensive outgrowths (Fig. 1). Two kinds of cells predominated in these outgrowths (Fig. 2), and it was these cells derived mainly from the ovariole sheath and intermediate layer which displayed mitosis in all stages (Figs. 3–10).

It was estimated from cell counts in cultures of different ages that over the first 12 days, which included an initial lag phase of about 2 days duration, the mitotic index averaged 0·5%. The maximum of 1·0% was reached on the 5th and 6th day. Thereafter the mitotic rate declined, being less than 0·3% after the 21st day (Fig. 12). A mitotic index of 0·5% over a 12-day period coupled with the fact that cells in culture took about 30 min to complete mitosis indicates that three to four generations of cells could have been produced in this time. The decrease in the mitotic rate after the 12th day is to be expected in hanging-drop primary cultures, because such preparations are also unfavourable to the growth of vertebrate cells which could otherwise be propagated continuously by other culture methods (Paul, 1959).

The establishment of primary cultures of insect tissues in which cell proliferation compared favourably with that in primary cultures of vertebrate tissues next gave rise to attempts to produce insect cell strains. Success in this was first reported by Grace (1962a), who obtained four lines of cells from cultures of dissociated cells derived from silkmoth ovarian tissue. Grace (1962a) observed that the cell-types of which the lines were composed resembled those described in the primary cultures of Jones and Cunningham (1960, 1961) (Figs. 1–10).

Grace (1962a) trypsinized the silkmoth ovarian tissue at 37°C, and cultured the dissociated cells in modified Wyatt's medium (1956). Large numbers of cells apparently degenerated after the 50th day, and by the 70th day only a few of the cells present appeared to be still viable. After these cultures of cells had been kept for 10 months, the medium being frequently changed throughout this period, the healthy cells began to increase in number sufficiently for them to be subcultured. These "adjusted" cells were in fact then subcultured for further periods of 3–15 months. It seems reasonable therefore to conclude from this behaviour of the cells that there emerged in the cultures of dissociated cells, after 10 months, cell-types with an altered metabolism which made them capable of utilizing the components of the medium sufficiently for them to display continuous growth by cell division. Although these cell-types of the four cell lines may have retained an appearance which resembled the cells present in the primary cultures described by Jones and Cunningham (1960, 1961), it is probable that

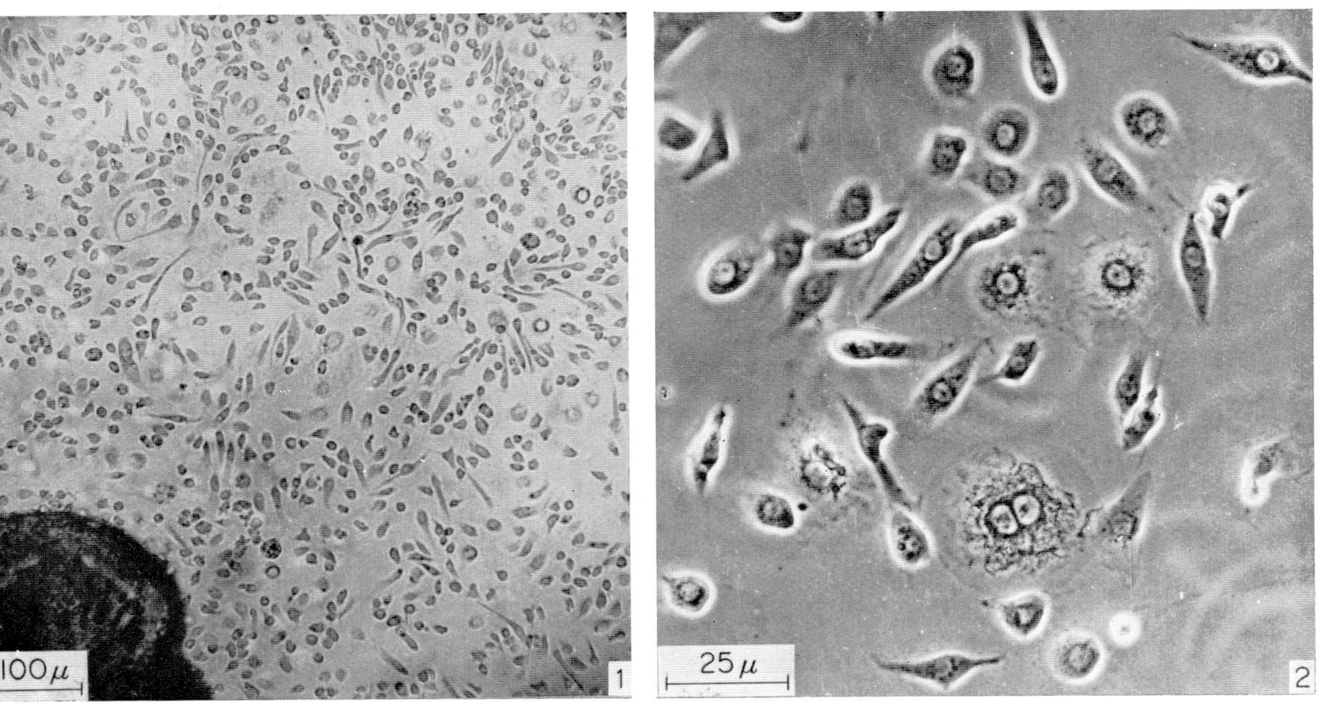

Fig. 1. Cellular outgrowth in a culture of silkmoth ovarian tissue, eighth day *in vitro*.
Fig. 2. Relatively large vacuolated cells and smaller cells assuming rounded and elongated shapes in cultures of silkmoth ovarian tissue, ninth day *in vitro*. Phase contrast.
(After Jones and Cunningham, 1960.)

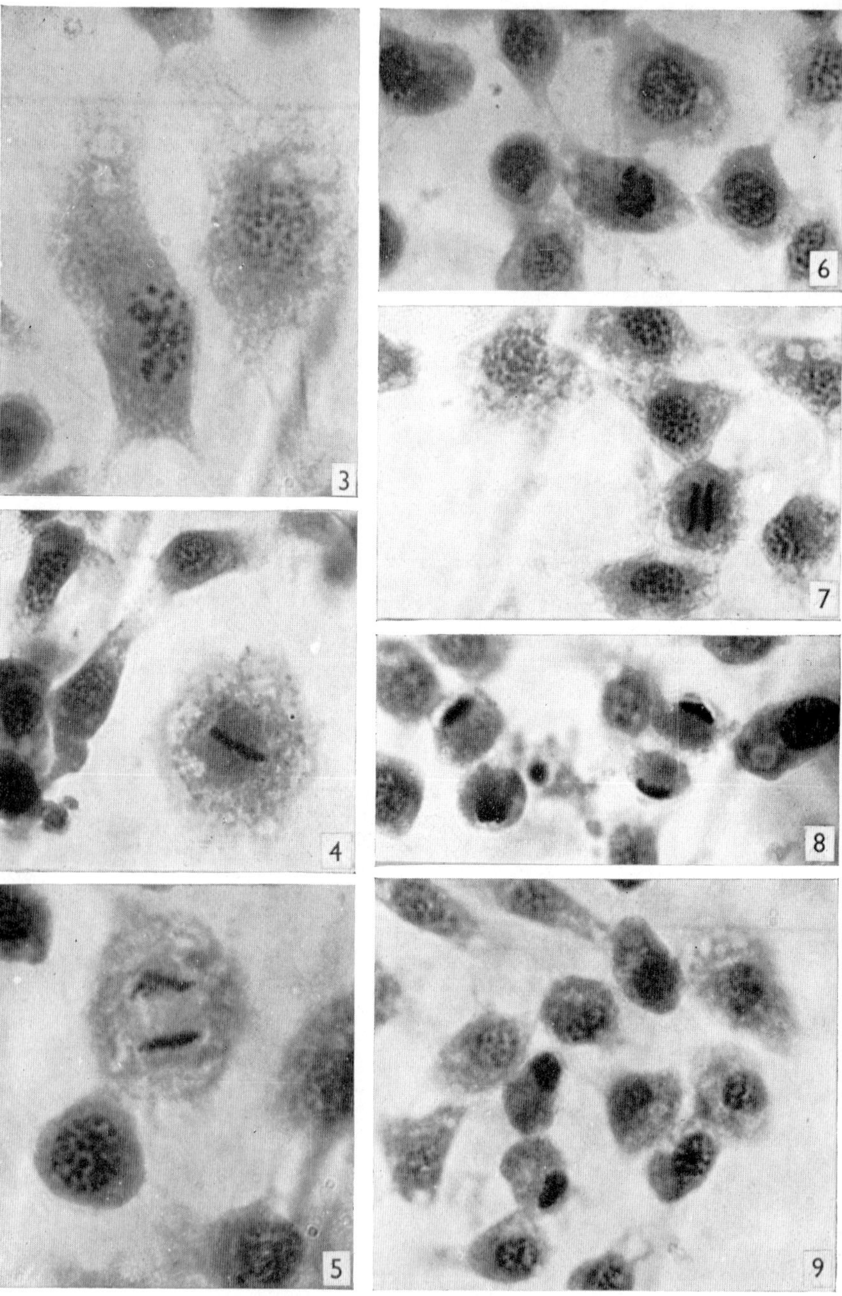

FIGS. 3–9. (After Jones and Cunningham, 1960).

FIG. 3. Prophase in large vacuolated cells in a culture of silkmoth ovarian tissue, 9-day-old culture. FIG. 4. Metaphase in same kind of cell, 9-day-old culture. FIG. 5. Late anaphase, 9-day-old culture. FIG. 6. Metaphase in smaller cell-type, 12-day-old culture. FIG. 7. Early anaphase of same kind of cell, 12-day-old culture. FIG. 8. Telophases, 9-day-old culture. FIG. 9. Daughter cells, 9-day-old culture.

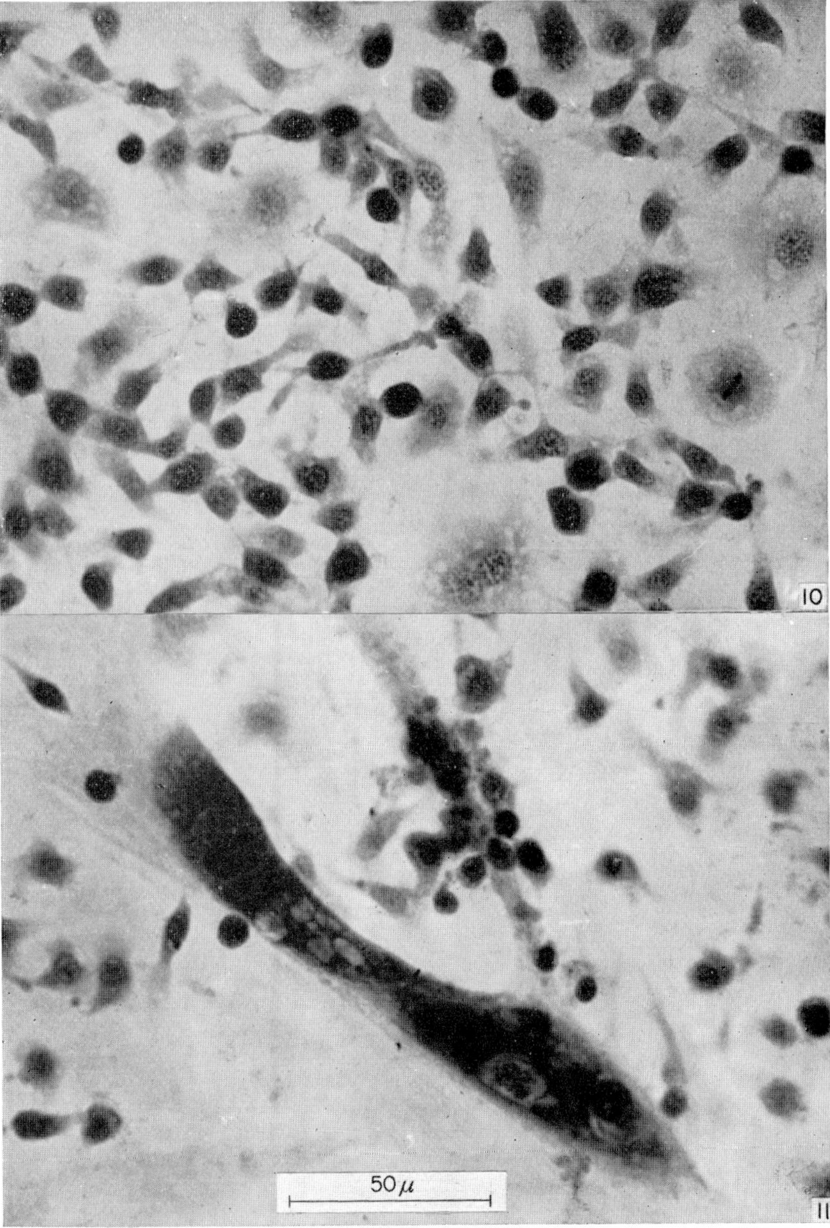

Fig. 10. Large vacuolated cells in isolation and smaller cells assuming fibroblast characteristics, 8-day-old culture of silkmoth ovarian tissue.
Fig. 11. Extremely large cap cells which have migrated into the medium, 8-day-old culture of silkmoth ovarian tissue.
(After Jones and Cunningham, 1961.)

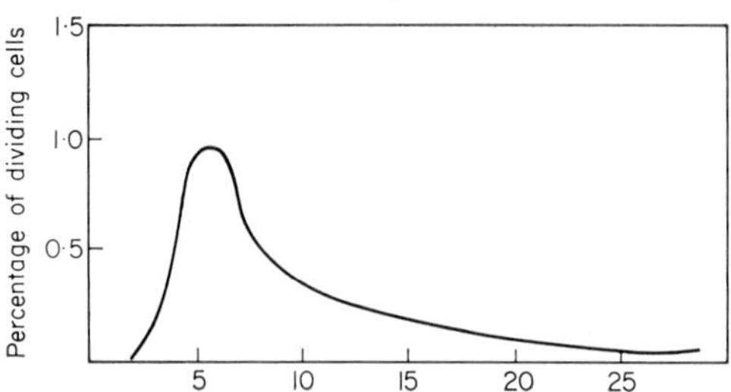

Fig. 12. Mean mitotic index for primary cell cultures of silkmoth ovarian tissue. (After Jones and Cunningham, 1960.)

some profound cellular or chromosomal modifications had taken place in the "adjusted" cell types to make them suitable for propagation by continuous subculture.

It is of particular interest that Rocca and Martin (1963) have reported on the ability of the white-body cells of *Octopus vulgaris*, which have been described by Bolognari (1951), to display a measurable mitotic activity in a medium that is a modification of Parker's T.C. 199 (Morgan, Morton and Parker, 1950), in which the Δ.T. was adjusted from 0·61 to 2·22 by the addition of 26·833 g NaCl. The percentage of cells undergoing mitosis was also calculated by counting the numbers of cells blocked at metaphase by the presence of colchicine in the medium.

The following physiological solution was also recommended as being favourable to the cultivation of the cells:

	g/l
NaCl	25·8
KCl	0·64
$CaCl_2$	0·64
$MgCl_2 . 6H_2O$	3·08
KH_2PO_4	0·02
Na_2HPO_4	0·08
$NaHCO_3$	0·20
Na_2SO_4	0·92
Na-pyruvate	1·50
Na-fumarate	1·05
L-glutamine	1·09

The pH of the solution is 7·5 and a feature of this solution is the compensation of the glucose by the sodium pyruvate and sodium fumarate. The presence of L-glutamine was apparently especially favourable to the cells. The cells remained healthy and were capable of "multiplication" for at least 96 h in this solution.

The nature and appearance of the cellular outgrowths produced in cultures of invertebrate tissues closely resemble those in primary cultures of vertebrate tissues. The cells emigrate from the explants in isolation, or in unison, or in small groups of fused cells (Fig. 11). These cells have been broadly classified into amoebocytes, which migrate singly; epitheliocytes, which do so in sheets; and fibroblast cells or mechanocytes, which tend to move out in a network pattern (Willmer, 1960).

One suspects, judging from the variety of shapes that an invertebrate tissue cell-type can assume in culture, that the ability of cells of invertebrates to express themselves heterotypically may be strongly developed. It recalled the ease with which the protozoan, *Naegleria gruberi,* will change from an amoeboid to a flagellate state, or vice versa, depending on the nature of the environmental conditions to which the protozoan is exposed (Willmer, 1956), and how the epithelial cells of a sponge blastula are capable of assuming the characteristics of either an amoeboid or flagellate-type cell (Willmer, 1960).

It would be interesting to learn whether the degree of plasticity in cells is related to the order of "primitiveness" of the organism from which the cells were derived.

VI. Aggregation of Dissociated Cells

Cell cohesion is an essential prerequisite for achievement of the multicellular state. Yet development of the multicellular organism is also marked by cells losing affinity for their neighbours and migrating to new places, where they will re-adhere to other cells. Indeed the sorting out of cells in this way points to adhesion and motility being closely associated phenomena, and this is equally well illustrated by cells crawling over a glass surface; for these cells must adhere to the glass to gain purchase in their efforts to move (Curtis, 1962a).

It is generally recognized that selective adhesion and the mechanism concerned lie at the root of the problem of morphogenesis. Thus the pressing need for information on how do like cells "recognize" each other in a mixed population, and acquire preferential affinities, thus implying some kind of coding device operating at the surfaces of cells. In order to gain insight into the nature of the cellular and environmental factors involved in the mutual and selective binding of cells, a great deal of attention is being given at the present time to studying the problem of how dissociated cells interact to form aggregates *in vitro,* and of how the cells sort themselves out and differentiate within the aggregates.

When mammalian or avian embryonic tissues are trypsinized, they dissociate into separate cells (Moscona and Moscona, 1952), but the effect of this treatment on the actual surfaces of the cells is little understood. It is generally known that mucoidal material is released around the treated cells, and it is presumed that since trypsin breaks peptide bonds linking arginine or lysine, the intercellular materials as well as a proportion of the material coating the cells are removed. How much disruption of the actual cell surfaces is brought about when the tissues are treated with tryptic enzymes, and what bearing this has on the re-aggregating capacity of the dissociated cells is not clear. But the disruptive effect of trypsin on cells must affect quantitative measurements of the effects of other factors such as temperature, pH and the presence or absence of proteins in the medium on cell aggregation.

When trypsin-dissociated embryonic mouse- and chick-cells are obtained from homologous tissues at corresponding stages in development, and mixed, they will intermingle to form interspecific mosaics and produce chimeric structures (Moscona, 1962). For example, kidney cells from both species cohere to form chimeric tubules; neural retina, chimeric rosettes; chondroblasts, chimeric cartilage, and so on (see Vol. 1, Chap. 14). This mixed system of vertebrate embryonic cells lacks species-specificity, and in this respect differs from mechanically dissociated sponge cells which appear to be species-specific (Wilson, 1907; Galtsoff, 1925a, b; Curtis, 1962b; Moscona, 1963).

In view of this apparent lack of specificity in embryonic vertebrate cells one cannot dismiss the possibility that treating embryonic mouse- and chick-cells with trypsin modifies their adhesive properties sufficiently to render them non-selective. The possibility is strengthened by the suggestion of Ambrose and Easty (1960) on evidence from their experiments that trypsin reacts with the surfaces of cells to alter the adhesive properties. It is also possible that the lack of species-specificity in the avian and mammalian cells, as displayed in cell-aggregation studies, may be coupled with their being embryonic. The species-specificity in sponge cells on the other hand might be an expression of adultness. Yet the dissociated cells of differentiated adult vertebrate tissues are apparently incapable of even forming aggregates in a rotated medium (Moscona, 1962), signifying a loss of ability to furnish an adhesive mechanism of any kind after dissociation.

It is therefore suggested that adult sponge cells have retained the ability of creating a self-made environment around them by exuding materials in the form of an outer coat. When these outer coats coalesce, they produce a matrix, and within this matrix the cells can move freely relative to each other. Thus the sorting out of cells necessary for producing a reconstituted sponge takes place in a separate environment of the cells' own making. Since the sponge cells are already differentiated, they are then presumably also capable of expressing cell-type specificity when mixed with cells of another type. When embryonic vertebrate cells are brought into contact with each other, they too are capable of forming similar-type aggregates within the confines of which the cells move from place to place in sorting themselves out. These embryonic cells when they form aggregates resemble sponge cells in that they reside in a matrix of their own making. It is also likely that some cells, for example epithelial cells, are inherently capable of exuding this matrix material more efficiently than others. Thus the necessity for two kinds of cells, epithelial and mesenchymal, to be mixed in experiments designed to induce cells to produce a differentiated structure assuming the shape of the organ from which the dissociated cells were derived. The production of a matrix would therefore seem to be a requirement for the formation of large aggregates in which cells are capable of differentiating.

The question which arises is whether cells are capable of initial adhesion in the complete absence of this matrix-type exudate at the surface. Moscona (1963) has marshalled evidence in favour of the view that this exudate or cell-binding material is essential for the initial adhesion of cells, whereas Curtis (1962b) prefers to believe that cells are capable of initial adhesion in the absence of the exudate.

We might therefore turn next to consider the contribution that *in vitro* studies on the self-aggregating ability of dissociated cells of invertebrate tissues have made to the background of information upon which current ideas on the nature of the mechanism of cellular adhesion are based. When Herbst (1900) first demonstrated that the mechanically dissociated blastomeres of sea-urchin embryos would re-adhere only in the presence of Ca^{++}, it was concluded that the adhesive mechanism was Ca-dependent. It was also suspected that in a Ca- and Mg-free medium the "hyaloplasm", which held the blastomeres together (Fig. 13b) was removed completely. It was this possibility that led to the assumption that the initial adhesion of blastomeres denuded of "hyaloplasm" was brought about by a separate Ca-dependent mechanism. It was therefore believed that two mechanisms were concerned with cell adhesion. Indeed A. R. Moore (1930) and M. M. Moore (1932) were of the opinion that the "hyaloplasm" simply maintained the shape of the embryo. It was Gray (1926) who first compared the chemical properties of the "hyaloplasm" which holds the cells of the ciliated epithelium of *Mytilus* gills together (Fig. 13a), with those of mucin and gluten, and Monné and Hårde (1951) later confirmed that "hyaloplasm" contained an acid polysaccharide associated with protein.

Hyaloplasm undoubtedly possesses adhesive properties, and when present even in small amounts at the surfaces of cells it could pre-

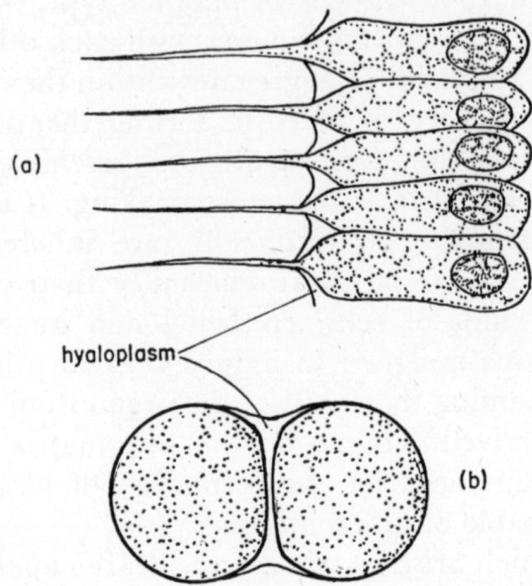

FIG. 13. (a) Epithelial cells of *Mytilus* gills held together by hyaloplasm. (b) Hyaloplasm between two blastomeres of a sea-urchin egg at the end of the first cleavage.

sumably cause cells which made contact with each other, to stick together. Galtsoff (1925a, b) took the view that the "hyaloplasm" was the cell-binding material of sponges from the standpoint that some "hyaloplasm" was retained at the surfaces of the mechanically dissociated cells. When Loeb (1922, 1927) observed that the blood cells of the King crab, *Limulus*, agglutinated to form aggregates in hanging-drops of haemolymph, he suggested that under these conditions the "hyaline ectoplasm" which coated the cells became adhesive. The role of the hyaline- or jelly-coat at the surfaces of sea-urchin eggs in adhesion was clearly defined by Lillie (1912) when he caused sea-urchin spermatozoa to agglutinate by placing them in sea-water containing the jelly-coat substance of the eggs of the same species. This result inferred some kind of immunological reaction in the process which brought the egg and sperm together in firm contact. In suggesting that a substance "fertilizin" from the egg combined with an "antifertilizin" of the sperm, Lillie pointed for the first time to the possibility of interpreting fertilization in terms of immunology. Tyler (1941) suggested that the fertilizin was emitted from the jelly-coat of the egg, and later on Tyler, Burbank and Tyler (1954a, b) showed it to be a polyfucose sulphate, while the antifertilizin appeared to be a globulin-like protein.

Tyler (1947, 1955) and Weiss (1950) extended the suggestion of Loeb (1927) that an adhesive mechanism resided at the surfaces of cells by proposing the existence of complementary macromolecules with linkage groups at the cell surface. These groups were thought of as interlocking on the principle of antibody-antigen systems, but since the relative movements of cells in a cohesive mass is not restricted (Townes and Holtfreter, 1955), it is unlikely that the interlocking device would be rigid. Since there is as yet no real evidence that the initial adhesion of cells is brought about by chemical bridging, the alternative suggestion that physical forces alone may be responsible for it, seems plausible (L. Weiss, 1960; Curtis, 1960, 1962a). One certainly cannot dismiss the importance of physical forces in bringing cells into close proximity with one another, but the nature of the charges at the surfaces of cells must in any case be dependent on the composition of the surface materials. Whether the secretion of an exudate is necessary to initiate cell adhesion is as yet uncertain. Galtsoff's view (1925a, b), however, that mechanically dissociated sponge cells reaggregated because a certain amount of the "hyaloplasm" or cell-binding material remained at the surfaces of the cells would seem to be confirmed by the recent work of Moscona (1963), who contends that dissociated sponge cells with their surfaces denuded of cell-binding material cannot re-adhere to each other to form aggregates until fresh cell-binding material is secreted.

On the view that the synthesis of this material was temperature-dependent, experiments have been designed to test the effects of temperature on cell re-aggregation. Moscona (1963) found that the exudate at the surfaces of sponge cells not only had a high cell-binding activity, but was also species selective. When the chemically dissociated cells of *Microciona prolifera* were placed in sea-water at 5°C, they failed to form aggregates. Yet at this same temperature they succeeded in producing aggregates provided the exudate extracted from the surfaces of the same species of cells was present. Curiously enough the cells of *Haliclona occulata* failed to aggregate at 5°C when the exudate extracted from *Microciona* cells was present. Thus it was suggested that the exudate was not only essential for cell adhesion, but was also species selective. Mechanically dissociated sponge cells on the other hand invariably aggregated at 5°C, the implication being that sufficient cell-binding material remained at the surfaces of the cells to make them adhesive.

Curtis (1962b), however, claimed that sponge cells completely denuded of the cell-binding material were still capable of adhering to each other at 3°C, when brought into contact. Even if one accepts that the sponge cells adhered to form groups of three or four cells at 3°C, it is difficult to reconcile these results with those of Moscona (1963), who makes it abundantly clear that sponge cells at 5°C remain single, even after being brought into contact by rotation. It could be that these differences in results may be accounted for in the preparation of the experimental cells, or indeed in the fact that the species of sponges used by these workers were different. Since Curtis (1962b) washed the dissociated sponge cells exceptionally thoroughly, it is also possible that the permeability of the cells was affected sufficiently for them to leach out materials with cell-binding properties.

It is less easy to explain the recent finding of Curtis (1965) that chick-embryo cells will form three-cell aggregates at 1°C when serum is absent from the medium. Apparently, serum contains a protein factor which inhibits cell aggregation at low temperatures, because the cells cannot hydrolyse the protein when this is adsorbed at their surfaces. At the higher temperatures, above 15°C, the cells, it is suggested, are able to break down this inhibitory protein, so that it cannot then interfere with the cells coming together to form aggregates. Although this may be an explanation of the failure of chick-embryo cells to adhere to each other at 15°C in a medium containing serum (1965), it serves mainly as an illustration of how environmental factors can have a modulating influence on cell adhesion. Curtis (1962a) had previously drawn attention to the effects of pH, ions, proteins, and mucopolysaccharides, when present in the medium, on cell reaggregation.

An example of how a medium containing a relatively high concentration of proteins and amino acids can promote aggregation is afforded by the aggregation behaviour of silkmoth haemocytes in citrated haemolymph. The haemocytes will form aggregates in about 15 min (Fig. 14). When chick-embryo fibroblasts were placed in the haemolymph from which the haemocytes had been removed, they too gathered into clumps. But whereas the clumps of chick-embryo cells could be mechanically dissociated, the aggregates of haemocytes could only be dispersed by chemical methods.

Both the silkmoth haemocytes and chick-embryo fibroblasts failed to produce aggregates in a culture medium containing 10% of preheated silkmoth blood (for composition of medium, see Table IV). They showed instead a preference for the glass surface, and as a consequence remained as a monolayer of cells on the glass.

These observations recall the effects of different proteins on the aggregation of cells to glass. For example, Lieberman and Ove (1957) obtained an α-globulin from serum which apparently promoted the adhesion of tissue cells to glass. Taylor (1961) showed that salmine adsorbed to a glass surface accelerated the adhesion of cells to the glass. Serum, on the other hand, had a pronounced inhibitory effect. It was presumed that since there are only basic groups on the salmine molecule, the adsorbed film would carry a positive charge, and that this being of opposite sign from that on the cells might be responsible for the rapid adhesion of the cells to the glass. The serum probably simply

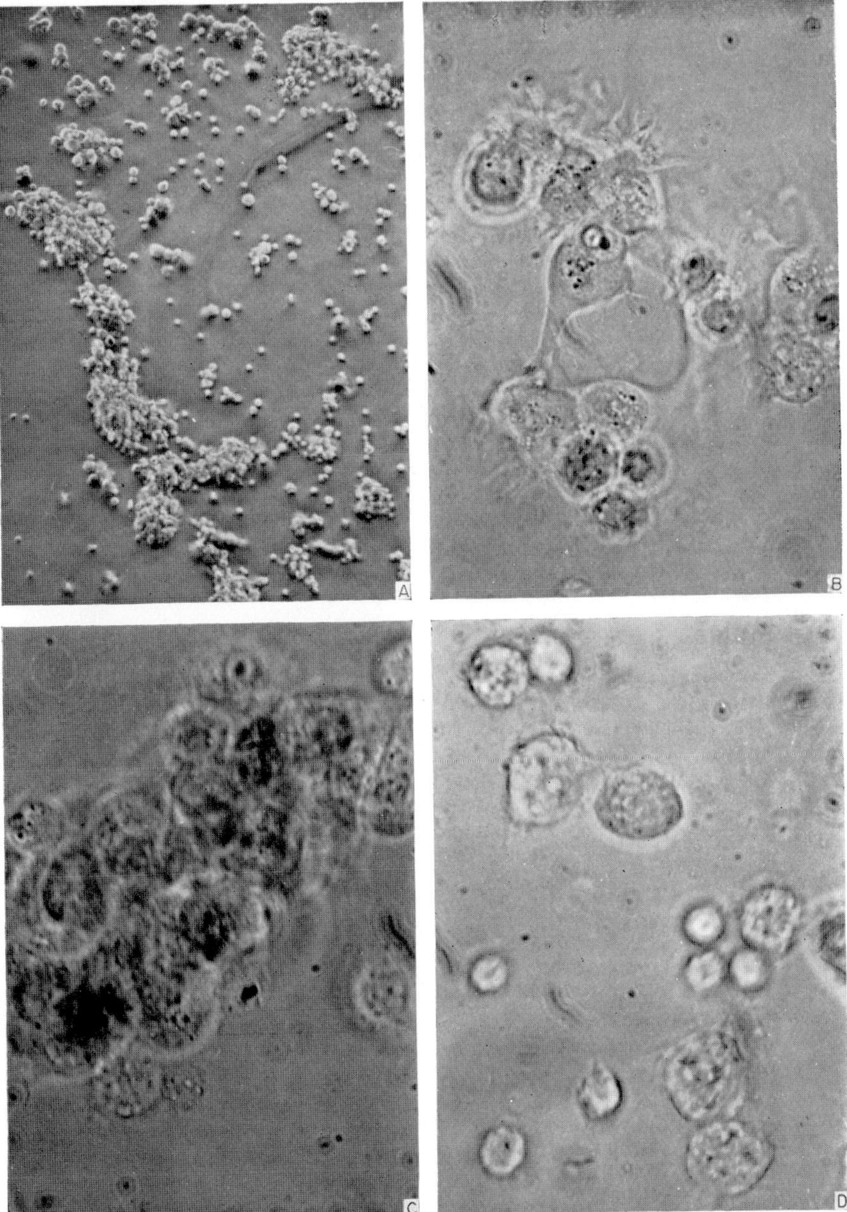

FIG. 14. Aggregation of silkmoth haemocytes *in virto*. Aggregation in citrated haemolymph after 30 min. Haemocytes in the process of forming an aggregate. Cohesive mass of haemocytes. Haemocytes in a physiological solution containing 10% preheated blood; they do not aggregate.

interfered with the cell to glass adhesion by its presence between the cell and glass surfaces (Fig. 15).

It is therefore likely that in the case of the silkmoth haemocytes, which adhered to each other in preference to the glass, that the protein being in high concentration in the haemolymph simply prevented the haemocytes adhering to the glass. It is suggested that in addition the haemocytes, once they had made contact with each other, were virtually held in position by the surrounding medium, due possibly to pressures exerted by the high protein content. The haemolymph thus had a "grouping" effect on the haemocytes as indeed it had on embryo-chick fibroblast cells.

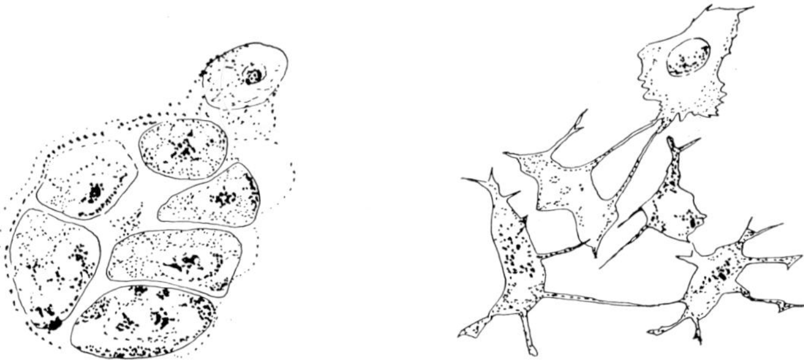

FIG. 15. Human conjunctiva cells as they appear 24 h after contact with the substratum. Left, in Eagle's medium with 10% horse serum; right, in Eagle's medium only, on clean glass. (Drawings from photographs after Taylor, 1961.)

Dissociated sponge cells in sea-water create their own immediate environment in the shape of an outer coating of protein and mucopolysaccharide materials. These materials seem to favour cell adhesion but prevent cell to glass adhesion as exemplified by the way isolated sponge cells will move over a glass surface (Galstoff, 1923). When the peripheral coatings of adjacent sponge cells coalesce, the motility of the cells is halted, presumably because the cell adhesion is strong. The secreted exudate at the surfaces of the sponge cells therefore prevents cell to glass adhesion, but favours cell to cell adhesion. It is therefore tempting to compare this role of the exudate in cell to glass adhesion with that of horse serum which inhibits the adhesion of chick-embryo cells to glass, but favours the grouping of cells when it surrounds the cells in the medium (Taylor, 1961).

Although cell migration, depending on the locomotory activity of the cells, plays a part in the "self-aggregation" of cells, a second and perhaps more important factor in the case of sponge cells is the apparent contraction of the matrix material in which the cells are embedded. Many years ago de Laubenfels (1932) pointed out that a mechanism other than amoeboid movement was involved in the production of aggregates. He observed that the initially formed aggregates were relatively small and that groups of cells seemed to be pulled in simultaneously from a given area. The larger the aggregate, the more expansive the space that surrounded it. Furthermore, the aggregates once formed, remained stationary. Galtsoff (1923) estimated that isolated archaeocytes were capable of crawling a distance of 185 μ in about 3 h over a glass surface, but de Laubenfels (1932) noticed that sponge cells at the fringe of a mass of these cells in the process of aggregating covered a distance of between 1000 and 10,000 μ in 2–6 h. This observation supported his conviction that sponge cell-sheets contracted into separate aggregates. Cells may at first escape from such a mass, but when the aggregate differentiates and produces a bounding layer of cells subjacent to a thick peripheral layer of the matrix material, the cells are retained. Embryonic vertebrate cells are also capable of producing a similar matrix material within which the cells aggregate and move around relative to each other before coming to a halt in positions within a boundary layer of flattened cells.

There still remains, however, the problem of how important is the secretion of the exudate in question for initiating cell adhesion. Is it possible for cell adhesion to be initiated in the complete absence of this exudate? Or, can initial adhesion be effected only when this exudate is present at the cell surface at a level of concentration sufficient to bind cells together? According to Moscona (1963) the initial adhesion of chemically dissociated sponge cells seems to depend on the secretion of such a cell-binding material. Since the aggregation of these cells is temperature-sensitive, in that the cells remain dispersed at 5°C (Humphreys, Humphreys and Moscona, 1960), it has been suggested that the cells are incapable of synthesizing and secreting the requisite cell-binding material at this low temperature. Thus the cells fail to aggregate (Moscona, 1963).

Since this cell-binding material is also apparently species-specific (Moscona, 1963), it could explain why cells from different species of sponges, when mixed, will form separate species-specific clumps (Wilson, 1907) or composite aggregates in which the aggregate of one species is in some way attached to another, as in the case of an aggregate of *Microciona* being surrounded by an aggregate of *Ciona* (Galtsoff, 1925a, b). The production of the composite aggregates has been explained by Curtis (1962b) in terms of a simultaneous mixing of cells of two species, which reaggregated at different rates. Hence the suggestion that a "temporal specificity" could account for the sorting out of cells (Curtis, 1962b).

From the foregoing consideration of the problem of cell-reaggregation, it will be apparent that it is as yet difficult to detect the existence of a separate mechanism concerned with initial cell adhesion. If a mechanism of cellular adhesion resides in the materials which lie close to or are even integrated with the lipid layer, then it is possible to draw a distinction between such a mechanism and the adhesive matrix material, which is produced by avian and mammalian embryonic cells and adult sponge cells. If two mechanisms concerned with cell adhesion do exist, as first suggested by Herbst (1900), is the difference between them qualitative or quantitative? So far the answer to this has been unexpectedly difficult to provide, but it is possible that the initial adhesion of cells can be effected by means which may be distinguished from those causing the subsequent fusion of cell-binding material exuded by cells. It has been suggested that initial cell adhesion depends partly on the degree of integration of the components at the cell surface (Jones, 1960), implying that when the components are loosely integrated the surface is less viscous, making it favourable to adhesion, and when closely integrated, perhaps due to increased bonding, the viscosity of the surface would be raised making it unfavourable to adhesion (Jones, 1965). We are reminded, however, that at the present time the problem of the behaviour of cells toward one another is full if imponderables (Abercrombie, 1964a), so it rules out any certainty about how the changing pattern of reactions of cells to one another is brought about.

Undoubtedly the technique of causing dissociated embryonic cells to collide by rotation to make them form aggregates, as first devised by Holtfreter (1944), is invaluable because, as Abercrombie points out (1964b), it permits a direct assessment of the interaction between cells with little interference by extracellular material. What sort of changes occur in these artificially constructed aggregates when two types of cells which were capable of adhering to each other initially begin to sort themselves out into separate territories? The problem is also a problem of cell contacts in morphogenesis which has been discussed by Abercrombie (1964b).

It is a matter of common observation that after treatment with tryptic enzymes, cells tend to round up. Even so, chemically dissociated cells, particularly those derived from very young embryos, quickly recover and soon form aggregates when they are brought into contact with each other. Thus despite the removal by the trypsin of the intercellular material and probably of part of the cell-surface material, two types of cells in a mixed suspension will on rotation adhere to each other to form aggregates. Hence initial adhesion is not cell-type specific. This implies that the adhesive mechanism of most cells may be similar. Since cells are not free of their environment, the sorting out process may be the result of factors in the environment interacting with the cell surface, thereby influencing the effectiveness of the adhesive mechanism.

It may well be that the sorting out of cells, entailing as it does de-adhesion and migration, is governed by secreted "conditioning" substances which diminish adhesiveness, and that these same substances are to be distinguished from the mucoprotein moiety, in which the adhesive mechanism seems to reside, and from the intercellular ground matrix as well. The initial adhesion of two different types of cells in aggregates may thus be explained in terms of their adhesive mechanisms being able to operate because they are unhindered by the presence of substances capable of modulating the properties of the cell surface. When the two types of cells begin to secrete, the substances produced interact with the cell surfaces to disrupt their adhesion, thereby causing a breach in the continuity of the cell-to-cell contact. The edges of the cells then become free and activated, and thus the cells are mobilized. The cells then move relative to each other and at random in the matrix. As cells move into an area where they are surrounded by like cells and substances of their own making in the matrix they are immobilized. The conditions favour adhesion and the cells in contiguity are once again held together.

I mention this speculation mostly because it illustrates the complexity of the interaction one may expect to find when cells are adjusting themselves to their surroundings. I have of course only touched on this problem, but sufficiently, it is hoped, to show that studies on the recohesion of the dissociated cells of invertebrate tissues are extremely important, because the adult as well as the embryonic cells of invertebrates have a propensity for adhesion *in vitro*, a characteristic not shared by the late embryonic and adult cells of vertebrates.

VII. Culture of Organs and Embryos in Developmental Studies

One of the most elegant examples of the use of organ culture in biological assay is provided by the investigations of Schmidt and Williams (1953) on the effects of the prothoracic gland hormone on the male sex cells of diapausing *cecropia* pupae.

There was ample circumstantial evidence in support of the presumption that a composite endocrine system composed of the brain and the prothoracic glands (or homologous glands) controlled growth and differentiation in insects. Under the tropic stimulation of the brain factor, released from highly specialized neurones in the cerebral ganglia the prothoracic glands secrete the "growth and differentiation" hormone. It is this same hormone which apparently reacts with the tissues to promote moulting and metamorphosis (Williams, 1952). The latter is in turn controlled by a third hormone, produced by the corpora allata (Wigglesworth, 1952) and when this hormone is present at a certain critical level, growth and differentiation is in the larval or immature stage direction.

Curiously enough, although the function of these endocrine centres can be demonstrated by extirpation and implantation of the glands, and parabiosis, none of the effects produced by these procedures is duplicated when blood transfusion methods are carried out on the test animal.

Thus Schmidt and Williams (1953) turned their attention to the possibility and hope that an *in vitro* system might furnish a method of biological assay. The organ chosen to provide the test tissue cells upon which to estimate the effect of blood containing varying amounts of the "growth and differentiation" hormone was the diapausing pupal testis.

The testes of the *cecropia* silkmoth are divided into four tubules, each tubule containing the germ cells, the majority of which are present as aggregates and enclosed by a layer of flattened cells to form testicular cysts (Fig. 16). In diapausing pupae the germ cells of the testes range

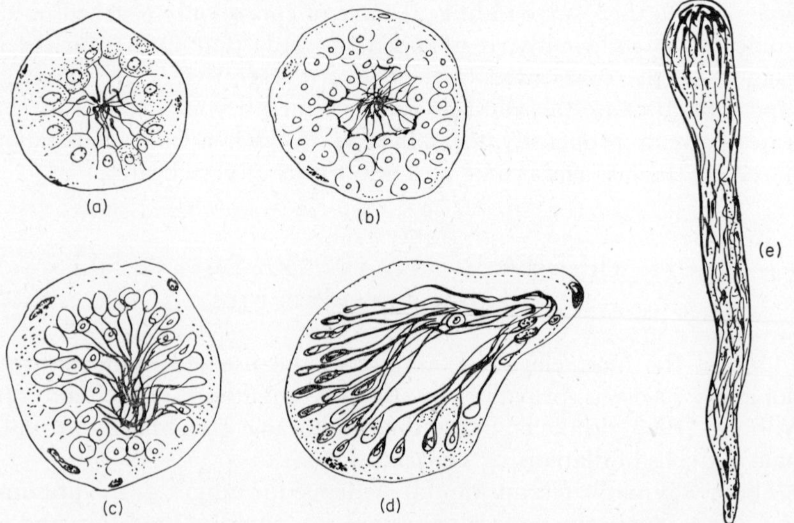

Fig. 16. Typical stages in the development of pupal *cecropia* sex cells in hanging-drops of "active" blood. (a) Testicular cyst of diapausing pupa with enclosed primary spermatocytes. (b) Cyst after several days in culture; the sex cells have just completed meiosis. (c) Further development to spermatids. (d) Continuation of differentiation of spermatids. (e) Elongated cyst containing well-differentiated spermatids. (Drawn from illustrations after Schmidt and Williams, 1953.)

in their development from spermatogonia to primary spermatocytes. On the termination of diapause mitosis is initiated in the immature cysts containing spermatogonia and meiotic division in the cysts containing primary spermatocytes. By the end of the first week of adult development, nearly all the sex cells in the testes have been transformed into spermatids.

When testicular cysts removed from diapausing pupae were placed in debris- and cell-free blood from larval, prepupal, pupal and developing adult donors, the results turned out as follows. Their spermatogonia and spermatocytes promptly developed into spermatids when cultured in hanging-drops of blood obtained from larvae entering the pupal stage (prepupae), or from developing adults (Fig. 16). Blood from mature larvae prior to the prepupal stage, or from diapausing pupae failed to stimulate comparable development. The prepupal and developing adult stages correspond to the periods when the prothoracic glands secrete the "growth and differentiation" hormone into the blood to react with the tissues and provoke their development. The fact that blood taken from these stages stimulated the conversion of the spermatogonia and primary spermatocytes of dormant pupae into spermatids *in vitro* was thus accepted as evidence in support of the conclusion that the development of the sex cells of the male organ was dependent upon the hormone secreted by the prothoracic glands.

It was also found by adopting the same organ-culture technique and the use of metabolic inhibitors, that the glycolytic system mobilizes substrates for spermatogenesis, that the tricarboxylic acid cycle is the main pathway of acetate utilization, and the oxidative phosphorylation energizes spermatogenesis (Schneiderman, Ketchel and Williams, 1953). This process is an aerobic one and is inhibited or retarded by several inhibitors of the cytochrome system according to the concentration of the inhibitor.

In the light of the demonstration by Schmidt and Williams (1953) of the stimulatory effect of blood containing a relatively high concentration of the prothoracic gland hormone upon the development of dormant testicular cysts of the *cecropia* silkworm *in vitro,* it is extremely interesting that Lender and Duveau-Hagege (1962, 1963) succeeded in initiating the development of both spermatogonia and oogonia of the Bee moth, *Galleria mellonella, in vitro* in the absence of the blood of this moth. The medium employed consisted of a balanced salt solution, embryo-chick extract and horse serum. When Bee moth blood was added to the medium, it did not apparently enhance development of the sex cells. In the absence of the embryo-chick extract in the medium used, the gonads rapidly deteriorated.

The gonads developed normally, however, in the medium described.

Testicular cysts containing spermatogonia from the last larval stage were converted to spermatids *in vitro*. In the female gonads, the oogonia multiplied, and the oocytes, nutritive cells and follicular cells differentiated, with the oocytes entering vitellogenesis. Thus both male and female gonads showed progress in development in the absence of the "growth and differentiation" hormone in the medium.

By implication it would seem that factors favourable to the development of the gonads *in vitro* are present in chick-embryo extract. Furthermore, since the ability to grow and differentiate resides in the cell, it is safe to assume that the primary role of the prothoracic gland hormone present in the hanging-drops of blood in which Schmidt and Williams (1953) cultured dormant spermatogonia to the spermatid stage, was to trigger off this development. Once this had occurred, one might assume that the blood medium provided favourable enough conditions for the subsequent progress in the development of the male gonads to take place. The progress of the development of the dormant male gonads in the cultures probably also depended on the extent of the reaction between the sex cells and the hormone, for there is abundant evidence (Wigglesworth, 1952; Williams, 1952) that the effectiveness of insect hormones seems to depend on concentration levels, and the balance of one hormone against the other.

It has to be made clear that the dormant pupal spermatogonia in the cultures of Schmidt and Williams (1953) probably required the stimulatory action of the hormone to initiate their development. But the state of the spermatogonia taken from the growing and developing stages of the Bee moth (Lender and Duveau-Hagege, 1963) was different in that they probably only required a medium that favoured further progress in their development. A medium containing chick-embryo extract to provide the growth stimulatory factors is obviously eminently suitable. It would be interesting to learn, however, whether spermatogonia derived from diapausing *cecropia* pupae would develop further in a similar medium containing chick-embryo extract.

The immature male and female gonads of the ascidian, *Molgula manhattensis,* failed to differentiate when placed in various media based on sea-water gelified by agar (Sengel and Kieny, 1962, 1963). Even their maintenance is short-lived, unless chicken plasma, or horse serum, or embryo-chick extract is added. The presence of the complex formed by the neural gland, the neural ganglion, and the vibratile organ was favourable to the survival of the gonads *in vitro,* and some oocytes were observed under these conditions to continue their development. But these same conditions did not stimulate the further development of the spermatocytes. Nonetheless, there is a suggestion in the results of this investigation that the neural gland-neural ganglion-vibratile-organ complex possesses a growth-initiating factor which can at least affect the development of the oocytes *in vitro*. This factor as far as its effect on development is concerned would seem to bear comparison with the prothoracic gland hormone of the *cecropia* silkmoth, but whether this resemblance is sufficient evidence for the neural gland of ascidians having an endocrine function is another question. That the neural gland present in the cultures of gonads of the ascidian had a stimulatory effect on the development of the oocytes is interesting, because there is no evidence that insect tissues in culture are stimulated in the same way by the presence of prothoracic glands.

When Bucklin (1953) cultivated fragments of diapausing embryos of the grasshopper, *Melanoplus, in vitro* the cells divided, signifying that those factors which exerted the inhibitory effect on cell growth in the intact diapausing embryo did not operate in fragments of the same embryo *in vitro*. There is also the possibility that the cells in the intact diapausing embryo were denied some factor or factors which favoured their growth. What is clear is that either those factors that were exerting the inhibitory effect were removed when the fragments of tissue were placed in hanging-drops of a balanced salt solution, or the *in vitro* conditions simply stimulated mitotic activity in the fragments of tissue which had been previously part of a closed system in which embryonic growth and development had been brought to a halt.

Fukuda (1951, 1952) demonstrated the source of a diapause hormone in *Bombyx* as being located in the sub-oesophageal ganglion of the female. When this hormone is released and apparently absorbed sufficiently by the eggs, its presence is expressed by the embryo passing into a diapause phase, during which time growth and development is inhibited. When the inhibitory effect of the hormone is no longer exerted, development recommences.

However, there is no evidence that a comparable hormone initiates diapause in lepidopterous pupae, or the diapause condition in grasshoppers, and locust embryos. Indeed the evidence (Williams, 1952) for diapause in *cecropia* pupae being simply a condition brought about by a denial of the growth stimulatory effect of hormonal factors to the cells is very acceptable. However, it is important not to lose sight of the possibility that the causal factors are probably interdependent, and that the failure of the prothoracic glands to function is also an effect, in much the same way as are the electrically dead state of the brain and the non-functioning state of the neurosecretory cells of the cerebral ganglia in diapausing *cecropia* pupae (Van der Kloot, 1955).

An insight into the relationship between the endocrine system and the diapause condition in embryos of *Locustana pardalina* was made possible by culturing embryos ligatured at different levels to test the effect of cutting off the flow of hormonal factors liberated by the composite brain-ventral head gland (homologous with prothoracic gland -corpus allatum system) (Jones, 1956a, b).

In the natural environment the embryo of *pardalina* at a certain point in its development enters a diapause period which lasts for about 6 months. At the end of this period the embryo recommences development, provided there is sufficient moisture. If dry conditions prevail in the post-diapause period development will still be held up, although the egg may then be regarded as being in a quiescent state, which can be terminated simply by immersing the eggs in water (Matthee, 1951).

When the dried quiescent eggs are placed on moist filter paper, they take in water through the hydropyle, a terminal sieve-like plate at one end of the egg, and enlarge until the turgor pressure inside is high. This triggers off development and initiates a sequence of events during the post-quiescent period which lasts for about 11 days at 30°C, and ends when the egg hatches out a young locust. Mitosis begins on the third day after wetting the egg, and preceding this is the appearance of distinguishable neurosecretory cells in the brain on the second day. But it is most doubtful if these cells are responsible for initiating mitosis, because Williams (1952) has demonstrated that brains with active neurosecretory centres are incapable alone of initiating mitosis and development.

The neurosecretory cells were large and apparently active on the fourth day and there were visible signs of progress in development. On the fifth day it was possible to distinguish the corpora allata and ventral head glands with the latter reaching a maximal size and activity on the sixth day. A moult occurred on the seventh day. Mitosis ended on the eighth day, and the ventral head glands were considerably reduced in size by the time the locust emerged. Isolated embryos were also capable of progressing in their development through the same stages *in vitro*.

The evidence converged convincingly in support of the conclusion that there was no participation of organized endocrine tissue or centres in the initiation of mitosis and development of the embryo on the termination of diapause. The observation therefore serves to explain why fragments of diapausing embryos of *Melanoplus* displayed mitosis when placed in hanging-drops of salt solution (Bucklin, 1953).

The role of the brain-ventral head gland-corpus allatum system in the post-diapause development stage of the embryo of *pardalina* was put into perspective by ligaturing experiments carried out on cultured embryos. Ligatures were placed at different levels before and after the periods of peak activity of the brain and the ventral head glands. The ligatures thus divided the embryos into two separate compartments. The serosal cuticle was removed and progress in development of the ligatured embryos *in vitro* was observed over the following 8 days. The organs of the abdomens of the experimental embryos were also examined at the end of this period.

Since the head contains the composite brain-ventral head gland-corpus allatum system, it follows that if this system was responsible for liberating a growth stimulatory factor then that part of the embryo which was cut off from a supply of the factor would not progress in its development. When ligatures were placed between the head and thorax (Fig. 17A), or the thorax and abdomen (Fig. 17B) before the critical period, the 6th day, the region posterior to the ligature failed to develop. When a ligature was placed in position after the critical period, the region posterior to the ligature was not prevented from displaying further development (Fig. 17C). It is significant, however, that evidence pointed to a continued supply of the secreted factor being necessary for the embryo to complete its development.

Excellent use of a successful method of cultivating grasshopper nerve tissue *in vitro* has been made by Carlson (1961) in radiobiological studies on the neuroblast cells. The tissue was obtained from embryos of *Chortophaga* at an age equivalent to 14 days at 26°C. Only the abdominal region extending from the 1st to the 3rd or 4th segment is retained for culturing. The ventral surface of this fragment is placed against a coverglass in a thinly spread drop of the culture medium, described in an earlier section (p. 413), in a hanging-drop preparation.

A major advantage of the neuroblast of the grasshopper, *Chortophaga,* as material for study, as Carlson (1961) pointed out, is the large size of this cell and its chromosomes. Neuroblasts measure approximately 25 μ in diameter at metaphase. The metaphase chromosome diameter is 1·5 μ, and the longer chromosomes measure 12–15 μ in length. The nucleoli are also relatively large and their disappearance at late prophase and reappearance in telophase is a well-marked feature in the mitotic cycle.

The neuroblasts are distributed in the prospective nerve cord as a ventral layer which is subjacent to the hypodermis (Fig. 18). Moreover, each neuroblast in this layer maintains a relatively constant position with respect to the neighbouring neuroblasts of the same segment (Fig. 19). In each segment the neuroblasts are arranged in about five rows and it is possible to observe mitosis in a number of selected cells in different embryos over the course of several hours or days.

In the radiobiological studies on mitosis in the neuroblast cells *in vitro,* a glass coverglass may be used in X-ray and gamma-ray experiments, thin mica for alpha particles, and a quartz coverslip for ultraviolet radiation.

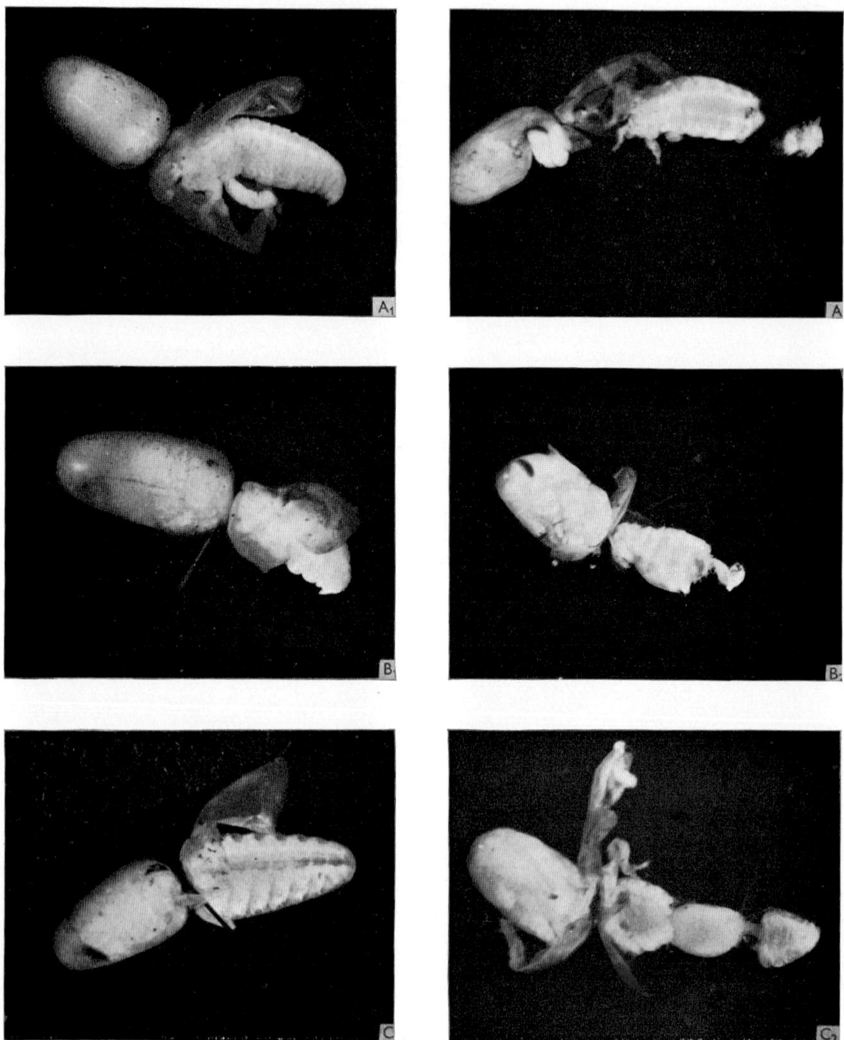

FIG. 17. Embryos of *Locusta migratoria* after 8 days *in vitro* showing unequal progress in development in front of and behind ligatures. The embryos were ligatured at different levels before and after the liberation of the "development" hormone from the head gland. A and B were ligatured before, and C after the critical period. A was ligatured between the head and thorax, and B and C between the thorax and abdomen.

A_1 and A_2: head developed, but thorax and abdomen showed no progress in development. B_1 and B_2: head and thorax developed but abdomen did not. C_1 and C_2: head, thorax and abdomen all developed. (After Jones, 1956b.)

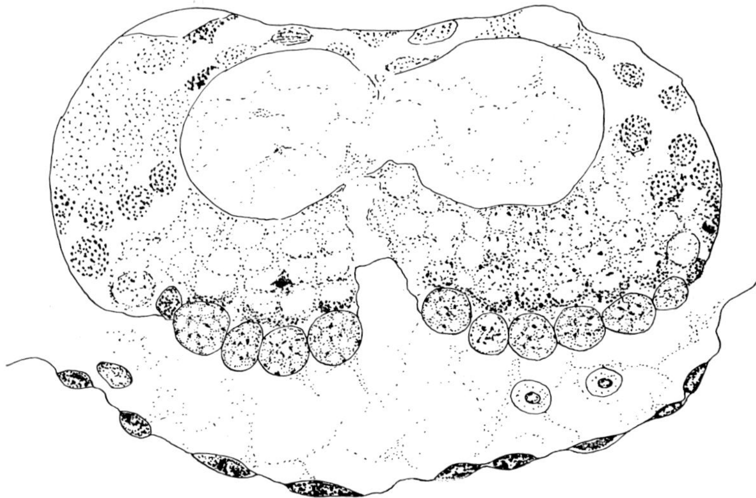

Fig. 18. Transverse section of prospective nerve cord of young locust embryo showing ventrally placed neuroblasts subjacent to the epidermis.

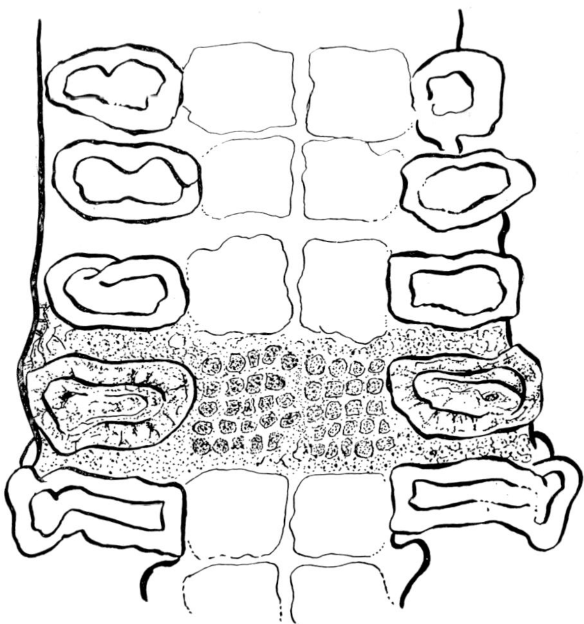

Fig. 19. Ventral view of prospective nerve cord of young locust embryo extending from the 1st to the 5th abdominal segment and showing the layer of neuroblasts in the 2nd segment.

The effects of ionizing and ultraviolet radiations on grasshopper neuroblasts have been reviewed (1954, 1958) and summarized (1961) by Carlson (see also Chapter 2). Since these results are part of the wider subject of radiobiology, all that need be said here is that grasshopper neuroblasts provide ideal experimental material for radiobiological studies.

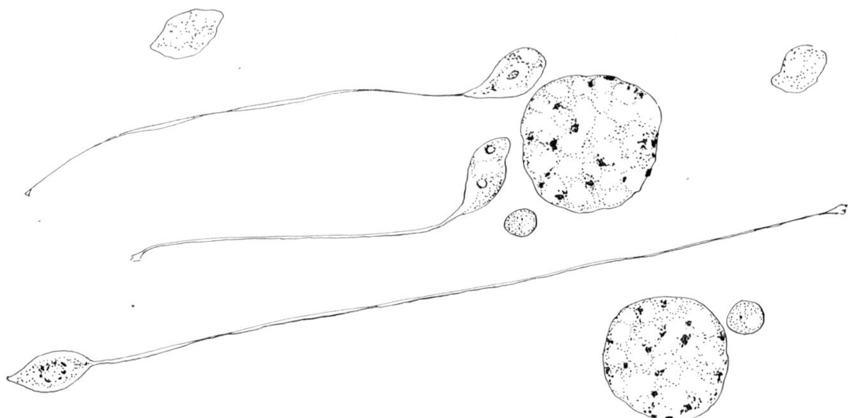

FIG. 20. Axons produced by nerve cells in 48 h *in vitro*. The larger cells are neuroblasts. (Drawn from preparations after J. Braeman, unpublished work.)

VIII. INVERTEBRATE TISSUE CULTURE IN PATHOLOGY

There has been an increasing tendency in recent years for research workers in the fields of virology and pathology in particular to replace experimental animals by isolated organs and tissues, and these, in turn, by cells maintained *in vitro*. This has inevitably led to a considerable demand for reliable methods of tissue and cell culture.

Since insects are natural "culture flasks" for viruses, bacteria, rickettsiae, and Protozoa, many of which are pathogenic to man as well as to his crops and domestic animals, the possibilities of a successful method of insect Tissue Culture as a research tool for investigating problems of insect-borne diseases were realized many years ago. Indeed one can in retrospect point to two requirements that initiated insect Tissue Culture work. The first was to maintain silkmoth spermatocytes *in vitro* since observations of their development would help to elucidate the problem of gametogenesis (Goldschmidt, 1915), and the second, which came much later, was to grow viruses known to develop naturally in insects, in insect tissues in cultures.

It was Trager (1935) who first used insect Tissue Culture successfully to meet this second requirement. Indeed his efforts to design a method of maintaining silkmoth ovarian tissue *in vitro* were primarily aimed to provide favourable conditions for studying the latent virus which causes the disease in silkmoths called polyhedrosis.

As described in an earlier section, Trager (1935) placed explants of *Bombyx* ovaries in a simple medium of balanced salts and silkmoth plasma in a hanging-drop preparation. The conditions induced a moderate number of cells to migrate from the tissues. When the explanted tissues were experimentally infected with the latent virus of grasserie, which causes polyhedrosis in silkmoths, the virus apparently multiplied in the cells.

Latent viruses are of course frequently met with in plants as well as in insects, and the existence of such viruses in organisms has been accepted readily enough and without question by most virus workers (Smith, 1952). Many of these latent viruses have been obtained in crystalline form; the first of these, in animals, to be crystallized was that of poliomyelitis, the second being the irridescent virus of the insect, *Tipula* (Smith, 1959).

The type of latent virus that occurs in insects can become virulent under the influence of appropriate stimuli. The latent virus is also transmitted from generation to generation and in "healthy" stocks of insects a high proportion are liable to carry the virus. Grace (1958c) found that if he altered the osmotic pressure of the medium in his cultures of silkmoth tissues, polyhedral viruses were produced in the tissue cells. Cunningham (1961) induced silkmoth blood cells to produce the viruses by adding phenylcarbamide to the culture medium. The development of the virus in *Bombyx* can also apparently be promoted in the carriers by feeding the larvae with nitrites (Yamafugi and Yoshihara, 1950), or acetoxime (Yamafugi and Omura, 1950). The development of the latent virus of *Bombyx* in the cell nucleus has been described by Smith and Xeros (1953) who tentatively compared the latent virus with a differentiated product of altered cell metabolism.

Martignoni and Scallion (1961) have successfully infected the blood cells of silkmoths *in vitro* with the polyhedrosis virus which then developed in the nuclei of the cells. Grace (1962b), however, has demonstrated the development of a cytoplasmic polyhedrosis in separate cultured cells obtained by dissociating the ovaries (Fig. 21). Since the viruses are apparently formed in the nucleus from rods of ribonucleic acid (RNA), each of which embeds itself in protein, which is just sufficient to form a well-fitting coat (Smith and Xeros, 1953), then one may presume from the findings of Grace (1962b) that rods of RNA originating in the cytoplasm are equally capable of forming, with protein, the nucleo-protein virus.

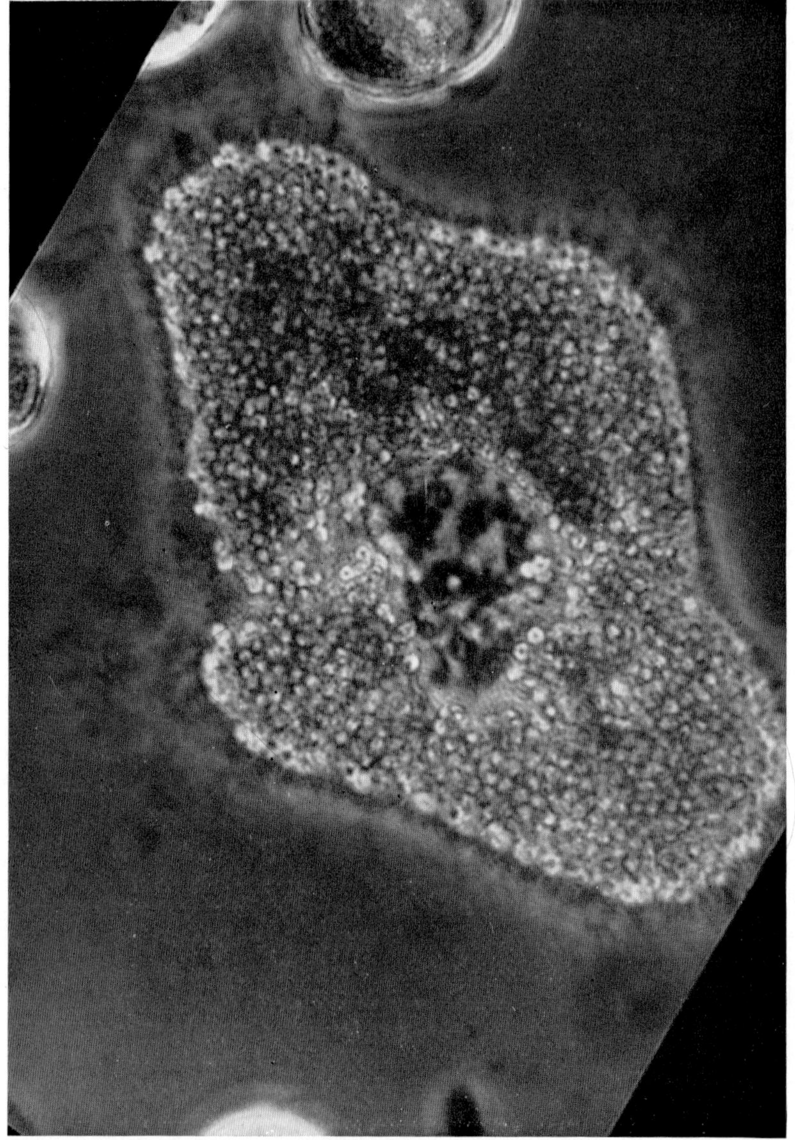

Fig. 21. A single cell from a culture of *Antheraea eucalypti* ovarian cells grown *in vitro* showing polyhedra present in the cytoplasm in which they developed. (After Grace, 1962b.)

Merrill, Lacaillade and Ken Broeck (1934) showed that the equine encephalomyelitis virus develops naturally in the mosquito, *Aedes aegypti*, and it was Trager (1938) who found that when the gut and ovary tissues of this mosquito were experimentally infected *in vitro* with the virus, the virus multiplied slowly, reaching at the end of 28 days *in vitro* a titre that was estimated as 100,000 times greater than that for the original virus suspension.

Attempts to develop pathogenic protozoa *in vitro* in the presence of insect tissues have so far been few. Weinman (1957) and Trager (1959a, b), however, have succeeded in stimulating the development of trypanosomes to the infective metacyclic form *in vitro* in the presence of tsetse-fly tissues. Curiously enough, when attempts have been made to cultivate mosquito gut bearing oocysts of *Plasmodium,* the malarial protozoan parasite, the oocysts have failed to develop further (Ball, 1947, 1948, 1954; Ragab, 1948, 1949). It has now been shown, however, that the oocysts will develop in a favourable medium even when isolated completely from the gut (Ball and Chao, 1957).

In vitro studies on insect tumours have so far been exploratory and tentative. Friedman and Burton (1956) have maintained a fragment of normal *Drosophila* tissue with an associated invasive-type tumour *in vitro* for 14 days. The cells of this tumour were amoebocytic and in their appearance resembled the melanoblasts in cultures of human, mouse and fish melanomas. They were stellate-shaped with fine dendrites and possessed pigment granules clustered around the nucleus. It was claimed that in the preparations containing the combined tumour and normal tissue explants the tumour tissue further invaded the normal tissue to which it was attached. That insect tumour cells have invasive properties is confirmed by their ability to metastasize in the host insect and develop secondary tumour growths (Sharrer, 1945; Harker, 1958). An interesting point about the exploratory investigations *in vitro* on insect tumour tissue is the juxtaposing of the normal and tumour tissues under organ-culture conditions, which is an approach to the problem of the invasiveness of tumour tissues that has obvious advantages over studies on separate tumour cells.

References

Abercrombie, M. (1964a). Behaviour of cells toward one another. *In* "Advances in Biology of Skin", Vol. 5, pp. 95–112. Pergamon Press, London.

Abercrombie, M. (1964b). Cell contacts in morphogenesis. *Arch. Biol.* (*Liège*) **75**, 351.

Ambrose, E. J. and Easty, G. C. (1960). Membrane structure in relation to cellular motility. *Proc. R. phys. Soc. Edinb.* **28**, 53.

Arvy, L. and Gabe, M. (1946). Sur la multiplication *in vitro* des cellules sanguines de *Forficula auricularia. C.R. Soc. Biol., Paris* **140**, 787.

Ball, G. H. (1947). Attempts to cultivate the mosquito phase of *Plasmodium relictum. Amer. J. trop. Med.* **27**, 301.

Ball, G. H. (1948). Extended persistence of *Plasmodium relictum* in culture. *Amer. J. trop. Med.* **28**, 533.

Ball, G. H. (1954). Prolonged contraction of mosquito digestive tract *in vitro* with partial development of oocysts of *Plasmodium relictum*. *Exp. Parasit.* **3**, 359.

Ball, G. H. and Chao, J. (1957). Development *in vitro* of isolated oocysts of *Plasmodium relictum*. *J. Parasit.* **43**, 409.

Barsa, M. C. (1954). The behaviour of isolated hearts of the grasshopper, *Chortophaga viridifasciata*, and the moth, *Samia walkeri*, in solutions with different concentrations of sodium, potassium, calcium and magnesium. *J. gen. Physiol.* **38**, 79.

Baumgartner, W. J. and Payne, M. A. (1930). Intravitam technique for the study of the living cells of insects. *Science* **72**, 199.

Bělăr, K. (1929). Beitrage zur Kausalanalyse der Mitose II. Untersuchungen an den Spermatocyten von *Chorthippus*. *Arch. EntwMech. Org.* **118**, 357.

Bevelander, G. and Martin, J. (1949). Culture of mantle tissue of marine molluscs. *Anat. Rec.* **105**, 614.

Bialaszewicz, K. and Landau, C. (1938). Sur la composition minérale de l'hémolymphe des vers à soie et sur les changements qu'elle subit au cours de la croissance et pendant la métamorphose. *Acta Biol. exp.* **12**, 307.

Bodine, J. H., Tahmisian, T. N. and Hill, D. L. (1944). Effect of heat on protyrosinase. Heat activation, inhibition and injury of protyrosinase and tyrosinase. *Arch. Biochem.* **4**, 403.

Bohuslav, P. (1932). Die Gewebezüchtung des postembryonalen Verdauungstraktus, der Glandula salivalis und des Receptaculum seminis bei Mollusken aus der Familie Helicidae. *Arch. exp. Zellforsch.* **13**, 673.

Bohuslav, P. (1933). Die Explantation des reinen postembryonalen Herzbindegewebes aus *Helix pomatia*. *Arch. exp. Zellforsch.* **14**, 139.

Bolognari, A. (1951). Morfologia, struttura e funzione del corpo vianco dei Cefalopodi. Parte 2. Strutturas e funzione. *Arch. zool. ital.* **36**, 253.

Buck, J. B. (1953). Physical properties and chemical composition of insect blood. *In* "Insect Physiology" (K. D. Roeder, ed.), pp. 147–90. Wiley, New York.

Bucklin, D. H. (1953). Termination of diapause in grasshopper embryos cultured *in vitro*. *Anat. Rec.* **117**, 539.

Carlson, J. G. (1946). Protoplasmic viscosity changes in different regions of the grasshopper neuroblast during mitosis. *Biol. Bull. Woods Hole* **90**, 109.

Carlson, J. G. (1954). Immediate effects on division, morphology and viability. *In* "Radiation Biology" (A. Hollaender, ed.). McGraw-Hill, New York.

Carlson, J. G. (1958). The immediate cytological effects of ionizing radiations. *Bios* **29**, 106.

Carlson, J. G. (1961). The grasshopper neuroblast culture technique and its value in radiobiological studies. *Ann. Acad. Sci. N.Y.* **95**, 932.

Castiglioni, M. C. and Raimondi, G. R. (1961). First results of *in vitro* cultivation of *Drosophila melanogaster* tissues. *Atti Ass. Genet. ital.* **6**, 139.

Chambers, R. (1925). Études de microdissection. IV. Les structures mitochondriales et nucléaires de cellules germinales males chez la Santalle. *Cellule* **35**, 105.

Collier, W. A. (1920). Biochemische feststellung der verwandtschaft bei insekten. *Z. wiss. Insektenbiol.* **16**, 1.

Cunningham, I. (1961). Studies on the maintenance and growth of insect tissues and cells *in vitro*. M.Sc. Thesis. University of Edinburgh.

Curtis, A. S. G. (1960). Cell contacts: some physical considerations, *Amer. Nat.* **94**, 37.

Curtis, A. S. G. (1962a). Cell contact and adhesion. *Biol. Rev.* **37**, 82.

Curtis, A. S. G. (1962b). Pattern and mechanism in the reaggregation of sponges. *Nature, Lond.* **196**, 245.

Curtis, A. S. G. (1965). The inhibition of cell aggregation by a pure serum protein. *J. Embryol, exp. Morph.* **13**, 309.

Demal, J. and Leloup, A. M. (1963). Essai de culture *in vitro* d'organes d'insectes. *Ann. Épiphyt.* **14**, 91.

Duchateau, G., Florkin, M. and Gromadska, M. (1958). La tréhalose émie du ver à soie. *Arch. int. Physiol.* **66**, 434.

Eagle, H. (1955). The specific amino acid requirements of a human carcinoma cell (strain HeLa) in tissue culture. *J. exp. Med.* **102**, 37.

Evans, D. R. and Dethier, V. G. (1957). The regulation of taste thresholds for sugars in the blowfly. *J. Insect Physiol.* **1**, 3.

Fauré-Fremiet, E. (1925). L'agglutination des ámibocytes d'arenicole *C.R. Soc. Biol., Paris* **92**, 1287.

Fauré-Fremiet, E. (1932). Morphogénèse expérimentale (reconstitution) chez *Ficulina ficus* L. *Arch. Anat. micr.* **28**, 1.

Fauré-Fremiet, E. (1934). Les transformations thixotropiques des amibocytes de *Nephtys* et d'*Arenicola. Arch. exp. Zellforsch* **15**, 373.

Fischer-Piette, E. (1929). Le tissu lymphocytogéne des crustacés étudié en survie *in vitro. C.R. Soc. Biol., Paris* **102**, 764.

Fischer-Piette, E. (1931). Culture de tissues de Crustacea. La glande lymphatique du Homard. *Arch. Zool. exp. gen.* **74**, 33.

Fischer-Piette, E. (1933). Proliferation *in vitro* dans le glande lymphatique des Crustacés. *Arch. exp. Zellforsch.* **14**, 345.

Flandre, O. and Vago, C. (1963). Culture de tissus de Gastéropodes en coagulum plasmatique. *Ann. Épiphyt.* **14**, 161.

Friedman, F. and Burton, L. (1956). Benign and invasive tumours induced in *Drosophila* by an inherited tumour inducing factor. *Cancer Res.* **16**, 1059.

Frew, J. G. H. (1928). A technique for the cultivation of insect tissues. *J. exp. Biol.* **6**, 1.

Fukuda, S. (1951). The production of the diapause eggs by transplanting the sub-oesophageal ganglion in the silkworm. *Proc. Imp. Acad. Japan* **27**, 672.

Fukuda, S. (1952). Function of the pupal brain and suboesophageal ganglion in the production of nondiapause and diapause eggs in the silkworm. *Annot. zool. jap.* **25**, 149.

Galtsoff, P. S. (1923). The amoeboid movement of dissociated sponge cells. *Biol. Bull. Woods Hole* **45**, 153.

Galtsoff, P. S. (1925a). Regeneration after dissociation (an experimental study on sponges). I. Behaviour of dissociated cells of *Microciona prolifera* under normal and altered conditions. *J. exp. Zool.* **42**, 183.

Galtsoff, P. S. (1925b). Regeneration after dissociation (an experimental study on sponges). II. Histogenesis of *Microciona prolifera. J. exp. Zool.* **42**, 223.

Gatenby, J. B. (1931). Outgrowth from pieces of *Helix aspersa*, the common snail. *Nature, Lond.* **128**, 1002.

Gatenby, J. B. (1932). Absence of mitosis in tissue culture and regeneration in *Helix aspersa. Nature, Lond.* **130**, 628.

Gatenby, J. B. and Duthie, E. S. (1932). On the behaviour of small pieces of the pulmonary cavity wall of *Helix aspersa,* kept in blood. *J. R. micr. Soc.* **52**, 395.

Gatenby, J. B. and Hill, J. C. (1933). Improved technique for non-aseptic tissue culture of *Helix aspersa*, with notes on molluscan cytology. *Quart. J. micr. Sci.* **76**, 331.

Gaulden, M. E. and Kokomoor, K. L. (1955). Influence of yolk on mitotic rate in untreated and X-rayed grasshopper neuroblasts *in vitro. Exp. Cell Res.* **2**, 416.

Gavrilov, W. and Cowez, S. (1941). Essai de culture *in vitro* de tissue de Montsiques et d'intestins de Lapins adultes infectés. *Ann. Parasit. hum. comp.* **18**, 180.

Gay, R. (1963). Essais de cultures de fragments de Lumbricides sur milieu gélosé synthétique. *Ann. Épiphyt.* **14**, 61.

Glaser, R. W. (1917). The growth of insect blood cells *in vitro*. *Psyche* **24**, 1.

Goldschmidt, R. (1915). Some experiments on spermatogenesis *in vitro*. *Proc. nat. Acad. Sci. Wash.* **1**, 220.

Goodchild, A. J. P. (1954). Culture of insect tissues. *Nature, Lond.* **173**, 504.

Gottschewski, G. and Fischer, I. (1939). Über das Pigment bildungsvermögen von *Drosophila in vitro*. *Naturwissenschaften* **27**, 584.

Grace, T. D. C. (1954). Culture of insect tissues. *Nature, Lond.* **174**, 187.

Grace, T. D. C. (1958a). Effects of various substances on growth of silkworm tissues *in vitro*. *Aust. J. exp. Biol.* **11**, 407.

Grace, T. D. C. (1958b). The prolonged growth and survival of ovarian tissue of the Promethea moth *Callosamia promethea, in vitro*. *J. gen. Physiol.* **41**, 1027.

Grace, T. D. C. (1958c). Induction of polyhedral bodies in ovarian tissue of the tussock moth *in vitro*. *Science* **128**, 249.

Grace, T. D. C. (1962a). Establishment of four strains of cells from insect tissues grown *in vitro*. *Nature, Lond.* **195**, 788.

Grace, T. D. C. (1962b). The development of a cytoplasmic polyhedrosis in insect cells grown *in vitro*. *Virology* **18**, 33.

Gray, J. (1926). The properties of an intercellular matrix and its relation to electrolytes. *J. exp. Biol.* **3**, 167.

Harker, J. (1958). Experimental production of mid-gut tumours in *Periplaneta americana*. *J. exp. Biol.* **35**, 251.

Harrison, R. G. (1906). Observations on the living developing nerve fibre. *Anat. Rec.* **1**, 116.

Heller, J. (1932). Über den Anteil der Haemolymphe am Stoffwechsel der Schmetter lingspuppen. *Biochem. Z.* **255**, 205.

Heller, J. and Moklowska, A. (1930). Über die Zusammensetzung des Raupenblutes bei *Deilephila euphorbiae* und deren Veränderungen im Verlauf der Metamorphose. *Biochem. Z.* **219**, 473.

Herbst, C. (1900). Über das Auseinandergehen von Furchungs-und Gewebezellen in Kalkfreiem Medium. *Arch. EntwMech. Org.* **9**, 424.

Hill, J. C. and Gatenby, J. B. (1934). On the behaviour of small pieces of mantle cavity wall of *Helix aspersa* kept in blood and various artificial media. *Arch. exp. Zellforsch.* **18**, 195.

Hirumi, H. and Maramorosch, K. (1964). Insect tissue culture. Further studies on the cultivation of embryonic leaf-hopper tissues *in vitro*. *Contrib. Boyce Thompson Inst.* **22**, 343.

Holtfreter, J. (1944). Experimental studies on the development of the pronephros. *Rev. canad. Biol.* **3**, 220.

Howden, G. F. and Kilby, B. A. (1956). Trehalose and trehalase in insects. *Chem. Ind., Lond.* 1453.

Humphreys, T., Humphreys, S. and Moscona, A. A. (1960). Rotation-mediated aggregation of dissociated sponge cells. *Biol. Bull. Woods Hole* **119**, 295.

Huxley, J. S. (1911). Some phenomena of regeneration in Sycon; with a note on the structure of collar cells. *Phil. Trans.* B, **202**, 165.

Huxley, J. S. (1921). Differences in viability in different types of regenerates from dissociated sponges, with a note on the entry of some somatic cells by spermatozoa. *Biol. Bull. Woods Hole* **40**, 127.

Jones, B. M. (1956a). Endocrine activity during insect embryogenesis. Function of the ventral head glands in locust embryos (*Locustana pardalina* and *Locusta migratoria*, Orthoptera). *J. exp. Biol.* **33**, 174.

Jones, B. M. (1956b). Endocrine activity during insect embryogenesis. Control of events in development following the embryonic moult (*Locusta migratoria* and *Locusta locustana*, Orthoptera). *J. exp. Biol.* **33**, 685.

Jones, B. M. (1960). Some studies relating to the cell surface. *Proc. R. phys. Soc. Edinb.* **28**, 35.

Jones, B. M. (1962). The cultivation of insect cells and tissues. *Biol. Rev.* **37**, 512.

Jones, B. M. (1965). Inhibitory effect of p-benzoquinone on the aggregation behaviour of embryo-chick fibroblast cells. *Nature, Lond.* **205**, 1280.

Jones, B. M. and Cunningham, I. (1960). Growth by cell division in insect tissue culture. *Nature, Lond.* **187**, 1072.

Jones, B. M. and Cunningham, I. (1961). Growth by cell division in insect tissue culture. *Exp. Cell Res.* **23**, 386.

Kagawa, Y., Kaneto, K., Takaoka, T. and Katsuta, H. (1960). Amino acid consumption by strain L cells (mouse fibroblasts) in protein-free media. *Jap. J. exp. Med.* **30**, 95.

Konicek, H. (1933). Über die Züchtung des Lungensack- und Herzgewebes bei *Helix pomatia*. Vorläufige Mitteilung. *Arch. exp. Zellforsch.* **13**, 709.

Laubenfels, M. W. de (1932). Physiology and morphology of Porifera exemplied by *Lotrochota birotulata. Tortugas Laboratory Papers Carnegie Inst. Wash.* **28**, 39.

Lazarenko, T. (1925). Beiträge zur vergleichenden Histologie des Blutes und des Bindegewebes. II. Die morphologische Bedeutung der Blut- und Bindegewebelemente der Insekten. *Z. mikr.-anat. Forsch.* **3**, 409.

Lender, Th. and Duveau-Hagege, J. (1962). La survie et la différenciation des gonades larvaires de *Galleria mellonella* en culture organotypique. *C.R. Acad. Sci., Paris* **254**, 2825.

Lender, Th. and Duveau-Hagege, J. (1963). la survie et la différenciation *in vitro* des gonades de larves de dernier âge de *Galleria mellonella* (Lepidoptère, Pyralididae). *Devl. Biol.* **6**, 1.

Lewis, M. R. (1916). Sea water as a medium for tissue cultures. *Anat. Rec.* **10**, 287.

Lewis, M. R. and Robertson, W. R. B. (1916). The mitochondria and other structures observed by the tissue culture method in the male germ cells of *Chorthippus curtipennis. Biol. Bull. Woods Hole* **30**, 99.

Levenbook, L. (1950). The composition of horse bot-fly (*Gastrophilus intestinalis*) larva blood. *Biochem. J.* **47**, 336.

Levenbook, L. (1951). Variation in phosphorus compounds during the development of the blowfly, *Calliphora erythrocephala. Fed. Proc.* **10**, 82.

Li, Yu-Ying Fu, Baker, F. D. and Andrew, W. (1963). A method for tissue culture of *Hydra* cells. *Proc. Soc. exp. Biol., N.Y.* **113**, 259.

Lillie, F. R. (1912). The production of sperm iso-agglutinins by ova. *Science* **36**, 527.

Lieberman, I. and Ove, P. (1957). Purification of a serum protein required by a mammalian cell in tissue culture. *Biochim. biophys. Acta* **25**, 449.

Lockwood, A. P. M. (1961). "Ringer" solutions and some notes on the physiological basis of their ionic composition. *Comp. Biochem. Physiol.* **2**, 241.

Loeb, L. (1922). Agglutination and tissue formation. *Science* **56**, 237.

Loeb, L. (1927). Amoeboid movement and agglutination in amoebocytes of *Limulus* and the relation of these processes to tissue formation and thrombosis. *Protoplasma* **2**, 514.

Martignoni, M. E. (1960). Problems of insect tissue culture. *Experientia* **16**, 125.

Martignoni, M. E. and Scallion, R. I. (1961). Multiplication *in vitro* of a nuclear polyhedrosis virus in insect amoebocytes. *Nature, Lond.* **190**, 1133.

Martignoni, M. E., Zitcer, E. M. and Wagner, R. P. (1958). Preparation of cell suspension from insect tissues for *in vitro* cultivation. *Science* **128**, 360.

Martin, H. M. and Vidler, B. O. (1962). *In vitro* growth of tick tissues (*Rhipicephalus appendiculatus*, Neumann, 1901). *Exp. Parasit.* **12**, 192.

Matthee, J. J. (1951). The structure and physiology of the egg of *Locustana pardalina. Sci. Bull. Dep. Agric. S. Afr.* no. 316.

Merrill, M. H., Lacaillade, C. W. and Ken Broeck, C. (1934). Mosquito transmission of equine encephalomyelitis. *Science* **80**, 250.

Millara, P. (1946). Recherches sur la cytologie des leucocytes d'Insectes et leur survie en milieu artificiel. *C.R. Soc. Biol., Paris* **140**, 1006.

Monné, L. and Hårde, S. (1951). On the formation of the blastocoele and similar embryonic cavities. *Ark. Zool.* **1**, 463.

Moore, A. R. (1930). Fertilization and development without membrane formation in the egg of the sea-urchin *Strongylocentrotus purpureus. Protoplasma* **9**, 9.

Moore, M. M. (1932). On the coherence of the blastomeres of sea-urchin eggs. *Arch. EntwMech. Org.* **125**, 487.

Morgan, J. F., Morton, H. J. and Parker, R. C. (1950). Nutrition of animal cells in tissue culture. I. Initial studies on a synthetic medium. *Proc. Soc. exp. Biol., N.Y.* **73**, 1.

Moscona, A. A. (1962). Analysis of cell recombinations in experimental synthesis of tissues *in vitro*. *J. cell comp. Physiol.* Suppl. 1, **60**, 65.

Moscona, A. A. (1963). Studies on cell aggregation. Demonstration of materials with selective cell-binding activity. *Proc. nat. Acad. Sci., Wash.* **49**, 742.

Moscona, A. A. and Moscona, H. (1952). The dissociation and aggregation of cells from organ rudiments of the early chick embryo. *J. Anat., Lond.* **86**, 287.

Murray, M. R. (1927). The cultivation of planarian tissues *in vitro*. *J. exp. Zool.* **47**, 467.

Murray, M. R. (1931). *In vitro* studies of planarian parenchyma. *Arch. exp. Zellforsch.* **11**, 656.

Nossal, P. M. (1952). Estimation of L-malate and fumarate by malic decarboxylase of *Lactobacillus arabinosus*. *Biochem. J.* **50**, 349.

Papenfuss, E. J. and Bokenham, A. H. (1939). The fate of the ectoderm and endoderm of Hydra when cultured independently. *Biol. Bull. Woods Hole* **76**, 1.

Paul, J. (1959). "Cell and Tissue Culture." Livingstone, Edinburgh.

Pfeiffer, H. H. (1937). Versuche mit Ganglionkulturen aus *Corethralarven. Arch. exp. Zellforsch.* **20**, 255.

Pfeiffer, H. H. (1939). Über Spannungswirkungen auf Zellen *in vitro* nach Messungen der Doppelbeugung. *Naturwissenschaften* **27**, 389.

Pfeiffer, H. H. (1943). Polarisationsmikroskopische Messungen an gerichtet gespannten Mutterstricken von Ganglionkulteren *in vitro*. *Naturwissenschaften* **31**, 47.

Ragab, H. A. (1948). The maintenance of the isolated mosquito gut *in vitro* with the object of studying the development of the malarial parasite. *Trans. R. Soc. trop. Med. Hyg.* **41**, 434.

Ragab, H. A. (1949). Observations on the isolated gut of the mosquito. *Trans. R. Soc. trop. Med. Hyg.* **43**, 225.

Řeháček, J. (1962). Propagation of tick-borne encephalitis (TE) virus in tick tissue cultures. *Ann. Épiphyt.* **14**, 199.

Ris, H. (1949). The anaphase movement of chromosomes in the spermatocytes of the grasshopper. *Biol. Bull. Woods Hole* **96**, 90.

Rocca, A. N. and Martin, R. (1963). The mitotic activity of the white body cells of *Octopus vulgaris in vitro*. *Ann. Épiphyt.* **14**, 23.

Roudabush, R. L. (1933). Phenomenon of regeneration in everted *Hydra*. *Biol. Bull. Woods Hole* **64**, 253.

Sarlet, H., Duchateau, G. and Florkin, M. (1952a). Sur les acides aminés, libres on combinés sous ferme non-protéinique, du plasma, sanguin de différents insects (phase, larva d'arbeille, Lepidoptères). *Arch. int. Physiol.* **60**, 103.

Sarlet, H., Duchateau, G. and Florkin, M. (1952b). Les acides aminés du milieu intérieur du Ver à soie au cours du filiage. *Arch. int. Physiol.* **60**, 126.

Schmidt, E. L. and Williams, C. M. (1953). Physiology of insect diapause. V. Assay of the growth and differentiation hormone of Lepidoptera by the method of tissue culture. *Biol. Bull. Woods Hole* **105**, 174.

Schmidtmann, M. (1925). Über die intracellulaire Wasserstoffionenkonzentration unter physiologischen und einigen pathologischen Bedingungen. *Z. ges. exp. Med.* **45**, 714.

Schneiderman, H. A., Ketchel, M. and Williams, C. M. (1953). The physiology of insect diapause. VI. Effects of temperature, oxygen tension, and metabolic inhibitors on *in vitro* spermatogenesis in the Cecropia silk-worm. *Biol. Bull. Woods Hole* **105**, 188.

Sengel, P. and Kieny, M. (1962). Action de divers liquides nutritifs et du complexe "glande neurale-ganglion nerveux-organe vibratile" sur les gonades de *Molgula manhattensis* (Tunicer Ascidiacé) cultivées *in vitro*. *C.R. Acad. Sci., Paris* **254**, 1682.

Sengel, P. and Kieny, M. (1963). Culture de gonades de *Molgula manhattensis*, isolées ou associées en complexe formé par la glande neurale, le ganglion nerveux et l'organe vibratile. *Ann. Épiphyt.* **14**, 95.

Sharrer, B. (1945). Experimental tumours after nerve section in an insect. *Proc. Soc. exp. Biol., N.Y.* **60**, 184.

Shaw, E. I. (1956). A glutamic acid-glycine medium for prolonged maintenance of high mitotic activity in grasshopper neuroblasts. *Exp. Cell Res.* **11**, 65.

Smith, K. M. (1952). Latency in viruses and the production of new virus diseases. *Biol. Rev.* **27**, 347.

Smith, K. M. (1959). Recent work on the electron-microscopy of viruses. *Nature, Lond.* **184**, 1440.

Smith, K. M. and Xeros, N. (1953). Development of virus in the cell nucleus in the silkworm *Bombyx mori*. *Nature, Lond.* **172**, 670.

St. Amand, G. S. and Tipton, S. R. (1954). The separation of neuroblasts and other cells from grasshopper embryos. *Science* **119**, 93.

Stein, W. H. and Moore, S. (1954). The free amino acids of human blood plasma. *J. biol. Chem.* **211,** 915.

Stern, C. (1940). Growth *in vitro* of the testes of *Drosophila*. *Growth* **4**, 377.

Takakuson, S. (1924). Beobachtungen über die Spermogenese *in vitro*. *Z. Zellforsch.* **1**, 22.

Taylor, A. (1935). Experimentally induced changes in the cell complex of the blood of *Periplaneta americana*. *Ann. ent. Soc. Amer.* **26**, 135.

Taylor, A. C. (1961). Attachment and spreading of cells in culture. *Exp. Cell Res.* Suppl. **8**, 154.

Tobias, J. M. (1948). The high potassium and low sodium in the body fluid and tissues of a phytophagous insect, the silkworm, *Bombyx mori*, and the change before pupation. *J. cell. comp. Physiol.* **31**, 143.

Townes, P. L. and Holtfreter, J. (1955). Directed movements and selective adhesion of embryonic amphibian cells. *J. exp. Zool.* **128**, 53.

Trager, W. (1935). Cultivation of the virus of grasserie in silkworm tissue cultures. *J. exp. Med.* **61**, 501.

Trager, W. (1938). Multiplication of the virus of equine encephalomyelitis in surviving mosquito tissues. *Ann. J. trop. Med.* **18**, 387.

Trager, W. (1959a). Development of *Trypanosoma vivax* to the infective stage in the tsetse fly tissue culture. *Nature, Lond.* **184**, 30.

Trager, W. (1959b). Tsetse fly tissue culture and the development of trypanosomes to the infective stage. *Ann. trop. Med. Parasit.* **53**, 473.

Treherne, J. E. (1958a). Facilitated diffusion and exchange in the absorption of glucose by the locust *Schistocerca gregaria. Nature, Lond.* **181**, 1280.

Treherne, J. E. (1958b). Absorption of glucose from the alimentary canal of the locust *Schistocerca gregaria. J. exp. Biol.* **35**, 297.

Treherne, J. E. (1958c). The absorption and metabolism of some sugars in the locust *Schistocerca gregaria. J. exp. Biol.* **35**, 611.

Tyler, A. (1941). The role of fertilizin in the fertilization of eggs of the sea-urchin and other animals. *Biol. Bull. Woods Hole* **81**, 190.

Tyler, A. (1947). An auto-antibody concept of cell structure, growth and differentiation. *Growth* **10**, 7.

Tyler, A. (1955). Ontogeny of immunological properties. *In* "Analysis of Development" (B. H. Willier, P. A. Weiss and V. Hamburger, eds.), p. 556. Saunders, Philadelphia.

Tyler, A., Burbank, A. and Tyler, J. S. (1954a). Sedimentation constants, viscosity, and diffusion of the fertilizins of *Arbacia* and *Echinarachnius. Biol. Bull. Woods Hole* **107**, 303.

Tyler, A., Burbank, A. and Tyler, J. S. (1954b). The electrophoretic mobilities of the fertilizins of *Arbacia* and *Echinarachnius. Biol. Bull. Woods Hole* **107**, 304.

Van der Kloot, W. G. (1955). Control of neurosecretion and diapause by physiological changes in the brain of the Cecropia silkworm. *Biol. Bull. Woods Hole* **109**, 276.

Waymouth, C. (1957). Nutrition and metabolism of animal tissue cultures. *J. nat. Cancer Inst.* **19**, 495.

Weinman, D. (1957). Cultivation of trypanosomes. *Trans. R. Soc. trop. Med. Hyg.* **51**, 600.

Weiss, L. (1960). The adhesion of cells. *Int. Rev. Cytol.* **9**, 187.

Weiss, P. (1950). Perspectives in the field of morphogenesis. *Quart. Rev. Biol.* **25**, 177.

Wigglesworth, V. B. (1952). Hormone balance and the control of metamorphosis in *Rhodnius prolixus* (Hemiptera). *J. exp. Biol.* **29**, 620.

Willmer, E. N. (1956). Factors which influence the acquisition of flagella by the *Amoeba, Naegleria gruberi. J. exp. Biol.* **33**, 583.

Willmer, E. N. (1960). "Cytology and Evolution." Academic Press, London and New York.

Williams, C. M. (1952). Physiology of insect diapause. IV. The brain and prothoracic glands as an endocrine system in the Cecropia silkworm. *Biol. Bull. Woods Hole* **103**, 120.

Wilson, H. V. (1907). On some phenomena of coalescence and regeneration in sponges. *J. exp. Zool.* **5**, 245.

Wilson, H. V. (1911). On the behaviour of the dissociated cells in hydroids, *Alcyonaria*, and *Asterias. J. exp. Zool.* **11**, 281.

Wyatt, G. R. (1961). The biochemistry of insect haemolymph. *Ann. Rev. Entomol.* **6**, 75.

Wyatt, G. R. and Kalf, G. F. (1956). Trehalose in insects. *Fed. Proc.* **15**, 388.

Wyatt, G. R., Loughheed, T. C. and Wyatt, S. S. (1956). The chemistry of insect haemolymph. Organic components of the haemolymph of the silkworm, *Bombyx mori*, and two other species. *J. gen. Physiol.* **39**, 853.

Wyatt, G. R. and Meyer, W. L. (1959). The chemistry of insect haemolymph. III. Glycerol. *J. gen. Physiol.* **42**, 1005.

Wyatt, S. S. (1956). Culture *in vitro* of tissue from the silkworm *Bombyx mori*. *J. gen. Physiol.* **39**, 841.

Yamafugi, K. and Yoshihara, F. (1950). On the virus production and oxime formation in silkworms fed with nitrites. *Enzymologia* **14**, 124.

Yamafugi, K. and Omura, H. (1950). Formation of silkworm virus by acetoxime feeding. *Enzymologia* **14**, 120.

Zalokar, M. (1960). Sites of ribonucleic acid and protein synthesis in *Drosophila*. *Exp. Cell Res.* **19**, 184.

CHAPTER 8

Introduction and Methods Employed in Plant Tissue Culture

H. E. STREET and G. G. HENSHAW

Department of Botany, University College of Swansea, Wales

I. Introduction

It is possible to trace three main lines of technical development which together constitute the methodology of Plant Tissue Culture. These lines of development have been concerned, respectively, with the culture of isolated plant organs (particularly of isolated roots but, to a lesser extent, of stem tips, leaf primordia, flower structures and immature embryos), the growth of callus masses on solidified media and, more recently, the growth in liquid media of mixed suspensions of separated cells and small cell groups.

These various forms of aseptic culture are of interest in that they make possible the study of certain problems in cell, tissue and organ physiology inaccessible to study by other means and they enable certain other aspects of plant physiology to be studied more elegantly than do any alternative techniques. Plant Tissue Culture comprises, therefore, a group of techniques now available and offering certain unique features to the experimental botanist. These techniques have already been exploited to great advantage in a number of important centres of botanical research but one, and perhaps the major factor which has deterred their more general use is the widespread view that the techniques required for the successful aseptic culture of plant material are difficult and excessively laborious. The following chapters will, therefore, deal first and, in outline, with the basic techniques and then go on to assess some of the more important contributions to our knowledge of plant growth and metabolism which have resulted from their experimental manipulation.

The establishment of suspension cultures and the development from such suspensions, and also from callus, of clones of single-cell origin, both achievements of the last decade, have taken us far towards the fulfilment of an objective first clearly formulated by Haberlandt some sixty years ago. Haberlandt, in a frequently quoted paper published in 1902, stated clearly the desirability of culturing the isolated vegetative cells of higher plants in order to examine their capacities to function as "elementary organisms" and in order to reveal the reciprocal influences to which the individual cells of a multicellular plant are subjected. Haberlandt foresaw that, if we could culture isolated plant cells, then we could demonstrate experimentally the suspected totipotency of all the living cells of higher plants and that, in so doing, the way might be opened to directing and reversing experimentally the processes of cellular differentiation. At the same time, the metabolic output of all kinds of tissue cells and of the meristematic cells from which they are derived would be revealed together with their environmental, nutrient and growth-factor requirements. It follows also that by working with cultured tissue masses and cultured plant organs we should reveal the nutritive interrelationships between these larger units and be able to study the origin and nature of the determinant patterns which are established when cells are associated together in a symplast and which control or initiate the patterns of tissue differentiation and organogenesis characteristic of the development of the multicellular plant.

These vistas are particularly exciting at the present stage of development of plant biology and, in consequence, it can be confidently predicted that Plant Tissue-Culture techniques will be used in the future to an increasing extent in studies of cellular physiology and of morphogenesis and differentiation in higher plants.

Following his prediction of the advances in knowledge which would be likely to follow from the successful *in vitro* culture of plant cells, many attempts were made in Haberlandt's laboratory to culture single cells of the palisade tissue of leaves, of medullary parenchyma, of the epidermis and of various plant hairs (Haberlandt, 1902; Winkler, 1902). These investigations were continued in Haberlandt's laboratory over a number of years (Bobilioff-Preisser, 1917; Lamprecht, 1918; Thielmann,

1924, 1925; Küster, 1928) and also in other laboratories (Czech, 1926; Kunkel, 1926; Börger, 1926; Kemmer, 1928; Úlehla, 1928; Schmucker, 1929; Scheitterer, 1931; Pfeiffer, 1931, 1933; LaRue, 1933). However, the experimental results were most discouraging and in no case could such isolated cells be induced to generate tissue masses by cell division.

However, during this period Kotte (1922a, b), working in Haberlandt's laboratory in Berlin, and Robbins (1922a, b), working at the New York Botanic Garden, had initiated studies on the growth of excised root tips in sterile culture solutions and thereby opened up the technique which, particularly in the hands of Philip White, has led to the establishment of continuously growing root cultures.

Kotte (1922a, b) examined the growth of apical and sub-apical fragments of *Pisum* and *Zea* roots on various media containing sugars, organic nitrogen compounds and inorganic salts. He reported considerable, but not indefinite growth of *Zea* root tips on a medium solidified with agar and containing a Knop's inorganic solution (Knop, 1865), 1% dextrose and Liebig's meat extract. The cultured roots gave rise to numerous laterals. Less effective than Liebig's meat extract were supplements of (1) α-alanine, (2) peptone, asparagine, alanine and glycine and (3) a pepsin-diastase digest of pea seeds.

In the same year, Robbins, working independently, reported the growth of root tips of *Pisum, Zea* and *Gossypium* on a liquid medium containing a balanced inorganic solution, dextrose and an extract of autolysed yeast. Immediately subsequent papers (Robbins and Maneval, 1923, 1924) reported the testing of root tips from a wider range of species and led to the discovery of the beneficial effect on growth of moderate illumination of the cultures. These workers studied the behaviour of the root tips after excision and transference to new flasks of culture medium and reported that growth continued through a number of subculture passages although such subculture led to marked and progressive decreases in growth rate. Prolonged but not continuous growth in culture was therefore achieved by these workers. Similarly, Gautheret, working from 1932 in the laboratory of Molliard at the Sorbonne, began a study of the growth of root tips and root fragments derived from a number of species and cultured in a number of different nutrient media and reported (1935a) that growth of the root explants was initially vigorous but strictly limited in duration. In the same year (1932), White commenced his work on excised root culture at the Rockefeller Institute for Medical Research, using seedling root tips of *Triticum* as experimental material. In attempts to obtain continuous growth of his excised wheat roots, White systematically varied such cultural factors as light and temperature, as well as aeration, volume, H-ion concentration and the inorganic and organic composition of the medium (White,

1932, 1933). Under the most favourable conditions established, the roots grew rapidly in culture for about 14 days but subsequently their growth rapidly declined to zero and this cessation of growth was hastened by attempts to subculture the root apices.

However, in 1934 White, using a similar culture medium, but with sucrose instead of dextrose as the source of carbon, succeeded in repeatedly subculturing excised tomato roots without diminution of growth rate and also, by subculturing the lateral root tips which developed during culture, was able to establish from the root tip of a single radicle, a clone of excised roots in continuous culture. By 1936, these roots had passed through 160 passages, each of 7 days' duration, and the mean linear growth rate of the roots had continued at *ca* 5 mm per day (White, 1934, 1936). These reports gave an immediate impetus to studies on excised root culture and led in the immediately succeeding years to the publication of a spate of papers reporting the successful culture of excised root tips of several species in defined liquid media.

Contemporary with these papers came reports by Gautheret that pieces of cambium removed under aseptic conditions from *Salix capraea, Populus nigra* and other trees and placed on a solidified medium containing Knop's solution, dextrose and cystein hydrochloride would continue to proliferate for some months, giving rise to algal-like outgrowths (Gautheret, 1934, 1935a). Influenced by contemporary work with root cultures, Gautheret added aneurin and indoleacetic acid to his medium and reported greatly enhanced growth in culture of the *Salix capraea* cambium (Gautheret, 1937, 1938). At the same time, Nobécourt (1937, 1938a, b) reported some success in culturing explants of cambium from carrots and potatoes using a medium containing Knop's solution (Knop, 1865) supplemented with Berthelot's (Berthelot, 1934) mixture of accessory salts. Gautheret (1939) then also examined the behaviour of carrot explants on a medium compounded of dextrose and the inorganic salt mixture of Nobécourt but also containing aneurin, cystein hydrochloride and a low concentration of indoleacetic acid. The carrot explants gave rise to an "undifferentiated" mass of tissue capable of repeated subculture. These results of Gautheret were reported to the French Academy of Sciences on 9 January 1939. A few days previously, on 30 December 1938, White (1939) had independently reported the continuous cultivation of a similar undifferentiated callus derived from the procambial tissue of young stems of a hybrid *Nicotiana* (*N. glauca* × *N. langsdorffii*) cultured in the medium he had developed for excised tomato roots but containing 0·5% agar. At the time of White's paper this callus culture had been maintained through forty passages, each of 1 week's duration, its weight having increased threefold during each passage. These callus cultures of Gautheret and White were the forerunners of similar cultures derived from the tissues of many dicotyledonous plants.

Work with such callus cultures indicated that there was a lower limit to the size of fragments which could be successfully subcultured. With tissue fragments approaching this size, growth was reported to be uncertain and frequently to occur only after a prolonged lag phase. Two developments in technique have, however, now taken us closer to the successful culture of isolated plant cells as envisaged by Haberlandt. The first has been the study of the growth of fragments of callus tissue when these are transferred to complex and agitated liquid media; the second the study of the behaviour of uninjured single cells in the presence of nutrients but out of direct contact with other cells.

In 1954, Muir, Hildebrandt and Riker reported from the Department of Plant Pathology of the University of Wisconsin the growth of liquid cultures containing single cells and small clumps of cells of *Tagetes erecta* and of *Nicotiana tabacum*. These cultures arose when fragments of callus cultures of these species were transferred to a liquid medium agitated on a reciprocal shaker. Similarly, in 1955, Steward and Shantz of Cornell University when studying the growth of carrot root phloem explants in liquid medium in specially constructed rotating culture vessels, reported that the supernatant fluid became turbid, owing to the development and growth of free-floating cells. From this initial suspension culture they serially propagated cultures containing only free-floating single cells and small groups of cells. In 1956, Reinert, working in White's laboratory at Bar Harbor, obtained evidence for the occurrence of cell divisions in a similar suspension of single cells and cell groups from *Picea glauca* and, in the same year, Nickell reported from the laboratories of Chas. Pfizer & Co., New York, that he had for 4 years continuously subcultured a suspension rich in single cells of the hypocotyl of *Phaseolus vulgaris*.

The second development is that some successes have now been reported in inducing single isolated cells to divide, thus leading in certain instances to the establishment of clones of plant tissue of single cell origin. In 1954, Muir *et al.* isolated single cells from their suspension cultures and from "friable" callus tissues of crown-gall origin and placed these singly on the upper surface of squares of filter paper whose lower surface made good contact with an actively growing "nurse" crown-gall callus. A high proportion of the single cells underwent a few divisions, a small proportion continued dividing to give small callus masses on the filter paper and again a number of these were successfully transferred to agar medium to give clones of single-cell origin. In 1960, Jones, Hildebrandt, Ricker and Wu examined the growth in hanging-drop culture of separated cells (2–30 cells per drop) from a callus of hybrid tobacco (*Nicotiana tabacum* × *N. glutinosa*). Using fresh culture medium they observed cell divisions only when a high number of cells was present in the drop. In such cultures some cells enlarged and differentiated while others remained quiescent. When these differentiated cells became senescent and died, some of the small cells of the culture, hitherto quiescent, divided, enlarged and differentiated. Divisions with a single cell per drop were also observed when the medium was "conditioned" by having previously supported the growth of a cell population. In the same year, Bergmann, starting with suspension cultures of *Nicotiana tabacum* var. Samsun and *Phaseolus vulgaris* var. Early Golden Cluster, obtained filtrates containing 90% of the cells as single cells and then spread these over the surface of a 1 mm layer of a culture medium solidified with 0·6% agar in a Petri dish. The plates were then sealed and incubated in diffuse light. Individual cells could be marked and examined at intervals by means of an inverted microscope. Under these conditions 20% of the cells underwent repeated divisions giving rise to small colonies and a number of these colonies of single-cell origin were subcultured to tubes of solidified medium.

It is with these various types of aseptic culture that we shall be concerned, considering first the basic techniques of culture and then going on in the ensuing chapters to assess how far their use has already contributed to various aspects of botanical research.

More detailed accounts of the pioneer work in this field are given by White (1931, 1936, 1941, 1943a) and by Gautheret (1959).

II. Techniques of Organ, Tissue and Free Cell Culture

A critical appreciation of techniques is an essential background to an evaluation of the potentialities of plant cultures in different fields of botanical research. With this in mind we shall endeavour, in presenting an outline of basic techniques, to stress their limitations and assess how far they permit of reproducible and quantitative studies of nutrition, metabolism, growth and differentiation. References will be given which will guide research workers to more detailed protocols.

A. Excised Root Culture

The basic technique of excised root culture was first clearly set out in White's "Handbook of Plant Tissue Culture" (1943a). Certain significant modifications and developments in technique have, however, occurred since this date and these are drawn together in the outline of present techniques set out below.

1. *Culture Vessels and Culture Apparatus*

The standard culture vessels used are of Pyrex or similar borosilicate glass. New culture vessels should be filled with water and autoclaved several times, being cleaned between autoclavings with chromic acid/sulphuric acid mixture. This "breaking in" process is necessary if uniform and high growth rates are to be obtained. Closure of the culture vessels is normally by plugs of non-absorbent cotton wool wrapped in a layer of open-wove bandage (previously freed from dressing by boiling in water). Such plugs should also be submitted to a preliminary autoclaving before use because there is a high yield of waxy material to the sides of the culture vessels during the first autoclaving. Such plugs can be used many times provided that they are stored in dust-tight containers when not in use. Any plugs which become saturated with water or contaminated with medium should be rejected and this also applies to plugs from cultures which reveal contamination during incubation.

The Pyrex culture vessels and all measures, pipettes and flasks used in the preparation and dispensing of culture media are traditionally cleaned each time by treatment with chromic acid/sulphuric acid mixture and then washed very thoroughly with jets of tap water (this takes at least 5 min) and subsequently twice rinsed with distilled water before use. Clean glassware should be protected from dust and, if not used immediately after cleaning, should be rinsed with distilled water immediately before use. The dried glassware can be most effectively sterilized by heating in an oven to 150°C for 1 h.

To facilitate the cleaning work it is desirable to have a special laboratory supplied with high-pressure water points, lead-topped benches and an acid-resistant floor. The washing out of the chromic acid mixture is most effectively carried out by washing machines constructed of a hard grade of polyvinyl chloride (PVC) and which not only provide strong uniform jets of water but effectively dilute the chromic acid as it enters the plumbing system. For immersion of pipettes, Petri dishes and small vessels in the chromic acid mixture, polythene or PVC buckets (with handles of the same material) are very suitable. Where workers are handling chromic-acid mixture, acid-resistant plastic clothing and rubber boots should be worn. Such a laboratory in operation is shown in Fig. 1. Certain modern detergents may well be equally effective and safer substitutes for the chromic-acid mixture but probably require even more effective rinsing of the vessels with water jets.

The laboratory illustrated in Fig. 1 also houses a refrigerator running

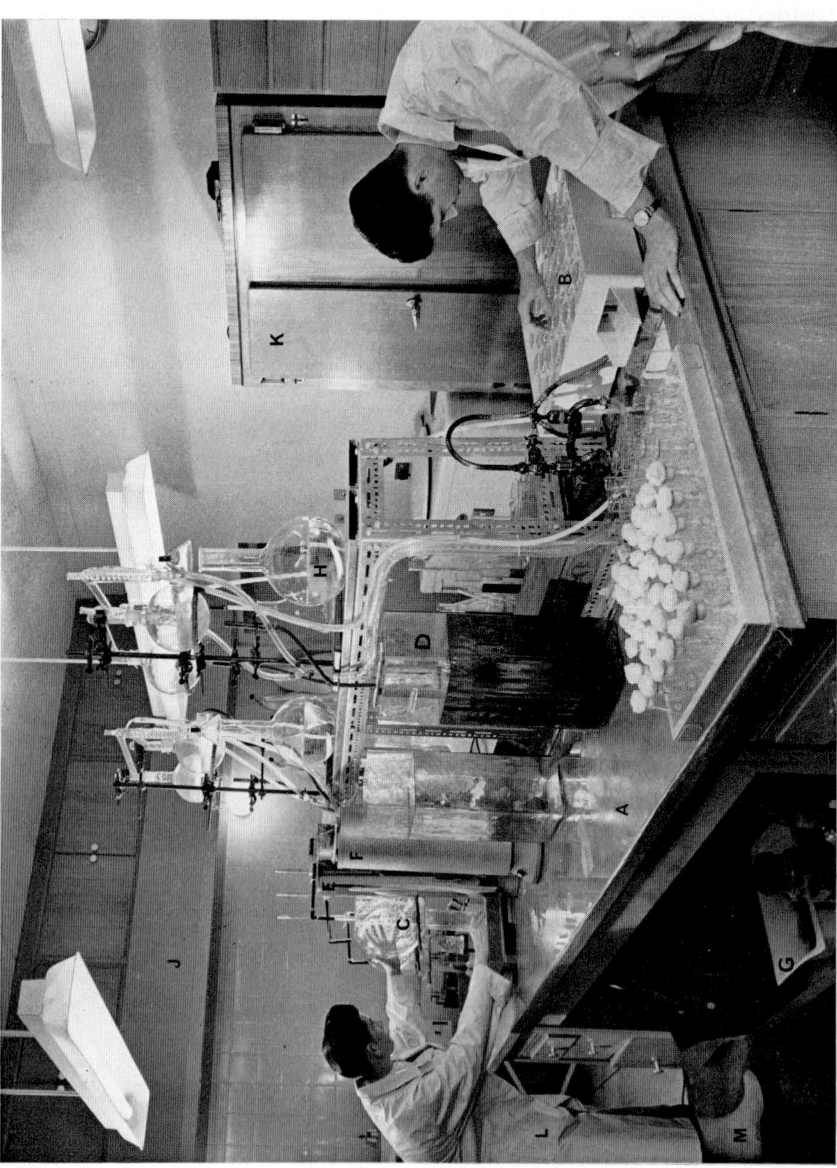

Fig. 1. Tissue Culture Laboratory used for cleaning of glassware, autoclaving of media, preparation of distilled water and storage of stock solutions used in media preparation. On the top of the lead-covered bench (A) can be seen polyvinyl chloride (PVC) washing machines used for the cleaning of the standard Erlenmeyer culture vessels (B) and the large flasks used in preparation of culture media (C), and glass tanks (D) containing chromic acid/sulphuric acid mixture, a stainless steel washer (E) and drier (F) for cleaning pipettes. Below the bench are polythene

at 2–4°C for the storage of inorganic stock solutions and a deep-freeze cabinet at −20°C for the storage of concentrated vitamin solutions and solutions of other organic supplements.

100 ml wide-mouthed Erlenmeyer flasks containing 50 ml of liquid culture medium are most generally used to initiate and maintain cultures and in growth experiments where a high degree of replication (10–20 replicate cultures per treatment) is desirable. Such culture vessels are normally inoculated with a single 10 mm root tip or sector initial (which in the case of excised tomato roots is a portion of the main axis of the cultured root bearing 4–5 laterals, each 3–8 mm long) (Fig. 2). These flasks are closed with cotton plugs as described, except where it is important to prevent any possibility of contamination with soluble material from the plugs when a collar of cotton wool supports an inverted Pyrex beaker (Fig. 2a). This kind of closure is used in studies on vitamin or micro-element nutrition. Where the standard cotton plugs are used these are covered with an inverted aluminium beaker which protects the outer surface of the plug from dust and from drips in the autoclave and which carries a reference number in coloured heat-resistant enamel enabling rapid identification of each culture after randomization of cultures during incubation.

Where it is desirable to extend the period of incubation of the cultures (in the case of excised tomato roots, beyond 7 days) larger culture vessels are required. Particularly suitable (by virtue of the large surface to volume ratio of the medium and ease of stacking in the culture room) are 1 and 2 litre Pyrex penicillin culture flasks, charged with 500 or 1000 ml of culture medium respectively. Such flasks can also be inoculated with up to ten or twenty root tips where the object is to obtain larger amounts of cultured root material for chemical study or for the study of the changes in composition of the culture medium which occur as a result of root growth (where "staled" medium is required for analysis) (Fig. 3). Such penicillin flasks are also very suitable for studies on the effects of aeration on root growth using sintered glass aerators, the leads of which can be passed through the cotton plugs, sterilized *in situ* and protected from contamination by soda-lime tubes packed with non-absorbent cotton wool.

Where it is desired to eliminate the effects on growth of changes in the composition of the culture medium, a system which allows of a continuous flow of sterile culture medium over the growing root culture must be used. One apparatus of this type described by Street and Roberts (1952) is illustrated in Fig. 4, I–IV, and its operation outlined in the legend. Provided the assembly procedure is carefully followed, this apparatus can be set up and growth allowed to proceed for at least 28 days with a low frequency of contamination.

Fig. 2. Technique of culture of excised tomato roots. (a) Culture vessel with a 6-day old "tip" culture; (b) sector culture; (c) sector initial; (d) root tip (10 mm) excised from a main lateral of the sector culture.

Fig. 3. 2000 ml Penicillin culture flask. This contains 1000 ml of culture medium and shows growth after 14 days incubation at 27°C following inoculation with ten 10 mm tomato root tips. An aluminium top protects the cotton wool plug from condensation in the autoclave and carries the identifying mark of the culture.

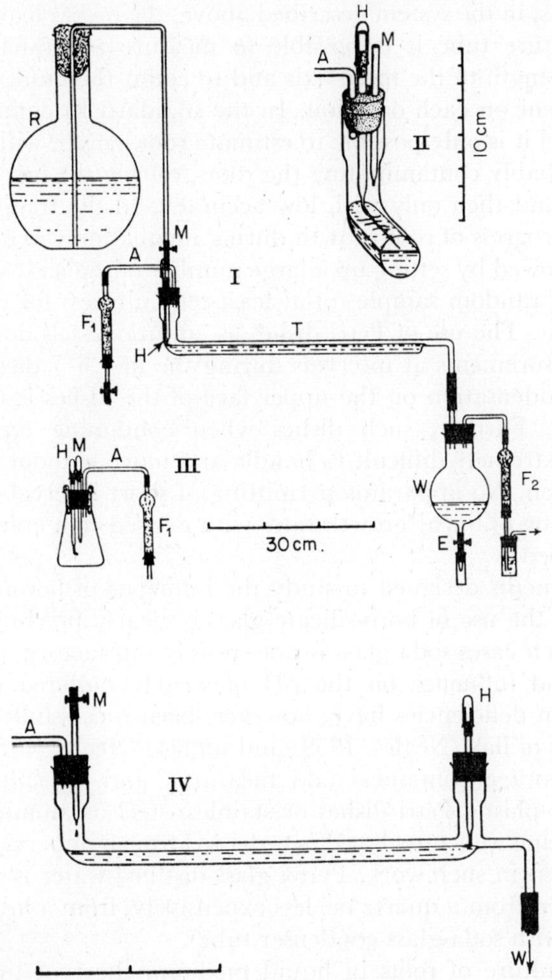

FIG. 4. Apparatus for growth of excised roots in flowing culture medium. I. Complete apparatus for growth of excised roots in flowing medium. II. Part of the growth tube showing attachment of the root in its holder. III. Rubber bung carrying root holder, medium feed tube and air inlet tube shown in the carrier conical flask ready for autoclaving. IV. Culture tube in which the culture medium flows counter to the direction of root growth so that the new medium first meets the main axis meristem and then flows over the older parts of the root. The 30 cm scale applies to I and III.

Key: R, Reservoir of sterile culture medium, fitted with siphon tube; M, culture medium feed tube; A, air inlet tube which is fitted to a low pressure compressed air supply; H, root holder; T, culture tube; W, graduated effluent trap; E, exit from which effluent medium can be withdrawn from W; F_1 and F_2, air filters packed with non-absorbent wool. From Street and Roberts (1952).

In so far as, in the system described above, the root is fixed and grows along a culture tube it is possible to measure accurately the daily increase in length of the main axis and to count the number of lateral roots emergent on each occasion. In the standard Erlenmeyer type of culture vessel it is only possible to estimate root length, without removing and probably contaminating the roots, during the first 3–4 days of incubation and then only with low accuracy. In the standard culture vessels the progress of root growth during incubation can only be satisfactorily followed by setting up a large number of replicate cultures and harvesting a random sample (of at least ten cultures) for each growth measurement. The use of Petri dishes as culture vessels does permit of growth measurements at intervals during the first 6–7 days of culture although condensation on the upper face of the dishes is usually very troublesome. Further, such dishes when containing liquid culture media are extremely difficult to handle and move without introducing contamination. No apparatus permitting of short interval (minutes or hours) plotting of linear growth rates with excised root cultures has yet been described.

In experiments designed to study the influence of boron on excised root growth the use of boro-silicate glass is clearly precluded (Neales, 1959). In such cases soda glass is not entirely satisfactory in view of its solubility and influence on the pH of weakly buffered root-culture media. Boron deficiencies have, however, been successfully induced in excised roots of flax (Neales, 1959) and tomato (Neales, 1964) by using polythene storage containers and measures, and, as culture vessels, either sterile plastic Petri dishes or stainless steel or aluminium dishes (the latter being well autoclaved in order to form an impervious alumina film). Further, in such work, Pyrex glass-distilled water is replaced by water distilled from a quartz or, less expensively, from a heavily tinned metal still (with soda-glass condenser tube).

For the culture of roots in liquid medium, the root tips or sector initials when transferred to the medium should float; the root then grows at or near to the surface of the medium until the advancing root tip meets the inner surface of the culture vessel when the growing apex is usually deflected deeper into the culture solution (this not being associated with any significant reduction in growth rate). If the initial inoculum sinks, this is due to infiltration of its intercellular air space system with liquid; such "sinkers" make very little growth and become abnormal in morphology and anatomy. With some species (such as wheat) careful handling of the root tips during excision and transfer may be important to prevent them becoming "sinkers". Liquid media are generally used because right from the pioneer work of White (1932) it has been general experience, to which there are few exceptions

(McClary, 1940), that slower growth rates or even complete failure of growth occur when root tips are transferred to the surface of media solidified with agar. The superiority of liquid to solidified media is illustrated by the comparative studies undertaken by Day (1943) with tomato roots. However, a development in technique was described in 1956 by Raggio and Raggio which involves the simultaneous use of solidified and liquid culture phases (Fig. 5). Here the basal cut end of the root tip is inserted into the solid phase and the apical part of the root tip bridges the gap between the two phases and dips into the liquid medium. This technique permits the organic constituents of the medium (sugar and organic growth factors) to be supplied through the

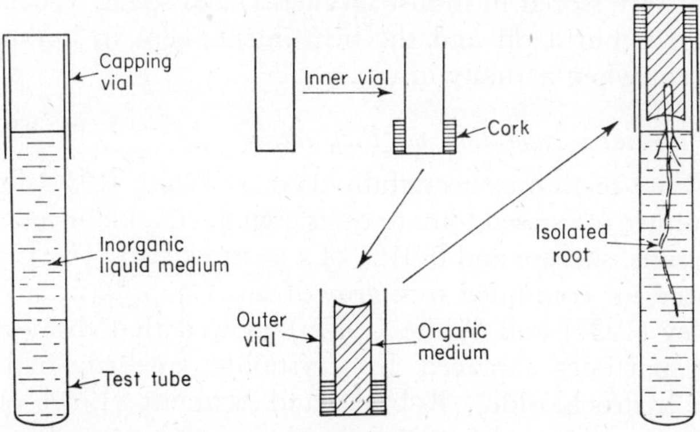

FIG. 5. Raggio and Raggio (1956) technique for excised root culture. The organic moiety of the medium is applied in agar (inner vial) and the inorganic moiety in the liquid form (in test tube).

mature basal tissues while the growing root (on which root hairs are particularly well developed) projects into the inorganic salt solution. The use of this technique has permitted the experimental nodulation of excised roots of *Phaseolus vulgaris* (black wax bean) and of *Glycine soja* var. *Biloxi* by *Rhizobium phaseoli*; the apical part of the root formed nodules as it grew into a nitrate-free inorganic solution containing *Rhizobium* (Raggio, Raggio and Torrey, 1957). This technique also demonstrates the ability of the basal mature cells to absorb and transport sugar and organic growth factors to the growing apex and expanding cells. It is claimed to be of value in studying the influence of auxins on tissue differentiation and cambial activity in cultured roots since, by feeding auxins to the root from the basal end, it seems possible to establish high levels of auxin in the growing regions without the inhibitory effects which result from the immersion of the whole cultured root in an auxin-containing medium (Torrey, 1963). This technique is not, however, generally well suited to quantitative growth studies due to variation in growth rate between individual cultures receiving the same nutrients, an effect which probably reflects the difficulty of achieving an optimum sugar uptake by feeding entirely through the basal part of the root.

The main instruments required for manipulation of root cultures are: stainless steel scalpels for excision of seedling root tips; fine-pointed stainless steel "iris" scissors for excision operations in Petri dishes, angle long-bladed stainless steel "Mayo" scissors for excision operations in the culture vessels, and platinum loops (Standard wire gauge 24) sealed in glass handles for transferring root apices and sector initials. These instruments are stored in industrial methylated spirit. When required, the alcohol is burnt off and the instruments kept in boiling distilled water except when actually in use.

2. *Culture Media: Composition and Preparation*

The culture medium, successfully used by White (1934) for the continuous culture of excised tomato roots contained a balanced solution of inorganic salts, sucrose and 0·01% of a yeast extract. The yeast extract was essential for continued root growth (see Chap. 9, p. 562. Robbins and Bartley (1937) and White (1937a) showed that the yeast extract could be partially replaced by crystalline aneurin hydrochloride (thiamine hydrochloride). Robbins and Schmidt (1939a-c) then reported that a mixture of aneurin and pyridoxine would permit the indefinite culture of excised tomato roots and therefore concluded that the growth-promoting activity of yeast extract was due to its content of these vitamins. Further addition of other B vitamins failed to enhance the growth of tomato roots of the strain used by Robbins and Schmidt. This was confirmed by Bonner (1943). However, Bonner and Devirian (1939) and Robbins (1941) showed that the growth of other tomato root clones was further enhanced by the addition of niacin (nicotinic acid). White (1937b) found that, with his clone of tomato roots, the yeast extract could be fully replaced by aneurin plus a mixture of nine amino acids and later reported that the nine amino acids could be fully replaced by an appropriate concentration of glycine. On the basis of all these observations, White (1943a), in formulating a basic synthetic medium for excised root culture, included a vitamin solution composed of a mixture of aneurin and pyridoxine hydrochlorides, niacin and glycine (Table I).

Different workers (Kotte, 1922a, b; Robbins, 1922a, b; White, 1934; Gautheret, 1935a; Bonner, 1936; Burström, 1941; Glasstone, 1947) all used different inorganic salt mixtures, based in each case on culture

TABLE I

Root-culture medium (after White, 1943a, as modified by Street and McGregor, 1952)

	Content per litre of medium expressed as weight of *anhydrous* compound
Calcium nitrate, $Ca(NO_3).4H_2O$	200 mg
Potassium nitrate, KNO_3	80 mg
Potassium chloride, KCl	65 mg
Sodium dihydrogen phosphate, $NaH_2PO_4.4H_2O$	16·5 mg
Manganese chloride, $MnCl_2.4H_2O$	4·5 mg
Zinc sulphate, $ZnSO_4.7H_2O$	1·5 mg
Potassium iodide, KI	0·75 mg
Sodium sulphate, $NaSO_4.10H_2O$	200 mg
Magnesium sulphate, $MgSO_4.7H_2O$	360 mg
Boric acid, H_3BO_3	1·5 mg
Molybdic acid, H_2MoO_4	0·0017 mg
Copper sulphate, $CuSO_4.5H_2O$	0·013 mg
Ferric chloride, $FeCl_3$	2·5 mg
Aneurin hydrochloride	0·1 mg
Pyridoxine hydrochloride	0·1 mg
Nicotinic acid	0·5 mg
Glycine	3·0 mg
Sucrose	20 g

solutions previously employed for the growth of whole plants (Table II). White, working with excised tomato roots, undertook some experimental work on the influence of the ionic composition of the inorganic salt mixture upon growth (White, 1937c, 1938a, 1943b) and evolved a modified Uspenski and Uspenskaia (1925) solution. This solution which is incorporated into White's basic synthetic medium (White, 1943a) has been widely used in root culture work since that date (Table I). The demonstration by Boll and Street (1951) that batches of White's medium prepared with analytical reagent grade salts may be deficient in copper and particularly in molybdenum has led to the generally adopted modification of White's inorganic solution by addition of 0·005 p.p.m. Cu and 0·001 p.p.m. Mo as first suggested by Street and McGregor (1952).

Excised roots require for growth a supply of a utilizable carbohydrate. This was recognized by the pioneers of excised root culture (Kotte, 1922a, b; Robbins, 1922a, b; Robbins and Maneval, 1923; White, 1932) who incorporated dextrose in their media. White, however, in his work (1934) leading to the continuous culture of excised tomato roots,

TABLE II

Various inorganic salt solutions which have been used in preparing root-culture media
(Concentrations expressed as mg/l of anhydrous salt.)

Inorganic salt	Robbins (1922a)	Robbins and White (1936)	Kotte (1922a)	White (1932)	White (1933)	White (1934)	White* (1943a)	Gautheret (1935a)	Bonner and Devirian (1939)	McClary (1940)	Burström (1941)	Almestrand (1949)	Heller (1953)**
$Ca(NO_3)_2.4H_2O$	333	50	1000	144	100	142	200	—	242	590	95	95	—
KNO_3	83	—	250	25	25	81	80	—	85	250	20	20	—
KCl	42	—	—	—	—	65	65	—	61	†	—	—	750
$MgSO_4.7H_2O$	83	10	250	50	25	73	360	200	42	25	49	49	250
$Na_2SO_4.10H_2O$	—	—	—	—	—	—	200	—	—	—	—	—	—
KH_2PO_4	83	10	250	25	25	12	—	1000	20	68	41	41	—
$NaH_2PO_4.H_2O$	—	—	—	—	—	—	16·5	—	—	—	—	—	125
NaCl	—	—	—	—	—	—	—	—	—	—	—	—	—
K_2CO_3	—	—	—	35	35	—	—	—	—	—	—	—	—
$CaCO_3$	—	—	—	—	—	—	—	2000	—	—	—	—	—
$CaSO_4$	—	—	—	—	—	—	—	—	—	—	14	—	—
$NaNO_3$	—	—	—	—	—	—	—	—	—	—	—	—	600
$CaCl_2.2H_2O$	—	—	—	—	—	—	—	—	—	—	—	—	75
$FeCl_3$	0·0008	1·0	t	—	—	—	2·5	—	—	—	—	—	1·0
$Fe_2(SO_4)_3$	—	—	—	1·25	1·25	2·4	—	100	—	4	1·0	1·0	—
Ferric tartrate	—	—	—	—	—	—	—	—	1·5	—	—	—	—
KI	—	—	—	—	—	—	0·75	—	—	—	0·02	0·02	0·01
$(NH_4)_2.SO_4$	—	—	—	—	—	—	—	250	—	—	—	—	—
$MnCl_2.4H_2O$	—	—	—	—	—	—	4·5	50	—	—	—	1·0	—
$ZnCl_2$	—	—	—	—	—	—	—	t	—	—	—	—	—
$ZnSO_4.7H_2O$	—	—	—	—	—	—	1·5	—	—	—	0·02	0·02	1·0
K_2SO_4	—	—	—	—	—	—	—	t	—	—	—	—	—
H_3BO_3	—	—	—	—	—	—	1·5	—	—	—	0·02	0·02	1·0
$CuSO_4.5H_2O$	—	—	—	—	—	—	0·013	—	—	—	0·02	—	0·03
H_2MoO_4	—	—	—	—	—	—	0·0017	—	—	—	—	—	—
$(NH_4)_2.MoO_4$	—	—	—	—	—	—	—	—	—	—	0·02	0·02	—
$MnSO_4.4H_2O$	—	—	—	—	—	—	—	—	—	—	1·0	—	0·1
$NiCl_2.6H_2O$	—	—	—	—	—	—	—	—	—	—	—	—	0·03
$AlCl_3$	—	—	—	—	—	—	—	—	—	—	—	—	0·03

*As Tables I, V and VI. **As Tables V and VI. †In later experiments McClary replaced KNO_3 by an equivalent amount (191 mg) of KCl, and also added 2 g/l NaCl. t, Trace.

found that sucrose was markedly superior to dextrose as a source of carbon; the increase in fresh weight with sucrose being about ten times that with dextrose. This pronounced superiority of sucrose for excised tomato-root growth was confirmed by Dormer and Street (1949) and Street and Lowe (1950) and its more detailed study will be reported upon later in this chapter (see also Chap. 9, p. 556). Sucrose has also been reported to be the carbohydrate of choice for the culture of a number of other dicotyledonous roots (Bonner and Addicott, 1937; White, 1938b; Addicott and Devirian, 1939; Bonner and Devirian, 1939; Bonner, 1940, 1942; David, 1954; Skinner and Street, 1954; Dawson and Street, 1959a, b). The standard White's root-culture medium is therefore normally prepared to contain 2% sucrose. However, for most monocotyledonous roots whose culture has been attempted, dextrose has proved superior to sucrose (Burström, 1941; Almestrand, 1949, 1957; Roberts and Street, 1955; Street, Carter, Scott and Sutton, 1961) and a basic medium for work with cereal roots should therefore contain dextrose at an initial concentration of 2%.

The composition of the modified White's basic root-culture medium, as currently prepared for the culture of excised tomato roots, is shown in Table I. With the exception of the calcium nitrate all the constituents are readily obtainable as analytical grade chemicals. The source of iron is shown as ferric chloride which is used in the form of a dilution of the "Specpure" solution of this compound obtainable from Johnson Matthey Ltd. This is used in place of the ferric sulphate, recommended by White, because of the very significant levels of contamination with manganese and other metal ions in samples of the sulphate and because it eliminates the repeated weighing of small amounts of a solid compound.

The inorganic salts are stored as a stock solution at ten times the strength of the culture medium and the vitamin mixture as a second stock solution at 100 times the final concentration. The sucrose is dissolved in distilled water; to this is then added, in turn, the vitamin solution, the ferric chloride solution and the inorganic stock solution before the solution is diluted almost to final volume with distilled water. The pH of this solution is then adjusted to 4·9–5·0 with the aid of a small volume of sodium hydroxide or hydrochloric acid and the medium made up to final volume and distributed to the culture vessels for sterilization.

White (1936) stressed the extreme sensitiveness of root cultures to iron deficiency in the culture medium. Street, McGonagle and Lowe (1951) and Street, McGonagle and McGregor (1952) studying the "staling" of the medium consequent upon the growth of excised tomato roots found that the pH of the medium drifts from an initial value of 4·8–4·9 to 5·8–6·0 during the standard incubation period of 7 days and that at a pH of 5·2 or above, growth of the roots becomes limited by the development of iron deficiency. The preparation and study of the growth-promoting properties of root culture media in which pure sucrose was incorporated by techniques which did not involve its autoclaving with the other constituents of the medium led to the discovery (Ferguson, Street and David, 1958) that the availability of iron in White's medium, as routinely prepared, is due to the complexing of iron with traces of sugar acids such as glucono-Δ-lactone and glucuronic acid arising during the autoclaving (these sugar acids are fully effective at a concentration of 0·002%). However, such complexes are ineffective in maintaining iron availability as the pH increases during culture. To do this a more stable chelate is required, and it was shown that if the iron is supplied as ferric citrate or ferric sodium ethylenediamine tetra-acetate (Fe-EDTA) it remains available over a wider pH range and that root growth then continues for much longer periods than in White's medium with ferric sulphate or chloride as the primary source of iron (Street *et al.*, 1952). A suitable preparation of Fe-EDTA which permits of a high rate of root growth and maintains iron availability up to pH 7·6–8·0 has now been formulated from data published by Bersworth (1952). Whenever it is desirable to extend the culture period beyond the standard period of 7 days the ferric chloride of Table I is replaced by this preparation. The Fe-EDTA preparation is compounded as follows: 0·8 g disodium ethylenediamine tetra-acetate is dissolved in water, 3·0 ml 10% solution of ferric chloride ("Specpure") added and the volume adjusted to 1 litre (Sheat, Fletcher and Street, 1959). 6·5 ml of this solution per litre of medium gives the standard iron concentration (0·7 p.p.m. Fe).

White's basic medium is very weakly buffered. This is reflected in the often significant drifts which occur during autoclaving, particularly when monosaccharides (dextrose and laevulose) are used as sources of carbon or other substances are present which yield traces of acids (or bases) during sterilization (Ferguson, 1957). Reference has previously been made to the rapid changes in pH which result during root growth primarily from selective ion uptake (Street *et al.*, 1951). However, effects of pH on root growth can be assessed in the standard basic medium over periods of up to 60 h. Because the pH changes occurring during autoclaving cannot be accurately predicted, particularly in modified media, this often involves adjustment to the desired pH value *after* sterilization of the medium. A procedure for this is described by Sheat *et al.* (1959). The experimental medium is divided into two portions and both are autoclaved. The small test portion of known volume is then accurately titrated with sterile 0·1 N NaOH (or HCl) to the required pH. From the titration readings the correct volume of the sterile alkali or acid to be added to the bulk portion of the medium is calculated (this will not exceed 5 ml per litre of medium) and then added aseptically. The medium is then distributed aseptically to sterile culture vessels. By this procedure, maximum variation of pH from the desired value should not exceed $\pm 0{\cdot}1$ of a pH unit.

The standard basic medium in which nitrogen is supplied as nitrate drifts towards alkalinity as a result of excised root growth and, if the nitrate is replaced by ammonium, an even more marked drift occurs towards acidity. These pH drifts reflect the rapid selective uptake of these nitrogen-containing ions. With ammonium nitrate as nitrogen source and with initial pH values in the range 4·4–4·7, a considerable stabilization of pH is achieved; only a slow acid drift occurs (Street *et al.*, 1951). On the other hand, growth is significantly inferior to that occurring in the basic nitrate-containing medium. However, if as little as 0·05 times the standard amount of nitrogen is added as ammonium to the standard nitrate medium of pH 4·7, it completely prevents the alkaline drift which would otherwise occur and does not affect the high level of root growth. In nitrate medium of pH 5·8, the pH can be effectively stabilized by as little as 0·02 times the standard amount of nitrogen added as ammonium (Sheat *et al.*, 1959).

Two alternative techniques have been explored for pH stabilization. The first of these has been the use of buffer mixtures of sodium dihydrogen phosphate and disodium hydrogen phosphate. The use of such buffer mixtures is, however, very limited because the relatively high concentrations of phosphate required to enhance buffer capacity significantly are markedly inhibitory to excised root growth, particularly at pH values above 6·0. A more attractive alternative which has been exploited in studying the relationships between root growth and pH, has been the use of "solid buffers" involving the sparingly soluble compounds, amorphous calcium dihydrogen orthophosphate $Ca(H_2PO_4)_2$, calcium phosphate precipitated (B.P.C.) and calcium carbonate. The composition of selected buffers involving these compounds singly and in combinations is shown in Table III. The technique of incorporating these buffers is as follows: the required amount of buffer is added to 10 ml of water in each 100 ml Erlenmeyer culture vessel and autoclaved. When the vessels are cool, 40 ml of a $\times$ 1·25 normal strength sterile medium is added aseptically to each. The pH values are checked electrometrically by allowing specimen vessels containing the completed medium to remain undisturbed for 12 h and then immersing the electrodes in the clear supernatant. If the "solid buffer" is autoclaved with the other medium constituents adsorption of micronutrient elements onto the solid phase reduces the growth-promoting activity of the medium (Sheat *et al.*, 1959).

TABLE III

Mixtures of sparingly soluble calcium salts used as "solid buffers" for root culture media (after Sheat *et al.*, 1959)

Key: A, Amorphous calcium dihydrogen orthophosphate; B, calcium phosphate precipitated (British Pharmaceutical Codex); C, calcium carbonate.

Salt mixture	Weight * (g) of mixture per 50 ml culture medium	Approx. pH† of media in presence of mixture
A only	0·033	4·2
34g A + 8·7g B	0·040	4·4
17g A + 8·7g B	0·025	4·8
17g A + 17·4g B	0·030	5·2
17g A + 34·8g B	0·024	5·6
B only	0·021	6·0
17g A + 17g C	0·028	6·4
C only	0·025	7·1
8·7g B + 34g C	0·039	7·5

*2 spoonfuls of a standard spoon designed to contain approx. 10 mg of C. This is added to 10 ml water and autoclaved, and then 40 ml of × 1·25 standard strength sterile culture medium is added.

†These vary with the samples of salts used and also the pH given by the mixtures changes slowly if they are stored after preparation. pH values are of supernatant after medium has stood undisturbed for 12 h.

Whenever one is studying the influence of the concentration of a major constituent of the medium, like the sugar, on the rate of root growth the question arises of how far the growth effects are modified by changes in the osmotic pressure of the medium. In this connection, Street and Lowe (1950) and Ferguson *et al.* (1958) have shown that raffinose and mannitol are almost inactive as carbon sources, are absorbed only very slowly and are, probably in consequence, only very slightly inhibitory at concentrations of 3% and 2%, respectively. These compounds are therefore valuable for adjusting the osmotic pressures of modified media.

Quantitative studies on the requirement and involvement in metabolism of the essential inorganic nutrients of root culture media are facilitated by the relative insensitivity of root cultures to changes in the concentration of sodium and chloride ions up to quite high levels of both ions. Thus, cations can be replaced by the corresponding sodium salts and anions by the corresponding chlorides. This can be illustrated by the technique of preparing N-omitted culture media and media containing different concentrations of nitrate and ammonium ions shown in Table IV from Sheat *et al.* (1959). In such media the glycine of White's vitamin solution is also omitted, since it is slightly inhibitory

TABLE IV

Basal inorganic stock solution for preparing a nitrogen-omitted root culture medium (after Sheat *et al.*, 1959)

Constituent	Content of *actual compound* (mg/l)
Sodium sulphate, $Na_2SO_4.10H_2O$	453
Potassium chloride, KCl	124
Calcium chloride, $CaCl_2.6H_2O$	268
Magnesium sulphate, $MgSO_4.7H_2O$	748
Sodium dihydrogen phosphate, $NaH_2PO_4.2H_2O$	21·5
Manganese chloride, $MnCl_2.4H_2O$	6
Zinc sulphate, $ZnSO_4.7H_2O$	2·6
Potassium iodide, KI	0·75
Molybdic acid, H_2MoO_4	0·0017
Copper sulphate, $CuSO_4.5H_2O$	0·013
Ferric chloride, $FeCl_3$	2·5
To add the standard nitrate concentration (45 mg NO_3N/l)	
Sodium nitrate, $NaNO_3$	274·8

to or without growth effect with a number of excised tomato root clones and on the root cultures of most other species tested.

In work on the requirements of excised root cultures for the micro-nutrient elements it is usually necessary to purify the inorganic salts by the traditional techniques used in this field (Hewitt, 1952). Difficulties may arise because the root cultures may be sensitive to residues from the reagents used and it is essential to test for full restoration of the growth-promoting activity of the purified medium by addition of an effective concentration of the omitted element. Very pure distilled water can be obtained by double distillation from Pyrex stills (Fig. 1) provided that the stills have effective baffles and are frequently cleaned (Boll and Street, 1951). Purification of the sugar is essential; this applies also to the induction of critical deficiences of certain of the macro-nutrient elements like sulphur. For this purpose recourse is made to exchange resins (Hannay and Street, 1954) which can very effectively purify concentrated solutions (up to 20%) of sugars. Particularly in the purification of oligosaccharides an exchange resin should be chosen which does not chemically modify the sugar. Reference has already been made to the special requirements needed to induce critical deficiencies of boron (Neales, 1959, 1964).

3. *Sterilization of Culture Media and Seeds*

The standard technique for the sterilization of culture media and culture apparatus is autoclaving at 15 lb/in² for 5–15 min. Culture apparatus and apparatus for aseptic filtration should be wrapped in cellophane sheet to prevent saturation of cotton filters and condensation of steam within the apparatus. Good quality rubber or silicone rubber bungs can be repeatedly autoclaved without deterioration but should, before use, be boiled for several hours to remove soluble material and dressing. Nylon or silicone rubber tubing is biologically inactive and resistant to autoclaving.

When certain constituents of the culture medium are thermolabile other techniques for sterilization of part or all of the medium have to be adopted. During autoclaving (5 min) of the standard basic root culture medium, sucrose (2%) yields up to 0·1% of reducing sugars and monosaccharides tend to yield small amounts of sugar acids. The decomposition of sugars during autoclaving is promoted by other constituents of the medium, particularly by ions which can act as electron carriers (e.g. iron) and by phosphate ions. For the critical testing of many such carbon sources it is sufficient simply to autoclave the carbohydrate separately in pure aqueous solution and then add this to the remainder of the medium, separately autoclaved. For substances which are more thermolabile two techniques are available.

(a) Sterilization by passage through Pyrex sintered-glass sterilizing filters (porosity H 5) (Street *et al.*, 1951). Such filters should be cleaned each time with 5% sodium nitrate in 70% H_2SO_4, washed well with filtered (porosity H 3 sinter) distilled water, autoclaved and then washed with sterile distilled water (to remove released alkali). Complete medium can be rapidly sterilized with such filters by filtration under vacuum provided that the medium is first clarified by filtration through a sintered-filter of porosity H 3. Alternatively, Millipore filters (Millipore Filter Corporation, Bedford, Massachusetts) may be used (Nitsch and Nitsch, 1957). These have the advantage that each filter membrane can be rejected after use, thereby facilitating repeated use of the apparatus. Seitz, Berkfeld and Pasteur filters are unsuitable because they adsorb constituents of the medium and also release alkaline material to the weakly buffered medium (Almestrand, 1950). When extremely dilute solutions of active growth-regulating substances are being sterilized by filtration through sintered filters it is necessary to reject the first portion of the filtrate which may have been reduced in concentration by adsorption.

(b) Treatment of the dry substance with Analar ethyl ether, removal of the ether at a temperature below 30°C and solution of the solid in sterile distilled water followed by aseptic addition to the remainder of the sterile medium (Ferguson *et al.*, 1958). Solid chemicals, as purchased, are often sterile and hence, when this technique is being used, they should be weighed into sterile containers and the ether treatment conducted in sterile vessels closed by large dry sterile cotton plugs. This technique has had very wide application for the incorporation into root culture media of thermolabile substances.

The technique for the sterilization of tomato seeds is as follows: the seeds are treated for 5 min in a 1% (w/v) solution of bromine in water, washed five times with sterile distilled water and then the seeds are transferred to sterile 9 cm Petri dishes each containing two Whatman No. 1 filter papers moistened with sterile water. Germination takes place in the dishes which are incubated in the dark at 27°C (25°C is a better general temperature). Because of the complete volatility of bromine and its effectiveness as a sterilant this is the technique of choice and alternatives are only sought where bromine treatment markedly reduces the percentage germination or gives rise to abnormality in the seedlings. Groundsel (*Senecio vulgaris*) seed cannot be sterilized by bromine without injury but seed sterilized by immersion for not more than 8 h in a bleaching powder filtrate containing 1% chlorine (Wilson, 1915) gives 96–100% germination in 48 h (Skinner and Street, 1954). Grains of Petkus II rye (Roberts and Street, 1955), Victory oats (Harris, 1956) and Atson Elite wheat (Street *et al.*, 1961) can be effectively sterilized by shaking with 1% of the detergent, Lissapol, for 1 min followed by 0·1% aqueous mercuric chloride for 20 min. Many seeds can be effectively sterilized without injury to the embryo by one of these techniques.

4. *Aseptic Manipulations: the Establishment and Maintenance of Root Clones*

All aseptic manipulations should be carried out in an inoculating cabinet large enough for the operator to have a good area of well illuminated working bench and to permit of the shelving of large numbers of culture vessels. Electric power and vacuum are also required. Such a cabinet is illustrated and briefly described in Fig. 6. The interior surfaces of this cabinet should be kept very clean and dust traps should be avoided. The interior of the cabinet and the hands of the operator should be sterilized by short exposure (up to 4 min) to the radiation of a Hanovia Bactericidal Ultraviolet tube (peak emission at 2537Å). The positive pressure of filtered air maintained in the cabinet not only assists asepsis but permits the operator to work in comfort for prolonged periods. Special overalls and caps should be reserved for work in the cabinet.

The following is an outline of the procedure followed to initiate and establish a clone of excised tomato roots. Sterilized seeds are allowed to germinate at 27°C for 4–5 days in the dark, by which time the radicles are 30–40 mm. The 10 mm apical tips of such radicles are excised with a scalpel and transferred with a platinum loop singly to the culture vessels containing 50 ml of the basic root culture medium. The cultures

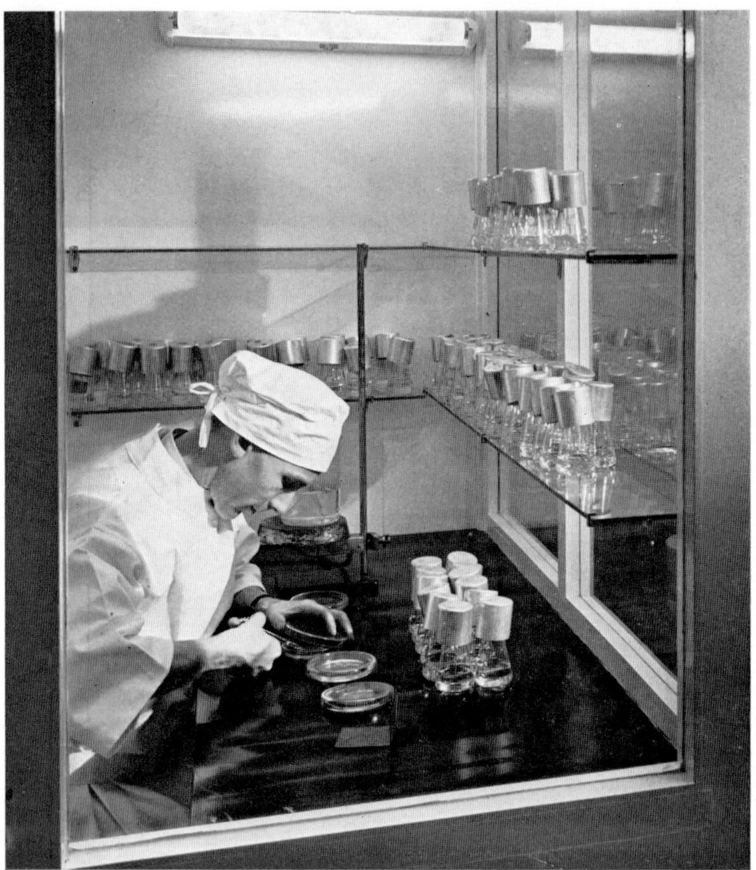

FIG. 6. Aseptic transfer cabinet. Root "sector" cultures are being subcultured from Petri dishes using iris scissors for the excisions.

are incubated at 27°C in the dark for 7 days. The cultured roots are then cut up either directly in the culture vessels using "Mayo" scissors or after transfer to Petri dishes containing sterile medium, using iris scissors, to give sector initials (each consisting of a portion of the main axis bearing four or five laterals, each 3–8 mm long). These sector initials are transferred to new culture vessels and again incubated for 7 days. The resulting "sector cultures" are composed of the original short length of the main axis, now bearing the elongated laterals which have, in turn, developed laterals. Such "*sector cultures*" can be cut up to yield four or five main lateral root tips, each 10 mm long and at least this number of sector initials. The sector initials can now be used to multiply the clone further. The main lateral root tips will grow into "*tip cultures*" similar in morphology to the root arising from the radicle root tip. These procedures are represented diagrammatically in Fig. 7 and typical "tip" and "sector" cultures are shown in Fig. 2. Clones of tomato roots can be grown for long periods entirely as sector cultures and since each such sector yields inocula for at least five new cultures each 7 days, the clone can be built up to any desired size. Experimental cultures can then also be established each week from the main lateral root tips. Such experimental tip cultures are very suitable for measurement of linear growth values.

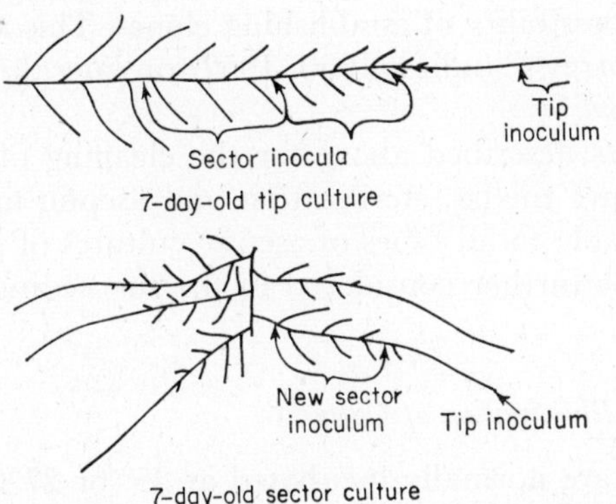

FIG. 7. Subculture of excised roots. "Tip" and "sector" cultures showing portions excised to again initiate both "sector" and "tip" cultures (see also Fig. 2, p. 468).

When clones of excised tomato roots are maintained week by week as sector cultures, the growth potential of the root tips of the first order laterals slowly declines. To ensure the vigour of these tips, which are used to initiate experimental cultures, it is necessary, as part of the clonal maintenance procedure, to interpose a tip passage between the successive sector passages every fifth or sixth subculture.

The optimum concentration of sucrose as assessed by linear growth and increase in dry weight is, for most tomato root clones, close to 2%. For clonal maintenance, however, it is found best to use a sucrose concentration slightly below this (1·5 or 1·75%).

This general technique is applicable when the root cultures develop a regular sequence of laterals and when such laterals are capable of rapid growth from sector initials. When working with different species which fulfil this general criterion it is, however, important to determine the optimum sugar concentration, duration of passage, length of root tip inoculum and size of laterals on the sector initials which are compatible with a continuing high and uniform growth rate in successive passages. Procedures for subculture based on this general pattern have now been worked out for several species other than tomato (David,

1954; Skinner and Street, 1954; Charles and Street, 1959; Dawson and Street, 1959a; Roberts and Street, 1955).

The roots of certain species are described as developing no, or only few, slow-growing laterals in culture and in a number of such cases the roots have been maintained in continuous culture by repeated excision and transfer of the main axis root tip (Bonner and Addicott, 1937; Bonner and Devirian, 1939; Bonner, 1940; White, 1938b; van Overbeek, 1939). In such cases, further work may lead to the development of culture procedures conducive to lateral root initiation and growth with the consequent possibility of establishing clones. This approach is foreshadowed by Torrey's studies (1950, 1952) on lateral root initiation in cultured pea roots.

The techniques described above for the cleaning of glassware, preparation of culture media, sterilization and aseptic manipulation are generally applicable to all types of aseptic cultures of plant origin and hence will not be further considered in the succeeding descriptions of basic techniques.

5. *Incubation and Illumination of Cultures*

Root cultures are normally incubated at 25° or 27°C and, in quantitative work, the air temperature should be maintained in the incubator or incubator room within ±1°C of this mean temperature. Such incubators usually mean that the cultures are in darkness. The now quite numerous observations on the influence of light on the growth of excised roots (Robbins and Maneval, 1924; White, 1932; Gautheret, 1935b; Robbins, 1940; Street, 1953; Roberts, 1954; Scott, Carter and Street, 1961), however, require that the light regime during incubation should be carefully controlled and described.

Apparatus for the controlled illumination of root cultures has been described by Scott *et al.* (1961) who used daylight fluorescent tubes, Ilford Spectrum filters and Jena Spectralfarbfilters.

6. *Measurement of the Growth of Excised Root Cultures*

With excised root clones very reproducible rates of growth can be obtained and by suitable replication (10–20 cultures per treatment) and statistical analysis, the significance of quite small differences can be established. Under the standard conditions described and with clonal tomato roots, differences of 10–15% in the values for mean linear extension of the main root axis under different treatments will, with twenty replicates, normally be significant at the 5% level. Occasion to occasion variation in growth cannot be entirely eliminated, probably because of variation in the physiological vigour of the root tip inocula but this variation is not large (by comparison with that encountered in work with other plant test organs grown under standardized conditions) and its extent can be checked by introducing a control treatment in each of a sequence of experiments.

Linear growth of the cultures is expressed by the following criteria: increase in length of the main axis (i.e. final length of main axis minus its initial length, in mm); number of emergent laterals visible to the naked eye (lateral number); total length of laterals per root (mm). Fresh and dry weights are most easily recorded by bulking five or ten roots. Reproducible fresh weights can be obtained by adopting a precise blotting technique and dry weights by gentle washing of the roots followed by drying to constant weight in small metal boats at 80°C.

Anatomical techniques suitable for work with root cultures have been described by Street and McGregor (1952) and used in studies of the influence of sugar supply (Street and McGregor, 1952) and auxins (Hughes and Street, 1960) on root anatomy.

Root growth is the outcome of cell division in the apical meristems and enlargement and differentiation of the new cells produced (see Chap. 10, p. 632). Measurement of cell expansion has been based upon measurements of the length and transverse diameter of exodermal cells in roots fixed in 70% alcohol and cleared with lactophenol. Usually ten cells are measured in each of five replicate roots at a point (5 mm or more from the extreme tip) where cell expansion is complete. By making such measurements at fixed intervals from the apex the process of cell expansion can be followed and plotted on a time scale by reference to the known linear growth rate during the previous 24 h. Measurements of the rate of production of new cells per 24 h and changes in the number of meristematic cells in the root apex can be carried out by the method of Brown and Rickless (1949) modified by centrifuging the cell suspension, removing the supernatant chromic acid and replacing this with 50% glycerol (Butcher and Street, 1960). In work with excised tomato roots each cell suspension is prepared from twenty replicate root segments (5–20 mm long) macerated for 16 h in 2 ml 5% chromic acid. The mean values for the cell densities (vacuolated and meristematic cells can be counted separately if desired) are based upon three haemocytometer counts of not less than 200 cells (which should be present in 0·9 mm^3 of the suspension). The appearance of a cell suspension prepared in this way is illustrated in Fig. 8. Where data are required regarding the rate of production of new cells during root growth, segments are taken which exclude the apical 2 mm (and hence the apical meristem and root cap) and which have a length equal to the linear growth increment of the main axis during the previous 24 h.

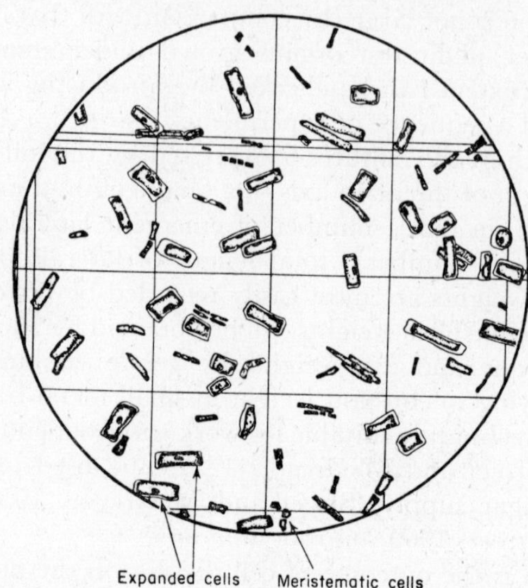

FIG. 8. A suspension prepared by maceration of root tissue as seen in the haemocytometer. Each square is 1/16 mm² in area and the depth of the suspension below the coverslip is 0·2 mm. (Drawn by Dr. D. N. Butcher, from Street, 1962).

B. EXCISED SHOOT APICES

Loo (1945) reported that stem tips (5 mm) from sterile seedlings of *Asparagus officinalis*, when supported at the surface of a liquid medium by plugs of glass wool and illuminated, underwent potentially unlimited growth without giving rise to roots. 5 mm tips were excised at intervals ranging from 5 to 23 days and the cultures were maintained by this technique for 9 months involving twenty successive transfers and at a growth rate of between 0·5 and 2·0 mm per day. The culture medium consisted of Bonner's (1943) solution of inorganic ions and 2% sucrose. Light was essential to continued growth. In the few cases where adventitious roots were initiated the growth rate immediately increased three or four times. Growth could not be enhanced by addition of the B vitamins used in root culture media or by the addition of the leaf growth substance, adenine. In a later paper (Loo, 1946a) the continuing growth of these cultures for 22 months was reported and it was found that the growth rate and appearance of cladophylls were both enhanced by the use of 0·5% agar instead of glass wool to support the cultures. Loo (1946b) has also successfully grown excised stem tips of dodder (*Cuscuta campestris*) on a similar agar medium and in light, some of the cultures reaching the stage were lateral buds and flowers were initiated. Growth rate after a fourth or fifth transfer to new medium was scarcely measurable and could not be enhanced by the addition of a number of growth factors. The amount of chlorophyll developed in the stems was clearly greater than when dodder grows parasitically on a host. Although Loo obtained cultures with flower buds, he did not investigate the control of flower-bud initiation in his cultures. Such a study has, however, been undertaken by Baldev (1962) with stem tips of *Cuscuta reflexa*, 1–1·5 cm long and bearing 3–5 vegetative buds. These tips were cultured on a modified White's medium solidified with 0·8% agar. The cultures flowered when maintained either in continuous darkness or exposed to 14 h daily dark periods, indicating *Cuscuta* to be a typical short-day plant. The presence of 5% sucrose in the medium substituted for the high intensity light exposure normally required for short-day plants, strongly indicating that the high intensity light reactions are reactions in photosynthesis. It seems that in this plant, the bud itself is sensitive to photo-induction since induction was not prevented by removal of the scale leaves.

The potential value of cultured stem apices for studies on the transition from vegetative to reproductive development is also indicated by work with the short-day plant, *Perilla*. Chailakhyan, Butenko and Lynbarskaya (1961), working with *Perilla ocymoides*, demonstrated that feeding a mixture of ribonucleosides plus casein, or even only kinetin or adenosine, stimulated flowering of apices cultured in darkness, in short-days, or even in long-days. Raghavan and Jacobs (1961), working with *P. frutescens*, found that even under long-days cultured apices devoid of leaves gave rise to sterile cone-like structures (termed Stage I); in the presence of attached leaves the shoots remained completely vegetative under long-days. The development of sporogenous tissue and normal flowers (Stage II) was dependent upon favourable photoperiods. Evidence was obtained that the leaves are not only involved in short-day induction in the sense of promoting Stage II development but that they produce, particularly under long-days, inhibitors of flowering capable of diffusing out into the medium from cultured leaves. The work was considered to support the concept of Stage II flowering being determined by a balance between a specific promoter formed under short days and inhibitor(s) developed in the leaves under all day length conditions. Stage I of the flowering process was regarded as an intrinsic property of the apical meristem, the expression of which could be inhibited by leaves exposed to long-days.

Morel (1958, 1966) has cultured stem apices of certain tropical orchids (particularly hybrid *Cymbidiums*) in a simple medium containing only inorganic salts and glucose. Such apices give rise to a protocorm (a juvenile stage in the development of the plant) and the cultures can be serially propagated by division into three or four fragments at each subculture. By contrast, apical meristems (60–80 μ in diam.) excised from sprouts of *Solanum tuberosum* and from seedlings of *Helianthus annuus* and transferred to the simple medium produced only a small amount of callus, then their growth ceased, and within one to two months the cultures were dead. Addition of 10^{-7} g/ml of gibberellic acid suppressed the development of callus and normal, although chlorotic, shoot development took place to give a culture 5 mm in length. The rate and duration of this shoot development were both increased by raising the potassium concentration of the medium to 500 mg/l.

Wetmore (1954) has emphasized that very small apices of vascular cryptogams will develop roots and grow into plants in a relatively simple medium. In this way, plants of *Adiantum pedatum, Selaginella willdenorii, Lycopodium cernuum* and *Equisetum hyemale* were developed from apices only 200–250 μ in length. To raise plants from dicotyledonous stem apices it was necessary to take a longer tip (rooting of 0·5 mm apices of *Syringa vulgaris* and *Parthenocissus tricuspidata* was reported). It was also noted that the angiosperm apices, in contrast to the vascular cryptogams, could not use nitrate as an effective source of nitrogen and that their growth depended upon supplying a mixture of amino acids.

Ball (1946) has cultured very small stem tips (400–430 μ^3) of *Tropaeolum majus* and *Lupinus albus*. These gave rise to plantlets bearing roots *when illuminated* and placed in a medium containing inorganic salts, dextrose and 0·3% agar. These apices were obtained sterile by dissection of intact buds previously immersed for 5 min in 1·75% solution of calcium hypochlorite. In later work, Ball (1960) has cultured larger apices of a number of species in a medium supplemented with 150 ml/l fresh coconut milk and 1 mg/l gibberellic acid, using as culture vessels Kolle flasks closed with sterile cover glasses. Such cultures have been maintained active for several weeks under conditions permitting of time-lapse photographic studies of cell division and alteration in position of individual cells in the apices.

C. EXCISED LEAF PRIMORDIA

It has long been known that detached leaves can often be maintained alive for very long periods and undergo some increase in size after detachment (Yarwood, 1946). Bonner, Haagen-Smit and Went, as early as 1939, reported the limited growth in culture of small whole leaves. The first really successful sterile cultures of leaf primordia were, however, obtained in work with leaves of various degrees of immaturity dissected out from the dormant subterranean apical buds of ferns and particularly of *Osmunda cinnamomea* (Sussex and Steeves, 1953; Steeves and Sussex, 1957; Sussex and Clutter, 1960; Steeves, 1961). These leaves were cultured in tubes at 24°C, received 12 h illumination per day and were nurtured by a medium solidified with 0·8% agar and containing inorganic salts and 2% sucrose. The leaves (even small primordia initially only 0·12 cm high) followed, during development in culture, a pattern of growth essentially similar to that of normal attached fronds except that the completion of growth was speeded up and the resulting leaves were smaller in size than normal, due to a reduced cell number per leaf (rather than to any reduction in mean cell size). The cultured leaves remained healthy for many weeks after reaching maturity. Additions to the basic medium of B vitamins, an auxin, acid casein hydrolysate and coconut milk separately or together did not profoundly influence development although the final weight of the cultures was increased.

Since the reduced size of cultured leaves is due primarily to a reduced total number of cells per leaf it can be argued that excision induces a precocious maturation. Excision may remove some influence (possibly of the older leaves) inhibitory to cell expansion or some influence promoting cell division. It could be that both such effects are aspects of the growth-regulating activity of a single substance reaching the developing primordium. Sussex (1958) working with *Leptopteris hymenophylloides* has shown that the development of cultured primordia does not immediately become one of maturation. The primordia show a reduced period of meristematic growth leading to crozier formation and the extent of this development is greater with young primordia even though the final leaf size attained is inversely related to the size of primordia at the time of their excision. Further, the normal formation and uncoiling of the crozier indicates that the balance between cell division on the abaxial and adaxial sides of the frond proceeds normally in cultured leaves (Caponetti and Steeves, 1963). The cultured leaves complete their development in a shorter time. This is partly due, in *Osmunda cinnamomea,* to the elimination of dormant periods which characterize the course of development of attached leaves, but even if we exclude these the cultured leaves show accelerated maturation. The contrast is not in the duration of the phases of crozier elevation, crozier uncoiling and elongation of the rachis but in the earlier phases of development (Caponetti and Steeves, 1963).

Steeves (1961), working with excised leaf primordia of *Osmunda cinnamomea* ranging from the first visible primordium (P_1) taking the form of a flat mound projecting a maximum of 30 μ beyond the surface of the apical meristem to P_{10} primordia slightly over 800 μ long, found that for a relatively long period the primordia are not irreversibly determined as leaf primordia. P_{10} primordia always developed into leaves in culture. P_1 primordia almost always became shoot apices in culture. Primordia of intermediate age at the time of excision showed, with increase in age, a decrease in their tendency to develop into leafy shoots. The shoot versus leaf expression of the primordia was not influenced by the mineral salt or sugar concentrations in the culture medium. The appearance of a distinct apical cell in the primordia occurred in advance of the time of irreversible determination. The shoot apex was shown to arise from the apex of the primordium and there was no evidence that the organization of a shoot apex was an injury response associated with excision or handling of the primordia. Steeves tentatively suggested that the progressively rising tendency to develop as a leaf with increase in the age of the primordium before excision and the irreversibility of leaf determination at P_{10} pointed to determination being the consequence of the gradual build up in the primordium of the concentration of some leaf-forming substance. That this rather than the development of some specific structural organization was determinative was supported by the demonstration (Kuehnert and Steeves, 1962) that leaf primordia P_4–P_{10} from *Osmunda,* when subjected to vertical longitudinal splitting after excision gave half primordia which gave rise in culture to leaves with normal morphology and with a similar frequency to the development of leaves (rather than leafy stems) from unsplit primordia of the same P number.

Steeves, Gabriel and Steeves (1957) have also reported the successful growth in culture of very young leaves of *Helianthus annuus* and *Nicotiana tabacum*. Even very small primordia were found to be capable of developing into leaves of normal morphology although of greatly reduced size. A tendency of the cultured leaves to become chlorotic as they matured was largely overcome by using ammonium nitrate instead of sodium nitrate as the source of nitrogen. Here again organic growth factors were not essential although, particularly with the youngest primordia, their addition to the medium caused marked increases in linear dimensions and in fresh weight of the cultures. These investigations by Steeves and co-workers emphasize that the complex patterns of leaf development are self-controlled within the young leaf primordium and are not dependent upon association with the shoot apex.

Sussex and Steeves (1958) have reported the production of sporangia on excised leaves of these ferns growing in sterile culture and reported that sporangia formation is promoted by a high sucrose and high inorganic nitrogen supply in the medium. The sporangia remained immature, only reaching a premeiotic stage of development.

D. CULTURE OF FLOWERS AND FLORAL ORGANS

The basic techniques of *anther* culture have been established by Gregory (1940), Taylor (1949), Sparrow, Pond and Kojan (1955) and

Vasil (1959, 1962). No one has succeeded in obtaining, in excised anthers, the whole development from microspore mother cell to mature pollen grains. In one case (*Trillium erectum*), formation of mature pollen grains from microspore mother cells at the pachytene stage has been reported (Sparrow *et al.*, 1955). In most cases anthers excised at the pachytene or diplotene-diakinesis stages can be reared *in vitro* up to the stage of formation of tetrads or one-celled microspores. Beyond this stage the cytoplasm of the microspore is usually consumed and this is accompanied by nuclear degeneration. The deoxyribonucleic acid (DNA) synthesis in the mother cells is completed by the diplotene stage and anthers excised *after* this stage can develop at least to the one-celled microspore stage in a simple medium supplying salts and sugar. Coconut milk assists in the continuation of development of anthers excised at the pachytene stage, presumably by supplying nucleic acid. Beneficial effects of DNA and particularly of ribonucleic acid (RNA) upon development from the leptotene-zygotene stage to tetrad formation are reported by Vasil (1959). Vasil has also reported (1963) the induction of mitosis of the microspore nucleus by feeding a mixture of the four nucleotides of RNA to anthers of *Allium cepa* excised at the one-celled microspore stage.

It is not clear how far the functioning of the tapetum is inhibited by excision and how far this accounts for our present inability to culture immature anthers through to the production of pollen.

Studies of sex expression in cultured excised floral buds of *Cucumis sativus* have been described by Galun, Jung and Lang (1963). Contamination of the buds was eliminated by immersion of the stem apices for 4 min in 1% hypochlorite, followed by dipping in ethanol and rinsing with distilled water. The buds excised at an early embryonic stage (0·5–0·7 mm) developed considerably during the 20 days of culture to buds at an advanced embryonic stage (1·0 cm). The culture medium contained salts, sucrose, B vitamins, tryptophane, casamino acids and 15% coconut milk. These studies showed that potentially male buds tended to develop ovaries when cultured and this tendency to produce female flowers was enhanced by early excision and by addition of IAA to the culture medium. This promotion of ovary development by IAA was antagonized by gibberellic acid. One difficulty in interpreting this result was that stamen development in excised buds was significantly retarded compared with that occurring in attached buds, whereas the culture medium seemed to supply all that was needed for ovary development. The development of potentially female and hermaphrodite buds was little affected by either IAA or gibberellic acid. Although all flowers are initiated as bisexual organs, there was no development of hermaphrodite flowers from buds expected to develop into unisexual flowers. A trigger mechanism operates in potentially unisexual flowers and auxin caused this trigger to operate in favour of ovary development. IAA and gibberellic acid failed to suppress stamen development in potentially hermaphrodite flowers; IAA, at a concentration converting male into female flowers did not give female flowers from potentially hermaphrodite buds. There is no trigger mechanism in the development of the hermaphrodite flowers.

Tepfer, Greyson, Karpoff and Gerimonte (1963) have also reported, so far only in abstract, that excised young floral buds of *Aquilegia* make extensive growth and development in a medium containing vitamins, coconut milk, IAA, gibberellic acid and kinetin. Kinetin was essential but had no distinctive morphogenetic effect. Omission of IAA led to abortion of carpel primordia. Gibberellic acid stimulated the elongation growth of all organs except the stamens. Normal petal expansion was particularly dependent upon the presence of gibberellic acid.

Nitsch (1951) initiated the study of fruit development on *excised flowers* cultured under aseptic conditions. Flowers whose pedicels were sealed with liquid paraffin were sterilized by short immersions (3–10 min) in a decanted 5% calcium hypochlorite solution and then washed with sterile water. The sealed ends of the pedicels were then cut and the flowers transferred to the culture tubes. With liquid media the flowers were supported on filter paper by the technique of Heller (1949) (see Fig. 9, p. 497), for solidifying media 0·7–1·0 agar was used. Fruit development of a number of species was reported in experiments using a simple medium containing inorganic salts and sucrose, provided that the flowers had been pollinated 2 or more days before separation of the flowers from the mother plant. Most such fruits contained viable seed although the percentage seed set was abnormally low (see also Chopra, 1958; Sachar and Baldev, 1958; Johri and Guha, 1963). When excised before pollination and transferred to simple medium the ovaries do not develop and no seed is present. Parthenocarpic fruits can, with appropriate species, be induced to develop in culture from unpollinated flowers by the use of synthetic auxins.

One feature of all the aseptically cultured fruits described by Nitsch (1951) was their relatively small size. However, fruits of *Iberis amara* (Maheshwari and Lal, 1958, 1961), *Althaea rosea* (Chopra, 1962), *Ranunculus scleratus* (Sachar and Guha, 1962), *Anethum graveolens* (Johri and Sehgal, 1963) and of *Allium cepa* (Johri and Guha, 1963) as large as or larger than those in nature have been obtained by culture on media supplemented with organic growth factors. Auxins (indole acetic acid, or phenoxy- or naphthoxyacetic acids), gibberellic acid and kinetin, particularly in combination, frequently stimulate fruit enlargement. A natural "kinin" has been detected in green and red tomato juice which will stimulate the growth of unpollinated tomato ovaries in culture (Nitsch, 1960).

E. OVULES AND EMBRYOS

The embryologist, Hannig (1904), was the first to demonstrate that embryos (of *Raphanus* and *Cochlearia*) could be successfully cultured in a medium containing certain mineral salts and sucrose. Later Laibach (1925) successfully used a technique of culturing embryos on cotton wool moistened with 15% dextrose to raise embryos of *Linum* hybrids which aborted if left *in situ*. Subsequently, and with improved techniques, embryo culture has been quite extensively used to obtain various hybrids otherwise difficult or impossible to grow (Jörgensen, 1928; Tukey, 1933, 1934; Werckmeister 1934; Brink, Cooper and Aushermann, 1944; Blakeslee and Satina, 1944).

In most studies the culture medium has included a balanced mixture of inorganic salts including micro-elements. Sucrose has, in general, proved superior to all other carbohydrates tested, high concentrations of sucrose often proving particularly important in the culture of young embryos as evidenced by the studies of Sanders (1950) and Rietsema, Satina and Blakeslee (1953) with *Datura,* of Rijven (1952) with *Capsella* and of Ziebur and Brink (1951) and Norstog and Smith (1963) with *Hordeum*. Recently it has been shown (Raghavan and Torrey, 1963) in work with globular embryos of *Capsella* (*ca* 80 μ long) that broadly similar development can be achieved either by high sucrose concentration (12–18%) or by enhanced levels of macronutrient ions or additions of growth factors (kinetin, adenine, IAA). Such results suggest a controlling influence of the intracellular sucrose level on certain pathways of biosynthesis within the embryo. While nitrate has, in general, proved to be a satisfactory source of nitrogen for mature embryos, immature embryos and even mature embryos during the initial stages of germination often require reduced forms of nitrogen such as glutamine (Rijven, 1952, working with *Capsella*) or amino acids (Sanders and Burkholder, 1948, with *Datura*). Raghavan and Torrey (1964a) and Raghavan (1964) have shown that very young seedlings of *Cattleya* cannot utilize nitrate (nitrate reductase is only slowly developed during germination) but can utilize, as effective nitrogen sources, ammonium, arginine, ornithine or urea and somewhat less effectively γ-aminobutyric acid and proline. There is also evidence that the various B vitamins may be important, particularly in the nutrition of immature embryos (Bonner, 1938; Bonner and Axtmann, 1937; van Overbeek, Conklin and Blakeslee, 1942). Embryo development may depend upon an appropriate balance being established between such hormonal factors as auxins, gibberellins and kinins and several studies point in this direction (Rijven, 1952; Rietsema, Satina and Blakeslee, 1953; DeMaggio and Wetmore, 1961; Raghavan and Torrey, 1963, 1964b).

Li (1934) and Li and Shen (1934) made the interesting observation that in order to culture *Ginkgo* embryos *in vitro* it was necessary to add to the medium an extract of *Ginkgo* seed endosperm. Then, in 1942, van Overbeek *et al.* found that unheated coconut milk permitted the growth in culture of very young *Datura* embryos (embryos of initial length 0·15 mm growing up to 8·0 mm long in 7 days). Milk from mature coconuts also enabled seedlings to be obtained from sugar-cane embryos of 66 μ length (Warmke, Rivera-Perez and Ferrer-Monge, 1946) and from *Hordeum* embryos of 60 μ length (Norstog, 1956, 1961). To promote the growth of isolated coconut embryos it was necessary to use coconut milk obtained from immature green nuts (Abraham and Thomas, 1962). It has also been shown that many other materials, such as yeast extracts, wheat germs, almond meal and extracts of *Datura* ovules have "embryo factor" activity although it is less than that of filter-sterilized coconut milk (van Overbeek, Sui and Haagen-Smit, 1944) and also that the coconut milk can be effectively replaced by a solution of powdered malt extract sterilized by filtration (Blakeslee and Satina, 1944). The "embryo factor" of coconut milk and of these other extracts has not been chemically identified. The use in the culture of immature embryos of liquid endosperms and endosperm extracts recalls the early work of Stingl (1907) which showed that isolated embryos could be cultured by placing them on the surface of endosperms and that a foreign endosperm was in this connection often superior to the endosperm of the species (e.g. wheat embryos grew better on rye endosperm than on wheat endosperm).

The culture of very young embryos still presents many problems. Reference to some of the papers quoted above will illustrate the difficulty of removing such embryos uninjured. They are very sensitive to the physical conditions of culture (pH, osmotic pressure, etc.). Their growth requirements are complex and as yet not defined. Often such young embryos germinate precociously and produce malformed or necrotic seedlings.

The difficulty of removing embryos much before they have reached the heart-shaped stage has led to attempts to culture ovules. Work along these lines has been undertaken by various workers with orchids and, as a result, information has been built up regarding the requirements of immature orchid embryos (Ito, 1961). These studies have found practical application in the development of organic culture media for the orchid growers.

In 1958, Maheshwari demonstrated that ovules of *Papaver somniferum* containing a zygote (or 2-celled proembryo) and a few endosperm nuclei could be cultured to give viable seeds using the medium of Nitsch (1951) supplemented with 0·4 p.p.m. kinetin. Later Kanta, Ranga Swamy and Maheshwari (1962), also from the Department of Botany, Delhi, demonstrated that, starting in this species with ripe pollen and with ovules just after anthesis, it was possible to effect in culture all stages from the germination of pollen and double fertilization to development of viable seeds. Sachar and Kapoor (1959a, b) cultured ovules of an unidentified species of *Zephyranthes* using as a basic medium that of Nitsch supplemented with B vitamins and calcium pantothenate. Ovules removed before pollination and cultured in this medium containing gibberellic acid, developed into seeds with normal testas but lacking embryo and endosperm and about half normal size. Ovules excised 2 days after pollination (zygote stage, with undivided primary endosperm nucleus) when cultured in the above medium grew up to the formation of a late globular embryo but the endosperm development was inhibited. Further development was not achieved by additions of kinetin, auxins or gibberellic acid. However, ovaries excised at this stage and cultured in the basic medium gave seeds with fully differentiated embryos indicating that the ovary wall contributes certain substances essential for the normal differentiation of the embryo. If excision of the ovules was delayed until 4–5 days after pollination (when they contain a young globular proembryo and a free nuclear endosperm) normal differentiation of the embryo occurred in culture and the seeds germinated *in situ*. Differentiation of the embryo required simultaneous endosperm development. In a later paper, Kapoor (1959) showed that normal development of viable seed could be achieved from ovules excised 2 days after pollination if the culture medium was supplemented by coconut milk and casamino acids. The casamino acids could be replaced by either histidine or arginine at appropriate concentration. The importance of endosperm for embryo differentiation is also indicated by the studies of Chopra and Sabharwal (1963) with *Gynandropsis gynandra*. Ovules could only be raised to maturity if they had at the time of excision a globular proembryo and a few endosperm nuclei. When cultured at this stage and in a medium supplemented by IAA and casamino acids (but not coconut milk) it was found that the rate and extent of development and size of the embryo were all increased by leaving the ovules attached to placental tissue. Mature seeds raised *in vitro* did not become dormant (as occurs *in vivo*) but could germinate immediately.

The Delhi School have also studied the behaviour in culture of excised *Citrus* ovules in which embryos can arise adventitiously from cells of the nucellus (nucellar embryos). In some species, such as *Citrus microcarpa*, polyembryony naturally occurs in this way. In 1961, and using this species, Ranga Swamy split the ovules open and obtained a callus of nucellar origin in continuous culture. The callus gave rise, in its growing upper part, to embryo-like structures which were termed "pseudobulbils" and from these, plantlets arose. Sabharwal (1963) cultured ovules, nucelli and embryos of a second species, *C. reticulata*, in which nucellar embryos also arise. Callus arose from proembryos in the ovule and from the nucellar tissue and both types of callus gave rise to pseudobulbils and weakly seedlings. Such callus cultures therefore represent tissue "banks" capable of initiating clones of adventive embryos, a phenomenon of both practical value and theoretical interest.

Ovoid embryos (0·5–1 mm) in *Cuscuta reflexa*, cultured in White's medium supplemented with IAA and casamino acids, were found by P. Maheshwari and Baldev (1962) to give rise to adventive embryos. From older embryos of this species a continuously growing callus culture was obtained which, on each subculture, gave rise to a fresh crop of adventive embryos. Similarly, a callus obtained from globular proembryos of *Dendrophthoe falcata* (Johri and Bajaj, 1963) gave rise to numerous proembryos.

For a fuller account of embryo culture and particularly of early work in this field the reader is referred to Rappaport (1954), and to Narayanaswami and Norstog (1964).

F. CALLUS CULTURES

As a very detailed description of the techniques of callus culture is given by Gautheret (1959) and since the general techniques of asepsis are common to those outlined in Section II, A, the present account will be confined to an outline of the special features of callus culture and will draw particular attention to certain practical problems and to recent advances in the development of more effective culture media.

1. *Culture Vessels*

Callus cultures are grown in tubes (1 in diam.), Erlenmeyer flasks (50–250 ml) or Petri dishes. If the cultures are to be grown on liquid media the tissue mass must be supported on some porous inert material such as ashless filter paper (Heller, 1949, 1953; White, 1954) (Fig. 9), or be alternately immersed in medium and exposed to air (see Section G, p. 509). The culture vessels may be closed with cotton wool plugs but, with the long incubation periods frequently adopted, it is also necessary to seal the vessels with aluminium foil, cellophane, polythene film or

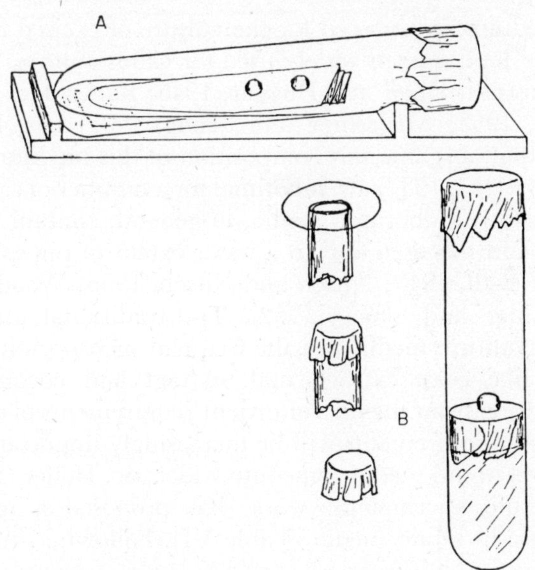

FIG. 9. Growth of callus with liquid medium. A. White's (1954) method of cultivating callus tissue on a folded strip of filter paper whose lower end rests in a liquid medium. B. Heller's (1949) method in which the explant is placed on a platform of filter paper formed around a mandril (left) and inserted into a vertical tube so as to dip into the liquid medium. Note closure of culture tubes with aluminium foil. (From White, 1954.)

"Parafilm" (thermoplastic film) in order to prevent desiccation of the medium. The plastic films are ideal in that they are impermeable to water vapour but permeable to oxygen and carbon dioxide but have the disadvantage that they cannot be autoclaved and must be sterilized with alcohol. The metal foils and cellophane can be autoclaved; the metal foils can also be effectively sterilized by flaming. When these anti-desiccation covers are employed it is often advantageous to dispense with the cotton wool plugs after the initial inoculation, particularly when using aluminium foil caps which can be flamed together with the neck of the culture vessel each time the cultures are opened in the transfer cabinet (Fig. 6, p. 482).

2. *Culture Media*

As will be discussed more fully in Chapter 9 some callus cultures can grow in a simple medium containing inorganic salts and a utilizable sugar (sucrose is usually the most effective carbon source), in other cases this medium must be supplemented by the addition of vitamins, auxins, amino acids or other organic substances, and in still other cases the only effective media contain a natural supplement of incompletely understood composition (e.g. coconut milk).

White's medium, introduced for the culture of excised roots (White, 1943a) (Table I), has been widely used for callus culture. More recent work (Hildebrandt, Riker and Duggar, 1946; Burkholder and Nickell, 1949; Heller, 1953; Murashige and Skoog, 1962) has, however, indicated that the inorganic salt composition of this medium and of that of Gautheret (1935a, 1937) are subotimal for a number of callus cultures. The more recently elaborated media, in general, contain higher levels of potassium and nitrogen and to a lesser extent of phosphorus (Burkholder and Nickell, 1949; Nitsch and Nitsch, 1956; Wood and Braun, 1961; Murashige and Skoog, 1962). The traditional use of agar to solidify callus culture media and the frequent incorporation of natural supplements like yeast extract, malt extract and coconut milk has diverted attention from the micronutrient requirements of callus tissues. However, these requirements will be increasingly important considerations as defined liquid media come into wider use. Heller (1953), on the basis of careful experimental work, has proposed a micronutrient solution for use in liquid media (Table VI). Following studies on iron availability in root culture media (p. 475 *et seq.*) various workers have used ferric-EDTA in media for the culture of callus (Klein and Manos, 1960; Tulecke, 1960; Murashige and Skoog, 1962).

The compositions of the various inorganic solutions used in callus culture are set out in Tables V and VI. The media of White (1943a) and Heller (1953) are probably the most suitable with which to attempt the culture of any new tissues since they have already been found to support the growth of a wide range of tissues. Sucrose (2–3%) would also be the first carbon source to use, again because it has proved to be very effective with a wide range of tissues (see Chap. 9, p. 554).

Where the tissue fails to grow in a simple medium containing sucrose and inorganic salts, this may be indicative of additional nutritional requirements either for growth-regulating substances (Chap. 9, p. 569) or organic nitrogenous compounds (Chap. 9, p. 546). The auxins most commonly used are β-indolylacetic acid (IAA), naphthaleneacetic acid (NAA) and 2, 4-dichlorophenoxyacetic acid (2, 4-D) and initially these should be tested over a wide concentration range (0·01–10 mg/l). Such auxins may be ineffective alone but may show strong synergistic interactions with other supplements such as kinetin (Skoog, 1944; Das, Patau and Skoog, 1956) or coconut milk (Steward and Caplin, 1951). While an auxin addition may be essential to initiate the callus and maintain it through an initial period of subculture, the tissue may in time become auxin-autotrophic (see Chap. 9, p. 587). Kinetin (tested over the concentration range 0·1–10·0 mg/l) may be essential for the continuous culture of callus tissue (Das *et al.*, 1956; Braun and Wood, 1962).

TABLE V

Various solutions of the macronutrient ions (m. moles/l) which have been incorporated into culture media used for callus tissues and suspension cultures

Ion	Gautheret (1939)	White* (1943a)	Hildebrandt *et al.* (1946) "Sunflower"	Hildebrandt *et al.* (1946) "Tobacco"	Burkholder and Nickell (1949)	Heller (1953)	Torrey (1954)	Nitsch and Nitsch (1956)	Fox and Miller† (1959)	Tulecke (1960)	Braun and Wood (1962)	Murashige and Skoog (1962)
Mg^{++}	0·5	3·0	2·9	0·7	2·0	1·0	0·2	1·0	0·3	3·0	3·0	1·5
Ca^{++}	2·1	1·2	3·4	1·7	3·0	0·5	1·0	0·2	0·6	1·2	1·2	3·0
Na^{+}	—	3·0	2·4	11·5	—	8·0	—	1·8	0·1	4·2	26·3	0·2
K^{+}	2·2	1·7	3·3	1·7	12·0	10·0	1·7	40·0	1·8	1·7	13·0	20·0
NH_4^{+}	—	—	—	—	—	—	—	—	5·0	—	12·0	20·6
SO_4^{--}	0·5	4·4	3·6	6·3	1·0	1·0	0·2	1·0	0·3	4·4	10·4	1·5
NO_3^{-}	5·5	3·2	8·4	4·2	8·0	7·1	2·8	19·8	7·0	3·2	24·4	39·4
Cl^{-}	—	0·9	1·8	0·9	10·0	11·0	0·8	20·6	0·9	0·9	12·2	6·0
H_2PO_4	0·9	0·14	1·0	0·3	8·0	0·9	0·1	1·8	0·09	1·4	2·3	1·0

*See also Tables I and IV.
†See also Murashige and Skoog (1962).

TABLE VI

Various solutions of the micronutrient elements which have been incorporated into culture media used for callus tissues and suspension cultures
(Concentrations all expressed in μmoles/l.)

Element	Gautheret (1939)	White* (1943a)	Hildebrandt *et al.* (1946) "Sunflower"	Hildebrandt *et al.* (1946) "Tobacco"	Burkholder and Nickell (1949)	Heller (1953)	Torrey (1954)	Nitsch and Nitsch (1956)	Fox and Miller† (1959)	Tulecke (1960)	Braun and Wood (1962)	Murashige and Skoog (1962)
Fe	125·0	13·0	18·0	143·0	9·0	4·0	10·0	—	53·0	7·2	13·0	100·0
B	0·4	25·0	50·0	6·0	10·0	16·0	25·0	—	26·0	8·0	25·0	100·0
Mn	4·5	30·0	20·0	20·0	2·0	4·5	26·6	—	29·0	13·3	30·0	100·0
Zn	0·2	10·0	1·0	2·2	4·6	3·5	5·25	—	9·4	1·75	10·0	30·0
I	1·5	4·5	2·2	8·0	—	0·06	—	—	4·5	—	4·5	5·0
Cu	0·1	—	—	—	1·6	0·12	0·16	—	—	0·1	—	0·10
Mo	—	—	—	—	1·0	—	0·16	—	—	0·1	—	1·0
Co	0·1	—	—	—	—	—	—	—	—	—	—	0·10
Ni	1·0	—	—	—	—	0·13	—	—	—	—	—	—
Ti	1·0	—	—	—	—	—	—	—	—	—	—	—
Be	0·3	—	—	—	—	—	—	—	—	—	—	—
Al	—	—	—	—	—	0·23	—	—	—	—	—	—

*See also Tables I and IV.
†See also Murashige and Skoog (1962).

The use of mixtures of nitrogenous compounds, particularly amino acids is summarized in Table VII. Most of these complex mixtures, although capable of supporting a high growth rate of the tissue for which they have been elaborated, are probably unnecessarily complex. Thus Straus (1960) found that excellent growth of maize endosperm tissue could be obtained in a synthetic medium containing L-asparagine as the source of reduced nitrogen instead of the yeast extract, casein hydrolysate or tomato juice previously thought to be necessary (Straus and LaRue, 1954). Steinhart, Standifer and Skoog (1961) working with spruce tissue (*Picea abies*) found that the malt extract of their original medium could be replaced by casein hydrolysate and that a synthetic medium containing, as its source of reduced nitrogen, L-arginine (400 mg/l) and urea (200 mg/l) would support a high growth rate. Risser and White (1963) have now demonstrated that the mixture of eighteen amino acids used to culture tumour tissue of *Picea glauca* by Reinert and White (1956) can be replaced by L-glutamine. When endeavouring to establish a new tissue in culture, the use of acid hydrolysed casein (at a concentration of 200–800 mg/l) as a supplement will usually test for a requirement for reduced nitrogen. When endeavouring to replace such a source of reduced nitrogen by defined compounds those to be tested first would be urea, arginine, the amides (glutamine and asparagine), and the dicarboxylic amino acids (glutamic and aspartic acids). These would be tested over the concentration range 50–400 mg/l (see Chap. 9, p. 546 *et seq.*).

In addition to the amino acids and their derivatives, certain other nitrogenous compounds, particularly those which may be implicated in nucleic acid synthesis have been shown to be essential for or to enhance callus growth. Such compounds include uracil, adenine, adenosine, hypoxanthine, guanine, cytosine, thymine (Skoog, 1950; Nickell, Greenfield and Burkholder, 1950; Henderson, Durell and Bonner, 1952; Wiggans, 1954; Lingappa, 1957) and cytidylic and guanylic acids (Wood and Braun, 1961).

Callus cultures are often autotrophic for vitamins (Chap. 9, p. 562). Aneurin is, however, either essential (Nickell, 1952; Paris, 1958) or stimulatory (Paris, 1955) for a number of callus tissues. Since the discovery of m-inositol as a constituent of coconut milk (Pollard, Shantz and Steward, 1961) it has been shown to be an essential nutrient for several callus tissues (Wood and Braun, 1961; Risser and White, 1963). Vitamin additions used by various workers in preparing media for callus and suspension cultures are summarized in Table VIII.

Coconut milk (coconut water) as a supplement to callus media has been widely used and proved effective in supporting the growth of many tissues still resistant to continuous growth in defined media.

TABLE VII

Amino acid mixtures used in preparing plant tissue-culture media (concentrations expressed as mg/l)
(Amino acids contributed by 10% coconut milk and 200 mg/l acid hydrolysed casein shown for comparison.)

Amino acids	Paris and Duhamet (1953)	Reinert and White (1956)	Constabel (1958)	Torrey and Reinert (1961)	10% coconut milk*	200 mg/l hydrolysed casein†
L-arginine	72·0	7·8	7·8	7·8	2·07	7·6
L-glutamic acid	140·0	14·0	14·0	14·0	10·50	10·2
L-glutamine	—	50·0	—	50·0	0·20	—
L-aspartic acid	21·0	6·0	—	6·0	1·14	1·0
L-asparagine	—	20·0	—	20·0	2·53	—
DL-alanine	30·0	—	—	—	19·80	—
L-leucine	18·0	15·6	—	15·6	3·30	19·8
L-lysine	21·0	15·6	15·6	15·6	1·30	13·4
L-tyrosine	18·0	40·0	—	40·0	t	3·8
L-histidine	12·0	2·6	2·6	2·6	t	4·6
L-phenylalanine	8·0	5·0	15·6	2·5	t	8·0
DL-serine	9·0	—	—	—	8·50	—
L-cysteine	12·0	—	1·5	—	—	—
L-cystine	—	1·5	—	1·5	—	—
DL-methionine	—	13·0	13·0	13·0	t	4·4
DL-threonine	—	13·0	13·0	—	2·74	7·8
L-threonine	—	—	—	6·5	—	—
DL-valine	—	13·0	13·0	13·0	1·55	14·4
DL-isoleucine	—	10·4	10·4	10·4	—	9·2
L-tryptophane	—	4·0	—	4·0	—	—
L-proline	—	5·0	5·0	5·0	1·29	—
Glycine	—	10·0	10·0	10·0	1·80	2·2
γ-aminobutyric acid	—	—	—	—	17·30	—
Hydroxy-L-proline	—	—	—	—	0·82	—
L-homoserine	—	—	—	—	0·88	—

*Autoclaved coconut milk from mature nuts after Tulecke, Weinstein, Rutner and Laurencot (1961). † Difco analysis. t, Trace.

TABLE VIII

Mixtures of vitamins used in media for callus tissues and suspension cultures
(Concentrations all in mg/l.)

Vitamins	White (1943a)	Morel (1948)	Gautheret (1948)	Jacquiot (1950)	Morel and Wetmore (1951)	Henderson *et al.* (1952)	Paris and Duhamet (1953)	Reinert and White (1956)	Torrey and Shigemura (1957)	Constabel (1958)	Torrey and Reinert (1961)
Aneurin	0·10	1·00	1·00	1·00	1·00	0·01	0·005	0·10	1·00	0·10	0·10
Pantothenic acid (calcium salt)	—	1·00	1·00	0·50	1·00	0·08	0·052	0·10	—	10·00	0·10
Biotin	—	0·01	0·01	0·10	0·01	0·005	0·002	0·01	—	0·10	0·01
m-Inositol	—	100·00	—	500·00	100·00	0·50	—	—	—	100·00	100·00
Riboflavin	—	—	—	0·10	—	0·05	0·001	0·10	—	0·10	0·10
Pyridoxine	0·10	—	—	—	1·00	0·10	0·001	0·10	—	—	0·10
p-Aminobenzoic acid	—	—	—	1·00	—	0·05	—	0·10	—	—	—
Niacin or niacinamide	0·50	—	—	1·00	1·00	0·50	0·064	0·50	5·00	0·50	0·50
Choline	—	—	—	—	—	0·10	—	10·00	—	10·00	10·00
Folic acid	—	—	—	0·01	—	0·10	0·0003	1·00	—	1·00	—
Ascorbic acid	—	—	—	—	—	—	—	0·10	—	—	0·10
Vitamin B_{12}	—	—	—	—	—	—	—	0·0015	—	—	—

Present knowledge regarding the chemical composition of coconut milk has been summarized by Tulecke, Weinstein, Rutner and Laurencot (1961) and Pollard *et al.* (1961) and the biological activities of coconut milk and other liquid endosperms in plant tissue culture has been reviewed by Steward and Shantz (1959). Since the active constituents of coconut milk are reported to be thermostable, the milk is routinely deproteinized by boiling, then filtered, autoclaved and stored at −20°C. It is usually used at concentrations of between 5 and 20% v/v. Most workers have used milk obtained from stored mature nuts. It is, however, clear that there are considerable differences in chemical composition between the milk of immature (green) and mature nuts (Tulecke *et al.,* 1961) and it might be rewarding to compare, by the use of plant tissue cultures, the biological activities of milk withdrawn from coconuts at various stages during their maturation.

Other natural extracts which have been used and which have made possible the first successful cultures of certain tissues are yeast extract (Jagendorf, Bonner and Naylor, 1952; Tryon, 1955; Torrey and Shigemura, 1957; Tulecke, 1957) and malt extract (Loewenberg and Skoog, 1952; Jablonski and Skoog, 1954; Wiggans, 1954; Tryon, 1955).

When attempting to bring into culture a new tissue it is desirable to use a simple medium and supplement it with defined constituents known to be effective in other cases. Resort to media containing natural fluids or extracts is only justified when simpler media are ineffective. It should, however, be borne in mind (a) that growth requirements may change as subculture proceeds, either because of gradual depletion of essential metabolites carried over with the initial piece of tissue or organ (the explant), or because the tissue develops an enhanced ability to synthesize certain metabolites when repeatedly subcultured, and (b) that defined media capable of sustaining the growth of a callus tissue may only permit of a very much lower rate of growth than media containing natural fluids or extracts.

The general principles of preparing a solution of the medium constituents for callus culture are as described in Section II, A, (p. 475). Callus-culture media usually contain, in addition, agar (0·6–1%) and, when this is to be incorporated, the medium is made at double strength and then mixed with an equal volume of double-strength solution of agar in boiling water. The medium is then cooled to 40°C, adjusted in pH, distributed to the culture vessels and autoclaved.

3. *Sterilization of Organs and Tissues, Isolation of Initial Explants, Initiation and Maintenance of Cultures*

It is necessary to effect a surface sterilization of the organ from which the tissue is to be aseptically excised or of the seed or spore whose germination will yield the tissue explant, and the most generally used sterilizing agents are those described in Section II, A, p. 481. Antibiotics, because of their relatively restricted range of bactericidal activity, are not generally used but most (e.g. penicillin, bacitracin, terramycin) are relatively non-toxic to plant tissues (at concentrations up to 100 mg/l) and therefore can be tried where the use of other sterilizing agents is precluded. Antibiotics have also been incorporated into culture media to assist in the maintenance of sterility in large-scale suspension cultures (Tulecke and Nickell, 1960; Byrne and Koch, 1962).

Surface sterilization followed by aseptic removal of tissues or embryos has been used to obtain callus from embryo tissues (van Overbeek, Conklin and Blakeslee, 1941; LaRue, 1947), from the parenchymatous and cambial tissues of woody stems (Gioelli, 1938; Morel, 1948; Skoog and Tsui, 1948; Barker, 1953; White, 1954; Karstens, 1955), from fleshy storage organs (Steward and Caplin, 1954), from fruits (Schroeder, 1955), and from buds and apical meristems (Kofler, 1945; Morel, 1956). Alternatively, seeds, spores or pollen grains may be sterilized, transferred to culture medium and the callus initiated from the seedling (Jagendorf *et al.,* 1952; Tryon, 1955), pollen (Tulecke, 1953, 1957, 1959) or fern sporeling (Morel, 1950; Morel and Wetmore, 1951; Steeves and Sussex, 1952). Sometimes the initiation of callus may take place *in situ* very readily, provided that germination takes place on a suitable culture medium. However, in other cases, a more complicated manipulative procedure may be required. Thus, Torrey and Shigemura (1957) obtained a pea root callus by transferring sterile excised seedling root tips, first to medium containing 10^{-5}M IAA which initiated divisions in the vascular cambium, and then dissecting out and transferring segments, consisting mainly of stelar tissue and vascular cambium, to a medium containing yeast extract (1 g/l) plus 2·4–D (10^{-6}M).

The initiation of callus growth from parenchyma or cambium is often promoted by the presence in the explant of some mature vascular tissue (Barker, 1953; Jablonski and Skoog, 1954). The callus tissue itself is usually derived either from active primary or secondary meristems or from immature parenchyma adjacent either to such meristems or to secondary vascular tissue. It is a general rule that the explant must not be below a critical size if callus is to develop and a number of observations indicate that the size of the explant can be smaller when it contains several different types of tissue cells than when it is uniformly parenchymatous. The questions raised by these observations on explant size and cellular composition will be further discussed when considering the special nutrient requirements of isolated cells (Chap. 9, p. 596) and the growth patterns in suspension cultures (Chap. 10, p. 665).

Many tissue explants possess some degree of polarity with the result that callus is formed most easily at one surface; in stem segments, callus is formed particularly from that surface which *in vivo* was directed towards the root (the morphologically basal surface). Further, the presence of auxin in the medium can accentuate this polarity because of its strongly polar transport. The effects of polarity in the explant are, however, complicated by the fact that callus often develops more readily from the tissue not in contact with and particularly not immersed in the solidified culture medium. Thus, stem segments inverted so that the morphologically apical surface is in contact with an auxin-containing medium will often initiate callus much more profusely than when upright in an auxin-free medium. With many tissues, however, the combined effects of polarity and contact with the medium cannot be predicted so that, in practice, the tissue or organ explant should be orientated in various ways to determine empirically the best orientation for callus growth.

Just as callus is only initiated on explants above a critical size, so the maintenance of growth in callus tissue by subculture requires the transfer on each occasion of a piece of healthy tissue above a certain critical mass. For most callus cultures this condition will be met by the transfer of pieces 5–10 mm in diameter and of 20–100 mg fresh weight. For routine maintenance of most callus cultures a suitable regime is to subculture every 28 days by transfer of such pieces singly to culture vessels containing 30 ml medium. Many cultures will, however, remain healthy and continue a slow rate of growth for much longer periods than this without subculture, particularly if the standard incubation temperature of 25°C is lowered to 15–20°C. Caplin (1959) has reported the preservation of cultures for long periods without loss of viability by covering them with a layer of mineral oil. Although the light requirements of callus cultures have not been examined critically it is clear that the growth of many cultures and particularly of those which form chlorophyll is stimulated by low-intensity illumination. Light (either on a 12 h cycle or continuously) is therefore usually provided in the incubation rooms by fluorescent tubes.

4. *Measurement of the Growth of Callus Cultures*

Techniques for quantitative work with callus cultures have been developed only to a very limited extent. Variation in growth between individual cultures established as replicates is clearly very much higher than with root cultures. This high level of variability is an outcome of the heterogeneous cellular composition of callus cultures even where the callus can be described as being parenchymatous. The growth of such callus masses is the outcome of cell division in localized meristematic layers or nodules (see Chap. 10, p. 652) and the expansion and differentiation of the cells so produced. Further, as the callus mass increases, a decreasing proportion of its cells remain meristematic and its growth, assessed in terms of weight increase, becomes increasingly a reflection of cell expansion and the deposition of cell wall material and of reserves of food substances like starch. The dissection of such a mass into pieces of uniform size and fresh weight does *not* yield inocula which are uniform in either cellular composition or growth behaviour.

Where quantitative work has been attempted the parameter measured has usually been fresh weight (taken with simple aseptic precautions), since this has enabled initial and final weights to be recorded for the same sample of tissue (Enderle, 1951; Heller, 1953; White, 1954). Less frequently, dry weights (drying to constant weight at 60–80°C) have also been determined. Such parameters give us a very limited understanding of the growth of the callus mass. The most important criterion additionally needed is the increase in number of cells. Steward and Shantz (1955) have described a technique for the maceration of carrot callus followed by a haemocytometer count of the number of cells in the resulting suspension. This approach has, however, not been generally adopted in studies of callus growth presumably because of the difficulty of working out rapid maceration techniques which effectively separate the cells without causing a high degree of cell destruction. Das *et al.* (1956) attempted to estimate cell numbers from counts of the nuclei in slices of tissue but such a method is clearly inaccurate and not applicable to routine growth studies.

Our knowledge of callus growth is not only limited by the difficulties encountered in describing it in terms of cell division, cell expansion and cell differentiation but also because, in most studies, measurements have only been made of the total growth as recorded at the end of the experiment and not at frequent intervals during the culture period. Nickell (1956) has expressed growth in terms of "growth values" (final size or weight divided by initial size or weight). Klein (1963) uses the term "growth increment" calculated thus: (final size–initial size) × 100 divided by initial size. Caplin (1947) has calculated the "relative growth rate" from the formula:

$$\frac{\log_e (S_t/S_0)}{t} \quad \text{where } S_t = \text{final size, } S_0 = \text{initial size and } t = \text{time.}$$

These means of expressing growth are, in view of the nature of the data, based upon weight measurements. Only as techniques are developed for cell counting will it be possible to supplement these parameters with values for "mean generation time" calculated at intervals during the experimental growth period. Mean generation time (G) is the calculated average time which would be required for the cell population of the callus mass to double. The value of G can be calculated from the equation:

$$G = \frac{t}{n} = \frac{t \log 2}{\log C_t - \log C_0}$$

where t = time; n = number of cell generations passed through in time t; C_t = number of cells after time t; C_0 = initial number of cells.

G. SUSPENSION CULTURES

1. *General Technique*

Suspension cultures are generally initiated by transferring an established callus tissue to an agitated liquid medium (media as described in Section II, F, p. 497) in an Erlenmeyer culture vessel (30–60 ml medium per 250 ml flask), this technique being most successful with very friable callus (see Chap. 10 p. 662). The release of cells and tissue fragments from less friable callus masses and the maintenance of a good degree of cell separation may often be promoted by the presence in the liquid medium of a high auxin concentration (Bergmann, 1960; Torrey and Reinert, 1961), an appropriate balance between auxin and yeast extract (Torrey and Shigemura, 1957), between auxin and coconut milk (Lamport and Northcote, 1960) or between auxin and kinetin (Earle and Torrey, 1963). There is also evidence that deficiencies of certain vitamins may assist cell separation (Reinert, 1956; Torrey and Reinert, 1961). These modifications of the culture medium designed to enhance cell separation often also reduce the growth rate of the suspension culture. Cell separation has not yet been enhanced by incorporating pectic enzymes or chelating agents into the medium.

Suspension cultures have also been successfully established by introducing tissue fragments into the liquid medium as soon as they are obtained from sterile roots by mechanical disruption with a sterile homogenizer (Goldacre, Unt and Kefford, 1962; Mehta, 1963). In such cases the tissue fragments first give rise to small callus masses from which free cells and small cell aggregates are later released. It must be emphasized that in the present state of knowledge, even if a suspension culture can be obtained, its rate of growth and its composition in terms of free cells and cell aggregates (the latter are always present) is very much determined by the strain of callus or plant tissue used. We are not yet able, by alteration of the composition of the culture medium or other cultural variables, to obtain suspension cultures from all tissues, nor are we able to control the cellular composition of suspension cultures except to a very limited extent.

Suspension cultures are usually incubated at 25°C in darkness or in low intensity fluorescent light. Continuous agitation of flask cultures is most commonly achieved by using a horizontal shaker which rotates at between 100 and 200 rev/min, each flask describing a 2 in diameter circle. The use of aluminium foil or film seals (see Section II, F, p. 496) to reduce evaporation is here very important. The use of a double aluminium foil seal secured with an elastic band maintains sterility and greatly reduces evaporation. Information regarding the gaseous exchange of cultures grown in this way is lacking. Steward, Mapes and Smith, (1958) designed a special roller-tube culture vessel, which was rotated on a specially designed wheel, for the culture of carrot root phloem explants and this has also been used for the growth of suspension cultures derived from this tissue (Fig. 10). This roller-tube technique employs a much slower rate of movement of the medium than occurs on horizontal shakers. Critical studies on the influence of turbulence in the medium, on growth and cell separation in suspension cultures have yet to be reported. Apparatus designed for the growth of larger volumes of suspensions have employed forced aeration, either alone or in combination with a magnetic stirrer for agitation of the medium. In this way, batch cultures ranging from 20 to 134 litres have been grown successfully (Tulecke and Nickell, 1959, 1960; Byrne and Koch, 1962) (Fig. 11). A semi-continuous culture apparatus has been devised and successfully operated by Melchers and Bergmann (1959) (Fig. 12). The limitations of present achievements in this direction must, however, be emphasized. Techniques of rapidly and continuously monitoring the growth of suspension cultures have yet to be devised and there is the even more difficult problem of achieving high growth rates and at the same time maintaining a high proportion of free cells and an upper limit to the size of the cell aggregates. The processes of cell division and cell separation tend to be mutually antagonistic.

Suspension cultures are subcultured by the transfer at regular intervals of untreated or fractionated aliquots of the suspension to fresh medium. Fractionation of aliquots is achieved by aseptic filtration through nylon fabrics of known mesh size and this technique can be used to remove cell debris (units below a certain size) or large aggregates (units above a certain size, usually 1000 μ) (Fig. 13). Such fractionation may be important in preventing a gradual accumulation of cell debris and dead cells or of visible callus masses as subculture proceeds. The inoculum transferred on each occasion must apparently establish a sufficiently high "cell" density if growth is to continue (although our present state of knowledge does not enable us to define "cell" density in specific terms). Higher densities than this critical level are required to shorten or eliminate a lag phase before growth occurs in a new culture. The retarding effect on the initial growth rate of a small

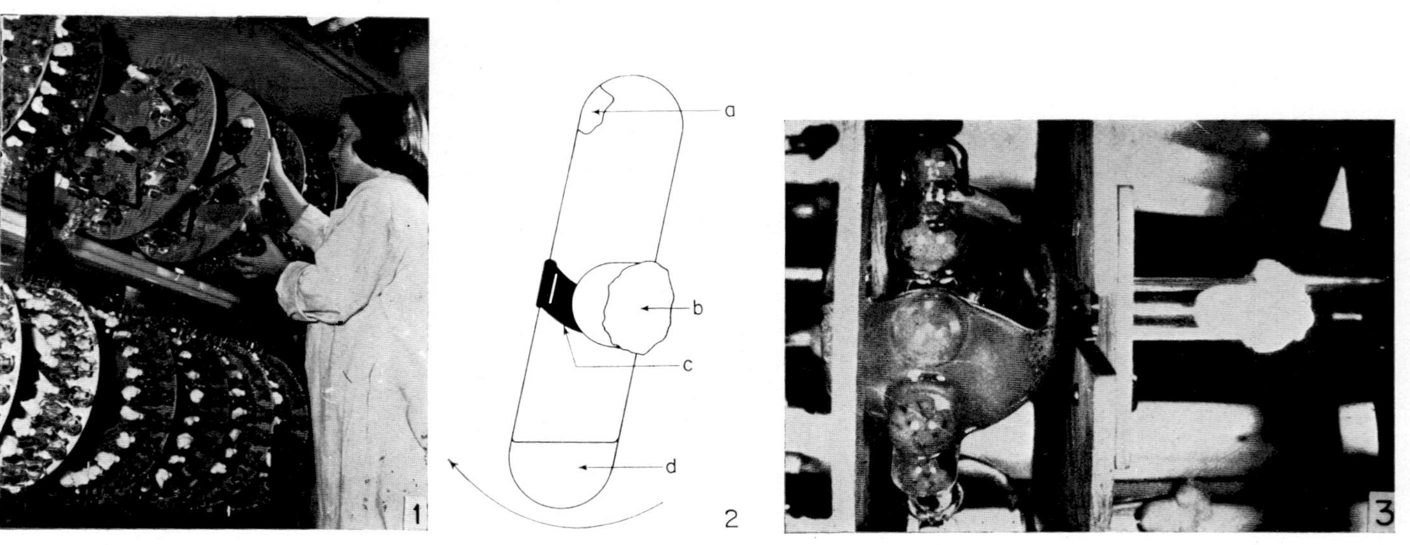

Fig. 10. Growth of carrot phloem explants and suspension cultures. 1. Rotating wheels (1 rev/min.) in culture room. Upper wheels carrying large culture flasks with a large number of explants and free floating cells in the ambient fluid (shown close up in 3). Lower wheels carrying culture vessels of type shown in 2. a, Explant; b, cotton plug; c, clip-on wheel; d, culture medium. Arrow shows direction of rotation of wheel. (After Steward *et al.*, 1958.)

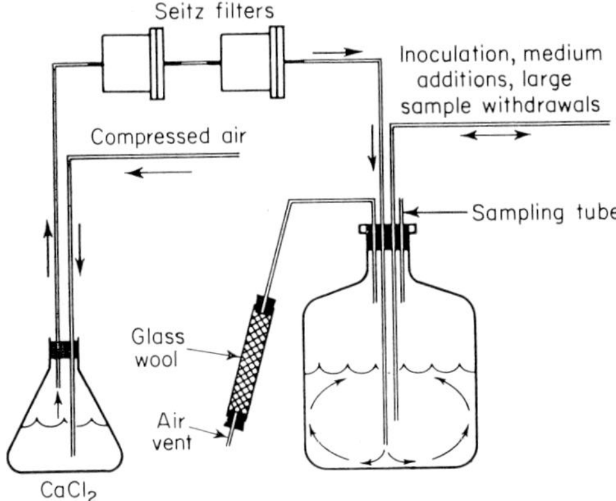

FIG. 11. A carboy culture system for growing a large batch of a plant suspension culture. (After Tulecke and Nickell, 1959, 1960.)

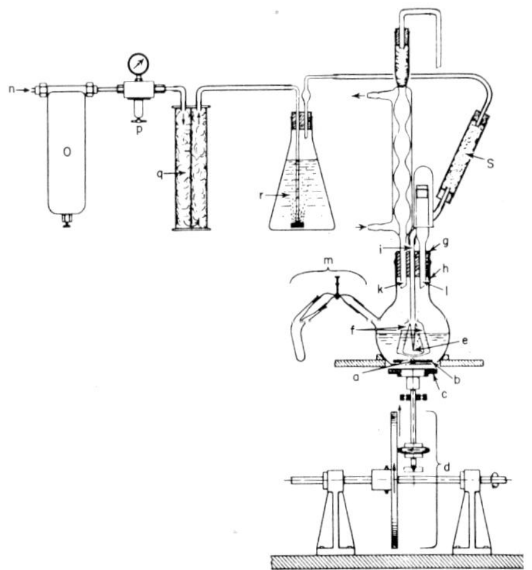

FIG. 12. Melchers and Bergmann (1959) apparatus for growth of a suspension culture. This apparatus permits the addition of new culture medium and the withdrawal of samples of the culture at intervals. Key: a, 750 ml culture vessel; b, c and d, magnetic stirrer; e and f, aerating tube and baffle; g and h, rubber bung and sleeve; i, air inlet; k, reflux condenser to check evaporation; l, tube to introduce inoculum or culture medium; m, sampling tube; o, coarse filter; p, reducing valve on compressed air line; q and s, cotton wool filters; r, humidifier containing sterile water.

inoculum is accentuated unless a sufficient volume of "conditioned" medium is transferred along with the cell material (see Chap. 9, p. 596). It is clear that the duration of culture between successive transfers must also be carefully considered in relation to inoculum size and volume of medium. If the inoculum is small, both the lag phase and the subsequent phase of experimental growth are more prolonged than

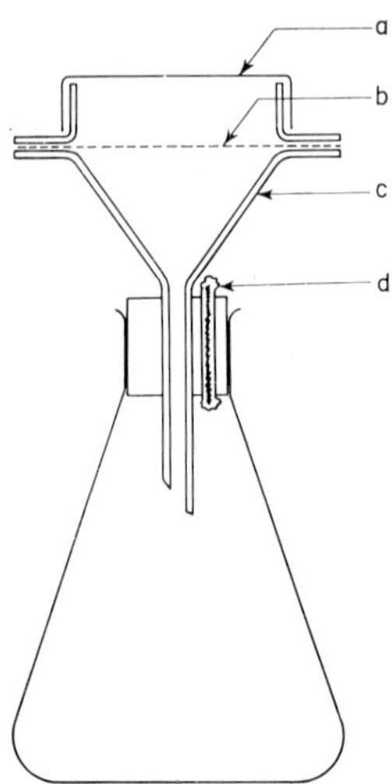

Fig. 13. Filtration apparatus for the aseptic fractionation of suspension cultures. a, Petri dish cover; b, nylon bolting fabric of known mesh size; c, Hartley funnel; d, air outlet plugged with cotton wool.

occurs with a larger inoculum. At this early stage of our knowledge of growth patterns in suspension cultures and of how these patterns are affected by inoculum size, inoculum composition and the time between subcultures (see Chap. 10, p. 665), it is very difficult to formulate general principles of subculture procedure. At present, most laboratories subculture their suspensions during the stationary phase of the growth curve (relating time to cell number) and before the culture has "aged" to the point where the cells are generally becoming senescent.

Although suspension cultures can be serially propagated as described above, a number of accounts of the nature of suspension cultures and of the growth potentialities of their free cells and cell aggregates relate to suspensions which have, on each occasion, been freshly established from large callus masses growing on a solid medium (see Section II, H, p. 504).

2. *Measurement of the Growth of Suspension Cultures*

Measurement of the growth of suspension cultures faces the same basic difficulties as are encountered with callus cultures, although quantitative studies with suspension cultures have been facilitated by the ease with which uniform aliquots can be removed without disturbing the progress of growth and by the greater, if still limited, degree of standardization of inocula which is possible. Certain pioneer studies on the growth patterns of such cultures have combined withdrawal of aliquots from the cultures at intervals during a fixed growth period with fractionation of the aliquots into different size classes of "cellular units" by the use of nylon fabrics of standardized mesh size. Determinations have then been made of the fresh and dry weights, and of the mitotic index (percentage of cells in a recognizable stage of mitosis) of each fraction (see Chap. 10, p. 666). To these criteria can now be added, at least for some suspension cultures, a determination of the mean generation time for the cells of each fraction based upon total cell counts following the use of a suitable maceration technique.

Mitotic index can be determined after Feulgen staining (Darlington and La Cour, 1947) as described by Bowen (1955). The protocol followed in our laboratory is as follows.

The aliquot is fixed in alcohol(3)-acetic acid (1) for 2–24 h and then stored in 70% alcohol at −20°C until required. The alcohol is removed by centrifuging and the fraction suspended in N HCl at 60°C and incubated at this temperature for 5–10 min. The hydrolysis is terminated by placing the centrifuge tube in ice-cold water and the acid removed by centrifuging. The fraction is then suspended in the Feulgen reagent and stored in the dark for 1–4 h. A drop of the suspension of cells in Feulgen reagent is then placed on a slide, covered with a coverslip and the excess reagent removed by squashing the coverslip under several layers of filter paper. The coverslip is then prized off and a drop of sulphur-dioxide water added and the coverslip replaced. The duration of the bleaching procedure (several seconds) which decolourizes the cytoplasm without removing stain from the nuclei is experimentally determined with a few test slides. The sulphur dioxide water is then largely removed by pressing the coverslip under several layers of filter paper, the coverslip immediately prized off and the stained cells mounted in a drop of glycerin jelly. The mitotic index is then determined by scanning such Feulgen-stained slides, in a regular manner, until 1000 nuclei have been scored.

For total cell counts it is necessary to disperse the cell aggregates present in the fractions without destroying the cell outlines. The most effective maceration technique must be worked out for each suspension culture on a trial and error basis. The following macerating agents should be tested: oxidizing agents such as chromic acid (Brown and Rickless, 1949; Butcher and Street, 1960; see Section II, A, p. 485), chelating agents (Letham, 1960, 1962) and pectic enzymes (Chayen 1952; McClendon and Somers, 1960; Yager, 1960). After maceration, the cells may be separated either by low-speed blending (Letham, 1960), by vigorous agitation, or by being forced back and forth through a hypodermic needle (Das *et al.*, 1956). If they are not too large, the cells in the suspension may then be counted in a haemocytometer slide.

If the cells are large it may be necessary to transfer a known small volume of the suspension to a slide with a micropipette and then count all the cells present. Attempts are being made to count such cell suspensions in the Coulter Counter (Coulter Electronics Inc. Florida) but the large size ($>200\ \mu$ diameter) and irregular shape of some of the cells encountered in suspension cultures presents formidable difficulties with this technique.

H. CULTURE OF ISOLATED CELLS

Work with suspension cultures has shown that cell division takes place actively in the cell aggregates but only with low frequency in the free cells. In order to eliminate a lag-phase in the growth of such cultures it is necessary either to use a very large inoculum or to transfer with the cellular material sufficient of the old medium already "conditioned" by supporting the growth of the culture during the previous passage. These two observations suggest that the induction of cell division may require the establishment in the cells of a critical level of some growth regulating substance(s) and that this level is more easily established in cell aggregates than in free cells, and in "conditioned" than in fresh culture medium.

These observations form a background for considering the various experimental approaches which have been made to the culture of single isolated higher plant cells. Muir *et al.* (1954) isolated single cells from "friable" callus masses of crown-gall origin and placed these singly on the upper surface of filter-paper squares whose lower surface made good contact with an actively growing "nurse" callus of the same strain. A high proportion of the cells underwent a few divisions, a small proportion went on dividing to give small callus masses on the filter paper (Fig. 14) and again a proportion of these were successfully transferred to agar medium to give clones of single cell origin. The initial criticism that the callus might have arisen by cells of the "nurse" callus growing through the filter paper was answered by the demonstration that the calluses obtained had the characteristics of the parent tissue when the "nurse" callus was of different origin, morphology and growth rate (Muir *et al.*, 1954). Torrey (1959) showed that calluses of single cell origin could be obtained when the filter paper was replaced by a membrane of small pore size ($0{\cdot}5$–$0{\cdot}75\ \mu$). This technique has the disadvantages that only a very limited number of cells can be cultured at any one time, that it involves mechanical manipulation of the single cells, that it is very difficult to standardize the conditions (such as degree of contact between cell, membrane and "nurse" and siting of cell in contact with a similar area of the callus mass), and that it is

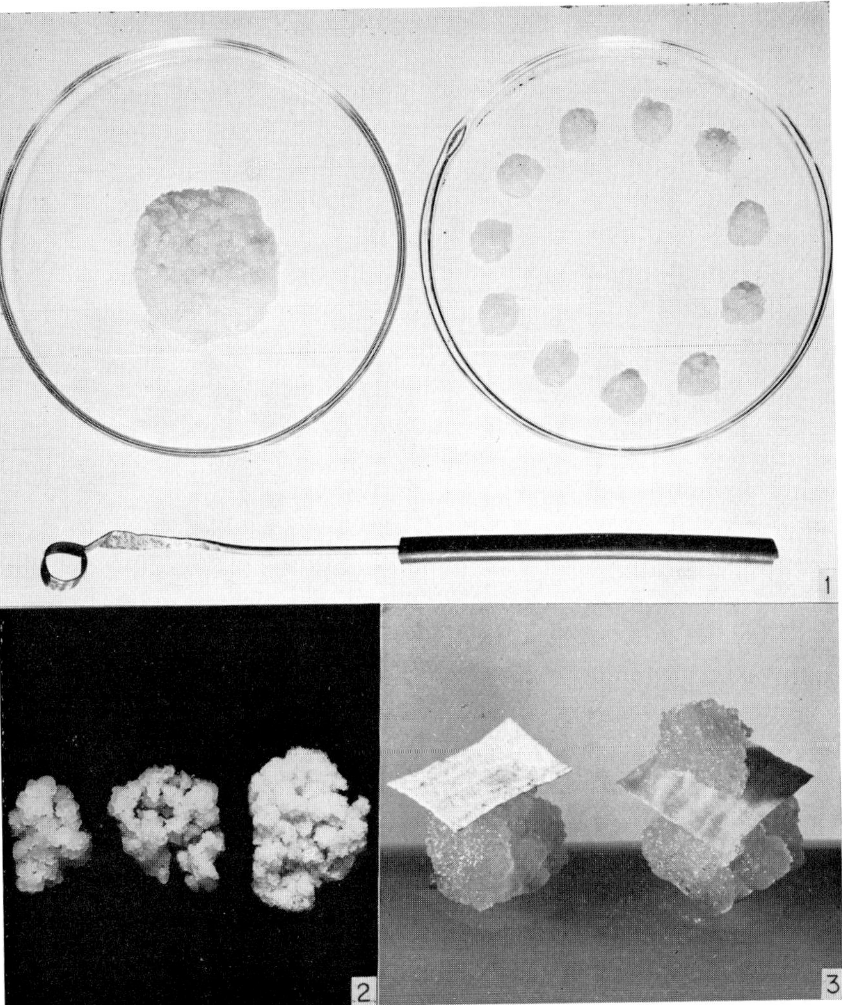

FIG. 14. Growth of single cells by the use of a "nurse" callus. 1. Subculture of parent "nurse" callus showing instrument used to obtain uniform explants. 2. Friable callus masses from which single cells can be isolated. 3. Growth of single cells on upper surface of filter paper in contact with the "nurse" callus. (After Muir, 1953.)

difficult to observe microscopically the "mother" cell and the divisions which lead it to initiate a callus.

A different approach was adopted by De Ropp (1955) when he tried to culture single cells in microchambers containing liquid medium, in which he could keep the cells under continuous observation in the phase-contrast microscope. Although many of the isolated cells observed by De Ropp remained alive for considerable periods, they did not divide and he concluded that ten to fifteen clumped cells was the lower limit from which a clone could be built up. Torrey (1957), working with a callus derived from the cambium of pea roots, also used a microchamber technique (Maximow's double coverslip method: Fig. 15) but

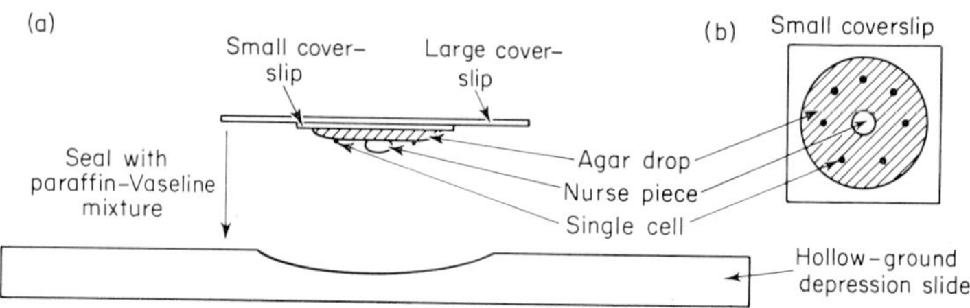

FIG. 15. Maximow's double coverslip method as used by Torrey (1957).

planted his cells on agar around a small "nurse" callus. However, of those cells still viable after 24 h only 8% underwent division and the largest group of cells achieved was of only seven cells and that after several weeks of culture. More recently, Jones *et al.* (1960) have examined the growth of separated cells (2–30 cells per drop) of a callus from a hybrid tobacco (*Nicotiana tabacum* × *N. glutinosa*) using a microchamber sealed with an inert mineral oil (Fig. 16). Using fresh culture

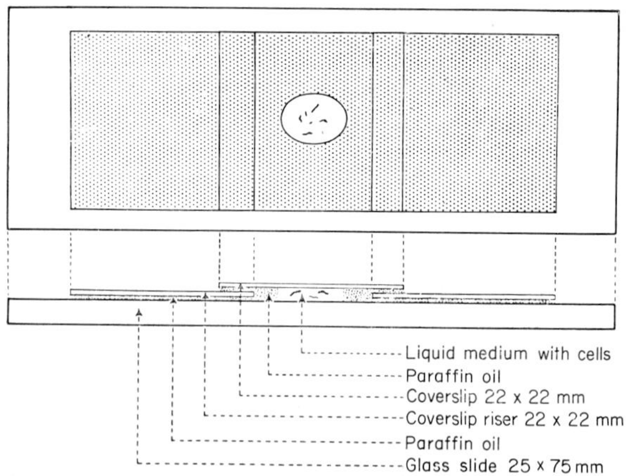

FIG. 16. Microchamber used by Jones *et al.* (1960) to observe the growth of free cells of hybrid tobacco.

medium they observed cell divisions only when a high number of cells were present in the drop. Divisions with a single cell per drop were, however, observed in a medium "conditioned" by having previously supported the growth of a cell population (see Chap. 9, p. 597). The report by Ball (1963) that single cells from suspension cultures of *Sequoia sempervirens* can become attached to glass surfaces cleaned by the method of Rappaport and Bishop (1960) should make possible observations on the growth and division of such attached cells in chambers through which liquid culture media can be circulated. These microchamber techniques are clearly elegantly suited for the microscopic observation of isolated cells (excellent phase-contrast films of dividing cells in such chambers have been made by the Wisconsin group of Hildebrandt and Riker; see also Chap. 10, p. 677) but they do not readily permit of studies on large cell populations and are not a satisfactory way of establishing clones of single cell origin.

A third, and it seems much more promising approach, involving the plating out of suspensions of free cells, was developed in 1960 by Bergmann using Petri dishes containing a thin layer (1 mm) of a medium solidified with agar (0·6%) and containing coconut milk (7%) and 2.4-D (0·5 p.p.m.). Starting with suspension cultures of *Nicotiana tabacum* (var. Samsun) and *Phaseolus vulgaris* (var. Early Golden Cluster), he obtained a filtrate, 90% of the cellular units of which were free cells. This was then spread on the surface of the soft agar and the Petri dishes were sealed to prevent desiccation and incubated in diffuse light. Under these conditions and with these strains, up to 20% of the cells underwent repeated divisions to give rise to small colonies which could be successfully transferred to tubes of agar medium. Subsequently, Torrey and Reinert (1961) obtained many small colonies in this way by plating out, on a complex synthetic medium, a suspension culture fraction of *Convolvulus arvensis* containing free cells and small cell clumps. Similarly, Blakely and Steward (1961) have reported that about 1% of the cellular units of a suspension culture of *Haplopappus* will give rise to colonies when plated out on a medium containing coconut milk (10%), NAA (0·5 p.p.m.) and casein hydrolysate (200 p.p.m.).

The technique used in our laboratory to test the ability of free cells and small cell aggregates to give rise to colonies on agar plates is as follows. An aliquot of the suspension culture is aseptically filtered through an appropriate grade of nylon bolting cloth to give a fraction rich in free cells and then, if necessary, concentrated by centrifuging. The number of free cells and cell aggregates in unit volume of this fraction is then determined by counting small samples removed aseptically and the volume adjusted with the sterile liquid medium so that 1 ml contains the number of cellular units to be distributed per Petri dish. 1 ml of this suspension is then mixed with 4 ml of the test medium containing agar (0·6% w/v) maintained at 38°C, and the mixture immediately poured to give a uniform layer in a sterile 9 cm polystyrene (disposable) Petri dish. Once the agar has set, the dishes are sealed with cloth adhesive tape and photomicrographic records are made of selected areas on the replicate dishes. The dishes are then incubated at 25°C in diffuse light or darkness for periods up to 35 days. During this period a record is made of visible colonies as they appear and the photographed areas are examined in order to follow the behaviour of the free cells and cell aggregates and to determine the origin of any visible colonies which develop in these areas.

Quantitative studies have been undertaken recently by Blakely and Steward (1962) and Mehta (1963) in which the origin of the colonies has been traced in this way and the percentages recorded of the free cells and cell aggregates undergoing division and giving rise to visible colonies. Figure 17 shows the changing picture of a photographed area of a plated suspension of carrot cells and small cell aggregates, and Fig. 18 the appearance of visible colonies from such a suspension at

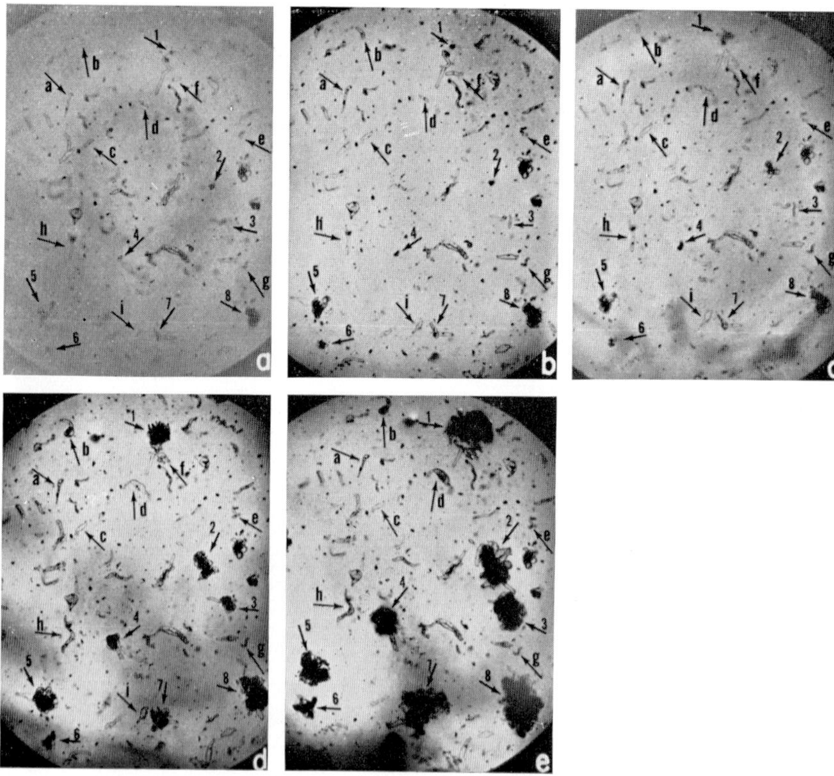

FIG. 17. Growth of single cells and cell aggregates on agar medium. Low magnification microphotographs of free cells and small cell aggregates of carrot tissue plated out on agar medium in Petri dishes. The numbered arrows point to cellular units (free cells and cell aggregates) that grew into colonies. The lettered arrows point to units which only underwent cell enlargement or a very limited number of cell divisions. (By courtesy of Blakely and Steward, 1962.)

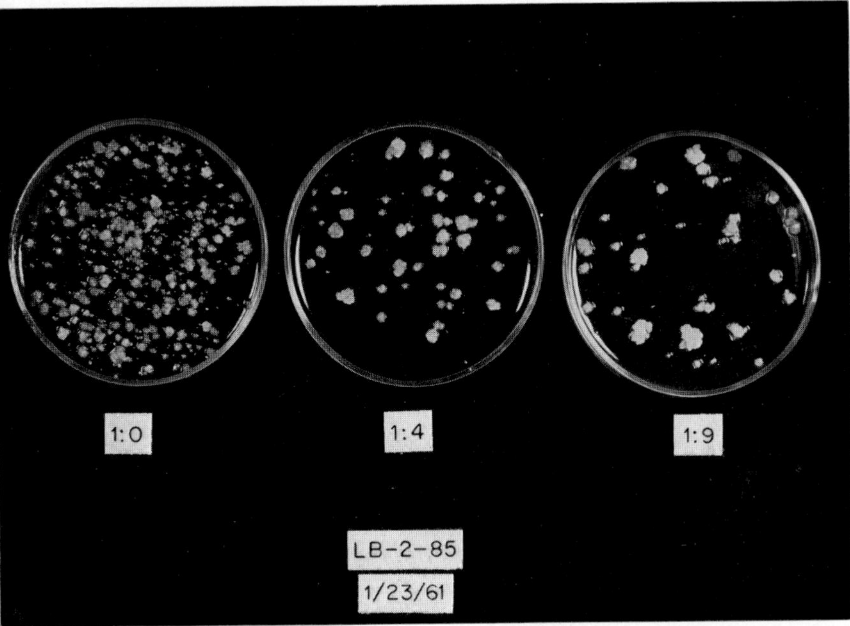

FIG. 18. Colonies arising on agar plates. The plates were inoculated with three densities of a carrot suspension culture. Centre plate 1/4 density and right-hand plate 1/9th density of the left-hand plate. Plates photographed after 35 days' incubation. (By courtesy of Blakely and Steward, 1962.)

three levels of density of cellular units and after 35 days' incubation (both after Blakely and Steward).

The importance of developing this plating technique to promote our understanding of the factors controlling cell division (see Chap. 9, p. 596) and to develop the biochemical genetics of higher plant cells (see Chap. 9, p. 578) merits a brief statement of findings from current research. The percentage of cellular units undergoing division and the percentage giving rise to visible colonies decreases and eventually becomes zero if the density of units plated is progressively reduced below a critical level. When the cellular units are washed with fresh medium before plating (so that no "conditioned" medium is carried over to the plates with the suspension fraction) the incidence of divisions and the formation of colonies are reduced. The introduction of large cell colonies on to the plates exercises a nurse effect and promotes cell divisions in the neighbouring free cells and small aggregates. The same action can be observed as visible colonies increase in area; free cells and small aggregates are induced to divide as the margin of the growing colony approaches their location on the agar. The importance of the physiological condition of the suspension in determining the ability of its cellular units to divide on the agar is illustrated by the observations that (1) samples taken when the suspension culture has a high mitotic index give the highest number of visible colonies, and (2) suspensions very recently derived from a growing callus mass have, in certain instances, been shown to give rise to more colonies than suspensions of the same tissue after they have been maintained by serial subculture in agitated liquid medium.

References

Abraham, A. and Thomas, K. J. (1962). A note on the *in vitro* culture of excised coconut embryos. *Indian Cocon. J.* **15**, 84–88.

Addicott, F. T. and Devirian, P. S. (1939). A second growth factor for excised pea roots—nicotinic acid. *Amer. J. Bot.* **26**, 667.

Almestrand, A. (1949). Studies on the growth of isolated roots of barley and oats. *Physiol. Plant.* **2**, 372.

Almestrand, A. (1950). Further studies on the growth of isolated roots of barley and oats. *Physiol. Plant.* **3**, 205.

Almestrand, A. (1957). Growth and metabolism of isolated cereal roots. *Physiol. Plant.* **10**, 521.

Baldev, B. (1962). *In vitro* studies of floral induction in stem apices of *Cuscuta reflexa* Roxb.—a short-day plant. *Ann. Bot., Lond.* **26**, 173.

Ball, E. (1946). Development in sterile culture of stem tips and subjacent regimes of *Tropaeolum majus* L. and of *Lupinus albus* L. *Amer. J. Bot.* **33**, 301.

Ball, E. (1960). Cell divisions in living shoot apices. *Phytomorphology* **10**, 377.

Ball, E. (1963). An optically efficient method for observing single plant cells from shake cultures during growth and division. *Nature, Lond.* **197**, 103.

Barker, W. G. (1953). Proliferative capacity of the medullary sheath region in the stem of *Tilia americana*. *Amer. J. Bot.* **40**, 773.

Bergmann, L. (1960). Growth and division of single cells of higher plants *in vitro*. *J. gen. Physiol.* **43**, 841.

Bersworth, F. C. (1952). "The Versenes", 5th ed. Tech. Bull. No. 2, Bersworth Chem. Co., Framingham, Mass., U.S.A.

Berthelot, A. (1934). Nouvelles remarques d'ordre chimique sur le choix des milieux de culture naturels et sur la manière de formuler les milieux synthétiques. *Bull. Soc. chim. biol. Paris* **16**, 1553.

Blakely, L. M. and Steward, F. C. (1961). Growth induction in cultures of *Haplopappus gracilis*. I. The behaviour of cultured cells. *Amer. J. Bot.* **48**, 351.

Blakely, L. M. and Steward, F. C. (1962). The growth of free cells. II. Observations on individual cells and their subsequent patterns of growth. III. The observation and isolation of variant strains. *Amer. J. Bot.* **49**, 653.

Blakeslee, A. F. and Satina, S. (1944). New hybrids from incompatible crosses in *Datura* through culture of excised embryos on malt media. *Science* **99**, 331.

Bobilioff-Preisser, W. (1917). Beobachtungen an isolierten Palisaden- und Schwammparenchymzellen. *Bot. Zbl.* **33**, 248.

Boll, W. G. and Street, H. E. (1951). Studies on the growth of excised roots. I. The stimulatory effect of molybdenum and copper on the growth of excised tomato roots. *New Phytol.* **50**, 52.

Bonner, D. M., Haagen-Smit, A. J. and Went, F. W. (1939). Leaf growth hormones. I. A bioassay and source for leaf growth factors. *Bot. Gaz.* **101**, 128.

Bonner, J. (1936). Plant tissue culture from a hormonal point of view. *Proc. nat. Acad. Sci., Wash.* **22**, 426.

Bonner, J. (1938). Nicotinic acid and the growth of isolated pea embryos. *Plant Physiol.* **13**, 865.

Bonner, J. (1940). On the growth factor requirements of isolated roots. *Amer. J. Bot.* **27**, 692.

Bonner, J. (1942). Culture of isolated roots of *Acacia melanoxylon*. *Bull. Torrey bot. Club* **69**, 130.

Bonner, J. (1943). Further experiments on the nutrition of isolated tomato roots. *Bull. Torrey bot. Club* **70**, 184.

Bonner, J. and Addicott, F. (1937). Cultivation *in vitro* of excised pea roots. *Bot. Gaz.* **99**, 144.

Bonner, J. and Axtmann, G. (1937). The growth of plant embryos *in vitro*. Preliminary experiments on the role of accessory substances. *Proc. nat. Acad. Sci., Wash.* **23**, 453.

Bonner, J. and Devirian, P. S. (1939). Growth factor requirements of four species of isolated roots. *Amer. J. Bot.* **26**, 661.

Börger, H. (1926). Uber die Kultur von isolierten Zellen und Gewebsfragmenten. *Arch. exp. Zellforsch.* **2**, 123.

Bowen, C. C. (1955). Feulgen staining of cell suspensions. *Stain Tech.* **30**, 135.

Brink, R. A., Cooper, C. D. and Aushermann, L. E. (1944). A new hybrid between *Hordeum jubatum* and *Secale cereale* reared by an artificially cultivated embryo. *J. Hered.* **35**, 67.

Braun, A. C. and Wood, H. N. (1962). On the activation of certain essential biosynthetic systems in cells of *Vinca rosea* L. *Proc. nat. Acad. Sci., Wash.* **48**, 1776.

Brown, R. and Rickless, P. (1949). A new method for the study of cell division and cell extension with some preliminary observations on the effect of temperature and of nutrients. *Proc. roy. Soc.* B, **136**, 110.

Burkholder, P. R. and Nickell, L. G. (1949). Atypical growth of plants. I. Cultivation of virus tumours of *Rumex* on nutrient agar. *Bot. Gaz.* **110**, 426.

Burström, H. (1941). Studies on the carbohydrate nutrition of roots. *LantbrHögsk. Ann.* **9**, 264.

Butcher, D. N. and Street, H. E. (1960). The effects of gibberellins on the growth of excised tomato roots. *J. exp. Bot.* **11**, 206.

Byrne, A. F. and Koch, R. B. (1962). Food production by submerged culture of plant tissue cells. *Science* **135**, 215.

Caplin, S. M. (1947). Growth and morphology of tobacco tissue cultures *in vitro*. *Bot. Gaz.* **108**, 379.

Caplin, S. M. (1959). Mineral oil overlay for conservation of plant tissue cultures. *Amer. J. Bot.* **46**, 324.

Caponetti, J. D. and Steeves, T. A. (1963). Morphogenetic studies on excised leaves of *Osmunda cinnamomea*, L. Morphogenetic studies of leaf development in sterile nutrient culture. *Canad. J. Bot.* **41**, 545.

Chailakhyan, M. Kh., Butenko, R. G. and Lynbarskaya, I. I. (1961). Effect of derivatives of nucleic acid metabolism on the growth and flowering of *Perilla nankinensis*. *Fiziol. Rast.* **8**, 101.

Charles, H. P. and Street, H. E. (1959). Studies on the growth of excised roots. VI. The effects of certain amino acids and auxins on the growth of excised groundsel roots. *New Phytol.* **58**, 75.

Chayen, J. (1952). Pectinase treatment for isolating plant cells. *Nature, Lond.* **170**, 1070.

Chopra, R. N. (1958). *In vitro* cultures of ovaries of *Althea rosea,* Cav. *In* Proc. Sem. Mod. Dev. Plant Physiol., University of Delhi (P. Maheshwari, ed.), pp. 87-89.

Chopra, R. N. (1962). Effect of some growth substances and calyx on fruit and seed development of *Althaea rosea,* Cav. *In* "Plant Embryology—A Symposium", pp. 170–181. C.S.I.R., New Delhi.

Chopra, R. N. and Sabharwal, P. S. (1963). *In vitro* culture of ovules of *Gynandropsis gynandra* (L) Briq. and *Impatiens balsamina,* L. *In* "Plant Tissue and Organ Culture—A Symposium" (P. Maheshwari and N. S. Ranga Swamy, eds.), pp. 257–263. International Society of Plant Morphologists, Delhi.

Constabel, F. (1958). La culture des tissus de *Juniperus communis. Rev. gen. Bot.* **65**, 390.

Czech, H. (1926). Kultur von pflanzlichen Gewebezellen. *Arch. exp. Zellforsch.* **3**, 176.

Darlington, C. D. and La Cour, L. F. (1947). "The Handling of Chromosomes". Allen and Unwin, London.

Das, N. K., Patau, K. and Skoog, F. (1956). Initiation of mitosis and cell division by kinetin and indoleacetic acid in excised tobacco pith tissue. *Physiol. Plant.* **9**, 640.

David, S. B. (1954). Studies on the nutrition of excised roots of *Medicago sativa* L. Ph.D. Thesis, University of Manchester.

Dawson, J. R. O. and Street, H. E. (1959a). The behaviour in culture of excised root clones of the "Dorset Marlgrass" strain of red clover, *Trifolium pratense* L. *Bot. Gaz.* **120**, 217.

Dawson, J. R. O. and Street, H. E. (1959b). The growth responses of a clone of excised roots of the "Dorset Marlgrass" strain of red clover, *Trifolium pratense* L. *Bot. Gaz.* **120**, 227.

Day, D. (1943). Growth of excised tomato roots in agar with thiamine plus pyridoxine, nicotinamide or glycine. *Amer. J. Bot.* **30**, 150.

DeMaggio, A. E. and Wetmore, R. H. (1961). Morphogenetic studies on the fern *Todea barbara.* III. Experimental biology. *Amer. J. Bot.* **48**, 551.

De Ropp, R. S. (1955). The growth and behaviour *in vitro* of isolated plant cells. *Proc. roy. Soc.* B, **144**, 86.

Dormer, K. J. and Street, H. E. (1949). The carbohydrate nutrition of tomato roots. *Ann. Bot., Lond.* **13**, 199.

Earle, E. D. and Torrey, J. G. (1963). Differentiation in colonies derived from isolated cells of *Convolvulus arvensis. Amer. J. Bot.* **50**, 613.

Enderle, W. (1951). Tagesperiodische Wachstums- und Turgorschwankungen an Gewebeculturen. *Planta* **39**, 570.

Ferguson, J. D. (1957). Studies in the carbohydrate nutrition of excised tomato roots. Ph.D. Thesis, University of Wales.

Ferguson, J. D., Street, H. E. and David, S. B. (1958). The carbohydrate nutrition of tomato roots. V. The promotion and inhibition of excised root growth by various sugars and sugar alcohols. *Ann. Bot., Lond.,* **22**, 513.

Fox, J. E. and Miller, C. O. (1959). Factors in corn steep water promoting growth of plant tissues. *Plant Physiol.* **34**, 577.

Galun, E., Jung, Y. and Lang, A. (1963). Morphogenesis of floral buds of cucumber cultured *in vitro. Devl. Biol.* **6**, 370.

Gautheret, R. J. (1934). Culture du tissu cambial. *C. R. Acad. Sci., Paris* **198**, 2195.

Gautheret, R. J. (1935a). Recherches sur la culture des tissus végétaux: essais de culture de quelques tissus méristématiques. Thèse, Université de Paris.

Gautheret, R. J. (1935b). Recherches sur la formation de chlorophyll dans les racines et la reduction des sels argent par les chloroplasts. *Rev. gen. Bot.* **47**, 401.

Gautheret, R. J. (1937). Nouvelles recherches sur la culture du tissu cambial. *C. R. Acad. Sci., Paris* **205**, 572.

Gautheret, R. J. (1938). Sur le repiquage des cultures de tissu cambial de *Salix capraea. C. R. Acad. Sci., Paris* **206**, 125.

Gautheret, R. J. (1939). Sur la possibilité de réaliser la culture indéfinie des tissus de tubercules de carotte. *C. R. Acad. Sci., Paris* **208**, 118.

Gautheret, R. J. (1948). Sur la culture indéfinie des tissus de *Salix caprea. C. R. Soc. Biol., Paris* **142**, 807.

Gautheret, R. J. (1959). "La culture des tissus végétaux, techniques et réalisations". Masson, Paris.

Gioelli, F. (1938). Morfologia, istologia, fisiologia e fisiopatologia di meristemi secondari *in vitro. Atti Acad. Sci. Ferrara* **16**, 1.

Glasstone, V. F. C. (1947). Inorganic micronutrients in tomato root tissue culture. *Amer. J. Bot.* **34**, 218.

Goldacre, P. L., Unt, H. and Kefford, N. P. (1962). Cultivation of isolated tissue derived from the pericycle of roots. *Nature, Lond.* **193**, 1305.

Gregory, W. C. (1940). Experimental studies on the cultivation of excised anthers in nutrient solution. *Amer. J. Bot.* **27**, 687.

Haberlandt, G. (1902). Kulturversuche mit isolierten Pflanzenzellen. *S. B. Akad. Wiss. Wien, Math-Naturw. Kl.* **111**, 69.

Hannay, J. W. and Street, H. E. (1954). Studies on the growth of excised roots. III. The molybdenum and manganese requirement of excised tomato roots. *New Phytol.* **53**, 68.

Hannig, E. (1904). Uber die kultur von Cruciferne Embryonen ausenhalb des Embryosachs. *Bot. Ztg.* **62**, 45.

Harris, G. P. (1956). Amino acids as sources of nitrogen for the growth of isolated oat embryos. *New Phytol.* **55**, 253.

Heller, R. (1949). Sur l'emploi de papier filtre sans cendres comme support pour les cultures de tissus végétaux. *C. R. Soc. Biol., Paris* **143**, 335.

Heller, R. (1953). Recherches sur la nutrition minérale des tissus végétaux cultivés *in vitro. Ann. Sci. nat. Bot. Biol. Veg. Ser.* **11**, 1.

Henderson, J. H. M., Durell, M. E. and Bonner, J. (1952). The culture of normal sunflower callus. *Amer. J. Bot.* **39**, 467.

Hewitt, E. J. (1952). "Sand and Water Culture Methods used in the Study of Plant Nutrition". Commonwealth Agricultural Bureaux, Farnham Royal, England.

Hildebrandt, A. C., Riker, A. J. and Duggar, B. M. (1946). The influence of the composition of the medium on growth *in vitro* of excised tobacco and sunflower tissue cultures. *Amer. J. Bot.* **33**, 591.

Hughes, E. W. D. and Street, H. E. (1960). Effects of inhibitory concentrations of 3-indolylacetic acid and 3-indolylacetonitrile on cell division and tissue differentiation in excised tomato roots. *J. exp. Bot.* **11**, 198.

Ito, I. (1961). *In vitro* culture of ovary and seed in orchids. Ph.D. Thesis, Kyoto Prefect University.

Jablonski, J. R. and Skoog, F. (1954). Cell enlargement and cell division in excised tobacco pith tissue. *Physiol. Plant.* **7**, 16.

Jacquiot, C. C. R. (1950). Sur la culture *in vitro* de tissu cambial de Châtaignier (*Castanea vesca,* Gaertn). *C. R. Acad. Sci., Paris* **231**, 1080.

Jagendorf, A. T., Bonner, D. M. and Naylor, A. W. (1952). An atypical growth of cabbage seedling roots. I. Morphology, histology and induction conditions. *Bot. Gaz.* **113**, 334.

Johri, B. M. and Bajaj, Y. P. S. (1963). *In vitro* response of the embryo of *Dendrophthoe falcata* (L.f.) Ettings. *In* "Plant Tissue and Organ Culture—A Symposium" (P. Maheshwari and N. S. Ranga Swamy, eds.), pp. 292–301. International Society of Plant Morphologists, Delhi.

Johri, B. M. and Sehgal, C. B. (1963). Growth of ovaries of *Anethum graveolens*, L. *In* "Plant Tissue and Organ Culture—A Symposium" (P. Maheshwari and N. S. Ranga Swamy, eds.), pp. 245–254. International Society of Plant Morphologists, Delhi.

Johri, B. M. and Guha, S. (1963). *In vitro* development of onion plants from flowers. *In* "Plant Tissue and Organ Culture—a Symposium" (P. Maheshwari and N. S. Ranga Swamy, eds.), pp. 215-223. International Society of Plant Morphologists, Delhi.

Jones, L. E., Hildebrandt, A. C., Riker, A. J. and Wu, J. H. (1960). Growth of somatic tobacco cells in microculture. *Amer. J. Bot.* **47**, 468.

Jörgensen, C. A. (1928). The experimental formation of heteroploid plants in the genus, *Solanum*. *J. Genet.* **19**, 133.

Kanta, K., Ranga Swamy, N. S. and Maheshwari, P. (1962). Test tube fertilisation in a flowering plant. *Nature, Lond.* **194**, 1214.

Kapoor, M. (1959). Influence of growth substances on the ovules of *Zephyranthes*. *Phytomorphology* **9**, 313.

Karstens, W. K. H. (1955). Observations on the proliferation of stem pith parenchyma *in vitro*. I. General introduction. *Acta bot. néerl.* **4**, 183.

Kemmer, E. (1928). Beobachtungen uber die Lebensdauer isolierter Epidermen. *Arch. exp. Zellforsch.* **7**, 1.

Klein, R. M. (1963). Interaction of ultraviolet and visible radiation on the growth of cell aggregates of *Ginkgo* pollen tissue. *Physiol. Plant.* **16**, 73.

Klein, R. M. and Manos, G. E. (1960). Use of metal chelates for plant tissue cultures. *Ann. N.Y. Acad. Sci.* **88**, 416.

Knop, W. (1865). Quantitative Untersuchungen uber die Ernahrungsprocesse der Pflanzen. *Landw. Vers. Sta.* **7**, 93.

Kofler, L. (1945). Bouturage de bourgeons de Rosier en milieu nutritif aseptique. *Bull. Soc. bot. Paris* **92**, 78.

Kotte, W. (1922a). Wurzelmeristem in Gewebekultur. *Ber. dtsch. bot. Ges.* **40**, 269.

Kotte, W. (1922b). Kulturversuche mit isolierten Wurzelspitzen. *Beitr. allg. Bot.* **2**, 413.

Kuehnert, C. C. and Steeves, T. A. (1962). Capacity of fragments of leaf primordia to produce whole leaves. *Nature, Lond.* **196**, 187.

Kunkel, W. (1926). Uber die Kultur von Perianthgeweben. *Arch. exp. Zellforsch.* **3**, 405.

Küster, E. (1928). Das Verhalten pflanzenlicher Zellen *in vitro* und *in vivo*. *Arch. exp. Zellforsch.* **6**, 28.

Laibach, F. (1925). Das Taubwerden der Kunstliche Aufricht fuhrabsterbender Bastardembryonen. *Z. Bot.* **17**, 417.

Lamport, D. T. A. and Northcote, D. H. (1960). The use of tissue culture for the study of plant cell walls. *Biochem. J.* **76**, 52P.

Lamprecht, W. (1918). Über die Kultur und Transplantation kleiner Blattstücken. *Beitr. allg. Bot.* **1**, 353.

LaRue, C. D. (1933). Regeneration in mutilated seedlings. *Proc. nat. Acad. Sci., Wash.* **19**, 53.

LaRue, C. D. (1947). Growth and regeneration of the endosperm of maize in culture. *Amer. J. Bot.* **34**, 585.

Letham, D. S. (1960). The separation of plant cells with ethylenediaminetetra-acetic acid. *Exp. Cell Res.* **21**, 353.

Letham, D. S. (1962). Separation of plant cells with hexametaphosphate and the nature of intercellular bonding. *Exp. Cell Res.* **27**, 352.

Li, T. T. (1934). The development of the embryo of *Ginkgo biloba.* *Nat. Tsing Hua. Univ. Sci. Rep.* B**2**, 29.

Li, T. T. and Shen, T. (1934). The effect of "pantothenic acid" on the growth of the radical of *Ginkgo* embryos in artificial media. *Nat. Tsing Hua Univ. Sci. Rep.* B**2**, 53.

Lingappa, T. (1957). Tissue cultures of *Solanum tuberosum* and *Ipomea pandurata. Amer. J. Bot.* **44**, 419.

Loewenberg, J. R. and Skoog, F. (1952). Pine tissue culture. *Physiol. Plant.* **5**, 33.

Loo, S. W. (1945). Cultivation of excised stem tips of *Asparagus* '*in vitro.*' *Amer. J. Bot.* **32**, 13.

Loo, S. W. (1946a). Further experiments on the culture of excised *Asparagus* stem tips *in vitro.* *Amer. J. Bot.* **33**, 156.

Loo, S. W. (1946b). Cultivation of excised stem tips of dodder *in vitro.* *Amer. J. Bot.* **33**, 295.

McClary, J. E. (1940). Synthesis of thiamin by excised roots of maize. *Proc. nat. Acad. Sci., Wash.* **26**, 581.

McClendon, J. H. and Somers, G. F. (1960). The enzymatic maceration of plant tissues: observation using a new method of measurement. *Amer. J. Bot.* **47**, 1.

Maheshwari, N. (1958). *In vitro* culture of excised ovules of *Papaver somniferum. Science* **127**, 342.

Maheshwari, N. and Lal, M. (1958). *In vitro* culture of ovaries of *Iberis amara,* L. *Nature, Lond.* **181**, 631.

Maheshwari, N. and Lal, M. (1961). *In vitro* culture of ovaries of *Iberis amara,* L. *Phytomorphology* **11**, 17.

Maheshwari, P. and Baldev, B. (1962). *In vitro* induction of adventive buds from embryos of *Cuscuta reflexa.* Roxb. *In* "Plant Embryology—A Symposium", pp. 129–138. C.S.I.R., New Delhi.

Mehta, A. R. (1963). Nutritional and morphogenetic studies with callus and suspension cultures derived from roots. Ph.D. Thesis, University of Wales.

Melchers, G. and Bergmann, L. (1959). Untersuchungen an Kulturen von haploid Geweben von *Antirrhinum majus.* *Ber. dtsch. Bot. Ges.* **71**, 459.

Morel, G. (1948). Recherches sur la culture associée de parasites obligatoires et de tissus végétaux. *Ann. Épiphyt.* **14**, 1.

Morel, G. (1950). Sur la culture des tissus d'*Osmunda cinnamomea.* *C. R. Acad. Sci., Paris* **230**, 2318.

Morel, G. (1956). Nouvelles méthodes permettant de réaliser des cultures de tissus végétaux. *Rev. gen. Bot.* **63**, 314.

Morel, G. (1958). Biochemistry of morphogenesis of plant shoots. Symposium VI. Biochemistry of Morphogenesis. *Proc. 4th int. Congr. Biochem.* 221–222.

Morel, G. (1966). La culture *in vitro* du meristeme apical. *Rev. Cytol., Paris* (in press).

Morel, G. and Wetmore, R. H. (1951). Fern callus tissue culture. *Amer. J. Bot.* **38**, 141.

Muir, W. H. (1953). Cultural conditions favouring the isolation and growth of single cells from higher plants *in vitro*. Ph.D. Thesis, University of Wisconsin.

Muir, W. H., Hildebrandt, A. C. and Riker, A. J. (1954). Plant tissue cultures produced from single isolated cells. *Science* **119**, 877.

Murashige, T. and Skoog, F. (1962). A revised medium for rapid growth and bio-assays with tobacco tissue cultures. *Physiol. Plant.* **15**, 473.

Narayanaswami, S. and Norstog, K. (1964). Plant embryo culture. *Bot. Rev.* **30**, 587.

Neales, T. F. (1959). The boron requirement of flax roots grown in sterile culture. *J. exp. Bot.* **10**, 426.

Neales, T. F. (1964). A comparison of the boron requirement of intact tomato plants and excised tomato roots grown in sterile culture. *J. exp. Bot.* **15**, 647.

Nickell, L. G. (1952). Vitamin B_1 requirement of *Rumex* virus tumor tissue. *Bull. Torrey bot. Club* **79**, 427.

Nickell, L. G. (1956). The continuous submerged cultivation of plant tissues as single cells. *Proc. nat. Acad. Sci., Wash.* **42**, 848.

Nickell, L. G., Greenfield, P. and Burkholder, P. R. (1950). A typical growth of plants. III. Growth responses of virus tumors of *Rumex* to certain nucleic acid components and related compounds. *Bot. Gaz.* **112**, 42.

Nitsch, J. P. (1951). Growth and development *in vitro* of excised ovaries. *Amer. J. Bot.* **38**, 566.

Nitsch, J. P. (1960). Presence d'une substance type "cinetine" dans le jus de tomate. *Bull. Soc. bot. Fr.* **107**, 263.

Nitsch, J. P. and Nitsch, C. (1956). Auxin-dependent growth of excised *Helianthus tuberosus* tissues. I. *Amer. J. Bot.* **43**, 839.

Nitsch, J. P. and Nitsch, C. (1957). Auxin-dependent growth of excised *Helianthus tuberosus* tissues. II. Organic nitrogenous substances. *Amer. J. Bot.* **44**, 555.

Nobécourt, P. (1937). Culture en série de tissus végétaux sur milieu artificiel. *C. R. Acad. Sci., Paris* **205**, 521.

Nobécourt, P. (1938a). Sur les proliférations spontanées de fragments de tubercules de carotte et leur culture sur milieu synthétique. *Bull. Soc. bot. Fr.* **85**, 1.

Nobécourt, P. (1938b). Sur la proliferation *in vitro* du parenchyme amylifère du tubercule de *Solanum tuberosum* L. *Bull. Soc. bot. Fr.* **85**, 490.

Norstog, K. J. (1956). The growth of barley embryos on coconut milk media. *Bull. Torrey bot. Club* **83**, 27.

Norstog, K. J. (1961). The growth and differentiation of cultured barley embryos. *Amer. J. Bot.* **48**, 876.

Norstog, K. J. and Smith, J. E. (1963). Growth of very small barley embryos on defined media. *Science* **142**, 1655.

Overbeek, J. van (1939). Evidence for auxin production in isolated roots growing *in vitro*. *Bot. Gaz.* **101**, 450.

Overbeek, J. van, Conklin, M. E. and Blakeslee, A. F. (1941). Factors in coconut milk essential for growth and development of very young *Datura* embryos. *Science* **94**, 350.

Overbeek, J. van, Conklin, M. E. and Blakeslee, A. F. (1942). Cultivation *in vitro* of small *Datura* embryos. *Amer. J. Bot.* **29**, 472.

Overbeek, J. van, Sui, J. R. and Haagen-Smit, A. J. (1944). Factors affecting the growth of *Datura* embryos *in vitro*. *Amer. J. Bot.* **31**, 219.

Paris, D. (1955). Action de quelques vitamines hydrosolubles sur les cultures de tissus végétaux. *Année biol.* **31**, 15.

Paris, D. (1958). Recherches sur la nutrition des tissus normaux d'Aubépine cultivées *in vitro*. *C. R. Acad. Sci., Paris* **246**, 449.

Paris, D. and Duhamet, L. (1953). Action d'un mélange d'acides aminés et de vitamines sur la prolifération des cultures de tissus de crown-gall de Scorsonère: comparaison avec l'action du lait de Coco. *C. R. Acad. Sci., Paris* **236**, 1690.

Pfeiffer, H. (1931). Beobachtungen an Kulturen nackter Zellen aus pflanzenlichen Beirenperikarpien. *Arch. exp. Zellforsch.* **11**, 424.

Pfeiffer, H. (1933). Uber das Migrationsvermögen pflanzlicher Zellen *in situ* und *in vitro*. *Arch. exp. Zellforsch.* **14**, 152.

Pollard, J. K., Shantz, E. M. and Steward, F. C. (1961). Hexitols in coconut milk: their role in nurture of dividing cells. *Plant Physiol.* **36**, 492.

Raggio, M. and Raggio, N. (1956). A new method for the cultivation of isolated roots. *Physiol. Plant.* **9**, 466.

Raggio, M., Raggio, N. and Torrey, J. G. (1957). The nodulation of isolated leguminous roots. *Amer. J. Bot.* **44**, 325.

Raghavan, V. (1964). Effects of certain organic nitrogen compounds on growth *in vitro* of the seedlings of *Cattleya*. *Bot. Gaz.* **125**, 260.

Raghavan, V. and Jacobs, W. P. (1961). Studies on the floral histogenesis and physiology of *Perilla*. II. Floral induction in cultured apical buds of *P. frutescens*. *Amer. J. Bot.* **48**, 751.

Raghavan, V. and Torrey, J. G. (1963). Growth and morphogenesis of globular and older embryos of *Capsella* in culture. *Amer. J. Bot.* **50**, 540.

Raghavan, V. and Torrey, J. G. (1964a). Inorganic nitrogen nutrition of the seedlings of the orchid, *Cattleya*. *Amer. J. Bot.* **51**, 264.

Raghavan, V. and Torrey, J. G. (1964b). Effects of certain growth substances on the growth and morphogenesis of immature embryos of *Capsella* in culture. *Plant Physiol.* **39**, 691.

Ranga Swamy, N.S. (1961). Experimental studies on female reproductive structures of *Citrus microcarpa* Bunge. *Phytomorphology* **11**, 109.

Rappaport, J. (1954). *In vitro* culture of plant embryos and factors controlling their growth. *Bot. Rev.* **20**, 201.

Rappaport, C. and Bishop, C. B. (1960). Improved method for treating glass to produce surfaces suitable for the growth of certain mammalian cells in synthetic medium. *Exp. Cell Res.* **20**, 580.

Reinert, J. (1956). Dissociation of cultures of *Picea glauca* into small tissue fragments and single cells. *Science* **123**, 457.

Reinert, J. and White, P. R. (1956). The cultivation *in vitro* of tumor tissue and normal tissue of *Picea glauca*. *Physiol. Plant.* **9**, 177.

Rietsema, J., Satina, S. and Blakeslee, A. F. (1953). The effect of sucrose on the growth of *Datura stramonium* embryos *in vitro*. *Amer. J. Bot.* **40**, 538.

Rijven, A. H. G. C. (1952). *In vitro* studies on the embryo of *Capsella bursa-pastoris*. *Acta Bot. néerl.* **1**, 158.

Risser, P. G. and White, P. R. (1963). Nutritional requirements of spruce tumor cells *in vitro*. *Plant Physiol.* **38**, Suppl. LII.

Robbins, W. J. (1922a). Cultivation of excised root tips and stem tips under sterile conditions. *Bot. Gaz.* **73**, 376.

Robbins, W. J. (1922b). Effect of autolyzed yeast and peptone on growth of excised corn root tips in the dark. *Bot. Gaz.* **74**, 59.

Robbins, W. J. (1940). Light and the growth of excised roots of *Datura*. *Bull. Torrey bot. Club* **67**, 761.

Robbins, W. J. (1941). Growth of excised roots and heterosis in tomatoes. *Amer. J. Bot.* **28**, 216.

Robbins, W. J. and Bartley, M. A. (1937). Vitamin B_1 and the growth of excised tomato roots. *Science* **86**, 290.

Robbins, W. J. and Maneval, W. E. (1923). Further experiments on growth of excised root tips under sterile conditions. *Bot. Gaz.* **76**, 274.

Robbins, W. J. and Maneval, W. E. (1924). Effect of light on growth of excised root tips under sterile conditions. *Bot. Gaz.* **78**, 424.

Robbins, W. J. and Schmidt, M. B. (1939a). Vitamin B_6, a growth substance for excised tomato roots. *Proc. nat. Acad. Sci., Wash.* **25**. 1.

Robbins, W. J. and Schmidt, M. B. (1939b). Further experiments on excised tomato roots. *Amer. J. Bot.* **26**, 149.

Robbins, W. J. and Schmidt, M. B. (1939c). Growth of excised tomato roots in a synthetic solution. *Bull. Torrey bot. Club* **66**, 193.

Robbins, W. J. and White, V. B. (1936). Limited growth and abnormalities of excised corn root tips. *Bot. Gaz.* **98**, 209.

Roberts, E. H. (1954). Factors controlling persistence of meristematic activity in excised roots. Ph.D. Thesis, University of Manchester.

Roberts, E. H. and Street, H. E. (1955). The continuous culture of excised rye roots. *Physiol. Plant.* **8**, 238.

Sabharwal, P. S. (1963). *In vitro* culture of ovules, nucelli and embryos of *Citrus reticulata* Blanco var. Nagpuri. *In* "Plant Tissue and Organ Culture—A Symposium" (P. Maheshwari and N. S. Ranga Swamy, eds.), pp. 265–273. International Society of Plant Morphologists, Delhi.

Sachar, R. C. and Baldev, B. (1958). *In vitro* growth of ovaries of *Linaria moroccana*, Hook. *Current Sci. India* **27**, 104.

Sachar, R. C. and Guha, S. (1962). *In vitro* growth of achenes of *Ranunculus scleratus*, L. *In* "Plant Embryology—A Symposium", pp. 244–253. C.S.I.R., New Delhi.

Sachar, R. C. and Kapoor, M. (1959a). *In vitro* culture of ovules of *Zephyranthes*. *Phytomorphology* **9**, 147.

Sachar, R. C. and Kapoor, M. (1959b). Gibberellin in the induction of parthenocarpy in *Zephyranthes*. *Plant Physiol.* **34**, 168.

Sanders, M. E. (1950). Development of self and hybrid *Datura* embryos in artificial culture. *Amer. J. Bot.* **37**, 6.

Sanders, M. E. and Burkholder, P. R. (1948). Influence of amino acids on growth of *Datura* embryos in culture. *Proc. nat. Acad. Sci., Wash.* **34**, 516.

Scheitterer, H. (1931). Versuche zur Kultur von Pflanzengeweben. *Arch. exp. Zellforsch.* **12**, 141.

Schmucker, T. (1929). Isolierte Gewebe und Zellen von Blutenpflanzen. *Planta* **9**, 339.

Schroeder, C. A. (1955). Proliferation of mature fruit pericarp tissue slices *in vitro*. *Science* **122**, 601.

Scott, E. G., Carter, J. E. and Street, H. E. (1961). Studies of the growth in culture of excised wheat roots. III. The quantitative and qualitative requirement for light. *Physiol. Plant.* **14**, 725.

Sheat, D. E. G., Fletcher, B. H. and Street, H. E. (1959). Studies on the growth of excised roots. VIII. The growth of excised tomato roots supplied with various sources of nitrogen. *New Phytol.* **58**, 128.

Skinner, J. C. and Street, H. E. (1954). Studies on the growth of excised roots. II. Observations on the growth of excised groundsel roots. *New Phytol.* **53**, 44.

Skoog, F. (1944). Growth and organ formation in tobacco tissue culture. *Amer. J. Bot.* **31**, 19.

Skoog, F. (1950). Chemical control of growth and organ formation in plant tissues. *Année biol.* **26**, 545.

Skoog, F. and Tsui, C. (1948). Chemical control of growth and bud formation in tobacco stem segments and callus cultured *in vitro*. *Amer. J. Bot.* **35**, 782.

Sparrow, A. H., Pond, V. and Kojan, S. (1955). Microsporogenesis in excised anthers of *Trillium erectum* grown in sterile media. *Amer. J. Bot.* **42**, 384.

Steeves, T. A. (1961). A study of the development potentialities of excised leaf primordia in sterile culture. *Phytomorphology* **11**, 346.

Steeves, T. A., Gabriel, H. P. and Steeves, M. W. (1957). Growth in sterile culture of excised leaves of flowering plants. *Science* **126**, 350.

Steeves, T. A. and Sussex, I. M. (1952). *In vitro* culture of a fern callus. *Nature, Lond.* **170**, 672.

Steeves, T. A. and Sussex, I. M. (1957). Studies on the development of excised leaves in sterile culture. *Amer. J. Bot.* **44**, 665.

Steinhart, C. E., Standifer, L. G. Jr. and Skoog, F. (1961). Nutrient requirement for *in vitro* growth of spruce tissue. *Amer. J. Bot.* **48**, 465.

Steward, F. C. and Caplin, S. M. (1951). A tissue culture from potato tuber, the synergistic action of 2·4-D and coconut milk. *Science* **113**, 518.

Steward, F. C. and Caplin, S. M. (1954). The growth of carrot tissue explants and its relation to the growth factors present in coconut milk. *Année Biol.* **30**, 385.

Steward, F. C., Mapes, M. O. and Smith, J. (1958). Growth and organised development of cultured cells. I. Growth and division of freely suspended cells. *Amer. J. Bot.* **45**, 693.

Steward, F. C. and Shantz, E. M. (1955). The chemical induction of growth in plant tissue cultures. *In* "The Chemistry and Mode of Action of Plant Growth Substances" (R. L. Wain and F. Wightman, eds.), pp. 165-186. Butterworth, London.

Steward, F. C. and Shantz, E. M. (1959). The chemical regulation of growth (some substances and extracts which induce growth and morphogenesis). *Annu. Rev. Plant Physiol.* **10**, 379.

Stingl, G. (1907). Experimentelle Studien über die Ernahrung von pflanzenlichen Embryonen. *Flora* **97**, 308.

Straus, J. (1960). Maize endosperm tissue grown *in vitro*. III. Development of a synthetic medium. *Amer. J. Bot.* **47**, 641.

Straus, J. and LaRue, C. D. (1954). Maize endosperm tissue grown *in vitro*. 1. Cultural requirements. *Amer. J. Bot.* **41**, 687.

Street, H. E. (1953). Factors controlling meristematic activity in excised roots. III. Light as a factor in the "location effect" noted with *Lycopersicum esculentum* Hill. *Physiol. Plant.* **6**, 466.

Street, H. E. (1962). The physiology of roots. *In* "Viewpoints in Biology", Vol. 1 (J. D. Carthy and C. L. Duddington, eds.), pp. 1-49, Butterworth, London.

Street, H. E., Carter, J. E., Scott, E. G. and Sutton, D. (1961). Studies of the growth in culture of excised wheat roots. I. The growth effects of an acid-hydrolysed casein and of light. *Physiol. Plant.* **14**, 621.

Street, H. E. and Lowe, J. S. (1950). The carbohydrate nutrition of tomato roots. II. The mechanism of sucrose absorption by excised roots. *Ann. Bot., Lond.* **14**, 307.

Street, H. E., McGonagle, M. P. and Lowe, J. S. (1951). Observations on the "staling" of White's medium by excised roots. *Physiol. Plant.* **4**, 592.

Street, H. E., McGonagle, M. P. and McGregor, S. M. (1952). Observations on the "staling" of White's medium by excised tomato roots. II. Iron availability. *Physiol. Plant.* **5**, 248.

Street, H. E. and McGregor, S. M. (1952). The carbohydrate nutrition of tomato roots. III. The effect of external sucrose concentration on the growth and anatomy of excised roots. *Ann. Bot., Lond.* **16**, 185.

Street, H. E. and Roberts, E. H. (1952). Factors controlling meristematic activity in excised roots. I. Experiments showing the operation of internal factors. *Physiol. Plant.* **5**, 498.

Sussex, I. M. (1958). A morphological and experimental study of leaf development in *Leptopteris hymenophylloides* (A. Rich.) Presl. *Phytomorphology* **8**, 96.

Sussex, I. M. and Clutter, M. E. (1960). A study of the effect of externally supplied sucrose on the morphology of excised fern leaves *in vitro*. *Phytomorphology*, **10**, 87.

Sussex, I. M. and Steeves, T. A. (1953). Growth of excised leaves in sterile culture. *Nature, Lond.* **172**, 624.

Sussex, I. M. and Steeves, T. A. (1958). Experiments on the control of fertility of fern leaves in sterile culture. *Bot. Gaz.* **119**, 203.

Taylor, J. H. (1949). Chromosomes from cultures of excised anthers. *J. Hered.* **40**, 86.

Tepfer, S. S., Greyson, R. I., Karpoff, A. J. and Gerimonte, J. A. (1963). *In vitro* culture of floral buds of *Aquilegia*. Effects of indoleacetic acid and gibberellic acid. *Amer. J. Bot.* **50**, 618.

Thielmann, M. (1924, 1925). Uber Kulturversuche mit spaltoffmingzellen. *Ber. dsch. Bot. Ges.* **42**, 429; *Arch. exp. Zellforsch.* **1**, 66.

Torrey, J. G. (1950). The induction of lateral roots by indoleacetic acid and root decapitation. *Amer. J. Bot.* **37**, 257.

Torrey, J. G. (1952). Effect of light on elongation and branching in pea roots. *Plant Physiol.* **27**, 591.

Torrey, J. G. (1954). The role of vitamins and micronutrient elements in the nutrition of the apical meristem of pea roots. *Plant Physiol.* **29**, 279.

Torrey, J. G. (1957). Cell division in isolated single plant cells *in vitro*. *Proc. nat. Acad. Sci., Wash.* **43**, 887.

Torrey, J. G. (1959). Experimental modification of development in the root. *In* "Cell, Organism and Milieu" (D. Rudnick, ed.), pp. 189-222. Ronald Press, New York.

Torrey, J. G. (1963). Cellular patterns in developing roots. *Symp. Soc. exp. Biol.* **17**, 285. Cambridge University Press.

Torrey, J. G. and Reinert, J. (1961). Suspension culture of higher plant cells in synthetic media. *Plant Physiol.* **36**, 483.

Torrey, J. G. and Shigemura, Y. (1957). Growth and controlled morphogenesis in pea root callus tissue grown in liquid media. *Amer. J. Bot.* **44**, 334.

Tryon, K. (1955). Root tumors on *Nicotiana affinis* seedlings grown *in vitro* on a malt and yeast extract medium. *Amer. J. Bot.* **42**, 604.

Tukey, H. B. (1933). Artificial culture of sweet cherry embryos. *J. Hered.* **24**, 7.

Tukey, H. B. (1934). Artificial culture methods for isolated embryos of deciduous fruits. *Proc. amer. Soc. hort. Sci.* **32**, 313.

Tulecke, W. (1953). A tissue derived from the pollen of *Ginkgo biloba*. *Science* **117**, 599.

Tulecke, W. (1957). The pollen of *Ginkgo biloba* in *in vitro* culture and tissue formation. *Amer. J. Bot.* **44**, 602.

Tulecke, W. (1959). The pollen cultures of C. D. LaRue: a tissue from the pollen of *Taxus*. *Bull. Torrey bot. Club* **86**, 283.

Tulecke, W. (1960). Arginine-requiring strains of tissue obtained from *Ginkgo* pollen. *Plant Physiol.* **35**, 19.

Tulecke, W. and Nickell, L. G. (1959). Production of large amounts of plant tissue by submerged culture. *Science* **130**, 863.

Tulecke, W. and Nickell, L. G. (1960). Methods, problems and results of growing plant cells under submerged conditions. *Trans. N.Y. Acad. Sci.* II, **22**, 196.

Tulecke, W., Weinstein, L. H., Rutner, A. and Laurencot, H. J. Jr. (1961). The biochemical composition of coconut water (coconut milk) as related to its use in plant tissue culture. *Contrib. Boyce Thompson Inst.* **21**, 115.

Ulehla, V. (1928). Vorversuche zur kultur des Pflanzengewebes. *Arch. exp. Zellforsch.* **6**, 370.

Uspenski, E. E. and Uspenskaia, W. J. (1925). Reinkultur und ungeschlectliche Fortplanzing des *Volvox minor* und *Volvox globator* in einer synthetischen Nahrlosung. *Z. Bot.* **17**, 273.

Vasil, I. K. (1959). Cultivation of excised anthers *in vitro*—effect of nucleic acids. *J. exp. Bot.* **10**, 399.

Vasil, I. K. (1962). Physiology of anthers. *In* "Proceedings of the Summer School of Botany", Darjeeling, pp. 477–487. New Delhi.

Vasil, I. K. (1963). Some new experiments with excised anthers. *In* "Plant Tissue and Organ Culture—a Symposium" (P. Maheshwari and N. S. Ranga Swamy, eds.), pp. 230-238. International Society of Plant Morphologists, Delhi.

Warmke, H., Rivera-Perez, E. and Ferrer-Monge, J. A. (1946). The culture of sugar cane embryos *in vitro*. *Inst. trop. Agric. Univ. Puerto Rico 4th Ann. Rep.* 22–23.

Werckmeister, P. (1934). Uber die kunstliche Aufzucht von Embryonen aus Iris Bastardsamen. *Gartenbauwiss* **8**, 607.

Wetmore, R. H. (1954). The use of *in vitro* cultures in the investigation of growth and differentiation in vascular plants. *In* "Abnormal and Pathological Plant Growth", *Brookhaven Symp. Biol.* **6**, 22.

White, P. R. (1931). Plant tissue cultures. The history and present status of the problem. *Arch. exp. Zellforsch.* **10**, 501.

White, P. R. (1932). The influence of some environmental conditions on the growth of excised root tips of wheat seedlings in liquid media. *Plant Physiol.* **7**, 613.

White, P. R. (1933). Concentrations of inorganic ions as related to growth of excised root tips of wheat seedlings. *Plant Physiol.* **8**, 489.

White, P. R. (1934). Potentially unlimited growth of excised tomato root tips in a liquid medium. *Plant Physiol.* **9**, 585.

White, P. R. (1936). Plant tissue cultures. *Bot. Rev.* **2**, 419.

White, P. R. (1937a). Vitamin B_1 in the nutrition of excised tomato roots. *Plant Physiol.* **12**, 803.

White, P. R. (1937b). Amino acids in the nutrition of excised tomato roots. *Plant Physiol.* **12**, 793.

White, P. R. (1937c). A comparison of nutrient salt solutions for the cultivation of excised tomato roots. *Growth* **1**, 182.

White, P. R. (1938a). Accessory salts in the nutrition of excised tomato roots. *Plant Physiol.* **13**, 391.

White, P. R. (1938b). Cultivation of excised roots of dicotyledonous plants. *Amer. J. Bot.* **25**, 348.

White, P. R. (1939). Potentially unlimited growth of excised plant callus in an artificial nutrient. *Amer. J. Bot.* **26**, 59.

White, P. R. (1941). Plant Tissue cultures. *Biol. Rev.* **16**, 34.

White, P. R. (1943a). "A Handbook of Plant Tissue Culture". J. Cattell, Lancaster, Pa.

White, P. R. (1943b). Nutrient deficiency studies with an improved inorganic nutrient for cultivation of excised tomato roots. *Growth* **1**, 53.

White, P. R. (1954). "The Cultivation of Animal and Plant Cells". Thames and Hudson, London.

Wiggans, S. C. (1954). Growth and organ formation in callus tissues derived from *Daucus carota*. *Amer. J. Bot.* **41**, 321.

Wilson, J. K. (1915). Calcium hypochlorite as a seed sterilizer. *Amer. J. Bot.* **2**, 420.

Winkler, H. (1902). Besprechung der Arbeit G. Haberlandt's "Culturversuche mit isolierten Pflanzenzellen". *Bot. Z.* **60**, 262.

Wood, H. N. and Braun, A. C. (1961). Studies on the regulation of certain essential biosynthetic systems in normal and crown-gall tumor. *Proc. nat. Acad. Sci., Wash.* **47**, 1907.

Yager, R. E. (1960). Possible role of pectic enzymes in abscission. *Plant Physiol.* **35**, 157.

Yarwood, C. E. (1946). Detached leaf culture. *Bot. Rev.* **12**, 1.

Ziebur, N. K. R. A. and Brink, R. A. (1951). The stimulative effect of *Hordeum* endosperms on the growth of immature plant embryos *in vitro*. *Amer. J. Bot.* **38**, 253.

CHAPTER 9

The Nutrition and Metabolism of Plant Tissue and Organ Cultures

H. E. STREET

Department of Botany, University College of Swansea, Wales

I. Introduction

In attempting to achieve the growth of plant organs, tissues or free cells in culture, recourse can be made to variation in external chemical factors (which, in a broad sense, can also be termed nutritional factors) and in physical factors such as light, temperature and water-regime. Success or failure has, in most cases, apparently been determined primarily by meeting, or failing to meet, the general and specific nutritional requirements of the living material. In this sense all studies with such cultures are either strictly nutritional studies or an extension of such studies. However, the objective of the research has frequently been to establish actively growing cultures rather than to define, still less to explain, in metabolic terms, the nutritional requirements. In consequence, there is a vast mass of nutritional data scattered through the literature of plant tissue culture, much of which is neither easy to tabulate nor capable of immediate interpretation.

The nutritional requirements of tissue and organ cultures must reflect their synthetic potentialities. However, it is much less clear how far such requirements are directly dependent on the particular conditions of culture and would, in fact, be significantly different under another regime of culture. Hence any interpretation of nutritional interrelationships within the whole organism which are inferred from the data of tissue and organ culture data must be accepted with caution (Street, 1959). For instance, how far can we argue from studies with root cultures to the interpretation of shoot-root relationships in the physiology of the whole plant? It is true that excised cultured roots have the morphology and detailed anatomy of seedling radicles. There is also evidence that, in several cases, they grow in culture at rates similar to those achieved during seedling growth. However, differences between the excised root and the "intact" root can be cited. Excised roots do not normally show secondary thickening and such secondary thickening as does occur in old cultures is abnormal (Dormer and Street, 1948). The roots of tomato seedlings show normal geotropic curvature, bending until their tips are orientated in the direction of gravity. Excised tomato root cultures when orientated at right-angles to gravity show only a "short-lived" curvature which does not continue to bring the root tip vertical, and after this initial curvature the root grows in a straight line even if this direction of growth makes a wide angle to the vertical (Marilyn E. Evans, unpublished). Perhaps even more significant are the differences in chemical composition between the cells of seedling pea roots and cultured excised pea roots reported by Abbott (1963). The apical 10 mm of both kinds of root contained a similar total number of cells but the seedling root tips had higher wet and dry weights and higher contents of total and of organic nitrogen per cell than the tips of the cultured roots. Further, the contents of both deoxyribonucleic acid (DNA) and ribonucleic acid (RNA) per cell were very much lower in the cultured than in the seedling roots.

Similarly, from experiments with callus cultures, examples can be quoted of changes in metabolism or limitations of synthetic ability induced by current techniques of culture. The early investigators expected that tissues derived from chlorophyllous organs would, in culture, possess the faculty of growing without an organic carbon source. Tissue colonies growing *in vitro* and in light have, however, in no case proved autotrophic in relation to carbon. Even where the callus is rich in chlorophyll, its growth, even in high light intensity, apparently still depends upon an external supply of sugar (Hildebrandt, Wilmar, Johns and Riker, 1963). More frequently, tissues in culture become pale green or almost completely depigmented. This indicates that under the conditions of culture, callus cells are, in most cases, deficient in some material or enzymes essential for active chlorophyll synthesis or chloroplast development. The chemical or physical conditions of culture in some way debar the formation of normal photosynthetic cells. This may well be some aspect of the mineral nutrition of cultured cells, for not only are certain metal ions known to be involved in chlorophyll synthesis but evidence is accumulating that the ionic composition of existing culture media may seriously limit the synthetic capacities of cultured plant cells. Further, and in a more general sense, it is also quite clear that, although on many grounds callus cultures can be described as tissue cultures, they correspond neither in the morphology of their cells nor in their physiology to any tissue of the plant body. Callus tissue is species specific in that callus cultures derived from different genomes differ recognizably from one another but the callus cultures of any one species can be derived from many different types of normal tissue cell.

When considering the differentiation of cells in culture we shall refer to the morphological variation occurring in suspension cultures of plant cells. In such cultures the dividing cells rarely resemble the cells of plant meristems and many of the non-dividing cells are quite unlike any type of normal tissue cell. Giant non-dividing cells are frequently encountered; these cells are so large as to indicate that the controlling mechanism which normally brings cell expansion to an end in tissue differentiation *in vivo* has failed to operate *in vitro*.

A further aspect of the study of nutritional requirements is their interpretation in terms of the involvement of individual nutrients in metabolism and in terms of the identification of the deficiencies in metabolic machinery which make the cultured cells dependent upon an external supply of a particular organic metabolite or growth factor.

In their initial successes in culturing excised roots and in establishing callus cultures, the botanists concerned contrasted their defined and relatively simple media with the complex and undefined media being employed by those who were doing contemporary pioneer work on animal Tissue Cultures. However, botanists have subsequently had to make increasing use of complex and undefined media in order to culture roots and callus tissues from a wider range of species, to establish suspensions of growing plant cells, to induce continuing division in single cells and finally to culture immature embryos. Informed discussion of the nutritive requirements of many plant cultures, therefore, now has to await positive identification of the important growth factors and other biologically active constituents of such supplements as coconut milk, other liquid endosperms and similar complex solutions of plant origin, or until the use of such supplements has been superseded by the development of equally effective media compounded entirely of purified chemicals.

Certain cells of higher plants are adapted for the absorption of inorganic ions through their external surfaces. This applies to the cells of the piliferous layer of the root, including the root hair cells. Many of the nutritive elements which thereby enter the plant body as inorganic ions are, however, transported to other cells, for example to the cells of the apical meristems in organic combination and via the protoplasmic continuity of plant tissues. Sugars arise *within* the photosynthetic cells and are then transported to the non-photosynthetic tissues via the symplast, including the phloem. Cells of organ and tissue cultures, and cells growing in suspension cultures or plated on agar are presented, not only with inorganic ions but also with sugars, amino acids, vitamins, growth hormones and other growth factors. Further, these substances must be presented at sufficiently high external concentrations to permit rates of uptake compatible with active growth and development of the cultures. In consequence, not only can cell permeability be profoundly affected but it seems reasonable to suppose that "non-physiological" concentrations of biologically active substances may frequently result at certain sites in the cell and particularly in the hyaloplasm. In consequence, nutritional studies can be complicated or even vitiated by the toxic actions of externally applied cell constituents even at concentrations below the mean cellular level.

In assessing the value of plant cultures for the study of aspects of cell and tissue nutrition, the considerations outlined above are on the debit side. However, on the credit side, plant cultures do offer certain unique opportunities for studies in plant nutrition. The sterile nature of the cultures allows the feeding of organic molecules which would suffer change in the presence of micro-organisms and it enables us to detect both inorganic and organic substances liberated by the cultures into the surrounding medium. The closed nature of the system and the absence of micro-organisms permits the construction of balance sheets showing the total chemical changes occurring in the tissue/medium system. By utilizing large volumes of medium or one of the techniques permitting intermittent or continuous renewal of the culture medium, organic compounds can be applied at low concentrations without significant depletion of their supply by absorption. Further, in such experiments other cultural variables both nutritive and environmental can be modified at will. Thus these culture techniques open up the possibility of defining the special nutritive requirements and of studying the individual metabolisms of the separate cells, tissues and organs of the multicellular plant; no other equally effective methods of approach to such problems have yet been discovered. In such studies the metabolic and structural changes which follow manipulation of nutritive and environmental factors can be followed.

In view of the above considerations and particularly the mass of published data bearing upon the nutrition of plant cultures, much of it albeit of a fragmentary nature, it has been thought most profitable to consider a selected series of examples chosen either because they illustrate the potentialities of the Tissue-Culture technique or because they seem to be very promising starting points for future significant advances in knowledge.

II. Aspects of Inorganic Nutrition

A. INTRODUCTION

Some consideration has been given in Chapter 8 (p. 497 *et seq.*) to the development of suitable solutions of the macronutrient cations and anions for the active growth of callus and suspension cultures. Studies initiated by Burkholder and Nickell (1949) and by Heller (1953), and continued by later workers, have led to the development of culture solutions with enhanced levels of nitrogen, phosphorus and potassium and reduced levels of calcium as compared with the original formulations by Gautheret (1939) and White (1943a). These fortified media, although usually developed in an effort to enhance the growth of a particular plant tissue, have proved to have wider usefulness. Before the development of such solutions many callus tissues, although capable of continuous culture, had very low rates of growth as was underlined when growth rate was considered in terms of the probable mean generation time of the constituent cells. The newly developed inorganic salt solutions have led to the availability of culture media which now permit the rapid growth of certain normal callus tissues and of the suspensions of cells and cell aggregates which can be developed from them.

One interesting aspect of the physiological activity of these fortified media is illustrated by work in Braun's laboratory on the different cultural requirements of normal as against crown-gall tumour tissues (Wood and Braun, 1961; Braun and Wood, 1962) (see also p. 565). These studies not only contribute to our understanding of the changes which occur when a normal cell is transformed into a tumour cell, but have wider implications relating to the control of the biosynthetic activities of plant cells. Furthermore, in so far as they reveal that requirements for particular organic metabolites may be the outcome of suboptimal conditions of inorganic nutrition, they are relevant to the problems of the resistance of many organs and tissues to continuous growth in culture, as discussed more fully in Section IX, p. 599.

The need to provide in plant culture media those macronutrient elements which are known to be required for the nutrition of the whole plant was established by the pioneer work of White (1943a) with root cultures and of Heller (1953) with callus cultures. Although deficiencies of most of these elements can be rapidly developed in plant cultures, the Tissue-Culture technique has not, with the exception of work on nitrogen (p. 542), contributed anything substantial to our knowledge of the uptake of these macronutrient elements and their involvement in metabolism. Work with the micronutrient elements, however, provides a more critical test of the potential value of plant tissue and organ cultures for studies in the field of mineral nutrition and hence it is to such studies that attention is now directed.

It has been argued (Street, 1956) that sterile root cultures are particularly suited to studies in inorganic nutrition on the following grounds. Root clones grown under rigorously controlled environmental conditions provide very uniform and actively growing experimental material. The purification of the synthetic liquid media employed does not present any special problems which have not already been tackled in work on the micronutrient requirements of fungi and other micro-organisms. The fact that growth proceeds rapidly from a small inoculum reduces carry-over effects and permits the rapid development of deficiencies. The aseptic conditions of culture exclude dust and contamination with micro-organisms and permit the feeding of organic substances whose biosynthesis may be controlled by enzymes for which micronutrient elements are essential. This line of reasoning has, however, been strongly criticized by Skoog (1956) who stated "I think that as far as plants are concerned, the Tissue-Culture method is singularly unsuitable for the study of mineral nutrition and that its unsatisfactory nature is clearly demonstrated by the record of recent achievements." An outline of some recent studies of the micronutrients required by cultured roots may enable the reader to assess these arguments by the acid test of experimental investigation.

B. IRON

Brown and Possingham (1957) have examined the effects of iron deficiency on the growth and metabolism of excised pea roots. Iron deficiency resulted in a cessation of cell division and in a loss of the cyanide-sensitive component of respiration. The cyanide-sensitive component of the respiration of plant tissues is usually regarded as being mediated by the cytochrome system and the work of James and Boulter (1955), with barley roots, indicates that this system is the main pathway of terminal oxidation in the root apex but is replaced in importance by ascorbic acid oxidase as the cells mature. Protein synthesis in the iron-deficient pea roots continued unimpaired for some time after the cessation of cell division but the newly synthesized protein accumulated in the mature cells adjacent to the apex, probably due to a lack of utilization of amino acids at the apical meristem. Subsequently, Possingham and Brown (1958) studied the intracellular incorporation of ^{59}Fe by autoradiography and demonstrated that iron is incorporated into the nuclei of the root cells to a much higher concentration than into the surrounding cytoplasm. These findings therefore implicated iron as critically important to the functioning of dividing cells and suggested that this might indicate that it is not only essential for the functioning of respiratory enzymes but also has a special role in intranuclear metabolism.

More recently, Abbott (1963), also working with cultured pea roots, has confirmed the importance of iron for the maintenance of cell divisions in the root apex and reported that iron deficiency results in enhanced levels of free amino acids and of DNA but in a reduced content of RNA. Feeding experiments with tritiated uridine indicated a reduced level of RNA synthesis in the iron-deficient cells and a confining of this RNA synthesis to the nucleoli. From these findings it was suggested that iron deficiency blocks RNA synthesis thus leading to reduced levels of RNA in both nucleus and cytoplasm and to an associated breakdown of protein synthesis and blocking of mitosis.

C. MANGANESE

That manganese is necessary for the growth of cultured tomato roots was demonstrated by Hannay and Street (1954). In these studies it was found that, when either manganese or molybdenum was omitted from the purified medium, then growth and survival of the roots could be significantly enhanced by raising the concentration of the other element. Further additions of relatively high concentrations of manganese (3 p.p.m. or higher), although beneficial in the absence of molybdenum, were markedly inhibitory in the presence of even 0·0001 p.p.m. molybdenum and this inhibition was intensified by a further increase in the molybdenum level. These observations are of interest primarily because they cannot be satisfactorily explained in terms of present knowledge of the activation of enzyme systems by these two elements.

Hannay, Fletcher and Street (1959) have also exposed an interesting interaction between manganese and magnesium in the growth of excised tomato roots. The deleterious effect of high manganese is alleviated by a further addition of magnesium and even at low concentrations of manganese the ratio of manganese to magnesium must be below a certain value for maximum growth rate. The importance of an appropriate manganese:magnesium ratio for a high growth rate may be because manganese can replace magnesium in a number of enzyme systems, with efficiencies ranging from less than 30% up to nearly double that of magnesium, and because certain combinations of these two metals may, through competitive interactions, differentially affect the activity of enzymes and disturb metabolism (Hewitt, 1957).

Abbott (1963), in work with excised pea roots, has demonstrated a failure of cell expansion and a consequent disruption of vascular differentiation resulting from manganese deficiency. The cells which fail to expand contain a high concentration of free amino acids and do not show the increase in protein content normally associated with cell expansion. Here again, as in iron deficiency, the RNA content of the cells was depressed. One possible action of manganese is that it is involved in the linkage of RNA to proteins which is essential for the development of the protein synthesizing centres of the cell, for Lyttleton (1960) has shown that manganese deficiency prevents the development of ribonucleoprotein particles in wheat embryos and that magnesium cannot replace manganese in this function. Further study, along these lines, of the role of manganese could lead to a better understanding of the determinative processes in cell expansion.

D. BORON

Neales (1959), by avoiding the use of borosilicate glassware, demonstrated boron deficiency in cultured flax roots. More recently, adopting the same technique, Neales (1964) has shown that excised tomato roots have an appreciable requirement for boron and that boron deficiency leading to cessation of growth can be developed after 3 days in the boron-free culture medium. In both these cases Neales found that a similar level of boron in the culture solution was required to prevent boron deficiency in seedlings grown in water cultures and in excised root cultures. The evidence strongly indicates that boron deficiency affects both cell division and cell expansion in roots (Odhnoff, 1957; Whittington, 1959) and the symptons of boron-deficient roots simulate those of roots inhibited by supra-optimal concentrations of auxin. One possibility therefore is that the concentration of boron may determine the level of the natural inhibitors of IAA-oxidase or other auxin-controlling systems.

Gauch and Dugger (1953, 1954) considered that a primary effect of boron was its promotion of sugar transport. The development of a lethal boron deficiency in cultures bathed in sucrose points, however, to the necessity for boron in aspects of metabolism other than sugar translocation.

E. IODINE

White (1938a) reported that the iodide ion was beneficial to the growth of excised tomato roots and subsequently included potassium iodide in his basic root-culture medium (White, 1943a). The beneficial effect of iodide was confirmed by Hannay (1956) who found that in its absence growth declined and, after the third weekly transfer, became very low and variable. Up to half of the tomato root cultures had completely ceased growth after three passages in iodide-free medium and did not resume growth on transfer to the complete medium. These findings point to the possibility that iodine must be added to the list of *essential* nutrient elements (the iodine deficiency reported was induced in a medium rich in chloride). The optimum concentration was 0·5 p.p.m. iodine as iodide, and the need for iodine could be met by either potassium iodide, or methylene iodide or iodoacetate. Reference is made later (p. 587) to the importance of iodide for the growth of *Vinca rosea* tissue and the ability of 1,3-di-iodotyrosine to meet this requirement. These observations fit in with the evidence that residues of iodoamino acids occur in plant proteins (Fowden, 1959).

F. MOLYBDENUM, COPPER AND ZINC

The need for molybdenum by root cultures was demonstrated by Hannay and Street (1954) and it was shown that, for a high level of growth, molybdenum was required even when ammonium or organic nitrogen compounds were used as the nitrogen sources (Hannay *et al.*, 1959). This clearly points to the involvement of molybdenum in activating some system additional to nitrate reductase. There is also strong but not conclusive evidence pointing to the necessity of copper and zinc for cultured roots and callus tissues.

This brief survey indicates that critical deficiencies of micronutrient elements can be rapidly induced under the techniques of sterile plant tissue culture and that such cultures are beginning to reveal interesting aspects of the roles of these elements. The view is reiterated that this relatively neglected aspect of the nutrition of plant cultures can be a rewarding field of research.

III. Aspects of Nitrogen Nutrition and Metabolism

It is possible to trace three main themes in the many studies which have been published on the nitrogen nutrition and metabolism of plant tissue and organ cultures: (1) studies of the ability of inorganic and organic nitrogenous substances to meet the nitrogen requirements of cultured tissues and organs; (2) studies of the effects on growth, both stimulatory and inhibitory, of externally applied amino acids and related compounds; (3) comparative studies of protein synthesis and turnover in quiescent cells and in cells induced to undergo active growth and division in culture.

A. THE ASSIMILATION OF INORGANIC NITROGEN

White's basic medium contains nitrate (45 mg NO_3-N/l) as the nitrogen source, the only other nitrogen-containing substances being the B vitamins, which are present only in trace amounts, and glycine (3 mg/l). Glycine is not an essential nutrient (White, 1939), is not stimulatory to the growth of most excised root cultures, including those of many tomato strains, and in those cases where its presence does enhance root growth it does not function as the primary source of nitrogen. This implies that those root cultures so far successfully established are able to reduce nitrate and thus synthesize their essential amino acids and other nitrogenous compounds. In line with this, Vaidyanathan and Street (1959a) have demonstrated that excised tomato root extracts in the presence of added nicotinamide adenine dinucleotide (NAD) and flavin mononucleotide (FMN) can effect the reduction of nitrate, nitrite, hyponitrite and hydroxylamine. Work with molybdenum-deficient roots indicates the necessity of this element for the reduction of nitrate to nitrite (Hannay and Street, 1954). The reduction beyond nitrite is activated by manganese. The excised tomato-root extracts also contain a thermolabile system for which ascorbate and iron are co-factors and which *in vitro* also effects nitrate reduction. Roots cultured with glutamine as the source of nitrogen have very low nitrate- and nitrite-reducing activities as compared with nitrate-grown roots indicating that, as in other plant tissues, the nitrate-reducing system of enzymes is formed adaptively in response to nitrate feeding.

Maintained high levels of growth of excised tomato roots can be obtained with nitrate as the nitrogen source over the pH range 4·0–7·2 when FeEDTA is used as the source of iron and solid buffers are incorporated (Sheat, Fletcher and Street, 1959). The growth is again improved at pH values close to neutrality if White's medium is further modified by reduction of its magnesium concentration to one-tenth and by lowering the manganese addition (Standard addition = 1·67 p.p.m. Mn) to 0·01 p.p.m. Mn and the zinc addition (Standard addition = 0·6 p.p.m. Zn) to 0·1 p.p.m. Zn (Hannay *et al.*, 1959).

When the nitrate of White's medium is replaced by ammonium at equivalent nitrogen concentration, the medium does not support the growth of excised tomato roots (Robbins and Schmidt, 1938) or groundsel roots (Skinner and Street, 1954). Ammonium has also been reported to be ineffective as a nitrogen source for a number of callus tissues (Riker and Gutsche, 1948; Burkholder and Nickell, 1949; Heller, 1953, 1954). The many comparative studies of ammonium and nitrate as sources of nitrogen, undertaken prior to work with tissue and organ cultures, have revealed interesting differences between species and emphasized the influence of environmental factors (Street and Sheat, 1958). However, no general understanding of the metabolic events which limit the value of ammonium as a nitrogen source has emerged.

Addition of ammonium ions to nitrate-containing medium does

not inhibit the growth of excised roots; a satisfactory root culture medium can be prepared with ammonium nitrate (Robbins and Schmidt, 1938; Street, McGonagle and Lowe, 1951; Skinner and Street, 1954). Furthermore, the addition of ammonium ions to nitrate-containing root culture medium reverses the rise in pH which otherwise accompanies root growth, strongly indicating that ammonium ions are absorbed and assimilated under these conditions.

Robbins and Schmidt (1938) suggested that there might be an oxygen deficiency in White's medium when the nitrogen was supplied as ammonium ions but work in our laboratory has shown no beneficial effect of forced aeration. Raising the sucrose concentration or adding a more complex vitamin mixture, including biotin (Winzler, Burk and Du Vigneaud, 1944), were also without significant effect.

A contrast between the pH optima for growth with ammonium as against nitrate as the nitrogen source has been reported many times in work on the nitrogen nutrition of whole plants (Nightingale, 1937, 1948; Street, 1949). In general, ammonium is only effective at pH values close to neutrality. The pH of White's medium is at pH 4·5–4·8 and if this pH is increased above pH 5·2 iron deficiency results (Street, McGonagle and McGregor, 1952). Further, White's medium is very weakly buffered and drifts rapidly towards neutrality with nitrate and even more rapidly towards acidity with ammonium as nitrogen source. It was in order to study the relationship between pH and growth in ammonium-containing media that FeEDTA was introduced as a source of iron and a series of sparingly soluble buffers was elaborated (Sheat *et al.*, 1959). With these technical modifications, it was possible to achieve a high rate of growth at a pH of 6·8–7·2 with ammonium as the sole source of nitrogen and when, in addition, the manganese concentration was lowered to 0·01 p.p.m., continuous culture of excised tomato roots was also achieved with this nitrogen source (Hannay *et al.*, 1959). Further, by stabilizing the pH at 6·0 it was possible to demonstrate the utilization of nitrite as a source of nitrogen for excised root growth provided the nitrite was supplied at low concentration (5 mg/l nitrite-N).

The activity of ammonium as a source of nitrogen for the growth of excised root decreases very rapidly as the pH is reduced below 6·8. Over the whole range of pH 4·0–6·4 a very low growth rate is recorded in the presence of ammonium and this further declines on subculture; it is this inability of plant tissues to grow satisfactorily with ammonium supplied within this pH range that has eluded satisfactory explanation. Various workers have postulated that the uptake of ammonium is adversely affected at pH values below neutrality. However, from studies with excised tomato roots there is evidence that both nitrate and ammonium are absorbed at similar and high rates over the pH range 5–7 and that a high proportion of the nitrogen is absorbed as ammonium from ammonium-nitrate media at pH 4–5 (media in which, incidently, high rates of growth occur). At pH values 4–5 a medium containing the standard nitrogen addition in the form of a nitrate to ammonium ratio of 1:10 is almost as effective in promoting root growth as the standard nitrate medium.

These results suggest that over a wide pH range most of the nitrogen requirement of the root tissues can be provided as ammonium, but that, except over a very narrow pH range, the roots have a requirement for nitrate, presumably because nitrate is the most effective precursor of some essential metabolite(s). This concept is supported by some recent work with excised wheat roots where it can be shown that, despite the high content of soluble organic nitrogen established in the absence of nitrate, a supply of nitrate is, nevertheless, essential to obtain the marked enhancement of growth and protein synthesis which can occur in response to illumination of the cultures (Sutton, Scott and Street, 1961; Derbyshire and Street, 1964).

This hypothesis suggests that the pH range over which ammonium functions as an effective sole source of nitrogen might be extended by supplying, simultaneously, organic nitrogenous substances whose availability in metabolism is otherwise limiting to growth. Some interest, therefore, attaches to the finding that although amino-acid mixtures based upon analyses of casein hydrolysate are ineffective as sole nitrogen sources for excised tomato roots, nevertheless, their addition to an ammonium-containing medium stimulates growth very significantly at pH values above 5·3. Further, a simplified mixture containing the basic amino acids (arginine, histidine, lysine, phenylalanine and tyrosine) was equally effective in enhancing growth under these same conditions (Street, Hughes and Lewis, 1960). In this connection it is recalled that Viets, Moxon and Whitehead (1946) noted that the marked increase in amino-acid nitrogen after ammonium feeding of corn plants was not paralleled by an increase in the basic amino acids so that the proportion of basic to total amino acids was low as compared with that of nitrate-fed plants and as compared with the proportion of basic amino acids in corn proteins. Weissman (1959) has also shown that the relative concentrations of the free amino acids in wheat seedlings are differentially affected by nitrate and ammonium and that this is reflected in the amino-acid composition of the total protein synthesized. This suggests that one consequence of ammonium feeding under conditions of suboptimal external pH may be the development of an imbalance in the amino-acid pool and particularly in the relatively low level of certain of the basic amino acids.

Two aspects of these findings call for comment. Firstly, they are apparently not the complete story because no supplement of organic nitrogen has yet been found which will permit active growth of excised tomato roots in ammonium medium at pH values below 5·3. Secondly, external pH would not be expected to affect the rate of synthesis of amino acids directly unless the sites of synthesis in the root cells are very weakly buffered or are readily accessible to the external ions by diffusion (i.e. are in the "free space"). Two alternative and perhaps more likely explanations of the effect of external pH are (1) that ammonium, at pH values towards the acid end of the physiological range, interferes with the uptake of some other essential inorganic nutrient(s), or (2) that the ammonium ions or excess hydrogen ions or a combination of both factors enhance, to a critical extent, the leakage of certain essential amino acids or other essential nitrogenous metabolites from the root cells into the external medium. So far many attempts to improve growth in ammonium media of pH below 5·3 by altering the absolute and relative concentrations of inorganic ions in the media have met with no success. On the other hand, Melhuish (1962) has shown that amino acids are released from living root cells into the medium in which the roots are growing, that the release is enhanced at pH 4·5 as compared with pH 7·0 and that the release is differentially affected by nitrate and ammonium ions. Further work along these lines in which balance sheets are constructed to show the net total gains of the separate amino acids arising during nitrate and ammonium feeding of root cultures and the distribution of each amino acid between newly synthesized protein, the amino-acid pool of the cells and the external medium should indicate definitively how far the lack of growth in ammonium-containing media of unfavourable pH is to be explained in terms of limitation of protein synthesis by the lack of certain amino acids. The important subject of the release of metabolites from plant cultures into their culture media will be further discussed in Section VIII, A, p. 591.

B. THE ASSIMILATION OF ORGANIC NITROGEN

Complex mixtures of amino acids or natural products rich in amino acids such as peptone, casein hydrolysate, and yeast extracts have been shown to be capable of meeting the nitrogen requirements of sunflower crown-gall tissue (Riker and Gutsche, 1948), cultured maize-endosperm tissue (Straus and LaRue, 1954; Tamaoki and Ullstrup, 1958), mature embryos of *Hordeum* (Harris, 1956), immature *Datura* embryos (Sanders and Burkholder, 1948) and immature embryos of *Capsella bursa-pastoris* (Rijven, 1952). For many tissues, however, complex mixtures of amino acids although rarely inhibitory to growth are usually poor as the only sources of nitrogen. This may indicate that the absorbed amino acids are not actively deaminated in the tissue cells, or that their deamination does not readily yield ammonium to the sites involved in the synthesis of essential metabolites from ammonium which is fed directly or arises from nitrate reduction.

When amino acid mixtures are ineffective as sole sources of nitrogen they are often reported to enhance growth when added as a supplement to a medium already containing nitrate. Thus Paris, Duhamet and Goris (1954), working with *Scorzonera* crown-gall tissue, reported that whilst individual amino acids were not stimulatory, a mixture of eleven amino acids dramatically increased the rate of proliferation. Similar stimulatory effects of amino-acid mixtures on the growth of carrot callus and Jerusalem artichoke tissue were reported by Nétien and Beauchesne (1954) and in sunflower tissues by Nitsch and Nitsch (1957). Shantz and Steward (1952) have also emphasized that the growth-promoting activity of fractions isolated from coconut milk when tested in their carrot system is very markedly enhanced by simultaneously feeding casein hydrolysate. Goldacre and Unt (1961), working with excised clover roots, showed that either casein hydrolysate, or a mixture of amino acids designed to represent the hydrolysate, stimulated main axis growth, lateral production and dry-weight increase of the cultures. Similarly, Sutton *et al.* (1961) showed that the activity of hydrolysed casein, in increasing the growth of cultured wheat roots, was primarily because it provided a balanced mixture of amino acids.

In a number of cases where supplements containing a mixture of amino acids have functioned as sources of nitrogen or have enhanced the growth of cultures simultaneously supplied with inorganic nitrogen, it has been possible to show that their activity could be reproduced or surpassed by a single amino acid or amino-acid amide. Thus Riker and Gutsche (1948) found that the following single amino acids, although inferior to nitrate, could support the growth of sunflower crown-gall tissue: alanine, glycine, arginine, glutamic acid, aspartic acid and asparagine. Frank, Riker and Dye (1951) showed that the callus tissue derived from tumours of the hybrid *Nicotiana langsdorffii* × *N. glauca* would grow at a slow rate when their nitrogen was supplied as glutamic acid or as alanine. Nickell (1950a) and Nickell and Burkholder (1950) found that aspartic acid enhanced the growth of sorrel-virus tumour tissue simultaneously supplied with nitrate, and Sandstedt and Skoog (1960) reported that the stimulating activity of a complex amino-acid mixture on the growth of tobacco tissue was due to its content of glutamic and aspartic acids. Nitsch and Nitsch (1957) reported that Jerusalem artichoke tuber tissue grew as well with alanine, γ-aminobutyric acid, glutamic acid, aspartic acid, glutamine or urea as with nitrate during a 21-day growth period. Glutamic acid and arginine have been reported to increase the growth of cultured *Asparagus* stem tips (Galston, 1948). Rijven (1952) reported that glutamine was superior to a complex mixture of amino acids and markedly superior to asparagine as a sole source of nitrogen for the growth of immature *Capsella* embryos. Street *et al.* (1960) found that, as organic nitrogen sources for the growth of excised tomato roots glutamine was the most effective, urea was next in effectiveness; asparagine, glutamic acid, aspartic acid, arginine and casein hydroysate were relatively poor, and all other amino acids tested were inactive. In contrast to glutamine, ammonium hydrogen glutamate was no more active than glutamic acid. Skinner and Street (1954) found arginine, ornithine, citrulline and lysine to support the growth of excised groundsel roots when supplied as sources of nitrogen. Addition of any one of these amino acids or of urea enhanced the growth of groundsel roots simultaneously supplied with nitrate. Harris (1959) found arginine and urea to be effective nitrogen sources for the growth of excised roots of red clover, and Burkholder, Castle and Smith (1948) found these two compounds each able to meet the nitrogen requirements of cultured protonemata and gametophytes of the moss *Catharinea undulata* (see also Chap. 8, p. 501).

The references above to the effectiveness of the dicarboxylic amino acids and their amides and to alanine suggests that the utilization of these compounds may arise from their activity in transamination reactions and to the ability of glutamic acid, into which they can be converted, to undergo oxidative deamination. The finding that L-glutamine is a particularly effective nitrogen source for excised tomato roots and for *Capsella* suggests that it should be more widely tested as a nitrogen source for plant cultures when aseptically incorporated into media of neutral pH. Its effectiveness is of interest in view of the large body of evidence for its central role in nitrogen metabolism and its possible role as an immediate nitrogen donor for protein synthesis (Steward and Street, 1947). In this connection it is interesting that the requirement of certain bacteria and of mammalian cells in tissue culture for glutamine cannot be met by supplying glutamic acid (Archibald, 1945; Street, 1949; Eagle, 1959), that glutamine has certain specific roles in biosynthesis (Ory, Hood and Lyman, 1954; Eagle, 1959) and that there is evidence for a specific glutamine transaminase (Meister, 1957). Further, certain tissues absorb and translocate glutamine more rapidly than other related compounds (Meister, 1957) and, in contrast to asparagine, its absorption does not seem to be associated with hydrolysis of the amide group (Fridhandler and Quastel, 1955).

Evidence for the operation of an "ornithine cycle" (Krebs and Henseleit, 1932) in plants came first from studies of X ray-induced mutants of *Neurospora* (Srb and Horowitz, 1944) and *Penicillium notatum* (Bonner, 1946). The finding (Arnow, Oleson and Williams, 1953) that *Chlorella vulgaris* is able to utilize as its sole nitrogen source, arginine, ornithine, citrulline or urea, and the studies of Skinner and Street (1954) on the nitrogen nutrition of groundsel roots, indicate strongly the operation of this cycle in these organisms. It seems likely that in functioning as sole nitrogen sources the amino acids of the "ornithine cycle" act through urea or by yielding ammonia.

The ability of urea to function as a nitrogen source has usually been explained by supposing that urease hydrolyses it to carbon dioxide and ammonia and undoubtedly this enzyme is widely distributed in plants (Fosse, 1916; Damodoran and Sivaramakrishnan, 1937). However, Shantz and Steward (1959), who found that urea could act in lieu of the most effective combination of inorganic nitrogen and amino acids for the growth of carrot tissue, have questioned this simple explanation. They point, for instance, to the different paths of carbon resulting from feeding ^{14}C-urea as against feeding $^{14}CO_2$ plus ammonia (Pollard, Bollard and Steward, 1957), to the evidence suggestive of the formation from urea of the carbamyl group which may then participate in a number of transfer reactions and to the possible participation of urea in purine and pyrimidine synthesis.

C. AMINO-ACID INHIBITIONS AND ANTAGONISMS

Reference has been made above to the fact that many single amino acids are quite inactive as sources of nitrogen, even where balanced amino-acid mixtures or other amino acids may either function as effective sole nitrogen sources or enhance the growth of tissues simultaneously supplied with nitrate. It must also be emphasized that such amino acids are often very inhibitory to the growth of cultured plant tissues and organs at concentrations well below those which would be needed to supply an adequate amount of nitrogen. For instance, the linear growth of excised tomato roots cultured in modified White's medium, is 50% inhibited by additions of less than 1 mg/l of L-methionine, DL-norvaline, L-norleucine, or hydroxy-L-proline and by additions of less than 5 mg/l of L-phenylalanine, L-isoleucine, L-leucine and L-threonine. L-Valine is slightly less active as a growth inhibitor of excised tomato roots, causing 50% inhibition within the concentration range 5–10 mg/l (Street *et al.*, 1960). Similar inhibitions of the growth of tissue and organ cultures and of aseptically cultured seedlings following incorporation of single amino acids into culture solutions have been reported by many other workers (White, 1937b; Steinberg, 1947; Spoerl, 1948; Riker and Gutsche, 1948; Gorham, 1950; Fries, 1951; Harris, 1956; David, 1958; Steward, Pollard, Patchett and Witkop, 1958b). In these studies the amino acids reported above to be inhibitory to the growth of tomato roots have regularly proved to be among the most toxic.

Three aspects of the growth-inhibitory activity of singly applied amino acids call for comment. Firstly, Nitsch and Nitsch (1957) have drawn attention to the general use of the DL-forms of the amino acids in most earlier studies. Both their results and those reported by Street *et al.* (1960) emphasize that D- and L-isomers differ markedly not only in their inhibitory activity but also in their ability to function as sources of nitrogen. Thus, for excised tomato roots, the D-isomers completely lack the activities of L-aspartic acid and of L-asparagine as nitrogen sources, and the D-forms of histidine, isoleucine, leucine and norleucine are all less inhibitory than the natural L-isomers, whereas the reverse is the case for the isomers of alanine and serine. The second aspect, also frequently not considered in earlier work, is that the inhibitory activity is nearly always more marked at neutral than at acid pH values, probably because of the greater uptake at neutral pH. The third and most interesting aspect is that the inhibitory activity of individual amino acids can be reduced by adding simultaneously one or more additional amino acids. This phenomenon of antagonism between pairs of amino acids or within simple mixtures was noted by Sanders and Burkholder (1948) and studied in some detail by Harris (1956) using as a bioassay the growth of roots of cultured oat embryos. Often very dramatic antagonisms between otherwise very inhibitory amino acids could be demonstrated. Harris revealed particularly marked antagonisms between L-phenylalanine and L-tyrosine, between L-leucine and DL-valine, between DL-isoleucine and DL-valine and between L-arginine and L-lysine. A similar strong antagonism between L-proline and the very inhibitory hydroxy-L-proline was noted by Fries (1951) when measuring root growth of decotylized pea seedlings and by Steward *et al.* (1958b) studying the growth of phloem explants from carrot. Similar and often quite specific interactions between amino acids in their effects on growth have also been frequently reported from work with bacteria and fungi (Woolley, 1952).

The most marked antagonisms are clearly between amino acids of similar structure and often known to be related in metabolism. There are, however, less specific antagonisms in which a number of relatively non-inhibitory amino acids mitigate the inhibitions caused by any one of a number of other amino acids. These two types of interaction may have different explanations. Thus the observation by Steinberg (1947) that tobacco seedlings inhibited in growth by single amino acids often show symptoms very similar to those of mineral deficiencies and the finding by Riggs, Coyne and Christensen (1954) that external glycine and tryptophane can promote excessive loss of potassium and gain of sodium by animal cells suggest that single amino acids may have unfavourable effects on cell permeability. Another concept (see Martin, 1951) is that protein synthesis and normal metabolism are dependent upon a proper and delicate balance between all the amino acids within the cell and that this is disturbed by the feeding of individual amino acids. This concept implies that a "balanced" mixture of inorganic ions or amino acids is one which promotes the establishment of favourable absolute and relative concentrations of its constituents within the cells. The quite highly specific antagonisms between certain amino acids are, however, more likely to involve competition at specific enzyme sites.

The interesting mutual antagonisms between leucine, isoleucine and valine reported by Gladstone (1939), working with *B. anthracis,* and by Harris, working with oat roots, are possibly to be explained by (1) the common transaminase which catalyses amino transfer between any two of the following: isoleucine, valine, leucine, norvaline and glutamic acid (Rudman and Meister, 1953), or by (2) the probable existence of a single enzyme promoting the dehydration of the dihydroxy-acid precursors of both isoleucine and valine (Myers and Adelberg, 1954). Similarly, Steward *et al.* (1958b), in considering the antagonisms between L-proline and hydroxy-L-proline have put forward the hypothesis that hydroxy-L-proline does not normally exist free in carrot cells and that it is a competitive inhibitor of the incorporation of free proline into protein. The hydroxyproline content of a protein fraction actively synthesized by dividing carrot cells is then interpreted as arising not by utilization of the hydroxyamino acid in protein synthesis but by the oxidation of certain already incorporated proline residues. This subject of amino-acid antagonisms has been considered here because tissue and organ cultures are particularly well adapted to the intensive study of this phenomenon and because the author agrees with Meister (1957) that such mutual antagonisms between natural amino acids may represent an important physiological mechanism for the control of growth and metabolism.

A phenomenon exposed in the study of the nitrogen nutrition of sunflower crown-gall tissue (Riker and Gutsche, 1948), although still inexplicable (Eberts, Burris and Riker, 1954), is worthy of further study. Glutamic and aspartic acids and alanine, when supplied as single amino acids, became sharply inhibitory at about 0·0001 M and within the concentration range from this point up to 0·002 M are very inhibitory. With increase in amino-acid concentration above 0·002 the growth inhibition markedly decreases only to reappear at still higher concentrations. By plotting growth against concentration they obtained what was described as a two maximum curve, the maxima (points of minimum inhibition) being separated by the intervening range at which inhibition was very marked. David (1954) working with excised roots of lucerne similarly noted that some amino acids (glutamic acid, lysine and proline) were more inhibitory at low than at higher concentrations, and Sutton *et al.* (1961) found an intermediate range of concentration over which tryptophane was inhibitory to main axis growth and lateral development of cultured wheat roots although at higher concentration it enhanced both of these aspects of root growth.

D. PROTEIN SYNTHESIS AND TURNOVER IN QUIESCENT AND ACTIVELY GROWING CELLS

Gregory and Sen (1937) from studies of the relationship of mineral nutrition to the metabolism of barley leaves concluded that the respiration of the leaves was geared to a "protein cycle" and that the degradative side of this cycle yielded amino acids by protein breakdown and that these amino acids were then the source of a significant part of the carbon dioxide liberated in respiration. Evidence interpreted as supporting the operation of such a cycle was also obtained by Steward, Stout and Preston (1940) working with potato tuber slices whose metabolism had been activated by washing and aeration. This general concept of a protein cycle was also strongly supported by the pioneer studies of Schoenheimer (1942) who, by feeding animal cells with amino acids whose amino groups were labelled with ^{15}N, obtained evidence that the body proteins are continually breaking down and being resynthesized. More recently, interesting new data bearing upon this question of how far respiration is tied in with the operation of a cyclic synthesis and degradation of protein has been obtained by Steward and his co-workers in their comparative studies of the nitrogenous composition and carbon metabolism of carrot explants placed under conditions of culture favourable or unfavourable to their rapid growth.

Steward, Thompson and Pollard (1958c) showed that the rapidly proliferating tissue has a higher ratio of protein to soluble organic nitrogen than the non-growing tissue and that this is due to a much *lower* content of amino acids and especially of glutamine, asparagine and arginine in the growing tissue (the only amino acid whose content rose as active growth was initiated was γ-aminobutyric acid). The rapidly growing cells were also characterized by the presence of hydroxy-L-proline residues in their protein fraction. Subsequently it was concluded that a protein rich in hydroxy-L-proline and metabolically inert (i.e. not undergoing much turnover) is characteristically synthesized in actively growing cells of carrot and other species (Pollard and Steward, 1959). The conspicuous example of the occurrence of hydroxyproline is in collagen and it is known that in various situations in the animal body, in which cells return to the growing state (as in wound-healing), collagen synthesis is markedly accentuated (Asboe-Hansen, 1954). Whether the presence of hydroxyproline in the protein of actively growing plant cells in culture is indicative of a similar protein and if so what functions it plays have yet to be determined.

Steward, Bidwell and Yemm (1958a) and Steward and Bidwell (1958) undertook an investigation, primarily designed to study the fate of labelled sugars, glutamine and γ-aminobutyric acid in carrot tissues when these were stimulated to active growth in a coconut-milk medium, with a view to comparing the metabolism of amides in growing and non-growing cells and thus determining the extent to which glutamine furnishes nitrogen and carbon for protein synthesis. Important aspects of the data obtained in these experiments were that (1) incorporation of sugar ^{14}C into certain amino-acid residues of the protein occurred much faster than would be expected from the net gain in protein; (2) ^{14}C-glutamine promoted an increase in glutamine content but of continuously declining specific activity, and (3) sugar ^{14}C was only slowly incorporated into free glutamine. From these observations four main conclusions were drawn. (1) In actively growing cells, as compared with non-growing cells, protein synthesis was more active and that this was correlated with a higher rate of protein breakdown as indicated by the increased rate of production of non-radioactive glutamine. (2) The free amino acids which exist in quantity in plant cells (probably to a considerable extent in the vacuoles) are not to be regarded as the immediate precursors of protein but rather as having originated largely from protein breakdown. (3) Protein synthesis takes place readily from sugar entering the cells; the carbon skeletons of the amino acids which *are* intermediates in protein synthesis are derived from the entering sugar and such "transitory" amino acids are not free to mingle with the general pool of soluble organic nitrogen compounds. (4) A very significant part of the carbon dioxide arising in respiration does not arise directly from sugar but by oxidation of the amino acid and amide units liberated by the continuous breakdown of protein. The design of these experiments by Steward and his co-workers was both novel and productive of a new kind of data and the results are of such general interest that it may be confidently anticipated that they will be extended not only within the carrot tissue system but to other cultured tissues and suspension cultures. An interesting critical evaluation of some of these new data has been presented by Yemm and Folkes (1958) and its interpretation further discussed by Steward and Bidwell (1962).

IV. Carbohydrate Requirements and Physiological Effects of Sugars and Sugar Alcohols

A. Carbohydrates as Carbon Sources for the Growth of Callus and Root Cultures

The carbohydrate requirements of a callus culture were first studied experimentally by Gautheret (1941, 1945) who examined the ability of various sugars to support the growth of normal carrot tissue cultures derived from the cambial cells of the carrot root. Similar studies, involving tissues from a number of dicotyledons, were subsequently made by Hildebrandt and Riker (1949, 1953), Nickell and Burkholder (1950) and Henderson (1954). Straus and LaRue (1954) have studied the carbohydrate requirements of a tissue culture derived from corn endosperm, and Ball (1953, 1955) has studied the effects of different sugars on the growth of *Sequoia* tissue. The above studies revealed that most tissues grow best when supplied with sucrose, dextrose or laevulose. Galactose has, in most cases, proved ineffective although for tissues of *Vinca rosea* (Hildebrandt and Riker, 1949, 1953) and of *Sequoia sempervirens* (Ball, 1953) it is reported to be a very satisfactory carbon source. Tissue of *Sequoia* is also unique in growing well when supplied with mannose; in general this is a very poor or quite ineffective carbon source. Tissues vary considerably in their ability to utilize raffinose and maltose. The pentoses and methyl-pentoses tested have failed to support growth. Natural polysaccharides are, in general, not utilizable although Hildebrandt and Riker (1949, 1953) have reported utilization of pectins, dextrin and even soluble starch by tissues of *Vinca rosea* and *Chrysanthemum frutescens* and Straus and LaRue (1954) the utilization of soluble starch by corn endosperm tissue. Nickell and Burkholder (1950) and Brakke and Nickell (1951, 1952, 1955) reported that the ability of sorrel-virus tumour tissue to utilize soluble starch was due to an active secretion of amylases into the medium. Gautheret (1948a) has reported that carrot tissue can be cultured indefinitely with glycerol as the sole carbon source and Hildebrandt and Riker (1949) and Nickell and Burkholder (1950) have obtained evidence for this substance acting as a carbon source for other tissues. Other poly-alcohols have proved inactive as carbon sources for callus tissues.

The studies quoted above indicate that callus tissues derived from different species differ, often quite dramatically, in their ability to utilize different carbohydrates. Such differences can occur even between closely related callus cultures as illustrated by the difference in response to added sugars shown by single-cell clones derived from a single-parent callus culture (Arya, Hildebrandt and Riker, 1962).

In many of the studies on carbohydrate nutrition of callus the range of sugars and related compounds tested has been very limited, and each has been tested either at a single concentration or at a very limited number of concentrations. The studies of Hildebrandt, Riker and Duggar (1946), however, clearly indicate the importance of covering effectively a wider concentration range of each sugar to determine its optimum concentration. Further, the growth effects have, in most cases, been assessed by determinations of fresh weight (and not of cell number or dry weight) resulting from a slow rate of growth proceeding over weeks or months in the undisturbed medium. It may be suggested that under these circumstances the applied carbohydrate may undergo chemical modification in the external medium (this is almost certainly the case with oligosaccharides which suffer hydrolysis) and that differences in the effectiveness of different carbohydrates may be obscured when rates of growth are limited by unappreciated factors, such as pH and the availability of inorganic ions (both initially and following callus growth). Ball (1953, 1955), for instance, explained the beneficial effect of autoclaving a medium containing sucrose upon the growth of his *Sequoia* callus as due to the liberation of the more readily utilizable sugar, laevulose. However, the work of Ferguson, Street and David (1958a) offers a possible alternative explanation. These workers demonstrated that the autoclaving of sugar with the salts of root culture media is important for maintaining availability of iron (when the iron source is supplied as inorganic salt) and that this is probably caused by the formation of very small amounts of sugar acids from laevulose and dextrose during the heating.

Excised roots, as would be expected, require for growth a supply of a utilizable carbohydrate. The pioneers of excised root culture envisaged this and incorporated dextrose into their culture media. These early attempts, however, as previously indicated (Chap. 8, p. 461) failed to establish roots in continuous culture. White (1932), although similarly unable to maintain wheat roots growing in culture, found that dextrose supported a higher and more prolonged growth rate than sucrose; a result confirmed by later workers (Almestrand, 1957; Street, Carter, Scott and Sutton, 1961). Roberts and Street

(1955), in establishing the first continuous cultures of a monocotyledonous root (Petkus II rye), found sucrose and dextrose to be satisfactory carbon sources although for the strain of rye roots cultured by Almestrand (1957) dextrose permitted and sucrose did not permit continuous culture. Other observations with monocotyledonous roots (McClary, 1940; Burström, 1941a, b) support the general conclusion that both dextrose and sucrose are effective carbon sources but that, at its optimum concentration, dextrose is significantly superior to the disaccharide.

In contrast to the conclusion above, White (1934), in first establishing tomato roots ("Bonny Best") in culture, found sucrose much better than dextrose as a carbon source; about ten times the increase in fresh weight occurring with sucrose as compared with dextrose. White (1940) in later work confirmed this superiority of sucrose; dextrose supported a very slow rate of growth, while maltose had even less activity as a carbon source. Many different samples of sucrose had almost identical activity. While the growth rate was maintained from passage to passage with sucrose, with dextrose the low rate of growth declined further on subculture. Dormer and Street (1949), using an excised root clone derived from the tomato variety "Best-of-All", found that roots cultured in a sucrose medium not only grew much faster but were more robust and of greater anatomical complexity than those obtained in dextrose medium. The delicate dextrose-grown roots were usually quite devoid of laterals whereas the sucrose-grown roots developed a regular two-ranked system of vigorous laterals. Strong evidence was obtained to show that the contrast in growth-promoting activity between these two sugars could not be explained in terms of impurities in the sugars, nor as arising from differences in the osmotic pressures of the solutions.

Although the superiority of sucrose to all other sugars for the growth of excised tomato roots was questioned by Robbins and Schmidt (1938, 1939b), their divergent results are clearly explicable in terms of their very long culture periods. Dormer and Street (1949) and Street and Lowe (1950) found that the utilization of sucrose by excised tomato roots involves its breakdown at the root surface; starting with a 10 mm root tip in 50 ml of a sucrose medium they found that, after 14–20 days culture, the medium contained no longer sucrose, but a mixture of laevulose and dextrose. This means that during a large part of the long growth periods adopted by Robbins and Schmidt the roots were in contact with a mixture of laevulose and dextrose which is inferior as a carbon source to the same level of carbon entirely as dextrose (Ferguson *et al.,* 1958a). Further, the alkaline drift in pH of the medium resulting from root growth induces iron deficiency and this is more severe in the sucrose medium than in a medium where the iron has been autoclaved with a monosaccharide (Street, 1959). The apparent contradiction between the findings of White and those of Robbins and Schmidt is a classical example of the importance, when attempting to interpret nutritional experiments, of careful standardization of conditions and of a proper appreciation of other aspects of nutrition and of changes occurring in the culture system with time.

The work of Skinner (1953) using roots of *Senecio vulgaris*, of Dawson (1958) with roots of *Trifolium pratense* and of David (1954) with *Medicago sativa* illustrate that the very great superiority of sucrose to all other sugars is commonly encountered with other cultured dicotyledonous roots.

B. THE SUPERIORITY OF SUCROSE AS A CARBON SOURCE FOR THE GROWTH OF CERTAIN ROOT CULTURES

A complete understanding of the unique activity of sucrose as a carbon source for the excised tomato root has not yet been achieved but a brief survey of studies designed to increase our understanding of this problem will illustrate clearly how nutritional studies can lead on to interesting studies of metabolism. Comparisons of the anatomy and growth of roots cultured in the optimum sucrose concentration, in a suboptimal level of sucrose (Street and McGregor, 1952) and of those grown in dextrose (without sucrose) strongly indicated that dextrose-grown roots were carbohydrate-deficient roots. Further, the finding that sucrose utilization was associated with the appearance in the medium of both dextrose and laevulose when considered along with other data then published led to the suggestion (Street and Lowe, 1950) that there might operate a surface enzyme or solute carrier system which was sucrose specific. It was postulated that this promoted a phosphorolytic splitting of the glycosidic bond in sucrose and a linked transfer of a hexose unit to the carrier.

However, a number of the experimental observations which appeared to support this attractive hypothesis have now received quite different explanations (Street *et al.*, 1952; Ferguson *et al.*, 1958a; Thomas, 1961). It now therefore seems more likely that the appearance of monosaccharides in the medium may be due, as Burström (1941a, 1957a) suggested, to the activity of a surface invertase unrelated to the process of sucrose uptake and that the sucrose molecule enters the root cells as such, as certainly seems to occur in the absorption of sucrose by tobacco leaf discs (Porter and May, 1955).

Morgan and Street (1959) showed that the oxygen uptake of sucrose-grown excised tomato roots fell to a low level (15 μl O_2/h/100 mg fresh weight) after a 60 h starvation period in a sugar-free medium. The oxygen uptake of the starved roots rose *at a similar rate* and reached, after 12 h, a value of 50–60 μl O_2/h/100 mg fresh wt. when they were fed *either* with sucrose, dextrose or laevulose and the respiratory quotients at this time were, in each case, close to unity. Similar effects of pH, dinitrophenol and azide on respiration were observed irrespective of which sugar was used as substrate. The almost identical activity of the three sugars as respiratory substrates was, therefore, in marked contrast to their dissimilar activities as sole carbon sources. Further, chromatography of root extracts revealed the presence of sucrose, dextrose, laevulose, raffinose and xylose in roots fed with each of these three sugars. Studies of carbon incorporation into cell fractions and carbon released as CO_2 in feeding experiments with uniformly labelled ^{14}C sucrose and dextrose failed to reveal any differences in carbon metabolism sufficient to suggest that they were the key to the differences in growth-promoting activity of the two sugars (Thomas, Craigie and Street, 1963). Studies, over periods up to 24 h, of rates of sugar uptake by starved roots showed that both sucrose and dextrose could be absorbed at high and very similar rates. Rates of absorption of these sugars into starved cells, therefore, offered no explanation of the divergence in growth-promoting activity between the sugars.

Analysis of sucrose-grown and dextrose-grown roots showed that the sucrose-grown roots had a higher percentage dry weight and a higher content of all carbohydrate fractions (wall constituents and soluble sugars) as a percentage of the fresh weight. When the content of these fractions was expressed as a percentage of dry weight the sucrose-grown roots had a significantly higher value for total sugars, mainly due to higher contents of the three major soluble sugars, sucrose, dextrose and laevulose. The concept of the dextrose-grown roots as low carbohydrate roots compared with the sucrose-grown roots was therefore confirmed.

In the experiments on the uptake of sugars and their utilization in respiration, not only had starved sucrose-grown roots been used but the roots used were 3–6 days old and hence consisted predominantly of mature tissues. Root growth (as expressed by cell production, cell expansion and the differentiation of tissue patterns) is, however, a process which occurs at the root apex (apical 5 mm). With this consideration in mind, Thomas *et al.* (1963) went on to demonstrate that: (1) in longer feeding experiments (beyond 24 h) with sucrose-grown starved root segments, sucrose feeding *did* lead to the establishment of a higher level of sucrose in the mature tissues and to higher levels of sucrose, dextrose and laevulose in the apical 5 mm of the root than did dextrose feeding; (2) the root tips of dextrose-grown roots have much lower levels of soluble sugars than those of sucrose-grown roots; (3) during sugar starvation of the roots the tips become almost completely depleted of sucrose before the levels of the monosaccharides fall. This last observation is paralleled by the preferential utilization of sucrose during auxin-stimulated extension of the *Avena* coleoptile; a finding which led Christiansen and Thimann (1950) to propose that sucrose was the direct precursor of cellulose and pectins. The technique of Raggio and Raggio (1956) (see Fig. 5, p. 471) demonstrated that the carbohydrate requirements of the cultured root apex can be met by translocation of sugar from mature cells. Evidence that such longitudinal movement of metabolites to the apex takes place when roots are cultured by the standard technique is to be found in the works of McGregor and Street (1953), Street (1954), Brown and Possingham (1957) and Pecket (1957). Heimsch (1960), also working with excised tomato roots, has noted that the increase in root diameter occurring at about 200 μ from the apex results mainly from cell divisions in the cortex and that these divisions are initiated opposite the phloem strands, presumably because these are the sites from which essential food substances and growth factors are being released. Swanson (1959) has summarized the very strong evidence that carbohydrate is transported in the phloem entirely as sucrose.

Against this background of recent experimental work it is now possible to suggest that the superiority of sucrose as a source of carbon for the growth of excised tomato roots is due to the establishment in its presence of a high level of sucrose in the mature cells of the root and that this leads to an effective flow of sucrose to the meristem, where it is a key metabolite. This hypothesis, however, requires confirmation by further study of the uptake and *transport* of the various sugars within the growing cultures. A full understanding of this problem also demands elucidation of the mechanism of sucrose uptake by root cells and of its involvement in the metabolism of meristematic and expanding cells. The work already enables us to define the questions which will have to be answered if we are to explain the varying responses of other cultured organs and tissues to carbohydrate supply.

C. INHIBITORY SUGARS: THE MECHANISM OF THE MANNOSE INHIBITION OF GROWTH AND RESPIRATION

The most detailed survey of the ability of various sugars and sugar alcohols (exclusive of sucrose) to act as carbon sources for the growth of excised roots is that undertaken by Ferguson *et al.* (1958a) for tomato roots. These workers found that dextrose and laevulose, and mixtures of these two sugars, supported a low but sustained level of root growth and that all other sugars and sugar alcohols were inactive as sources of carbon. In these studies the carbohydrates were incorporated into the media without heating, and iron availability was effectively maintained by the use of the ethylenediamine tetra-acetate (EDTA) complex of iron. David (1954) had also tested fourteen sugars and sugar alcohols as carbon sources for the growth of excised roots of *Medicago sativa* and found that dextrose, laevulose, maltose and raffinose support low levels of root growth. Dawson and Street (1959b) also reported that dextrose, laevulose and maltose supported a very slow growth of the roots of *Trifolium pratense*.

In these studies on the ability of excised roots to utilize sugars, other than sucrose, as carbon sources, it was observed that certain sugars (and particularly D-mannose and D-galactose), when added to a medium containing the optimum concentration of sucrose, markedly inhibited the growth of excised roots. Thus, L-sorbose, L- and D-arabinose and D-xylose at a concentration of 0·5% caused not less than 80% inhibition of the growth of excised tomato roots cultured in the presence of 2% sucrose. D-Mannose and D-galactose completely inhibited growth at 0·1%. This toxicity of galactose and mannose to plant roots was first reported by Knudson (1915, 1917). Wachtel (1943), working with cress seedlings, Steinberg (1947), working with tobacco seedlings, and Stenlid (1957), working with wheat seedlings, also reported that these sugars, and particularly mannose, were strongly inhibitory to root growth. A full metabolic explanation of these toxic effects of natural sugars cannot yet be advanced but some progress has been made, particularly towards our understanding of the inhibitory activity of mannose.

Ferguson, Street and David (1958b), in a more detailed examination of the toxicities of galactose and mannose, reported that 0·005–0·01% mannose reduces by 50%, and 0·03–0·04% reduces by not less than 90% the growth of excised tomato roots cultured in 1% sucrose medium. These toxicities of mannose and galactose are antagonized by the simultaneous addition of dextrose. Thus the inhibitory effect of concentrations of mannose up to 0·4% could be fully reversed by dextrose and the minimum ratio of dextrose:mannose for maximum antagonism of the growth inhibition was 3·5:1. A similar reduction of mannose inhibition by dextrose was reported by David (1954) working with roots of *Medicago sativa*. These observations and data presented by Stenlid (1957) were considered by Ferguson *et al.* (1958b) to be compatible with a competitive interaction between dextrose and mannose at an enzyme surface.

Morgan and Street (1959) found, with excised tomato roots, that mannose is a strong inhibitor of respiration in cultures depending on sucrose and, if present in a sufficiently high relative concentration, also of cultures depending on dextrose. The inhibition of the utilization of sucrose as a respiratory substrate by low concentrations of mannose could be fully reversed by the addition of a level of dextrose which would reverse the growth inhibition of the mannose. Additions of laevulose failed to reverse either the inhibitions of growth or of respiration caused by mannose. When mannose was applied to starved roots their endogenous respiration was decreased and the RQ of the endogenous respiration fell from 0·83 to 0·60, suggesting that mannose was inhibiting the carbohydrate component of the endogenous respiration.

Further studies recently undertaken by Goldsworthy (1964) indicate that the mannose absorbed by excised tomato roots appears in the tissues almost entirely in the form of mannose-6-phosphate, that mannose-6-phosphate can be oxidized at only a very slow rate, that mannose competitively inhibits the phosphorylation of dextrose by the hexokinase which can be detected in low activity in root extracts and that mannose-6-phosphate is a strong competitive inhibitor of the enzyme phosphoglucose isomerase. These findings clearly take us far towards a metabolic explanation of the inhibition of respiration by mannose. Reversal of this inhibition by dextrose seems to be primarily due to its inhibiting the uptake of mannose, an action which could involve competition for a hexokinase-like enzyme (Höber, 1946; Dixon, 1949).

Stenlid (1954, 1957, 1959a) working with freshly excised roots of wheat seedlings has reported that mannose inhibits the uptake of chloride and nitrate, a result to be expected in view of its activity as an inhibitor of respiration. However, Stenlid (1959b) has also reported that inhibitory concentrations of mannose can actually stimulate phosphate uptake, an effect which could result from the reduction of the phosphate level in the cells by the trapping of phosphate in mannose-6-phosphate. This, in turn, could also be a factor involved in the inhibition of respiration by mannose.

These studies of mannose toxicity in excised roots suggest the desirability of a comparative study of mannose metabolism in *Sequoia* callus for which mannose is reported to be an effective carbon source (Ball, 1953).

References to the inhibition of ion uptake by mannose, and the inhibition, in turn, of mannose uptake by dextrose emphasize the importance of uptake phenomena in studies on the nutrition of plant cultures. This can be further illustrated by the work on mannose toxicity. Morgan and Street (1959) using carbohydrate-depleted roots were able to demonstrate a small but significant enhancement (persisting for at least 8 h) of oxygen uptake by feeding sodium pyruvate and that this effect was inhibited by added mannose. This led them to suggest that the mannose "block" in respiration was probably either in the TCA cycle or in terminal oxidation. The discovery (Goldsworthy 1964; Goldsworthy and Street, 1965) that mitochondria from excised tomato roots can oxidize pyruvate if a "sparker" amount of malate is also present and that this oxidation is *not* inhibited by mannose strongly suggests that the mannose inhibition of pyruvate oxidation by intact root tissues may be due to an inhibition of pyruvate uptake.

Despite our very considerable knowledge of the sugar biochemistry of plant cells, recent studies of the carbohydrate responses of organ and tissue cultures emphasize that there is still much to be learned regarding carbohydrate uptake, translocation and metabolism in plant organs and tissues and that sterile plant tissue cultures are particularly suited to such studies.

V. Vitamin Nutrition

A. Introduction

The vitamins with which we shall be concerned here are vitamins of the B complex. We shall consider particularly aneurin (thiamin, vitamin B_1) and pyridoxine (vitamin B_6), since of the vitamins reported to be essential for or markedly stimulatory to the growth of plant cultures these are the only two that have been submitted to any detailed study. Both these vitamins are involved as prosthetic groups or co-enzymes of enzymes essential to all living cells. Aneurin in the form of aneurin pyrophosphate or co-carboxylase (Lohman and Schuster, 1937) is an essential co-factor for pyruvate and α-keto-glutarate decarboxylations and of a transketolase concerned in the formation of sedoheptulose from ribulose phosphate (Racker, de la Haba and Leder, 1953). Pyridoxine is the precursor of pyridoxal phosphate the prosthetic group of the transaminases (Lichstein, Gunsalus and Umbreit, 1945; Schlenk and Snell, 1945) and of glutamic acid decarboxylase (Schales, Mims and Schales, 1946; Schales and Schales, 1946) and other amino-acid decarboxylases.

The culture medium successfully used by White (1934) contained 0·01% of a yeast extract and this supplement was essential for continued growth of his excised tomato root cultures. Robbins and Bartley (1937a) and White (1937a) showed that the yeast extract could be partially replaced by crystalline aneurin. Robbins and Schmidt (1939a-c) then reported that a mixture of aneurin and pyridoxine would permit the indefinite culture of excised tomato roots and with their strain, addition of other B vitamins failed to enhance the growth rate further. Bonner (1943) confirmed this with a different clone of tomato roots. Bonner (1940) and Bonner and Devirian (1939) also examined the vitamin requirements of excised roots of ten other species. For "full" growth rate all required the presence of aneurin in the external medium; carrot roots also required pyridoxine, while sunflower and *Datura* roots required both pyridoxine and niacin in addition to aneurin. A similar requirement for all three B vitamins was found in certain strains of tomato roots, a result confirmed by Robbins (1941) for three of his tomato root clones.

Aneurin, therefore, in all the cases cited, is either "essential" for excised root growth (in the sense that cultures cannot be maintained in its absence) or markedly stimulatory to it. The classical example of the latter situation is the work of Bonner and Devirian (1939) on flax roots. These roots can grow through many subcultures and probably indefinitely in a medium containing no vitamins. The growth of these roots is, however, increased more than ten times by the addition of aneurin (optimum concentration 2 μg per culture) to the medium. Roots of white clover (Bonner and Bonner, 1948) are similarly stimulated in their growth by addition of aneurin, although they can be maintained in a medium in which the only vitamin added is niacin.

There is no evidence for a pyridoxine requirement from work with callus cultures. Aneurin also fails to enhance the growth of many callus cultures, but in other cases, although not essential, it has enhanced the extent and rate of cell proliferation (Czosnowski, 1952a; Paris, 1955). The only clear cases where aneurin is known to be essential for growth are the callus tissue from hawthorn studied by Paris (1955), and the virus tumour tissue from sorrel (*Rumex*) studied by Nickell (1952).

B. ANEURIN (THIAMINE, VITAMIN B_1)

The aneurin requirement of root cultures immediately raises a number of interesting questions. Gautheret (1956) has remarked "I have always been surprised that the nutritional requirements of roots appear to be different from those of true tissue cultures. It is sometimes possible to obtain a callus from a root culture and the reverse can also be obtained; that is, a callus culture may give rise to roots. The genetics of the cells should be the same, yet there are changes in the nutritional requirements." In illustration we may take a strain of carrot callus which can be grown on a simple medium containing mineral salts and sugar; as already indicated, excised carrot roots require aneurin and pyridoxine. Again, although all root cultures seem to be stimulated in their growth by addition of aneurin to the culture medium, they vary from roots which can be grown continuously in its absence to clones of tomato roots, for instance, where withholding aneurin brings growth to a stop in a few days.

At this point it is possible to formulate and to go on to give at least partial answers to two questions. First, is the root as an organ normally dependent upon the rest of the plant for the whole or part of its aneurin requirement? If so, does the study of root cultures enable us to determine whether roots can be entirely heterotrophic for aneurin in the sense that the roots of certain species or strains may completely lack the ability to synthesize this vitamin? Our knowledge of the aneurin economy of whole plants is based upon studies by Bonner (1942b), Burkholder and Snow (1942), Burkholder and McVeigh (1942) and Geddes and Levine (1942) in which aneurin was assayed by the *Phycomyces* test (Schopfer, 1934) which, although very sensitive, responds not only to aneurin but to a mixture of the two moieties from which, at least in some organisms, aneurin is synthesized, viz. aneurin pyrimidine and aneurin thiazole. The studies of these workers, which involved the girdling technique, strongly indicated that the main site of aneurin synthesis was the leaves and that aneurin was exported particularly from mature leaves to the roots. The methods used, while indicating transport of aneurin from shoot to root did not resolve whether the quite high aneurin content of roots (which may be of the order of 6–8 μg/g dry wt.) arises entirely or only in part by translocation from the leaves.

Czosnowski (1952b) found, as might have been expected, that certain callus cultures, which were not enhanced in growth by external aneurin, contained this vitamin; the concentrations reported were of the order of 5×10^{-2} μg/ml fresh volume of tissue. Bonner and Bonner (1948) concluded that excised flax roots synthesized 0·02 μg and excised white clover roots 0·01 μg per root per week. The question posed is whether these root cultures were exceptional in retaining the ability to synthesize aneurin albeit at a markedly suboptimal rate. When aneurin is withheld, excised tomato roots show a decrease in growth rate within the first 4 days of culture; growth ceases within 7–8 days and after that the roots quickly and irreversibly lose their growth potentiality. Their aneurin requirement is, however, extremely low; over the range of external concentration 0·1–1·0 μg/l growth is proportional to concentration and the full requirement is met by a maintained concentration of as little as 1·0 μg/l. Such roots seem particularly suitable to test whether excised root cultures can have a zero ability to synthesize aneurin.

Street and Jones (1963) approached this problem of testing the ability of excised tomato roots to synthesize aneurin by using the sensitive and specific thiochrome method of Jansen (1936) which, when combined with a prior hydrolysis of phosphorylated forms of aneurin, enables total aneurin, exclusive of precursor molecules, to be estimated. Because the root cultures so quickly cease to grow in the absence of an external supply of aneurin these workers used a test medium containing initially 1·0 μg/l of the vitamin, and allowed this to be depleted by growth over a period of 3 weeks. Aneurin in the root material and medium was measured at zero time and again at the end of the 3 weeks of incubation. Under these conditions a decrease in aneurin content of the system (by virtue of aneurin instability) would be expected if the root had no ability to synthesize the vitamin. In practice, small gains in aneurin were recorded (*ca* 0·4 μg per culture in 21 days), strongly indicating that the roots did slowly synthesize it.

This finding is of interest because it raises the possibility that many or even all of the genes which control the synthesis of those enzymes and their co-factors which function directly in the pathways of energy release and in the synthesis of the essential structural constituents of plant cells are never completely suppressed during differentiation. It also raises the question of how far the enzymic activities and hence the nutritional requirements of cultured cells are a reflection of the *conditions of culture* or a reflection of changes involved in the normal processes of cell differentiation. Do roots have a requirement for an external supply of aneurin or is the requirement revealed in culture a reflection of the particular conditions imposed by the techniques of excised root culture? Do meristematic cells have very complex nutritional requirements or are the indications to this effect obtained in work with free cell cultures a reflection of the special environmental conditions thereby imposed upon the cells? If many or any of the nutritional requirements of plant organ and tissue cultures are, in this sense, a reflection of the conditions of culture, it may be expected that simplification of the nutritional requirements should follow from suitable alterations of the supply of inorganic nutrients, primary energy and carbon sources, conditions of gaseous exchange, light or temperature.

Some recent work on crown-gall tumour cells seems to be very relevant to this contention. The crown-gall tumour cell has been shown to have, in culture, an enhanced ability to synthesize nucleic acids, mitotic proteins and other substances concerned specifically with cell growth and division (Braun, 1961), and this has been described by saying that the induction of the tumorous state in such plant cells involves the permanent activation of a series of biosynthetic systems. Further, in a series of elegant experiments, Braun (1943, 1947, 1951) has shown that the transformation process can be interrupted at intervals to obtain tissues showing varying grades of neoplastic change ranging from slow-growing and benign to rapidly-growing and fully autonomous tumour cell types. Work with such cell types from *Vinca rosea,* shows that the fully transformed crown-gall tumour cells are capable of rapid growth in White's basic medium containing only inorganic salts and sucrose. Partially transformed tumour cells could be grown at a similar high rate only when this basic medium was supplemented with an auxin (naphthaleneacetic acid), m-inositol and glutamine; to achieve a similar growth rate of the normal tissue it was necessary also to add to the medium a kinin (6-furfurylaminopurine), asparagine, and cytidylic and guanylic acids (Braun, 1958). However, if the inorganic salt mixture of the medium was fortified by the addition of a solution of potassium chloride, sodium nitrate and sodium dihydrogen phosphate, the partially transformed tumour cells showed a very high growth in the absence of m-inositol and glutamine and normal cells grew in a medium supplemented with auxin, kinin and inositol at a rate equal to that in the basic medium supplemented with the seven growth factors listed above (Wood and Braun, 1961; Braun and Wood, 1962). The normal cells and, to a lesser extent, the partially transformed tumour cells required significantly higher levels of nitrate, phosphate and potassium ions than are present in White's basic medium to synthesize certain essential metabolites in amounts required for their rapid growth. Clearly, work along these lines with other types of plant cultures may be expected to clarify our understanding of their special nutritional requirements.

From the argument developed above we may postulate that when a natural organic substance either enhances or is essential for the continuation of growth in culture, then either this substance is not being adequately synthesized in the cultured tissues or it is being destroyed or lost to the external surroundings. In the case of aneurin there is no evidence of loss to the external medium; root cultures can indeed very effectively remove added aneurin from the culture medium. Further, extracts of excised tomato roots prepared by a number of methods do not have detectable aneurinase activity; thus it is unlikely that they destroy the vitamin at an appreciable rate. It is, therefore, tempting to try and discover the step or steps in metabolism which limit aneurin synthesis in tomato root cultures. As early as 1937, Robbins and Bartley (1937b) showed that the aneurin requirement of excised tomato roots can be fully replaced by an equimolar mixture of aneurin thiazole and aneurin pyrimidine, and that some strains required only an adequate supply of aneurin thiazole. With the clone of excised tomato roots used in our laboratory by Jones (1963), each moiety alone supported a very low level of growth in the first passage and this declined further on subculture. There was no evidence of a significant enhancement of aneurin content from feeding either moiety. A mixture of the two moieties did, however, fully satisfy the aneurin requirement and was associated with a highly significant increase in the aneurin content of the roots. Bonner (1938), working with pea roots, had similarly found each moiety to be individually quite inactive, but that a mixture of the two satisfied the aneurin requirement.

The activity of the mixture of pyrimidine and thiazole in the cases studied by Jones and by Bonner strongly suggests that either the level of both precursors is limiting in tissues which require aneurin as against tissues autotrophic for this vitamin or that the steps involved in their condensation can only be made to proceed, in aneurin-requiring tissues, by establishing experimentally levels of both precursors not normally established in plant cells. Attempts to demonstrate the presence in extracts of excised tomato roots, seedling tomato roots and tomato leaves of the complex enzyme system involved in the synthesis of aneurin from pyrimidine and thiazole in yeasts (Camiener and Brown, 1959; Leder, 1959; Nose, Ueda and Kawasaki, 1959) have, however, so far yielded negative results (Jones, 1963). The final steps in aneurin synthesis in higher plants are therefore unknown. Furthermore, no attempts to study pyrimidine and thiazole levels in cultured tissues and the raising of these levels in feeding experiments have yet been undertaken, although the availability as test organisms of pyrimidine- and thiazole-less mutants of *Neurospora* makes such studies feasible. The important objective of a full metabolic explanation of the aneurin requirement of excised root cultures is therefore far from being achieved.

C. PYRIDOXINE (VITAMIN B_6)

Certain studies on the requirement of excised tomato roots for pyridoxine undertaken by Boll (1954a-c, 1959) illustrate another approach towards the understanding of the physiology of vitamins in cultured tissues. Reference has already been made to the work of Robbins and Schmidt (1939a-c) and of Bonner (1943) which showed that a mixture of aneurin and pyridoxine fully replaced the yeast extract hitherto required for the continuous culture of excised tomato roots at a high growth rate. However, White (1937b) had found earlier that the growth-promoting effect of yeast extract could also be achieved by aneurin plus a mixture of nine amino acids, and in 1939 that the nine amino acids could be replaced by an appropriate concentration of the single amino acid, glycine, or by a mixture of amino acids which need not include glycine. More recently Boll (1954a) found, for two newly cultured inbred lines of tomato and for the crosses between them, that to replace the effect of pyridoxine completely it was necessary to add both glycine and niacin. However, if the roots were supplied with suboptimal levels of pyridoxine growth could be fully restored to that obtained with the optimum level of pyridoxine by the addition of glycine only (Boll, 1954b). Boll (1954c) further showed that excised roots growing in White's basic medium supplemented only with thiamine did synthesize pyridoxine although the optimum external supply of pyridoxine very significantly raised this internal level. This suggested that the partial or complete removal by glycine of the need for an external supply of pyridoxine might be explained if either glycine enhanced the synthesis of pyridoxine or if it exerted a "sparing" action on the limited pyridoxine synthesized by the roots; a "sparing" action in the sense that in its presence pyridoxine was no longer involved in the activation of certain enzymes, so that the limited amount of pyridoxine synthesized was then exclusively used to activate other enzymes still essential to growth and metabolism. Further work (Boll, 1954c) showed that a number of other single substances could replace the pyridoxine requirement, and that in fact glycine was not the most active substance which would enhance growth in a medium containing also aneurin and niacin. The most active substances, in order of decreasing efficiency, were dimethylaminoethanol, ethanolamine, glycine, choline, DL-norvaline and L-valine. Several other substances could also partially substitute for pyridoxine; examples of this group are L-serine, DL-norleucine and L-methionine.

Boll (1954c) interpreted, as evidence against the possibility that these various pyridoxine substitutes enhanced pyridoxine synthesis, his finding that roots receiving aneurin plus ethanolamine grew faster than roots receiving only aneurin and contained a greater total pyridoxine content but a lower pyridoxine concentration (content per unit dry weight) and hence presumably a lower pyridoxine content per cell. Boll therefore attempted to obtain indirect evidence which would test the "sparing" action hypothesis. He assumed that ethanolamine is normally synthesized in the root cells, that a "serine decarboxylase" activated by pyridoxine is involved in this synthesis, and that in presence of added ethanolamine this enzyme is repressed by a negative feedback mechanism with consequent release of pyridoxine. He then (1959) went on to demonstrate (1) that very low concentrations of certain amino acids, which are without growth effect on roots cultured in a medium containing aneurin plus niacin, were stimulatory to growth in presence of suboptimal levels of ethanolamine, and (2) that at higher concentrations certain amino acids were more inhibitory to growth in presence of the optimum ethanolamine addition than in its absence. These results were both regarded as explicable in terms of the "sparing" action of ethanolamine, this being in case 1 supplemented by the added amino acid and in case 2 permitting metabolism of the added amino acid to proceed sufficiently for it to have a toxic effect. Clearly, this work on the pyridoxine requirement of excised tomato roots is still only at its beginning. Its discussion here is, however, justified on the grounds that it raises the question of the factors controlling the partition of common co-factors between the enzymes which they activate and suggests the possibility, for further study, that negative feedback mechanisms involving suppression of enzyme synthesis may occur in higher plant cells.

VI. Requirements for Growth-regulating Substances

A. Auxins

"The only irrefutable result is that while some tissues can be cultured without auxin, others require a substance of this type" (Gautheret, 1955a).

Most crown-gall tissues not only proliferate in the absence of an external supply of auxin but their growth is not enhanced by such additions (de Ropp, 1947; Gautheret, 1948b; Hildebrandt and Riker, 1947; Morel, 1948). Gall tissues arising as a result of insect attack may, however, require auxin for their growth, as shown by the work of Démétriadès (1953) on the gall tissue of *Salvia pomifera*. Many normal tissues require auxin for their growth in culture, and the media employed for their successful culture have contained one of the following auxins: β-indolylacetic acid (IAA), naphthaleneacetic acid (NAA), 2,4-dichlorophenoxyacetic acid (2,4-D), or *para*-chlorophenoxyacetic acid. A comprehensive summary, in tabular form, of the auxin requirements of normal callus cultures is presented in Gautheret's review (1955a).

For the culture of a number of normal callus tissues, auxin is the only essential supplement which needs to be added to a basic medium supplying inorganic ions and sugar. Examples of such tissues are cited by Gautheret (1942, 1959), Morel (1948) and Ball (1950). For many other callus cultures, and for most suspension cultures, the culture medium must contain, in addition to auxin, vitamins or vitamins and reduced nitrogen compounds, or a complex supplement such as coconut milk.

Tissue from different varieties of the same species may show different auxin requirements. Thus, some workers have been able to culture carrot callus without auxin (Gautheret, 1950b), others by the addition of an auxin (Nobécourt, 1939a, b; Levine, 1951; Wiggans, 1954) and others only by adding coconut milk (de Ropp, Vitucci, Hutchings and Williams, 1952). Similarly, while Morel (1948) found NAA essential for the growth of Virginia creeper tissue, Bertossi (reported by Gautheret, 1955a) isolated a strain of this tissue having no auxin requirement.

Roberts and Street (1955) have grouped excised roots on the basis of their behaviour towards externally applied auxins as follows: (1) roots that are either unaffected or inhibited by external auxin, e.g. excised roots of tomato (Street, McGregor and Sussex, 1954; Hughes and Street, 1960) and *Acer rubrum* (Bachelard and Stowe, 1963); (2) roots whose growth in culture is enhanced by an appropriate concentration of IAA, e.g. pine (Slankis, 1951), groundsel (Charles, 1959), white lupin (Duhamet, 1939), pea (Bonner and Koepfli, 1939; Naylor and Rappaport, 1950), maize (Fiedler, 1936; Kandler and Vieregg, 1953; Kandler and Eberle, 1955) and wheat (Burström, 1942); (3) roots whose growth in culture is dependent upon an external supply of auxin or an auxin precursor, e.g. rye (Roberts and Street, 1955).

The requirements of certain tissue cultures for auxins make them potentially valuable for auxin bioassays, and comparative studies on the activities of natural and synthetic auxins have been undertaken with callus cultures (Raoul and Gautheret, 1947, 1949; Bouriquet, 1955; Bouriquet and Mentzer, 1951; Bouriquet and Pachéco, 1952).

The sensitivity of plant tissue and organ cultures to auxins, both as regards growth promotion and inhibition also makes possible the investigation of the metabolic effects of auxins. Studies have been made of the influence of auxins on the rate of sugar depletion when callus cultures are transferred to sugar-free medium (Goris, 1947, 1948a, b) and of sugar accumulation in response to addition of auxin to a sugar-containing medium (Goris, 1954; Lioret, 1955; Wiggans, 1954). Such studies point to greater rates of uptake and metabolism of sugars in response to auxin. The classification of excised tomato roots as being unaffected or inhibited by auxin (Roberts and Street, 1955) applies to roots cultured in presence of the standard (2%) or higher concentrations of sucrose. However, when excised tomato roots are cultured in media containing lower sucrose concentrations (0·75 and 0·5%), then NAA very significantly enhances their linear growth, the initiation and development of laterals, and the increase in dry weight (Butcher and Street, 1960a). The symptoms induced by supra-optimal sucrose concentrations (retarded linear growth, enhanced root diameter, enhanced percentage dry weight) can be very closely simulated at suboptimal sucrose concentrations by the addition of partially inhibitory concentrations of IAA or NAA. Concentrations of auxin strongly inhibitory to linear growth can actually produce increased dry weights per culture in excised roots of tomato and wheat (Sutton *et al.,* 1961). The resemblance between auxin-inhibited and sucrose-inhibited roots extends to details of their anatomy, including the development of a greater number of lignified xylem elements (Street and McGregor, 1952; Hughes and Street, 1960). These studies with excised roots again suggest that auxin may enhance the uptake of sugar and its conversion into cell wall constituents. Plant tissue cultures are particularly suitable for studies of the sugar:auxin interrelationship, and further studies with ^{14}C-labelled sugars, auxins and plant cultures along the lines recently reported in a study of auxin-controlled coleoptile growth (Baker and Ray, 1965) are urgently needed.

Lachaux (1944a-d), Nickell (1950c), and Lioret (1952a, b, 1953a, b) have reported that auxins can enhance the respiration of cultured tissues. Morel and Démétriadès (1955) have reported that IAA and 2,4-D enhance the activity of peroxidase and polyphenoloxidase in cultured Jerusalem artichoke tissue, and Bryan and Newcomb (1954) that auxin enhances pectin-methylesterase activity in tissue cultures of tobacco pith. One enzyme of particular interest in connection with auxin is the auxin-destroying enzyme, IAA-oxidase, reported by Galston and Dalberg (1954) and Pilet and Galston (1955) to be an adaptive enzyme, its level of activity increasing in response to the addition of IAA. Subsequent studies by Burström (1957b), working with wheat seedlings, and by Audus and Bakhsh (1961), working with sub-apical segments of pea roots growing in sucrose solutions, have shown that pre-treatment with IAA certainly leads to a decreased sensitivity of the cell-expansion process of root cells to auxin inhibition. However, from detailed analyses of this adaptation phenomenon and from parallel studies on adaptation to 2,4-D it has been concluded by both Burström and Audus that, while augmentation of IAA-oxidase activity may be involved, there also occurs a change in real sensitivity of the cells to auxin, probably involving changes in activity of the enzymes mediating cell wall growth.

This leads us to consider why certain cultured tissues require an external supply of auxin whereas others do not. The most obvious hypothesis is that those tissues which do not require an external auxin meet their auxin requirement by biosynthesis and a number of workers have obtained evidence of the development of adequate endogenous levels of auxin in crown-gall and auxin-autotrophic normal callus tissues (Link and Eggers, 1941; Kulescha, 1952; Henderson and Bonner, 1952; Bitancourt, 1949, 1955). From work with root cultures (Nagao, 1936, 1937, 1938; van Overbeek and Bonner, 1938; van Overbeek, 1939a, b; Britton, Housley and Bentley, 1956; Thurman and Street, 1960) there is evidence of endogenous auxin production to "seedling" levels in cultured roots whose growth is not enhanced by an external supply and to detectable but abnormally low levels in roots which can be enhanced in their growth by an appropriate external auxin concentration. Further, the complex pattern of auxin activity revealed by the chromatography of extracts of excised tomato root cultures closely resembles the auxin patterns which have been described for extracts of seedling roots of tomato and other species (Audus and Gunning, 1958; Lexander, 1953; Britton *et al.*, 1956; Thurman and Street, 1960).

The high auxin content often found in tumour tissues as compared with normal tissues of the same species could be due to a greater rate of synthesis in the tumour tissue and Henderson and Bonner (1952), working with *Helianthus* tissues, considered that this was so. However, Bitancourt (1955) has interpreted his results to indicate that the difference is due to a lower activity of the auxin-destroying enzymes in the tumour tissue. Neither of these studies can, however, be regarded as definitive in view of the recent work indicating (1) the presence in tissues of a number of indoles with auxin activity, (2) our uncertainty regarding the nature of the "active auxin" directly concerned in growth regulation, and (3) our lack of knowledge of the reactions mediating the synthesis and interconversion of natural indoles.

There is a large body of evidence that tryptophane can be converted to IAA in many tissues and is probably the precursor of the indole auxins (Gordon, 1954). Henderson and Bonner (1952) considered that the system limiting auxin production in normal *Helianthus* tissue was the slow rate of its formation from tryptophane. Work with cereal root cultures also strongly indicates that these may be unable to synthesize their natural auxins from tryptophane. Roberts and Street (1955) in reporting that auxin (IAA or the corresponding nitrile, IAN) was essential for the continuous culture of excised rye roots drew attention to the inactivity of unheated tryptophane. Autoclaving of the tryptophane, particularly in presence of the other constituents of the medium, however, caused an "activation" and such heated tryptophane solutions could meet the auxin requirement of the rye roots. Similarly, in work with cultured wheat roots, autoclaved tryptophane enhanced growth whereas unheated tryptophane was inactive (Sutton *et al.*, 1961). In these studies it was shown that unheated tryptophane, although inactive as an auxin, was absorbed by the roots to an extent which greatly increased the indole content of the root cells. Later work (Carter and Street, 1963) showed that the autoclaving of the tryptophane led to the presence in the medium of a small amount of IAA and of a second unidentified indole and that the activation of the tryptophane was due to the production of these active auxins.

Plant tissue and organ cultures are potentially of great value for the study of the synthesis and involvement in metabolism of growth regulatory substances like IAA and related indoles. By our ability to establish many different conditions of culture and to define these in terms of environmental and nutritive variables it should be possible to study (1) both the relationships between growth phenomena and the endogenous levels of growth regulatory substances, and (2) the *in vivo* synthesis of the active molecules which regulate the processes of growth and differentiation. The carrying out of work of this kind is at present handicapped by our lack of knowledge of the chemical nature of the natural indoles and of their metabolism. Preliminary work directed towards these objectives is reported in studies designed to separate and identify the natural auxins present in cultured roots (Thurman and Street, 1960; Street, 1960; Winter and Street, 1963; Street, Butcher, Handoll and Winter, 1964) and in studies of the metabolism of auxins absorbed from the culture medium (Thurman and Street, 1962).

B. KININS

When slabs of pith removed from segments of tobacco stems (*Nicotiana tabacum* var. Wisconsin 38) are placed on the surface of an agar medium containing mineral salts, sucrose, B vitamins and glycine, callus tissue develops by cell division at the morphologically basal surface. The callus tissue, however, does not continue to grow and cannot be subcultured. Addition of IAA augments the early growth but does not prolong the period of growth (Jablonski and Skoog, 1954). However, in 1955 (Miller, Skoog, Okumura, von Saltza and Strong) a crystalline material was obtained from autoclaved slurries of DNA from herring sperm which, when added to a medium also containing IAA, permitted the continuous culture of the tobacco stem callus. This crystalline material, known as kinetin, was shown to be 6-furfurylaminopurine (Miller, Skoog, Okumura, von Saltza and Strong, 1955, 1956). The demonstration that a number of analogs of kinetin also made continuing cell division possible in the tobacco callus led to the use of the term "kinins" (from cytokinesis) to describe this class of substances (Miller *et al.*, 1956). Although kinetin has its most dramatic effect on tobacco pith cultures (Skoog and Miller, 1957), it also very significantly enhances the growth of tissue derived from the phloem of the carrot root (Shantz, Mears and Steward, 1958), soybean cotyledon callus (Miller, 1960), pea root callus (Torrey, 1958a) and cocklebur stem callus (Fox and Miller, 1959).

Marked effects of kinetin on the growth of cultured roots have not been reported. Danckwardt-Lillieström (1957), working with root cultures of *Isatis tinctoria*, found that kinetin promoted root growth at low concentrations and was inhibitory at higher concentrations. Kinetin at low concentration enhanced the growth of roots of *Convolvulus arvensis* cultured in darkness, but in light it enhanced the inhibition of growth caused by light (Torrey, 1958b). Butcher and Street (1960a) in a more detailed study of the influence of kinetin on the growth of excised tomato roots found that kinetin was either without effect or was inhibitory to growth in media containing 1·5% or less sucrose. However, with higher sucrose concentrations and particularly at 3% or higher, kinetin promoted linear growth by enhancing the rate and prolonging the occurrence of cell divisions in the root tip meristem and by enhancing the process of cell expansion. Further, in these high sugar media auxins and gibberellic acid decrease the duration of meristematic activity in individual root meristems and these effects are antagonized by kinetin. This may possibly be a consequence of the establishment of an auxin:kinin ratio more favourable to cell division or due to a kinetin inhibition of auxin uptake (Wickson and Thimann, 1960).

Guttman (1957) and Jensen and Pollock (1958) have obtained evidence that kinetin causes an increase in the nucleic acid, and particularly in the RNA of onion root cells. Recently a more detailed study has been made of the changes in RNA and DNA content of the cells of the onion root following treatment for periods up to 48 h with a high external concentration of kinetin (1 mg/l) (Jensen, Pollock, Healey and Ashton, 1964). After only 30 min treatment with kinetin the RNA content of the cells in the region 1200–2000 μ from the apex was doubled. With continuation of kinetin treatment the RNA content per cell dropped to a plateau value 30% above the control and this level was maintained for 12 h. Thereafter a second decline in RNA content occurred and after 48 h kinetin treatment the RNA content per cell was only about half of that of the corresponding cells from the control roots. As indicated earlier there is an increase in the DNA content of nuclei during expansion and differentiation of root cells; after 48 h kinetin treatment the DNA content of the nuclei of such cells had fallen to that typical of the meristematic cells. There were no significant changes in the RNA and DNA content of the cells of the meristem. The authors conclude that their results show that kinetin enters the root rapidly and that its immediate effect is to inhibit turn-over of RNA, thereby leading to enhanced accumulation of RNA in the expanding cells. Subsequently, a new equilibrium between synthesis and breakdown is established and this gives place to a decline in RNA as its synthesis is inhibited by a reduction in nuclear DNA. The significance of this decline is doubtful in view of the high level of kinetin applied in these experiments. In another study (Steinhart, Mann and Mudd, 1964), it was found that kinetin treatment of seedling barley roots caused an increase over the whole length of the roots in the activity of the enzyme, tyramine methylpherase. Kinetin did not affect the activity levels of four other enzymes examined. The kinetin-induced rise in tyramine methylpherase activity was prevented by the simultaneous addition of inhibitors of protein synthesis suggesting that kinetin promoted an enhanced rate of synthesis of this enzyme protein. This again suggests that kinetin may influence the growth of root cells via an influence on RNA. The evidence from work with leaves and stem segments, that kinetin may promote protein synthesis (Mothes, Engelbrecht and Kulajewa, 1959; Thimann and Laloraya, 1960; Osborne, 1961) may also be related to the promotion by kinetin of RNA synthesis.

These studies which point to an influence of kinetin on RNA synthesis and, in consequence, upon protein synthesis do not establish either the specificity of these effects or that they are the basis of all the physiological consequences of kinetin treatment. Evidence that auxin can promote RNA synthesis and that the effectiveness of auxin in promoting cell expansion is reduced by ribonuclease has been obtained by Masuda (1965) in work with tuber tissue of *Helianthus tuberosus*. In line with this, Key and Shannon (1964) have reported that auxin enhances ^{14}C-nucleotide incorporation into RNA in excised soybean hypocotyls. Any hypothesis that the primary actions of auxins or kinins are on RNA synthesis must at present be accepted with caution. Masuda (1965) concluded that the primary effect on RNA synthesis in the *Helianthus* tuber tissue might be mediated by neither an auxin nor kinin but by a gibberellin. The possibility that all these types of growth regulator act via effects on some key aspect of metabolism, such as RNA synthesis, is of interest in view of the evidence that it is the balance between them that is determinative in certain aspects of tissue differentiation and in the initiation of organ meristems in callus (see Chapter 10, Section III, B, p. 659).

This subject of the mechanism of action of kinetin and related compounds, will have a renewed interest as work progresses on the isolation of natural kinins from plant tissues (see Section IX, D, p. 607).

C. GIBBERELLINS

Nickell and Tulecke (1959) have studied the responses of fifty-nine strains of callus tissue from twenty-five species to 10 p.p.m. gibberellin (described as Pfizer Lot No. 76088, a mixture of gibberellins A and X). The monocotyledonous tissues and most of the dicotyledonous tissues examined were inhibited by the gibberellin. Where the gibberellin application was stimulatory to growth, the enhancement varied from + 6% (*Solanum* tuber tissue) to + 84% of control growth (*Melilotus* stem virus-tumour tissue). A survey of this kind, involving an arbitary concentration of gibberellin applied to tissues growing in a variety of culture media (some containing auxins and some auxin-free) has a severely limited value and it is now necessary to undertake more detailed studies with a few selected tissue cultures. We do not at present know of any callus tissue for which a gibberellin is an essential nutrient.

In 1957, Whaley and Kephart, using excised radicle tips of certain strains of maize, briefly reported that gibberellic acid (GA) can stimulate the extension growth of cultured roots. Lee (1959), however, reported GA to inhibit the main axis growth of excised roots in clones from both a tall and a dwarf variety of tomato. Butcher and Street (1960b), working with a different clone of excised tomato roots, found GA to increase the growth of the main axis and the number of emergent laterals when the roots were cultured in a medium of low sucrose content. GA promoted extension growth of the lateral roots over a wider range of sucrose concentration; this effect occurred even at sucrose levels where GA was inhibiting growth of the main axis. Both the stimulatory and inhibitory effects of GA were mediated through effects on both cell division and cell extension. GA closely resembled auxin (particularly NAA) in its effects on excised tomato root growth except that (1) auxin stimulation of the growth of newly initiated laterals was only observed in media containing 1% or less sucrose, and (2) GA was at high concentrations only a weak inhibitor of root growth. Sutton *et al.* (1961) found that GA strongly inhibited the growth of excised wheat roots cultured in a medium containing a stimulatory concentration of autoclaved tryptophane although at the same concentration it did not depress the lower level of growth occurring in a tryptophane-free medium. In a basic root culture medium wheat roots grow better when illuminated. GA, at a concentration which promoted lateral initiation and development in dark-grown cultures, was strongly inhibitory to the illuminated cultures. Since there is evidence that autoclaved tryptophane is a way of supplying "auxin" and that light enhances an endogenous auxin of the cultured wheat roots, it appears as if GA "sensitizes" the root cells to endogenous or externally applied auxin. A similar hypothesis would explain the resemblance between the effect of GA and auxin on the excised tomato root. In this connection it is interesting to note that GA has been reported to depress the activity of IAA-oxidase (Pilet, 1957; Galston and Warburg, 1959) and to lead to an increase in endogenous auxin level in various woody shoots (Nitsch, 1957).

Further work designed to elucidate the role of gibberellins in organ and tissue growth requires the identification of the natural gibberellins present and the development of more sensitive and specific biological or chemical assay techniques. As a first step in this direction Butcher (1963) has examined excised tomato roots for their natural gibberellins and obtained evidence for the occurrence of gibberellin A_1.

D. POSTSCRIPT

The levels of growth regulators developed by biosynthesis *in vitro* are clearly often a limitation to the growth of many tissues and organs in culture. However, only very limited contributions to our knowledge of the involvement of these natural regulators in metabolism or of their routes of biosynthesis have so far followed from work with plant tissue cultures. A more encouraging picture will emerge when we go on to consider the use of plant cultures in studies of the role of growth-regulating substances in cellular differentiation and organogenesis (Chap. 10).

VII. Pathways of Biosynthesis, "Biochemical Genetics" and Adaptation in Organ and Tissue Cultures

A. BIOSYNTHESIS OF SECONDARY PLANT PRODUCTS

Potentially, the techniques of plant tissue culture are well suited for studying the environmental and nutritive control and chemical pathways involved in the synthesis of particular metabolites. Reference has already been made to the very limited progress made with excised root cultures towards elucidating pathways of vitamin biosynthesis (p. 567). The work of Dawson (1942), Solt (1954), Solt, Dawson and Christman (1960) and Schroter and Engelbrecht (1957) has shown that work with excised root cultures of *Nicotiana tabacum* can contribute to the study of the synthesis of nicotine and nornicotine and that of West and Mika (1957) that both root and callus cultures of *Atropa belladonna* can be used in the study of atropine biosynthesis. Recently (Hadwiger and Waller, 1964), in a study with cultured roots of *Ricinus communis*, ^{14}C-labelled ricinine has been isolated from both roots and culture medium after feeding with niacin-7-^{14}C and succinic acid-2-3-^{14}C. Evidence that allantoin is synthesized in *Symphytum* from glycine via purine intermediates was obtained in work with excised root cultures (Butler, Ferguson and Allison, 1961). The successful growth of callus and suspension cultures of *Agave toumeyana* and *Dioscorea compositae* (Nickell and Tulecke,1960; Tulecke and Nickell, 1959; Weinstein, Nickell, Laurencot and Tulecke, 1959) open up possibilities yet to be exploited on the biosynthesis of hecogenin and diosgenin, respectively.

A number of workers (von Wacek, Härtel and Meralla, 1953, 1954; Barnoud, 1956; Bardinskaya, 1961) have used tissue cultures of herbaceous and woody species in studies of the biological activity of possible lignin precursors such as coniferin, syringin and vanillin as expressed by their effects on growth and lignin formation. Hasegawa, Higuchi and Ishikawa (1960) have used a callus derived from the cambium of *Pinus strobus* in studying the formation of shikimic acid and lignin consequent upon feeding glucose-1-^{14}C, shikimic acid-G-^{14}C, sodium acetate-1-^{14}C and sodium acetate-2-^{14}C. Lamport and Northcote (1960a, b) have used suspension cultures derived from a stem callus of *Acer pseudoplatanus* (sycamore) for studies on cell walls and reported the presence in the walls of the cultured cells of a hydroxyproline-containing protein. Preliminary studies with tissue cultures have also been reported on factors controlling the development of anthocyanins (Slabecka-Szweykowska, 1952, 1955; De Capite, 1955; Straus, 1959, 1960a).

No attempt has been made above to cover comprehensively the literature relating to the applications of tissue and organ cultures to studies in biosynthesis, but the limited number of citations given illustrate that in this field there are as yet no major advances to report although it is evident that plant cultures are well suited to such studies, particularly when combined with the use of isotopic tracers. Additional references to this aspect of work with plant cultures are given in a recent paper (Street, Henshaw and Buiatti, 1965).

B. BIOCHEMICAL MUTANTS AND INTRASPECIFIC VARIATION

Another and possibly more far-reaching development is foreshadowed by the isolation of arginine-requiring strains of tissue from pollen of *Ginkgo biloba* L. by Tulecke (1960). These arginine-requiring strains probably each arose from a separate pollen grain and can be interpreted as a reflection of the genetic differences to be expected between the separate pollen grains. Tulecke therefore regarded these strains as biochemical mutants selected by an appropriate culture medium from a large population of pollen grains.

Blakely and Steward (1962, 1964) have described the detection, by the Bergmann (1960) plating technique and the use of a medium favouring anthocyanin production, of green anthocyanin-free colonies amongst the large number of red colonies derived from their *Haplopappus* cell suspensions. The variant colonies remained essentially anthocyanin-free on subculture and some of the variants were reported to have karyotypes differing from normal. The same workers using suspensions of carrot cells have found that, while nearly all colony formation is suppressed by incorporating 0·5 p.p.m. acriflavine into the medium, occasional colonies arise with varying degrees of resistance to acriflavine (Fig. 1). Single-cell clones isolated by the technique of Muir, Hildebrandt and Riker (1958) have also been shown to differ from one another in colour, texture and response to sugars (Arya *et al.*, 1962).

Here then we have the description of different strains characterized by their modified metabolic activities, strains which in these differences reflect the genetic heterogeneity within the parent cell populations from which they have arisen. In the case of pollen this heterogeneity is the outcome of segregation at meiosis expressing itself in the metabolism of haploid cells. In the other cases quoted it would seem to be the outcome of random genetic changes occurring spontaneously in somatic cells. This genetic instability of cultured cells is probably involved, not only in the sectoring which has often been observed in pigmented callus cultures, but in the recent report by Sievert, Hildebrandt, Burris and Riker (1961) that single-cell clones differing in colour, texture and growth rate can be isolated from callus masses, themselves of known single cell origin. This instability is reflected in changes in nuclear cytology (polyploidy and chromosomal abnormalities) reported by a number of workers (Partanen, 1959; Mitra, Mapes and Steward, 1960; Mitra and Steward, 1961; Denes and Roderick, 1961; Blakely and Steward, 1964). Further, there is evidence that certain media may promote, and other media may suppress, the development of polyploidy in cultured tissues. Thus Torrey (1958a) found that a pea root callus remained predominantly diploid when cultured in a simple medium but that supplementation of this medium with either kinetin (5×10^{-6}M) or with yeast extract (1 g/l) plus 2,4-D (10^{-5}M) caused an increased proportion of the cells to be tetraploid. In old cultures in such media it was possible to demonstrate all degrees of ploidy from diploid (2n) to 12n, aneuploids

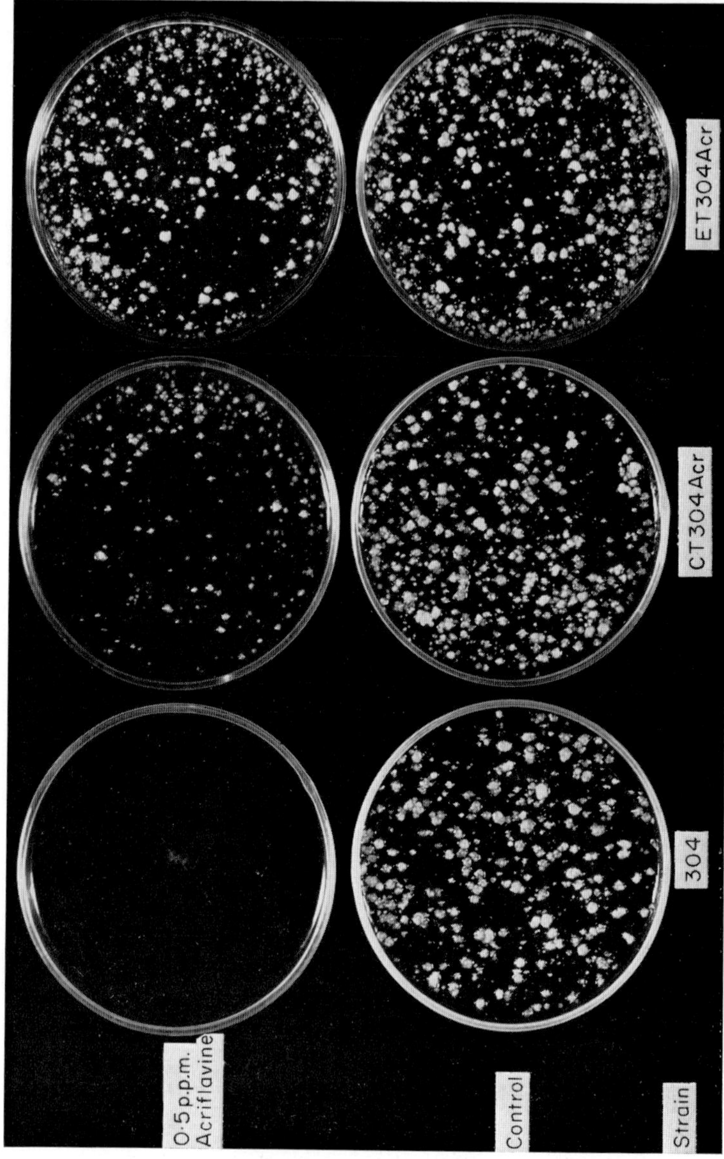

Fig. 1. Acriflavine resistance of two selected strains (CT 304. Acr) (ET 304. Acr) of carrot tissue (strain 304). Resistance revealed by plating suspension on to agar medium in Petri dishes. (By courtesy of F. C. Steward and co-workers.)

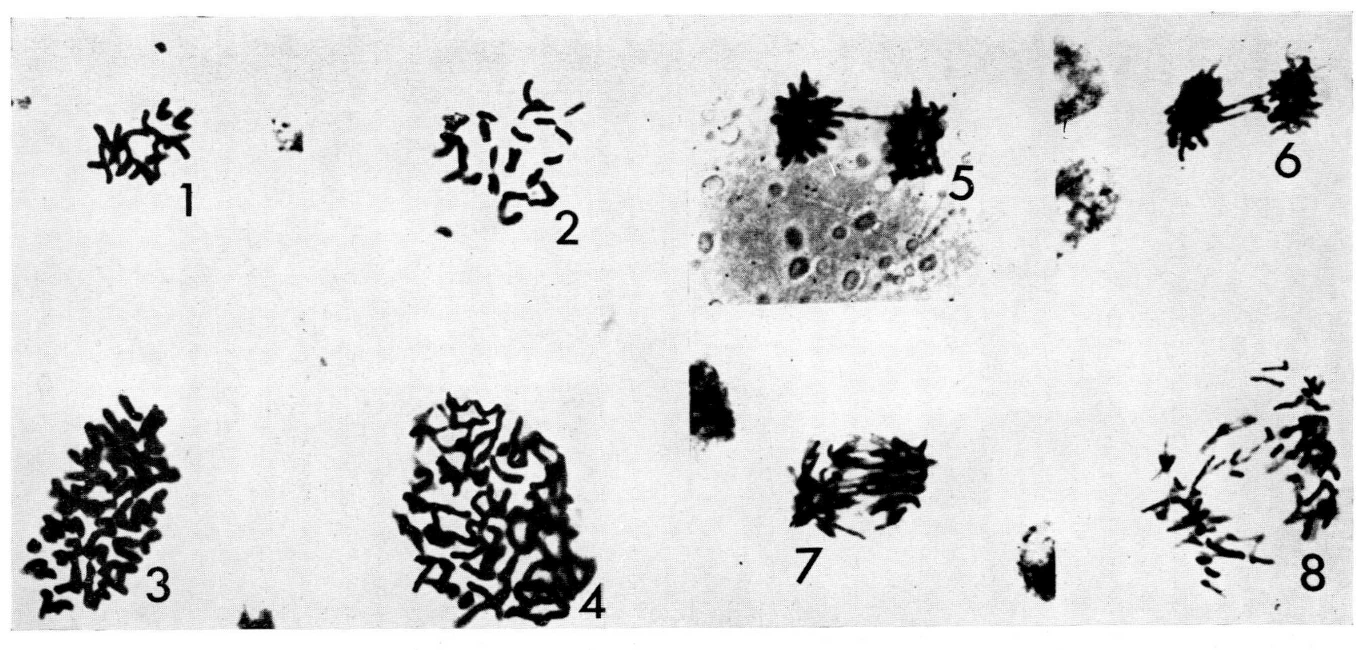

Fig. 2. Feulgen-stained squash preparations of pea root callus tissue cells. Tissue cultured in a yeast extract—2,4-D medium. 1–4, Metaphase division figures; 5–8, anaphase division figures of tetraploid nuclei. 1, Diploid; 2, tetraploid; 3, octoploid; 4, 12n nucleus; 5, 6, chromosome bridges; 7, chromosome loops; 8, chromosome rings. (After Torrey, 1959.) × 1125.

(especially around 4n ± 1) and cells showing aberrant mitoses (anaphase bridges, chromosome loops and rings) (Fig. 2). While such genetic instability clearly can be exploited, work should also be developed to see whether cell lines can be selected, either from existing tissue cultures or from new and appropriate species, which would maintain a higher degree of nuclear stability under a wide range of cultural conditions.

These studies on "mutant" strains arise from attempts to assess the feasibility of using cultures of the cells of higher plants for microorganism-like biochemical genetics. To test this intriguing possibility further it is urgently necessary to be able, by developing techniques like that of Bergmann, to obtain a high efficiency of colony formation when plating separated cells on media of known composition. It also needs to be shown that biochemical mutants, comparable with those produced in bacteria and fungi, can be induced in higher plant cells. Where, as in the African violet, plantlets arise from single cells of the petiole (Naylor and Johnson, 1937), it has been possible to produce viable mutants by irradiation (Sparrow, Sparrow and Scharrer, 1960). Currently, the action of radiomimetic agents and ultraviolet radiation on cultured cells of *Haplopappus* is being studied in the Department of Physiological Botany, Uppsala, by Kihlmann and Eriksson. Further studies along these lines may be expected from a number of laboratories in the immediate future.

Intraspecific genetic differences, either not expressed in the phenotype of the whole plant or expressed in small morphological differences, are often revealed by excised roots as marked differences in growth habit or in growth responses to nutritive variables in culture. Outstanding examples are the differences revealed between excised roots of tomato varieties (Bonner, 1940; Robbins, 1941; White, 1943b; Whaley and Long, 1944), of pea varieties (Naylor and Rappaport, 1950) and of geographic strains of *Senecio vulgaris* (Skinner, 1952, 1953; Harland and Skinner, 1954). The apparently successful culture of maize roots by McClary (1940) as contrasted with many unsuccessful attempts by other workers, probably depended upon the use of a particular strain. An attempt to repeat results such as those reported by White (1938b) or Bonner (1940) will immediately show the importance of the strain used in determining the behaviour of the excised roots in culture. The only attempt at genetic analysis linked to work with excised root cultures is that of Skinner (1952, 1953). Crosses were made between geographic strains of *Senecio vulgaris* that differed markedly in the growth rate of their excised roots under the standard conditions of culture. Excised root cultures from the F_2 generation were intermediate in growth rate between those of the parent strains, the variation within the F_1 population was small and its distribution quite distinct from those of either parent. Neither dominance nor hybrid vigour were therefore detected in the excised roots of the hybrids. Excised roots from the successful crosses (F_1) were identifiable by their growth rate in culture and this identification was checked by raising plants from the aseptically cultured seedlings from which the root cultures had been established. Segregation for excised root characters occurred in the F_2 generations of all crosses. The reciprocal hybrids did not differ in the behaviour of their F_2 segregates so that no evidence of cytoplasmic inheritance was obtained. Some of the excised roots of the F_2 segregates had growth rates in culture equal to that of the faster-growing parent of F_1, some as slow as the slow-growing parent. There was also transgressive segregation with growth rates in F_2 roots above those of the faster and below those of the slower-growing parents. In certain cases, there were indications of differences in the segregations of F_2 families pointing to heterozygosity in the parent strains; a study of F_3 roots also gave evidence of heterozygosity in the parent strains. The low variability of the parent strains and F_1 progeny, the overlapping and transgression of the parent distributions by those of the F_2 generation and the fairly true breeding of the F_2 individuals suggested to Skinner that the growth rates of the excised roots were determined by a small number of major genes subjected to the action of a large number of modifiers. Further, Harland and Skinner (1954) postulated that the biochemical variability exposed by root culture probably represented the outcome of a large amount of mutation not subjected to selection since it did not result in conferring a selective advantage or disadvantage on the growth of the whole plant under natural conditions.

Some of these intraspecific differences have been analysed physiologically in terms of vitamin requirements and responses to growth-regulating substances. Reference has already been made to differences in the requirement for B vitamins exhibited by the excised roots of different tomato varieties (Section V, A, p. 569; see also Street, 1957). In the case of the groundsel strains, first studied by Skinner, more recent work by Charles (1959) has produced strong evidence that the growth differences in culture are due to differences in auxin physiology. Four strains, "Iceland", "Czechoslovakian", "Peruvian" and "Wetherley" which grew at very different rates in the basic arginine-supplemented medium, could all be raised to a uniformly high growth rate by using for each strain an appropriate concentration of the auxin, 2-naphthoxyacetic acid. The slower growing strains required a higher dosage of external auxin than the faster growing strains. The results strongly suggested that the different behaviour in culture of the roots of the various strains was determined by their different and suboptimal levels of a natural auxin.

In the above examples, genetic information regarding the strains has been lacking. However, in 1958, Lee established in culture several clones of a strain of tomato roots carrying the gene for dwarfism, *wd*, and also clones carrying the normal allele, wd^+. The roots carrying wd^+ had a higher growth rate than those carrying *wd*, apparently mainly due to a higher rate of cell division at the main apices. An attempt was then made (Lee, 1959) to see whether any growth factor (e.g. auxin, kinin, gibberellin) or antimetabolite (e.g. an antiauxin) would enhance differentially the growth of the slowly growing *wd*-carrying roots. The only factors acting at all in the sense required, and then not very definitively, were light (growth of *wd* roots was favoured in the dark, that of wd^+ in the light) and treatment with eosin at 10^{-9}g/ml in both light and dark (difficult to interpret for eosin is only reported to promote auxin destruction in the light). It was thus not possible to make any tentative identification of the cell constituent whose level in the roots might be determining the difference in growth rate between the normal and mutant clones. Whaley and Kephart (1957) have reported differences in the response to GA of roots derived from different inbred lines of maize (lines not carrying dwarfism genes) but they did not follow up the work to relate the response to any particular combination of genes. Venketeswaran and Mahlberg (1962) have recently obtained in culture, callus tissues derived from three normal strains of tobacco and from an albino strain. Albinism in this species apparently arises in presence of the double recessive of two Mendelian characters located on different chromosomes (Clausen and Cameron, 1950). In culture, the three different normal strains all formed chlorophyll although there seemed to be reduced chlorophyll synthesis in one of the heterozygotes. No critical work on the gene control of chlorophyll synthesis in these strains has yet been attempted through these tissue cultures, but the authors express the view that the cultures obtained could be employed to advantage in "gaining an insight into cytogenetical, biochemical and morphological phenomena".

What seems to be overlooked in much of this work is that, even within species which have been intensively worked upon by plant geneticists, there may be many genetic differences over and above those known to distinguish the strains and that, in culture, these differences may modify or even overshadow the genetic differences apparently being studied. The controlled irradiation of populations of single cells (particularly haploid cells), themselves of recent single cell origin and the selection of clearly defined nutritional, thermal or other mutants by appropriate cultural conditions seems to be the most suitable approach if we wish to gauge the possibilities of opening up the biochemical genetics of higher plant cells.

C. INTRA-STRAIN VARIATION

The differences with which we have been concerned above are those manifested between varieties or strains within species. There are also a considerable number of examples of *intra-strain* variation revealing itself in excised root culture by the different behaviour of roots derived from different seeds, often seeds which are part of a common harvest from a highly inbred line. In a pioneer paper, Robbins and Maneval (1923) refer to the establishment of ten root clones each from a separate seed of *Lupinus albus*. Nine of the ten roots ceased growth and became necrotic, the tenth root survived and was apparently repeatedly subcultured. Bonner (1942a) reported that of eighty-two roots established from separate seedlings of *Sterculia diversifolia*, eighty had ceased growth by the fourth subculture but the remaining two roots continued to grow, one being retained for thirteen weekly growth periods and the other for twenty-one similar subcultures. Similar exceptional roots were obtained from seedlings of *Bauhinia purpurea*, *Wisteria sinensis* and *Acacia melanoxylon*. Naylor and Rappaport (1950) were able, by selection from a large initial population of excised pea roots (var. "Perfection") to obtain a few cultures which would grow vigorously without the addition to the medium of a mixture of tryptophane and cysteine. Roberts and Street (1955), although able to establish clones of excised Petkus II rye roots in continuous culture, found that only 10% of the seed sample would yield cultures capable of indefinite growth on subculture. Robbins (1941) and Boll (1954a) have made careful studies using highly inbred strains of tomato as sources for root cultures. For instance, Boll starting with seed harvested from a single fruit of a highly inbred, highly homozygous plant of the "Red River" strain was able to select from fifty-one initial cultures, six clones which covered the main range of variation and which continued to differ consistently and significantly in both quantitative and qualitative features over many subculture passages. It is clear that a similar phenomenon can be encountered in the establishment of callus cultures (Gautheret, 1959).

D. ADAPTATION PHENOMENA

In all these intra-strain differences there is a strong element of doubt as to how far the differences have a genetic basis, and this applies particularly to differences within highly inbred lines. This uncertainty arises from a number of observations. For example, there is the question of how far certain rather long-term "adaptive" physiological changes occur before tissues reach a "steady state" of growth and metabolism in culture. Certainly, if such processes are involved, then initial physiological vigour rather than genetic constitution may determine which cultures achieve this adjustment before, for instance, metabolites carried over with the initial explant are exhausted to a critical level. Bonner and Addicott (1937), working with excised pea roots grown in medium supplemented with yeast extract, found that with both 1-week and 2-week culture periods, there was, after the second subculture, a steady increase in growth rate through successive subcultures. Bonner (1940), working with roots of *Helianthus annuus,* noted that in the last 2 weeks of an experiment involving seventeen weekly subcultures, the growth rate was 200% of the average for the first 5 weeks. White (1943b) found that various strains of tomato grew equally well in media supplemented with either aneurin plus glycine or with aneurin plus pyridoxine. Three of the clones were maintained for a number of passages in the medium supplemented with aneurin plus glycine. When one of these clones was transferred to aneurin plus pyridoxine medium it grew poorly during the first culture period in the new medium (30% of that in the aneurin plus glycine control) but by its third growth period the growth rate had risen to a value of 82% of that in the simultaneous aneurin plus glycine control. The roots apparently required, after growth in aneurin plus glycine, a period of "adaptation" to aneurin plus pyridoxine. Similarly, in studies on the growth of excised tomato roots with organic forms of nitrogen it has been found that the growth rate may not stabilize or reach its maximum value for a number of culture periods (Joyce Hughes, unpublished work) suggesting a form of "adaptation". The evidence obtained by Abbott (1963) and referred to on p. 535 shows that significant changes in chemical composition occur as the seedling root tip grows in culture. Evidence that certain enzyme systems may be activated by culture comes from the demonstration of a much higher phosphatase activity in the mature cortical cells of cultured as compared with seedling tomato roots (McGregor and Street, 1953). The detection by Vaidyanathan and Street (1959b) of a natural inhibitor of glutamotransferase in excised tomato roots and the demonstration that the level of this inhibitor is increased in response to feeding L-glutamine as the sole nitrogen source, can also be interpreted as an adaptive change to the conditions of culture. Gautheret (1953) has reported that various callus tissues, if subjected to a period of stimulated proliferation by receiving coconut milk plus auxin, develop a growth requirement for the coconut milk, indicating the possibility of the repression of enzyme systems active before the coconut milk feeding.

Gautheret (1942) observed that strains of normal carrot tissue capable of culture in the absence of added auxin (IAA) gradually altered in their response to IAA. The proliferation of freshly isolated explants was stimulated by additions of IAA at appropriate concentrations. However, after a period of culture in presence of IAA, the tissue no longer responded in this way. Various investigators (Morel, 1948; Kandler, 1952; Henderson, 1954) have reported, in work with various other callus tissues, a similar change in response to auxin. Gautheret referred to this phenomenon first as "accoutumance à l'auxine" (1942, 1946) and later as "anergie à l'auxine" (anergy) (1955b). This anergy can occur not only with tissues initially capable of proliferation without added auxin but also with tissues, like that of *Scorzonera,* which must be supplied with auxin when first put into culture. Such tissues can, after numerous transfers, acquire the ability to grow in the absence of external IAA and are then no longer capable of showing an IAA-stimulation. These "anergized" tissues differ from normal tissues not only in their insensitivity to IAA but in being translucent, friable and incapable of initiating roots. Kulescha (1952) has shown that they contain a higher content of free auxin than normal tissues. The "anergized" tissue also shows more or less pronounced tumour-forming properties as evidenced by grafting (Camus and Gautheret, 1948a, b; Braun and Morel, 1950; Henderson, 1954). In tobacco this is particularly marked, the "anergized" tissue being more malignant than crown-gall tissue (Limasset and Gautheret, 1950).

Recently, Braun (private communication) has observed an interesting example of anergy in tissue cultures of *Vinca rosea.* Normal tissue of this species does not grow on White's basic culture medium but requires the following organic growth factors, auxin, m-inositol, kinetin, glutamine, asparagine, cytidylic and guanylic acids (see p. 566). A large number of fragments of such tissue were planted on White's medium in which the total salt concentration had been raised sixfold. With one exception, these tissue fragments did not grow. In that one instance, growth developed from one small portion of the tissue fragment. The new growth was isolated and again planted on White's medium in which the salt concentration had been raised sixfold. The tissue grew very profusely and indefinitely on that medium or on a medium in which the only change in the inorganic salt composition was a sixfold increase in potassium iodide. 1,3-diodotyrosine added to White's basic medium also permitted the growth of this tissue. Addition of kinetin plus cytidylic acid to White's basic medium similarly permitted good growth of the tissue. The metabolic block preventing the growth of the altered tissue on White's basic medium appeared, therefore, to be in the area of purine and pyrimidine biosynthesis. The enzyme systems concerned with auxin, m-inositol, glutamine, and asparagine biosynthesis appeared to have been unblocked. A very large number of fragments of the tissue that grew profusely on White's medium in which the salt concentration was raised sixfold were planted on White's basic medium. Of these, one fragment showed, after prolonged culture, a new growth originating from one of the pieces of tissue. This new growth was isolated and cultured on White's basic medium where it grew well and continuously. Such tissue had acquired the capacity to synthesize all of the seven growth factors required by the original normal tissue and, therefore, nutritionally resembled fully transformed tumour tissue.

This phenomenon of anergy is regarded by Gautheret (1955b) as a form of enzymatic adaptation, since its reproducibility seems to preclude mutation or selection of cells with a special genotype. This leads to the proposition that IAA application induces in the tissue a capacity for auxin synthesis. Clearly this is not a very special phenomenon confined to auxin metabolism and occurring only with certain tissues and under particular cultural conditions. Cultured plant tissue and organs seem generally to be capable of multiple "adaptations" affecting their powers of synthesis and assimilation. Gautheret (1950a, 1955b) cites the case of willow tissue initiated in a complex medium which became able to grow actively without several of the growth factors initially important for its proliferation; in particular, the tissue lost its need for an external supply of pantothenic acid. Similarly, the virus tumour tissue of *Rumex acetosa* has recently been reported (Nickell, 1961) to have no longer any need for aneurin. Several growth-factor synthesizing systems appear to be activated in Braun's studies on *Vinca rosea* tissue.

Examples can also be found from work with excised root cultures which can be interpreted as indicating both repression and activation of synthetic activities. Robbins and Stebbins (1949) report the maintenance of a clone of excised tomato roots in culture for many passages (96) at a reasonably constant growth rate by supplying only the thiazole moiety of aneurin. Then, fairly rapidly, the growth rate of the cultures declined (it was very poor by the 100th passage) although the clone exhibited active growth in medium supplemented with aneurin. The authors suggested that the roots cultured with the thiazole addition had lost the ability to synthesize the pyrimidine moiety of aneurin. Boll (1954b), studying the growth of the roots of tomato strains on pyridoxine-free medium, occasionally encountered roots which grew abnormally well and whose main axis tips were exceptional in their healthy appearance. However, clones derived from these roots by subculturing lateral apices showed the normal pyridoxine requirement. In this case the altered metabolism permitting growth in the absence of pyridoxine was limited to individual main axes and apparently was not transmitted to the newly initiated laterals. This, combined with the fact that these exceptional roots arose on a number of occasions, was regarded as indicating that a mutant was not involved. More recently, Willemot and Boll (1962) have reported that a *clone* of excised tomato roots, originally selected for its marked requirement for pyridoxine and grown for 6 years in a medium containing this vitamin, now grows much more readily in a pyridoxine-free medium than when originally isolated. The reported results do not indicate when or how suddenly or slowly the change in ability to grow on the pyridoxine-free medium occurred. Willemot and Boll exclude a mutational basis for *this* change on the grounds that, with the generally accepted view of the histogenesis of lateral root meristems, the mutation would have to take place in several cells (!) and that the mutation would possibly need to be in two alleles because of the highly inbred nature of the parent plant. Further, it was considered very unlikely that a variant arising in a single meristem had been selected since the mechanism of clonal maintenance involved at least several stock cultures on each occasion and there was no evidence of any significant change in the growth rate or morphology of the clone as maintained in the pyridoxine-containing medium.

These various but inconclusive indications that adaptive physiological changes involving the biosynthetic activity of cultured plant tissues and organs may occur relatively slowly (that is, over a number of subculture periods of 7 days or more each) prompts consideration of whether any similar phenomena have been reported from work with whole organisms. Hinshelwood (1946) reported that the bacterium, *Bacillus lactis aerogenes,* can, over a number of successive subcultures, be trained to utilize glycerol as a carbon source and, if fully trained, can retain, at least for a time, this ability when grown in the absence of glycerol and supplied with dextrose. The work of Shrift (1954) and Shrift, Nevyas and Turndorf (1961a, b) shows that *Chlorella vulgaris* can slowly develop a resistance to the antimetabolite, selenomethionine. At an intermediate stage in this adaptation all the cells showed some, but variable, degrees of adaptation. Here the adaptation is due to enhanced activity of the enzymes responsible for the reduction of sulphate leading to methionine synthesis, and the resistance persists in the absence of the inducing antimetabolite. However, sulphur starvation or methionine feeding leads to a decrease in the activities of the sulphate-assimilating enzymes and, in consequence, loss of resistance to the antimetabolite. Thresher and Street (1962), working with a particular strain of the same organism cultured in darkness, have also reported slow training to utilize galactose as an effective carbon source and have reported that the trained cells have increased galactokinase activity. In this case, the activity of the galactokinase and the associated ability to utilize galactose very quickly decreases when galactose is replaced by the readily utilizable sugar, dextrose. *Chlorella* also provides an example of more rapid adaptation, that to the utilization of α-glucosides (Neish, 1951). From higher plants the only reports of enzymic adaptation known to the author are those of glycolic acid oxidase (Tolbert and Cohan, 1953), indoleacetic acid oxidase (Galston and Dalberg, 1954) and nitrate reductase (Tang and Wu, 1957). This is in marked contrast to the numerous examples and intensive studies of adaptation in bacteria and fungi (Hinshelwood, 1946; Pollock, 1959). The indications of the rather widespread occurrence of adaptation phenomena in plant tissue culture are thus of interest, not only because of the possible importance of induction and repression of enzyme synthesis in cellular differentiation (Monod and Jacob, 1961), but because of the poverty of established instances of such phenomena from higher plants and the fact that no such instances have been intensively studied.

A second factor which may be relevant to a proper interpretation of the so-called intra-strain differences exposed by root culture relates to the behaviour of excised root meristems under suboptimal conditions. In some cases, where it has been reported that only one or a few cultures survived from a number established from separate seeds or seedlings, the technique of subculture adopted was that of repeated excision of main axis root tips. Excised tomato root clones can probably be established from all or almost all normal tomato seedlings. However, if the main axis root tips from within any easily cultured clone are subjected to repeated subculture (which involves the continuous survival of activity in individual meristems) and if this is attempted in a suboptimal medium (for instance in a medium containing a supra-optimal concentration of sucrose), then after a few weeks many of the meristems will have completely ceased to grow and eventually the whole population of meristems will be inactive (Street, McGonagle and Roberts, 1953). Within a large population there will be a wide time difference between the first appearance of this "ageing" phenomenon in the apices and the cessation of growth activity in the most persistent meristems. Study of the week-by-week growth of those roots which persist indicates that they have passed through a succession of growth crises at fairly regular intervals but that at these times the apices have not quite ceased growth and have subsequently undergone a process of physiological regeneration carrying with it again the liability to a complete loss of growth activity (Street and McGonagle, 1953). Each root thus shows a repeating growth pattern in which sequences of increasing growth values alternate with sequences of decreasing growth values, and analysis of the data by Gleissberg's (1946) method gives strong statistical evidence for a cyclic growth behaviour. Again, survival or meristematic activity is greatly affected by the length of the apical portion transferred on each occasion; the larger the amount of mature tissue transferred, the higher the incidence of loss of growth activity. The apparent superiority of individual roots, sometimes interpreted as indicating genetic variation, could then well reflect either physiological variability or lack of standardization of technique. There is here, however, again the complication of adaptation. Street and McGonagle (1953), starting from clonal material (material built up from a single meristem) and adopting this technique of repeated subculture of the main axis meristems, were able to isolate roots and develop from them, clones having much better chances of survival on repeated subculture, together with a higher mean growth rate and a lower variability as between successive passages.

VIII. The Release of Metabolites into the Culture Medium

A. Release of Organic Metabolites and Enzymes

The sterility of plant cultures ensures that the metabolites detected in their culture media have not been derived from or modified by the activity of micro-organisms. Care is, however, required if one wishes to exclude the possibility that the compounds detected are not being released mainly or entirely by dead cells. To test critically that the detected substances are being released by living cells of the culture, it is necessary to remove carefully all sloughed off cells and to examine the ability of the older and superficial cells to be plasmolysed or to fulfil some other criterion indicating that they are alive. Further, it is only when release is then followed over short test periods under conditions favourable to growth that one can feel confident that release from living cells is being studied and is not being modified by release from cells dying from unfavourable conditions of culture or as a consequence of differentiation. Emphasis will here be given to studies of release from sterile plant cultures but unfortunately, in most of the cases which will be mentioned, the question of how far the release is from dead cells has not been critically examined. With excised root and stem tips there is the further complication of exposing open ends of conducting elements and cut surfaces with damaged cells and thereby obtaining substances in the culture medium, some of which may be escaping from cut surfaces and others from intact tissue cells. Such surfaces usually become sealed over with wound callus during culture and once this has occurred there is no evidence of any mass flow of vascular fluids into the medium. With root culture the technique of Raggio and Raggio (1956) permits the cut surface to be removed from contact with the liquid culture medium. This aspect of the release of substances by organ culture has, however, rarely been subject to critical examination and reservations of this kind must be borne in mind in considering much of the evidence that the living cells of plant tissues do release metabolites into their culture media.

Dawson (1942) noted the excretion of nicotine by excised root cultures of *Nicotiana tabacum* but suggested that the origin of the excretion was from the cut xylem or phloem elements. However, the demonstration (see p. 577) that root callus cultures of *Atropa belladonna* synthesize and release atropine into the culture medium strongly suggests that alkaloids can be released through the membranes of growing tissue cells (West and Mika, 1957). Bonner (1940, 1942c) has demonstrated the synthesis and release into the culture medium of biotin and riboflavin from the root cultures of a number of species. The earlier demonstration by West (1939) that aneurin and biotin are released from the surface of intact young roots of flax seedlings in sterile culture suggested strongly that Bonner's observations probably indicated release of vitamins from intact cells of the cultured roots.

Lundegårdh and Stenlid (1944) obtained evidence that nucleotides, inorganic ions and sugars are released by excised pea and wheat roots and that wheat roots release, in addition, a flavone. From studies of absorption spectra it was concluded that adenosine monophosphate was the main constituent of the nucleotide fraction. Evidence was obtained that the rate of release of organic substances was related to the rate of ion uptake by the root cells, that release of nucleotides took place mainly from the apical 5–10 mm of the roots and that release of xylem sap from the cut surface contributed very little to this release. In relation to the nucleotide release it was postulated that the growth of young cells is dependent upon a supply of nucleotides from the nucleus to the cell membranes from which they were progressively lost to the culture media by diffusion. It was further suggested that the cessation of growth and of nucleotide secretion as the cells matured was related to a depletion of nucleotides by this loss to the external environment. Stenlid went on to show, in work with excised wheat roots, that the release was enhanced when oxygen uptake of the root cells was inhibited by cyanide or azide (Stenlid, 1948) and also enhanced by levels of methylene blue and α-α-dipyridyl which did not affect oxygen uptake but were regarded as interfering with the energy transfer required for the maintenance of cellular membranes (Stenlid, 1950). More recently, Wright (1962) has demonstrated a promotion of leakage of previously accumulated ^{14}C-labelled glycine from excised roots of wheat, barley and mustard by addition of the protein-synthesis inhibitor, chloramphenicol, or the enzyme, ribonuclease.

Fries and Forsman (1951) detected the release of lysine, arginine, methionine, uridine, cytidine, adenine and guanine (or their nucleosides), traces of adenosine and unidentified ultraviolet absorbing substances from cultured excised pea roots and from the roots of sterile seedlings. They concluded, in line with Lundegårdh and Stenlid, that these compounds were released mainly from the root apices.

Kandler (1951) has shown that excised maize roots, cultured in a dextrose-containing medium, release amino acids, prominent amongst which are glutamine, alanine, serine, aspartic acid, valine, asparagine, leucine, isoleucine, and glutamic acid. When the culture solution becomes depleted of nitrate some reabsorption takes place, particularly of the released glutamine, but while this happens other amino acids are also being released. Kandler considered that the amino acid composition of the "staled" medium sufficiently resembled that of the free amino acids of the roots to suggest that the excretion mechanism is one of free diffusion from the root cells modified by reabsorption under conditions of nitrate deficiency. Tesar and Kutacek (1955) studied the amino acids released from the roots of sterile wheat plants and excised wheat root cultures. They found that the basic amino acids were relatively more prominent in the mixture released by the whole plant, and threonine, valine and methionine in the mixture released by the root cultures. However, in both cases, they concluded that the free amino acid composition of the culture medium after supporting root growth was sufficiently similar to that of the roots to support strongly Kandler's hypothesis that free outward diffusion of soluble organic constituents takes place from root cells. Anomalies in the distribution of γ-aminobutyric acid and proline were explained by postulating that the former arose from glutamic acid and the latter from either glutamic acid or ornithine by the action of enzymes located on the external surface of the root.

Melhuish (1962) has demonstrated that the roots of sterile tomato seedlings and cultured excised tomato roots both secrete a complex mixture of some seventeen amino acids and has studied the influence of various factors on the release by the cultured excised roots. This release of amino acids from the root cultures was followed after the development of a sealing callus over the cut surface and after removal of sloughed off cells and washing of the root surface in fresh medium. From several lines of evidence it was concluded that the release was normally an expression of the behaviour of growing cells of unimpaired metabolism. The release was sensitive to the ionic composition of the medium (e.g. omission of Ca^{++} decreased release), to pH (increased by lowering the pH from 7·0 to 4·4), and to temperature (Q_{10} of release *ca* 1·4). Release only proceeded at a high rate under conditions conducive to amino acid synthesis (adequate carbohydrate and availability of a utilizable source of nitrogen). By appropriate feeding with nitrate or ammonium nitrogen, roots with differing free amino-acid pools were obtained. When release from these roots into medium containing their own nitrogen source was studied, there was a strong similarity between the composition of the released amino-acid mixture and that of the cellular pool. However, when nitrate-grown roots were placed in ammonium medium, or vice versa, the released amino-acid mixture resembled more closely that of the pool which tends to build up from the nitrogen source present in the external medium than that of the existing cellular pool of the test roots. To explain their results, Tesar and Kutacek (1955) endorsed the view that roots are "open systems" from which free diffusion of metabolites can take place. The results of Melhuish suggest a modification of this to the effect that most of the amino-acid pool of the roots is in a non-free space from which they do not readily diffuse but that amino-acid synthesis is taking place in a "free space" and that, in consequence, the released amino-acid mixture closely resembles that of the mixture of amino-acids being currently synthesized. The recent studies of Oaks (1965) on the incorporation of leucine into protein in the growing region of the maize root provides independent evidence for two distinct amino-acid pools. The larger of these pools (designate the "soluble pool") is strongly enriched by externally supplied leucine but only very slowly yields leucine for incorporation into protein and is probably in the "non-free space" of the cells. The second and smaller pool (designated the "metabolic pool") yields most of the leucine for protein synthesis and contains the leucine being synthesized at the apex or reaching the apex by translocation. The release of amino acids, studied by Melhuish, seems to occur from a pool of this kind.

Melin and co-workers have demonstrated the release, by cultured pine roots and cultured roots of several dicotyledonous species, of metabolites which are essential for the growth of certain tree mycorrhizal fungi (Melin, 1954; Melin and Das, 1954). The metabolites concerned are apparently not any of the well known vitamins or amino acids but they have not been identified and are referred to as factor M (Melin, 1954).

A number of workers have reported the release of enzymes from different kinds of tissue cultures (Nickell and Burkholder, 1950;

Brakke and Nickell, 1951; Lampton, 1952; Straus and LaRue, 1954; Ball, 1955; Constabel, 1960, 1961, 1963; Straus and Campbell, 1963). In most of these cases, the release has not been convincingly shown to occur from living cells and in certain instances the results could be explained in terms of the activity of surface-localized enzymes whose products accumulate in the medium. Szember (1960) observed that, with radish roots grown in an agar medium containing phytin, there rapidly developed a clear area around the roots strongly indicative of the diffusion from the root of a phytin-degrading enzyme. Similarly, Lipetz and Galston (1959) have produced evidence for the release of peroxidase from growing cultures of normal and crown-gall callus of *Parthenocissus*. Chang and Bandurski (1964) have demonstrated that maize roots release, as soluble exoenzymes, invertase and a nuclease. It therefore seems likely that enzymes may be released from intact cultured cells. In the case of roots, studies of fine structure suggest that the root cap cells are specialized secretory cells in which Golgi bodies are particularly prominent. Vesicles apparently derived from the Golgi bodies occur outside the plasmalemma and the evidence suggests that these vesicles move from the Golgi bodies across the hyaloplasm and through the plasmalemma (Mollenhauer, Whaley and Leech, 1961; Mollenhauer and Whaley, 1963). Although the mechanism of this transfer is not fully understood, freeze-etched surface views of the plasmalemma show dissolution of circular areas of the membrane, 200–300 Å wide (Branton and Moor, 1964). Until recently there also seemed to be a growing body of evidence that plant cells could actively absorb foreign proteins (McLaren, Jensen and Jacobson, 1960; Jensen and McLaren, 1960) and that this uptake was by pinocytosis (Bhide and Brachet, 1960). However, further experimental work has cast serious doubt on the validity of the earlier evidence for such inward transport of protein (Bradfute, Chapman-Andreson and Jensen, 1964; Bradfute and McLaren, 1964; Barton, 1964).

These selected examples, indicative of the release of identifiable metabolites from organ and tissue cultures, have been briefly reviewed here in view of the many reports of the release of biologically active organic substances from the roots and other organs of higher plants (Börner, 1960) and the evidence that such compounds are of importance in the interactions between higher plants, including cases of parasitism, and in the establishment of root nodules, the "rhizosphere" (Katznelson, Lochhead and Timonin, 1948; Rovira, 1956) and mycorrhizas (Harley, 1959). Release of metabolites from higher plant cells may therefore have wide biological significance and involve many different metabolites and growth-regulating substances. Plant tissue and organ cultures seem particularly well suited for more precise studies of the influence of environmental and nutritive factors on this release and for elucidating the metabolic or physical processes through which the release is mediated.

B. CONDITIONED MEDIA

This phenomenon of metabolite release may have a direct and immediate bearing on our ability to grow cells and tissues in culture. Thus, if as a result of tissue growth, a culture medium decreases in its growth-promoting activity we describe it as "staled" medium. This "staling" may involve both depletion of nutrients and accumulation of metabolic products. Thus, excised tomato roots as a result of growing in White's medium not only render that medium iron-deficient and lacking in sucrose (the depletion of sucrose being accompanied by the appearance in the medium of dextrose, laevulose and traces of inhibitory sugars), but at the same time many organic metabolites including phenolic substances (prominent among which is salicylic acid) strongly inhibitory to root growth are liberated (Winter and Street, 1963).

Alternatively, when as a consequence of tissue growth a medium develops enhanced growth-promoting activity, and particularly when this phenomenon is involved in the transition from a lag-phase of growth to a phase characterized by exponential growth of the culture, we talk of a "conditioning" of the medium. Such "conditioned" media are media enriched by the release of organic substances from living cells and the conditioning is complete when these metabolites attain a critical concentration in the medium. Thus, in the conventional methods of animal cell culture, an inoculum of about 10^5 cells is usually required for self-sustaining growth to be initiated (Earle, Sanford, Evans and Shannon, 1951), although it was shown (Sanford, Earle and Likely, 1948) that single cells of certain tissues could be induced to divide by introducing them into fine capillaries containing a medium previously "conditioned" by supporting the growth of a mass of cells. Further, although certain cell types (e.g. the HeLa strain of malignant epithelial cells) could, with high efficiency, give rise to colonies from single cells when plated out in Petri dishes of a suitable new medium (Scherer, Syverton and Gey, 1953), this method is not uniformly successful with other mammalian tissue cells, though the introduction (Puck, Marcus and Cieciura, 1956) of a "feeder" system of cells whose own reproduction had been terminated by a previous exposure to X-irradiation allowed single-cell survival where it had previously failed. This technique has shown that cells of different origins differ greatly in their effectiveness as "feeders" to induce other types to generate clones of single cell origin. Presumably the effective "feeder" cells are cells which selectively and, in adequate quantities, release metabolites not provided by the culture medium and essential to the nutrition and division of the test cells.

This concept guided Muir, Hildebrandt and Riker (1954, 1958) when they successfully established callus cultures of single cell origin by isolating single cells from suspension cultures and friable callus masses and by placing them on the upper surface of filter-paper squares whose lower surface made good contact with an actively growing "nurse" callus of the same crown-gall origin (Chap. 8, Fig. 14, p. 515). That induction of division in the single cells had occurred and not simply growth through the paper of the nurse callus mass seemed almost certain. This was confirmed by Torrey (1959) who successfully established single cell clones of a pea root callus by interposing a millipore membrane (pore size 0·5–0·75 μ) between the single cells and the nurse callus. In experiments of this kind only some of the isolated cells divide and a still smaller proportion continue division to give rise to a callus sufficiently large to permit its subculture and the establishment of a clone. However, for such cells, the release of inorganic and organic nutrients by the nurse callus has met their requirements for division and growth in a way which cannot yet be achieved with media of known composition.

A different approach, but one which also involves the conditioning principle is illustrated by studies with a hanging-drop techniquc undertaken by Jones, Hildebrandt, Riker and Wu (1960) (Chap. 8, Fig. 16, p. 516) using cells derived from a callus of a tobacco hybrid (*Nicotiana tabacum* × *N. glutinosa*). Using fresh culture medium they observed cell divisions only when numerous cells were present in the drop. In such cultures some cells divided, enlarged and differentiated, while others remained quiescent. When these differentiated cells became senescent or died, some of the smaller cells of the culture were again stimulated to divide, enlarge and differentiate. Increase in cell number occurred in surges. Divisions with a single cell per drop were, however, observed in a medium "conditioned" by having previously supported the growth of a cell population.

A third technique involving plating out suspensions of free cells has been developed by Bergmann (1960) using a medium solidified with agar (0·6%) and containing coconut milk and 2,4-dichloro-phenoxyacetic acid. Starting with suspension cultures of *Nicotiana tabacum* var. Samsun and *Phaseolus vulgaris* var. Early Golden Cluster, he obtained a fraction in which 90% of the units were single cells and these were then spread on the surface of the soft agar medium. Under these conditions and with these tissue strains, up to 20% of thc cells underwent repeated divisions to give rise to small colonies which could be successfully subcultured in tubes of agar medium. Although cell aggregates constituted some 10% of the units it seems likely that some of the clones established by this technique were from single cells. Subsequent work by Blakely and Steward (1961, 1962) (Chap. 8, Figs. 17, 18, pp. 518, 519) with suspensions of *Haplopappus* and carrot has shown that the total number of units plated influences the frequency with which colonies arise, that washing the cellular units before plating decreases the incidence of colonies and that introduction of nurse pieces of callus on to the plates promotes colony formation, particularly when using a "washed" suspension otherwise limited to single cells and small cell aggregates by appropriate filtration. By a detailed photographic study, these workers showed that a few of the visible colonies were of single-cell origin (in one experiment of 235 single cells whose behaviour was followed, thirty-four showed some enlargement or division and of these seven went on to give rise to small colonies). When pieces of nurse callus were introduced, it was clearly seen that colony formation was enhanced in their vicinity. Torrey and Reinert (1961) have obtained visible colonies by plating suspensions of *Convolvulus* containing a mixture of single cells and cell aggregates onto a completely synthetic medium solidified with agar, but whether any of these colonies were derived from single cells was not determined. Results, some still unpublished (Mehta, 1963, and others), obtained by the use of this plating technique not only confirm the importance of cell density on the plates and the promotive influence of the larger ("feeder") aggregates but also indicate that incorporation of "conditioned" medium into the agar may be beneficial to colony formation, that the physiological condition of the cells at the time of plating may be critical and that cell lines can be selected for their ability to form colonies after plating. At least with certain tissue strains, it has been found that suspensions freshly prepared from callus masses give rise to colonies with much greater frequency than do suspensions which have been repeatedly subcultured in liquid medium. Further, where samples for plating are removed from suspension cultures at intervals during a culture passage it is found that colonies do not develop with a high frequency unless the culture is actively growing; highest frequencies are often recorded with samples taken immediately *after* the peak of cell division activity has been passed in the suspension culture. Several of these observations stress the importance of metabolite release from non-dividing cells and cell masses for the initiation of division in single cells and the continuation of division in the small cell groups so formed.

The nature of the metabolites involved in the conditioning of plant culture media is obscure. It is, therefore, of interest that the release of indole compounds by excised root cultures has recently been reported (Winter and Street, 1963; Street *et al.*, 1964). One of these, on present evidence, appears to be a 5-hydroxytryptophane peptide which is active at very low concentrations in a number of bioassays involving both cell division and cell enlargement.

Further study of culture media which have supported the growth of plant tissues and organs and, particularly, attempts to detect and isolate growth-active substances from such media may clearly lead us to a better understanding of the special growth requirements of actively dividing cells.

IX. The Resistance to Growth in Culture Encountered with some Organs, Tissues and Cells

A. Introduction

Any worker seeing the potential value to his research of growing a particular organ or tissue in sterile culture will find it difficult from the literature to assess whether this is likely to be easily achieved. In general, the literature describes instances of successful culture rather than those of abortive efforts. Often it is not at all clear whether the techniques of culture described represent a successful first attempt or have been developed as a result of a long process of trial and error and therefore must be followed quite meticulously. Further, as stressed in Section VII, B and C, p. 578 *et seq.*, the successful culture of an organ or tissue may be restricted to a particular variety or strain or even to a single sample of seed or parent individual and the method used may not apply to other varieties, strains or even individuals within that species. At the present stage in the development of plant tissue culture, estimates of the probability that a given organ or tissue can be cultured by the use of some well established manipulative procedure and one of a small range of recognized culture media are entirely precluded. Nevertheless, it is possible to set out the present position in very general terms, particularly from work with root cultures and to a lesser extent with callus tissues of normal and tumour origin.

White (1938b), using a medium capable of sustaining the continuous culture of excised tomato roots, studied the growth in culture of the roots of thirty-one dicotyledonous species drawn from eight families. Roots of nineteen species were apparently capable of culture; roots of the remaining species were quite refractory. White drew attention to the interest attached to this intractability of certain roots to culture, particularly where those of closely related species grew well.

Bonner (1942a) and Bonner and Bonner (1948) have also drawn attention to the intractability of the roots of many tree species, of all members of the Cucurbitaceae tested, and of all monocotyledonous species. The root tips from citrus seedlings and from most cucurbits when transferred to root-culture media show virtually no growth at all; cell division ceases within 24 h and any subsequent increase in length is due to cell expansion. The more general situation is that the root tips grow more or less vigorously in the period following excision, but this gives place to a declining rate of growth, and this decline is enhanced by subculture so that continuous culture cannot be achieved. This latter situation is well illustrated by the many unsuccessful attempts to culture the roots of cereals (Robbins, 1922a, b; Robbins and Maneval, 1924; Robbins and White, 1936, 1937; Fiedler, 1936; Bonner and Bonner, 1948; Almestrand, 1949, 1950, 1951, 1957).

A summary of published information regarding species from which excised roots have been grown in sterile culture is now available in tabulated form (Butcher and Street, 1964). Gautheret (1959) lists details in tabulated form for many of the callus cultures which have been established.

B. SUBCULTURE PROCEDURES

Some root tips when placed in culture give rise to a rapidly growing main root axis but lateral roots develop slowly, or not at all. When this is the case subculture must inevitably take place by repeated excision of the main axis root tips which precludes the development of clones and carries with it the problem of "ageing" of the initial meristems as described on p. 590. Undoubtedly, some and possibly all roots can be cultured indefinitely by this technique provided the culture medium contains all the essential nutrients at appropriate concentration and an appropriate subculture technique is adopted. Roots of several species were first continuously cultured by such repeated excisions of the main root tips (Bonner and Addicott, 1937; Bonner and Devirian, 1939; Bonner, 1940; White, 1938b; van Overbeek, 1939b). However, in cases of this kind, resistance to culture may mean that the culture conditions did not prevent "ageing" of the meristems. If this is so then success may well follow alteration of the duration of each culture passage, or of the size of the apical segment transferred on each occasion, or of the concentration of a major constituent of the medium such as the sugar. This draws attention to the fact that resistance to culture may not imply that an essential nutrient is missing from the culture medium but that an inappropriate manipulative procedure is being used. This necessity for adopting an appropriate procedure of subculture applies equally to roots which readily form laterals in culture and in which "sector cultures" can be grown and hence clones established and multiplied. As examples, one may cite the importance of passage length, as demonstrated by Roberts and Street (1955) working with rye roots, the importance of alternating sector with tip cultures as shown by Skinner and Street (1954) using roots of *Senecio vulgaris,* and the importance of using a standardized sequence of passages of unequal duration and involving subculture through both main axis and lateral tips as worked out by Dawson and Street (1959a) to obtain reproducibly active root tips for experimental work with *Trifolium pratense.*

An important variant in procedure, involving alternating two different culture media in succeeding passages and the two media together meeting the specific nutrient requirements of the roots, was introduced by Charles and Street (1959). Working with certain geographic strains of *Senecio* they obtained high growth rates in an arginine-containing medium by growing the roots in a previous passage in a medium lacking arginine but containing an appropriate concentration of tryptophane or an auxin. A technique of this kind subsequently enabled Bausá Alcalde (1961) to culture successfully the excised roots of the liliaceous plant, *Androcymbium gramineum.* Here a passage in Morel's medium (1950) supplemented with the auxin, γ-3-indolyl-n-butyric acid, was alternated with one in a medium containing adenine. The auxin promoted the initiation of laterals and then their active growth was promoted in the adenine-containing medium. This approach may be particularly valuable in establishing clones from roots which do not readily initiate laterals in standard root-culture media.

C. PHYSICAL FACTORS

Consideration of the importance of physical factors must enter into any analysis of why certain organs and tissues cannot at present be successfully grown in culture. Callus tissues have traditionally been cultured on media solidified with agar or silica gel (Gautheret, 1945) but more recently, and consequential to the work of Steward, Caplin and Millar (1952) and Heller (1949, 1953), liquid media have been used to an increasing extent and it is their introduction which has led to the development of suspension cultures. Liquid media have almost always been employed for root cultures and, in general, solidified agar media have proved either unsuitable or have supported significantly lower growth rates (Day, 1943). With certain media, where nutrient availability may become limiting because of such effects as pH change, the use of agar may promote uptake through the operation of contact-exchange phenomena (Chapman, 1939). Agar samples may also contain traces of growth-active substances or may adsorb substances released by the growing cells. Liquid media may, however, more effectively present nutrients to the culture and allow the dispersion of toxic exudates by virtue of a greater contact area and the development of convection currents. Probably more important is the question of how far gaseous exchange may differ in the two types of culture. A callus tissue growing on the surface of agar has the greater part of its surface in air. This was preserved in the technique developed by Heller (1953) in which the culture was supported on filter paper maintained moist by liquid medium. The technique adopted by Steward *et al.* (1952) subjected the tissue mass to alternate immersion in liquid medium and exposure to air. To make oxygen available effectively to callus cultures may, therefore, require their exposure to air, although this has not been critically tested. To obtain actively growing suspension cultures recourse is made to constant agitation, either by shaking the culture flasks, by forced aeration, or by magnetic stirring (see Chap. 8, Section II, G, p. 508) but, here again, these procedures have not been critically analysed and hence it is only surmise that they are of importance in meeting the oxygen requirement of the cells. Aeration of liquid media supporting the growth of excised tomato and wheat roots has not, in our experience, significantly enhanced growth rates and this may indicate that the oxygen requirements of excised root culture are effectively met in undisturbed liquid cultures.

An unappreciated aspect of gaseous exchange in plant tissue culture is that of the pressure of carbon dioxide. The knowledge that many heterotrophic micro-organisms are capable of carbon dioxide assimilation and that the presence of carbon dioxide or carbonate may be essential for their growth raises the possibility that carbon dioxide may be an essential nutrient for higher plant tissues in culture. A "dark" fixation of carbon dioxide has been shown to occur in succulent leaves (Thurlow and Bonner, 1948; Thomas, 1949) and in roots (Poel, 1953). More recently, Geisler (1963) has reported that appropriate levels of carbon dioxide applied to the root environment markedly stimulate extension growth, lateral development and dry-weight increase of the roots of pea plants growing in water culture. The superiority of liquid media for excised root cultures may, therefore, be related to a need for carbon dioxide or bicarbonate ions by the growing root cells. Recent unpublished results in our laboratory show that aeration with air containing 5% carbon dioxide, as contrasted with aeration with carbon dioxide-free air, enhances the growth of excised wheat roots.

Many callus cultures when exposed to light become green and contain chloroplasts. However, most such tissues are only pale green and many callus tissues remain without chloroplast pigments when grown in the light. The photosynthetic activity of green cultured tissues has not been investigated but at present the growth of all such tissues depends upon an external supply of sugar (see p. 535). White (1943a) reviewing the situation as it applies to both tissue and organ cultures concluded that they are, for the most part, relatively insensitive to light and can be grown equally well in either darkness or in diffuse light. This statement may be justified in so far as it indicates that photosynthesis is not essential for the growth of cultured tissues. It is, however, possible that a low light dosage operating through other pigment systems may still prove to be of real importance to continued growth in culture. This possibility arises from two considerations. The first is that there are no published papers reporting the continuous culture of plant organs or tissues under conditions rigorously excluding intermittent exposure to light, such as normally occurs during the subculture procedure, even if the cultures are incubated in strict darkness. Evidence that very small amounts of light may be essential for normal growth and cell division in an organism otherwise capable of heterotrophic nutrition is illustrated by the work of Killam and Myers (1956) with the Emerson strain of *Chlorella pyrenoidosa*. The second line of evidence comes from observations on the effect of light on the growth of excised root cultures. Robbins and Maneval (1924) noted that light from a north-facing window, as against darkness, prolonged the duration of growth of excised maize roots subcultured every 14 days. White (1932) seems to have observed some stimulation of growth of excised wheat root by daylight and artificial light and, more recently, Street *et al.* (1961) found that illumination dramatically enhanced both the level and duration of growth of excised roots of a wheat variety when they were cultured in a casein-containing medium. In a further study (Scott *et al.*, 1961), they showed that fluorescent light at an intensity as low as 1·5 lux (0·62 ergs/cm^2 sec) caused full expression of the enhancement of the linear growth of their cultured wheat roots, although increasing dry weight values were obtained up to an intensity of 300 lux or even higher. Gautheret (1935) reported that light promoted the growth of excised roots of *Lupinus albus* and Roberts (1954) observed that diffuse light prolonged the duration of growth and enhanced apical dominance in roots of *Lycopersicum pimpinellifolium* repeatedly subcultured by excision of their main axis tips. Street (1953) similarly reported that tungsten filament light of low intensity (4–97 lux) increased the rate and duration of main-axis growth of excised tomato roots. Against these reports of enhanced and prolonged growth following illumination can be placed a number of observations upon the inhibitory effects of light on the growth of cultured roots (Malyschev,

1932; Segelitz, 1938; Delarge, 1941; Burström and Hejnowicz, 1958; Burström, 1959, 1960). These inhibitory effects have generally occurred where relatively high levels of illumination have been used. It is also clear that a level of illumination which may be inhibitory to a root culture newly initiated from a seedling root tip may, as growth in culture continues, become either no longer inhibitory or significantly activating to growth (Fujiwara and Ojima, 1954; Ojima and Fujiwara, 1959, 1962; Street *et al.*, 1961).

For any established plant culture growing under standard conditions there is an optimum temperature for growth, and temperatures a few degrees above this optimum are usually injurious. In all quantitative studies, cultures are therefore incubated at a fixed temperature, usually within the range 25–30°C. To what extent temperatures of incubation have influenced reports on culturability cannot be judged from the literature, and long term experiments at different fixed temperatures within the range 5–30°C or with alternating "day" and "night" temperatures do not seem to have been undertaken with plant cultures. Temperature is clearly one of the variables which should be studied in connection with the adaptation phenomena referred to in Section VII, D, p. 585.

D. NUTRITIONAL FACTORS

Although manipulative procedures and physical factors may be important to the question of the culturability of plant tissues, it is also clear that in some and probably in many cases our inability to culture a particular organ or tissue arises from our inability to meet its specific nutrient requirements. The concept that existing culture media are lacking in nutrients essential to the growth of some tissues is favoured as explaining many instances of resistance to growth in culture despite the possibility, raised by Boll (1960), that some tissues may be inhibited or may cease their growth because of excessive accumulation of certain metabolites. Initially vigorous growth, declining and ultimately ceasing in culture, could be the outcome of either depletion of essential metabolites or accumulation of by-products of metabolism. What really favours the depletion hypothesis are the examples where continuous growth in culture has followed upon further elaboration of the basic culture media of White and Gautheret.

In our experience, certain roots can be cultured in a medium containing yeast extract and this has not yet been replaced by a supplement of known composition. However, in other cases where yeast extract was needed as a supplement to White's medium the growth requirements of the roots have been studied and the activity of the yeast traced to a single constituent (Skinner and Street, 1954; Roberts and Street, 1955) and a satisfactory synthetic medium prepared. Similarly, the stimulating effect of casein hydrolysate on the growth of excised wheat roots can be reproduced by a mixture of pure amino acids (Sutton *et al.*, 1961) and this applies to a number of other cases where protein hydrolysates have proved essential for, or have enhanced the growth of plant cultures.

In 1941, van Overbeek, Conklin and Blakeslee succeeded in growing immature *Datura* embryos in culture by including the liquid endosperm of *Cocos nucifera* (coconut milk) in their culture medium. In 1948, Caplin and Steward were unable to culture fragments of carrot root phloem in presence of IAA but obtained a high rate of proliferation when coconut milk was added. After this pioneer work, coconut milk was quickly shown to stimulate cell division in other cultured tissues and its use as a supplement was adopted in many laboratories (Duhamet, 1949, 1950a, b, 1951; Duhamet and Gautheret, 1950; Morel, 1950; Nickell, 1950b; Henderson, Durrell and Bonner, 1952; De Ropp *et al.*, 1952; Archibald, 1954; Wiggans, 1954). A number of tumour tissues and "anergized" tissues insensitive to auxin were also found to be markedly stimulated by coconut milk. Moreover, it was reported that when tissues were sensitive to auxin there occurred a synergistic interaction between auxin (IAA or 2,4-D) and coconut milk, and such a synergistic effect of this kind was exploited quite early in order to bring potato tuber tissue into culture (Steward and Caplin, 1951).

Other complex plant juices and liquid endosperms have been shown to possess stimulatory properties more or less similar to those of coconut milk. Nétien, Beauchesne and Mentzen (1951) and Steward and Caplin (1952) have demonstrated stimulation of carrot-tissue explants with liquid endosperm from immature corn and immature fruits of other grasses. Tomato juice first tested against crown-gall tissue by Nitsch (1951) has subsequently been shown to be stimulatory to the growth of other tissues and was used in the medium which first established corn endosperm tissue in culture (Straus and LaRue, 1954). Stimulatory juices have also been obtained from a number of other immature fruits (including *Juglans regia* and *Aesculus woerlitzensis*) and seeds (Steward and Caplin, 1952; Kovoor, 1953, 1954; Nitsch, 1954; Steward and Shantz, 1959a). Steward and Caplin (1952) also found that the female gametophyte of *Ginkgo* yields an extract stimulatory to the growth of carrot cells.

Coconut milk is at present necessary for the growth of many normal callus tissues and it enhances the growth of many more. It has recently been reported as an essential ingredient of media for the growth of excised roots of *Eucalyptus camaldulensis* (Bachelard and Stowe, 1963).

Almost all suspension cultures (other than those of tumour tissues) show active growth with a coconut-milk medium and, until very recently, such media were used in all attempts to induce divisions in isolated plant cells.

Great interest therefore attaches to the identification of the active constituents of natural fluids like coconut milk. Straus (1960b) showed that the tomato juice, yeast extract or casein hydrolysate, required for the growth of corn endosperm tissue, functioned by supplying an acceptable form of organic nitrogen (a mixture of amino acids) and that this requirement of the tissue could be even better met by addition of asparagine. A spruce tissue culture which previously required a medium supplemented by malt extract can now be cultured in a synthetic medium containing an auxin, kinetin, m-inositol, urea and arginine (Steinhart, Standifer and Skoog, 1961). De Maggio and Wetmore (1961) reported that the coconut-milk requirement of 17-day-old embryos of *Todea barbara* could be met by a mixture of m-inositol and sorbitol. In some cases, the stimulatory action of coconut milk appears to be mainly or entirely due to its content of organic nitrogen and of vitamins and this may well be the case for *Scorzonera* crown-gall tissue where a similar stimulation of growth can be obtained with a mixture of eleven amino acids plus seven B vitamins (Paris *et al.*, 1954). Similarly, other and more complex supplements of known amino acids, purines and vitamins, based upon present knowledge of the composition of coconut milk (Tulecke, Weinstein, Rutner and Laurencot, 1961) have been found to substitute for coconut milk in maintaining the growth of certain suspension cultures (Shigemura, 1958; Reinert, 1959; Torrey and Reinert, 1961; Torrey, Reinert and Merkel, 1962). It must be emphasized, however, in connection with these very complex synthetic media, that the essentiality of the individual compounds has not been critically tested and that while such media are apparently satisfactory for the strains of tissue for which they were developed they do not have the general growth-promoting activity of coconut milk-containing media.

Pollard, Shantz and Steward (1961) have divided the active components of coconut milk into three fractions, namely, a *nitrogenous* component (consisting of reduced nitrogen compounds particularly amino acids and their amides), a *neutral* component (in which the most prominent constituents are m-inositol, scyllo-inositol and sorbitol) and an *active* component. The composition of this active component has so far resisted analysis but is regarded as including auxin or auxin precursors and a factor or factors which "specifically stimulate cell division". The discovery of the activity of 6-furfurylaminopurine (kinetin) in promoting cell division in tobacco and carrot cells (Miller *et al.*, 1956) and the subsequent preparation of a number of active analogs of this compound led to the introduction of the term "kinins" to describe this class of cell division-promoting compounds (Skoog and Miller, 1957; Strong, 1958) (see Section VI, B, p. 573). The recent evidence that kinins occur in plant tissues (Goldacre and Bottomley, 1959; Zwar, Bottomley and Kefford, 1963; Letham and Bollard, 1961; Miller, 1961; Beauchesne, 1962; Letham, 1963a; Loeffler and van Overbeek, 1964; Weiss and Vandra, 1965) and that they are, at least in some cases, purine derivatives related closely to kinetin (Letham, 1963b; Letham, Shannon and McDonald, 1964) raises the question of the importance of such substances in accounting for the activity of natural fluids like coconut milk. In this connection, however, it has been reported that the effects of the active component of coconut milk certainly cannot be replaced by kinetin or its synthetic analogs (Steward and Shantz, 1959b). There is also evidence that the active component contains biologically active substances, for instance leucoanthocyanin-like compounds (Steward and Shantz, 1959b), chemically distinct from the known kinins.

Further progress in our understanding of the specific growth requirements of certain tissue cultures now awaits advances in our knowledge of the chemical nature of the active component of coconut milk and of the kinins detected in an increasing number of plant tissues. Such discoveries, by permitting the use of simpler supplements (supplements containing the active components of natural extracts but devoid of associated inactive or even inhibitory constituents), may not only enable us to use synthetic media for the growth of tissues which now require complex natural supplements, but may make possible the culture of tissues resistant even to such active growth stimulants as coconut milk.

References

Abbott, A. J. (1963). The growth and development of excised roots in relation to trace element deficiencies. Ph.D. Thesis, University of Bristol.

Almestrand, A. (1949). Studies on the growth of isolated roots of barley and oats. *Physiol. Plant.* **2**, 372.

Almestrand, A. (1950). Further studies on the growth of isolated roots of barley and oats. *Physiol. Plant.* **3**, 205.

Almestrand, A. (1951). The effects of pyridoxine on the growth of isolated grass roots. *Physiol. Plant.* **4**, 224.

Almestrand, A. (1957). Growth and metabolism of isolated cereal roots. *Physiol. Plant.* **10**, 521.

Archibald, J. F. (1954). Culture *in vitro* of cambial tissues of cacao. *Nature, Lond.* **173**, 351.

Archibald, R. M. (1945). Chemical characteristics and physiological roles of glutamine. *Chem. Rev.* **37**, 161.

Arnow, P., Oleson, J. J. and Williams, J. H. (1953). The effect of arginine in the nutrition of *Chlorella vulgaris*. *Amer. J. Bot.* **40**, 100.

Arya, H. C., Hildebrandt, A. C. and Riker, A. J. (1962). Clonal variation of grape stem and *Phylloxera* gall callus growing *in vitro* in different concentrations of sugars. *Amer. J. Bot.* **49**, 368.

Asboe-Hansen, G. (1954). "Connective Tissue in Health and Disease". Munksgaard, Copenhagen.

Audus, L. J. and Bakhsh, J. K. (1961). On the adaptation of pea roots to auxins and auxin homologues. *In* "Plant Growth Regulation" (R. M. Klein, ed.), pp. 109-124. Iowa State University Press, Ames, Iowa.

Audus, L. J. and Gunning, B. E. S. (1958). Growth substances in the roots of *Pisum sativum*. *Physiol. Plant.* **11**, 685.

Bachelard, E. P. and Stowe, B. B. (1963). Growth *in vitro* of roots of *Acer rubrum*, L. and *Eucalyptus camaldulensis*, Dehn. *Physiol. Plant.* **16**, 20.

Baker, D. M. and Ray, P. M. (1965). Direct and indirect effects of auxin on cell wall synthesis in oat coleoptile tissue. *Plant Physiol.* **40**, 345. The effect of auxin on synthesis of oat coleoptile cell wall constituents. *Plant Physiol.* **40**, 353. Relation between effects of auxin on cell wall synthesis and cell elongation. *Plant Physiol.* **40**, 360.

Ball, E. (1950). Differentiation in a callus culture of *Sequoia sempervirens*. *Growth* **14**, 295.

Ball, E. (1953). Hydrolysis of sucrose by autoclaving media, a neglected aspect in the technique of culture of plant tissues. *Bull. Torrey bot. Club* **80**, 409.

Ball, E. (1955). Studies of the nutrition of the callus culture of *Sequoia sempervirens*. *Année biol.* **31**, 80.

Bardinskaya, M. S. (1961). Plant lignification and some questions of cell growth. *Doklady Akad. Nauk, SSSR* **136**, 1486.

Barnoud, F. (1956). Influence de la coniférine et de la syringine sur les processus de lignification dans les cultures de tissue cambial de deux essences ligneuses. *C. R. Acad. Sci., Paris* **243**, 1545.

Barton, R. (1964). Electron microscope studies on the uptake of ferritin by plant roots. *Exp. Cell Res.* **36**, 432.

Bausá Alcalde, M. (1961). Sobre el cultivo *in vitro* de raices aisladas de *Androcymbium gramineum* (Cav.) McBride. *Farmacognosia* **21**, 71.

Beauchesne, G. (1962). Recherches sur les substances de croissance du mais immature. *Rev. Bot.* **69**, 493.

Bergmann, L. (1960). Growth and division of single cells of higher plants *in vitro*. *J. gen. Physiol.* **43**, 841.

Bhide, S. V. and Brachet, J. (1960). Study of the uptake of ribonuclease by onion root-tip cells. *Exp. Cell Res.* **21**, 303.

Bitancourt, A. A. (1949). Mecanismo genetico da tumorizacao nos vegetais. "Programma da 2a. semana de genética", p. 7 Puacicaba, 8–12 de Fevereiro.

Bitancourt, A. A. (1955). Recherches physiologiques sur les auxines. *Rev. gen. Bot.* **62**, 498.

Blakely, L. M. and Steward, F. C. (1961). Growth induction in cultures of *Haplopappus gracilis*. I. The behaviour of cultured cells. *Amer. J. Bot.* **48**, 351.

Blakely, L. M. and Steward, F. C. (1962). The growth of free cells. II. Observations on individual cells and their subsequent patterns of growth. III. The observation and isolation of variant strains. *Amer. J. Bot.* **49**, 653.

Blakely, L. M. and Steward, F. C. (1964). Growth and organized development of cultured cells. VII. Cellular variation. *Amer. J. Bot.* **51**, 809.

Boll, W. G. (1954a). Studies on the growth of excised roots. V. Growth of excised roots of two inbred lines of tomato and their reciprocal crosses in media supplemented with various growth factors. *New Phytol.* **53**, 406.

Boll, W. G. (1954b). Investigations into the function of pyridoxin as a growth factor for excised tomato roots. *Plant Physiol.* **29**, 325.

Boll, W. G. (1954c). The role of vitamin B_6 and the biosynthesis of choline in the excised tomato root. *Arch. Biochem. Biophys.* **53**, 20.

Boll, W. G. (1959). Evidence for negative feedback in the control of ethanolamine biosynthesis in excised tomato roots. *Canad. J. Bot.* **37**, 1071.

Boll, W. G. (1960). Ethionine inhibition and morphogenesis of excised tomato roots. *Plant Physiol.* **35**, 115.

Bonner, D. (1946). Production of biochemical mutants in *Penicillium*. *Amer. J. Bot.* **33**, 788.

Bonner, J. (1938). Thiamine (vitamin B_1) and the growth of roots: the relation of chemical structure to physiological activity. *Amer. J. Bot.* **25**, 543.

Bonner, J. (1940). On the growth factor requirements of isolated roots. *Amer. J. Bot.* **27**, 692.

Bonner, J. (1942a). Culture of isolated roots of *Acacia melanoxylon*. *Bull. Torrey bot. Club* **69**, 130.

Bonner, J. (1942b). Transport of thiamin in the tomato plant. *Amer. J. Bot.* **29**, 136.

Bonner, J. (1942c). Riboflavin in isolated roots. *Bot. Gaz.* **103**, 581.

Bonner, J. (1943). Further experiments on the nutrition of isolated tomato roots. *Bull. Torrey bot. Club* **70**, 184.

Bonner, J. and Addicott, F. (1937). Cultivation *in vitro* of excised pea roots. *Bot. Gaz.* **99**, 144.

Bonner, J. and Bonner, H. (1948). The B vitamins as plant hormones. *Vitam. Horm.* **6**, 225.

Bonner, J. and Devirian, P. S. (1939). Growth factor requirements of four species of isolated roots. *Amer. J. Bot.* **26**, 661.

Bonner, J. and Koepfli, J. B. (1939). The inhibition of root growth by auxins. *Amer. J. Bot.* **26**, 557.

Börner, H. (1960). Liberation of organic substances from higher plants and their role in the soil sickness problem. *Bot. Rev.* **26**, 393.

Bouriquet, R. (1955). Action de diverses substances synthétiques sur le développement des tissus végétaux cultivés *in vitro*. *Année biol.* **30**, 371.

Bouriquet, R. and Mentzer, C. (1951). Recherches sur l'action comparée de l'acide α-naphtylvinyl-acétique et de l'acide α-naphtalène-acétique sur les cultures de tissus de Topinambour et de Carotte. *C. R. Acad. Sci., Paris* **232**, 1574.

Bouriquet, R. and Pachéco, H. (1952). Action du chlorhydrate de N-méthyl-N-phenylglycolle sur les cultures de tissus de Topinambour et de Carotte. *C. R. Acad. Sci., Paris* **234**, 234.

Bradfute, O. E., Chapman-Andresen, C. and Jensen, W. A. (1964). Concerning morphological evidence for pinocytosis in higher plants. *Exp. Cell Res.* **36**, 207.

Bradfute, O. E. and McLaren, A. D. (1964). Entry of protein molecules into plant roots. *Physiol. Plant.* **17**, 667.

Brakke, M. K. and Nickell, L. G. (1951). Secretion of α-amylase by *Rumex* virus tumors *in vitro*. Properties and assay. *Arch. Biochem. Biophys.* **32**, 28.

Brakke, M. K. and Nickell, L. G. (1952). Lack of effect of plant growth-regulators on the action of alpha amylase secreted by virus tumor tissue. *Bot. Gaz.* **113**, 482.

Brakke, M. K. and Nickell, L. G. (1955). Secretion of an enzyme from intact cells of a higher plant tumor. *Année Biol.* **31**, 215.

Branton, D. and Moor, H. (1964). Fine structure in freeze-etched *Allium cepa* root tips. *J. Ultrastructure Res.* **11**, 401.

Braun, A. C. (1943). Studies on tumor inception in the crown-gall disease. *Amer. J. Bot.* **30**, 674.

Braun, A. C. (1947). Thermal studies on the factors responsible for tumor initiation in crown-gall. *Amer. J. Bot.* **34**, 234.

Braun, A. C. (1951). Cellular anatomy in crown-gall. *Phytopathology* **41**, 963.

Braun, A. C. (1958). A physiological basis for autonomous growth of the crown-gall tumor cell. *Proc. nat. Acad. Sci., Wash.* **44**, 344.

Braun, A. C. (1961). Plant tumors as an experimental model. *Harvey Lect.* Ser. 56, 191.

Braun, A. C. and Morel, G. (1950). A comparison of normal, habituated and crown-gall tumor tissue implants in the European grape. *Amer. J. Bot.* **37**, 499.

Braun, A. C. and Wood, H. N. (1962). On the activation of certain essential bio-synthetic systems in cells of *Vinca rosea*, L. *Proc. nat. Acad. Sci., Wash.* **48**, 1776.

Britton, G., Housley, S. and Bentley, J. A. (1956). Studies in plant growth hormones. V. Chromatography of hormones in excised and intact roots of tomato seedlings. *J. exp. Bot.* **7**, 239.

Brown, R. and Possingham, J. V. (1957). Iron deficiency and the growth of pea roots. *Proc. roy. Soc.* B, **147**, 145.

Bryan, W. H. and Newcomb, E. H. (1954). Stimulation of pectin methylesterase activity of cultured tobacco pith by indoleacetic acid. *Physiol. Plant.* **7**, 290.

Burkholder, P. R., Castle, H. and Smith, P. H. (1948). Studies on the nutrition of the moss *Catharinea undulata*, L. *Amer. J. Bot.* **35**, 807.

Burkholder, P. R. and McVeigh, I. (1942). The increase in B vitamins in germinating seeds. *Proc. nat. Acad. Sci., Wash.* **28**, 440.

Burkholder, P. R. and Nickell, L. G. (1949). Atypical growth of plants. I. Cultivation of virus tumors of *Rumex* on nutrient agar. *Bot. Gaz.* **110**, 426.

Burkholder, P. R. and Snow, A. G., Jr. (1942). Thiamine in some American trees. *Bull. Torrey bot. Club* **69**, 421.

Burström, H. (1941a). Studies on the carbohydrate nutrition of roots. *LantbrHogsk. Ann.* **9**, 264.

Burström, H. (1941b). On formative effects of carbohydrates on root growth. *Bot. Notiser*, p. 310.

Burström, H. (1942). The influence of heteroauxins on cell growth and development. *LantbrHogsk. Ann.* **10**, 209.

Burström, H. (1957a). Root surface development, sucrose inversion and free space. *Physiol. Plant.* **10**, 741.

Burström, H. (1957b). On the adaptation of roots to β-indolylacetic acid. *Physiol. Plant.* **10**, 187.

Burström, H. (1959). Growth and formation of intercellularies in root meristems. *Physiol. Plant.* **12**, 371.

Burström, H. (1960). Influence of iron and gibberellic acid on the light sensitivity of roots. *Physiol. Plant.* **13**, 597.

Burström, H. and Hejnowicz, Z. (1958). The formation of chlorophyll in isolated roots. *K. fysiogr. Sällsk. Lund Förh.* **28**, 65.

Butcher, D. N. (1963). The presence of gibberellins in excised tomato roots. *J. exp. Bot.* **14**, 272.

Butcher, D. N. and Street, H. E. (1960a). The effects of gibberellins on the growth of excised tomato roots. *J. exp. Bot.* **11**, 206.

Butcher, D. N. and Street, H. E. (1960b). Effects of kinetin on the growth of excised tomato roots. *Physiol. Plant.* **13**, 46.

Butcher, D. N. and Street, H. E. (1964). Excised root culture. *Bot. Rev.* **30**, 513.

Butler, G. W., Ferguson, J. D. and Allison, R. M. (1961). The biosynthesis of allantoin in *Symphytum.* *Physiol. Plant.* **14**, 310.

Camiener, G. W. and Brown, G. M. (1959). The biosynthesis of thiamine and thiamine phosphates by extracts of Baker's yeast. *J. Amer. chem. Soc.* **81**, 3800.

Camus, G. and Gautheret, R. J. (1948a). Sur le caractère tumoral des tissus de Scorsonère ayant subi le phenomène d'accoutumance aux hétéro-auxines. *C. R. Acad. Sci., Paris* **226**, 744.

Camus, G. and Gautheret, R. J. (1948b). Sur le repiquage des proliférations induites sur les fragments de racines de Scorsonère par des tissus de crown-gall et des tissus ayant subi le phénomène d'accoutumance aux hétéro-auxines. *C. R. Soc. Biol., Paris* **142**, 771.

Caplin, S. M. and Steward, F. C. (1948). Effect of coconut milk on the growth of explants from carrot root. *Science* **108**, 655.

Carter, J. E. and Street, H. E. (1963). Studies on the growth in culture of excised wheat roots. IV. The activation of *dl*-tryptophane by autoclaving. *Physiol. Plant.* **16**, 347.

Chang, C. W. and Bandurski, R. S. (1964). Exocellular enzymes of corn roots. *Plant Physiol.* **39**, 60.

Chapman, H. D. (1939). Absorption of iron from finely ground magnetite by citrus seedlings. *Soil Sci.* **48**, 309.

Charles, H. P. (1959). Studies on the growth of excised roots. VII. Effects of 2-naphthoxyacetic acid on excised roots from four strains of groundsel. *New Phytol.* **58**, 81.

Charles, H. P. and Street, H. E. (1959). Studies on the growth of excised roots. VI. The effects of certain amino acids and auxins on the growth of excised groundsel roots. *New Phytol.* **58**, 75.

Christiansen, G. S. and Thimann, K. V. (1950). The metabolism of stem tissue during growth and its inhibition. I. Carbohydrates. *Arch. Biochem.* **26**, 230.

Clausen, R. E. and Cameron, D. R. (1950). Inheritance in *Nicotiana tabacum.* XXIII. Duplicate factors for chlorophyll production. *Genetics* **35**, 4.

Constabel, F. (1960). Zur Amylasesekretion pflanzlicher Gewebekulturen. *Naturwissenschaften* **47**, 17.

Constabel, F. (1961). Das Wachstum der *Juniperus communis* Gewebekulturen in Gegenwart verschiedener Kohlenhydrate, insbesondere von Staike. *Planta* **57**, 331.

Constabel, F. (1963). Quantitätive Untersuchungen über die extracellulare Hydrolase von Kohlenhydraten durch *Juniperus communis* Gewebekulturen. *Planta* **59**, 330.

Czosnowski, J. (1952a). Charakterystyka fizjoligiczna trzech typow tkanek *Vitis vinifera*: normalnej, tumora bakteryjnego (crown-gall) i tumora chemicznego hodowanych *in vitro.* *Poznanskie towarzystwo przyjaciól nauk, Prace Kom. Biol.* **13**, 189.

Czosnowski, J. (1952b). Badania nad gospodarka witaminowa tkanek roślinnych. Hodowanych *in vitro* na tle ich gospodarki substancjami wzrostowymi typu auksyny. *Poznanskie towarzystwo przyjaciól nauk, Prace Kom. Biol.* **13**, 209.

Damodoran, M. and Sivaramakrishnan, P. M. (1937). New sources of urease for determination of urea. *Biochem. J.* **31**, 1041.

Danckwardt-Lilliesträm, C. (1957). Kinetin induced shoot formation from isolated roots of *Isatis tinctoria.* *Physiol. Plant.* **10**, 794.

David, S. B. (1954). Studies on the nutrition of excised roots of *Medicago sativa,* L. Ph.D. Thesis, University of Manchester.

David, S. B. (1958). Studies on the amino acid nutrition of excised roots of *Medicago sativa* L. "Modern Developments in Plant Physiology", Department of Botany, Delhi.

Dawson, J. R. O. (1958). Studies on the comparative physiology of excised roots derived from strains of red clover, *Trifolium pratense,* L. Ph.D. Thesis, University of Wales.

Dawson, J. R. O. and Street, H. E. (1959a). The behaviour in culture of excised root clones of the "Dorset Marlgrass" strain of red clover, *Trifolium pratense,* L. *Bot. Gaz.* **120**, 217.

Dawson, J. R. O. and Street, H. E. (1959b). The growth responses of a clone of excised roots of the "Dorset Marlgrass" strain of red clover, *Trifolium pratense,* L. *Bot. Gaz.* **120**, 227.

Dawson, R. F. (1942). Nicotine synthesis in excised tobacco roots. *Amer. J. Bot.* **29**, 813.

Day, D. (1943). Growth of excised tomato roots in agar with thiamine plus pyridoxine, nicotinamide or glycine. *Amer. J. Bot.* **30**, 150.

De Capite, L. (1955). Azione degli zuccheri e delle basse temperatura sulla formazione degli antociani in radici di *Daucus carota,* L. cultivate *in vitro. Rec. Scient.* 25^{e}an. **7**, 2091.

De Maggio, A. E. and Wetmore, R. H. (1961). Morphogenetic studies on the fern *Todea barbara.* III. Experimental biology. *Amer. J. Bot.* **48**, 551.

De Ropp, R. S. (1947). The response of normal plant tissues and of crown-gall tumor tissues to synthetic growth hormones. *Amer. J. Bot.* **34**, 53.

De Ropp, R. S., Vitucci, J. C., Hutchings, B. L. and Williams, J. H. (1952). Effect of coconut fractions on growth of carrot tissues. *Proc. Soc. exp. Biol., N.Y.* **81**, 704.

Delarge, L. (1941). Étude de la croissance et de la ramification des racines *in vitro. Arch. Inst. bot. Univ. Liége* **17**, 1.

Démétriadès, S. D. (1953). Essais de culture *in vitro* des tissus des galles du *Salvia pomifera* L. *Ann. Inst. Phytopathol. Benaki* **7**, 61.

Denes, de Torok and Roderick, T. H. (1961). Association between growth rate and chromosome number in a plant tissue culture. *Plant Physiol.* **36** (Suppl.) XXIX.

Derbyshire, E. and Street, H. E. (1964). Studies of the growth in culture of excised wheat roots. V. The influence of light on nitrate uptake and assimilation. *Physiol. Plant.* **17**, 107.

Dixon, M. (1949). "Multi-enzyme Systems". Cambridge University Press.

Dormer, K. J. and Street, H. E. (1948). Secondary thickening in excised tomato roots. *Nature, Lond.* **161**, 483.

Dormer, K. J. and Street, H. E. (1949). The carbohydrate nutrition of tomato roots. *Ann. Bot., Lond.* **13**, 199.

Duhamet, L. (1939). Action de l'hétéro-auxine sur la croissance de racines isolées de *Lupinus albus. C. R. Acad. Sci., Paris* **208**, 1838.

Duhamet, L. (1949). Action du lait de Coco sur la croissance des tissus du tubercule de Topinambour cultivés *in vitro. C. R. Acad. Sci., Paris* **229**, 1353.

Duhamet, L. (1950a). Action du lait de Coco sur la croissance des tissus de crown-gall de Scorsonère cultivés *in vitro. C. R. Acad. Sci., Paris* **230**, 770.

Duhamet, L. (1950b). Action du lait de Coco sur la croissance des tissus de *Parthenocissus tricuspidata* cultivés *in vitro. C. R. Soc. Biol., Paris* **144**, 59.

Duhamet, L. (1951). Action du lait de Coco sur la croissance des cultivés de tissus de crown-gall de Vigne, de Tabac, de Topinambour et de Scorsonère. *C. R. Soc. Biol., Paris* **145**, 1781.

Duhamet, L. and Gautheret, R. J. (1950). Structure anatomique de fragments de tubercules de Topinambour cultivés en presence de lait de Coco. *C. R. Soc. Biol., Paris* **144**, 177.

Eagle, H. (1959). The growth requirement and metabolic activities of human and animal cells in culture. *In* "Proceedings of the Fourth International Congress of Biochemistry. Symposium VI. Biochemistry of Morphogenesis", pp. 1–19. Pergamon Press, Oxford.

Earle, W. R., Sanford, K. K., Evans, H. K. W. and Shannon, J. E. (1951). The preparation and handling of replicate tissue cultures for quantitative studies. *J. nat. Cancer Inst.* **11**, 907.

Eberts, F. S., Burris, R. H. and Riker, A. J. (1954). The metabolism of nitrogenous compounds by sunflower crown gall tissue cultures. *Plant Physiol.* **29**, 1.

Ferguson, J. D., Street, H. E. and David, S. B. (1958a). The carbohydrate nutrition of tomato roots. V. The promotion and inhibition of excised root growth by various sugars and sugar alcohols. *Ann. Bot., Lond.* **22**, 513.

Ferguson, J. D., Street, H. E. and David, S. B. (1958b). The carbohydrate nutrition of tomato roots. VI. The inhibition of excised root growth by galactose and mannose and its reversal by dextrose and xylose. *Ann. Bot., Lond.* **22**, 525.

Fiedler, H. (1936). Entwicklungs-und veizphysiologische untersuchungen and kulturen isolierter Wurzelspitzen. *Z. Bot.* **30**, 385.

Fosse, R. (1916). Origine et distribution de l'urée dans la nature. *Ann. Chim.* N.S. **6**, 198.

Fowden, L. (1959). Radioactive iodine incorporation in organic compounds of various angiosperms. *Physiol. Plant.* **12**, 657.

Fox, J. E. and Miller, C. O. (1959). Factors in corn steep water promoting growth of plant tissues. *Plant Physiol.* **34**, 577.

Frank, E. M., Riker, A. J. and Dye, S. L. (1951). Comparisons of growth of tobacco and sunflower tissue on synthetic media containing various sources of organic nitrogen. *Plant Physiol.* **26**, 258.

Fridhandler, L. and Quastel, J. H. (1955). Absorption of amino acids from isolated surviving intestine. *Arch. Biochem. Biophys.* **56**, 424.

Fries, N. (1951). The influence of amino acids on growth and lateral root formation in cotyledonless pea seedlings. *Experientia* **7**, 378.

Fries, N. and Forsman, B. (1951). Quantitative determination of certain nucleic acid derivatives in pea root exudate. *Physiol. Plant.* **4**, 410.

Fujiwara, A. and Ojima, H. (1954). Physiological studies of plant roots. I. Influence of some environmental conditions on the growth of isolated roots of the rice plant and wheat. *Tohoku J. agric. Res.* **5**, 53.

Galston, A. W. (1948). On the physiology of root initiation in excised *Asparagus* stem tips. *Amer. J. Bot.* **35**, 281.

Galston, A. W. and Dalberg, L. Y. (1954). The adaptive formation and physiological significance of indoleacetic acid oxidase. *Amer. J. Bot.* **41**, 373.

Galston, A. W. and Warburg, H. (1959). An analysis of auxin-gibberellin interaction in pea stem tissue. *Plant Physiol.* **34**, 16.

Gauch, H. G. and Dugger, W. M. (1953). The role of boron in the translocation of sucrose. *Plant Physiol.* **28**, 457.

Gauch, H. G. and Dugger, W. M. (1954). The physiological action of boron in higher plants: a review and interpretation. *Bull. Md agric. exp. Sta.* A80 (technical).

Gautheret R. J. (1935). Recherches sur la formation de chlorophyll dans les racines et la reduction des sels argents par les chloroplasts. *Rév. gén. Bot.* **47**, 401.

Gautheret, R. J. (1939). Sur la possibilité de réaliser la culture indéfinie des tissus de tubercules de Carotte. *C. R. Acad. Sci., Paris* **208**, 118.

Gautheret, R. J. (1941). Action du saccharose sur la croissance des tissus de Carotte. *C. R. Soc. Biol., Paris* **135**, 875.

Gautheret, R. J. (1942). Hétéro-auxines et cultures de tissus végétaux. *Bull. Soc. Chem. Biol., Paris* **24**, 13.

Gautheret, R. J. (1945). "Une voie nouvelle en biologie végétale. La culture des tissus". Gallimard, Paris.

Gautheret, R. J. (1946). Comparaison entre l'action de l'acide indole-acétique et celle du *Phytomonas tumifaciens* sur la croissance des tissus végétaux. *C. R. Soc. Biol., Paris* **140**, 169.

Gautheret, R. J. (1948a). Sur l'utilization du glycérol par les cultures de tissus végétaux. *C. R. Soc. Biol., Paris* **142**, 808.

Gautheret, R. J. (1948b). Action de l'acide indole-acétique sur le développement de trois types de tissus de Scorsonère: tissus normaux, tissus de crown-gall et tissus accoutumes à l'hétéro-auxine. *C. R. Soc. Biol., Paris* **142**, 774.

Gautheret, R. J. (1950a). Remarques sur les besoins nutritifs des cultures de tissus de *Salix caprea*. *C. R. Soc. Biol., Paris* **144**, 173.

Gautheret, R. J. (1950b). Nouvelles recherches sur les besoins nutritifs des cultures de tissus de Carotte. *C. R. Soc. Biol., Paris* **144**, 172.

Gautheret, R. J. (1953). Remarques sur l'emploi du lait de Coco pour la réalisation des cultures de tissus vegetaux. *C. R. Acad. Sci., Paris* **235**, 1321.

Gautheret, R. J. (1955a). The nutrition of plant tissue cultures. *Annu. Rev. Plant Physiol.* **6**, 433.

Gautheret, R. J. (1955b) Sur la variabilité des propriétés physiologiques des cultures de tissus végétaux. *Rev. gen. Bot.* **62**, 1.

Gautheret, R. J. (1956). Proceedings of the Decennial Review Conference on Tissue Culture. *J. nat. Cancer Inst.* **19**, 489.

Gautheret, R. J. (1959). "La culture des tissus végétaux, techniques et realisations". Masson, Paris.

Geddes, W. F. and Levine, M. N. (1942). The distribution of thiamine in the wheat plant at successive stages of kernel development. *Cereal Chem.* **19**, 547.

Geisler, G. (1963). Morphogenetic influence of (CO_2 + HCO_3) on roots. *Plant Physiol.* **38**, 77.

Gladstone, G. P. (1939). Inter-relationships between amino acids in the nutrition of *B. anthracis*. *Brit. J. exp. Path* **20**, 189.

Gleissberg, W. (1946). A criterion for the reality of cyclic variation. *Nature, Lond.* **157**, 663.

Goldacre, P. L. and Bottomley, W. (1959). A kinin in apple fruitlets. *Nature, Lond.* **184**, 555.

Goldacre, P. L. and Unt, H. (1961). The cultivation of isolated roots of subterranean clover and effects of amino acids on their growth. *Amer. J. biol. Sci.* **14**, 323.

Goldsworthy, A. (1964). Studies in the carbohydrate metabolism of excised roots. Ph.D. Thesis, University of Wales.

Goldsworthy, A. and Street, H. E. (1965). The carbohydrate nutrition of tomato roots. VIII. The mechanism of the inhibition by D-mannose of the respiration of excised roots. *Ann. Bot., Lond.* **29**, 45.

Gordon, S. A. (1954). Occurrence, formation and inactivation of auxins. *Annu. Rev. Plant Physiol.* **5**, 341.

Gorham, P. R. (1950). Heterotrophic nutrition of seed plants with particular reference to *Lemna minor*, L. *Canad. J. Res.* C. **28**, 356.

Goris, A. (1947). Hydration de fragments de tubercules de Carotte et de Topinambour cultivés *in vitro* sur milieux dépourvus de sucres. Influence de l'acide indole-3-acétique. *C. R. Soc. Biol., Paris* **141**, 1205.

Goris, A. (1948a). Épuisement des réserves glucidiques de souches de tissus et de fragments de tubercules de carotte maintenus *in vitro* sur milieux dépourvus de sucres. *C. R. Acad. Sci., Paris* **226**, 105.

Goris, A. (1948b). Épuisement des réserves glucidiques de fragments de tubercules de Topinambour cultivés *in vitro* sur milieux dépourvus de sucres: influence de l'acide indole-3-acétique. *C. R. Acad. Sci., Paris* **226**, 742.

Goris, A. (1954). Transformations glucidiques intratissulaires. *Année biol.* **30**, 297.

Gregory, F. G. and Sen, P. K. (1937). Physiological studies in plant nutrition. VI. The relation of respiration rate to carbohydrate and nitrogen metabolism of barley leaves as determined by nitrogen and potassium deficiency. *Ann. Bot.* N.S. **1**, 521.

Guttman, R. (1957). Alterations in nuclear ribonucleic acid metabolism induced by kinetin. *J. biophys. biochem. Cytol.* **3**, 129.

Hadwiger, L. A. and Waller, G. R. (1964). Biosynthesis of ricinine in excised roots of *Ricinus communis*. *Plant Physiol.* **39**, 244.

Hannay, J. W. (1956). A study of the micronutrient nutrition of excised roots of *Lycopersicum esculentum*, Mill. Ph.D. Thesis, University of Manchester.

Hannay, J. W., Fletcher, B. H. and Street, H. E. (1959). Studies on the growth of excised roots. IX. The effects of other nutrient ions upon the growth of excised tomato roots supplied with various nitrogen sources. *New Phytol.* **58**, 142.

Hannay, J. W. and Street, H. E. (1954). Studies on the growth of excised roots. III. The molybdenum and manganese requirement of excised tomato roots. *New Phytol.* **53**, 68.

Harland, S. C. and Skinner, J. C. (1954). Genetic aspects of excised roots in *Senecio vulgaris*, L. Atti del IX Congresso Internationale de Genetica. *Caryologia Suppl.* pp. 719–724.

Harley, J. L. (1959). "The Biology of Mycorrhiza". Leonard Hill, London.

Harris, G. P. (1956). Amino acids as sources of nitrogen for the growth of isolated oat embryos. *New Phytol.* **55**, 253.

Harris, G. P. (1959). Amino acids as nitrogen sources for the growth of excised roots of red clover. *New Phytol.* **58**, 330.

Hasegawa, M., Higuchi, T. and Ishikawa, H. (1960). Formation of lignin in tissue culture of *Pinus strobus*. *Plant and Cell Physiol.* (*Japan*) **1**, 173.

Heimsch, C. (1960). A new aspect of cortical development in roots. *Amer. J. Bot.* **47**, 195.

Heller, R. (1949). Sur l'emploi du papier filtre sans cendres comme support pour les cultures de tissus végétaux. *C. R. Soc. Biol., Paris* **143**, 335.

Heller, R. (1953). Recherches sur la nutrition minérale des tissus végetaux cultivés *in vitro*. *Ann. Sci. nat., Bot. et Biol.* Veg. Ser II, 1.

Heller, R. (1954). Les besoins minéraux des tissus en culture. *Année biol.* **30**, 361.

Henderson, J. H. M. (1954). The changing nutritional pattern from normal to habituated sunflower callus tissue *in vitro*. *Année biol.* **30**, 329.

Henderson, J. H. M. and Bonner, J. (1952). Auxin metabolism in normal and crown-gall tissue of sunflower. *Amer. J. Bot.* **39**, 444.

Henderson, J. H. M., Durrell, M. E. and Bonner, J. (1952). The culture of normal sunflower callus. *Amer. J. Bot.* **39**, 467.

Hewitt, E. J. (1957). Some aspects of micronutrient element metabolism in plants. *Nature, Lond.* **180**, 1020.

Hildebrandt, A. C. and Riker, A. J. (1947). Influence of some growth-regulating substances on sunflower and tobacco tissue *in vitro*. *Amer. J. Bot.* **34**, 421.

Hildebrandt, A. C. and Riker, A. J. (1949). The influence of various carbon compounds on the growth of marigold, Paris-daisy, periwinkle, sunflower and tobacco tissue *in vitro*. *Amer. J. Bot.* **36**, 75.

Hildebrandt, A. C. and Riker, A. J. (1953). Influence of concentrations of sugars and polysaccharides on callus tissue growth *in vitro*. *Amer. J. Bot.* **40**, 66.

Hildebrandt, A. C., Riker, A. J. and Duggar, B. M. (1946). The influence of the composition of the medium on growth *in vitro* of excised tobacco and sunflower tissue cultures. *Amer. J. Bot.* **33**, 591.

Hildebrandt, A. C., Wilmar, J. C., Johns, H. and Riker, A. J. (1963). Growth of edible chlorophyllous plant tissues *in vitro*. *Amer. J. Bot.* **50**, 248.

Hinshelwood, C. H. (1946). "The Chemical Kinetics of the Bacterial Cell". Clarendon Press, Oxford.

Höber, R. (1946). "Physical Chemistry of Cells and Tissues". Churchill, London.

Hughes, E. W. D. and Street, H. E. (1960). Effects of inhibitory concentrations of 3-indolylacetic acid and 3-indolylacetonitrile on cell division and tissue differentiation in excised tomato roots. *J. exp. Bot.* **11**, 198.

Jablonski, J. R. and Skoog, F. (1954). Cell enlargement and cell division in excised tobacco pith tissue. *Physiol. Plant.* **7**, 16.

James, W. O. and Boulter, D. (1955). Further studies of the terminal oxidases in the embryos and young roots of barley. *New Phytol.* **54**, 1.

Jansen, B. C. P. (1936). A chemical determination of aneurin by the thiochrome method. *Rec. Trav. Chem.* **55**, 1046.

Jensen, W. A. and McLaren, A. D. (1960). Uptake of proteins by plant cells—the possible occurrence of pinocytosis in plants. *Exp. Cell Res.* **19**, 414.

Jensen, W. A. and Pollock, E. G. (1958). Effect of kinetin on the protein and nucleic acid content of root tip cells. *Plant Physiol.* **33**, Suppl. XV.

Jensen, W. A., Pollock, E. G., Healey, P. and Ashton, M. (1964). Kinetin and the nucleic acid content of onion root tips. *Exp. Cell Res.* **33**, 523.

Jones, L. E., Hildebrandt, A. C., Riker, A. J. and Wu, J. H. (1960). Growth of somatic tobacco cells in microculture. *Amer. J. Bot.* **47**, 468.

Jones, O. P. (1963). The thiamine metabolism of excised roots. Ph.D. Thesis, University of Wales.

Kandler, O. (1951). Papierchromatographischer Nachweis der Aminosauerenausscheidung *in vitro* kultivierter Maiswurzeln. *Z. Naturf.* **66**, 437.

Kandler, O. (1952). Über eine physiologische Umstimmung von β-Indolylessigsaure. *Planta* **40**, 346.

Kandler, O. and Eberle, G. (1955). Über den einfluss von α-parachlorphenoxy-isobuttersaure auf den Stoffwechsel *in vitro* kultivierter Maiswurzeln. *Phyton* **5**, 31.

Kandler, O. and Vieregg, A. (1953). Über den einfluss von β-Indolylessigsaure auf den Stoffwechsel *in vitro* kultivierter Maiswurzeln und Spargelsprosse. *Planta* **41**, 613.

Katznelson, H., Lochhead, A. G. and Timonin, M. I. (1948). Soil micro-organisms and the rhizosphere. *Bot. Rev.* **14**, 543.

Key, J. L. and Shannon, J. C. (1964). Enhancement by auxin of ribonucleic acid synthesis in excised soybean hypocotyl tissue. *Plant Physiol.* **39**, 360.

Killam, N. and Myers, J. (1956). A special effect of light on the growth of *Chlorella pyrenoidoso*. *Amer. J. Bot.* **43**, 569.

Knudson, L. (1915). Toxicity of galactose for certain of the higher plants. *Ann. Mo. bot. Gdn.* **2**, 659.

Knudson, L. (1917). The toxicity of galactose and mannose for green plants and the antagonistic action of sugars towards these. *Amer. J. Bot.* **4**, 430.

Kovoor, A. (1953). Action comparée du liquide intra-calicinal de *Spathodea campanulata* Beauv. sur la croissance des cultures de tissus végétaux. *C. R. Acad. Sci., Paris* **237**, 832.

Kovoor, A. (1954). Action de quelques substances stimulantes d'origine naturelle sur le développement des tissus végétaux cultivés *in vitro*. *Année Biol.* **30**, 417.

Krebs, H. A. and Henseleit, K. (1932). Untersuchungen über die Havastoffbildung im Tierkörper. *Hoppe-Seylers Z.* **210**, 33.

Kulescha, Z. (1952). Recherches sur l'élaboration des substances de croissance par les tissus végétaux. *Rev. gen. Bot.* **59**, 19, 92, 127, 195, 241.

Lachaux, M. (1944a). Respiration des tubercules de Carotte et de Topinambour. Ses variations sous l'influence du traumatisme. *C. R. Acad. Sci., Paris* **219**, 218.

Lachaux, M. (1944b). Respiration des tissus des tubercules de Carotte et de Topinambour. Influence du glucose et de l'acide indole-3-acétique. *C. R. Acad. Sci., Paris* **219**, 244.

Lachaux, M. (1944c). Étude de la respiration de tissus végétaux isolés cultivés *in vitro*. Tissus de tubercule de Topinambour. *C. R. Acad. Sci., Paris* **219**, 258.

Lachaux, M. (1944d). Étude de la respiration de tissus végétaux isolés cultivés *in vitro*. Influence de l'acide indole-3-acetique sur la respiration des tissus de Topinambour. *C. R. Acad. Sci., Paris* **219**, 291.

Lamport, D. T. A. and Northcote, D. H. (1960a). The use of tissue culture for the study of plant cell walls. *Biochem. J.* **76**, 52P.

Lamport, D. T. A. and Northcote, D. H. (1960b). Hydroxyproline in primary cell walls of higher plants. *Nature, Lond.* **18**, 665.

Lampton, R. K. (1952). Developmental and experimental morphology of the ovule of *Asimina triloba,* Dunal. Thesis, University of Michigan.

Leder, I. G. (1959). Enzymatic synthesis of thiamine. *Fed. Proc.* **18**, 270.

Lee, A. E. (1958). Comparative growth of excised tomato roots of clones carrying dwarf and normal alleles. *Amer. J. Bot.* **45**, 744.

Lee, A. E. (1959). The effect of various substances on the comparative growth of excised tomato clones carrying dwarf and normal alleles. *Amer. J. Bot.* **46**, 16,

Letham, D. S. (1963a). Purification of factors inducing cell division extracted from plum fruitlets. *Life Sciences* 1963, 152.

Letham, D. S. (1963b). Zeatin, a factor inducing cell division isolated from *Zea mays*. *Life Sciences* 1963, 569

Letham, D. S. and Bollard, E. G. (1961). Stimulant of cell division in developing fruits. *Nature, Lond.* **191**, 1119.

Letham, D. S., Shannon, J. S. and McDonald, I. R. (1964). The structure of zeatin, a factor inducing cell division. *Proc. chem. Soc.* 1964, 230.

Levine, M. (1951). The effect of growth substances and chemical carcinogens on fibrous roots of carrot tissue grown *in vitro*. *Amer. J. Bot.* **38**, 132.

Lexander, K. (1953). Growth-regulating substances in roots of wheat. *Physiol. Plant.* **6**, 406.

Lichstein, H. C., Gunsalus, I. C. and Umbreit, W. W. (1945). Function of the vitamin B_6 group. Pyridoxal phosphate (codecarboxylase) in transamination. *J. biol. Chem.* **161**, 311.

Limasset, P. and Gautheret, R. J. (1950). Sur le caractère tumoral des tissus de Tabac ayant subi le phénomène d'accoutumance aux hétéro-auxines. *C. R. Acad. Sci., Paris* **230**, 2043.

Link, G. K. K. and Eggers, V. (1941). Hyperauxiny in crown-gall of tomato. *Bot. Gaz.* **103**, 87.

Lioret, C. (1952a). Échanges gazeux respiratoires des tissus de crown-gall de Scorsonère (*Scorzonera hispanica*, L.) cultivés *in vitro* en presence d'acide α-naphtalène-acétique. *C. R. Acad. Sci., Paris* **234**, 237.

Lioret, C. (1952b). Action du lait de Coco sur les échanges gazeux respiratoires de tissus de crown-gall de Scorsonère (*Scorzonera hispanica*, L.) cultivés *in vitro*. *C. R. Acad. Sci., Paris* **234**, 648.

Lioret, C. (1953a). Action de l'acide α-naphtalène-acétique sur le metabolisme des tissus de racine de Scorsonère, cultivés *in vitro*. I. Accroissement des cultures et variations des constituants azotes et glucidiques. *C. R. Acad. Sci., Paris* **236**, 311.

Lioret, C. (1953b). Action de l'acide α-naphtalène-acétique sur le metabolism des tissus de racine de Scorsonère, cultivés *in vitro*. II. Variations des échanges gazeux respiratoires. *C. R. Acad. Sci., Paris* **236**, 504.

Lioret, C. (1955). Recherches sur le métabolisme des cultures de tissus normaux et pathologiques. *Année biol.* **31**, 185.

Lipetz, J. and Galston, A. W. (1959). Indole acetic acid oxidase and peroxidase activities in normal and crown gall tissue cultures of *Parthenocissus tricuspidata*. *Amer. J. Bot.* **46**, 193.

Loeffler, J. E. and Overbeek, J. van (1964). Kinin activity in coconut milk. *In* "Régulateurs Naturels de la Croissance Végétale," pp. 76–96. C.N.R.S., Paris.

Lohman, L. and Schuster, P. (1937). Co-carboxylase. I. *Naturwissenschaften* **25**, 26.

Lundegårdh, H. and Stenlid, G. (1944). On the exudation of nucleotides and flavonone from living roots. *Ark. Bot.* **31** A, 1.

Lyttleton, J. W. (1960). Stabilisation by manganese ions of ribosomes from embryonic plant tissue. *Nature, Lond.* **187**, 1026.

McClary, J. E. (1940). Synthesis of thiamine by excised roots of maize. *Proc. nat. Acad. Sci., Wash.* **26**, 581.

McGregor, S. M. and Street, H. E. (1953). The carbohydrate nutrition of tomato roots. IV. The nature and distribution of acid phosphatases. *Ann. Bot., Lond.* **17**, 385.

McLaren, A. D., Jensen, W. A. and Jacobson, L. (1960). Absorption of enzymes and other proteins by barley roots. *Plant Physiol.* **35**, 549.

Malyschev, N. (1932). Das Wachstum des isolierten Wurzelmeristems auf sterilen Nährböden. *Biol. Zbl.* **52**, 257.

Martin, G. J. (1951). "Biological Antagonism." Blakiston, New York.

Masuda, Y. (1965). RNA in relation to the effect of auxin, kinetin and gibberellic acid on the tuber tissue of Jerusalem artichoke. *Physiol. Plant.* **18**, 15.

Mehta, A. R. (1963). Nutritional and morphogenetic studies with callus and suspension cultures derived from roots. Ph.D. Thesis, University of Wales.

Meister, A. (1957). "The Biochemistry of Amino Acids." Academic Press, New York.

Melhuish, F. M. (1962). Aspects of the amino acid metabolism of roots. Ph.D. Thesis, University of Wales.

Melin, E. (1954). Growth factor requirements of mycorrhizal fungi of forest trees. *Svensk bot. Tidskr.* **48**, 86.

Melin, E. and Das, V. S. R. (1954). Influence of root-metabolites on the growth of the mycorrhizal fungi. *Physiol. Plant.* **7**, 851.

Miller, C. O. (1960). An assay for kinetin-like materials. *Plant Physiol.* **35**, Suppl. XXVI.

Miller, C. O. (1961). A kinetin-like compound in maize. *Proc. nat. Acad. Sci., Wash.* **47**, 170.

Miller, C. O., Skoog, F., Okumura, F. S., von Saltza, M. H. and Strong, F. M. (1955). Structure and synthesis of kinetin. *J. Amer. chem. Soc.* **77**, 2662.

Miller, C. O., Skoog, F., Okumura, F. S., von Saltza, M. H. and Strong, F. M. (1956). Isolation, structure and cell synthesis of kinetin, a substance promoting cell division. *J. Amer. Chem. Soc.* **78**, 1375.

Mitra, J., Mapes, M. O. and Steward, F. C. (1960). Growth and organized development of cultured cells. IV. The behaviour of the nucleus. *Amer. J. Bot.* **47**, 357.

Mitra, J. and Steward, F. C. (1961). Growth induction in cultures of *Haplopappus gracilis*. II. The behaviour of the nucleus. *Amer. J. Bot.* **48**, 358.

Mollenhauer, H. H. and Whaley, W. G. (1963). An observation on the functioning of the Golgi apparatus. *J. Cell Biol.* **17**, 222.

Mollenhauer, H. H., Whaley, W. G. and Leech, J. H. (1961). A function of the Golgi apparatus in outer root cap cells. *J. Ultrastructure Res.* **5**, 193.

Monod, J. and Jacob, F. (1961). General conclusions: Teleonomic mechanisms in cellular metabolism, growth and differentiation. *Cold Spr. Harb. Symp. quant. Biol.* **26**, 389.

Morel, G. (1948). Recherches sur la culture associée de parasites obligatoires et de tissus végétaux. *Ann. Epiphyt.* **14**, 1.

Morel, G. (1950). Sur la culture des tissus de deux monocotylédones. *C. R. Acad. Sci., Paris* **230**, 1099.

Morel, G. and Démétriadès, S. (1955). Action de régulateurs de croissance sur l'activité oxydasique de tissus de Topinambour. *Année biol.* **31**, 227.

Morgan, D. R. and Street, H. E. (1959). The carbohydrate nutrition of tomato roots. VII. Sugars, sugar phosphates and sugar alcohols as respiratory substrates for excised roots. *Ann. Bot., Lond.* **23**, 89.

Mothes, K. Engelbrecht, L. and Kulajewa, O. (1959). Über die Wirkung des Kinetins auf Stickstoffverteilung und Eiweiss-synthese in isolierten Blattern. *Flora* **147**, 445.

Muir, W. H., Hildebrandt, A. C. and Riker, A. J. (1954). Plant tissue cultures produced from single isolated cells. *Science* **119**, 877.

Muir, W. H., Hildebrandt, A. C. and Riker, A. J. (1958). The preparation, isolation and growth in culture of single cells from higher plants. *Amer. J. Bot.* **45**, 589.

Myers, J. W. and Adelberg, E. A. (1954). The biosynthesis of isoleucine and valine. I. Enzymic transformation of the dihydroxy acid precursors to the keto acid precursors. *Proc. nat. Acad. Sci., Wash.* **40**, 493.

Nagao, M. (1936). Studies on the growth hormones of plants. I. The production of growth substances in root tips. *Sci. Rep. Tohoku Univ.* (Biol.) **10**, 721.

Nagao, M. (1937). Studies on the growth hormones of plants. III. The occurrence of growth substances in isolated roots grown under sterilised conditions *Sci. Rep. Tohoku Univ.* (Biol.) **12**, 191.

Nagao, M. (1938). Studies on the growth hormones of plants. IV. Further experiments on the production of growth substances in root tips. *Sci. Rep. Tohoku Univ.* (Biol.) **13**, 221.

Naylor, A. W. and Rappaport, B. N. (1950). Studies on the growth factor requirements of pea roots. *Physiol. Plant.* **3**, 315.

Naylor, E. E. and Johnson, B. (1937). A histological study of vegetative reproduction in *Saintpaulia ionantha*. *Amer. J. Bot.* **24**, 673.

Neales, T. F. (1959). The boron requirement of flax roots grown in sterile culture. *J. exp. Bot.* **10**, 426.

Neales, T. F. (1964). A comparison of the boron requirements of intact tomato plants and excised tomato roots grown in sterile culture. *J. exp. Bot.* **15**, 647.

Neish, A. C. (1951). Carbohydrate nutrition of *Chlorella vulgaris*. *Canad. J. Bot.* **29**, 68.

Nétien, G. and Beauchesne, G. (1954). Essai d'isolement d'un factor de croissance présent dans un extrait laiteux de caryopses de Maïs immatures. *Année Biol.* **30**, 437.

Nétien, G., Beauchesne, G. and Mentzer, C. (1951). Influence du "lait de Maïs" sur la croissance des tissues de Carotte *in vitro*. *C. R. Acad. Sci., Paris* **233**, 92.

Nickell, L. G. (1950a). Effect of aspartic acid on growth of plant-virus tumour tissue. *Nature, Lond.* **166**, 351.

Nickell, L. G. (1950b). Effect of coconut milk on the growth *in vitro* of plant virus tumour tissue. *Bot. Gaz.* **112**, 225.

Nickell, L. G. (1950c). Effect of certain plant hormones and colchicine on the growth and respiration of virus tumor tissue from *Rumex acetosa*. *Amer. J. Bot.* **37**, 829.

Nickell, L. G. (1952). Vitamin B_1 requirement of Rumex virus tumor tissue. *Bull. Torrey bot. Club* **79**, 427.

Nickell, L. G. (1961). Sur la perte des besoins en vitamin B_1 par des tissus végétaux cultivés *in vitro*. *C. R. Acad. Sci., Paris* **253**, 182.

Nickell, L. G. and Burkholder, P. R. (1950). Atypical growth of plants. II. Growth *in vitro* of virus tumors of *Rumex* in relation to temperature, pH and various sources of nitrogen, carbon and sulphur. *Amer. J. Bot.* **37**, 538.

Nickell, L. G. and Tulecke, W. (1959). Responses of plant tissue cultures to gibberellin. *Bot. Gaz.* **120**, 245.

Nickell, L. G. and Tulecke, W. (1960). Submerged growth of cells of higher plants. *J. biochem. microbiol. techn. Engng* **2**, 287.

Nightingale, G. T. (1937). The nitrogen nutrition of green plants. *Bot. Rev.* **3**, 85.

Nightingale, G. T. (1948). The nitrogen nutrition of green plants. II. *Bot. Rev.* **14**, 185.

Nitsch, J. P. (1951). Growth and development *in vitro* of excised ovaries. *Amer. J. Bot.* **38**, 566.

Nitsch, J. P. (1954). L'action sur la croissance des cultures de tissu, du liquide seminal d'*Allanblackia parviflora*, A. Chev. *C. R. Acad. Sci., Paris* **238**, 141.

Nitsch, J. P. (1957). Growth responses of woody plants to photoperiodic stimuli. *Proc. Am. Soc. hort. Sci.* **70**, 512.

Nitsch, J. P. and Nitsch, C. (1957). Auxin-dependent growth of excised *Helianthus tuberosus* tissues. II. Organic nitrogenous substances. *Amer. J. Bot.* **44**, 555.

Nobécourt, P. (1939a). Sur la pérennité et l'augmentation de cultures de tissus végétaux. *C. R. Soc. Biol., Paris* **130**, 1270.

Nobécourt, P. (1939b). Sur les radicelles naissant des cultures de tissus du tubercule de Carotte. *C. R. Soc. Biol., Paris* **130**, 1271.

Nose, Y., Ueda, K. and Kawasaki, T. (1959). Enzyme synthesis of thiamine. *Biochim. biophys. Acta* **34**, 277.

Oaks, A. (1965). The soluble leucine pool in maize root tip. *Plant Physiol.* **40**, 142. The effect of leucine on the biosynthesis of leucine in maize root tips. *Plant Physiol.* **40**, 149.

Odhnoff, C. (1957). Boron deficiency and growth. *Physiol. Plant.* **10**, 984.

Ojima, K. and Fujiwara, A. (1959). Studies on the growth promoting substance of the excised wheat roots. I. Effects of peptone on growth. *Tohoku J. agric. Res.* **10**, 111.

Ojima, K. and Fujiwara, A. (1962). Studies on the growth promoting substance of the excised wheat root. III. Effects of tryptophane and some related substances. *Tohoku J. agric. Res.* **31**, 69.

Ory, R. L., Hood, D. W. and Lyman, C. M. (1954). The role of glutamine in arginine synthesis by *Lactobacillus arabinosus*. *J. biol. Chem.* **207**, 267.

Osborne, D. J. (1961). Rapid bioassay for kinetin and kinins using senescing leaf tissue. *Plant Physiol.* **36**, 219.

Overbeek, J. van (1939a). Is auxin produced in roots? *Proc. nat. Acad. Sci., Wash.* **25**, 245.

Overbeek, J. van (1939b). Evidence for auxin production in isolated roots growing *in vitro*. *Bot. Gaz.* **101**, 450.

Overbeek, J. van and Bonner, J. (1938). Auxin in isolated roots growing *in vitro*. *Proc. nat. Acad. Sci., Wash.* **24**, 260.

Overbeek, J. van, Conklin, M. E. and Blakeslee, A. F. (1941). Factors in coconut milk essential for growth and development of very young *Datura* embryos. *Science* **94**, 350.

Paris, D. (1955). Action de quelques vitamines hydrosolubles sur les cultures de tissus végétaux. *Année biol.* **31**, 15.

Paris, D., Duhamet, L. and Goris, A. (1954). Action des vitamines et des acides aminés contenus dans le lait de Coco sur la proliferation d'une souche de tissus de Carotte. *C. R. Soc. Biol., Paris* **148**, 296.

Partanen, C. R. (1959). Quantitative chromosome changes and differentiation in plants. *In* "Developmental Cytology" (D. Rudnick, ed.). Ronald Press, New York.

Pecket, R. C. (1957). The initiation and development of lateral meristems in the pea root. I. The effect of young and mature tissues. *J. exp. Bot.* **8**, 172.

Pilet, P. E. (1957). Action des gibberellins sur l'activité auxin oxydasique de tissus cultivé *in vitro*. *C. R. Acad. Sci., Paris* **245**, 1327.

Pilet, P. E. and Galston, A. W. (1955). Auxin destruction, peroxidase activity and peroxidase genesis in the root of *Lens culinaris*. *Physiol. Plant.* **8**, 888.

Poel, L. W. (1953). Carbon dioxide fixation by barley roots. *J. exp. Bot.* **4**, 157.

Pollard, J. K., Bollard, E. G. and Steward, F. C. (1957). The relative utilisation of C^{14} from urea and $C^{14}O_2$. *Plant Physiol.* **32**, Suppl. XLV (Abst.).

Pollard, J. K., Shantz, E. M. and Steward, F. C. (1961). Hexitols in coconut milk: their role in nurture of dividing cells. *Plant Physiol.* **36**, 492.

Pollard, J. K. and Steward, F. C. (1959). The use of C^{14}-proline by growing cells: its conversion to protein and to hydroxyproline. *J. exp. Bot.* **10**, 17.

Pollock M. R. (1959). Induced formation of enzymes. *In* "The Enzymes" (P. D. Boyer, H. Lardy and K. Mybäck, eds.), Vol. 1, pp. 619–680. Academic Press, New York.

Porter, H. K. and May, L. H. (1955). Metabolism of radioactive sugars by tobacco leaf discs. *J. exp. Bot.* **6**, 43.

Possingham, J. V. and Brown, R. (1958). The nuclear incorporation of iron and its significance in growth. *J. exp. Bot.* **9**, 277.

Puck, T. T., Marcus, P. I. and Cieciura, S. J. (1956). Clonal growth of mammalian cells *in vitro*. II. Growth characteristics of colonies from single HeLa cells with and without a "feeder" layer. *J. exp. Med.* **103**, 273.

Racker, E., de la Haba, G. and Leder, I. G. (1953). Thiamine pyrophosphate, a co-enzyme of transketolase. *J. Amer. chem. Soc.* **75**, 1010.

Raggio, M. and Raggio, N. (1956). A new method for the cultivation of isolated roots. *Physiol. Plant.* **9**, 466.

Raoul, Y. and Gautheret, R. J. (1947). Action de l'acide naphtoxy-acétique et de l'acide 2,4-dichlorophénoxy-acétique sur le développement des tissus de Carotte et de Topinambour. *C. R. Soc. Biol., Paris* **141**, 129.

Raoul, Y. and Gautheret, R. J. (1949). Recherches sur l'action conjugée de l'acide indole-acrylique et du tryptophane sur les cultures de tissus de Carotte et de Topinambour. *Bull. Soc. chim. Biol.* **31**, 1635.

Reinert, J. (1959). Über die Kontrolle der Morphogenese und die Induktion von Adventioembryonen an Gewebekulturen aus Karotten. *Planta* **53**, 318.

Riggs, T. R., Coyne, B. A. and Christensen, H. N. (1954) Amino acid concentration by a free cell neoplasm. Structural influences. *J. biol. Chem.* **209**, 395.

Rijven, A. H. G. C. (1952). *In vitro* studies on the embryo of *Capsella bursa-pastoris. Acta bot. néerl.* **1**, 158.

Riker, A. J. and Gutsche, A. E. (1948). The growth of sunflower tissue *in vitro* on synthetic media with various organic and inorganic sources of nitrogen. *Amer. J. Bot.* **35**, 227.

Robbins, W. J. (1922a). Cultivation of excised root tips and stem tips under sterile conditions. *Bot. Gaz.* **73**, 376.

Robbins, W. J. (1922b). Effect of autolized yeast and peptone on growth of excised corn root tips in the dark. *Bot. Gaz.* **74**, 59.

Robbins, W. J. (1941). Growth of excised roots and heterosis in tomatoes. *Amer. J. Bot.* **28**, 216.

Robbins, W. J. and Bartley, M. A. (1937a). Vitamin B_1 and the growth of excised tomato roots. *Science* **86**, 290.

Robbins, W. J. and Bartley, M. A. (1937b). Thiazole and the growth of excised tomato roots. *Proc. nat. Acad. Sci., Wash.* **23**, 285.

Robbins, W. J. and Maneval, W. E. (1923). Further experiments on growth of excised root tips under sterile conditions. *Bot. Gaz.* **76**, 274.

Robbins, W. J. and Maneval, W. E. (1924). Effect of light on growth of excised root tips under sterile conditions. *Bot. Gaz.* **78**, 424.

Robbins, W. J. and Schmidt, M. B. (1938). Growth of excised roots of tomato. *Bot. Gaz.* **99**, 671.

Robbins, W. J. and Schmidt, M. B. (1939a). Vitamin B_6, a growth substance for excised tomato roots. *Proc. nat. Acad. Sci., Wash.* **25**, 1.

Robbins, W. J. and Schmidt, M. B. (1939b). Further experiments on excised tomato roots. *Amer. J. Bot.* **26**, 149.

Robbins, W. J. and Schmidt, M. B. (1939c). Growth of excised tomato roots in a synthetic solution. *Bull. Torrey. bot. Club.* **66**, 193.

Robbins, W. J. and Stebbins, M. (1949). An additional report on the growth of excised tomato roots. *Bull. Torrey bot. Club* **76**, 136.

Robbins, W. J. and White, V. B. (1936). Limited growth and abnormalities of excised corn root tips. *Bot. Gaz.* **98**, 209.

Robbins, W. J. and White, V. B. (1937). Effect of extracts from the corn plant on growth of excised root tips. *Bot. Gaz.* **98**, 520.

Roberts, E. H. (1954). Factors controlling persistence of meristematic activity in excised roots. Ph.D. Thesis, University of Manchester.

Roberts, E. H. and Street, H. E. (1955). The continuous culture of excised rye roots. *Physiol. Plant.* **8**, 238.

Rovira, A. D. (1956). Plant root excretions in relation to the rhizosphere effect. I. The nature of the root exudate from oats and peas. *Plant and Soil* **7**, 178.

Rudman, D. and Meister, A. (1953). Transamination in *Escherichia coli. J. biol. Chem.* **200**, 591.

Sanders, M. E. and Burkholder, P. R. (1948). Influence of amino acids on growth of *Datura* embryos in culture. *Proc. nat. Acad. Sci., Wash.* **34**, 516.

Sandstedt, R. and Skoog, F. (1960). Effects of amino acid components of yeast extract on the growth of tobacco tissue *in vitro*. *Physiol. Plant.* **13**, 250.

Sanford, K. K., Earle, W. R. and Likely, G. D. (1948). The growth *in vitro* of single isolated tissue cells. *J. nat. Cancer Inst.* **9**, 229.

Schales, O., Mims, V. and Schales, S. S. (1946). Glutamic acid decarboxylase of higher plants. I. Distribution; preparation of clear solutions; nature of prosthetic group. *Arch. Biochem.* **10**, 455.

Schales, O. and Schales, S. S. (1946). Glutamic acid decarboxylase of higher plants. II. pH-activity curve, reaction kinetics, inhibition by hydroxylamine. *Arch. Biochem.* **11**, 155.

Scherer, W. F., Syverton, J. T. and Gey, G. O. (1953). Studies in the propagation *in vitro* of poliomyelitis virus. IV. Viral multiplication in a stable strain of human malignant epithelial cells (strain HeLa) derived from an epidermoid carcinoma of the cervix. *J. exp. Med.* **97**, 695.

Schlenk, F. and Snell, E. E. (1945). Vitamin B_6 and transamination. *J. biol. Chem.* **157**, 425.

Schoenheimer, R. (1942). "The Dynamic State of Body Constituents". Harvard University Press, Cambridge, Mass.

Schopfer, W. H. (1934). Versuche über die Wirkung von reinen Kristallisierter vitamin B_1 auf *Phycomyces*. *Ber. dtsch. Bot. Ges.* **52**, 308.

Schroter, H. B. and Engelbrecht, L. (1957). Nachweis der Nornicotin-bildung in isolierten Tabakwurzeln, *Arch. Pharm.* **290**, 204.

Scott, E. G., Carter, J. E. and Street, H. E. (1966). Studies on the growth in culture of excised wheat roots. III. The quantitative and qualitative requirement for light. *Physiol. Plant.* **14**, 725.

Segelitz, S. (1938). Den Einfluss von Licht und Dunkelheit auf Wurzelbildung und Wurzelwachstum. *Planta* **28**, 617.

Shantz, E. M., Mears, K. and Steward, F. C. (1958). Comparison between the growth-promoting effects on carrot tissue of coconut milk and of kinetin and certain of its analogues. *Plant Physiol.* **33**, Suppl. XVI.

Shantz, E. M. and Steward, F. C. (1952). Coconut milk factor: the growth-promoting substance in coconut milk. *J. Amer. chem. Soc.* **74**, 6133.

Shantz, E. M. and Steward, F. C. (1959). Investigations on growth and metabolism of plant cells. VII. Sources of nitrogen for tissue cultures under optimal conditions for their growth. *Ann. Bot., Lond.* **23**, 371.

Sheat, D. E. G., Fletcher, B. H. and Street, H. E. (1959). Studies on the growth of excised roots. VIII. The growth of excised tomato roots supplied with various sources of nitrogen. *New Phytol.* **58**, 128.

Shigemura, Y. (1958). The nutritional and auxin requirements for the growth of pea root callus tissue. Ph.D. Thesis, University of California, Berkeley.

Shrift, A. (1954). Sulphur-selenium antagonism. II. Antimetabolite action of selenomethionine on the growth of *Chlorella vulgaris*. *Amer. J. Bot.* **41**, 345.

Shrift, A., Nevyas, J. and Turndorf, S. (1961a). Mass adaptation to selenomethionine in populations of *Chlorella vulgaris*. *Plant Physiol.* **36**, 502.

Shrift, A., Nevyas, J. and Turndorf, S. (1961b). Stability and reversibility of adaptation to selenomethionine in *Chlorella vulgaris*. *Plant Physiol.* **36**, 509.

Sievert, R. G., Hildebrandt, A. C., Burris, R. H. and Riker, A. J. (1961). Growth *in vitro* of single cell clones isolated from a single cell clone. *Plant Physiol.* **36**, (Suppl.) XXVIII.

Skinner, J. C. (1952). Genetical variation in excised root cultures of *Senecio vulgaris*, L. *J. Hered.* **43**, 299.

Skinner, J. C. (1953). Genetical and physiological studies of the behaviour of excised root cultures of the groundsel, *Senecio vulgaris,* L. Ph.D. Thesis, University of Manchester.

Skinner, J. C. and Street, H. E. (1954). Studies on the growth of excised roots. II. Observations on the growth of excised groundsel roots. *New Phytol.* **53**, 44.

Skoog, F. (1956). Nutrition and metabolism of plant tissue cultures. Discussion. *J. nat. Cancer Inst.* **19**, 493.

Skoog, F. and Miller, C. O. (1957). Chemical regulation of growth and organ formation in plant tissue cultures *in vitro.* *Symp. Soc. exp. Biol.* **11**, 118.

Slabecka-Szweykowska, A. (1952). On the conditions of anthocyanin formation in the *Vitis vinifera* tissue cultivated *in vitro.* *Acta Soc. Bot. Polon.* **21**, 537.

Slabecka-Szweykowska, A. (1955). On the influence of the wavelength of light on the biogenesis of anthocyanin pigment in the *Vitis vinifera* tissue *in vitro.* *Acta Soc. Bot. Polon.* **24**, 3.

Slankis, V. (1951). Uber den Einfluss von β-Indolylessigsäure und anderen Wuchsstoffen auf das Wachstum von Kiefernwurzeln. I. *Symb. bot. upsaliens.* **11**, 1.

Solt, M. L. (1954). Nicotine production and growth of excised tobacco root cultures. *Plant Physiol.* **22**, 480.

Solt, M. L., Dawson, R. F. and Christman, D. R. (1960). Biosynthesis of anabasine and of nicotine by excised roots of *Nicotiana glauca,* Grah. *Plant Physiol.* **35**, 887.

Sparrow, A. H., Sparrow, R. C. and Scharrer, L. A. (1960). The use of X-rays to induce somatic mutations in *Saintpaulia.* *African Violet Mag.* **13**, 32.

Spoerl, E. (1948). Amino acids as sources of nitrogen for orchid embryos. *Amer. J. Bot.* **35**, 88.

Srb, A. M. and Horowitz, N. H. (1944). The ornithine cycle in *Neurospora* and its genetic control. *J. biol. Chem.* **154**, 129.

Steinberg, R. A. (1947). Growth responses to organic compounds by tobacco seedlings in aseptic culture. *J. agric. Res.* **75**, 81.

Steinhart, C. E., Mann, J. D. and Mudd, S. H. (1964). Alkaloids and plant metabolism. VII. The kinetin-produced elevation in tyramine methylpherase levels. *Plant Physiol.* **39**, 1030.

Steinhart, C. E., Standifer, L. G., Jr. and Skoog, F. (1961). Nutrient requirements for *in vitro* growth of spruce tissue. *Amer. J. Bot.* **48**, 465.

Stenlid, G. (1948). The effect of sodium azide on the exudation and oxygen consumption of excised pea roots. *Physiol. Plant.* **1**, 185.

Stenlid, G. (1950). Methylene blue and α-α-'dipyridyl, two different types of inhibitors for aerobic metabolism in young wheat roots. *Physiol. Plant.* **3**, 197.

Stenlid, G. (1954). Toxic effects of D-mannose, 2-desoxy-D-glucose and D-glucosamine upon respiration and ion absorption in wheat roots. *Physiol. Plant.* **7**, 173.

Stenlid, G. (1957). A comparison of the toxic effects of some sugars upon growth and chloride accumulation in young wheat roots. *Physiol. Plant.* **10**, 807.

Stenlid, G. (1959a). Studies on the inhibitory effects of sugars upon plant roots. Inaugural dissertation, Uppsala.

Stenlid, G. (1959b). On the effect of some sugars and of 2,4-dinitrophenol upon the absorption of phosphate ions by excised roots. *Physiol. Plant.* **12**, 199.

Steward, F. C. and Bidwell, R. G. S. (1958). Nitrogen metabolism, respiration and growth of cultured plant tissue. *J. exp. Bot.* **9**, 285.

Steward, F. C. and Bidwell, R. G. S. (1962). The free nitrogen compounds in plants considered in relation to metabolism, growth and development. *In* "Amino Acid Pools", pp. 667–693. Elsevier, Amsterdam.

Steward, F. C., Bidwell, R. G. S. and Yemm, E. W. (1958a). Nitrogen metabolism, respiration and growth of cultured plant tissue. *J. exp. Bot.* **9**, 11.

Steward, F. C. and Caplin, S. M. (1951). A tissue culture from potato tuber, the synergistic action of 2,4-D and coconut milk. *Science* **113**, 518.

Steward, F. C. and Caplin, S. M. (1952). Investigation on growth and metabolism of plant cells. IV. Evidence on the role of the coconut milk factor in development. *Ann. Bot., Lond.* **16**, 491.

Steward, F. C., Caplin, S. M. and Millar, F. K. (1952). Investigations on growth and metabolism of plant cells. I. New techniques for the investigation of metabolism, nutrition and growth of undifferentiated cells. *Ann. Bot., Lond.* **16**, 57.

Steward, F. C., Pollard, J. K., Patchett, A. A. and Witkop, B. (1958b). The effects of selected nitrogen compounds on the growth of plant tissue cultures. *Biochem. biophys. Acta* **28**, 308.

Steward, F. C. and Shantz, E. M. (1959a). "Biochemistry of Morphogenesis" (W. J. Nickerson, ed.), pp. 223–226. Pergamon Press, New York.

Steward, F. C. and Shantz, E. M. (1959b). The chemical regulation of growth (some substances and extracts which induce growth and morphogenesis). *Annu. Rev. Plant Physiol.* **10**, 379.

Steward, F. C., Stout, P. R. and Preston, C. (1940). The balance sheet of metabolites for potato discs showing the effects of salt and dissolved oxygen on metabolism at 23°C. *Plant Physiol.* **15**, 409.

Steward, F. C. and Street, H. E. (1947). The nitrogenous constituents of plants. *Annu. Rev. Biochem.* **16**, 471.

Steward, F. C., Thompson, J. F. and Pollard, J. K. (1958c). Contrasts in nitrogenous composition of rapidly growing and non-growing plant tissues. *J. exp. Bot.* **9**, 1.

Straus, J. (1959). Anthocyanin synthesis in corn endosperm tissue cultures. I. Identity of the pigment and general factors. *Plant Physiol.* **34**, 536.

Straus, J. (1960a). Anthocyanin synthesis in corn endosperm tissue cultures. II. Effect of certain inhibitory and stimulatory agents. *Plant Physiol.* **35**, 645.

Straus, J. (1960b). Maize endosperm tissue grown *in vitro*. III. Development of a synthetic medium. *Amer. J. Bot.* **47**, 641.

Straus, J. and Campbell, W. A. (1963). Release of enzymes by plant tissue cultures. *Life Sciences*, 50.

Straus, J. and LaRue, C. D. (1954). Maize endosperm tissue grown *in vitro:* I. Cultural requirements. *Amer. J. Bot.* **41**, 687.

Street, H. E. (1949). Nitrogen metabolism of higher plants. *Advanc. Enzymol.* **9**, 391.

Street, H. E. (1953). Factors controlling meristematic activity in excised roots. III. Light as a factor in the "location effect" noted in *Lycopersicum esculentum,* Mill. *Physiol. Plant.* **6**, 466.

Street, H. E. (1954). Factors controlling meristematic activity in excised roots. V. Effects of β-indolylacetic acid, β-indolylacetonitrile and α-(l-naphthylmethylsulphide)-propionic acid on the growth and survival of roots of *Lycopersicum esculentum,* Mill. *Physiol. Plant.* **7**, 212.

Street, H. E. (1956). Nutrition and metabolism of plant tissue cultures. *J. nat. Cancer Inst.* **19**, 467.

Street, H. E. (1957). Excised root culture. *Biol. Rev.* **32**, 117.

Street, H. E. (1959). Special problems raised by organ and tissue culture. Correlation between organs of higher plants as a consequence of specific metabolic requirements. "Encyclopaedia of Plant Physiology" (W. Ruhland, ed.), Vol. II, pp. 153–178. Springer-Verlag, Berlin.

Street, H. E. (1960). Hormones and the control of root growth. *Nature, Lond.* **188**, 272.

Street, H. E., Butcher, D. N., Handoll, C. and Winter, A. (1964). Natural regulators of root growth. "Régulateurs Naturels de la Croissance Végétale" pp. 529–541. C.N.R.S., Paris.

Street, H. E., Carter, J. E., Scott, E. G. and Sutton, D. (1961). Studies of the growth in culture of excised wheat roots. I. The growth effects of an acid-hydrolysed casein and of light. *Physiol. Plant.* **14**, 621.

Street, H. E., Henshaw, G. G. and Buiatti, M. C. (1965). The culture of isolated plant cells. *Chem. & Ind.* 1965 (1), 27.

Street, H. E., Hughes, J. C. and Lewis, M. S. J. (1960). Studies on the growth of excised roots. X. Individual amino acids and acid-hydrolysed casein as nitrogen sources for the growth of excised tomato roots. *New Phytol.* **59**, 273.

Street, H. E. and Jones, O. P. (1963). Nutritional problems raised by work with root cultures. *In* "Plant Tissue and Organ Culture—a Symposium," pp. 58–81. Int. Soc. Plant Morphologists, Delhi.

Street, H. E. and Lowe, J. S. (1950). The carbohydrate nutrition of tomato roots. II. The mechanism of sucrose absorption by excised roots. *Ann. Bot., Lond.* **14**, 307.

Street, H. E. and McGonagle, M. P. (1953). Factors controlling meristematic activity in excised roots. IV. Habituation of the main axis meristem of excised tomato roots to repeated subculture. *Physiol. Plant.* **6**, 707.

Street, H. E., McGonagle, M. P. and Lowe, J. S. (1951). Observations on the "staling" of White's medium by excised roots. *Physiol. Plant.* **4**, 592.

Street, H. E., McGonagle, M. P. and McGregor, S. M. (1952). Observations on the "staling" of White's medium by excised tomato roots. II. Iron availability. *Physiol. Plant.* **5**, 248.

Street, H. E., McGonagle, M. P. and Roberts, E. H. (1953). Factors controlling meristematic activity in excised roots. II. Experiments involving repeated subculture of the main axis meristems of roots of *Lycopersicum esculentum*, Mill. and *Lycopersicum pimpinellifolium*, Dunal. *Physiol. Plant.* **6**, 1.

Street, H. E. and McGregor, S. M. (1952). The carbohydrate nutrition of tomato roots. III. The effect of external sucrose concentration on the growth and anatomy of excised roots. *Ann. Bot., Lond.* **16**, 185.

Street, H. E., McGregor, S. M. and Sussex, I. M. (1954). Effects of 3-indolylacetic acid and 3-indolylacetonitrile on the growth of excised tomato roots. *J. exp. Bot.* **5**, 204.

Street, H. E. and Sheat, D. E. G. (1958). The absorption and availability of nitrate and ammonia. *In* "Encyclopaedia of Plant Physiology" (W. Ruhland, ed.), Vol. 8, pp. 150–161. Springer, Berlin.

Strong, F. M. (1958). Kinetin and kinins. *In* "Topics in Microbial Chemistry," pp. 98–158. Wiley, New York.

Sutton, D., Scott, E. G. and Street, H. E. (1961). Studies on the growth in culture of excised wheat roots. II. The growth promoting activity of amino acids. *Physiol. Plant.* **14**, 712.

Swanson, C. A. (1959). Translocation of organic solutes. *In* "Plant Physiology" (F. C. Steward, ed.), Vol. 2, pp. 481–558. Academic Press, New York.

Szember, A. (1960). Influence on plant growth of the breakdown of organic phosphorus compounds by micro-organisms. *Plant and Soil* **13**, 147.

Tamaoki, T. and Ullstrup, A. J. (1958). Cultivation *in vitro* of excised endosperm and meristem tissue of corn. *Bull. Torrey bot. Club* **85**, 260.

Tang, P. S. and Wu, H. Y. (1957). Adaptive formation of nitrate reductase in rice seedlings. *Nature, Lond.* **179**, 1355.

Tesar, I. S. and Kutacek, M. (1955). Root excretions of higher plants. I. Excretion of amino acids by the roots of wheat in culture. *Ann. Acad. tchécosl. Agric.* **28**, 927.

Thimann, K. V. and Laloraya, M. M. (1960). Changes in nitrogen in pea stem sections under the action of kinetin. *Physiol. Plant.* **13**, 165.

Thomas, D. R. (1961). Studies in the carbohydrate nutrition and metabolism of excised roots. Ph.D. Thesis, University of Wales.

Thomas, D. R., Craigie, J. S. and Street, H. E. (1963). Carbohydrate nutrition of the excised tomato root. "Plant Tissue and Organ Culture—a Symposium." Int. Soc. Plant Morphologists, Delhi, pp 26–43.

Thomas, M. (1949). Physiological studies in acid metabolism in green plants. I. CO_2 fixation and CO_2 liberation in Crassulacean acid metabolism. *New Phytol.* **48**, 390.

Thresher, C. L. and Street, H. E. (1962). The heterotrophic nutrition of *Chlorella vulgaris* (Brannon No. 1 strain). II. "Adaptation" to galactose as carbon source. *Indian J. Plant Physiol.* **5**, 117.

Thurlow, J. and Bonner, J. (1948). Fixation of atmospheric CO_2 in the dark by leaves of *Bryophyllum*. *Arch. Biochem.* **19**, 509.

Thurman, D. A. and Street, H. E. (1960). The auxin activity extractable from excised tomato roots by 80% methanol. *J. exp. Bot.* **11**, 188.

Thurman, D. A. and Street, H. E. (1962). Metabolism of some indole auxins in excised tomato roots. *J. exp. Bot.* **13**, 369.

Tolbert, N. E. and Cohan, M. S. (1953). Activation of glycolic acid oxidase in plants. *J. biol. Chem.* **204**, 639.

Torrey, J. G. (1958a). Differential mitotic response of diploid and polyploid nuclei to auxin and kinetin treatment. *Science* **128**, 1148.

Torrey, J. G. (1958b). Endogenous bud and root formation by isolated roots of *Convolvulus* grown *in vitro*. *Plant Physiol.* **33**, 258.

Torrey, J. G. (1959). Experimental modification of development in the root. *In* "Cell, Organism and Milieu" (D. Rudnick, ed.), pp. 189–222. Ronald Press, New York.

Torrey, J. G. and Reinert, J. (1961). Suspension cultures of higher plant cells in synthetic media. *Plant Physiol.* **36**, 483.

Torrey, J. G., Reinert, J. and Merkel, N. (1962). Mitosis in suspension cultures of higher plant cells in a synthetic medium. *Amer. J. Bot.* **49**, 420.

Tulecke, W. (1960). Arginine-requiring strains of tissue obtained from *Ginkgo* pollen. *Plant Physiol.* **35**, 19.

Tulecke, W. and Nickell, L. G. (1959). Production of large amounts of plant tissue by submerged culture. *Science* **130**, 863.

Tulecke, W., Weinstein, L. H., Rutner, A. and Laurencot, H. J., Jr. (1961). The biochemical composition of coconut water (coconut milk) as related to its use in plant tissue culture. *Contr. Boyce Thompson Inst.* **21**, 115.

Vaidyanathan, C. S. and Street, H. E. (1959a). Nitrate reduction by aqueous extracts of excised tomato roots. *Nature, Lond.* **184**, 531.

Vaidyanathan, C. S. and Street, H. E. (1959b). A non-dialysable inhibitor of glutamotransferase present in excised tomato roots. *Nature, Lond.* **184**, 347.

Venketeswaran, S. and Mahlberg, P. G. (1962). Proliferation of albino and pigmented genetic strains of *Nicotiana* in tissue culture. *Physiol. Plant.* **15**, 639.

Viets, E. G., Jr., Moxon, A. L. and Whitehead, E. I. (1946). Nitrogen metabolism of corn (*Zea mays*) as influenced by ammonium nutrition. *Plant Physiol.* **21**, 271.

Wacek, A. von, Härtel, O. and Meralla, S. (1953). Über den Einfluss von Coniferinzusatz auf die Verholzung von Karottengewebe bei Kultur *in vitro*. *Holzforschung* **7**, 58.

Wacek, A. von, Härtel, O. and Meralla, S. (1954). Über die Wirkung von Coniferinzusatz auf die Verholzung von Fichtengewebe bei Kultur *in vitro*. *Holzforschung* **8**, 65.

Wachtel, H. K. (1943). Inhibitory action of mannose upon the growing plant. *Arch. Biochem.* **2**, 395.

Weinstein, L. H., Nickell, L. G., Laurencot, H. J., Jr. and Tulecke, W. (1959). Biochemical and physiological studies of tissue cultures and the plant parts from which they are derived. I. *Agave toumeyana*. *Contrib. Boyce Thompson Inst.* **20**, 239.

Weiss, C. and Vaadra, Y. (1965). Kinetin-like activity in root apices of sunflower plants. *Life Sciences* 1965, 1323.

Weissman, G. S. (1959). Influence of ammonium and nitrate on the protein and free amino acids in shoots of wheat seedlings. *Amer. J. Bot.* **46**, 339.

West, F. R., Jr. and Mika, S. (1957). Synthesis of atropine by isolated roots and root-callus cultures of belladonna. *Bot. Gaz.* **119**, 50.

West, P. M. (1939). Excretion of thiamin and biotin by the roots of higher plants. *Nature, Lond.* **144**, 1050.

Whaley, W. G. and Kephart, J. (1957). Effect of gibberellic acid on growth of maize roots. *Science* **125**, 234.

Whaley, W. G. and Long, A. L. (1944). The behaviour of excised roots of heterotic hybrids and their inbred parents in culture. *Bull. Torrey bot. Club* **71**, 267.

White, P. R. (1932). The influence of some environmental conditions on the growth of excised root tips of wheat seedlings in liquid media. *Plant Physiol.* **7**, 613.

White, P. R. (1934). Potentially unlimited growth of excised tomato root tips in a liquid medium. *Plant Physiol.* **9**, 585.

White, P. R. (1937a). Vitamin B_1 in the nutrition of excised tomato roots. *Plant Physiol.* **12**, 803.

White, P. R. (1937b). Amino acids in the nutrition of excised tomato roots. *Plant Physiol.* **12**, 793.

White, P. R. (1938a). Accessory salts in the nutrition of excised tomato roots. *Plant Physiol.* **13**, 391.

White, P. R. (1938b). Cultivation of excised roots of dicotyledonous plants. *Amer. J. Bot.* **25**, 348.

White, P. R. (1939). Glycine in the nutrition of excised tomato roots. *Plant Physiol.* **14**, 527.

White, P. R. (1940). Sucrose versus dextrose as carbohydrate source for excised tomato roots. *Plant Physiol.* **15**, 355.

White, P. R. (1943a). "A Handbook of Plant Tissue Culture". J. Cattell, Lancaster, Pa.

White, P. R. (1943b). Further evidence on the significance of glycine, pyridoxine and nicotinic acid in the nutrition of excised tomato roots. *Amer. J. Bot.* **30**, 33.

Whittington, W. J. (1959). The role of boron in plant growth. II. The effect on the growth of the radicle. *J. exp. Bot.* **10**, 93.

Wickson, M. and Thimann, K. V. (1960). The antagonism of auxin and kinetin in apical dominance. II. The transport of IAA in pea stems in relation to apical dominance. *Physiol. Plant.* **13**, 539.

Wiggans, S. C. (1954). Growth and organ formation in callus tissues derived from *Daucus carota*. *Amer. J. Bot.* **41**, 321.

Willemot, C. and Boll, W. G. (1962). Changed response of excised tomato roots to pyridoxin deficiency following prolonged sterile culture. *Can. J. Bot.* **40**, 1107.

Winter, A. and Street, H. E. (1963). A new natural auxin isolated from "staled" root culture medium. *Nature, Lond.* **198**, 1283.

Winzler, R. J., Burk, D. and du Vigneaud, V. (1944). Biotin in fermentation, respiration, growth and nitrogen assimilation by yeast. *Arch. Biochem.* **5**, 25.

Wood, H. N. and Braun, A. C. (1961). Studies on the regulation of certain essential biosynthetic systems in normal and crown-gall tumor. *Proc. nat. Acad. Sci., Wash.* **47**, 1907.

Woolley, D. W. (1952). "A Study of Antimetabolites". Chapman and Hall, London.

Wright, D. E. (1962). Amino acid uptake by plant roots. *Arch. Biochem. Biophys.* **97**, 174.

Yemm, E. W. and Folkes, B. F. (1958). The metabolism of amino acids and proteins in plants. *Annu. Rev. Plant Physiol.* **9**, 245.

Zwar, J. A., Bottomley, W. and Kefford, N. P. (1963). Kinin activity from plant extracts. II. Partial purification and fractionation of kinins in apple extract. *Aust. J. biol. Sci.* **16**, 407.

CHAPTER 10

Growth, Differentiation and Organogenesis in Plant Tissue and Organ Cultures

H. E. STREET

Department of Botany, University College of Swansea, Wales

I. INTRODUCTION

Growth and differentiation can be described in terms of increase in mass and changes in form and structure. These changes are the outcome of nutrition and metabolism and these processes are, in turn, an expression of the potentialities of the genotype. Any separation between nutrition and metabolism on the one hand, and growth and differentiation on the other, is thus artificial and cannot be rigidly followed. Hence, in this chapter many references will be made to the previous discussion of nutrition and metabolism of plant cultures (Chap. 9).

The major objective of studies on growth, differentiation and organogenesis in tissue and organ cultures is a better understanding of these processes as they occur in the multicellular body of higher plants. Thus, discussion of these processes, firstly by reference to organ cultures, then to callus cultures and finally to suspension cultures (the sequence followed in this chapter), can again only be justified in terms of convenience and will not be strictly adhered to whenever cross-reference leads to a more satisfactory treatment.

The survey will follow the pattern generally adopted in the previous chapter of selecting subjects which have been mainly developed by utilizing plant Tissue-Culture techniques or are clearly subjects in which the further use of these techniques can be expected to contribute significantly in the immediate future. This implies that no attempt has been made at comprehensive coverage of all researches in the field of growth and differentiation which have used Tissue-Culture techniques although it is hoped that no major application has been completely omitted.

In this field the dominant concept is that growth and differentiation are controlled by specific growth-regulating substances (phytohormones) of high biological activity. Hence, most of the researches which will be reported have sought to demonstrate the operation of such chemical control mechanisms, to identify the operative regulators and to elucidate their mode of action. However, in most cases, the actual achievement does not extend beyond the first of these objectives. It cannot, therefore, be too strongly emphasized that our knowledge of the chemistry, biosynthesis and degradation of the natural growth-regulating substances of plants is most unsatisfactory and that we have hardly any understanding of their mode of action. This inevitably gives a tentative and purely descriptive character to the account of most of the researches available for discussion.

II. Growth and Differentiation in Cultured Roots

A. Meristems: The Division, Enlargement and Maturation of Root Cells

The growth of an organ like the root is the expression of an increase in the number of its constituent cells by cell division, enlargement of the new cells and their development (differentiation) into the different kinds of tissue cells. These processes are localized in growing centres or meristems. In the root the primary meristems are at the root tips and, in addition, there are secondary meristems or cambia which in the developing plant give rise to additional vascular tissues and to protective layers of cork. The general morphology of the cultured root system is determined by the level and duration of activity at the apical meristems, the extent to which lateral root tips are initiated and the interactions between the older and more recently initiated growth centres. Actively functioning apical root meristems exert an inhibitory influence on the functioning of more recently initiated lateral root meristems and this phenomenon of growth correlation is usually termed apical dominance.

The extreme tip of the root is occupied by a protective cap of cells (the root cap) derived from an underlying group of cells in the permanently dividing tissue or promeristem. All the new cells formed by the growing root have their ultimate origin in this promeristem, although some of the cells arising from the promeristem cells may undergo a limited number of further divisions before differentiating into the mature tissue cells. Our knowledge of this apical region of plant roots has recently been reviewed by Clowes (1961a). The region is both variable and complex and there has been much controversy, particularly regarding the number of cells constituting the promeristem. One type of organization which seems to apply to the root tip of a number of species is that the promeristem is composed of a group of dividing cells lying on the surface of a hemisphere. The proximal (basal) curved surface of this hemisphere is delimited by a plate of promeristem cells which give rise to the stele, cortex and piliferous layer and sometimes also to the outer cells of the root cap. The hemisphere is filled with a group of cells (as many as 500–1000 cells) which rarely divide and constitute a quiescent centre of the meristem. The distal (apical) flat surface of this hemisphere of quiescent cells is covered by a further plate of dividing cells which give rise to the central cells of the root cap (Fig. 1).

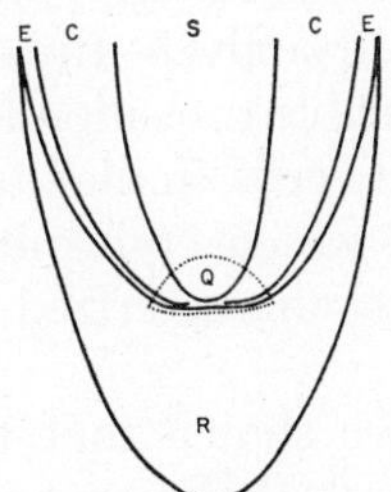

Fig. 1. Diagrammatic median section of the root apex of maize. The sites of the initial cells of the promeristem are indicated by dots. E, Piliferous layer; C, cortex; S, stele; Q, quiescent centre; R, root cap. (Drawn by L. Clowes. From Street, 1962.)

This description implies that the apex can contain both actively dividing and quiescent cells. Evidence that this may be so comes from autoradiography of sections of the root tip after feeding with radioactive substances. By feeding tritium-labelled thymidine, which is incorporated only into deoxyribonucleic acid (DNA), it is possible to detect the quiescent centre as a group of cells in which DNA synthesis is either not proceeding, or is proceeding very slowly, and that these cells are surrounded by promeristem cells in which DNA synthesis has led to the incorporation of labelled thymidine into the chromosomes during the 24 h test period (Clowes, 1959, 1961a, 1962). Experiments of this kind show that the numbers of both dividing and quiescent cells may vary during development. In young lateral root tips and embryonic roots, the quiescent centre is apparently either absent or represented by very few cells.

A pattern of growth behaviour to be observed in the growth of unicellular organisms is a continuing and regular sequence of cell divisions, each separated by a period of growth whose extent and duration is curtailed by the cell again entering mitosis. The cell growth here does not create any block to mitosis and the unicells can be described as permanently meristematic. Further, such cells can frequently become dormant and then again resume the pattern of alternating growth and division. This contrasts with the fate of those cells which are derived from the promeristem and which differentiate into the tissue cells. These will normally not divide again but mature, age and ultimately die. The meristems of embryonic roots and of newly initiated laterals either lack a quiescent centre or contain very few quiescent cells. However, as such meristems develop, a prominent quiescent centre may appear. If, in such a meristem, the actively dividing promeristem cells are injured by exposure to the β-radiation of tritium-labelled thymidine of high specific activity, then the subsequent meristem regeneration almost certainly involves conversion of cells of the quiescent centre into actively dividing cells (Clowes, 1961b). Here, then, we have a reversible transition from dividing (promeristem) cells to dormant (quiescent) cells similar to that observed in unicells. Quiescent cells are cells in which both mitosis and differentiation are blocked and such cells are characterized by their very low rate of metabolic activity.

Studies of root cells have shown that the process of mitosis is of short duration compared with the interphase separating the successive mitoses, and that increase in temperature speeds up cell division, mainly through a shortening of interphase (Brown, 1951). Studies of the respiration rate of dividing cells show that their metabolism, as expressed by this index, is at a particularly low level during the period of mitosis. The synthesis of DNA and of proteins from cytoplasmic precursors and the passing of energy-rich compounds into the nucleus occurs during interphase and once prophase commences the completion of the mitotic process is autonomous (Mazia, 1961). Cytoplasmic events following mitosis therefore determine whether the cell will again divide and whether such divisions will continue (i.e. the cell will remain in the promeristem) or will immediately, or after one or two further divisions, be blocked by specific changes in metabolism (initiation of differentiation) proceeding to a point which normally destines the cell to develop into a mature tissue cell. Which of these two alternative pathways is followed is determined in some way, not fully understood, by the micro-environment of the cell within the organized meristem. If mitosis supervenes sufficiently early, then the associated disorganization of cytoplasmic structure and function restores the meristematic state. We shall return to this question in considering the hormonal control of growth and differentiation in cultured roots.

The organization of the apical meristems of cultured roots as examined by microscopy corresponds closely with that of seedling radicle apices of the same species (Street and McGregor, 1952; Heimsch, 1960) and it is clear that their lateral apices only reach their full size and growth activity after several days of growth in culture following their emergence. Examination of cultured pea roots by autoradiography after feeding with labelled precursors of DNA and protein has, however, given no indication of a group of cells of low metabolic activity within the apical meristem (Abbott, 1963) so that the apices of cultured roots may resemble embryonic root meristems in lacking a quiescent centre. This aspect of the meristem structure of cultured roots, however, warrants further study particularly in roots allowed to grow for longer periods without subculture as can be achieved by the use of large volumes of medium per root.

The problems of structural and physiological differentiation in root apices can now also be approached by studies of their fine structure with the electron-microscope (Whaley, Mollenhauer and Leech, 1960; Esau, 1963). This approach, when applied to normal roots, not only emphasizes the contrast between promeristem and quiescent centre cells but also shows how far the structure of root cap cells supports the view that they are involved in the secretion of organic metabolites (Mollenhauer, Whaley and Leech, 1961; Chrispeels, Vatter and Hanson, 1963; see p. 591). However, at the time of writing, there is not yet any published work on the fine structure of the meristems of cultured roots.

The pattern in the arrangement of cells in the apical root meristem is maintained by the planes along which division walls are laid down in cell division and by a balance between the rate of cell division on the one hand and the rates and directions of cell expansion on the other. The orientation of the division walls is apparently, in turn, determined by the shape and orientation of the mitotic apparatus arising during the nuclear division which precedes cytokinesis. These planes of division are an expression of polarity in the cells of the meristems. When cell division in root meristems is inhibited by auxins this polarity is disturbed (Levan, 1939; Burström, 1942; Åberg, 1957). Hughes and Street (1960), working with excised tomato roots, noted increased numbers of longitudinally orientated divisions in cells destined to give vessel units, so that more vessels were formed and their individual units were of greater vertical height despite the strong inhibition of extension growth caused by the applied β-indolylacetic acid (IAA). Similar reorientation of division walls also clearly occurred in the cells generating the piliferous layer (to give a greater number of cells as seen in cross section) and in those generating the cortex (to give an increased number of layers of cortical cells). A similar reorientation of division walls giving an increased number of cells in the cross section of excised tomato roots was also reported by Butcher and Street (1960a) using naphthaleneacetic acid (NAA) at concentrations ranging from those which stimulate to those which inhibit extension growth. No such reorientation occurred in response to a range of gibberellic acid (GA) treatments. However, changes in orientation leading to an increased number of cells in the root diameter can also be induced by changes in sugar supply as shown by Burström (1941) and Street and McGregor (1952).

By studying the growth rate and by recording, by microscopic observation, the cell dimensions at known distances from the root apex, the time course of cell expansion in different cell layers can be worked out. Growth curves for particular tissue cells can thus be constructed, relating cell dimension to distance from the promeristem or to time. Curves so constructed for the elongation of the developing piliferous layer cells of the cultured tomato root (Street and McGregor, 1952) agree closely with those for seedling roots of *Phleum pratense* (Goodwin and Stepka, 1945) and other species. Such curves enable the effects of environmental and nutritive factors on cell growth to be analysed in terms of the changing rate with time and the total duration of the expansion process. Studies of this kind by Burström (1954, 1955) on wheat roots led him to advance the controversial hypothesis that cell extension takes place in two phases. The first stage is regarded as involving a plastic stretching of the wall and is independent of calcium and promoted by auxin. The second phase, for which calcium is essential, involves the deposition of cellulose and is inhibited by auxin.

If we follow the process of expansion by following changes in cell length in a cell whose major direction of expansion is longitudinal, as in the case of expanding exodermal and piliferous layer cells, the expansion starts very slowly, goes through a period of increasing rate, continues at a maximum rate for a time and then progressively declines until it ceases fairly abruptly. Studies of expansion in the piliferous layer suggest that the cells have a limited capacity for expansion. The longest cells of the piliferous layer are either without hairs or produce the shortest root hairs, while the shortest piliferous layer cells produce the longest hairs. Thus each piliferous layer cell appears to have a certain capacity for growth which may be expressed either longitudinally (as cell length) or horizontally (as an extending root hair). In some species, the piliferous layer shows a regular pattern of long cells without root hairs and short cells with root hairs. This highly controlled cell expansion to be observed in cultured roots contrasts sharply with the behaviour of expanding single cells in suspension cultures. Cells in suspension culture and thus freed from the "restrictions" of the organized multicellular body, not only give rise to cells of many and frequently novel shapes, but also to cells of giant size (see p. 672). In such cells the control mechanism, whose nature is not understood but which normally brings the expansion process to a sharp halt, seems to have been removed.

The mature cortical cells of the root may have twenty or more times the volume of the meristematic initials from which they are derived. These cells of the promeristem are isodiametric, have a high ratio of nucleus to cell volume and are filled with cytoplasm. The process of cell expansion is associated with the uptake of water leading first to the appearance of a number of small vacuoles and ultimately to a single central vacuole. It has been strongly argued that the uptake of water is a consequence of, rather than a motive force in, cell expansion since, as cells enlarge, their dry weight, protein content and content of cell wall material all increase (Thimann, 1960). Simultaneously, changes occur in the physiological activity of the cells. Expansion involves real growth and some degree of differentiation.

Brown and co-workers (Brown and Broadbent, 1950; Brown and Robinson, 1955; Brown, 1959) have studied the growth potential, cellular composition, respiratory activity, enzymic composition and ribonucleic acid (RNA) content of isolated segments of seedling pea roots cut at successive intervals of 1 mm from the apex. Associated with cell expansion there was found to be a progressive increase, on a per cell basis, in respiration, in protein and in the activities of invertase, a phosphatase and a dipeptidase. The conclusion was reached that the growing cell is an expanding metabolic system in which enzymes come to represent a higher proportion of the total protein. Moving back from the root tip through the first 8 mm of the roots (the distance examined) they found parallel increases in the protein and RNA contents per cell. Moreover the base composition of the RNA changed in the sense that the proportion of purines to pyrimidines rose as the cells became more mature. Heyes (1960) showed that this change in base composition was a reflection of a change in the relative amount of two RNA fractions (the base composition of each fraction being constant). The fraction dominant in young cells tended to decrease during expansion but an increase in the second fraction more than compensated for this and led to an overall increase in RNA content per cell. Abbott (1963), working with excised pea roots in culture, confirmed that the RNA content per cell rose during cell expansion (a process completed within 5 mm from the apex in both seedling and cultured roots), but that beyond this point the RNA content slowly declined. This led him to suggest that at least part of the increase in RNA occurring in seedling roots after the cells were fully expanded, was probably not related to cell maturation but represented an enrichment of the cells from seed reserves.

The concept that the cellular RNA changes in amount and chemical nature during differentiation requires a turn-over of RNA to mediate the transition from one state to another. Presumably the succession of RNA and protein states are regarded not only as mediating the expansion and differentiation but as limiting the duration and determining the rate of change of each stage in the overall process. On this basis, interference with RNA synthesis could therefore either prevent expansion and differentiation or prolong the expansion by blocking transformation to the state which forecloses expansion and initiates subsequent aspects of differentiation. Rather surprising enhancements of elongation in roots of *Pisum sativum* and *Zea mays* resulting from treatment with low concentrations of ribonuclease (Yeoman, 1962) and appropriate additions of 2-thiouracil (Woodstock and Brown, 1963) have been interpreted in these terms. The ribonuclease appears to disperse RNA from the nucleolus and to block the synthesis of the RNA required for further differentiation, thereby prolonging expansion. The stimulation induced in intact roots by thiouracil can be reversed by uracil and autoradiographic evidence suggests that uracil effectively prevents incorporation of the analogue into newly synthesized RNA, and thereby permits differentiation to proceed. The inability of uracil to antagonize the effect of 2-thiouracil on the elongation of isolated root segments (2·0–4·0 mm from the apex) can then be explained from the observation that during the expansion of the isolated segments there is a net decrease in RNA in contrast to the net increase in the same region during expansion in the intact root. The lack of new synthesis of RNA prevents replacement of the stable thiouracil-containing RNA by the normal RNA of the subsequent stage of differentiation.

The concept of a rising RNA content as characterizing the whole duration of the expansion process does not seem to apply to all roots and in work with *Vicia faba* there appears to be conflict between the results obtained in different laboratories as to the point at which the maximum RNA content per cell is reached. Thus, with *Vicia faba*, the RNA content has been reported to reach a peak at the end of cell expansion (4–8 mm from the root apex) by Holmes, Mee, Hornsey and Gray (1955) and at a much earlier stage in the expansion process (1·7 mm from the apex) by Jensen (1958). In studies on *Allium cepa* roots, Jensen (1957, 1958) found that from the region of the apical initials (350 μ from the tip) up to the point where rapid cell elongation *commences* (1000–1200 μ from the tip) the cells synthesize and accumulate RNA and there is little simultaneous RNA turn-over. There was a gain in total RNA during the stage of radial cell enlargement but not during the subsequent phase of rapid cell elongation. During cell elongation there was rapid RNA synthesis but a balancing rate of turn-over so that the RNA content per cell remained at first constant and ultimately declined. Woodstock and Skoog (1960, 1962) in studies with inbred lines of *Zea mays* obtained data indicating that the amount of RNA synthesized by the cells while still in the meristematic zone of the root apex determined the rate but not the duration of their subsequent elongation. Final cell size appeared to be determined by the RNA content reached early in the expansion process, subsequent expansion occurring either without further net gain or even with a small net loss in RNA per cell. These workers concluded that cell expansion is determined by RNA synthesis during a preparatory phase rather than by synthesis occurring during the phase of elongation.

Uniformity regarding the relationship of RNA to cell expansion is hardly to be expected since there is the possibility that only that part of the total cellular RNA which is directly concerned in determining the pattern and rate of protein synthesis has significance in the processes of cell expansion and differentiation. In bacteria a particular fraction of the total RNA, which has been shown to have a base composition similar to that of the chromosomal DNA, and to undergo a high rate of turn-over (as judged by its rate of labelling with ^{32}P- phosphate) has been designated "messenger RNA". It is postulated that this is responsible for carrying the genetic information from DNA to the ribosomes where protein synthesis takes place (Jacob and Monod, 1961). The recent demonstration that an RNA fraction of this kind can be detected in pea root cells (Loening, 1962) should open up the possibility of more critical studies on the flow of genetic information during cell expansion and differentiation in root cultures.

By treatment of roots with 2,4-D or IAA it has been possible to induce mitosis in differentiated root tissue cells (Levan, 1939; D'Amato,

1950; Holzer, 1952). From chromosome counts made on the dividing nuclei of such cells and from studies of nuclear volume, which is related to the ploidy of the nucleus (Bradley, 1954), it is clear that the mature tissue cells of both seedling and cultured roots are frequently polyploid or have multistrand chromosomes. These polyploid nuclei are not randomly distributed; usually each tissue is characterized by a predominant level of ploidy in its cells. Thus cortical cells are frequently tetraploid, vessel units of the metaxylem often tetra- or octoploid and endodermal cells frequently tetraploid (D'Amato, 1952; Chouinard, 1955). The significance of these changes in relation to differentiation is not clear, although various authors have emphasized that polyploidy and tissue differentiation are intimately related (Torrey, 1959a). The close correlation found by Wipf and Cooper (1940) between the presence of naturally occurring tetraploid cells and the origin of root nodules in leguminous roots strongly suggests that physiological changes may be correlated with changes in ploidy arising by endomitosis. The fact, however, that the cells of a particular tissue are rarely if ever *all* at the same degree of ploidy suggests that changes in ploidy are a consequence of or a late aspect of differentiation rather than an essential determining step in this process. The increasing extent of polyploidy (or polyteny) with increase in distance from the root apex is roughly paralleled by the increase in mean cell size and it could be that the polyploidy has the biological significance in large tissue cells of controlling a larger volume of cytoplasm (see p. 671). Recently, from studies on roots of several species (List, 1963), evidence has been obtained that the growth of xylem cells may be described as a fluctuating alternation or stepwise growth of cell and nucleus rather than by the allometric growth equation. Plots were made of log. nuclear against log. cell volume from measurements on a large number of metaxylem cells. The points on the graphs were considered to fall into clusters. There were size classes in the nuclei and associated with these, cell volume classes.

Although polyploidy is a feature of mature root tissues the apical meristem and lateral root meristems of cultured roots remain persistently diploid, indicating the preservation of the diploid condition in the pericycle from which new lateral meristems arise. As will be discussed later, organized meristems which arise in highly polyploid callus tissues and give rise to roots or shoot buds also seem always to be diploid. The development of polyploidy, during differentiation, could follow a blocking of mitosis in a phase of nuclear activity subsequent to DNA duplication. Patau, Das and Skoog (1957) concluded that both IAA and kinetin were required for active and continuing cell division in excised tobacco-pith tissue. Very low concentrations of IAA or kinetin would induce DNA doubling, higher concentrations of these regulators were required to induce mitosis and a further increase in kinetin concentration was required to induce cell division (cytokinesis). Changes, therefore, in the absolute and relative levels of natural auxins and kinins, during differentiation, could determine the blocking of mitosis and the extent to which DNA duplication continues to give polyploid nuclei. Further, there is evidence that, once the nucleus has become polyploid, low concentrations of IAA and kinetin are then less effective in promoting DNA duplication.

As indicated, division in polyploid root-tissue cells was first induced by high levels of auxin. However, kinetin has subsequently been shown to be an effective agent in inducing a *continuing* process of cell division in polyploid cells (Torrey, 1961) indicating that it is probably necessary to raise the endogenous kinin level (effective for mitosis in diploid cells) in order to activate the division process in polyploid nuclei. When pea root segments were placed in an auxin-containing medium, callus started to develop within 24 h from the diploid pericycle and the stelar parenchyma. However, if kinetin was added in sufficient concentration (1 mg/l), then, after a lag period of 48 h, callus arose also from the polyploid cortical cells. It should be emphasized that in all such cases where the cells of mature tissues (such as the epidermis, cortex or pith) are induced to divide and give rise *in vitro* to a callus, mitosis has been unblocked and thereby dedifferentiation initiated, either (1) by a particular manipulative treatment (usually involving separation or partial separation of the tissue from the whole organism), or (2) by a nutritional treatment (usually involving a culture medium containing growth-regulating substances), or (3) by a combination of these treatments.

B. HORMONAL CONTROL OF ROOT GROWTH

The demonstrations that the continuous culture of excised roots of rye requires the use of a culture medium containing auxin (Roberts and Street, 1955) and that an increase in the rate and duration of the growth of excised wheat roots results from the addition of a mixture of IAA and unaltered tryptophane to the culture medium (Carter and Street, 1963) point to the necessity of auxin for root growth. This conclusion is now supported by an impressive body of data. Work with isolated root segments has demonstrated that auxins can greatly increase their linear extension (a consequence of cell expansion) (Leopold and Guernsey, 1953; Audus, 1959a). The work of Butcher and Street (1960a) in excised tomato roots indicates that auxins not only promote root cell expansion but can also increase the rate of cell division at the apical meristems. A number of classical studies indicated that isolated root tips released substances active in Went's (1928) *Avena* curvature test (Hawker, 1932; Boysen-Jensen, 1933a; van Raalte, 1936) and that auxins could be extracted from roots by chloroform (Thimann, 1934). The studies of Nagao (1937, 1938) and van Overbeek (1939a, b) and more recently of Britton, Housley and Bentley (1956) and Thurman and Street (1960) all yield evidence for the presence of auxins in excised roots cultured in auxin-free medium. These results indicate that auxins are synthesized in roots and are essential for their growth. Similarly, the demonstration (Butcher, 1963) of the presence of gibberellins in cultured roots also points to their involvement in the regulation of root growth, a conclusion strengthened by the demonstration that they can, under appropriate conditions, enhance cell expansion and cell division in cultured roots (Butcher and Street, 1960a) (see also Chap. 9, p. 576). Evidence has also been obtained that kinins are synthesized in roots and may be exported from the root to the shoot (Loeffler and van Overbeek, 1964; Weiss and Vaadra, 1965).

Despite the very convincing evidence now available that auxins are essential for root growth it is interesting to recall that most of the pioneer workers reported an inhibition of root growth in response to externally applied auxin, even when used in very low concentration (Cholodny, 1924, 1926, 1927, 1931; Nielsen, 1930; Boysen-Jensen, 1933b, 1936; Lane, 1936). These authors concluded that auxin was a promoter of shoot growth and an inhibitor of root growth. To explain these reports of the inhibitory activity of low auxin concentrations it is necessary to consider the action of *externally* applied auxin and the information regarding the endogenous levels of auxin established in growing root systems. Audus (1959b) has drawn attention to the fact that the natural levels of endogenous auxin present in roots, when expressed as IAA equivalents, are usually of a higher order of magnitude than the low levels of auxin which, applied externally, are significantly inhibitory. Assuming that expressing endogenous levels in terms of IAA equivalents of activity does not give an entirely false picture, this means that external applications of IAA or other auxins may have an inhibitory action *not* explicable in terms of the raising of the overall internal auxin level to a supra-optimal value. External auxins may thus have an inhibitory action because they develop supra-optimal concentrations at particular sites in the tissue and meristem cells. The same kind of problem has already been raised in considering the inhibitory activities of externally applied amino acids (see Chap. 9, p. 549). One recent observation made in studies with cultured wheat roots is very relevant to this discussion. Autoclaved tryptophane increases the growth of these roots; unheated tryptophane, although readily absorbed, is inactive. The growth-promoting activity of autoclaved tryptophane cannot be replaced by IAA alone. However, the incorporation into the culture medium of 0·025 mg/l IAA plus 50 mg/l unheated tryptophane fully reproduces the growth stimulation resulting from 50 mg/l of autoclaved tryptophane (Carter and Street, 1963). It can be argued here that the unheated tryptophane blocks the inhibitory activity of external IAA and allows the IAA absorbed into the cells to show its growth-promoting activity.

The second consideration relevant to explaining the inhibitory action of auxins in root growth relates to our knowledge of endogenous auxin levels and how they change as the root system develops. Pilet (1951a, b, 1961a, c) in a series of studies with seedling roots of *Lens culinaris* has determined their endogenous auxin level, IAA-oxidase activity and growth responses to external IAA. His results indicate that the natural auxin level in the root meristem is higher than in the mature tissues and that the overall natural auxin level rises as the root continues to grow. The rate of growth of the root is for a short time at its maximum value and this corresponds to the point of transition in auxin content from suboptimal to supra-optimal. Before this point, externally applied IAA promotes root growth, and afterwards inhibits it. The period during which the endogenous auxin level is suboptimal is very short and, therefore, many experiments involving seedling roots have probably involved the application of auxins to roots with a supra-optimal endogenous level. Although there is also a rise in the activity of IAA-oxidase, with time (probably in response to the rising endogenous level of auxin), this does not prevent a continuing auxin accumulation. Furthermore, the rise in auxin content is greatest in the meristem and the rise in IAA-oxidase most marked in the older tissue cells. Lahiri and Audus (1960, 1961) working with roots of *Vicia faba* have also studied changes in endogenous auxins with age. They submitted the acid-ether soluble fraction of the roots to chromatography and detected three zones of auxin activity which they labelled AP_{i}, AP_{ii} and AP_{iii}. From studies of the content of these fractions in successive segments along the root they concluded that AP_{ii} (which corresponded in chromatographic properties with IAA) and AP_{iii} were synthesized in the meristem. Throughout the growth period, AP_{ii} remained at a suboptimal level in the zone of elongation and it was suggested that it was the factor promoting cell expansion. AP_{iii}, however, accumulated during growth to supra-optimal levels particularly in the apical meristem and was regarded as the factor possibly responsible for the increasing retardation of growth coincident with the ageing of the root tip meristem. These observations on the development of supra-optimal levels of auxin in the apical meristems of root systems growing *in vivo* are closely paralleled by studies undertaken in the author's laboratory with cultured excised tomato roots.

As previously indicated (Chap. 9, p. 590) most clones of excised tomato roots cannot be cultured indefinitely in the basic root-culture medium of White by repeated excision of the main axis tips. Nearly all the tips continue growth through 4–6 passages each of 7 days duration, but after this the number of functional meristems begins to decline and in many experiments of this kind all the meristems have, in due course, ceased to grow (Street, McGonagle and Roberts, 1953). Similarly, when the roots are allowed to continue growth, either in large volumes of medium or in continuously renewed medium, their main axis meristems cease activity whilst the more recently initiated lateral meristems are still actively growing (Street and Roberts, 1952). This decline and ultimate and apparently irreversible loss of meristematic activity in the individual meristems has been regarded as an "ageing" phenomenon. Under appropriate cultural conditions it can be demonstrated in many root cultures; published studies apply not only to tomato but to *Lycopersicum pimpinellifolium* (Street *et al.*, 1953), *Trifolium pratense* (Dawson and Street, 1959) and *Senecio vulgaris* (Hannay and Butcher, 1961).

Although the meristems age under a regime of regular subculture, nevertheless, the act of excision (involving removal of the root tip from the root system to which it has given rise) does prolong meristematic activity, particularly if each passage is not of prolonged duration and if the length of the root tip transferred does not exceed 10 mm (thus limiting the amount of mature tissue transferred). The duration of activity can be even more effectively extended and the growth can be better maintained in the successive culture passages by application of certain anti-auxins such as α-(l-naphthylmethyl sulphide)- propionic acid (NMSP) and l-naphthoxyacetic acid (1-NOA) at appropriate and increasing concentrations in the successive passages (Street, 1954a, 1955). Similarly, a marked extension of the duration of main axis growth can be obtained by growing the roots in large volumes of medium containing an anti-auxin (Street, 1954b) (Fig. 2). On the assumption that such effective anti-auxins antagonize the activity of a natural auxin synthesized in the roots, it is possible, from experiments involving a range of anti-auxin concentrations and measurement of the time course of the growth of the main and lateral roots, to conclude that newly initiated meristems contain a suboptimal level of a natural growth regulator essential for their activity but that, as growth proceeds, this level rises until it first becomes optimal, then supra-optimal and ultimately reaches a critical supra-optimal level which brings meristematic activity to an end. In excised tomato roots this tendency towards ageing of the meristems can be prevented (the individual meristems remaining continuously active) by lowering the sucrose

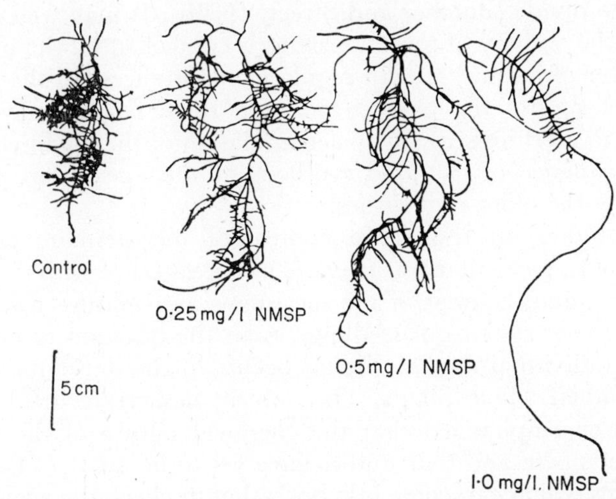

FIG. 2. Excised tomato roots cultured for 31 days in culture vessels containing 1 litre of medium (as Fig. 3, p. 468). White's standard medium (control) and this medium containing an addition of the anti-auxin, α(-1-naphthylmethyl sulphide)-propionic acid (NMSP) at the concentrations indicated. Note the increasing apical dominance of the main axis and of the first-order lateral roots with the higher concentrations of NMSP. (After Street, 1954b.)

concentration of the medium below a critical level (this level being sub-optimal for growth as judged over a 7-day growth passage). By contrast, the ageing can be accelerated and induced to occur in media of low sucrose content by addition of the synthetic auxin, NAA. IAA is, in this respect, ineffective. In this connection it may be noted that the anti-auxins effective as anti-ageing factors also reverse the inhibition of root growth caused by NAA but not by IAA. It may therefore be postulated that NAA reinforces the action of the natural auxin which controls meristematic activity in the root apex. Gibberellic acid also promotes ageing and can be postulated, in line with certain other evidence (Chap. 9, p. 576) to enhance the sensitivity of the cells to the natural auxin or to check the destruction of auxin in the root cells. From a number of observations (see Chap. 9, p. 573 and this Chap., p. 659) there is evidence of the importance of the auxin:kinin balance in determining the growth behaviour of tissues. It is interesting, therefore, that kinetin shows an activity similar to that of the anti-auxins in its effect upon the growth of excised roots. When roots are cultured in a medium of sufficiently low sucrose content to prevent ageing, then kinetin is an inhibitor of their growth. However, under conditions where ageing occurs, and particularly if this is intensified by using sucrose concentrations above 2%, then kinetin enhances growth rate and prolongs the period over which the cells of the apical meristem continue to divide (Butcher and Street, 1960b). It may well be, therefore, that the activity of root meristems is controlled by the interaction of a number of natural growth-regulating substances. In the roots of a number of species the balance between these factors may then be disturbed to a critical extent by accumulation of the auxin component as a consequence of its rapid synthesis at the apex from precursors supplied by the older root tissues.

These studies on the auxin control of meristematic activity in cultured roots, particularly as they are not at variance with the reported changes in auxin content of the meristems and mature tissues of the developing root systems of seedlings, raise the question of how far an ageing of individual root meristems occurs in the development of the root systems of whole plants. This subject deserves critical study. It must also be emphasized that the chemical nature of the operative auxin is unknown and that studies have yet to be made of the cellular mechanisms which can come into operation to check the accumulation of the auxin to a critical level. Lahiri and Audus (1961) have suggested that their AP_{iii} auxin resembles in some of its properties, the hypothetical "ageing" auxin postulated by Street (1955). A preliminary study of AP_{iii} in our laboratory indicates that this auxin is indolic and that it yields amino acids on hydrolysis (Street, Butcher, Handoll and Winter, 1964). It may, therefore, be a similar compound to the 5-hydroxytryptophane peptide isolated by Winter and Street (1963) from the culture medium which had supported the growth of excised tomato roots for 21–28 days without subculture.

Certain studies on the effects of inhibitory auxin concentrations on cell differentiation in roots have indicated that auxin may speed up this process, particularly in xylem elements, so that xylem units "invade" the apex (Torrey, 1953). This raises the possibility that, as auxin accumulates in the growing apex, an enhanced rate of differentiation in the cytoplasm of the dividing cells may lead to complete transformation of the promeristem cells into tissue cells. Work with excised tomato roots shows that in aged meristems there remain a small number of cells in what may be an arrested state of differentiation; the cells have undergone a limited degree of enlargement and their cytoplasm contains numerous small vacuoles. Such meristems seem unable to resume their meristematic function. It now seems important to examine more critically, in a number of species, whether the apices of cultured roots have quiescent centres and whether the presence of a quiescent centre would modify the ageing phenomenon and, particularly, the powers of regeneration of apices in which cell division had ceased. There is much evidence that in perennial plants the root apex can become dormant and again resume growth. It has been suggested that the quiescent centre may be the site of auxin synthesis (Clowes, 1961a) and/or kinin synthesis (Torrey, 1962) in the meristem. If this is the case it could be that the persistent, partially enlarged, cells of a fully aged apex are disorganized cells of what was earlier a functional quiescent centre and that all the promeristem cells have developed into mature tissue cells. Studies of the growth activity of individual meristems during successive culture passages have shown that a decrease in the rate of production of cells at the apex such as normally foretells an impending complete loss of meristematic activity can be reversed, so that gradually the apex again becomes highly active before it is in further danger of ageing (Street and McGonagle, 1953; see also Chap. 9, p. 590). Here we may have a partial differentiation of the quiescent centre with a subsequent rebuilding of the promeristem from any quiescent cells whose metabolism has not been irreversibly deranged. These problems should prompt more detailed studies of the changing structure and activity of the apical meristems of cultured roots by electron-microscopy and isotope techniques.

C. LATERAL INITIATION

Lateral root primordia in cultured roots arise in the pericycle at positions related to the primary xylem poles of the central cylinder. The extent to which laterals are developed by cultured roots varies markedly as between species and as between strains within species (Street, 1957). This is well illustrated by roots derived from different geographic strains of *Senecio vulgaris* (Skinner and Street, 1954; Charles and Street, 1959, Charles, 1959). In an arginine-supplemented medium the roots of the Czechoslovakian strain produced only a few short laterals whereas the roots of the Iceland strain were characterized by producing numerous vigorously growing laterals. Lateral production in the roots of the Czechoslovakian strain was greatly increased by incorporating either IAA or the synthetic auxin, 2-NOA into the culture medium.

The work of Torrey (1950, 1952, 1956, 1959b) and of Pecket (1957a, b) with seedling and cultured pea roots has also implicated auxin in lateral-root initiation. Decapitation experiments also indicate that the main axis meristem exerts an inhibitory effect decreasing in intensity with distance from the root apex. This creates a zone immediately below the main apex which remains free of laterals while the main axis meristem is active. Torrey (1959b) has attempted by acid-alkali ether fractionation and chromatography to detect the hypothetical inhibitor secreted by the main apex and maintaining its dominance. Two inhibitors of lateral development, the most active of which appeared to be phenolic, were detected in the alkaline fraction by a bioassay. However, it remains to be shown whether either or both of these are of physiological significance in controlling lateral initiation and emergence in the root.

Pecket (1957a) has shown that the basal (most mature) part of the root is of importance in the promotion of lateral initiation in the regions of the root nearer to the growing apex. This suggests that some substances involved in lateral initiation are synthesized in mature cells. In line with this, Torrey (1956) obtained evidence that thiamine, niacin, adenine and certain mineral ions were essential for lateral development. Later (Torrey, 1962), it was found that kinetin had a more pronounced effect on auxin-induced lateral root initiation than did adenine. The stimulatory effect of kinetin was observed at 0·01 p.p.m. (5×10^{-8}M). At higher concentrations, kinetin was inhibitory to lateral initiation; at 5·0 p.p.m. lateral initiation was completely suppressed. Probably the auxin-kinin balance is as important in the control of lateral initiation as it is for root initiation in callus (see p. 659). Goldacre (1959), in studies on lateral development in cultured flax roots, noted that IAA treatment increased the number of laterals per root by inducing the formation of additional lateral primordia closely adjacent to already functioning lateral meristems. From this observation he suggested that active meristems might release a kinin which, in presence of externally applied IAA, induced new primordia at the appropriate point in the kinin diffusion gradient. Goldacre further concluded that this endogenous kinin could not be replaced by either kinetin or diphenylurea for these did not enhance lateral initiation in presence of IAA at the concentrations tested.

Some early observations indicated that light may suppress lateral initiation in cultured roots and root segments and that, in this respect, red light was more active than blue or green light (Torrey, 1952; Street, 1953). Recently, this phenomenon has been investigated in more detail using root segments of *Pisum sativum* (Furuya and Torrey, 1964) and it has been shown, with segments of cultured roots, 4–10 mm from the tip, that maximum inhibition of auxin-induced lateral formation can be achieved by a single exposure to red light (10–20 kergs cm^{-2}). Further, it was found that this could be completely reversed by far-red irradiation (120 kergs cm^{-2}). This must be regarded as strong evidence that the phytochrome system is involved in some way in the process of auxin-dependent lateral root formation.

These studies on lateral development in roots, in common with many others, emphasize the complexity of the factors controlling morphogenetic processes. This "appearance of complexity" may, however, only reflect the particular state of our knowledge at this time; further study may well simplify the picture by distinguishing primary from secondary factors.

D. VASCULAR PATTERNS

The arrangement of the different root tissues is not only characteristic of root anatomy in general but, in its details, of each species of root. The question therefore arises as to how this pattern is determined. The view has been advanced that the pre-existing pattern extends itself upwards into the region of newly formed cells; that the formative influences are transmitted from the mature to the young cells. This hypothesis faces the immediate difficulty of explaining the original development of the characteristic tissue pattern both in the embryonic root and again whenever a new meristem arises, as in lateral initiation. The alternative hypothesis that the pattern is determined in the meristem has experimental support. Torrey (1954, 1955) was able to grow roots of pea in culture from very small root tips (0·5 mm which included the root cap and only about 200 μ of apical meristem) by reinforcing the culture medium with thiamine and niacin and the micronutrient elements, zinc, manganese and molybdenum. These tips included no mature tissue; nevertheless, the roots which developed had normal tissue distribution except that a few of the roots were di- or mon-arch instead of typically tri-arch. This simplification was probably the outcome of some injury to the meristems during excision of the 0·5 mm tips because on continuing culture the triarch stelar arrangement was re-established. Torrey (1957) also found that, if the apical 0·5 mm of a well-developed pea root culture was removed then the root stump was capable of generating a new meristem, and the vascular pattern that developed did not necessarily line up with that in the mature tissues. If this new meristem was allowed to regenerate in the presence of 10^{-5} M IAA the new meristem gave rise to a hexarch vascular pattern and this pattern was maintained as long as the root was allowed to grow in the presence of this inhibitory IAA concentration but reverted to the normal triarch pattern when growth continued in an auxin-free medium (Fig. 3). These studies strongly indicate that organization within the meristem determines the vascular pattern.

White (1943) states that secondary thickening does not occur in excised root cultures of dicotyledonous roots and, as a generalization, this is justified. Dormer and Street (1948), in investigating the anatomy of excised tomato roots which had been kept for periods of up to 6 months in small volumes of medium, found no organized development of secondary vascular tissues but disorganized cambial activity within the stele and differentiation of lignified xylem elements from some of the cambial derivatives. Torrey (1951) found that after decapitation of pea root cultures, cell divisions occurred in the stele of the root stump to an extent which could double the root diameter and that such roots

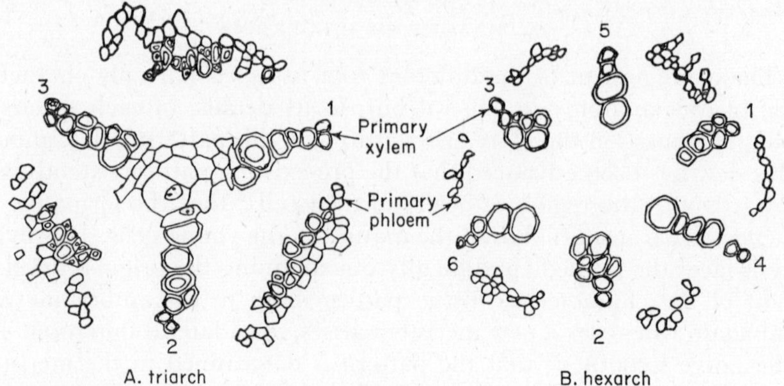

FIG. 3. Transverse sections showing the vascular pattern in cultured pea roots (diagrammatic). A, Triarch root base; B, newly regenerated hexarch pattern developed in the presence of medium containing 10^{-5} M indolylacetic acid. (After Torrey, 1959a.)

contained increased numbers of xylem elements. Root tips from pea seedlings, when cultured in a medium containing a relatively high concentration of IAA, gave rise to roots which showed a vascular cambium; however, when the root tips used were obtained from roots which had been maintained in culture *for several passages,* no vasuclar cambium was produced. These results suggested that, in culture, some substance(s), essential for the development of a vascular cambium and derived from the seedling shoot system, is depleted. Fries (1954) interpreted his findings on cambium development in pea roots along similar lines. Excised pea roots in their first passage produced a vascular cambium and a limited amount of secondary vascular tissue. When *decotylized* pea seedlings were similarly cultured, no cambial activity occurred in the roots. The growth of roots on such cultured decotylized seedlings was increased by adding amino acids and adenine to the culture medium. The more rapid growth of the excised roots was not, however, enhanced by these supplements. Fries, therefore, concluded that the roots of the decotylized seedlings are depleted by the demands of the plumule and that this reduces their growth and ability to initiate a vascular cambium.

The initiation of cambium may well depend, not only on the presence in the root of the essential growth regulators or their precursors, but upon the internal *distribution* of such regulators in the root tissues. Thus, in excised tomato roots, indole-3-acetonitrile (IAN) inhibits cell division at the apical meristem and the initiation of lateral primordia; it does not markedly affect cell expansion, but it causes generalized divisions in the pericycle, leading to a larger number of cells in the stele some of which give rise to secondary xylem vessels. By contrast, IAA at similarly inhibitory concentrations does not appreciably reduce the rate of cell division at the main tip meristem; it enhances the initiation of lateral primordia; it strongly inhibits cell expansion and does *not* promote generalized divisions in the pericycle (enhanced stelar diameter in this case being due to changed orientation of division walls at the apical meristem) (Street, McGregor and Sussex, 1954; Hughes and Street, 1960). These differential effects of IAN and IAA suggest either that the activity of IAN does not depend on its being a precursor of IAA (Thurman and Street, 1962) or that feeding IAN establishes a different pattern of auxin distribution within the roots. The work of Torrey (1963), using a modification of the technique of Raggio and Raggio (1956), also illustrates this concept. Taking 15 mm pea-root apical segments with the basal 5 mm inserted into a separate agar vial and the remainder of the root growing on the surface of agar in a Petri dish, he found that 10^{-5} M IAA was very inhibitory to root growth when incorporated into the Petri dish medium but that the same concentration of IAA in the vial medium did not inhibit extension growth of the apical part of the root but did induce formation of a vascular cambium for some distance along the root and beyond the confines of the vial. Cambium development in first passage roots of radish (*Raphanus sativus*) can also be stimulated by applying auxin to the basal end of the root or by leaving a small amount of hypocotyl tissue attached to the root (Jones, 1954). More recently, Loomis and Torrey (1964) have obtained more extensive secondary thickening in cultured radish roots by using the Raggio and Raggio (1956) technique and applying via the vial sucrose, 6-benzylaminopurine (1 mg/l) or other active kinin, IAA and m-inositol. The importance of a kinin in cambial initiation and function had been indicated by previous studies with the pea epicotyl (Sorokin, Mathur and Thimann, 1962). In cultured radish roots, application of the growth factors listed above does not permit of continuing cambial activity or cambial initiation in subcultured roots. Some additional and as yet unidentified factor is critically depleted during growth in culture.

A rather different approach has been adopted by Goldacre, Unt and Kefford (1962). They cultured excised flax roots in a medium containing IAA, gently homogenized the root tissue and transferred the homogenate, which contained many unbroken cells, to a medium containing 6% coconut milk and 10^{-5} M IAA and, by agitating the cultures for 4 weeks, obtained a growing cell suspension. This suspension contained large vacuolated cells which apparently had failed to divide and whose tissue origin was uncertain, together with isolated small cells and clumps of such cells which were considered to be of pericyclic origin. Some of these cell clumps which could be further cultured in the coconut milk-IAA medium contained lignified cells and tended to give rise to recognizable root primordia. Such studies could lead on to the definition of the nutrients and growth factors required to induce division in cells of the pericycle and also to studies of how far such cultured cells retain the potentialities of the pericycle cells of the organized root.

III. Histogenesis in Callus Cultures

A. Vascularization

Gautheret and his co-workers (Gautheret, 1957, 1959) have established a very large number of different callus cultures by transferring fragments of plant organs to the surface of agar media (see Chap. 8, p. 496). They have fixed, embedded and sectioned many such cultures and submitted them to microscopic study. These studies reveal that such callus masses are heterogeneous in cell composition and that the appearance and diversity of the constituent cells and their associations vary according to (1) the origin of the callus, (2) the extent to which it has been maintained in culture, (3) the composition of the culture medium, (4) the extent to which the culture is immersed or is above the surface of the medium, and (5) the growth activity of the culture at the time of histological fixation. When such cultures are actively growing, they usually contain a high proportion of vacuolated parenchymatous cells together with more localized groups of smaller and obviously meristematic cells (Figs. 4 and 5). Such cultures may contain very few or even no vascular tissues. When such cultures become very slow growing as a result of a prolonged period without subculture or are inhibited in their growth by appropriate concentrations of auxins, then vascular tissues are often much more prominent. Such vascular tissues may vary from isolated tracheid-like cells to organized vascular bundles or nodules containing xylem and phloem (Fig. 6). Sometimes, sheets of cambial-like cells can be observed to give rise on one side to xylem and on the other side to phloem. For a fuller and documented account of these observations the reader is referred to Gautheret (1959). The challenge of these observations is whether patterns of vascularization in callus masses can be duplicated experimentally and hence the determinative factors identified.

Camus (1949) first showed that buds of *Cichorium* grafted into agar-lined V-shaped cuts in storage or cultured tissue of this species caused the differentiation mainly below the bud of vascular strands and that these, if they continued to develop, did so in a direction tending to

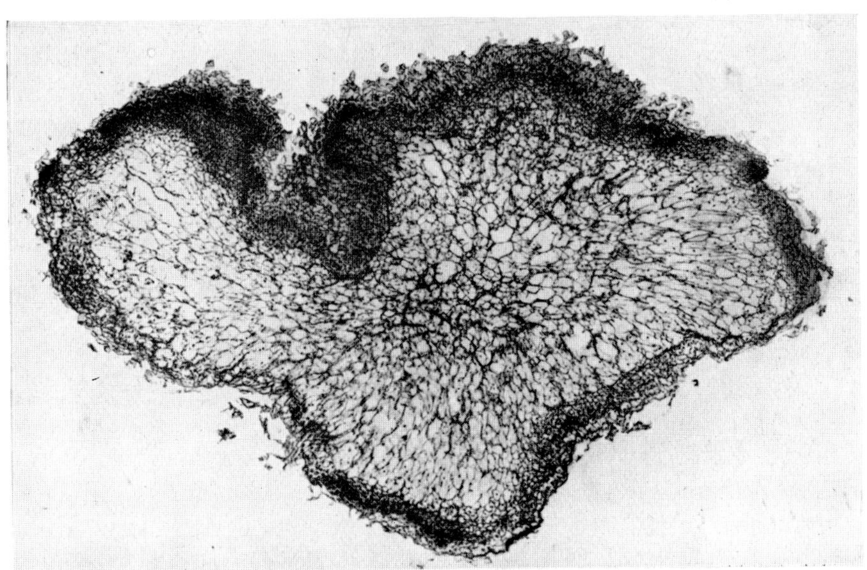

Fig. 4. A section of a callus mass of *Agave toumeyana* showing central large vacuolated cells and a peripheral meristematic zone. (After Gautheret, 1959.)

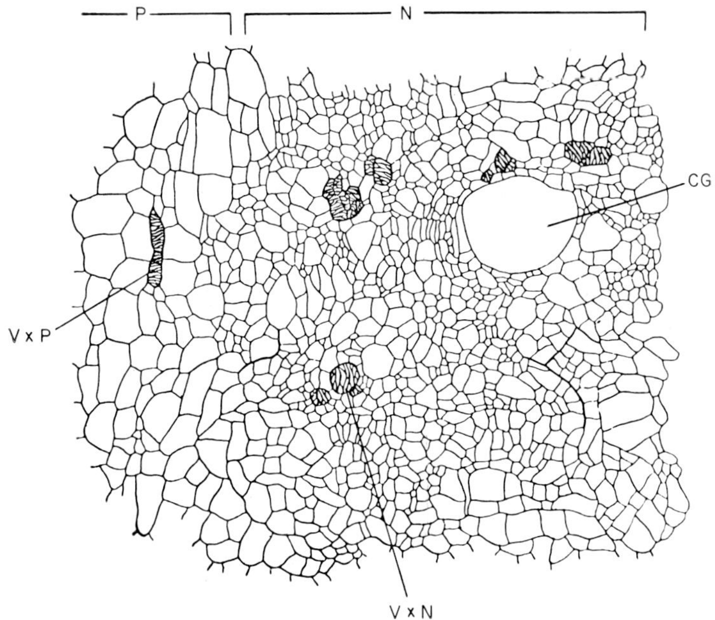

Fig. 5. Callus (N) arising from an explant of tissue (P) from the xylem of the carrot root. The callus contains small groups of meristematic cells separated by intervening vacuolated parenchymatous cells, giant cells (CG) and tracheidal cells (VxN). (After Gautheret, 1959.)

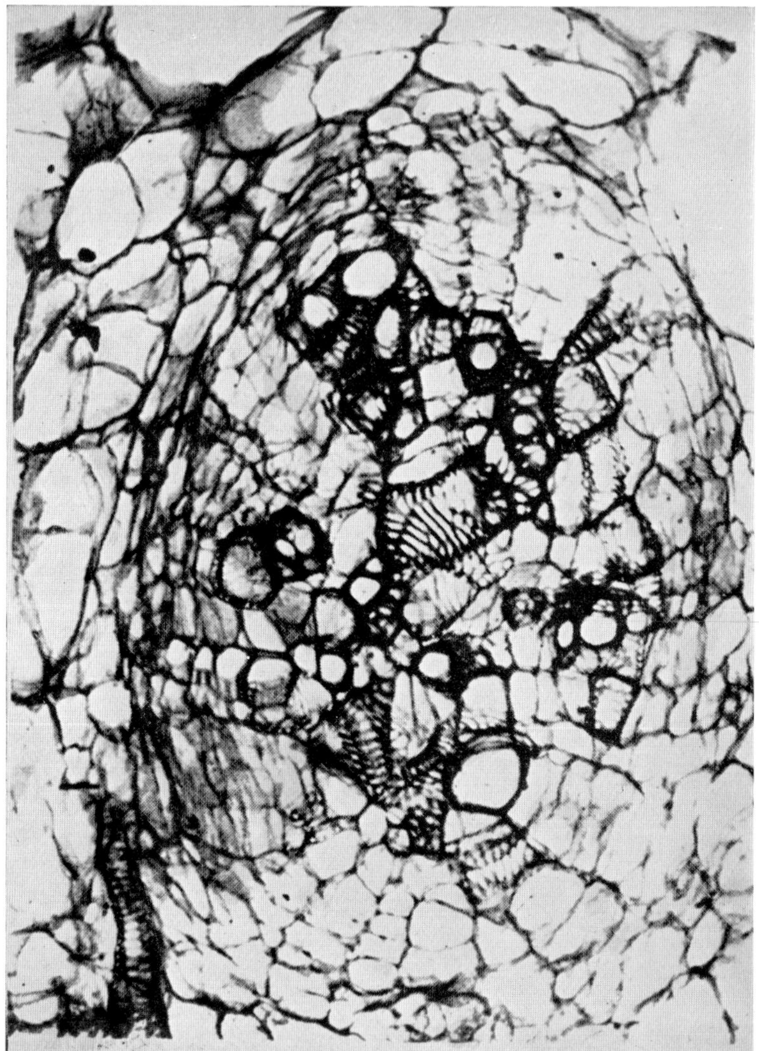

FIG. 6. A vascular nodule formed in a callus derived from carrot phloem. An islet of meristematic cells gave rise to a mass of tracheidal cells at its centre and superficially to phloem cells. Between these two types of vascular cells a circular meristematic zone has arisen. (After Gautheret, 1957.)

connect the bud with vascular strands already present in the stock (Fig. 7). A similar, if less marked development of vascular strands occurred even when the bud was separated from the stock tissue by cellophane, indicating that the induction of the vascular strands probably depended upon a diffusable substance released from the bud.

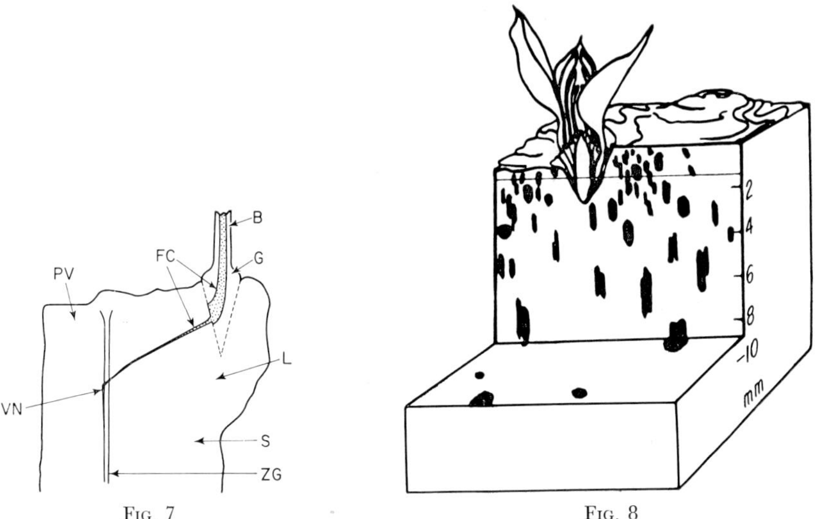

FIG. 7 FIG. 8

FIG. 7. Bud (B) of *Cichorium* grafted (G) into a callus of the same species (S). The graft has induced vascularization (FC) in the growing region of the callus and below and lateral to the graft. This vascular strand has extended to connect up with a vascular trace (VN) in the callus. (After Camus, 1949.)

FIG. 8. A stereogram of a piece of lilac (*Syringa vulgaris*) callus into which has been grafted an apex of lilac bearing two or three pairs of leaf primordia. The incision was filled with 1% agar containing naphthalene acetic acid (0·05 mg/l). Drawing made 54 days after grafting. Vascular strands developing in the callus shown black. Near to the graft all strands containing only xylem elements; close to the medium on which the callus rested, the strands contained xylem and phloem cells. (After Wetmore and Sorokin, 1955.)

Similar studies were undertaken by Wetmore and Sorokin (1955) using a homogeneous parenchymatous callus tissue of *Syringa vulgaris* into which they grafted apical portions of the shoot of this species or into which they introduced agar containing auxin or a coconut milk medium by means of V-shaped incisions. The insertion of the shoot apex induced mitotic activity in the callus below, particularly on the lower flanks of the scion. This mitotic activity gave rise to columns of cells of relatively short vertical extent. Later, and particularly after development of the graft union, these cells differentiated into lignified and pitted xylem elements (Fig. 8). These workers did not detect any phloem in the vascular columns. The use of a shoot apex and incorporation of auxin into the sealing agar revealed that, with low concentrations of NAA (0·01 mg/l), there was enhanced vascularization in the same regions as in absence of the auxin, while with higher auxin concentrations (1·0 mg/l) the strands differentiated away from the scion and towards the outside of the callus mass. More recently, Wetmore and Rier (1963) have extended these studies using a number of callus tissucs derived from woody and herbaceous species. By supplying an auxin (both IAA and NAA were used) and a sugar at an incision, they have successfully induced the development of vascular strands in the otherwise uniformly parenchymatous callus tissues. In these later experiments it has been possible to induce both xylem and phloem tissue, and the balance between these two tissues has been shown to be determined by the concentration of sugar applied. An intermediate concentration of 2·5–3·5% sucrose favoured the presence of both tissues, usually with a recognizable cambium between them. When the callus was sectioned transversely to its orientation in the medium, the vascular nodules were seen to be arranged in a roughly circular pattern and the diameter of the circle was increased by increasing the concentration of auxin at the site of incision (Fig. 9).

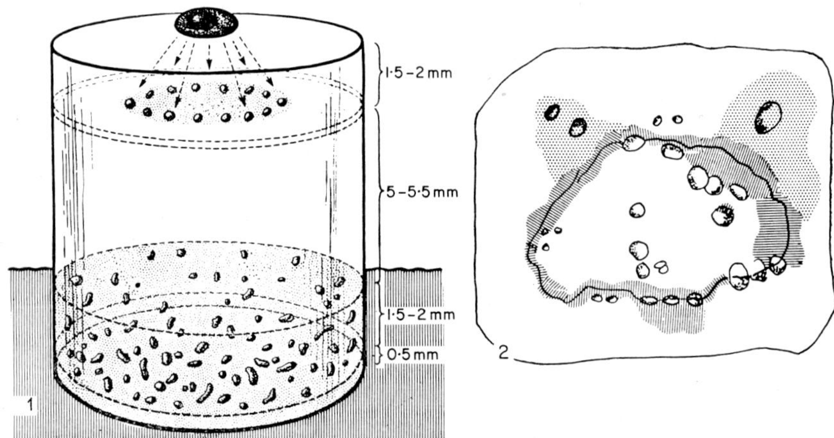

FIG. 9. (1) Stereogram of a piece of callus of *Syringa vulgaris* to a small area on the top of which has been applied 1% agar containing naphthalene acetic acid (0·1 mg/l) and sucrose (3%). Callus killed for study 35 days after application of the auxin-sugar agar. Note circle of vascular nodules (containing tracheids towards the centre and sieve elements towards the periphery) formed near to point of application of the agar. The diameter of this circle of nodules increases with increase in the concentration of auxin (NAA) applied. The relative amounts of xylem and phloem depend upon the concentration of sugar (see text). Below the medium (hatched) occur spherical or irregular vascular nodules showing haphazard distribution. (2) Transverse section through such a callus showing the ring-like distribution of the vascular nodules and the formation of a definite cambium (solid line) involving the nodules and becoming more or less continuous across the interfascicular regions. Cellular regions laid down by cambial activity shown by radial parallel lines. (Section 450μ below surface of a 54-day-old callus; agar containing 4% sucrose and 0·5 mg/l NAA.)
(Both after Wetmore and Rier, 1963.)

Xylem was characteristically orientated towards the centre and phloem towards the periphery of the callus mass.

These observations implicate both the sugar supply and the auxin level as factors in the induction of cambial activity and the differentiation of vascular elements. The relationship between the auxin concentration at the point of application and the distance away in the tissue at which vascular tissue develops suggest that a critical auxin level, established by diffusion, interacts with the endogenous growth-regulating substances in the callus cells to induce the formation of a vascular cambium. This assumes that auxin is a limiting factor, a situation which may not prove to be universally the case. It also suggests that the action of auxin is determined by concentration although it could be that as the auxin diffusion gradient develops a particular "slope" it induces the necessary cell divisions and orientates the division walls. Clearly much further work is required to identify the factors essential to the development of a cambium and to distinguish these factors from those which determine whether the new cells formed shall differentiate into xylem or phloem and at what rate this differentiation shall proceed. (See discussion of cambium initiation and function in cultured roots, p. 649.)

B. DEVELOPMENT OF MERISTEMS AND ORGANS

White (1939) showed that a callus tissue of the tobacco hybrid *Nicotiana glauca* × *N. langsdorffii* which remained uniformly parenchymatous when cultured on agar medium underwent differentiation when transferred to a liquid medium and gave rise, at its surface, to leafy buds. Skoog (1944), working with the same strain of callus, concluded that high light intensity, high temperature and a solid medium were favourable to maintaining the cultures in an undifferentiated (parenchymatous!) condition, whereas low light intensity, relatively low temperature and liquid medium (probably involving a lower oxygen tension) favoured bud formation.

Root development from callus cultures, first reported by Nobécourt (1939), is a more widespread phenomenon and occurs not only in normal but in virus-tumour tissues (Nickell, 1955).

With the hybrid tobacco callus of White, any roots which arise do not have their origin in the callus but develop adventitiously in the stems of the developing buds. Some tissues are, however, observed to give rise either to shoot or root meristems according to the conditions (Nobécourt, 1955; Jacquiot, 1955; Skoog, 1957; Pilet, 1961b).

In considering experimental work on the initiation of organ meristems in callus, it becomes clear that some tissues cannot yet be made to initiate organs (Nobécourt and Hustache, 1954) and that many of the successful experiments have involved newly initiated callus (in some cases, callus still attached to the organ fragment from which it had developed). Further, such callus tissues, when maintained in culture and repeatedly subcultured, often lose their ability to initiate organs (Morel, 1948; Jacquiot, 1951, 1955; Miller and Skoog, 1953; Mayer, 1956). Old-established callus cultures which retain the ability to initiate organs, even under conditions known to be stimulatory, are, therefore, at present exceptional (Gautheret, 1945; Morel and Wetmore, 1951).

From the above considerations, it follows that the initiation of organ primordia by a particular inductive treatment in one tissue by no means indicates that the treatment will be effective in another tissue. Nevertheless, the ability of substances like auxin and kinetin to induce the development of a meristem probably means that these substances are generally implicated in organogenesis although in unresponsive tissues they are not the limiting factors. Thus, we are led to the conclusion that there are, as yet, unknown controlling factors in organogenesis and that such factors may be depleted by existing cultural techniques. The loss of the ability to form roots associated with "anergy" (see Chap. 9, p. 587) could imply loss of some such rhizogenic factor but could, in this case, be the outcome of the development of a sufficiently high endogenous auxin level.

The general statement is frequently made in relation to plant cuttings that appropriate auxin treatments will enhance the number of cuttings which root and the number of the roots which they develop, only if the cuttings of the species show some ability to root in the absence of auxin treatment. Similar statements have also been made in relation to the action of kinetin in bud induction. Thus, Miller (1961) states "To be kept in mind is that all of the plants reported to respond to kinetin in terms of increased budding show some formation of shoot structures even in the absence of kinetin. Thus kinetin is known to cause bud formation only in those plant materials with an inherent tendency for formation; the compound must not be regarded as a specific 'bud-former'." In view of the experimental results which will be outlined below the import of this kind of statement is by no means clear. Since all plants form buds they surely all have some of the "inherent tendency" to do so. Again, when do we conclude that a given plant material does not have a tendency to form organs? Referring to the formation of roots by the virus-tumour tissue of *Rumex acetosa,* Nickell (1955) states "Root formation has been more frequent, having occurred 16 different times in over 75,000 subcultures."

The discovery of kinetin arose out of studies of the behaviour of cylinders of stem pith of *Nicotiana tabacum* var. Wisconsin No. 38 undertaken in Professor F. Skoog's laboratory. When these pith cylinders were placed on an agar medium containing mineral salts, sucrose, B vitamins and glycine, small masses of callus developed at the morphologically basal ends. This callus, however, quickly decreased its rate of growth and then stopped. The addition of IAA augmented the early growth but did not prolong the duration of growth. Increase in the concentration of auxin caused the cells to enlarge further but did not prolong the period during which cell divisions occurred. The continuous growth of this callus required the addition to the medium of yeast extract. Fractionation of the yeast extract yielded an active fraction of unknown composition but which, from its chemical properties and peak absorption at 268 mμ, was probably a purine. This directed attention to nucleic acid as a possible source of the active principle. A sample of DNA was found to be active and again the active constituent was partially purified. However, other samples of DNA were inactive and it was not until it was discovered that such samples could be activated by autoclaving under acid conditions that the active principle, 6-furfurylamino-purine (kinetin), was obtained in crystalline form (see Chap. 9, p. 573). This substance, when added to the medium containing IAA, permitted the continuous culture of the callus initiated from the columns of tobacco pith. It also proved to be able to stimulate cell division in a number of other tissues (Shantz, Mears and Steward, 1958; Torrey, 1958a; Fox and Miller, 1959; Miller, 1960).

Work with the tumour tissue isolated from a tobacco hybrid by White, and which spontaneously forms buds, revealed that bud development could be suppressed by IAA or NAA (Skoog, 1944) or enhanced by the addition of the purines, adenine or adenosine (Skoog and Tsui, 1951). Kinetin, which was essential for the growth of the pith callus of the Wisconsin No. 38 strain, was therefore tested with tissue of this strain for its interaction with auxin both with regard to growth and to the initiation of organs (Skoog and Miller, 1957). The tissue grows actively and remains parenchymatous in a medium containing the appropriate proportion of auxin (IAA) to kinetin (K) (e.g. 2·0 mg/l IAA: 0·2 mg/l K). If the ratio of auxin to kinetin is decreased either by increasing the concentration of kinetin (e.g. 2·0 mg/l IAA: 0·5 or 1·0 mg/l K) or by lowering that of auxin (e.g. 0·03 mg/l IAA: 1 mg/l K) the cultures initiate leafy shoots. By contrast, buds are suppressed and roots initiated with a sufficiently high ratio of auxin to kinetin (2·0 mg/l IAA: 0·02 mg/l K). With a medium containing an auxin:kinetin ratio which already promotes bud initiation, addition of casein hydrolysate (3 g/l) further enhances this and promotes the subsequent bud development (Fig. 10). This effect of the hydrolysate can be almost completely reproduced by the addition of a single amino acid, namely, tyrosine (210 mg/l). Kinetin is also reported to promote bud formation on the protonemata of *Tortella caespitosa* (Gorton and Eakin, 1957) and *Pohlia nutans* (Mitra and Allsopp, 1959). However, Sastri (1963), work-

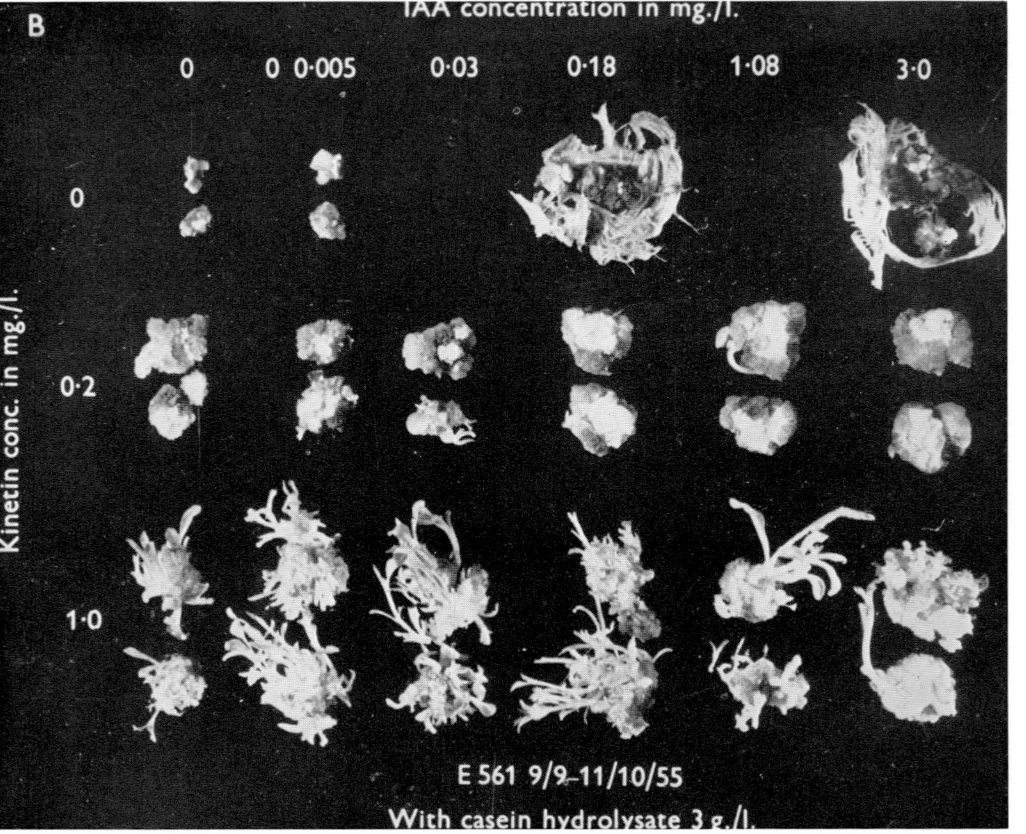

FIG. 10. Organogenesis in tobacco callus. Effects of increasing IAA concentration at different kinetin levels and in the presence of casein hydrolysate (3 g/l) on the growth and organ formation in tobacco callus cultured on a modified White's nutrient agar. Age of cultures 62 days. Note root formation in absence of kinetin and in the presence of 0·18 and 3·0 mg/1 IAA and shoot formation in the presence of 1·0 mg/1

ing with tissue cultures of *Armoracea rusticana* var. Y′, has reported bud formation in response to additions of IAA and NAA to the culture medium and suppression of bud formation by additions of kinetin.

Very few of the roots which have been successfully grown in culture have given rise to shoot buds. Norton and Boll (1954) reported that a particular clone of excised roots of hybrid tomato produced shoots from the callus developed at the cut surface. These buds arose when the roots were grown on a solid medium containing adenine but the conditions controlling their development were not further investigated. A similar development of buds from callus which had formed at the cut ends of the roots was reported by Danckwardt-Lillieström (1957) working with cultured roots of *Isatis tinctoria*. In the first passage these roots often gave rise to shoots after about a month in culture. On subculture, this tendency was lost, particularly by the third passage. Initiation of shoots during the second and third passage was promoted by adding kinetin to the culture medium but, nevertheless, the response to kinetin gradually diminished and with subculture kinetin became ineffective. Torrey (1958b) has reported the development of shoot-bud primordia in the pericycle and in the normal positions of lateral root primordia (opposite the xylem poles) in segments taken from a clone of excised roots of *Convolvulus arvensis* maintained in culture for several years. 15 mm segments of these roots, on incubation in culture medium in the *dark*, usually initiate a single lateral root and one or two bud primordia; in *low light* intensity (100 ft candles) the bud primordia develop into shoots (Fig. 11). The addition to the medium of 0·1 mg/l kinetin causes the segments to initiate an increased number of buds, particularly at their distal ends. More recent studies, so far only briefly reported (Bonnett and Torrey, 1963), indicate that the rate of growth of both lateral buds and roots is influenced by the length of the root segments and that their initiation and position can be altered by the concentration and direction of application of kinetin and of an auxin.

Reinert (1959, 1963) has studied the phenomena of organogenesis in a strain of carrot callus maintained on a medium supplemented with 7% coconut milk (CM) and IAA (10^{-5} g/ml). When such cultures were transferred to auxin-free medium or allowed to deplete the added auxin by prolonged growth without subculture, then the callus developed roots. When the cultures were grown on a complex *synthetic* medium containing auxin (Reinert and White, 1956) they at first showed an enhanced capacity to form roots on transference to auxin-free medium. However, callus maintained for 2–3 months on the synthetic medium underwent a change in texture and morphology, the outer surface becoming covered with "horny nodules" and when such cultures were transferred to auxin-free medium they produced shoots (*not* roots) of two kinds ("larger" and "smaller"). The "smaller" shoots when examined were found to correspond "except for a more or less marked fission or splitting of the cotyledons . . . to normal bipolar carrot embryos." These embryos developed into plantlets when the cultures were transferred back to the CM medium and illuminated. This initiation of embryos emphasizes the ability of at least some cells of the callus to give rise to structures which then recapitulate the development of a new plant which normally follows sexual reproduction.

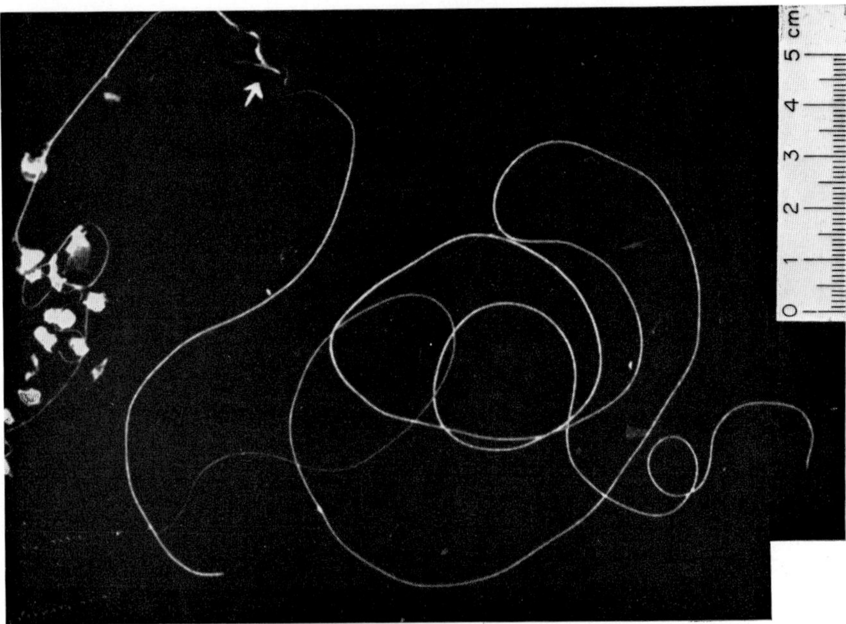

FIG. 11. Shoot initiation on segment of excised *Convolvulus* root. 10 mm root segment indictated by arrow derived from cultured root as shown on right. Lateral root from segment gives rise to a second lateral and this develops as a shoot with leaves. Segment placed in liquid culture medium in alternating 12 h periods of dark and light of 100 ft candles from white fluorescent tubes. (After Torrey, 1958b.)

It opens up the possibility that single diploid cells of the callus can behave like zygotes and follow the segmentations of early embryology. Such observations with callus tissues, therefore, naturally lead us on to consider the potentialities of separate cells in culture to develop organized structures, a subject to be developed later in this chapter (p. 677).

C. FRIABILITY

There are a number of detailed reports of variations in morphology in callus cultures of common origin (Gautheret, 1955; Nobécourt, 1955). The particular contrasting tissue forms to which attention is drawn here are those between a solid, round, smooth parenchymatous callus and a friable form readily breaking up into small nodular pieces or even single cells (Figs. 12 and 13). Transitions from smooth to friable (conditions for the reverse change have not been clearly established) are described in two pioneer studies. Reinert (1956) found that cultures of *Picea glauca* became particularly friable in liquid media when folic acid and vitamin B_{12} were withdrawn from the complex synthetic medium used for the growth of this tissue. Torrey and

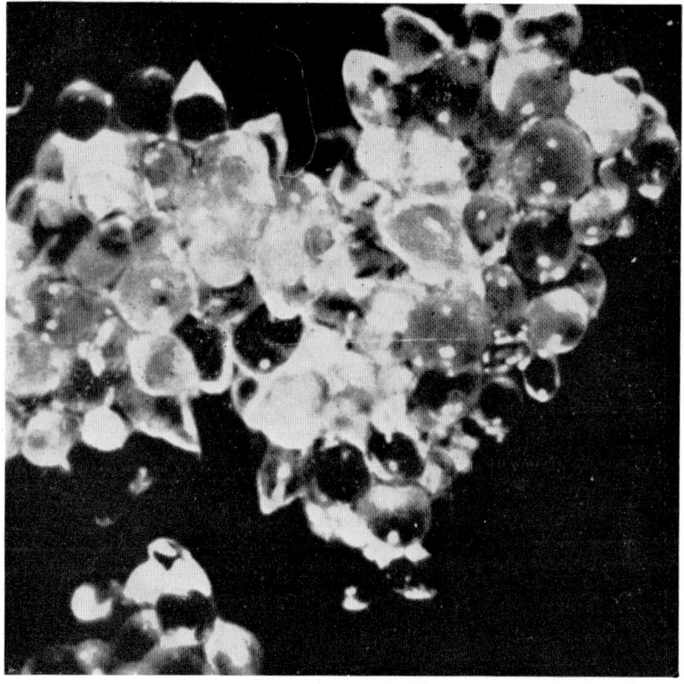

FIG. 12. Friable tobacco callus tissue. Obtained by culture on a medium containing 2×10^{-6} g/l IAA. (After Jablonski and Skoog, 1954.)

Shigemura (1957) made a more detailed study of factors influencing the degree of friability of a pea-root callus. Growth was rapid in a liquid medium containing 1 g/l yeast extract and 10^{-6} M 2,4-D, and a smooth, rounded callus developed. By contrast, friable, slow-growing tissue developed in presence of the standard amount of yeast extract when no auxin was added, and also in a medium containing auxin but with an increased concentration of the yeast extract (5 g/l). The friable tissue was shown to contain numerous incipient root meristems capable of giving rise to root primordia on an auxin-free medium.

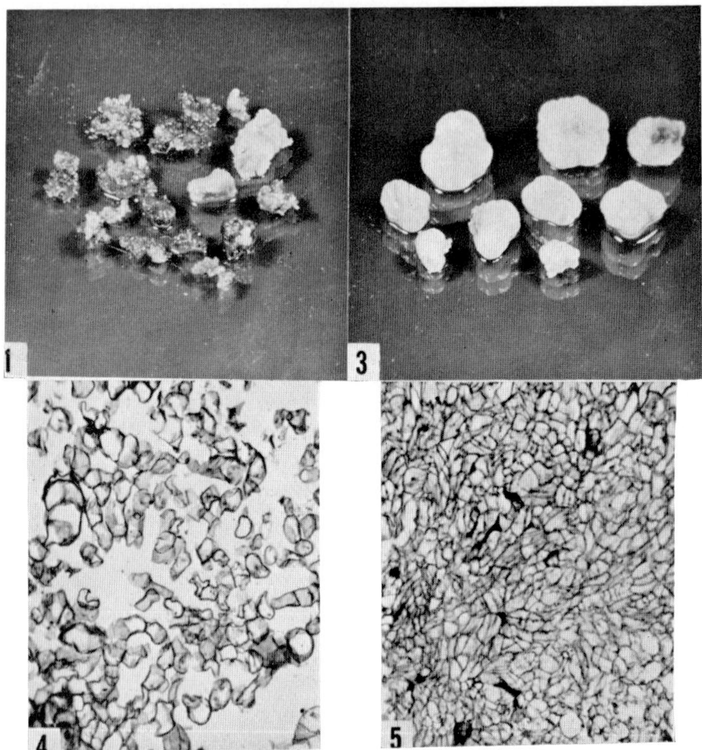

Fig. 13. Friable and compact cultures of *Haplopappus gracilis*. (1) Friable callus; (3) compact callus; (4) friable callus in section; (5) compact callus in section. (After Blakely and Steward, 1961.)

The transition of callus to a friable state is an important step towards the development of liquid suspension cultures by agitation. Its interest is that it opens up the important question of how far it may be possible, by modification of cultural conditions, to prevent dividing cells of higher plant from sticking together to form cellular aggregates. If we could do this it would not only advance our knowledge of the control of middle lamella formation but make it possible to replace the present suspension cultures (which contain free cells *and* cell aggregates) by true free cell cultures. Torrey and Shigemura have suggested that friability develops from enhanced activity of an enzyme solubilizing pectic substances but this is at present quite hypothetical. The very limited development of plant cell-wall biochemistry handicaps an informed approach to the experimental control of middle lamella chemistry (see Northcote, 1963).

IV. Growth and Differentiation in Suspension Cultures

A. GROWTH PATTERNS

Formidable difficulties stand in the way of developing quantitative analytical studies of the growth of suspension cultures. The suspensions are heterogeneous in the sense that they contain "cellular units" ranging from free cells to aggregates; the aggregates often ranging from a very few to several hundred cells. Further, the proportions of the different cellular units may change markedly and the free cells may alter significantly in mean size and morphology during a period of batch culture (culture for a fixed period in a fixed volume of medium). The techniques adopted for maintenance and subculture may not only permit an increasing proportion of dead cells to accumulate but cause long-term drifts in growth potentiality. These drifts in growth potentiality arise because, with a regime involving a succession of passages of equal length and a fixed size of inoculum at each transfer, it by no means follows that under these arbitrarily fixed conditions there is any standardization from passage to passage in the inoculum either in terms of cellular composition or the physiological state of the constituent cellular units. It is even difficult to decide how to standardize the inoculum since no *one* criterion of size, such as fresh weight, dry weight, number of cellular units, or total number of cells is satisfactory as an index of growth potentiality. Only as our understanding of the patterns of growth in such cultures advances will it become possible to standardize inocula in terms of their predictable capacity for growth. The same problem is encountered in choosing parameters by which growth can be expressed. Further, as will become evident in the ensuing discussion, some clearly valuable parameters are technically difficult to measure.

The first basis adopted for measuring growth was that of increase in fresh weight expressed as a *growth value* (final wet weight/initial wet weight) (Nickell and Tulecke, 1960). It is now clear, however, that increases in the fresh weight of suspension cultures, particularly towards the later part of the rather long incubation periods usually adopted (4–6 weeks), involve primarily increases in water content of the cells and that simultaneous increases in dry weight reflect depositions of starch and wall material rather than increases in cell number. If we make the assumption that fresh weight is a measure of the number of cells present (an assumption which implies that during the test period there is little change in mean cell size), then most of the published growth values indicate 10–30-fold increases in fresh weight after 4 weeks' incubation, such values corresponding at a maximum to 3–5 successive divisions of the initial population over the whole period of incubation. To understand the meaning of such low growth value it is necessary to endeavour to follow the progress of growth with time and to determine more directly the contributions to weight increase made by cell multiplication, cell expansion and cell differentiation (particularly, by deposition of storage substances within the cells and by growth and modification of cell walls). Further, to elucidate the pattern of growth it is necessary to try to assess the separate contributions made to these aspects of growth by the free cells on the one hand and by the various size-classes of cell aggregates on the other. These considerations emphasize the importance of developing reliable techniques for separating the different size classes of cellular units (such as aseptic filtration), for cell counting (such as maceration techniques which effectively separate but do not destroy the cells), and for determination of mitotic frequencies (see Chap. 8, p. 508).

The work of Torrey, Reinert and Merkel (1962) which seeks to expose more clearly the growth pattern of suspension cultures already goes far towards explaining the low average growth rates reported above and also the previously encountered difficulty of finding mitotic figures in these cultures. Working with a suspension culture derived from *Convolvulus* root-callus, they found a conspicuous peak in mitoses about 7 days after inoculation, a fall in this frequency after 2 weeks and no mitoses after 3 weeks. Mitoses were most frequent in tissue pieces which failed to pass a 100 μ filter, were rather less frequent in the cell groups (of up to ten cells) passing this filter and were relatively rare in the free cells. Although mitoses were rare after 14 days' culture, fresh and dry weight values continued to increase, and the proportion of the tissue in the fraction passing the 100 μ filter and as free cells continued to increase, presumably by release of cells from the tissue masses (Fig. 14). Similar studies with *Haplopappus* root-callus suspensions showed a peak of mitosis after only 3 days of incubation. Again mitoses were most frequent in the cell-aggregate fraction. Street and Henshaw (1963) have followed growth in a suspension culture of *Rubus fruticosus* using an inoculum prepared by passage through a 1000 μ filter and during an incubation period of 24 days. At each sampling, the suspension was fractionated by means of a 200 μ filter. The peak of mitotic activity in the fraction retained by the 200 μ filter (i.e. the larger aggregates) occurred on the sixth day, the peak in the $> 200\ \mu$ fraction on the ninth day of incubation. Both fractions showed very low mitotic frequencies on and after the fifteenth day. Through the 24 days of culture the total number of cells in the $< 200\ \mu$

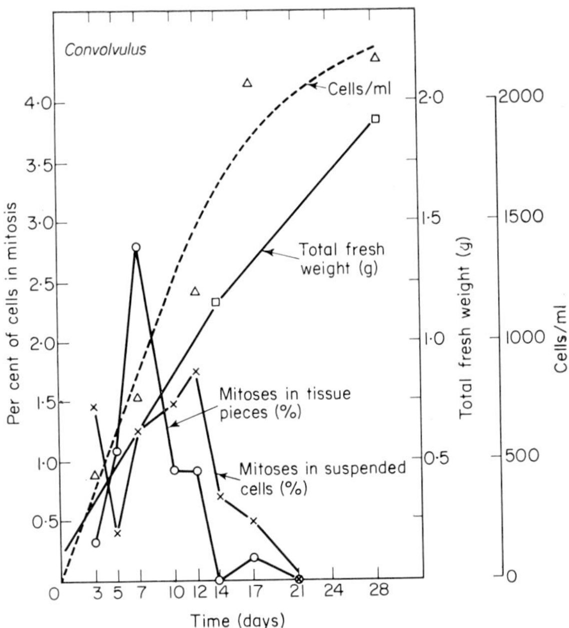

FIG. 14. Growth of a suspension of *Convolvulus* root cells. Tissue pieces > 100 μ diam.; suspended "cells" < 100 μ diam. % mitoses calculated from counts of 1000 or more nuclei. (After Torrey *et al.*, 1962.)

fraction (small aggregates and free cells) first decreased and then began to rise, reaching the initial value by the end of incubation. Total dry weight only rose very slowly during the first 9 days but, in the > 200 μ fraction, subsequently rose very steeply throughout the period of culture despite evidence that increase in cell number was proceeding very slowly after the fifteenth day (Fig. 15). Similar studies by Mehta (1963), using suspension cultures of *Phaseolus vulgaris, Linum usitatissimum* and a crown-gall tissue of *Parthenocissus tricuspidata,* emphasize that (1) mitotic activities rise sharply to reach high levels (2–6% of the cells in a recognizable stage of mitosis) for a very short time (1 or 2 days) and then decline equally sharply; (2) that the mitotic peak in the fraction containing only the smaller aggregates tends to be delayed as compared with that in the larger aggregates and, when the mitoses occur, they tend to increase the size of these smaller aggregates so that some of them pass into the larger size class; (3) that very few mitoses take place in the free cells and that the number of free cells does not increase appreciably until the culture ages and the larger cell aggregates begin to break up, releasing both free cells and small aggregates; (4) that while cell division is proceeding actively, the total

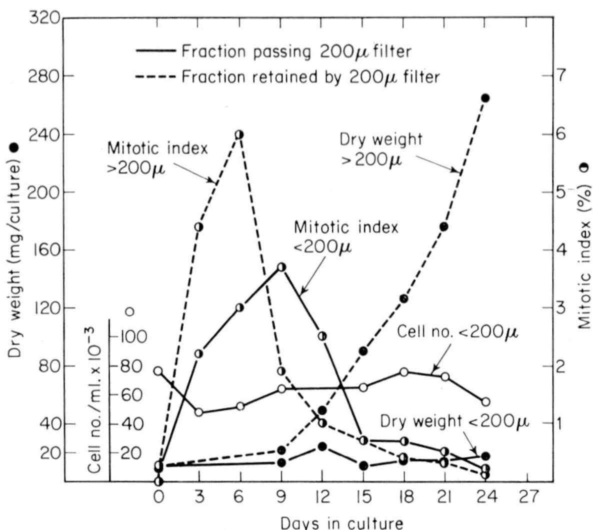

FIG. 15 Growth of a suspension culture of *Rubus fruticosus*. Mitotic index calculated as described in legend to Fig. 14. (After Street and Henshaw, 1963.)

dry weight does not rise in proportion to the increase in the number of cells (many small new cells arising with a consequent decrease in mean cell size) but that later, marked increases in fresh and dry weight occur which are mainly due to enlargement and differentiation of existing cells. Since the fate of many of the separate cells, released from the aggregates as the culture ages, is that they do not divide but enlarge and ultimately become senescent, there arises the danger of dead cells or cell debris accumulating in suspensions subcultured by transferring aliquots of cultures in which cell division has ceased and the cells have matured. Further, since some of the larger aggregates may fail to break up or may release only a limited number of superficial cells, there can also arise the problem of the gradual appearance of a number of callus-like lumps exceeding, say, 1000 μ in diameter.

The pattern of growth revealed by these studies poses a number of questions, both in relation to scientific objectives and practicability. One can, at this stage, formulate the objective of being able to grow a suspension composed entirely of free cells, each cell undergoing division regularly and the products of the division separating before mitosis recurs in the daughter cells. After that a chemostat could be developed which would maintain a predetermined cell density by frequent harvesting of cells and simultaneous replacement of culture medium. A medium would have been elaborated which was capable of maintaining cells in a meristematic condition and, at the same time, of controlling middle lamella formation so as to enable the cells to float apart. With the help of such suspensions studies on the cellular physiology of higher plants could proceed with a rapidity hitherto only possible in the case of unicellular micro-organisms. Cultures would be available for studies of the factors which pilot cells along the many pathways of differentiation that occur in the development of the diverse tissues of the multicellular plant body. We would have ideal material for studies in the biochemistry of mutant cells (see Chap. 9, p. 578) and even for plant breeding since whole plants could be derived from such individual cells (see p. 678). It is, however, very difficult to assess how far this is a realistic objective for immediate future research (see Vol. 1, Chap. 4). One immediate possible development could be the chance discovery of a tissue which just happened to give cultures approaching true free cell cultures as envisaged above.

Studies to date have been very restricted in the species and strains used but, nevertheless, they emphasize that tissues differ in the relative proportions of cell aggregates and free cells and in the size range of the cell aggregates to which they give rise under the currently available culture techniques. A fruitful approach here might well be the screening of clones of single cell origin already shown to differ in growth rate and physiology (see Chap. 9, p. 597). A number of unpublished observations indicate already that it may be possible to select by this approach, from within tissue strains, cell lines of particularly high growth rate in suspension culture.

Another immediate possibility might be that some quite empirical alteration of the culture medium or other aspect of the culture environment would have the effect of permitting free cells to divide actively in suspension or of promoting the separation of cells. Developments which would lead to more effective cell separation could arise from an extension to suspension cultures of the studies on the friability of callus (see p. 662) and work along these lines, indicating that concentrations of auxins and complex supplements like coconut milk can influence the degree of cell separation in suspension cultures, has already been published (Torrey and Shigemura, 1957; Lamport and Northcote, 1960; Bergmann, 1960). It may well be, however, that the problem of how to obtain cultures of truly free cells will only be solved after major advances in our knowledge of the growth and metabolism of cultured plant cells have been made.

It is therefore, perhaps, more immediately instructive to consider how our knowledge of the growth patterns of existing cultures and of the factors controlling these patterns could be developed. One aspect to consider is whether it is possible to represent with greater precision the changes occurring as suspension cultures grow. The assessments of rates of cell division so far reported have been mainly based on mitotic frequencies (mitotic index = per cent of cells in division at the time of sampling) (see Chap. 8, p. 513) and such assessments may be seriously in error. Dry-weight estimations should be supplemented by determinations of cellular protein and of cell wall fractions. Steward and Mohan Ram (1961) have commented upon the metabolism of carrot cells induced to active growth and cell division in culture. They draw attention to the relatively high resistance of their respiration to cyanide inhibition and the reduced extent to which carbon monoxide inhibition of their respiration is reversed by light as compared with that of quiescent cells. We have already referred to the comparative studies made by Steward and his associates on the protein metabolism of actively dividing, as compared with quiescent cells (see Chap. 9, p. 552). Such observations only serve to draw attention to our almost complete ignorance of the metabolism of cells growing and maturing in suspension cultures. It should at least be possible to study changes in respiration (rate, respiratory quotient, and sensitivity to inhibitors) and in the uptake of nutrients during the progress of batch cultures.

Evidence that nuclear changes can occur in suspension cultures initiated from normal diploid carrot tissue was first advanced by Mitra, Mapes and Steward (1960). Such changes included haploid (only one cell was considered to show this condition), tetraploid and more highly polyploid nuclei and nuclei showing such chromosomal aberrations as di- and tri-centric bridges. Nevertheless, such "abnormal" cells were only occasionally present and when cell masses from such cultures were induced to give rise to root and shoot growing points, these were apparently in all cases composed entirely of diploid cells. Similarly, haploid and polyploid nuclei and nuclei showing "pseudo-chiasmata", chromosome breaks, reunions and bridges were also observed in suspension cultures of *Haplopappus gracilis* by Mitra and Steward (1961) and studied further by Blakely and Steward (1964). The original stock cultures were found to give rise to variants which retained their distinctive character. These variants were characterized by such characters as growth form and pigmentation when cultured on an agar medium by the Bergmann (1960) technique. These variants were regarded as being isolated from a pool of genetic variation in the cell population. Some evidence was obtained that these variants had altered karyotypes; in one case, chromosome 2 of the variant cells lacked the characteristic satellite of this chromosome and had additional chromatin on the short arm. The authors, however, stress that, at present, the biochemical differences cannot be linked to particular locations on chromosomes.

These observations are in line, as far as detecting polyploid cells is concerned, with studies on differentiating tissue cells and cells of callus cultures (see Chap. 9, Section VII, B, p. 578). They also emphasize that cells which have the capacity to give rise to meristems seem to retain or regain the diploid condition. Polyploid nuclei in these studies were recognized by the study of mitotic figures. There are, however, also a number of observations indicating increases in nuclear volume (Monshau, 1930; Bradley, 1954; List, 1963) and in nuclear DNA content (Swift, 1950; List, 1963) proportional to increases in cell volume which may or may not be indicative of polyploidy. An alternative explanation could be that these nuclei have polytene chromosomes, that the increases in DNA arise from chromonemal reproduction and that following this there may occur nucleolar enlargement and synthesis of protein in the nucleus. Work with certain unicellular algae shows that, by appropriate illumination and nutrition, the cells may cease division, grow large and their nuclei accumulate abnormally large amounts of DNA. Then, on transfer to darkness or other conditions conducive to division, these cells divide rapidly to give as many as eight or sixteen smaller cells with a reduced content of nuclear DNA (Buffaloe, 1959; Tamiya, 1963). These observations not only emphasize the importance of studying the ploidy of cells in suspension cultures by cytological techniques but also the value of studying changes in DNA content per cell during the progress of growth. It could be that, in the period of culture characterized by increase in dry weight and cell volume and during which the cell number increases very little, the DNA content per chromosome undergoes successive duplications to give nuclei with polytene chromosomes. When such cells are subcultured and conditions promoting mitosis again established, their nuclei may undergo a quick series of mitoses to restore the normal diploid DNA content. Alternatively, DNA replication may not occur until the lag phase after subculture.

However, it is not only necessary to study in more detail the pattern of growth observed under a particular and arbitrary culture regime but to see how far this pattern is modified by such variables as the duration of the culture passage, the absolute size of inoculum, the ratio of size of inoculum to volume of medium, the cellular composition of the inoculum, the composition of the culture medium, light and temperature. No comprehensive experiments on the effects of these variables on the growth patterns in suspension cultures have yet been published. Preliminary work along these lines in our laboratory (Mehta, 1963; Street, Henshaw and Buiatti, 1965) indicates that if the cellular units being transferred are first washed with fresh medium then the lag phase preceding active increase in cell number is lengthened, particularly as the size of the inoculum is decreased. These studies have also shown that the number of cells produced and the total dry weight of the cultures is determined primarily by the volume of medium used rather than by the size of the initial inoculum or the timing and duration of the period of high mitotic frequency. These observations suggest that the transfer with the cellular units of some "conditioned" medium is important for the reduction of the lag phase of growth. Evidence was also obtained in these and related plating experiments (Bergmann's technique, see Chap. 8, p. 517) that the onset of the stationary phase is determined either by exhaustion of some essential constituents of the medium or by some factor related to cell density, such as oxygen availability or carbon dioxide tension, rather than by the biosynthesis and release of a growth inhibitor. In these experiments the use of small inocula while delaying the onset of the period of high relative increase in cell number (period of short mean generation time), prolongs its duration. This suggests that prolonged periods, during which a uniform and high rate of cell division occurs may be achieved by the controlled and continuous addition of fresh medium to the growing cultures. Whether such prolonged high growth rates can be achieved without profound changes in the cellular composition of the cultures is, however, doubtful since existing growth patterns indicate antagonism between the processes of cell division and cell separation. This, of course, raises the question of the nature of the cell aggregates. Does the aggregation of the cells make it possible for them to divide (in contrast to the free cells which rarely divide) simply by reducing the ratio of the external surface to the cellular unit volume and thereby assisting the intracellular retention of essential metabolites, or is there differentiation within these aggregates into meristematic and "feeder" cells? (see Chap. 9, p. 596). To answer these and related questions requires experiments which will make very high demands on labour and patience. Nevertheless, the further experimental study of growth patterns in suspension cultures will so obviously advance our knowledge of the factors controlling the division of plant cells that it can confidently be predicted that such studies will increasingly be the concern of those botanical laboratories from which pioneer studies have already been published.

B. CELL STRUCTURE AND CELL DIVISION

Whenever growing suspensions have been examined microscopically observers have recorded not only the presence of cell aggregates together with free cells but have drawn attention to the range of cell sizes and shapes encountered within the free cell fraction. Thus, Nickell (1956) found in suspension cultures of *Phaseolus vulgaris* mainly spherical cells, 12–40 μ in diameter, but also slipper shaped (30–60 × 10–20 μ) and gourd shaped cells (95 × 40 μ). Muir, Hildebrandt and Riker (1958) found in suspension cultures of a number of tissues spherical cells varying widely in diameter (from 15 to 220 μ diameter) together with elongated cells. In suspensions of crown-gall tissues of marigold and sunflower these elongated cells ranged from 20 to 150 μ in diameter and from 40 μ to 1·2 mm in length. In suspensions derived from normal and hybrid tobacco, giant elongated cells, often becoming multinucleate, were observed up to 300 μ in diameter and up to 2·5 mm long. These workers also observed small numbers of short tracheidal cells with spiral, lignified thickening. Steward, Mapes and Smith (1958b) have reported the presence in their carrot suspension cultures of spherical cells (50–100 μ in diameter), giant cells (100–150 × 300 μ) and of elongated tubular cells. Suspension cultures from the tuber of *Solanum tuberosum* and from the cotyledons of *Arachis hypogea* also showed a similar range of cell morphology. Street and Henshaw (1963) have depicted the main types of free cells encountered in suspensions of *Rubus fruticosus* and *Parthenocissus tricuspidata* crown-gall tissue.

This leads us to consider the origin and behaviour of these different kinds of free cells, bearing in mind the evidence that cell divisions do occur amongst free cells but with a very low frequency. Steward *et al.* (1958b) have reported division of spherical free cells in a typical equatorial fashion to give two-celled units. They also noted rows of three cells, the central cell of which was smaller than the two "wing" cells and suggested that such groups arose from a further division in these two-celled units. It was also postulated that "dense moruloid masses of actively dividing cells" arose from such three-celled units by divisions occurring both at right angles to and along their axis. To complete this cycle it was further suggested that the "moruloid" masses as they matured released free spherical cells again able to regenerate the cell aggregates. The giant cells of these cultures were, in a number of cases, observed to contain more than one nucleus and cells of this type were noted in which very unequal divisions had occurred (the small daughter cell being uninucleate) or which had apparently divided into a row or mass of uninucleate cells by internal divisions within the original cell wall and without cell expansion taking place. Enlarged and roughly isodiametric cells, usually among the superficial cells of aggregates, were seen, from which filamentous outgrowths had developed. Division by transverse walls in such filamentous outgrowths of cells was presumably the way in which uniseriate, filamentous structures had arisen. Rather infrequently in carrot cultures, but more prominently in their suspension cultures of peanut cotyledon tissue, these workers encountered spherical cells in which it appeared that small papillae had grown out from the surface, received cytoplasm and a nucleus from the "mother" cell and had then become constricted at their point of attachment. Other cells of the cultures suggested that such papillae may then enlarge and become "pinched off" at the base so that new cells arise by a process reminiscent of "budding" in yeasts. Similar cell types and probably division patterns (as indicated by cell associations) have also been described for the free cells of suspension cultures of *Haplopappus gracilis* (Blakely and Steward, 1961). The controversial questions here are those concerning the origin of the observed structures. Thus, Street and Henshaw (1963) who observed in cultures of *Parthenocissus tricuspidata* similar "moruloid" masses ranging from few (less than 10) cells to many (several 100) cells and associated and individual uniseriate and branched filaments conclude that these arose not from single cells but by fragmentation of larger cell aggregates and were, in turn, the precursors of such aggregates. Their observations suggested that the fate of most, if not of all, the single cells was to enlarge, senesce and die (Fig. 16). Bergmann (1960) has observed small cell associations in tobacco suspension cultures indicative of equatorial divisions in isodiametric cells and in elongated cells of division figures corresponding closely to those found in dividing fusiform cambium initials. In line with the conclusions of Steward and associates he has postulated internal segmentation within large cells and the development of multicellular aggregates from such groups. Jones, Hildebrandt, Riker and Wu (1960) noted a most peculiar behaviour of the giant elongated cells ($330\ \mu \times 2{\cdot}5$ mm) of tobacco in old suspension cultures (cultures incubated for 25–40 days). Uninucleate *free-floating* cells were formed within the wall of the giant cell and, when such giant cells were transferred to fresh medium, the endogenous free-floating cells divided first into filaments and then into cell masses until the giant cell contained several hundred cells. At this stage the enclosing parent wall burst and the aggregates of spherical cells were released (Fig. 17).

As pointed out by Steward *et al.* (1958b) the now considerable numbers of papers describing the diversity of cell morphology to be observed in suspension cultures "do not deal with the causative agents and limiting factors which regulate the stages of growth and development that are portrayed." At the moment one can merely say that in suspension cultures the cells show a great range of growth and form and that in their form and behaviour such cells do not correspond with recognized cell types in normal plant tissues or meristems. The giant cells suggest the absence of factors which normally limit cell expansion. The observation that in such large cells, the mitochondria may become joined end-to-end to form filiform aggregates of 2–12

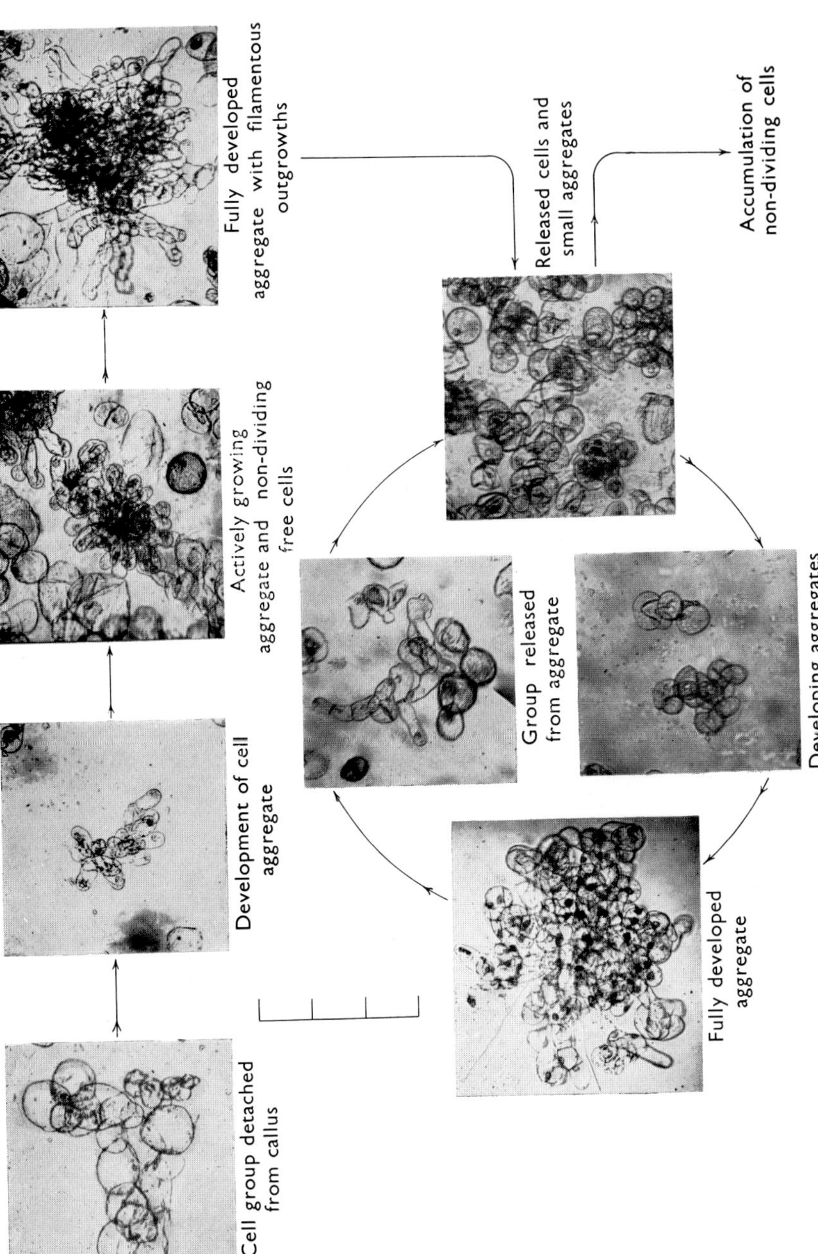

FIG. 16. Pattern of growth in suspension cultures of *Parthenocissus tricuspidata* crown-gall tissue. The initial cell aggregates formed during the establishment of the suspension culture from callus have more prominent filamentous outgrowths than the aggregates formed during subsequent culture passages. The pattern portrayed is that occurring when subculture takes place every 28 days. Each scale division = 100 μ. (After Street and Henshaw, 1963.)

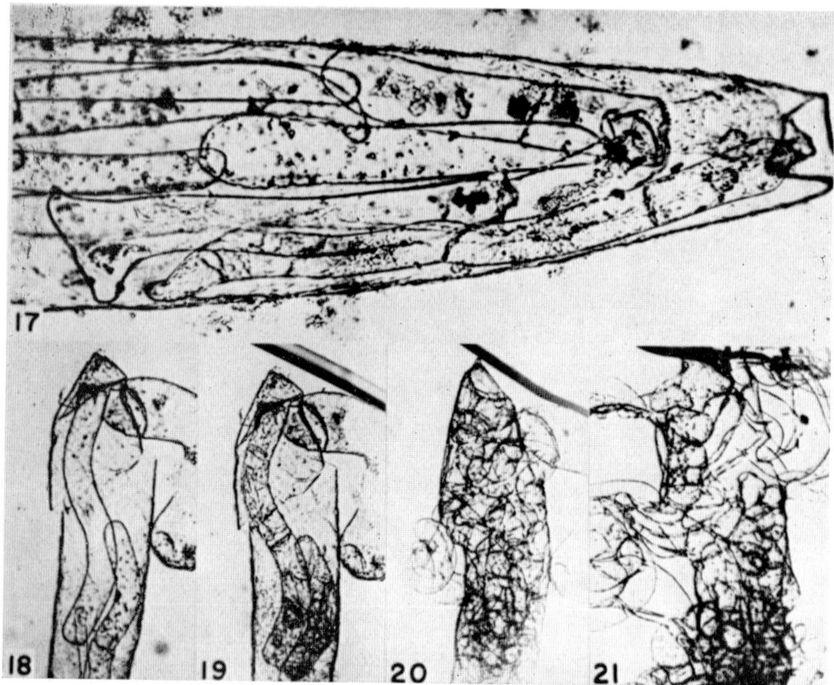

FIG. 17. "Giant" parenchyma cell of tobacco containing free-floating endogenous cells (17). (18–21) Behaviour following transfer of giant cell to new medium in a microchamber (see Fig. 16, Chap. 8, p. 516). 18, Initial condition; 19, 5 days later; 20, 10 days later; 21, 18 days later (see text). (After Jones *et al.*, 1960.)

units and that such mitochondria accumulate in the parietal sheath of cytoplasm where they exhibit "worm-like" movements similar to those described by Sorokin (1955) is regarded as indicative of their senescence and impending death (Jones *et al.*, 1960).

The free cells of suspension cultures characteristically have a large central vacuole and show active cytoplasmic streaming extending into the transvacuolar strands of cytoplasm which may suspend the nucleus. Study by phase-contrast microscopy of cell division in the roughly isodiametric free cells and in the similar cells of small aggregate shows it to resemble, in timing and cytological detail, the process as it occurs in the vacuolated cell of the regions of active elongation of the stem and root (Bergmann, 1960; Jones *et al.*, 1960) (Fig. 18). The development of the phragmoplast across the vacuole is as described by Sinnott and Bloch (1941). Excellent research films showing streaming and mitosis as revealed by the phase-contrast microscope have been made with tobacco cells in suspension culture by Jones and Muir of the Wisconsin Group.

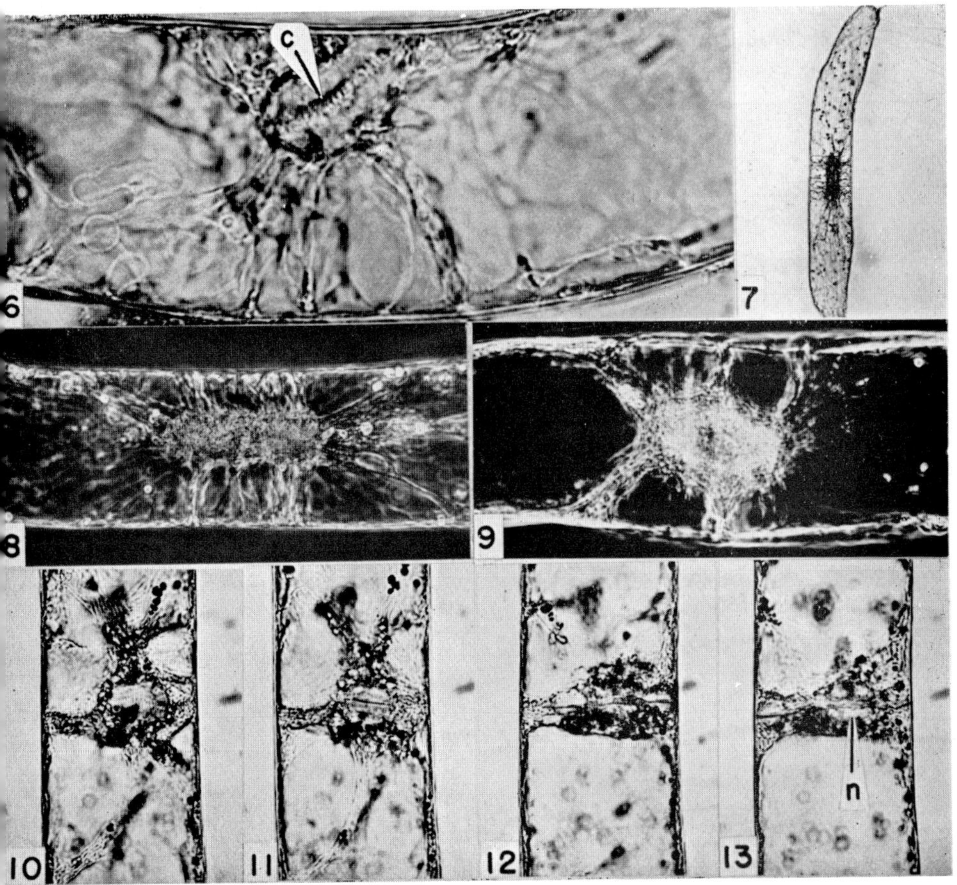

'IG. 18. Observation of cell division by phase contrast in tobacco cells in microculture (Jones *et al.*, 1960). ·, Mitosis in vacuolated cell, c, chromosomes at metaphase; 7, early prophase at 14.18 h; 8, early prophase .t 14.20 h, note numerous thin strands of cytoplasm surrounding the nucleus; 9, late prophase, cytoplasmic trands are coalescing; 10, late metaphase at 16.47 h, phragmosome of cytoplasm already formed; 11, arly telophase at 16.57 h, cell plate has started to form; 12, mid-telophase at 17.10 h; 13, cell plate is nearly ompleted at 17.22 h, daughter nuclei (n) are adjacent to the new cell wall. 6 × 510; 7 × 85; 8 – 13 × 305.

C. ORGANIZED GROWTH FROM FREE CELLS

The theme of this section can be summarized by quoting from the review of Steward and Mohan Ram (1961): "The capacity to produce the plant body does not, however, reside in the zygote alone—indeed in the light of recent work it may well persist, even though suppressed, in almost any living cell of the plant body . . . cells which have passed through many cell generations in culture, may still retain a degree of totipotency which is comparable with that of the zygote."

One way in which this ability of single cells to generate the whole plant could be expressed is by the following sequence: (1) a single cell gives rise to a callus mass, either by the technique of Bergmann (1960) or by the use of a nurse callus as first described by Muir, Hildebrandt and Riker (1954); (2) spontaneous or induced differentiation of a shoot growing point begins in this callus as described by Skoog and Miller (1957); (3) the growing point develops to give a leafy shoot and adventitious roots; (4) the "seedling structure" so developed is separated from the callus and grown on to give an independent autotrophic plant. Although the separate steps in this sequence have been achieved with tobacco stem cells the total sequence, starting with a single tobacco cell and ending with a tobacco plant, has not been carried out.

The observation of embryo-like structures ("adventive embryos") arising in a carrot callus by Reinert (1959) raises a more intriguing possibility, namely that a single cell of the callus gives rise to an embryo by a sequence of cleavages which follow the normal embryology of the zygote. This possibility has been strengthened by the observation, in suspension cultures of carrot (Steward, Mapes and Mears, 1958a) and tobacco (Bergmann, 1959), of embryo-like growth-forms which can be arranged in a sequence corresponding very closely with the early stages of the embryology of the species (Fig. 19). Further, Steward and his associates (Steward *et al.*, 1958a, b; Mitra *et al.*, 1960; Steward, Shantz, Pollard, Mapes and Mitra, 1961) have isolated young plantlets with normal radicle and plumule from cellular aggregates in

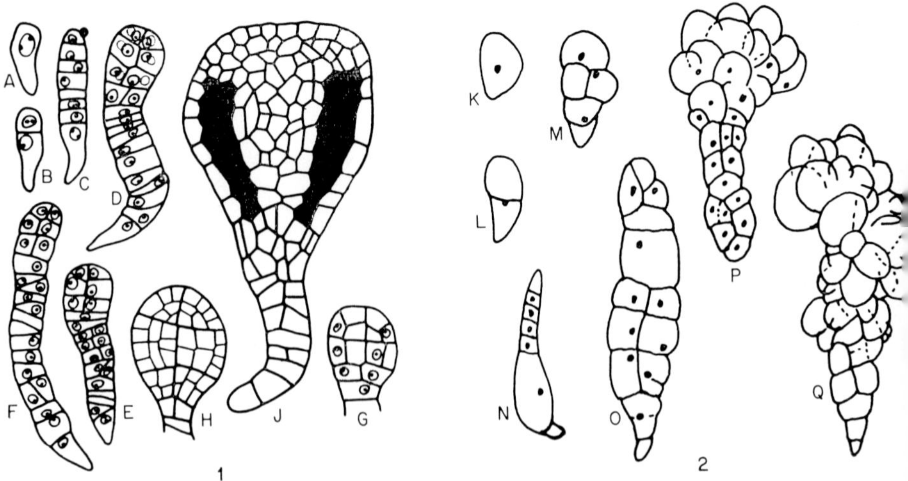

Fig. 19. Embryo-like forms in suspension cultures of carrot tissue. (1) A—J, The embryogeny of *Daucus carota*. (2) K—Q, Embryo-like structures observed in suspension cultures derived from carrot phloem callus. (From Steward *et al.*, 1961.)

these suspension cultures and grown these on to produce normal carrot plants. More recently, Steward, Mapes, Kent and Holsten (1964) have described the very high frequency with which such embryos arise on agar plates from cell aggregates recently derived from the cells of carrot embryos. Since the plantlets capable of being grown into carrot plants have been obtained from cell aggregates this sequence is incomplete in so far as the origin of such plantlets has not been traced back to a single cell (and this applies equally to the "adventive embryos" described by Reinert).

The development of embryos involves the appearance of polarity and in most flowering plants this is established with the first division of the zygote, a division which isolates the vacuole in the basal cell of the two-celled proembryo. This polarity would appear to be a response to some asymmetry in the environment. The first division of the zygote is nearly always at right angles to the direction of the micropyle of the ovule. In the case of free cells in a constantly agitated culture medium, the possibility cannot be completely excluded that unilateral stimuli of light, or gravity or contact with the culture vessels could serve to establish such polarity. If, in fact, single free-floating cells do segment to give polarized proembryos then either some stimulus of this kind is determinative or cell division establishes by chance the uneven distribution of the cell contents between the daughter cells necessary to initiate the required biochemical gradient. However, another possibility, certainly not excluded by the published data and seeming to the author much more probable, is that the free-floating plantlets observed in suspension have been released from the cell aggregates simultaneously present. If this is the case, then the gradient inducing polarity in the mother cell(s) of the plantlet is one already developed within the cellular aggregate in which it may be expected that there are gradients of oxygen, carbon dioxide, nutrients and metabolites.

The second condition that must be fulfilled for the development of an embryo or meristem would seem to be (1) in suspension cultures, a response of the initial cell(s) to the special nutrients contained in liquid endosperms, nutrient fluids specially designed to nurture embryos, and (2) in callus cultures, a response to those chemical stimulants (auxin, kinetin, certain amino acids) which are not only essential for cell division but act as morphogenetic stimuli.

The third condition, rightly stressed by Steward, is that in order to re-express their totipotency, cells must be released from the limitations imposed upon them by the plant body. Here we are probably concerned with a two-step process; first, the removal of the restriction of the "chemical" environment of the organism and, second, a remoulding of cellular metabolism (dedifferentiation!) probably dependent upon the cells being induced to undergo rapid division and being provided with a suitable source of growth regulators and metabolites.

These immediately preceding paragraphs draw attention to the importance of the interrelationships between the cytoplasm and nucleus in determining directions of cellular development and morphogenesis. The nucleus exercises a controlling influence on cytoplasmic activity probably through the export across the nuclear envelope of messenger molecules whose structure is determined by the functional genes. In turn, the cytoplasm not only provides the nucleus with energy-rich compounds and with the metabolites used in the synthesis of nuclear constituents but may also export molecules which activate or repress the genes. Thus the cytoplasm and the nucleus in turn control one another's activities and both the internal environment of the organism and external factors act upon this system probably in the first instance by their influence on cytoplasmic structure and function. The relative permanence of the changes, which together are usually considered to constitute the process of differentiation, is a reflection of the inertia of cytoplasmic and nuclear organization to change. The importance of cell division for the remoulding of this system reflects the effectiveness with which cytoplasmic organization is disturbed or eliminated during mitosis and even more dramatically during meiosis. The importance of appropriate nutrition at this time is presumably that it makes available the essential starting materials for the building of the nuclear and cytoplasmic organizations characteristic of cells capable of expressing their inherent totipotency. The importance in the induction of cell division and in directing the subsequent cellular development of specific growth-regulating substances is emphasized by the studies of growth and morphogenesis reviewed in this chapter. The crucial question which therefore arises is whether these substances are the molecules or immediate precursors of the molecules which, passing from the cytoplasm into the nucleus, determine the patterns of gene activation and repression (determine nuclear differentiation), or whether the known growth regulators and those yet to be isolated from such fluids as coconut milk act indirectly by involvement in cytoplasmic metabolism. If this latter is the case then such growth-regulating substances probably influence the synthesis of, as yet, quite unknown cytoplasmic products which are the direct determinants of cell growth and behaviour by virtue of their ability to control the functioning of the genes. The elucidation of the mode of action of the chemical regulators of growth and development and the identification of the determinants of nuclear differentiation are long-range objectives to which the work with plant cultures reviewed in this chapter are directed.

V. General Conclusions

The contributions made by organ, tissue and cell cultures to botanical research clearly relate to a very wide range of problems in the physiology of higher plants. The use of these techniques offers a unique avenue of approach to the further analysis of the metabolic potentialities of higher plant cells, for studies of the physiological inter-relationships between cells, tissues and organs within the multicellular plant and for controlling the expression, in differentiation and morphogenesis, of the totipotency of such cells.

The range of usefulness of Tissue-Culture techniques in botanical research, already very wide, is likely to be extended in the immediate future, particularly by developments in the field of the culture of isolated cells. Further, as with all techniques, their usefulness is enhanced when they are combined with other methods of approach. It is from the combined use of Tissue-Culture methods with chemical techniques such as isotopic tracers and with physical techniques such as electron-microscopy and mutagenic radiations, that we can expect most exciting advances in the biology of higher plants.

Acknowledgements

Grateful acknowledgement is made to my colleagues, Drs. D. N. Butcher and G. G. Henshaw, for many useful discussions and for their criticisms of the manuscript of this chapter and of Chapter 9, and to Miss Patricia Phillips for her care in preparing these manuscripts for the press.

References

Åberg, B. (1957). Auxin relations in roots. *Annu. Rev. Plant Physiol.* **8**, 153.

Abbott, A. J. (1963). The growth and development of excised roots in relation to trace element deficiencies. Ph.D. Thesis, University of Bristol.

Audus, L. J. (1959a). "Plant Growth Substances", 2nd ed. Leonard Hill, London.

Audus, L. J. (1959b). Some problems concerning root growth-hormones. *Zeszyty Naukowe Universytetu Mikolaja Kopernika w Toruniu. Naukl. Matemat-Przurodnicze* **6**, *Biol.* **4**, 9.

Bergmann, L. (1959). A new technique for isolating and cloning cells of higher plants. *Nature, Lond.* **184**, 648.

Bergmann, L. (1960). Growth and division of single cells of higher plants *in vitro*. *J. gen. Physiol.* **43**, 841.

Blakely, L. M. and Steward, F. C. (1961). Growth induction in cultures of *Haplopappus gracilis*. I. The behaviour of cultured cells. *Amer. J. Bot.* **48**, 351.

Blakely, L. M. and Steward, F. C. (1964). Growth and organized development of cultured cells. VII. Cellular variation. *Amer. J. Bot.* **51**, 809.

Bonnett, H. T. and Torrey, J. G. (1963). Comparative anatomy of the development of endogenous buds and roots from Convolvulus roots cultured *in vitro*. *Amer. J. Bot.* **50**, 613.

Boysen-Jensen, P. (1933a). Über den Nachweis von Wuchstoff in Wurzeln. *Planta* **19**, 345.

Boysen-Jensen, P. (1933b). Die Bedeutung des Wuchstoffes für das Wachstum und die geotropische Krummung der Wurzeln von *Vicia faba*. *Planta* **20**, 688.

Boysen-Jensen, P. (1936). "Growth Hormones in Plants". (Transl. revised G. S. Avery Jr. and P. K. Burkholder). New York.

Bradley, M. V. (1954). Cell and nuclear size in relation to polysomaty and the nuclear cycle. *Amer. J. Bot.* **41**, 398.

Britton, G., Housley, S. and Bentley, J. A. (1956). Studies in plant growth hormones. V. Chromatography of hormones in excised and intact roots of tomato seedlings. *J. exp. Bot.* **7**, 239.

Brown, R. (1951). The effect of temperature on the durations of the different stages of cell division in the root tip. *J. exp. Bot.* **2**, 96.

Brown, R. (1959). The regulation of growth and differentiation in the root. Proc. 4th int. Congr. Biochem., Symposium **6**, 77–94.

Brown, R. and Broadbent, D. (1950). The development of cells in the growing zones of the root. *J. exp. Bot.* **1**, 249.

Brown, R. and Robinson, E. (1955). Cellular differentiation and the development of enzyme proteins in plants. *In* "Biological Specificity and Growth" (E. G. Butler, ed.), pp. 93–118. Princeton University Press.

Buffaloe, N. D. (1959). Some effects of colchicine on cells of *Chlamydomonas eugametos* Moewus. *Exp. Cell Res.* **16**, 221.

Burström, H. (1941). On formative effects of carbohydrates on root growth. *Bot. Notiser.* p. 310.

Burström, H. (1942). The influence of heteroauxins on cell growth and development. *LantbrHogsk. Ann.* **10**, 209.

Burström, H. (1954). Studies on growth and metabolism of roots. IX. The influence of auxin and coumarin derivatives on the cell wall. *Physiol. Plant.* **7**, 548.

Burström, H. (1955). Zur Wirkungsweise chemischer Regulatoren des Wurzelwachstums. *Bot. Notiser* **108**, 400.

Butcher, D. N. (1963). The presence of gibberellins in excised tomato roots. *J. exp. Bot.* **14**, 272.

Butcher, D. N. and Street, H. E. (1960a). The effects of gibberellins on the growth of excised tomato roots. *J. exp. Bot.* **11**, 206.

Butcher, D. N. and Street, H. E. (1960b). Effects of kinetin on the growth of excised tomato roots. *Physiol. Plant.* **13**, 46.

Camus, G. (1949). Recherches sur le rôle des bourgeons dans les phenomènes de morphogénèse. *Rev. Cytol. Biol. Veg.* **9**, 1.

Carter, J. E. and Street, H. E. (1963). Studies on the growth in culture of excised wheat roots. IV. The activation of *dl*-tryptophane by autoclaving. *Physiol. Plant.* **16**, 347.

Charles, H. P. (1959). Studies on the growth of excised roots. VII. Effects of 2-naphthoxyacetic acid on excised roots from four strains of groundsel. *New Phytol.* **58**, 81.

Charles, H. P. and Street, H. E. (1959). Studies on the growth of excised roots. VI. The effects of certain amino acids and auxins on the growth of excised groundsel roots. *New Phytol.* **58**, 75.

Cholodny, N. (1924). Über die hormone Wirkung der Organspilze bei der geotropischen Krümmung. *Ber. dtsch. Bot. Ges.* **42**, 356.

Cholodny, N. (1926). Beitrage zur Analyse der geotropischen Reaktion. *Jahrb. Wiss. Bot.* **65**, 447.

Cholodny, N. (1927). Wuchshormone und Tropismen bei den Pflanzen. *Biol. Zbl.* **47**, 604.

Cholodny, N. (1931). Verwundung Wachstum und Tropismen. *Planta* **13**, 665.

Chouinard, A. L. (1955). Nuclear differences in *Allium cepa* root tissues as revealed through induction of mitosis with indoleacetic acid. *Canad. J. Bot.* **33**, 628.

Chrispeels, M. J., Vatter, A. E. and Hanson, J. B. (1963). On the development of cristae mitochondriales and endoplasmic reticulum during growth and differentiation in the roots of *Zea mays*. *Plant Physiol.* **38**, Suppl. XV.

Clowes, F. A. L. (1959). Apical meristems of roots. *Biol. Rev.* **34**, 501.

Clowes, F. A. L. (1961a). "Apical Meristems". Blackwell, Oxford.

Clowes, F. A. L. (1961b). Effects of β-radiation on meristems. *Exp. Cell Res.* **25**, 529.

Clowes, F. A. L. (1962). Rates of mitosis in a partially synchronous meristem. *New Phytol.* **61**, 111.

D'Amato, F. (1950). Differenziazione istologica per endopoliploidia nelle radici di alcune monocotiledoni. *Caryologia* **3**, 11.

D'Amato, F. (1952). Polyploidy in the differentiation and function of tissues and cells in plants. *Caryologia* **4**, 311.

Danckwardt-Lillieström, C. (1957). Kinetin induced shoot formation from isolated roots of *Isatis tinctoria*. *Physiol. Plant.* **10**. 794.

Dawson, J. R. O. and Street, H. E. (1959). The behaviour in culture of excised root clones of the 'Dorset Marlgrass' strain of red clover, *Trifolium pratense*, "L." *Bot Gaz.* **120**, 217.

Dormer, K. J. and Street, H. E. (1948). Secondary thickening in excised tomato roots. *Nature, Lond.* **161**, 483.

Esau, K. (1963). Ultrastructure of differentiated cells in higher plants. *Amer. J. Bot.* **50**, 495.

Fox, J. E. and Miller, C. O. (1959). Factors in corn steep water promoting growth of plant tissues. *Plant Physiol.* **34**, 577.

Fries, N. (1954). Chemical factors controlling the growth of the decotylised pea seedling. *Symb. bot. upsaliens.* **13**, 1.

Furuya, M. and Torrey, J. G. (1964). The reversible inhibition by red and far-red light of the auxin-induced lateral root initiation in isolated pea roots. *Plant Physiol.* **39**, 987.

Gautheret, R. J. (1945). "Une Voie nouvelle en Biologie végétale, la Culture des Tissus." Gallimard, Paris.

Gautheret, R. J. (1955). Sur la variabilité des propriétés physiologiques des cultures de tissus végétaux. *Rev. gen. Bot.* **62**, 1.

Gautheret, R. J. (1957). Histogenesis in plant tissue cultures. *J. nat. Cancer Inst.* **19**, 555.

Gautheret, R. J. (1959). "La Culture des Tissus végétaux, Techniques et Realisations." Masson, Paris.

Goldacre, P. L. (1959). Potentiation of lateral root induction by root initials in isolated flax roots. *Austr. J. biol. Sci.* **12**, 388.

Goldacre, P. L., Unt, H. and Kefford, N. P. (1962). Cultivation of isolated tissue derived from the pericycle of roots. *Nature, Lond.* **193**, 1305.

Goodwin, R. H. and Stepka, W. (1945). Growth and differentiation in root tip of *Phleum pratense*. *Amer. J. Bot.* **32**, 36.

Gorton, B. S. and Eakin, R. E. (1957). Development of the gametophyte in the moss, *Tortella caespitosa*. *Bot. Gaz.* **119**, 31.

Hannay, J. W. and Butcher, D. N. (1961). An ageing process in excised roots of groundsel (*Senecio vulgaris*, L.). *New Phytol.* **60**, 9.

Hawker, L. E. (1932). Experiments in the perception of gravity by roots. *New Phytol.* **31**, 231.

Heimsch, C. (1960). A new aspect of cortical development in roots. *Amer. J. Bot.* **47**, 195.

Heyes, J. K. (1960). Nucleic acid changes during cell expansion in the root. *Proc. roy. Soc. Lond.* B, **152**, 218.

Holmes, B. E., Mee, L. K., Hornsey, S. and Gray, L. H. (1955). The nucleic acid content of cells in the meristematic, elongating and fully elongated segments of roots of *Vicia faba*. *Exp. Cell Res.* **8**, 101.

Holzer, K. (1952). Untersuchungen zur karyologischen Anatomie der Wurzel. *Oestrr. Bot. Z.* **99**, 118.

Hughes, E. W. D. and Street, H. E. (1960). Effects of inhibitory concentrations of 3-indolylacetic acid and 3-indolylacetonitrile on cell division and tissue differentiation in excised tomato roots. *J. exp. Bot.* **11**, 198.

Jablonski, J. R. and Skoog, F. (1954). Cell enlargement and cell division in excised tobacco pith tissue. *Physiol. Plant.* **7**, 16.

Jacquiot, C. C. R. (1951). Action du méso-inositol et de l'adénine sur la formation de bourgeons par le tissue cambial d'*Ulmus campestris* cultivé *in vitro*. *C. R. Acad. Sci., Paris* **233**, 815.

Jacquiot, C. C. R. (1955). Formation d'organes par le tissu cambial d'*Ulmus campestris*, L. et de *Betula verrucosa*, Gaerth. cultivés *in vitro*. *C. R. Acad. Sci., Paris* **240**, 557.

Jacob, F. and Monod, J. (1961). Genetic regulatory mechanisms in the synthesis of proteins. *J. molec. Biol.* **3**, 318.

Jensen, W. A. (1957). The incorporation of C^{14}-adenine and C^{14}-phenylalanine by developing root tips. *Proc. nat. Acad. Sci., Wash.* **43**, 1038.

Jensen, W. A. (1958). The nucleic acid and protein content of root tip cells of *Vicia faba* and *Allium cepa*. *Exp. Cell Res.* **14**, 575.

Jones, L. E., Hildebrandt, A. C., Riker, A. J. and Wu, J. H. (1960). Growth of somatic tobacco cells in microculture. *Amer. J. Bot.* **47**, 468.

Jones, R. W. (1954). Secondary thickening in isolated roots of White Icicle radish. Ph.D. Thesis, University of California, Los Angeles.

Lahiri, A. N. and Audus, L. J. (1960). Growth substances in the roots of *Vicia faba*. *J. exp. Bot.* **11**, 341.

Lahiri, A. N. and Audus, L. J. (1961). Growth substances in the roots of *Vicia faba*. II. The effects of ageing and excision of the main tap root meristem. *J. exp. Bot.* **12**, 364.

Lamport, D. T. A. and Northcote, D. H. (1960). The use of tissue culture for the study of plant cell walls. *Biochem. J.* **76**, 52P.

Lane, R. H. (1936). The inhibition of roots by growth hormone, *Amer. J. Bot.* **23**, 532.

Leopold, A. C. and Guernsey, F. S. (1953). Auxin polarity in the *Coleus* plant. *Bot. Gaz.* **115**, 147.

Levan, A. (1939). Cytological phenomena connected with the root swelling caused by growth substances. *Hereditas* **25**, 87.

List, A., Jr. (1963). Some observations on DNA content and cell and nuclear volume growth in the developing xylem cells of certain higher plants. *Amer. J. Bot.* **50**, 320.

Loeffler, J. E. and van Overbeek, J. (1964). Kinin activity in coconut milk. *In* "Regulateurs Naturels de la Croissance Végétale," pp. 77–96. C.N.R.S., Paris.

Loening, U. E. (1962). Messenger ribonucleic acid in pea seedlings. *Nature, Lond.* **195**, 467.

Loomis, R. S. and Torrey, J. G. (1964). Chemical control of vascular cambium initiation in isolated radish roots. *Proc. nat. Acad. Sci., Wash.* **52**, 3.

Mayer, L. (1956). Wachstum und organbildung an *in vitro* Kultivierten Segmenten *Cyclamen persicum. Planta* **47**, 401.

Mazia, D. (1961). Mitosis and the physiology of cell division. *In* "The Cell" (J. Brachet and A. E. Mirsky, eds.), Vol. 3, pp. 77–412. Academic Press, New York.

Mehta, A. R. (1963). Nutritional and morphogenetic studies with callus and suspension cultures derived from roots. Ph.D. Thesis, University of Wales.

Miller, C. O. (1960). An assay for kinetin-like materials. *Plant Physiol.* **35**, Suppl. XXVI.

Miller, C. O. (1961). Kinetin and related compounds in plant growth. *Annu. Rev. Plant Physiol.* **12**, 395.

Miller, C. O. and Skoog, F. (1953). Chemical control of bud formation in tobacco stem segments. *Amer. J. Bot.* **40**, 768.

Mitra, G. C. and Allsopp, A. (1959). Effects of kinetin, gibberellic acid and certain auxins on the development of shoot buds on the protonema of *Pohlia nutans. Nature, Lond.* **183**, 974.

Mitra, J., Mapes, M. O. and Steward, F. C. (1960). Growth and organized development of cultured cells. IV. The behaviour of the nucleus. *Amer. J. Bot.* **47**, 357.

Mitra, J. and Steward, F. C. (1961). Growth induction in cultures of *Haplopappus gracilis.* II. The behaviour of the nucleus. *Amer. J. Bot.* **48**, 358.

Mollenhauer, H. H., Whaley, W. G. and Leech, J. H. (1961). A function of the Golgi apparatus in outer root cap cells. *J. Ultrastructure Res.* **5**, 193.

Monshau, M. (1930). Untersuchungen über das Kernwachstum bei Pflanzen. *Protoplasma* **9**, 536.

Morel, G. (1948). Recherches sur la culture associée de parasites obligatoires et de tissus vegetaux. *Ann. Épiphyt.* **14**, 1.

Morel, G. and Wetmore, R. H. (1951). Tissue culture of monocotyledons. *Amer. J. Bot.* **38**, 138.

Muir, W. H., Hildebrandt, A. C. and Riker, A. J. (1954). Plant tissue cultures produced from single isolated cells. *Science* **119**, 877.

Muir, W. H., Hildebrandt, A. C. and Riker, A. J. (1958). The preparation, isolation and growth in culture of single cells from higher plants. *Amer. J. Bot.* **45**, 589.

Nagao, M. (1937). Studies on the growth hormones of plants. III. The occurrence of growth substances in isolated roots grown under sterilised conditions. *Sci. Rep. Tohoku Univ.* (*Biol.*) **12**, 191.

Nagao, M. (1938). Studies on the growth hormones of plants. IV. Further experiments on the production of growth substances in root tips. *Sci. Rep. Tohoku Univ.* (*Biol.*) **13**, 221.

Nickell, L. G. (1955). Nutrition of pathological tissues caused by plant viruses. *Année biol.* **31**, 107.

Nickell, L. G. (1956). The continuous submerged cultivation of plant tissues as single cells. *Proc. nat. Acad. Sci., Wash.* **42**, 848.

Nickell, L. G. and Tulecke, W. (1960). Submerged growth of cells of higher plants. *J. Biochem. microbiol. techn. Engng.* **2**, 287.

Nielsen, N. (1930). Untersuchungen über einen neuen Wachstumregulierenden Stoff, Rhizopin, *Jahrb. Wiss. Bot.* **73**, 125.

Nobécourt, P. (1939). Sur les radicelles naissant des cultures de tissus du tubercule de Carotte. *C. R. Soc. Biol., Paris* **130**, 1271.

Nobécourt, P. (1955). Variations de la morphologie et de la structure de cultures de tissus végétaux. *Bull. Soc. bot. Suisse* **65**, 475.

Nobécourt, P. and Hustache, G. (1954). Évolution des caractères morphologiques et anatomiques dans des cultures de tissus végétaux. *Congr. Int. Bot.* **8**, 192.

Northcote, D. H. (1963). Changes in the cell walls of plants during differentiation. *Symp. Soc. exp. Biol.* **17**, 157.

Norton, J. P. and Boll. W. G. (1954). Callus and shoot formation from tomato roots *in vitro*. *Science* **119**, 220.

Overbeek, J. van (1939a). Is auxin produced in roots? *Proc. nat. Acad. Sci., Wash.* **25**, 245.

Overbeek J. van (1939b). Evidence for auxin production in isolated roots growing *in vitro*. *Bot. Gaz.* **101**, 450.

Patau, K., Das, N. K. and Skoog, F. (1957). Induction of DNA synthesis by kinetin and indoleacetic acid in excised tobacco pith tissue. *Physiol. Plant.* **10**, 949.

Pecket, R. C. (1957a). The initiation and development of lateral meristems in the pea root. I. The effect of young and mature tissues. *J. exp. Bot.* **8**, 172.

Pecket, R. C. (1957b) The initiation and development of lateral meristems in the pea root. II. The effect of indole-3-acetic acid. *J. exp. Bot.* **8**, 181.

Pilet, P. E. (1951a). Répartition et variations des auxines dans la racine du *Lens culinaris,* Med. *Experientia* **7**, 762.

Pilet, P. E. (1951b). Contribution à l'étude des hormones de croissance (auxines) dans la racine de *Lens culinaris*. *Mem. Soc. Vaud. Sci. Nat.* **10**, 137.

Pilet, P. E. (1961a). "Les Phytohormones de Croissance." Masson, Paris.

Pilet, P. E. (1961b). Culture *in vitro* de tissus des Carotte et organogenèse. *Ber. schweiz. bot. Ges.* **71**, 189.

Pilet, P. E. (1961c). Auxins and the process of ageing in root cells. *In* "Plant Growth Regulation", pp. 167–180. Iowa State University Press, Ames, Iowa.

Raalte, M. H. van (1936). On the influence of glucose on auxin production by the root tip of *Vicia faba*. *Proc. Kon. Akad. Wetensch.* (Amsterdam) **39**, 261.

Raggio, M. and Raggio, N. (1956). A new method for the cultivation of isolated roots. *Physiol. Plant.* **9**, 466.

Reinert, J. (1956). Dissociation of cultures of *Picea glauca* into small tissue fragments and single cells. *Science* **123**, 457.

Reinert, J. (1959). Über die Kontrolle der Morphogenese und die Induktion von Adventurembryonen an Gewebekulturen aus Karotten. *Planta* **53**, 318.

Reinert, J. (1963). Experimental modification of organogenesis in plant tissue cultures. "Plant Tissue and Organ Culture—a Symposium," p. 168. Int. Soc. Plant Morphologists, Delhi.

Reinert, J. and White, P. R. (1956). The cultivation *in vitro* of tumor tissue and normal tissue of *Picea glauca*. *Physiol. Plant.* **9**, 177.

Roberts, E. H. and Street, H. E. (1955). The continuous culture of excised rye roots. *Physiol. Plant.* **8**, 238.

Sastri, R. L. N. (1963). Morphogenesis in plant tissue cultures. "Plant Tissue and Organ Culture—a Symposium", p. 105. Int. Soc. Plant Morphologists, Delhi.

Shantz, E. M., Mears, K. and Steward, F. C. (1958). Comparison between the growth-promoting effects on carrot tissue of coconut milk and of kinetin and certain of its analogues. *Plant Physiol.* **33**, Suppl. XVI.

Sinnott, E. W. and Bloch, R. (1941). Division in vacuolate plant cells. *Amer. J. Bot.* **28**, 225.

Skinner, J. C. and Street, H. E. (1954). Studies on the growth of excised roots. II. Observations on the growth of excised groundsel roots. *New Phytol.* **53**, 44.

Skoog, F. (1944). Growth and organ formation in tobacco tissue culture. *Amer. J. Bot.* **31**, 19.

Skoog, F. (1957). Proceedings Decennial Review Conference in Tissue Culture. *J. nat. Cancer Inst.* **19**, 578.

Skoog, F. and Miller, C. O. (1957). Chemical regulation of growth and organ formation in plant tissue cultures *in vitro*. *Symp. Soc. exp. Biol.* **11**, 118.

Skoog, F. and Tsui, C. (1951). Growth substances and the formation of buds in plant tissues. *In* "Plant Growth Substances" (F. Skoog, ed.), pp. 263–285. Wisconsin University Press.

Sorokin, H. P. (1955). Mitochondria and spherosomes in the living epidermal cell. *Amer. J. Bot.* **42**, 225.

Sorokin, H. P., Mathur, S. N. and Thimann, K. V. (1962). The effects of auxins and kinetin on xylem differentiation in the pea epicotyl. *Amer. J. Bot.* **49**, 444.

Steward, F. C., Mapes, M. O., Kent, A. E. and Holsten, R. D. (1964). Growth and development of cultured plant cells. *Science* **143**, 20.

Steward, F. C., Mapes, M. O. and Mears, K. (1958a). Growth and organised development of cultured cells. II. Organisation in cultures grown from freely suspended cells. *Amer. J. Bot.* **45**, 705.

Steward, F. C., Mapes, M. O. and Smith, J. (1958b). Growth and organised development of cultured cells. I. Growth and division of freely suspended cells. *Amer. J. Bot.* **45**, 693.

Steward, F. C. and Mohan Ram, H. Y. (1961). Determining factors in cell growth: some implications for morphogenesis in plants. *Advanc. Morphogen.* **1**, 189.

Steward, F. C., Shantz, E. M., Pollard, J. K., Mapes, M. O. and Mitra, J. (1961). Growth induction in explanted cells and tissues: metabolic and morphogenetic manifestations. *In* "Syntheses of Molecular and Cellular Structures" (D. Rudnick, ed.), pp. 193–246. Ronald Press, New York.

Street, H. E. (1953). Factors controlling meristematic activity in excised roots. III. Light as a factor in the "location effect" noted with *Lycopersicum esculentum*, Mill. *Physiol. Plant* **6**, 466.

Street, H. E. (1954a). Factors controlling meristematic activity in excised roots. V. Effects of β-indolylacetic acid, β-indolylacetonitrile and α-(l-naphthylmethylsulphide)-propionic acid on the growth and survival of roots of *Lycopersicum esculentum*, Mill. *Physiol. Plant.* **1**, 212.

Street, H. E. (1954b). Effects of alpha (l-naphthylmethylsulphide)-propionic acid on the growth of excised tomato roots. *Nature, Lond.* **73**, 253.

Street, H. E. (1955). Factors controlling meristematic activity in excised roots. VI. Effects of various "anti-auxins" on the growth and survival of excised roots of *Lycopersicum esculentum*, Mill. *Physiol. Plant.* **8**, 48.

Street, H. E. (1957). Excised root culture. *Biol. Rev.* **32**, 117.

Street, H. E. (1962). The physiology of roots. *In* "Viewpoints in Biology" (J. D. Carthy and C. L. Duddington, eds.), Vol. 1, pp. 1–49. Butterworth, London.

Street, H. E., Butcher, D. N., Handoll, C. and Winter A. (1964). "Règulateurs Naturels de la Croissance Végétale." Proceeds 5th Int. Conf. Natural Plant Growth Regulators, p. 529. C.N.R.S., Paris.

Street, H. E. and Henshaw, G. G. (1963). Cell division and differentiation in suspension cultures of higher plant cells. *Symp. Soc. exp. Biol.* **17**, 234.

Street, H. E., Henshaw, G. G. and Buiatti, M. C. (1965). The culture of isolated plant cells. *Chem. & Ind.* 1965, 27.

Street, H. E. and McGonagle, M. P. (1953). Factors controlling meristematic activity in excised roots. IV. Habituation of the main axis meristem of excised tomato roots to repeated subculture. *Physiol. Plant.* **6**, 707.

Street, H. E., McGonagle, M. P. and Roberts, E. H. (1953). Factors controlling meristematic activity in excised roots. II. Experiments involving repeated subculture of the main axis meristems of roots of *Lycopersicum esculentum*, Mill. and *Lycopersicum pimpinellifolium*, Dunal. *Physiol. Plant.* **6**, 1.

Street, H. E. and McGregor, S. M. (1952). The carbohydrate nutrition of tomato roots. III. The effect of external sucrose concentration on the growth and anatomy of excised roots. *Ann. Bot.* **16**, 185.

Street, H. E., McGregor, S. M. and Sussex, I. M. (1954). Effect of 3-indolylacetic acid and 3-indolylacetonitrile in the growth of excised tomato roots. *J. exp. Bot.* **5**. 204.

Street, H. E. and Roberts, E. H. (1952). Factors controlling meristematic activity in excised roots. I. Experiments showing the operation of internal factors. *Physiol. Plant.* **5**, 498.

Swift, A. (1950). The constancy of desoxyribose nucleic acid in plant nuclei. *Proc. nat. Acad. Sci., Wash.* **36**, 643.

Tamiya, H. (1963). Cell differentiation in *Chlorella*. *Symp. Soc. exp. Biol.* **17**, 188.

Thimann, K. V. (1934). Studies on the growth hormones of plants. VI. The distribution of the growth substances in plant tissues. *J. gen. Physiol.* **18**, 23.

Thimann, K. V. (1960). "Fundamental Aspects of Normal and Malignant Growth," Chap. 10, pp. 748–822. Elsevier, Amsterdam.

Thurman, D. A. and Street, H. E. (1960). The auxin activity extractable from excised tomato roots by 80% methanol. *J. exp. Bot.* **11**, 188.

Thurman, D. A. and Street, H. E. (1962). Metabolism of some indole auxins in excised tomato roots. *J. exp. Bot.* **13**, 369.

Torrey, J. G. (1950). The induction of lateral roots by indoleacetic acid and root decapitation. *Amer. J. Bot.* **37**, 257.

Torrey, J. G. (1951). Cambial formation in isolated pea roots following decapitation. *Amer. J. Bot.* **38**, 596.

Torrey, J. G. (1952). Effect of light on elongation and branching in pea roots. *Plant Physiol.* **27**, 591.

Torrey, J. G. (1953). The effect of certain metabolic inhibitors on vascular tissue differentiation in isolated pea roots. *Amer. J. Bot.* **40**, 525.

Torrey, J. G. (1954). The role of vitamins and micronutrient elements on the nutrition of the apical meristem of pea roots. *Plant Physiol.* **29**, 279.

Torrey, J. G. (1955). On the determination of vascular patterns during tissue differentiation in excised pea roots. *Amer. J. Bot.* **42**, 183.

Torrey, J. G. (1956). Chemical factors limiting lateral root formation in isolated pea roots. *Physiol. Plant.* **9**, 370.

Torrey, J. G. (1957). Auxin control of vascular pattern formation in regenerating pea root meristem grown *in vitro*. *Amer. J. Bot.* **44**, 859.

Torrey, J. G. (1958a). Differential mitotic response of diploid and polyploid nuclei to auxin and kinetin treatment. *Science* **128**, 1148.

Torrey, J. G. (1958b). Endogenous bud and root formation by isolated roots of *Convolvulus* grown *in vitro*. *Plant Physiol.* **33**, 258.

Torrey, J. G. (1959a). Experimental modification of development in the root. *In* "Cell, Organism and Milieu" (D. Rudnick, ed.), pp. 189–222. Ronald Press, New York.

Torrey, J. G. (1959b). A chemical inhibitor of auxin-induced lateral root initiation in roots of *Pisum*. *Physiol. Plant.* **12**, 873.

Torrey, J. G. (1961). Kinetin as a trigger for mitosis in mature endomitotic plant cells. *Exp. Cell Res.* **23**, 281.

Torrey, J. G. (1962). Auxin and purine interactions in lateral root initiation in isolated pea root segments. *Physiol. Plant.* **15**, 177.

Torrey, J. G. (1963). Cellular patterns in developing roots. *Symp. Soc. exp. Biol.* **17**, 285.

Torrey, J. G., Reinert, J. and Merkel, N. (1962). Mitosis in suspension cultures of higher plant cells in a synthetic medium. *Amer. J. Bot.* **49**, 420.

Torrey, J. G. and Shigemura, Y. (1957). Growth and controlled morphogenesis in pea root callus tissue grown in liquid media. *Amer. J. Bot.* **44**, 334.

Weiss, C. and Vaadra, Y. (1965). Kinetin-like activity in root apices of sunflower plants. *Life Sciences* 1965, 1323.

Went, F. W. (1928). Wuchstoff und Wachstum. *Rec. Trav. Bot. Néerl.* **25**, 1.

Wetmore, R. H. and Rier, J. P. (1963). Experimental induction of vascular tissues in callus of angiosperms. *Amer. J. Bot.* **50**, 418.

Wetmore, R. H. and Sorokin, S. (1955). On the differentiation of xylem. *J. Arnold Arbor.* **36**, 305.

Whaley, W. G., Mollenhauer, H. H. and Leech, J. H. (1960). The ultrastructure of the meristematic cell. *Amer. J. Bot.* **47**, 401.

White, P. R. (1939). Controlled differentiation in a plant tissue culture. *Bull. Torrey bot. Club* **66**, 507.

White, P. R. (1943). "A Handbook of Plant Tissue Culture". J. Cattell, Lancaster, Pa.

Winter, A. and Street, H. E. (1963). A new natural auxin isolated from "staled" root culture medium. *Nature, Lond.* **198**, 1283.

Wipf, L. and Cooper, D. C. (1940). Somatic doubling of chromosomes and nodular infection in certain *Leguminoseae*. *Amer. J. Bot.* **27**, 821.

Woodstock, L. W. and Brown, R. (1963). The effect of 2-thiouracil on the growth of cells in the root. *Ann. Bot., Lond.* **27**, 403.

Woodstock, L. W. and Skoog, F. (1960). Relationship between growth rates and nucleic acid content in the roots of inbred lines of corn. *Amer. J. Bot.* **47**, 713.

Woodstock, L. W. and Skoog, F. (1962). Distributions of growth, nucleic acids and nucleic acid synthesis in seedling roots of *Zea mays*. *Amer. J. Bot.* **49**, 623.

Yeoman, M. M. (1962). The effects of ribonuclease on the growth of pea roots. *J. exp. Bot.* **13**, 390.

CHAPTER 11

The Use of Tissue Culture in Phytopathology

ARMIN C. BRAUN and JACQUES LIPETZ*
The Rockefeller University, New York, New York, U.S.A.

I. Introduction

Tissue-Culture methods, as applied to the field of phytopathology, have served a most useful purpose in studies dealing with the plant tumour problem. Such concepts as autonomy, tumour progression, the regulation of essential biosynthetic systems, as well as the nature of the heritable changes that lead to the autonomous growth in plant tumour cell types have found their explanation, in large part, through the use of Tissue-Culture methods.

Plant tumours, like animal tumours, may be initiated by physical, chemical, and biological agencies of the most diverse type. Three non-self-limiting tumours, the first of which has a genetic basis, the second is caused by a typical virus, while the third is initiated by a tumour-inducing principle elaborated by a specific bacterium, have been most thoroughly studied. Although these plant neoplasms are caused by different and distinct agencies, the physiological and biochemical basis for the autonomous growth of the tumour cells appears to be similar in all instances.

*Present address: Department of Biology, Manhattan College, New York 71, N.Y., U.S.A.
The survey of the literature pertaining to this article was concluded in February 1962.

Experimental findings reported in the plant field have now clearly demonstrated that as the result of the transformation of a normal plant cell to a tumour cell, a radical reorientation in synthetic activities occurs. This metabolic reorientation progresses from the precisely regulated metabolism concerned with differentiated function, which is characteristic of a normal resting cell, to one involving a permanently increased synthesis of the nucleic acids, mitotic proteins and other substances concerned specifically with cell growth and division. This switch in metabolism is in all instances triggered by irritation. It may be permanently fixed in a cell by any one of several distinct types of oncogenic agencies, and it is maintained in the plant tumour cell by virtue of the fact that all of those agencies permanently activate a series of biosynthetic systems, the products of which are concerned specifically with cell growth and division. The experimental evidence upon which those statements are based is summarized below.

II. The Crown-gall Disease

The crown-gall disease of plants has been used as the experimental model in the field of plant oncology for more than half a century. No attempt has been made here to cover the literature in that area. For a more complete description of the disease the reader is referred to the following recent review articles: Braun (1961, 1962); Braun and Stonier (1958); Braun and Wood (1961); Klein and Link (1955).

Crown gall is a non-self-limiting neoplastic disease of plants that is initiated by a tumour-inducing principle (TIP) elaborated by a specific bacterium, *Agrobacterium tumefaciens*. The TIP produced by the bacterium possesses the ability to transform regularly and irreversibly normal plant cells to tumour cells in short periods of time. When that transformation process, which takes place gradually and progressively over a period of several days, has been fully accomplished, the continued rapid, abnormal and autonomous proliferation of the tumour cells becomes entirely independent of any recognizable infectious agent. Sterile tumour tissue isolated from many plant species and maintained in culture for more than a decade has not shown the slightest tendency to become less autonomous. Such tumours are transplantable. These are, then, composed of permanently altered tumour cells that reproduce true to type and against the growth of which there is no adequate control mechanism in a host.

Crown gall was for many years considered to be a bacterial-stimulated hyperplasia, the continued development of which was dependent upon continued stimulation by the inciting bacterium, and this despite the fact that, as early as 1910, C. O. Jensen had brilliantly demonstrated that the beet tumour cells with which he worked were capable of autonomous development when implanted into healthy beet plants. It was not, however, until 1942 (White and Braun, 1942) when plant tissue-culture methods had been developed that the truly autonomous nature of the crown-gall tumour cell was unequivocally established. It had been observed by Smith, Brown and McCulloch (1912) and by Braun (1941) that many of the secondary tumours that arise in certain plant species at points distant from the seat of the primary growth were free of the inciting bacterium. When tissues from such bacteria-free secondary tumours were isolated and planted on White's simple, chemically defined culture medium, they grew profusely and indefinitely, though the same medium did not support the growth of normal cells of the type from which the tumour cells were derived. White's medium thus served as a selective culture medium that permitted the profuse growth of tumour cells but not of most normal cell types. Fragments of sterile tumour tissue implanted into a healthy host of the same species from which the tumour fragment was derived developed again into tumorous overgrowths that were similar to those originally produced by the bacteria except that such implants were sterile. Subsequently, tissues isolated from primary tumours of many plant species were found to behave similarly. These results indicated that a profound and heritable cellular change had resulted from the action of the bacteria. Much work has been done in culture on the nutritional aspects of tumour growth (see Braun, 1954, 1962; Gautheret, 1959; Riker and Hildebrandt, 1958).

Riker and Hildebrandt together with their associates have published a series of papers on the influence of the physical as well as the chemical environment on the growth of crown gall and *Nicotiana* hybrid tumour tissues. In the first paper of the series these workers studied the effects of temperature, hydrogen-ion and sugar concentrations on tissue growth (Hildebrandt, Riker and Duggar, 1945). This was followed by a successful attempt to improve the composition of White's medium for the growth of different tumour species (Hildebrandt, Riker and Duggar, 1946a). Subsequently, the effects on growth of large numbers of carbon- and nitrogen-containing compounds were investigated. In those studies (Hildebrandt and Riker, 1949), the influence on the growth of marigold, Paris daisy, periwinkle, sunflower and tobacco tumour tissues of various sugars, polysaccharides, organic acids and alcohols was studied. Dextrose, levulose or sucrose were found to be excellent carbon sources for tumours of all five plant species. In addition, marigold tissue increased significantly in weight on mannose, maltose or cellobiose; tobacco on maltose or cellobiose; periwinkle on lactose, galactose, maltose, cellobiose or raffinose. Marigold tissue increased slightly in weight in basal media containing starch, dextrin or pectin; Paris daisy on maltose, lactose, cellobiose, raffinose, dextrin or pectin; periwinkle on rhamnose, mannose, starch, inulin, dextrin or pectin; and tobacco on xylose, mannose, lactose, raffinose, starch, dextrin or pectin. It was found that all organic acids at a 0·5% concentration when used as the sole carbon source were unfavourable for growth. Slight increases in tissue weights were, nevertheless, found in marigold cultures on media containing succinic, stearic or fumaric acids; Paris daisy on succinic, fumaric or glutaric acids or calcium gluconate; periwinkle tissue on acetic, malic, succinic, formic, tartaric, pyruvic, propionic or stearic acids or calcium gluconate; sunflower tissue on malonic, malic, succinic, formic, tartaric, pyruvic, stearic, glycolic, fumaric or glutaric acids, and tobacco tissue on succinic, fumaric and glutaric acids. In the presence of sucrose, all five tissues grew well on media containing 0·5% of one of the following organic acids: stearic, succinic, fumaric or malic acids or calcium gluconate. In addition, marigold tissue grew well on media containing pyruvic, malonic, fumaric, malic and tartaric acids; periwinkle on pyruvic acid; and sunflower on malonic, malic or tartaric acid.

Marigold tissue was strongly inhibited on media containing glycolic, lactic, glutaric or citric acid; Paris daisy on pyruvic or malonic acid; periwinkle on glutaric or tartaric acid; sunflower on pyruvic, glutaric, fumaric or citric acid; and tobacco on media with pyruvic, malonic or tartaric acid. Alcohols at a concentration of 0·5% as a sole source of carbon were unfavourable for growth. When sucrose was present in the medium, all species grew well in the presence of 0·5% methanol glycerol, erythritol or dulcitol. Only periwinkle grew well on ethanol, while all except Paris daisy did well on mannitol.

Riker and Gutsche (1948) studied the influence of a number of different inorganic and organic nitrogen sources on the growth of sunflower tumour tissue. Nitrate and urea were found to be excellent sources of nitrogen, while most amino acids when used as the sole source of nitrogen failed to support growth of the tissue. However, a number of amino acids including arginine, alanine, glutamic and aspartic acids, when incorporated into a medium containing nitrate nitrogen, encouraged growth of the tissues.

The question as to whether the transformation of a normal cell to a fully autonomous crown-gall tumour cell takes place in one step or whether it is a gradual process was investigated (Braun, 1947, 1951a). By interrupting the transformation process at intervals following inoculation, by thermal treatment that selectively killed the bacteria without affecting the capacity of the host cells to respond with tumour formation to whatever alteration had occurred prior to the time that the bacteria were destroyed, it was possible to obtain tumour tissue that showed varying grades of neoplastic change that ranged from very slowly growing tumours to rapidly growing, fully autonomous tumour-cell types. Since such tumour tissues, which represent an excellent example of tumour progression, were obtained from the same tissues of the same plant species and since they maintained their characteristic growth patterns indefinitely on White's basic culture medium, they were used for a study of the factors required for rapid autonomous growth (Braun, 1958).

A physiological and biochemical study of three tumour tissues which showed varying grades of neoplastic change has demonstrated that, as a result of the transition of a normal plant cell to a fully autonomous tumour cell, a series of quite distinct biosynthetic systems, which represent the entire area of metabolism concerned with cell growth and division, become progressively and permanently activated. This leads to the synthesis by the tumour cell of essential growth-promoting substances that have been found to include two intracellular growth-regulating substances one of which, an auxin, is concerned with cell enlargement and the other of which, a kinin, acts synergistically with the first to promote growth and cell division (Braun, 1956). In addition, the vitamin myo-inositol, glutamine, aspartic acid or asparagine as well as purine and pyrimidine synthesizing systems are permanently activated (Braun, 1958). The degree of activation of those systems within a tumour cell appears, moreover, to determine the rate at which that cell type grows. Normal cells of the type from which the tumour cells were derived do not synthesize any of those substances when planted on White's basic culture medium. Thus, the development of a capacity for autonomous growth finds its explanation in terms of cellular nutrition. The tumour cells can synthesize all of the essential growth factors that their normal counterparts require for cell growth and division but cannot themselves make.

It is also clear from these studies that as a result of the transformation process, a profound and persistent reorientation in the pattern of synthesis occurs. This switch in metabolism is triggered by irritation accompanying a wound. It is permanently fixed in the crown-gall cell by an oncogenic principle elaborated by a specific bacterium. That pattern of synthesis is maintained in the tumour cell because the two hormones that regulate cell growth and division are continually synthesized by such cell types. The other metabolites shown to be produced by the tumour cells in excessive amounts are required for the synthesis of the nucleic acids, mitotic proteins and, in the case of inositol, the membrane systems of the cells. These metabolites are essential to provide the building blocks that permit the pattern of synthesis concerned with cell growth and division to be expressed.

The question as to whether this new pattern of synthesis found in the plant tumour cell results in the irreversible loss of the previous pattern concerned with differentiated function or whether it simply overwhelms the latter has been studied (Braun, 1959). The results of those studies are summarized below.

As previously indicated, the typical fully autonomous crown-gall tumour cell shows every indication of being a permanently altered cell type. There are, however, produced in certain plant species, the cells of which possess highly developed regenerative capacities, morphologically quite different types of tumours. These overgrowths, which are initiated by a TIP associated with moderately virulent strains of the inciting bacterium, are composed in part of morphologically highly abnormal leaves and buds. When tissues from such teratomata were planted on a basic culture medium, they grew profusely and indefinitely, though that medium did not support the growth of normal cells of the type from which the tumour cells were derived. Tissues from the teratomata differed from typical crown-gall tumour tissue in that they retained indefinitely in culture, as in the host, a striking capacity to organize morphologically highly abnormal leaves and buds. That teratoma tissue is composed entirely of tumour cells was recently demonstrated unequivocally by isolating a number of single-cell clones of such tissue according to the methods of Muir, Hildebrandt and Riker (1958) and demonstrating that such clones behaved in every respect as did the teratoma tissue from which they were derived (Braun, 1959). Since teratoma tissues of single-cell origin possessed a capacity to organize tumour buds, they were used for a study on the origin of the crown-gall tumour cell.

A study of this type was possible only because of the unique manner in which dicotyledonous plant species grow. Primary growth of such species is a result of the very rapid division and subsequent elongation of the meristematic cells at the extreme apex of a root or shoot. Such meristematic cells in a rapidly growing root or shoot divide at far faster rates than do the most rapidly growing tumour cells. By forcing tumour shoots derived from tumour buds into very rapid but organized growth as a result of a series of consecutive graftings to healthy plants, such shoots gradually recovered and ultimately became normal in every respect (Braun, 1951b, 1959). Tissues isolated from tumour shoots following the initial graft grew well and organized morphologically abnormal structures on a chemically defined culture medium. Tissue isolated from recovered shoots following three successive graftings did not grow on that medium. Since teratoma tissues used in such studies were of single-cell origin and since perfectly normal tobacco plants were ultimately obtained after a series of graftings from tissues derived from single cells, these studies demonstrated unequivocally that a single somatic cell of tobacco may possess all of the potentialities needed to reconstitute an entire tobacco plant.

Findings such as those reported above make nuclear changes of a mutation type appear highly unlikely as a possible explanation of the nature of the cellular alteration in crown gall. They suggest, instead, that we are dealing in this instance with a change in the expression rather than with a change in the integrity of the genetic information that is present in a cell.

It is quite clear from studies on the crown-gall disease that, as a result of the transformation of a normal plant cell to a tumour cell, a profound switch in the pattern of synthesis occurs leading to the activation of biosynthetic systems required for the synthesis of nucleic acids, mitotic proteins, and other substances required specifically for cell growth and division. Studies on the recovery of the crown-gall tumour cell demonstrate, moreover, that enzyme systems activated during transformation may again be blocked under certain special experimental conditions. These findings suggest that the area of metabolism concerned with differentiated function found in a normal cell is not irreversibly lost but is simply overwhelmed by the more primitive metabolism that is characteristic of a plant tumour cell. These results are not inconsistent with the concept that we are dealing here with the induction of self-maintaining steady-state mechanisms in which two areas of metabolism compete with one another for ascendancy in a cell. Such steady states, which, in this instance, appear to reflect changes in the phenotype without corresponding changes in the genotype, could persist indefinitely if the cellular system responsible for the maintenance of such states at particular functional levels was precisely regulated in a cell.

It is clear that some very fundamental cellular mechanism is concerned in accomplishing the simultaneous or perhaps sequential activation of the diverse biosynthetic systems found to be permanently unblocked in the crown-gall tumour cell. By comparing the growth of two types of tumour cells with normal cells on White's basic culture medium and on that medium in which the concentration of three salts, KCl, $NaNO_3$ and NaH_2PO_4, were raised, it was concluded that five and in part six of the seven biosynthetic systems shown to be permanently unblocked in the plant tumour cell are rendered functional by specific ions. Only the biosynthetic system concerned with the synthesis of the mitogenic hormone, kinin, cannot as yet be accounted for on that basis (Braun and Wood, 1962; Wood and Braun, 1961). These studies indicate, then, that progressive changes in the properties of the membrane systems accompany the cellular transformation and, as a result of such changes, essential ions penetrate to proper loci in the fully autonomous tumour cells but are unable to do so in the normal cell types when both tissues are grown on White's basic culture medium. Subsequent studies have shown that the observed changes in the properties of the membrane systems reflect progressive alterations in the permeability of the cell membrane. Active or metabolically dependent mechanisms for the transport of ions do not appear to be involved in this system. The fully autonomous tumour cells take up ions very efficiently from dilute salt solutions; the normal cells do not. This, then, represents a fundamental difference between a plant tumour cell and a normal cell since it accounts for the permanent activation by ions of a large segment of metabolism concerned with cell growth and division.

III. Genetic Tumours

Tumours that have a genetic basis arise regularly in certain interspecific hybrids within the genus *Nicotiana*. No external agency such as a virus or an oncogenic chemical is involved in the inception or development of such tumours. When, for example, two plant species such as *Nicotiana glauca* and *N. langsdorffii* are crossed and the seed of such hybrids sown, the resulting plants commonly grow normally during the period of their active growth. Once the plants reach maturity and terminal growth ceases, a profusion of tumours invariably arises on all parts of the plant (Kostoff, 1930). These tumours develop at points of irritation such as in areas where leaf petioles and flower petals have abscissed or where roots, stems, and leaves have been injured. Feeding such hybrid plants with radioactive phosphorus or irradiating them hastens the onset of tumour formation and increases significantly the number of tumours that develop (Sparrow and Gunckel, 1956; Sparrow, Gunckel, Scharrer and Hagen, 1956).

In 1930 Kostoff reported that nine interspecific hybrids within the species *Nicotiana* produced spontaneous tumours. Since these initial studies, about fifty different hybrid combinations have been investigated. Näf (1958) has reported that the parents of the tumorous hybrids may be divided into two groups which he arbitrarily designated as "plus" and "minus". It was found that if an intragroup cross was made between two species in the "plus" or two in the "minus" group, the resulting offspring did not develop tumours. On the other hand, crosses between a "plus" and a "minus" species produced tumorous offspring. From these studies it was concluded that the critical contributions of the "plus" parents differ from those of the "minus" parents.

Smith (1958, 1962) has recently provided evidence to indicate that in these hybrids neither spontaneous tumour formation nor radiation-induced tumour formation involves the process of mutation at the nuclear gene level. Such hybrid tumours and particularly those that develop in the cross between *N. glauca* × *N. langsdorffii* represent a lower grade of neoplastic change than is found in the fully transformed crown-gall tumour cell. Such tumours appear to be more comparable to the crown-gall teratomata since they frequently retain a capacity to organize abnormal tissues and organs in culture as well as in a host.

From an historical point of view these hybrid tumours are interesting. They were the first plant tumour tissues to be cultured continuously on a chemically defined medium (White, 1939a), although they were not shown to be transplantable until 1944 (White, 1944). Of greater significance was the role that these tissues played in initiating studies on controlled growth and development of plants. The hybrid tumour tissues do not ordinarily organize structures when planted on an agar-containing medium. White (1939b) found, however, that when such tissue was immersed in a liquid medium, it differentiated into leaves and shoots (Fig. 1). It was presumed by White that oxygen gradients were instrumental in the differentiation process. Skoog (1944) found that White's hybrid tumour tissue still differentiated when immersed

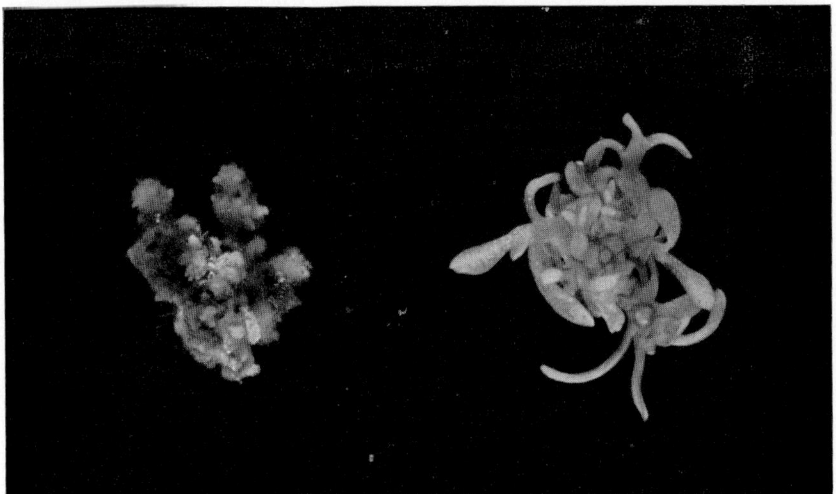

FIG. 1. Left: Callus culture undivided for 20 weeks, grown on a semi-solid culture medium. Right: A similar culture grown for 10 weeks on a medium like that at the left, then transferred for 10 weeks to a liquid medium containing the same nutrient materials. × 2·75. (From White, 1939b.)

in liquid following 144 passages on an agar medium. This worker also found that the tendency to form buds and shoots in liquid medium could be completely suppressed by the addition of 0·2 p.p.m. of indole acetic acid (IAA). In liquid culture the low concentration of added IAA not only suppressed differentiation and organization but stimulated growth so that fresh weights of such tissues were 50% more than those found in the controls. This IAA inhibition of organization was reversible by raising the level of certain nutrients such as sucrose, KH_2PO_4, and $Fe_2(SO_4)_3$ in the liquid medium. It was thus possible to control the development of organized structures in this system. Subsequent studies based on the observations above and carried out with the use of normal *N. tabacum* tissue culminated in the now classical discovery that the organization of buds and leaves is largely controlled in such a system by the ratio of two growth-regulating hormones, the auxins and the kinins (Skoog and Miller, 1957).

As indicated above, these hybrid tumours grow indefinitely on a simple, chemically defined culture medium. Normal cells isolated from either parent do not grow on that medium. Like the crown-gall tumour cells, the hybrid tumour cell types apparently synthesize all of the substances required for their continued growth from the mineral salts and sucrose present in White's basic culture medium.

Anders and Vester (1960) and Vester and Anders (1960) suggested that an abnormally high free amino-acid content of the hybrid plant is connected with spontaneous formation of tumours. Hagen and Gunckel (1958) reported that γ irradiation caused the leaf abnormalities of the parent species and their hybrid and a concomitant increase in the free amino-acid content of these leaves.

The alkaloids, sugars, organic acids, and amino acids of *N. glauca* and *N. langsdorffii* and of the tumorous and visibly non-tumorous portions of F_1 hybrid were studied (Tso, Burk, Sorokin and Engelhaupt, 1962). The chemical composition of the tumorous tissue varied with the culture medium and with the portion of the plant on which the tumour developed. Newly formed tumours accumulated high levels of free amino acids irrespective of the age of the plant itself.

IV. Virus Tumours

A third non-self-limiting neoplastic disease of plants, Black's wound-tumour disease, is caused by a virus (Black, 1945, 1949). The virus has been isolated and found to be a polyhedron having a diameter of about 80mμ (Brakke, Vatter and Black, 1954). The virus has a large host range and on many plant species the signs resulting from virus infection involve morphogenetic disturbances. In certain hosts such as sorrel (*Rumex acetosa* L.) and sweet clover (*Melilotus alba* Desr.), however, the response to infection involves the production of tumours which possess a capacity for unlimited unorganized growth *in vitro* as well as *in vivo*.

Although the wound-tumour disease is caused by a specific virus, the tumorous expression, as in the other two neoplastic diseases described above, is limited to areas of irritation of one sort or another. In addition to the virus and an area of irritation, the genetic constitution of the host plays an important role in the expression of the disease. Clones within the species *M. alba* may show striking differences with respect to the frequency, distribution, size, and shape of the resulting tumours (Black, 1951). It is interesting to note that the highly inbred B21 clone of sweet clover, which responds readily with tumour formation to virus infection, has also been found to give rise occasionally to spontaneous tumours in the non-infected state (Littau and Black, 1952).

Tissue isolated from sorrel tumours and planted on White's basic medium grows slowly but indefinitely on that chemically defined medium. The tissue approximately doubled in volume every 3 weeks. Such tissue was still found to contain virus after 14 months in culture (Black, 1949). Subsequently, Burkholder and Nickell (1949) modified White's basic medium and achieved far better growth of the tumour tissues. The tumour tissue was found to require high levels of phosphorus as well as vitamin B_1 in the medium for optimal growth. The requirement of high levels of phosphorus by such tissues was interpreted to reflect the need for phosphorus for replication of the virus (Burkholder and Nickell, 1949). It was found, further, that ribonucleic acid (RNA) hydrolysate and particularly uracil incorporated into the medium stimulated the growth of the tissues. Guanine, xanthine, and hypoxanthine were also found to be stimulatory. Deoxyribonucleic acid (DNA) hydrolysates, on the other hand, were inhibitory (Nickell, Greenfield and Burkholder, 1950). The tumour tissues were found to secrete significant amounts of the enzyme α-amylase into the culture medium (Brakke and Nickell, 1951, 1955). Tumour tissues, in general, appear to be more "leaky" than are their normal counterparts (Lipetz and Galston, 1959; Reinert, Schraudolf and Tazawa, 1957).

Although the virus commonly replicates in the cells of the tumour, a tumour line has now been isolated in which the virus is no longer demonstrable. This apparently virus-free tissue retains its tumorous properties. This raises the interesting question as to whether the oncogenic viruses are responsible only for the initiation of the new pattern of synthesis in a cell that leads to autonomous growth, or whether such agencies are responsible for its maintenance as well. It is commonly assumed that in those instances in which a virus cannot be demonstrated in a cell, the genetic material of the virus becomes integrated into the genome of the cell and is, in that form, responsible for the continuity of the tumorous properties from one cell generation to the next. Such findings are, nevertheless, equally consonant with an alternative interpretation that certain of the oncogenic viruses merely establish the particular pattern of synthesis that results in autonomous cell growth and which, once established, is maintained in a self-maintaining steady-state equilibrium in the absence of the virus.

The three non-self-limiting tumorous diseases of plants described above have much in common. In all instances irritation is one requisite for the initiation of the new growth. Irritation of one sort or another appears to be needed to switch the cellular metabolism from that found in a normal resting cell to that present in a dividing cell. When this metabolic reorientation has been accomplished, it can be permanently fixed by any of the oncogenic agencies. Once fixed, the tumour cells in all instances synthesize essential metabolites needed for the production of the nucleic acids, mitotic proteins, and other substances required specifically for cell growth and division. These biosynthetic systems are solidly blocked in most normal cell types.

There is no evidence to indicate, moreover, that the cellular changes that lead to autonomous growth in plant tumour-cell types result from somatic mutations at the nuclear level. Studies in this area suggest, rather, that such changes are of an epigenetic type and involve simply the permanent activation of that segment of the normal genome that is concerned specifically with cell growth and division.

V. Spruce Tumours

Massive overgrowths of unknown etiology have been found to develop on twigs, branches, trunks, and roots of the white spruce, *Picea glauca*, in certain highly restricted localities (White, 1957, 1958). Aside from their massive size, the most striking feature of such overgrowths is the high degree of cellular differentiation and organization found in them. The growth ring of the tumour wood is continuous with that found in the stem but differs from the latter in that the tumour wood may have ten times as many cells as does the adjacent normal wood. According to White (1957, 1958), this difference in numbers of cells in normal and tumour wood appears to result from a greatly prolonged growth season for the cells of the tumour. The tumour cells grow and divide for 8–9 months of the year, as compared with only about 2 months for the normal wood.

Because of the very high degree of differentiation and organization of the cells of such tumours and because the growth of the tumours appears simply to reflect the ability of the tumour cells to grow and divide for longer periods of time during the growing season, such overgrowths appear to represent an example of a very low grade of plant tumour in which cellular autonomy, if present at all, would appear to be but poorly developed. This interpretation appears to be further borne out by the results of tissue-culture studies. Early studies (Reinert and White, 1956) suggested that the cultivation *in vitro* of both normal and tumour tissues was not a simple matter. These spruce tissues appeared to require a wide range of vitamins including folic acid and B_{12} as well as a large number of amino acids which are not normally required by most plant tissue cultures. The high tannin and oxidase content of the spruce tissues caused further difficulties and resulted in a rapid blackening of the excised tissues and an inhibition of their growth. This blackening reaction was controlled in part by the use of non-metallic instruments when making subcultures of the tissues.

On the standard nutrient medium, all cultures from normal trees or from normal cambium present in tumour-bearing trees grew at uniform rates as firm, white, compact growths. These growths changed to gelatinous, rapidly developing masses of isolated cells when cultivated on a medium lacking folic acid and B_{12} (Reinert, 1956). Tumour tissue, on the other hand, was unpredictable on either medium. Some isolates were white, some brown, some compact, some gelatinous, others crustose. This suggests that the tumour cells may be unstable and undergo changes in growth pattern. It should be recalled, however, that the normal cells were isolated from the region of cambium while the tumour cells were probably largely xylem-parenchymatous in origin.

Of particular interest in these studies was the finding that the tumour tissues were strictly auxin-dependent, while the normal cells did not require an exogenous source of auxin for growth. This is exactly opposite to the results obtained with other pairs of tumour and normal tissues described above.

Reinert and Schraudolf (1959) confirmed earlier results showing that normal spruce tissue grew without auxin but found a 50% promotion of growth of the tissues when optimal concentration of IAA was applied to the culture medium. More recently, de Torok and Thimann (1961) reported that they found no such growth promotion with auxin. These workers greatly simplified the complex culture medium developed earlier and noted that with the use of the new medium the effective concentration of auxin for growth of the tumour tissue was twenty times less than the amount considered optimal in the earlier studies.

The tyrosine which caused so much blackening and toxicity in the earlier studies was omitted altogether from the medium with improved results.

De Torok and Thimann (1961) demonstrated, further, that an auxin antagonist, *p*-chlorophenoxy-isobutyric acid (pCiBA) inhibited the growth of tumour cells but did not affect the growth of the normal cells. Removal of the tumour cells from the pCiBA-containing medium to normal auxin-containing medium permitted the return, after some lag, of their original capacity for growth. This represents an interesting example in which the growth of a plant tumour can be inhibited for considerable periods of time by a single chemical substance and can fully recover from the effects of that substance when the tissue is removed from its influence.

The cytology of the spruce tumours is interesting. Smear preparations of cells taken from primary explants of normal and adjacent tumour wood showed completely regular mitotic behaviour with the great majority of the cells diploid, some tetraploid, and a few aneuploid. Tumour tissue, on the other hand, was more unstable with chromosome numbers ranging from 3 to more than 70, with a significant number of aneuploids. These findings are entirely consonant with results reported above on the nutritional behaviour of normal versus tumour tissue in culture. The normal wood was consistent in its growth pattern while the tumour wood was variable.

De Torok and Roderick (1962) recently compared subcultures derived from an explant of normal spruce tissues and subcultures derived from an explant of spruce-tumour tissue. They found in these studies significant correlation among growth rate, rate of cell division, and chromosome number in both tumour and normal subcultures. A most important finding was a correlation between chromosome number and growth rate over the entire aneuploid series. It was suggested by these authors that there is a cause-and-effect relationship from chromosome number through rate of cell division to growth rate.

VI. Fern Tumours

Frequent departures from the characteristic morphology of prothalli of several species of ferns growing in sterile culture have been reported (Hurel-Py, 1950; Morel and Wetmore, 1951; Steeves, Sussex and Partanen, 1955). The last-mentioned authors described five distinctive types of abnormal development in the growth of prothalli of *Pteridium aquilinum* (L.) Kuhn. Two general types of proliferations were distinguished in this study. Included in the first type were the filamentous pincushion and coralloid proliferations which were considered to be no more than abnormal prothallial colonies because they gave rise to functional sex organs and retained through long periods of culture the ability to regenerate normal prothalli. In the second group were included filamentous pseudocallus and the parenchymatous callus. These growths no longer gave rise to sex organs and they deviated more radically from the normal than did the growth abnormalities in the first group. Of particular interest to this discussion is the parenchymatous callus which grew continuously in culture in a completely unorganized manner on a simple, chemically defined medium.

Cytological studies on these tumorous growths showed that initially all of the chromosome numbers were haploid. In subsequent culture the chromosome numbers in the dividing cells reached an approximate tetraploid level. Superimposed upon this polyploidy, variable aneuploidy was commonly observed (Steeves, Sussex and Partanen, 1955).

Partanen (1956) measured the DNA in individual nuclei present in the normal and in the tumorous growth by photometric means. The normal as well as certain non-tumorous aberrant growth forms showed DNA amounts in the 1 C to 2 C range. Newly isolated tumour strains were found to be essentially like the normal prothalli in DNA pattern. In subsequent passages in culture they developed a spectrum of DNA values that ranged from the normal to much higher values. Partanen concluded that in this system, at least, polyploidy is neither causal to nor even present in the initiation of this type of tumorous growth. It appears clearly to be secondarily acquired.

The number of tumours appearing in culture on prothalli of the bracken fern *P. aquilinum* could be increased very significantly by treating the ungerminated spores or young prothalli with either X rays or γ rays (Partanen and Steeves, 1956). Such tumorous growths were similiar to those that arose spontaneously. The response in tumour frequency was found to be linear with respect to the total dose of X rays in a range up to 16,000r (Partanen, 1958).

Subsequent studies (Partanen, 1960a) demonstrated that the addition of amino acids to the basic medium on which X ray-treated spores were grown reduced the frequency of tumours by approximately 50%. Further studies showed that the tumour-suppressing ability was widely distributed among the amino acids rather than being confined to any one or a few (Partanen, 1960b). The most effective amino acids were found to be methionine and lysine. The effect of lysine could, moreover, be nullified by equimolar concentrations of arginine. On the other hand, one amino acid, glutamic acid, enhanced significantly the tumour frequency. Similar results were observed when ammonium salts were added in optimal amounts to the culture medium. As a result of these findings, Partanen suggested that in the initiation of tumours the reduction of nitrate to ammonium is impaired, but given an exogenous source of reduced nitrogen the tumours are able to develop. Hence, the increased tumour frequency when either ammonium salts or glutamic acid were supplied to the tumours.

VII. Insect Galls

Among the most interesting types of growth abnormalities found in plants are those that result from the activity of certain of the gall-forming insects. The distinguishing feature of insect galls is the determinate growth of those structures. So striking is this feature that it has been suggested that such galls are comparable in their determinate growth to a leaf or a fruit. Galls initiated by particular insect species are of constant size and form and possess their own polarity and symmetry. Although the cells forming such galls dedifferentiate as a result of the initial stimulus elaborated by an insect, they again redifferentiate into an orderly rearrangement of cells and cell layers which possess a degree of differentiation that is seldom if ever below that normally found in a host. Many of these highly specialized overgrowths and particularly those caused by the gall wasps or cynipids appear to represent beautiful examples of dependent differentiation. An examination of such structures leaves one with the unmistakable impression that highly specific morphogenetic stimuli of chemical nature and elaborated by certain of the gall-forming insects are capable of initiating, stimulating, and directing most precisely the differentiation of plant cells as well as encouraging the development of new and most unusual growth patterns.

It is clear from an examination of the literature (Anders, 1958; Boysen-Jensen, 1952; Lewis and Walton, 1958) that the growth of many such cells is dependent upon the continued administration to the host cells of growth-regulating substances produced by the insects. If the insects die prematurely, growth of the gall stops. Such galls are then self-limiting structures, the growth and development of which is dependent upon continued stimulation by the insect.

Of the considerable number of insect-gall tissues that have thus far been successfully cultivated *in vitro,* all have been obtained from galls of simple structure which showed very little internal cellular differentiation. Certain attempts to establish cultures of tissues isolated from highly organized cynipid galls have thus far failed (Pelet, 1959), although Démétriadès (1953) found that cells from a *Salvia* gall required exogenous auxin for growth in culture, as did the normal tissue. Perhaps the most comprehensive study as yet carried out in this area was that recently reported by Pelet, Hildebrandt, Riker and Skoog (1960) in which tissues from the simple *Phylloxera* gall of the grape were compared in culture with stem tissues of the normal plant. The general requirements for optimal growth were similar for all tissues, although each stem and gall tissue tended to have its own distinctive pattern of growth on a particular medium. It was reported, further, that the composition of the medium exerted strikingly different influences on both the rates and pattern of growth of the various isolates. Since these gall cells arise from temporary local stimulation of normal cells, they behave essentially as do normal cells. As might be expected, fragments of such gall tissue, when implanted into a healthy host of the same species from which it was derived, fused with the host and failed to develop into overgrowths. It is of interest to note that Pelet *et al.* (1960) successfully reared five successive generations of *Phylloxera* on callus tissue grown *in vitro*. The insect developed best on roots that grew from the callus tissue.

VIII. Nematodes

Although plant diseases may be due to nematode infections, the demonstration of the role of a particular nematode as the inciting agent is not always easy. Unless axenic cultures of these organisms can be obtained, the fulfilment of Koch's postulates remains a serious problem. The concomitant infection of plant roots with nematodes, bacteria, and fungi often leaves some doubt as to the identity of the primary pathogen. For these reasons the ability to grow mixed cultures of bacteria-free nematodes and sterile plant tissue has attracted the attention of plant pathologists for almost half a century.

As early as 1914 Byars was able to demonstrate, by sterile culture methods, that *Heterodera radicicola* was a disease agent in tomato and cowpea. He placed sterile egg masses in a soft agar medium with mineral salts in which sterile plants were growing. Characteristic galls were formed on the roots and the nematode population increased. Ferguson (1948) obtained root knots or galls on excised tomato roots grown in White's medium and infected with *H. marioni* (now known as *Meloidogyne*). Mountain (1954, 1955), using similar techniques of root culture, demonstrated that *Pratylenchus minyus* is the primary causative agent of brown root rot in tobacco. Widdowson, Doncaster and Fenwick (1958) grew tomato roots and were able to infect them with *H. rostochiensis*. "Egg to egg" cultures were reported by many of these investigators.

Sayre (1958) found that excised tomato roots in liquid culture media could not be successfully infected with *Meloidogyne incognita*, whereas they could be in solid medium. Once infected, these roots can be kept this way and grown in liquid medium. The composition of the medium is critical to the maintenance of the galls. Iron chelate prevented the formation of female nematodes, increased the growth rate of the root, and prevented infection even on solid medium. Iron sulphate, on the other hand, caused slower root growth, better infection, and more typical galls.

The problem of "attractiveness" of certain plant parts to the nematodes has been the subject of some controversy. Wieser (1955) reported that the apical 2 mm of tomato-seedling roots were "repellent" to *M. hapla* larvae. Sandstedt, Sullivan and Schuster (1961) found no part of the tomato root preferentially invaded by *M. incognita*. Mountain (1954) reported that in mixed cultures of corn and tobacco roots *P. minyus* preferentially invades the corn roots. Sayre (1958) reported that *M. incognita* attacks tomato-seedling roots in preference to excised tomato roots. In a study of relative attractiveness, Sayre (1958) demonstrated that attached roots were more attractive than excised roots, which were, in turn, more attractive than undifferentiated tissue. Using potato-tuber tissue and tobacco-stem tissue, this investigator was able to demonstrate that vascular tissue was needed in the plant tissue if complete development of the nematode was to occur in culture. By varying the adenine to IAA ratio, tobacco and potato tissues were grown in callus and differentiated states. The differentiated tissue in each case was more attractive than the corresponding callus tissue. It would thus seem that the vascular tissue is necessary not only for the complete life cycle of the parasite but may also provide some attracting factor.

Darling, Faulkner and Wallendal (1957) reported that *Ditylenchus destructor* Thorne, the nematode causing potato rot, could be grown in undifferentiated potato, carrot, clover, and tobacco tissue. Their report has not been confirmed or expanded since the original abstract appeared. Krusberg (1961) reported that *D. dipsaci* and *Aphelenchoides ritzemabosi* could be grown on alfalfa callus tissue. An examination of the illustrations, however, reveals that this so-called callus tissue is replete with roots and leafy shoots. Despite this nomenclatural problem, this paper contains much valuable histological and histochemical information obtained from parasitized tissue grown in culture.

IX. Bacterial Diseases

The lack of obligate phytoparasitic bacteria and the simple growth requirements of facultative parasites have made attempts to grow bacterially infected plant tissue *in vitro* necessarily lead to a systematic infection of the culture medium by the pathogen. Conceivably, media incorporating highly selective antibiotics, or possibly "killer phage", might be devised to surmount this problem, but at this time such a possibility remains remote.

Volcani, Riker and Hildebrandt (1953) demonstrated that the soft-rot bacteria (*Erwinia carotovorum,* and others) can act upon various tissues in culture, causing typical soft-rot injury, and that the bacteria-free filtrate of the bacterial growth medium contains the factors causing tissue dissolution. Garber and Goldman (1956), using twenty-seven mutants of *E. carotovorum* requiring specific amino acids for growth, reported that all mutants were capable of attacking *Vitis* tissue *in vitro,* although at slightly different rates. At the time, these authors interpreted their data as reflecting the concentrations of required nutrilites in the host tissue. More recently, Garber (1960) reported that the mere presence of a required nutrilite in sufficient concentration in the host tissue is not the limiting factor in successful pathogenesis by a mutant organism.

Kandler (1951) was able to demonstrate a decrease in the growth of corn roots infected with various soil bacteria and grown *in vitro*. He also reported that the filtrate of a culture of *Bacillus subtilis* inhibited the growth of these roots by means of a heat labile substance active at relatively high concentrations. The culture filtrate of *Azotobacter chroococcum* was relatively less inhibitory than infection of the roots with these bacteria and was still less toxic if the filtrate was prepared from a culture grown in a peptone-free medium. Attempts to modify the inhibition of root growth caused by the presence of the bacteria by using a nitrate-free medium were unsuccessful.

Other workers have also used tissue cultures to assay the properties of bacterial extracts, bacteria-free culture medium, and dead bacteria (Gioelli, 1940; Hildebrandt, Riker and Duggar, 1946b). The reported results of these experiments thus far have been of a preliminary nature and have not led to any findings of interest.

Fallot (1958) reported that stem sections of *Vitis vinifera* var. *Syrah* would callus and grow in tissue cultures regardless of the season of tissue selection. On the other hand, *V. rupestris* var. *Lot* would callus and grow *in vitro* only if taken before leaf fall occurs on the plant. Attempts to induce growth of the latter tissue by the addition of IAA or naphthalene acetic acid were unsuccessful. However, during the course of this study one of the cultures of *V. rupestris* began to show abundant growth, although the tissue was isolated after leaf fall. Examination of the growing culture revealed that the tissue was infected by a bacterium later identified as *B. megaterium*. Further experiments demonstrated that several available clones of *B. megaterium* were able to induce the growth of the otherwise dormant *V. rupestris* tissue. Regrettably, these interesting observations have not been the subject of further reports.

X. Fungal Diseases

In contrast to bacterial diseases, plant diseases of fungal origin may be caused by obligate parasites. This leads to the difficulty in obtaining and maintaining axenic or even monoxenic cultures of the parasite. Three approaches have been used to obtain monoxenic cultures of obligately parasitic phytopathogenic fungi: detached leaf culture, embryo culture, and tissue culture. Yarwood (1946) has carefully reviewed the use of detached leaves and leaf discs as substrates for growing these parasites. More recently, the use of embryo culture has yielded interesting results in the study of *Claviceps purpurea* (Tonolo, 1961). The use of tissue cultures for the monoxenic cultivation of obligately parasitic fungi dates to Morel's first paper on the cultivation of *Plasmopora* on grape callus tissue (1944).

Three methods have been employed to start monoxenic cultures of these obligate parasites. (1) The infection of callus tissue. (2) The culture of infected plant tissues. (3) The culture of specialized structures formed on the host plant as a result of infection.

The first method has the additional problem of obtaining a pure culture of the parasite, a problem not always easily solved. Morel (1948) used this technique to grow monoxenic cultures of *Plasmopora viticola,* a phycomycete, and *Uncinula necator,* an ascomycete, on *Vitis* tissue cultures. He reported that the dual cultures grew in a manner suggesting normal host–parasite relationships. *P. viticola* formed an aerial mycelium not seen in natural infections, and both parasites germinated more slowly and developed more slowly *in vitro* than in natural infections. In no case were sexual stages found. The best growth occurred in the most recently isolated tissues and growth became progressively poorer as tissue became less differentiated. Black (1957) suggested that the poorer growth of the parasite in tissue culture might be due to the comparatively unhealthy state of the tissue cultures as opposed to intact healthy plants.

Heim and Gries (1953) reported that only 2% of sunflower tumour tissue inoculated with spores of *Erysiphe cichoracearum* became infected. These authors did not report the establishment of a continuous monoxenic culture of plant and parasite.

Morel (1948) also attempted to use the second method of starting monoxenic cultures to grow *Puccinia antirrhini* and *P. malvacearum* but was unable to attain this end. Rossetti and Morel (1958) demonstrated that *P. antirrhini* spores would germinate on snapdragon tissues in culture, but mycelium would infect only stem sections covered by epidermis; callus tissue and decorticated stem tissue were not invaded.

The third method of starting monoxenic cultures of obligate parasites has been used extensively in studies of the cedar-apple-gall organism, *Gymnosporangium juniperi* (Cutter, 1951, 1959; Hotson, 1953; Hotson and Cutter, 1951). These authors maintain that they have been able to grow the host–parasite complex in tissue culture for some time without loss of either partner. Constabel (1957), however, in spite of many attempts was unable to maintain this dual culture for more than a few transfers. Rossetti and Morel (1958) also claim failure in attempting to grow this tissue-fungus combination for any length of time. Morel (1948) reported his inability to maintain a monoxenic culture of *G. clavariaeforme* but this may be due to his admitted lack of uniformly growing cultures of the plant tissue (*Juniperus communis*).

Cutter (1960) reported on a long series of experiments designed to obtain axenic cultures of the autoecious, obligately parasitic rust *Uromyces ari-triphylli.* This rust is parasitic on *Arisaema triphyllum,* a monocotyledon belonging to the Araceae. He reported the successful culture of infected and non-infected host corm on defined media. These tissues grew slowly and formed a suberized periderm which had to be surgically removed for further growth. Aecia and aeciospores were formed on some of the infected tissues. The conditions necessary for the formation of these fungal organs, however, could not be completely described; the author states that stripping of the periderm, followed by growth in light intensities of 350–890 ft candles, induced aecia on some of the cultures. Uredia, telia, and pycnia were never observed. Mycelium, when found in infected tissues, was localized to the parenchymal portion and never found in the periderm of the culture.

The author reports that in a few cases the fungus-tissue complex would give rise to a mycelium that would grow on a non-living substrate. Only a very small number of isolates were observed to undergo this change, which he believes to be a mutation.

This non-obligately parasitic fungus was demonstrated to be able to infect sterile callus tissue of the host and host plants in the field and greenhouse. The data presented are of great interest but, regrettably, not entirely convincing. The difficulty of growing *Arisaema* in the greenhouse or from sterile seed makes it difficult to obtain hosts which are definitely not infected. The data presented, however, does make it seem likely that these difficulties have in part been overcome. It is regrettable that the untimely death of this investigator interrupted this most interesting work.

It is somewhat disappointing that the reported cultures of these obligate fungal parasites in plant tissue culture have yielded very little new knowledge on the nature of obligate parasitism and have in general been rather sparse except for the major works of Morel (1948) and Cutter (1959, 1960). Although Hotson and Cutter (1951) reported the isolation of a strain or mutation of *G. juniperi* that would grow on a defined culture medium, Constabel (1957) was unable to observe such phenomena in spite of many attempts to repeat the work of Hotson and Cutter. Allen (1954) points out that Hotson makes no further mention of this isolation in his 1953 paper; Cutter (1959), however, has re-established his claim to the isolation of a strain or mutation of the fungus after several passages in tissue culture. He does not, however, make any reference to Constabel's inability to do so. It would certainly seem that the inability of other investigators to repeat the work of Hotson and Cutter leaves the entire problem in a state of doubt.

XI. Virus Diseases

The possibilities of growing obligate fungal parasites axenically present a difficult problem. Similarly, the axenic culture of viruses has not as yet been reported. It is partly for this reason that much of virus research in general has been dependent upon the use of tissue-culture techniques. The use of *in vitro* techniques in animal virus culture has led to many theoretical and practical gains. In spite of the greater simplicity and ease of plant tissue culture, relatively little use has been made of this technique in the study of viruses. Schmelzer (1961) in a recent review of this subject lists six reasons ranging from the greater health hazard to the investigator of animal viruses than of plant viruses, to the economics of plant growth as factors which historically have aided in the present dearth of plant virus research using *in vitro* techniques. Whatever the reasons, it must be admitted that compared with the literature on animal viruses grown in tissue culture, that on plant viruses is sparse.

Plant viruses have been grown continuously in association with normal, habituated, and crown-gall callus tissue, in suspended cell cultures, and for more limited periods in isolated roots. In all cases the infected tissues were macroscopically indistinguishable from their non-infected counterparts, a marked contrast to the situation in many virus-infected animal cells. This is probably due in part to the lack of a lysogenic response of plant cells when infected.

White (1934) was able to grow tomato roots infected with aucuba and tobacco mosaic virus (TMV) *in vitro*. He demonstrated that the meristematic region was essentially free of virus and the titre low in the young tissues, increasing in the older and more slowly growing tissues. Since continuous culture of roots *in vitro* is dependent upon the continuous subculturing of meristematic tissue, it was not possible to maintain the virus-infected roots indefinitely. Stanley (1938) demonstrated that these infected roots did indeed contain a virus with identical properties to those shown by the aucuba virus isolated from greenhouse-infected plants.

The freedom of stem and root apices from systemic viruses has been of great practical use in horticulture and agronomy. It has been possible to free a plant of virus by growing the apical region in tissue culture, and later rooting the new shoot. A number of virus-free clones have been obtained in this way. Much of this work is reviewed by Schmelzer (1961).

Although Segretain (1948) and Segretain and Hirth (1953) were able to grow TMV on pieces of tobacco stem tissue grown *in vitro,* they were unable to maintain these cultures for more than a few months. Morel (1948) first demonstrated the possibility of continuous culture of virus-infected callus tissue. He was able to grow TMV in normal, habituated, and crown-gall tobacco tissue. In contrast to White's (1934) earlier experiences, both Segretain (1943, 1948) and Morel (1948) were unable to infect tissues *in vitro* by applying juice expressed from infected plants to the wounded callus. It remained for Bergmann (1959b) to infect roots *in vitro*. A recent report by Hirth and Lebeurier (1962) states that they have been able to infect habituated tobacco tissue with TMV ribonucleic acid.

Morel (1948) was also able to grow potato virus X and Y in normal and crown-gall tobacco tissue and in *Hyoscyamus* tissue. Augier de Montgremier, Limasset and Morel (1948) were able to maintain a complex infection of TMV and cucumber mosaic I in tissue culture. Maramorosch (1958) reported that cultures of corn tissue infected with corn stunt virus could be grown as free-floating cells and cell clumps in liquid culture.

In summarizing his monumental 1948 paper, Morel states that none of these infections altered the infected tissues, that the virus maintained its virulence even after extended passage through tissue cultures, and that the virus titre was lower in tissue culture than in infected intact plants. Augier de Montgremier and Morel (1948) demonstrated that crown-gall tissue infected with TMV had a titre thirty to forty times lower than infected leaves on intact plants; habituated tissue had an even lower titre, so low, in fact, that it could not be detected serologically but only by means of biological assay on tobacco plants. These results were essentially confirmed by Kassanis (1957), using Morel's original isolates which had been maintained since first isolation in the late 1940's.

In intact plants, virus diseases can only be established through some kind of wound. As previously mentioned, White (1934) was unable to infect tomato roots with TMV *in vitro*. Bergmann and Melchers (1959) were somewhat more successful by wounding the roots with a quartz powder mixed with TMV. Kassanis, Tinsley and Quak (1958) obtained a degree of correlation between virus infection and degree of wounding of callus and root cultures. Wu, Hildebrandt and Riker (1960) were also able to infect tobacco cells growing in free-floating suspension in liquid medium with TMV. These authors reported that the younger, more meristematic cells were more resistant to infection or virus multiplication than the older cells. The well documented low viral titre of meristematic tissue in most virus infections tends to favour the latter, especially since there is considerable evidence that more rapidly growing tissues tend to have lower virus titres. The conflicting report by Kassanis (1957) and the greater titre in rapidly growing crown-gall tissue than in more slowly growing habituated tissue reported by Augier de Montgremier and Morel (1948) must, however, be borne in mind.

Kassanis, Tinsley and Quak (1958) reported that the rate of travel of TMV in strips of callus tissue is at most 4 mm in 32 days, a figure consonant with some reports of the rate of movement of this virus in intact leaves. It has been generally agreed that the virus travels from cell to cell via plasmodesmata; however, on the basis of electron-micrographs and conventional histological techniques, these authors report that they saw no evidence of plasmodesmata in habituated tissue cultures. Their published electron-micrographs, however, do not clearly establish this point.

Kutsky and Rawlins (1950) reported that 10^{-4} % naphthalene acetic acid (NAA) incorporated into the medium upon which TMV infected tobacco tissue is growing decreased the virus concentration in the tissue to 0·2–0·4 that of the control tissues without affecting the growth of the tissues. Kutsky (1952) stated that indole butyric acid (IBA) at 100 mg/l reduced virus concentration in the same system without inhibiting growth. These authors do, however, point out that the tissues in question have a brownish appearance. Hildebrandt, Riker and Watertor (1952) reported that both NAA and tryptophan only lowered virus titre at concentrations inhibitory to growth. In intact plants NAA and IBA have been observed to retard the appearance and to decrease the severity of the symptoms of TMV infection (Nichols, 1952).

In 1952 Segretain reported that coconut milk (CCM) favoured the growth of TMV in tobacco tissue cultures. A later paper by Hirth and Segretain (1956), however, reports that CCM favours callus cell division and lowers virus titre. These authors state that these results are not in contradiction, as they used callus tissue cultures in the later paper and stem isolates in the earlier paper. They report, further, that aspartic acid lowers virus titre and slightly inhibits growth, whereas glutamic acid favours virus increase at concentrations not affecting tissue growth. This had previously been reported by Segretain and Hirth (1953). Kassanis (1957) reported an increase in virus titre and tissue growth of TMV in crown-gall tissue caused by coconut milk.

Bergmann (1959a) demonstrated that concentrations of the anti-metabolite thiouracil inhibited the growth of TMV infected tomato roots at concentrations between 10^{-6} and 10^{-5} g/ml. Virus production, however, increased between 10^{-6} and 3×10^{-6} g/ml and dropped sharply at higher concentrations. This increase in virus concentration is not considered significant by the author. At about the same time, Hildebrandt (1958) and Hildebrandt and Riker (1958) reported an increase in virus titre with low concentrations of thiouracil (0·01 mg/l) with a corresponding decrease in tissue growth. Kassanis (1957) reported that thiouracil affected both virus and tissue growth in crown-gall tissue infected with TMV, and that uracil can stimulate both virus and tissue growth as well as partially reverse the effects of the analogue. This author also reported that autoclaved TMV added to the tissue-culture medium inhibited tissue growth and increased virus titre. Kurtzman, Hildebrandt, Burris and Riker (1960) reported that 6-methyl purine showed a greater virus toxicity than tissue toxicity at 0·01 mg/l. These authors reported that those antimetabolites and analogues that slowly and progressively inhibit growth increased virus titre, whereas those that rapidly cause a precipitous decrease in tissue growth cause a decrease in virus titre. Their data led them to conclude that there is a competition between the cell and the virus for nucleoprotein synthesis.

Lebeurier (1959) reported that TMV in tobacco tissue decreased if the tissue was grown at 37°C rather than 21°C. Commensurate with the decrease in virus titre was a decrease in tissue wet weight, protein nitrogen, DNA, RNA and amylogenesis. Exposure to 37°C for periods as short as 3–4 days followed by 3 weeks at 21°C still led to a decrease in virus titre.

Hildebrandt, Riker and Watertor (1954) reported that normal and crown-gall TMV infected tissues grew well at temperatures between 16 and 37°C with the best growth between 20 and 30°C. Virus titre was highest between 24 and 28°C and lowest at 36°C.

It is important to note that the uses of different tissue-culture media may account for some of the controversies noted above. The recent reports of Wood and Braun (1961) and Lipetz (1962) on the profound effects of mineral concentrations in tissue-culture media may account for some of the reported controversies. Furthermore, as Lance (1957) points out, fresh weight is by no means always the preferred base for measuring growth in tissue cultures.

Acknowledgements

Certain of the investigations reported herein were supported in part by a research grant (PHS C-6346) from the National Cancer Institute, Public Health Service, to the senior author. This review was written while the junior author held a postdoctoral fellowship (CF-7607) from the National Cancer Institute, Public Health Service.

The authors are greatly indebted to Dr. Philip R. White for permission to use the illustration shown in Fig. 1.

References

Allen, P. J. (1954). Physiological aspects of fungus diseases of plants. *Annu. Rev. Pl. Physiol.* **5**, 225.

Anders, F. (1958). Aminosäuren als gallenerregende Stoffe der Reblaus (*Viteus* [*Phylloxera*] *vitifolii*, Shimer). *Experientia* **14**, 62.

Anders, F. and Vester, F. (1960). Genetisch bedingte Tumoren und der Gehalt an freien Aminosäuren bei *Nicotiana*. *Experientia* **16**, 65.

Augier de Montgremier, H., Limasset, P. and Morel, G. (1948). Sur le maintien d'une maladie à virus complexe dans des tissus de tabac cultivés *in vitro*. *C. R. Acad. Sci., Paris* **227**, 606.

Augier de Montgremier, H. and Morel, G. (1948). Sur la diminution de la teneur en virus (*Marmor tabaci* Holmes) de tissus de tabac cultivés *in vitro*. *C. R. Acad. Sci., Paris* **227**, 688.

Bergmann, L. (1959a). Plant viruses in tissue culture. *Trans. N.Y. Acad. Sci.* ser. II, **21**, 227.

Bergmann, L. (1959b). Über den Einfluss von Thiouracil und Cytovirin auf das Wachstum und die Virusproduktion isolierter Tomatenwurzeln. *Phytopath. Z.* **34**, 209.

Bergmann, L. and Melchers, G. (1959). Infektionsversuche an submers kultivierten Geweben mit Tabakmosaikvirus. *Z. Naturf.* **14b**, 73.

Black, L. M. (1945). A virus tumor disease of plants. *Amer. J. Bot.* **32**, 408.

Black, L. M. (1949). Virus tumors. *Survey biol. Progr.* **1**, 155.

Black, L. M. (1951). Hereditary variation in the reaction of sweet clover to the wound-tumor virus. *Amer. J. Bot.* **38**, 256.

Black, L. M. (1957). Viruses and other pathogenic agents in plant tissue cultures. *J. nat. Cancer Inst.* **19**, 663.

Boysen-Jensen, P. (1952). Untersuchungen über die Bildung der Galle von *Mikiola fagi*. *K. Danske Videnskab. Selskab. Biol.* **18**, no. 18.

Brakke, M. K. and Nickell, L. G. (1951). Secretion of α–amylase by *Rumex* virus tumors *in vitro*. Properties and assay. *Arch. Biochem. Biophys.* **32**, 28.

Brakke, M. K. and Nickell, L. G. (1955). Secretion of an enzyme from intact cells of a higher plant tumor. *Année Biol.* **31**, 215.

Brakke, M. K., Vatter, A. E. and Black, L. M. (1954). Size and shape of wound-tumor virus. *In* "Abnormal and Pathological Plant Growth," Brookhaven Symposia in Biology, No. 6, pp. 137-156.

Braun, A. C. (1941). Development of secondary tumors and tumor strands in the crown gall of sunflowers. *Phytopathology* **31**, 135.

Braun, A. C. (1947). Thermal studies on the factors responsible for tumor initiation in crown gall. *Amer. J. Bot.* **34**, 234.

Braun, A. C. (1951a). Cellular autonomy in crown gall. *Phytopathology* **41**, 963.

Braun, A. C. (1951b). Recovery of crown-gall tumor cells. *Cancer Res.* **11**, 839.

Braun, A. C. (1954). The physiology of plant tumors. *Annu. Rev. Pl. Physiol.* **5**, 133.

Braun, A. C. (1956). The activation of two growth-substance systems accompanying the conversion of normal to tumor cells in crown gall. *Cancer Res.* **16**, 53.

Braun, A. C. (1958). A physiological basis for autonomous growth of the crown-gall tumor cell. *Proc. nat. Acad. Sci., Wash.* **44**, 344.

Braun, A. C. (1959). A demonstration of the recovery of the crown-gall tumor cell with the use of complex tumors of single-cell origin. *Proc. nat. Acad. Sci., Wash.* **45**, 932.

Braun, A. C. (1961). Plant tumors as an experimental model. *Harvey Lect.* **56**, 191.

Braun, A. C. (1962). Tumor inception and development in the crown-gall disease. *Annu. Rev. Pl. Physiol.* **13**, 533.

Braun, A. C. and Stonier, T. (1958). Morphology and physiology of plant tumors. *Protoplasmatologia* **10**, pt. 5a.

Braun, A. C. and Wood, H. N. (1961). The plant tumor problem. *Advanc. Cancer Res.* **6**, 81.

Braun, A. C. and Wood, H. N. (1962). On the activation of certain essential biosynthetic systems in cells of *Vinca rosea* L. *Proc. nat. Acad. Sci., Wash.* **48**, 1776.

Burkholder, P. R. and Nickell, L. G. (1949). Atypical growth of plants. I. Cultivation of virus tumors of *Rumex* on nutrient agar. *Bot. Gaz.* **110**, 426.

Byars, L. P. (1914). Preliminary notes on the cultivation of the plant parasitic nematode, *Heterodera radicicola*. *Phytopathology* **4**, 323.

Constabel, F. (1957). Ernährungsphysiologische und manometrische Untersuchungen zur Gewebekultur der *Gymnosporangium*-Gallen von *Juniperus*-Arten. *Biol. Zbl.* **76**, 385.

Cutter, V. M., Jr. (1951). The isolation of plant rusts upon artificial media and some speculations on the metabolism of obligate plant parasites. *Trans. N.Y. Acad. Sci.* **14**, 103.

Cutter, V. M., Jr. (1959). Studies on the isolation and growth of plant rusts in host tissue cultures and upon synthetic media. I. *Gymnosporangium*. *Mycologia* **51**, 248.

Cutter, V. M., Jr. (1960). Studies on the isolation and growth of plant rusts in host tissue cultures and upon synthetic media. II. *Uromyces ari-triphylli*. *Mycologia* **52**, 726.

Darling, H. M., Faulkner, L. R. and Wallendal, P. (1957). Culturing the potato rot nematode. *Phytopathology* **47**, 7 (Abstract).

Démétriadès, S. D. (1953). Essais de culture, *in vitro*, des tissus des galles du *Salvia pomifera* L. *Ann. Inst. Phytopath. Benaki* **7**, 61.

Fallot, J. (1958). Induction, par *Bacillus megaterium*, de la prolifération *in vitro* des tissus de tiges de *Vitis rupestris*, prélevées pendant la période de repos végétatif. *C. R. Acad. Sci., Paris* **246**, 295.

Ferguson, M. S. (1948). Culture experiments with *Heterodera marioni*. *J. Parasit.* **34**, Section 2 (Suppl.), 32.

Garber, E. D. (1960). The host as a growth medium. *Ann. N.Y. Acad. Sci.* **88**, 1187.

Garber, E. D. and Goldman, M. (1956). The response of grape tissue cultures to inoculation with biochemical mutants of *Erwinia aroideae*. *Bot. Gaz.* **118**, 128.

Gautheret, R. J. (1959). "La Culture des Tissus Végétaux; Techniques et Réalisations." Masson, Paris.

Gioelli, F. (1940). L'azione di filtrati di "*Bacterium tumefaciens*" su colture "*in vitro*" di tessuti vegetali. *Riv. Pat. veg.* **30**, 117.

Hagen, G. L. and Gunckel, J. E. (1958). Free amino acid levels in *Nicotiana glauca*, *N. langsdorffii* and their interspecific hybrid following gamma irradiation. *Plant Physiol.* **33**, 439.

Heim, J. M. and Gries, G. A. (1953). The culture of *Erysiphe cichoracearum* on sunflower tumor tissue. *Phytopathology* **43**, 343.

Hildebrandt, A. C. (1958). Stimulation or inhibition of virus of infected and insect-gall tissues and single-cell clones. *Proc. nat. Acad. Sci., Wash.* **44**, 354.

Hildebrandt, A. C. and Riker, A. J. (1949). The influence of various carbon compounds on the growth of marigold, Paris-daisy, periwinkle, sunflower and tobacco tissue *in vitro*. *Amer. J. Bot.* **36**, 74.

Hildebrandt, A. C. and Riker, A. J. (1958). Viruses and single cell clones in plant tissue culture. *Fed. Proc.* **17**, 986.

Hildebrandt, A. C., Riker, A. J. and Duggar, B. M. (1945). Growth *in vitro* of excised tobacco and sunflower tissue with different temperatures, hydrogen-ion concentrations and amounts of sugar. *Amer. J. Bot.* **32**, 357.

Hildebrandt, A. C., Riker, A. J. and Duggar, B. M. (1946a). The influence of the composition of the medium on growth *in vitro* of excised tobacco and sunflower tissue cultures. *Amer. J. Bot.* **33**, 591.

Hildebrandt, A. C., Riker, A. J. and Duggar, B. M. (1946b). Influence of crown-gall bacterial products, crown-gall tissue extracts, and yeast extract on growth *in vitro* of excised tobacco and sunflower tissue. *Cancer Res.* **6**, 368.

Hildebrandt, A. C., Riker, A. J. and Watertor, J. L. (1952). Growth and virus activity in tobacco tissue cultures with naphthalene acetic acid or tryptophan. *Phytopathology* **42**, 467 (Abstract).

Hildebrandt, A. C., Riker, A. J. and Watertor, J. L. (1954). Virus infectivity and host tissue growth on synthetic media at different temperatures and acidities. *Phytopathology* **44**, 492 (Abstract).

Hirth, L. and Lebeurier, G. (1962). Infection de cultures de tissus de tabac au moyen de l'acide ribonucléique extrait du virus de la mosaique du tabac. *C. R. Acad. Sci., Paris* **254**, 1495.

Hirth, L. and Segretain, G. (1956). Quelques aspects de la multiplication du virus de la mosaique du tabac en culture de tissus. *Ann. Inst. Pasteur* **91**, 523.

Hotson, H. H. (1953). The growth of rust in tissue culture. *Phytopathology* **43**, 360.

Hotson, H. H. and Cutter, V. M., Jr. (1951). The isolation and culture of *Gymnosporangium juniperi-virgini[a]nae* Schw. upon artificial media. *Proc. nat. Acad. Sci., Wash.* **37**, 400.

Hurel-Py, G. (1950). Recherches préliminaires sur la culture aseptique des prothalles de filicinées. *Rev. gen. bot.* **57**, 637.

Jensen, C. O. (1910). Von echten Geschwülsten bei Pflanzen. Deuxième Conférence International pour l'Etude du Cancer. Rapport. Paris. *K. Vet. Højsk Aarsskr.* **7**, 243.

Kandler, O. (1951). Über den Einfluss von Bodenbakterien und deren Filtraten auf das Wachstum in vitro kultivierter Wurzeln. *Arch. Mikrobiol.* **15**, 430.

Kassanis, B. (1957). The multiplication of tobacco mosaic virus in cultures of tumorous tobacco tissues. *Virology* **4**, 5.

Kassanis, B., Tinsley, T. W. and Quak, F. (1958). The inoculation of tobacco callus tissue with tobacco mosaic virus. *Ann. appl. Biol.* **46**, 11.

Klein, R. M. and Link, G. K. K. (1955). The etiology of crown-gall. *Quart. Rev. Biol.* **30**, 207.

Kostoff, D. (1930). Tumors and other malformations on certain *Nicotiana* hybrids. *Zbl. Bakt.* Abt. 2, **81**, 244.

Krusberg, L. N. (1961). Studies on the culturing and parasitism of plant parasitic nematodes, in particular *Ditylenchus dipsaci* and *Aphelenchoides ritzemabosi* on alfalfa tissue. *Nematologica* **6**, 181.

Kurtzman, R. H., Hildebrandt, A. C., Burris, R. H. and Riker, A. J. (1960). Inhibition and stimulation of tobacco mosaic virus by purines. *Virology* **10**, 432.

Kutsky, R. J. (1952). Effects of indolebutyric acid and other compounds on virus concentration in plant tissue cultures. *Science* **115**, 19.

Kutsky, R. J. and Rawlins, T. E. (1950). Inhibition of virus multiplication by naphthalene acetic acid in tobacco tissue cultures as revealed by a spectrophotometric method. *J. Bact.* **60**, 763.

Lance, C. (1957). Remarques sur l'emploi de differents critères de croissance dans le cas de tissus végétaux cultivés *in vitro*. *Rev. gen. bot.* **64**, 123.

Lebeurier, G. (1959). Remarques sur l'influence de la témperature sur la multiplication du virus de la mosaique du tabac en cultures de tissus. *C. R. Acad. Sci., Paris* **249**, 795.

Lewis, I. F. and Walton, L. (1958). Gall-formation on *Hamamelis virginiana* resulting from material injected by the aphid *Hormaphis hamamelidis*. *Trans. Amer. micr. Soc.* **77**, 146.

Lipetz, J. (1962). Calcium and the control of lignification in tissue cultures. *Amer. J. Bot.* **49**, 460.

Lipetz, J. and Galston, A. W. (1959). Indole acetic acid oxidase and peroxidase activities in normal and crown gall tissue cultures of *Parthenocissus tricuspidata*. *Amer. J. Bot.* **46**, 193.

Littau, V. C. and Black, L. M. (1952). Spontaneous tumors in sweet clover. *Amer. J. Bot.* **39**, 191.

Maramorosch, K. (1958). Viruses that infect and multiply in both plants and insects. *Trans. N.Y. Acad. Sci.*, ser. 2, **20**, 383.

Morel, G. (1944). Le développement du mildiou sur des tissus de vigne cultivés *in vitro*. *C. R. Acad. Sci., Paris* **218**, 50.

Morel, G. (1948). Recherches sur la culture associée de parasites obligatoires et de tissus végétaux. *Ann. Épiphyt.* [N.S.] **14**, 123 (*Sér. Pathol. vég. Mém.* 5).

Morel, G. and Wetmore, R. H. (1951). Fern callus tissue culture. *Amer. J. Bot.* **38**, 141.

Mountain, W. B. (1954). Studies of nematodes in relation to brown root rot of tobacco in Ontario. *Canad. J. Bot.* **32**, 737.

Mountain, W. B. (1955). A method of culturing plant parasitic nematodes under sterile conditions. *Proc. helm. Soc. Wash.* **22**, 49.

Muir, W. H., Hildebrandt, A. C. and Riker, A. J. (1958). The preparation, isolation, and growth in culture of single cells from higher plants. *Amer. J. Bot.* **45**, 589.

Näf, U. (1958). Studies on tumor formation in *Nicotiana* hybrids. I. The classification of the parents into two etiologically significant groups. *Growth* **22**, 167.

Nichols, C. W. (1952). The retarding effect of certain plant hormones on tobacco mosaic symptoms. *Phytopathology* **42**, 579.

Nickell, L. G., Greenfield, P. and Burkholder, P. R. (1950). Atypical growth of plants. III. Growth responses of virus tumors of *Rumex* to certain nucleic acid components and related compounds. *Bot. Gaz.* **112**, 42.

Partanen, C. R. (1956). Comparative microphotometric determinations of deoxyribonucleic acid in normal and tumorous growth of fern prothalli. *Cancer Res.* **16**, 300.

Partanen, C. R. (1958). Quantitative technique for analysis of radiation-induced tumorization in fern prothalli. *Science* **128**, 1006.

Partanen, C. R. (1960a). Suppression of radiation-induced tumorization in fern prothalli. *Science* **131**, 926.

Partanen, C. R. (1960b). Amino acid suppression of radiation-induced tumorization of fern prothalli. *Proc. nat. Acad. Sci., Wash.* **46**, 1206.

Partanen, C. R. and Steeves, T. A. (1956). The production of tumorous abnormalities in fern prothalli by ionizing radiations. *Proc. nat. Acad. Sci., Wash.* **42**, 906.

Pelet, F. (1959). Growth *in vitro* of grape, elm, poplar, willow, and oak tissues isolated from normal stems and insect galls. Ph.D. Thesis, University of Wisconsin, Madison.

Pelet, F., Hildebrandt, A. C., Riker, A. J. and Skoog, F. (1960). Growth *in vitro* of tissues isolated from normal stems and insect galls. *Amer. J. Bot.* **47**, 186.

Reinert, J. (1956). Dissociation of cultures from *Picea glauca* into small tissue fragments and single cells. *Science* **123**, 457.

Reinert, J. and Schraudolf, H. (1959). Über die physiologischen Eigenschaften von Gewebekulturen aus Tumor- und normalem Gewebe von *Picea glauca*. *Planta* **53**, 18.

Reinert, J., Schraudolf, H. and Tazawa, M. (1957). Extrazelluläre Enzyme und Auxinbedarf von Gewebekulturen. *Naturwissenschaften* **44**, 588.

Reinert, J. and White, P. R. (1956). The cultivation *in vitro* of tumor tissues and normal tissues of *Picea glauca*. *Physiol. Plant.* **9**, 177.

Riker, A. J. and Gutsche, A. E. (1948). The growth of sunflower tissue *in vitro* on synthetic media with various organic and inorganic sources of nitrogen. *Amer. J. Bot.* **35**, 227.

Riker, A. J. and Hildebrandt, A. C. (1958). Plant tissue cultures open a botanical frontier. *Annu. Rev. Microbiol.* **12**, 469.

Rossetti, V. and Morel, G. (1958). Le développement du *Puccinia antirrhini* sur tissus de muflier cultivés *in vitro*. *C. R. Acad. Sci., Paris* **247**, 1893.

Sandstedt, R., Sullivan, T. and Schuster, M. L. (1961). Nematode tracks in the study of movement of *Apeloidogyne incognita*. *Nematologica* **6**, 261.

Sayre, R. M. (1958). Plant tissue culture as a tool in the study of the physiology of the root-knot nematode *Meloidogyne incognita* Chit. Ph.D. Thesis, University of Nebraska, Lincoln.

Schmelzer, K. (1961). Gewebekulturen in der pflanzlichen Virusforschung. *Z. Pfl-Krankh.* **68**, 489.

Segretain, G. (1943). Culture d'un virus et son inoculation sur fragments de tige de tabac cultivés *in vitro*. *Ann. Inst. Pasteur* **69**, 61.

Segretain, G. (1948). Virus et culture de tissus de tabac et de tomate. *C. R. Acad. Sci., Paris* **226**, 594.

Segretain, G. (1952). Action du lait de coco et de l'acide naphtalène acétique sur la multiplication d'un virus en culture de tissus. *C. R. Acad. Acad. Sci., Paris* **235**, 1342.

Segretain, G. and Hirth, L. (1953). Action de substances azotées sur la multiplication du virus de la mosaique du tabac en culture de tissus. *C. R. Soc. Biol., Paris* **147**, 1042.

Skoog, F. (1944). Growth and organ formation in tobacco tissue cultures. *Amer. J. Bot.* **31**, 19.

Skoog, F. and Miller, C. O. (1957). Chemical regulation of growth and organ formation in plant tissues cultured *in vitro*. *Symp. Soc. exp. Biol.* No. 11, 118.

Smith, E. F., Brown, N. A. and McCulloch, L. (1912). The structure and development of crown gall. A plant cancer. *U.S. Dept. Agric., Bur. Plant Indus. Bull.* No. 255. 61 p.

Smith, H. H. (1958). Genetic plant tumors in *Nicotiana*. *Ann. N.Y. Acad. Sci.* **71**, Art. 6, 1163.

Smith, H. H. (1962). Genetic control of *Nicotiana* plant tumors. *Trans. N.Y. Acad. Sci.* ser. II, **24**, 741.

Sparrow, A. H. and Gunckel, J. E. (1956). Induction of tumours by ionising radiation on stems, leaves and roots of an interspecific *Nicotiana* hybrid. *In* "Progress in Radiobiology" (J. S. Mitchell *et al.*, eds.), pp. 485-488. Oliver and Boyd, Edinburgh and London.

Sparrow, A. H., Gunckel, J. E., Scharrer, L. A. and Hagen, G. L. (1956). Tumor formation and other morphogenetic responses in an amphidiploid tobacco hybrid exposed to chronic gamma irradiation. *Amer. J. Bot.* **43**, 377.

Stanley, W. M. (1938). Aucuba mosaic virus protein isolated from diseased, excised tomato roots grown *in vitro*. *J. biol. Chem.* **126**, 125.

Steeves, T. A., Sussex, I. M. and Partanen, C. R. (1955). *In vitro* studies on abnormal growth of prothalli of the bracken fern. *Amer. J. Bot.* **42**, 232.

Tonolo, A. (1961). Colture artificiali di *Claviceps purpurea* (Fr.) Tul. I. Infezione e produzione di sclerozi su piante di cereali cresciute in ambiente sterile. *R.C. Ist. Super. Sanita* **24**, 452.

Torok, D. de and Roderick, T. H. (1962). Associations between growth rate, mitotic frequency, and chromosome number in a plant tissue culture. *Cancer Res.* **22**, 174.

Torok, D. de and Thimann, K. V. (1961). The auxin requirement and the effect of an auxin-antagonist on tumorous and normal tissues of *Picea glauca*. *Physiol. Plant.* **14**, 543.

Tso, T. C., Burk, L. G., Sorokin, T. P. and Engelhaupt, M. E. (1962). Genetic tumors of *Nicotiana*. I. Chemical composition of *N. glauca, N. langsdorffii,* and their F_1 hybrid. *Plant Physiol.* **37**, 257.

Vester, F. and Anders, F. (1960). Der Gehalt an freien Aminosäuren des spontan tumorbildenden Artbastards von *Nicotiana glauca* und *N. langsdorffii*. *Biochem. Z.* **332**, 396.

Volcani, Z., Riker, A. J. and Hildebrandt, A. C. (1953). Destruction of various tissues in culture by certain bacteria. *Phytopathology* **43**, 92.

White, P. R. (1934). Multiplication of the viruses of tobacco and aucuba mosaics in growing excised tomato root tips. *Phytopathology* **24**, 1003.

White, P. R. (1939a). Potentially unlimited growth of excised plant callus in an artificial nutrient. *Amer. J. Bot.* **26**, 59.

White, P. R. (1939b). Controlled differentiation in a plant tissue culture. *Bull. Torrey bot. Club.* **66**, 507.

White, P. R. (1944). Transplantation of plant tumors of genetic origin. *Cancer Res.* **4**, 791.

White, P. R. (1957). An epiphytotic tumor of white spruce, *Picea glauca*. *In* "The Physiology of Forest Trees" (K. V. Thimann, ed.), pp. 493-510. Ronald Press, New York.

White, P. R. (1958). A tree tumor of unknown origin. *Proc. nat. Acad. Sci., Wash.* **44**, 339.

White, P. R. and Braun, A. C. (1942). A cancerous neoplasm of plants. Autonomous bacteria-free crown-gall tissue. *Cancer Res.* **2**, 597.

Widdowson, E., Doncaster, C. C. and Fenwick, D. W. (1958). Observations on the development of *Heterodera rostochiensis* Woll. in sterile root cultures. *Nematologica* **3**, 308.

Wieser, W. (1955). The attractiveness of plants to larvae of root-knot nematodes. I. The effect of tomato seedlings and excised roots on *Meloidogyne hapla* Chitwood. *Proc. helm. Soc. Wash.* **22**, 106.

Wood, H. N. and Braun, A. C. (1961). Studies on the regulation of certain essential biosynthetic systems in normal and crown-gall tumor cells. *Proc. nat. Acad. Sci., Wash.* **47**, 1907.

Wu, J. H., Hildebrandt, A. C. and Riker, A. J. (1960). Virus-host relationships in plant tissue culture. *Phytopathology* **50**, 587.

Yarwood, C. E. (1946). Detached leaf culture. *Bot. Rev.* **12**, 1.

Author Index

(*Numbers in italics refer to pages in the References at the end of each chapter.*)

B

C

D

G

H

I

J

L

N

Q

R

S

T

Taxonomic Index

E

G

H

I

J

L

M

Subject Index

B

D

I

J

K

L

M

N

O

V